BIRDS OF WESTERN PENNSYLVANIA

Birds

OF WESTERN PENNSYLVANIA

BY W. E. CLYDE TODD

CURATOR OF ORNITHOLOGY

CARNEGIE MUSEUM, PITTSBURGH

WITH TWENTY-TWO PLATES

IN COLOR

ILLUSTRATING 118 specie S

FROM THE ORIGINAL DRAW

BY

GEORGE MIKSCH SU ON

UNIVERSITY OF PITT BURGH PRESS 1940

PRINTED IN U. S. A., BY EDWARD STERN & COMPANY, INCORPORATED

THE PUBLICATION OF THIS BOOK

BY THE UNIVERSITY OF PITTSBURGH PRESS

FOR THE CARNEGIE MUSEUM, PITTSBURGH

WAS MADE POSSIBLE BY A GRANT

FROM THE BUHL FOUNDATION

FOREWORD

MORE THAN forty years have passed since I first conceived the idea of writing the *Birds of Western Pennsylvania* and began to amass data for its preparation. Indeed, the germ of the idea dates back to 1890, when I realized that the bird life of western Pennsylvania was virtually unknown. In 1893 I began systematic field work with a definite object in view, as described in detail below. In the course of my investigations I visited and became more or less familiar with every county in the western half of the state. Also, I invited and received from my correspondents in this area, most of whom are or were personally known to me, authentic annotated lists of the birds of their respective localities. When I joined the staff of the Carnegie Museum in 1899, I had planned to complete my report for publication within two or three years at most, but owing to causes beyond my control and to increasing demands on my time, the project was necessarily laid aside. In any event, clerical help was needed to collate the accumulation of field notes and published records, and such help was not immediately forthcoming. Finally, however, through generous financial aid from the local Audubon societies, competent secretarial assistance was engaged, and in due course the data for the proposed work were compiled and arranged. With this necessary groundwork laid, the actual writing of the book was begun in 1933, and, with some unavoidable intermissions, was carried forward to completion in 1939. The task has been undertaken with the full approval of the present director of the Museum, Dr. Andrey Avinoff.

The original plan for the work limited it to a technical discussion of local distribution and migration, but with the entrance of the Audubon societies into the project an expansion of scope became desirable. As it now stands, the book is no less scientific than was at first intended, but its plan has been enlarged and somewhat changed in order to give it a wider appeal. This end has been achieved by including a series of color plates, and a field description of each species with an account of its habits. The addition of these extra features has more than doubled the time and labor involved; the reader must judge whether or not the results have justified the effort. Had the book been brought out on the basis of the data available when the project was first undertaken, its preparation would have been comparatively simple, since the published records were then so few. But in the interim the literature dealing with the birds of western Pennsylvania has expanded greatly—even if not always wisely and scientifically. The long delay in the appearance of this volume has entailed a vast amount of additional work in its compilation, but the final result is a fuller and better book than I ever expected. When I began my work in the nineties, western Pennsylvania was a virtual terra incognita, ornithologically speaking, whereas it is now better known than any area of similar size in the eastern United States, and the distribution of bird life within its borders is better understood than is that of any like area. The distribution maps of the various species of birds shown herewith bear out this assertion.

In another sense the *Birds of Western Pennsylvania* is a résumé of my local ornithological studies during the past fifty years—a period when marked changes in ecological conditions and in bird life were taking place. This consideration explains (even if it does not excuse) the frequent injection of the personal element into the narrative. Much of the credit for the contents of the present work, however, must go to other observers who have generously placed their records at my disposal. The main object of this volume is to collate and interpret the records, from whatever source derived, in a way that will present a faithful picture of the bird life of our area. Obviously it is too much to expect in this day and age that all records, or even all those of an unusual character, be validated by specimens. In admitting records based on sight identifications I have been governed mainly by two considerations: the intrinsic probabilities and circumstances of each case; and my personal estimate of the ability and experience of the observer. A more conservative stand might have relegated certain species to a hypothetical list; instead I have decided to include them in normal sequence, with a full statement of the evidence and authority in each case to enable an independent judgment. At the same time every care has been taken to exclude records out of accord with recognized possibilities, and to question those that have appeared in print.

It remains to render grateful acknowledgment to those institutions and individuals that have had a share in making the *Birds of Western Pennsylvania* a reality. First of all, I wish to thank formally those who have supplied notes and records especially for this volume, as listed on pages 24 to 26. I am particularly indebted to Messrs. Edmund W. Arthur, Rudyerd Boulton, Thomas D. Burleigh, Bayard H. Christy, Samuel S. Dickey, Reinhold L. Fricke, Harry A. McGraw, Edward A. Preble, Ralph B. Simpson, and George M. Sutton, and to Miss Ruth Trimble, for write-ups on the habits of twenty-seven species. Dr. Frank M. Chapman, Professor Francis H. Herrick, Colonel Henry W. Shoemaker, and the commonwealth of Massachusetts (through Dr. John B. May) have authorized extracts from certain of their copyrighted books.

The Audubon Society of Western Pennsylvania and that of the Sewickley Valley, as already explained, have a large interest in the present undertaking, their financial assistance having made possible the necessary preliminary work. The following persons generously helped to defray the cost of typing the manuscript: Messrs. George E. Alter, Carl E. Behrhorst, John S. Fisher, Ralph E. Flinn, Charles B. Horton, Robert T. Houlden, H. L. Mason, Jr., D. M. Miller, James S. Pates, and Frank Semple, Jr.; Miss Anna M. Deens, Mrs. Tracy W. Guthrie, and Miss M. M. Alice Haworth. Publication of this book has been made possible by the co-operation of The Buhl Foundation, whose recognition of the scientific and educational significance of this project has been expressed in a grant of funds sufficient to cover the entire cost of issue. The University of Pittsburgh Press is responsible for the design of the book; and under its direction the book was printed, and the water colors reproduced in aquatone, by Edward Stern and Company of Philadelphia. I am grateful to the members of the University Press staff for their unselfish interest in the undertaking.

The original drawings for the colored illustrations have been prepared especially for this volume by that chief of bird-artists, George Miksch Sutton. They are designed to convey a suggestion of the local habitat of each species depicted, and all the figures are reproduced on the same scale (approximately one-third natural size). The species selected for illustration are not those that are rare or casual within the region, nor yet those that are strikingly colored or otherwise well known, but instead those that are hard for the amateur observer to identify in the field. Thus will a limited number of plates be made to serve the greatest number of readers. Dr. Sutton also made for this book the pen and ink drawings in the text. The map has been drawn by James R. Sweer and is based on a map of the United States Geological Survey; the contours, however, were transferred and reduced from the regular topographic sheets by Fred S. Datres and Frank A. Morrison, while contours for those parts of several counties not yet thus surveyed, including Cameron, Elk, and Forest, were supplied by Professor Raymond E. Murphy of The Pennsylvania State College. Miss Mary J. Cleeves is responsible for the construction of the relief map from the contours. The distribution maps in the text have been reduced from my series of large-scale working maps, which are deposited in the Carnegie Museum. Acknowledgment is due to the National Association of Audubon Societies for permission to use their cut illustrating the flight patterns of eastern hawks.

Portions of the manuscript have been examined by Mr. Arthur C. Bent, Dr. Alexander Wetmore, and Dr. Frank M. Chapman, whose suggestions and criticisms have been invaluable. Mr. Harry A. McGraw, Mr. Ansel B. Miller, Mr. W. M. Guynes, Professor Lawrence E. Hicks, Mr. Bayard H. Christy, and Mr. E. H. McClelland have also given me the benefit of their advice. Mr. Roger T. Peterson has been good enough to check over the field descriptions of all the species on the list. Miss Emily Alter (Mrs. Harwood Werkheiser) has read the manuscript and clarified the language at many points. For a critical and final editing of the book, I am deeply indebted to Elisabeth M. Sellers. It is a pleasure also to acknowledge my obligations to my loyal and able associate, Miss Ruth Trimble, for the vast amount of work she has done in connection with the preparation and publication of this volume. Not only has she compiled most of the data from the original sources, but she has also prepared all the family accounts that follow the Charadriidae, and several of the write-ups under "Habits." She has checked the references; read, reread, and corrected the manuscript and proofs; ironed out inconsistencies; offered pertinent advice, criticism, and sometimes much-needed encouragement; and in many other ways has earned the grateful thanks of the author.

W. E. Clyde Todd

CONTENTS

LIST OF FAMILIES

CONTENTS (Continued)

LIST OF COLOR PLATES

CONTENTS (*Continued*)

Part One

INTRODUCTION

INTRODUCTION

More than any other kind of wild life, birds arouse the interest and excite the curiosity of even casual observers of nature. Abundant and easily observed, they combine beauty of form and color with the appealing gift of song. Their aesthetic value, great though it may be, is transcended by their economic importance as natural enemies of noxious insects and rodents and as destroyers of weed seeds. Study of these highly organized, sensitive creatures reveals to the scientist the working of natural laws; he is concerned with the problems of origin and relationship, distribution in time and space, variation in form and color, nesting habits, and all the details of structure and life that comprise the science of ornithology.

To the student of the distribution of bird life the rugged mountains, high plateaus, deep, broad valleys, rivers, and lakes of Pennsylvania present a fascinating problem. Within the western half of the state there is sufficient variation in both latitude and altitude to support a diverse avifauna and to produce marked differences in the breeding ranges of many species of birds. The watercourses are important highways for transient waterfowl and shore birds; and many other migratory species pass through on their northward and southward flights.

The need for an ornithological investigation of this region to supplement studies in near-by states and to aid the local bird student has long been apparent. It is hoped that the present work may encourage the widespread interest in nature in general, and in birds in particular. This book has been written to serve a dual purpose: that of extending the knowledge of the distribution of birds in eastern North America, and of providing descriptive accounts of the birds occurring in western Pennsylvania.

GEOGRAPHY AND PHYSIOGRAPHY

Geographical limits—As used in this book, the term "western Pennsylvania" pertains to approximately the western half of the state. Its eastern limit has been arbitrarily fixed as the meridian of 77° 36′+ W., marking the eastern boundary of Potter County (not here a true north-and-south line). Twenty-nine counties are wholly included within these limits, and five others partially. The range in latitude is from 39° 43′ + at the Maryland–West Virginia line to about 42° on the New York line, with an extension reaching 42° 16′ in the northwest on the state's Lake Erie frontage of not quite fifty miles. The area described by these limits comprises roundly 24,500 square miles.

Physiographical Regions—The dominant feature of the topography of Pennsylvania is of course the Appalachian Mountain System, which traverses the state from northeast to southwest and separates it into two markedly distinct parts. Traveling by train or motor from Philadelphia to Pittsburgh, we pass from the fertile plains of Chester and Lancaster counties into a region of mountain ridges, with valleys between, all running in the same general direction. This type of country continues to the base of the steep Allegheny Front, or Escarpment. Ascending this we find ourselves on a plateau that slopes gradually away to the west. Two minor ridges intervene before we come to the rough and broken country of the Ohio Valley, where level lands are mainly confined to the flood plains of the streams. In western Pennsylvania, at least four fairly distinct physiographical regions can be recognized, as follows:

The Ridge and Valley Section comprises that part lying east of the main Allegheny Front. It includes (in our region) Bedford, Fulton, Huntingdon, and Blair counties; the larger part of Franklin, Mifflin, and Centre counties; and the western part of Juniata County. Its drainage is wholly to the east into the Potomac, Juniata, and West Branch of the Susquehanna, the tributaries of which in turn interlock according to the lay of the mountain ridges. The general northeast-southwest trend of these ridges is more marked toward the north. For the most part they are evenly topped hogbacks of sandstone or conglomerate (with occasional areas of slide-rock) that roughly parallel each other; but in some cases they meet and join, forming a valley closed at one end called a "cove." The Juniata River and its affluents have cut notches or gaps in many of these ridges; otherwise they remain unbroken for many miles. Tussey Mountain, for example, can be traced from the Maryland line all the way to southern Centre County, where it is lost in the wild jumble of hills and ridges known as the Seven Mountains. At points it reaches an altitude of 2,500 feet, but the average elevation is about 2,000 feet. The other ridges are somewhat lower, while the valley country proper seldom rises above 1,000 feet.

The Allegheny Plateau, as here restricted, includes the highlands west of the main Allegheny divide and north to the New York line. It is a part of the Appalachian Plateau, which, as generally understood, comprises all that part of the state west and north of the Allegheny Front (except a narrow strip along Lake Erie) and which in this work has been somewhat arbitrarily divided into two sections, one of which is the Allegheny Plateau and the other the Ohio Valley. Potter, McKean, and eastern Warren counties fall in the Allegheny Plateau region; also the counties south of these—Clinton (the western half), Cameron, Elk, Clearfield, and part of Centre. The general elevation of this section is 2,000 feet, with isolated spots in Potter County reaching 2,500 feet, but the surface has been so deeply gouged and trenched by erosion along the streams that it is decidedly uneven. Tributaries of the Allegheny River drain the northern and western parts of these northern counties (taken as a whole), but the main drainage is to the east into the West Branch of the Susquehanna, which has cut a deep gash through the Allegheny divide to reach the main stream. Beech Creek, an affluent of the West Branch, has also penetrated the divide, isolating a part of the same mountain range. In the apparent absence of a local name for this outlying ridge, it is here provisionally called Beech Creek Mountain.

South of Clearfield County the Allegheny Plateau contracts to include only Cambria and Somerset counties, but its general elevation increases. On the east it is sharply defined by the main crest of the Alleghenies, and on the west by Laurel Hill, a parallel ridge of about equal height. Through gaps in this ridge flow the Conemaugh and Youghiogheny rivers, the waters of which eventually reach the Ohio. Along these ridges the land rises to 2,500 feet, while Negro Mountain, an outlying spur of the Alleghenies proper in southern Somerset County, reaches an elevation of 3,220 feet—the highest point in the state.

West of and parallel with Laurel Hill, separated therefrom by the broad Ligonier Valley, lies Chestnut Ridge, which enters the state from the south at about the middle of the southern boundary of Fayette County, whence it spreads out and attains a height of 2,500 feet, contracting and falling off to the northward but not merging into the general level until it reaches Indiana County. Its continuity is interrupted, as is that of Laurel Hill, by the Conemaugh and Youghiogheny rivers, as well as by Loyalhanna and Blacklick creeks. Chestnut Ridge can scarcely be regarded, however, as an integral part of the Allegheny Plateau as here understood.

The Ohio Valley, in the restricted sense in which the term is used in this work, applies only to the immediate environs of the Ohio River in Beaver and Allegheny counties. In its larger and proper sense, however, it includes all that part of the state west of the Allegheny Plateau save a narrow strip along the Lake Erie shore. It is drained mainly by the Allegheny River, coming in from the north, and the Monongahela, from the south. These streams unite at Pittsburgh to form the Ohio, which before leaving the state receives the waters of another fair-sized tributary, the Beaver, which drains the northern counties of the western border. North of the Conemaugh River the Allegheny Plateau merges gradually into the Ohio Valley region as the general elevation falls off, but south of this stream the transition is abrupt and well defined. The region as a whole is irregular, broken, and hilly in character. Erosion is most marked near the larger streams, although at the headwaters the hills are round topped and the country more rolling. North and west of the terminal moraine, however, the land is much flatter, and there are parts of Erie and Crawford counties that in their level character suggest the western plains.

The Lake Shore Plain is a narrow strip, only a few miles wide, along Lake Erie, which is 573 feet above sea level. The plain is a level terrace forming the original basin of the lake and running back to the hills marking the original shore line; all the streams entering the lake have cut deep gorges in this terrace. Presque Isle, a semicircular peninsula jutting out from the mainland near Erie and enclosing a capacious but shallow bay, is the prominent feature of the lake shore proper.

The lakes and swamps of western Pennsylvania are mostly confined to the glaciated area, the drainage elsewhere being too rapid to permit their formation. Conneaut Lake, the largest natural lake in the state, which is situated in Crawford County a few miles west of Meadville, is only two and a half miles long and less than a mile wide. A few other small lakes occur in the Erie-Crawford district. Pymatuning Swamp, originally comprising 10,400 acres, once occupied a large depression in the western part of Crawford County that extended into the adjoining state of Ohio. It was a wooded bog of the sphagnum-tamarack type, fed by cold underground springs and supporting a flora and fauna of a boreal character. This highly interesting area, a relict of postglacial times, has been cleared in large part and converted into a shallow lake. Only at its upper end, near Hartstown, do original conditions still obtain. Smaller bogs of this type are found elsewhere in the northwestern part of the state, also in northern Clinton County and in the extreme southern portion of Centre County (Bear Meadows). Alder swamps also occur in the northwestern counties, particularly in Mercer County, but open swamps of the cattail variety are as a rule of small extent. They occur, however, on Presque Isle, at Hartstown, and south as far as New Galilee in northwestern Beaver County. In the plateau region there is little swampy ground; the largest areas are the Glades in southern Somerset County. There is a small open swamp near Bellefonte, Centre County, and another at Center Furnace in the same county.

While there are thus no natural lakes of any size outside the glaciated area, a number of artificial reservoirs in various other parts of the state have been formed by the damming of streams, and in some cases these are acquiring an ecological significance.

ECOLOGICAL CONDITIONS

In prehistoric times Pennsylvania must have been covered by heavy forest, but the glory of "Penn's Woods" has long since departed. Clearing and commercial exploitation began early in the history of the colony, and the stands of original forest are now reduced to a few pitiful remnants. The state and federal governments have finally intervened to save some of these from threatened extinction and to reforest large areas of cutover lands bought for the purpose. But over the greater part of the state there is nothing to prevent private owners from cutting timber as they please; thanks to an indifferent public sentiment, the destruction still continues. So far has deforestation progressed in many parts of the country that it is difficult to reconstruct a true picture of the original forest conditions from the few scattered fragments that remain. By far the greater part of our present forest is second growth—not necessarily composed of the same species as the original. During the nineties, when most of the writer's work in western Pennsylvania was done, there still remained some sizable areas of virgin forest which have since been lumbered over; his records, therefore, can never be duplicated. There is nothing to show that any considerable areas of prairie originally existed in western Pennsylvania; but the settlement of the country, which was well under way during the latter half of the eighteenth century, involved extensive clearing that created semiprairie conditions. Deforestation has gone forward steadily to the present day, and has entailed corresponding changes in the wild life.

The ridges in the ridge and valley section are in general forested from base to summit, while the intervening valleys have been cleared and cultivated. Pitch pine (*Pinus rigida*) is the dominant tree on the tops and upper slopes of these ridges, while black oak, chestnut oak, chestnut (formerly), black birch, and big-toothed aspen are also prevalent. The soil here is scanty and rocky, and the vegetation sparse and composed chiefly of bracken and huckleberries. On some of the steeper slopes there are rockslides, originating from the gradual weathering and disintegration of the cliffs above. On the lower and gentler slopes of these ridges, where the soil holds more moisture, the forest and lesser growth are much more luxuriant. Ravines in the valleys and on the mountainsides often support good stands of hemlock and rhododendron. The Pine Barrens in Centre County, and a similar area, the Tussey Mountain Barrens in Huntingdon County, are dry, sandy and stony plains with subterranean drainage that support much the same type of vegetation as that of the rocky summits of the ridges already described. In Fulton County there are also pine barrens, but of a somewhat different type, since the prevailing tree is not the pitch pine but the short-leaved pine (*Pinus echinata*), a species that enters from the south.

On its eastern face the Allegheny Escarpment, like the ridges to the eastward, is largely forested. Even before reaching the summit, however, a change is obvious, and becomes more marked after passing the crest and entering the plateau country. Not much remains of the original forest, which consisted mainly of white pine and hemlock; the latter was not confined to ravines, but spread over the level lands, especially in swampy places, where the undergrowth was rhododendron. The sugar maple, the beech, and the yellow birch were the principal deciduous trees in this area; they attained a good size, and left the ground beneath comparatively open. A mixed evergreen and deciduous forest of this general type once occupied all the plateau area, but it has now been largely extirpated by the lumber interests. In northern Pennsylvania in particular, hundreds of square miles have been lumbered over in the most wasteful manner and have then been swept by fire. In course of time these denuded areas, or "slashings," as they are called, grow up to blackberry canes and various bushes that form dense thickets, with here and there a charred stub projecting above the general level. It is the rule that the coniferous forest, once removed, is not succeeded by a forest of the same type, but by deciduous growth of a more austral, or southern, character. Hence it comes about that throughout the entire plateau area the conifers are receding, while the hardwood trees are pushing in from both sides to take their place. This fact has a most important bearing upon the distribution of bird and animal life. It is generally recognized that, since the Glacial period, life has been flowing toward the north—a tendency that has been greatly accelerated in recent years by human agency.

Deforestation has progressed farther in the Ohio Valley region than elsewhere in western Pennsylvania; at any rate, a larger proportion of this area has been brought under cultivation. While a fringe of sycamore, willow, and elm often remains along the streams, the lowlands, where the soil is richer and better adapted for farming, have generally been denuded. The uplands, too, have largely been cleared. What forest remains grows mostly on slopes too steep for cultivation or in narrow ravines or "hollows." The upland forest of this region, where any is left, is a deciduous forest of oak of several species, hickory, red maple, and chestnut (formerly). Hemlock, if it occurs at all, is strictly confined to the narrow floor and the steep sides of ravines. Other trees characteristic of the bottomlands are red maple, black birch, beech, basswood, white ash, and black and red oak, which form a rich, high forest with plenty of shrubbery and lush herbage beneath. White pine, which along the Ohio River is rare and local, becomes increasingly common to the northward as the country flattens out, and there is reason to believe that originally it must have predominated over the Erie-Crawford district generally, where now are left only a few isolated stands of large trees. The predominance of white pine in this area was probably an extension of the main range of this tree in the highlands to the eastward. There is a great deal of second-growth deciduous timber in the western counties, as well as much waste land, grown up to underbrush and briers that form heavy thickets, where many species of birds find suitable shelter. But there is no systematic effort being made here to reforest cutover lands that are unsuitable for cultivation.

The Lake Erie shore plain has been almost completely deforested, but there is reason to believe that its forest aspect was originally about the same as that of the region just to the south. The peninsula of Presque Isle is a sand-dune formation. Its open areas comprise marshes, ponds, and sandy flats, which support a type of vegetation that is unique in our region.

That there have been several successions of plant societies since the close of the Glacial period is obvious. These successions, as shown by O. E. Jennings,[1] depend primarily upon the stage of reduction to the condition of peneplain through which the region under consideration is passing. Dr. Jennings holds that all stages lead up to a climax stage in which a forest of the sugar maple–beech type is predominant. We are not so much concerned here with this point as with his expressed opinion that the sphagnum-tamarack bogs, with their characteristic growth of black spruce, balsam fir, and other conifers, are relicts of a type of forest that once prevailed over much of our area but that receded northward as the ice moved in that direction.

[1]*Proceedings Pennsylvania Academy of Science*, 1927, 1:23–55.

CLIMATE

Temperature—The southwestern counties of our region, and Franklin County in the extreme southeast, have the mildest climate. At Pittsburgh the average summer temperature in June, July, and August is 73.4° F.[2] At Erie it is 69° for the same period. At Bradford, McKean County, on the edge of the northern highlands, the summer mean is a little lower (67°), as it is also at Somerset in the southern part of the plateau region. There is thus a difference of over 6° of temperature between the upper Ohio Valley and the highlands in general. Temperatures of 100° or more are sometimes recorded in the western counties in July and August, while midwinter temperatures of –20° or even lower are occasional in the highlands and in the mountains southward almost to the state line. Our winters vary greatly in character. Thus, the winter of 1935–36 was noted for its severity, while that of 1931–32, when no ice formed on Lake Erie until March, was excessively mild. Not only are the summers cooler in the highlands, but they are also shorter. From frost to frost is less than 100 days in northern Potter County, as against 170 days in the Ohio and Monongahela valleys. The tempering effect of Lake Erie upon the climate makes for an equally long growing-season in its immediate vicinity.

Precipitation—The highlands of Somerset County have the heaviest annual precipitation; there the yearly mean exceeds fifty inches. This is because of their position with reference to Chestnut Ridge and Laurel Hill, which intercept the prevailing westerly winds and condense their moisture. The Ohio Valley and the Lake Shore Plain have the lowest annual precipitation, which averages less than forty inches. Centre County, too, has a somewhat lower average than the northern part of our region in general. In the highlands and northern counties the snowfall is heavier and lasts longer. In recent years there has been a perceptible change in the distribution of precipitation, which tends to occur in connected periods, so to speak, with long dry intervals between. The spring seasons in particular are backward, cold, and wet, as compared with those of forty or fifty years ago, while the autumns are often dry and unduly prolonged. Deforestation may possibly be a cause of these developments.

[2]A more detailed discussion of the climatic conditions at Pittsburgh is in W. S. Brotzman, *Cardinal*, 1925, v. 1, no. 5, p. 1–6.

DISTRIBUTION OF BIRD LIFE

A STUDY of the foregoing considerations necessarily makes for a better understanding of the local distribution of our avifauna. It is at once obvious, for instance, why aquatic and paludicoline (marsh-inhabiting) species are so largely confined to the northwestern counties, where alone they find conditions tolerable. But ecological factors, important as they may be, are by no means all that enter into the equation; climate likewise plays an important part. Remembering that a bird's home is where it nests and considering breeding data alone as significant, we find that birds are governed by precisely the same distributional laws as are other animals. They are similarly sensitive to heat and cold; temperature is therefore a controlling factor in their distribution. But temperature in turn depends upon latitude and altitude. There is enough variation in both these elements within our region, comparatively restricted though it is, to produce wide differences in the respective breeding ranges of many species of birds. These differences are the more marked because western Pennsylvania as a whole occupies debatable ground between the northern, or boreal, life forms on the one hand and the southern, or austral, forms on the other.

The life-zone concept, as developed by Allen, Merriam[1], and other authors, assumes that the facts of distribution, insofar as North America is concerned, are best expressed by dividing the continent into seven transcontinental belts or zones, each characterized by a certain assemblage of species. Beginning in the north, these life zones are the Arctic, Hudsonian, Canadian, Transition, Upper Austral, Lower Austral, and Tropical. The first three of these comprise the Boreal region with its characteristic fauna, and the next three the Austral, while the Tropical is in a class by itself. But many species of birds of undoubted austral affinities penetrate far into the Boreal region, and some boreal species similarly range into the Austral. The terms "Canadian Life Zone" and "Canadian Fauna" are used interchangeably in the present work, although properly speaking the latter is the eastern division of the former. The eastern division of the Transition Life Zone is known as the Alleghanian Fauna, and the corresponding division of the Upper Austral as the Carolinian Fauna. The boundaries between these faunas are of course not hard and fast lines; one passes into the other gradually; some species thin out and others take their places—until finally the whole faunal aspect of the country has changed. In western Pennsylvania we are concerned with only three faunas: the Canadian, the Alleghanian, and the Carolinian.

Ornithologists have generally accepted this proposed arrangement and have used it freely in defining distribution—as we do, provisionally, in the present work. Zoologists and botanists, on the other hand, have found it unacceptable and unworkable. The life-zone concept as a whole, including its fundamental basis of temperature control, has been challenged by several recent authors on apparently valid grounds.[2] Our present problem therefore is to discover to what extent the theory is supported or contraindicated by the facts at hand, insofar as the bird life of western Pennsylvania is concerned. Since no other area of comparable size in the East has received so much attention from this particular angle, such a study takes on peculiar significance.

Analysis of the avifauna discloses that of the 295 species of birds attributed to western Pennsylvania, approximately 180 breed within our limits. A few of these, such as the Caspian Tern (*Hydroprogne caspia imperator*) and the Painted Bunting (*Passerina ciris*), are merely accidental as breeding species and may therefore be disregarded in our study. A second group, almost wholly composed of water birds (swimmers and waders) but including such Passerine forms as the Long-billed Marsh Wren (*Telmatodytes palustris palustris*) and Grinnell's Water-Thrush (*Seiurus noveboracensis notabilis*), is virtually confined to the northwestern part of the state in glaciated territory, for reasons already specified. About seventy-three species breed throughout our area, although not all of them are evenly distributed; in the main these are species of wide latitudinal range. Omitting the water birds above mentioned and certain rare species the local ranges of which are as yet imper-

[1]J. A. ALLEN, *Bulletin Museum Comparative Zoölogy*, 1871, 2:375–425; C. H. MERRIAM, *National Geographic Magazine*, 1894, 6:229–238.
[2]Compare S. C. KENDEIGH, *Wilson Bulletin*, 1932, 44:129–143; V. E. SHELFORD, *Wilson Bulletin*, 1932, 44:144–157.

fectly worked out, there remain at least fifty-four species with a partial distribution within our area—a condition primarily dependent, we believe, upon the factor of temperature.

We shall first consider the species of admittedly southern affinities—the group commonly supposed to characterize the Carolinian Fauna (as generally understood) insofar as its northern limit is concerned. These are as follows:

*†Turkey Vulture (*Cathartes aura septentrionalis*)
*†Barn Owl (*Tyto alba pratincola*)
*†Red-bellied Woodpecker (*Centurus carolinus*)
*†Acadian Flycatcher (*Empidonax virescens*)
* Carolina Chickadee (*Penthestes carolinensis carolinensis*)
*†Tufted Titmouse (*Baeolophus bicolor*)
*†Bewick's Wren (*Thryomanes bewicki bewicki*)
*†Carolina Wren (*Thryothorus ludovicianus ludovicianus*)
* Eastern Mockingbird (*Mimus polyglottos polyglottos*)
*†Blue-gray Gnatcatcher (*Polioptila caerulea caerulea*)
* Prothonotary Warbler (*Protonotaria citrea*)
*†Worm-eating Warbler (*Helmitheros vermivorus*)
*†Cerulean Warbler (*Dendroica cerulea*)
†Northern Prairie Warbler (*Dendroica discolor discolor*)
*†Kentucky Warbler (*Oporornis formosus*)
*†Louisiana Water-Thrush (*Seiurus motacilla*)
*†Yellow-breasted Chat (*Icteria virens virens*)
*†Hooded Warbler (*Wilsonia citrina*)
*†Eastern Cardinal (*Richmondena cardinalis cardinalis*)
* Bachman's Sparrow (*Aimophila aestivalis bachmani*)

The most striking characteristic of the local ranges of these several species is a frequent discontinuity. The species enter from the southeast and southwest, either or both, to occupy areas of greater or less extent but separated from each other by the Allegheny Plateau. A few species, however, have apparently bridged the gap by crossing the southern part of Somerset County, where latitude finally counteracts altitude. In the above list the asterisk (*) indicates that the species occurs west of the highlands, while the dagger (†) indicates that it occurs east of the highlands. Only a few species seem actually to be restricted to one side or the other, but there are several that are rare in the east although common and characteristic in the west.

Comparison of the respective ranges of the species on this list as plotted on the maps shows wide discrepancies. Indeed, scarcely any two species have identical ranges. Even though we allow for the incompleteness of the available data and the imperfections of the maps based thereon, the disparities are yet too great and too varied to be ascribed wholly to these causes. In the west, for instance, the Carolina Chickadee, Eastern Mockingbird, Bewick's Wren, and Bachman's Sparrow range north only to the Ohio and lower Allegheny valleys and east, presumably, to Chestnut Ridge. Bewick's Wren, however, occurs irregularly as far north as Butler and Mercer counties. The Worm-eating Warbler and the Kentucky Warbler are definitely known to reach Chestnut Ridge, and the latter to pass it. The Worm-eating Warbler ascends the Allegheny Valley at least as far as Redbank Creek, and while it has been reported from the Pymatuning region in May, its breeding there has not been definitely established. There has been only one record of the Kentucky Warbler as far north as Mercer County. The Carolina Wren agrees in general with the two warblers just mentioned in its local breeding range, except for an isolated record from Warren on the upper Allegheny River. Species that regularly reach Crawford County, but are only accidental farther north, are the Turkey Vulture, Red-bellied Woodpecker, and Blue-gray Gnatcatcher. Eight species in the above list reach Lake Erie: the Barn Owl, Acadian Flycatcher, Tufted Titmouse, Cerulean Warbler, Louisiana Water-Thrush, Yellow-breasted Chat, Hooded Warbler, and Eastern Cardinal. On the other hand, one species, the Prothonotary Warbler, is known to breed only in Erie County.

East-and-west variation in the ranges of the species in this list is no less marked. In general, those species that range farther north in the westernmost counties tend to range higher up (that is, farther east) on the western slope of the Allegheny Plateau, but there are exceptions. The Turkey Vulture, for example, invades the central highlands, while the Red-bellied Woodpecker and the Blue-gray Gnatcatcher do not. Of the eight species that reach Lake Erie on the north, at least three, the Tufted Titmouse, Yellow-breasted Chat, and Eastern Cardinal, continue across the southern highlands and thereby merge their respective ranges on either side. But the Hooded Warbler, although known to breed at an elevation of two thousand feet in McKean County, as well as on the summit of Laurel Hill, apparently does not cross.

East of the main divide, variations in range within this particular group of species are somewhat less marked. Only one species, the Northern

Prairie Warbler, is peculiar to this area, and its range is restricted. The Kentucky Warbler barely enters the eastern edge of the region. Several other species common in the western part of the state are rare here. Apparently unaffected by elevation, such species as the Worm-eating Warbler, Yellow-breasted Chat, Hooded Warbler, and Bewick's Wren range indiscriminately across the valleys and mountains of this eastern section. The Louisiana Water-Thrush is a good example of a bird that has advanced its altitudinal range by following its particular habitat along streams to their headwaters. Together with several other species of southern predilections, it has entered Clinton County from the east along the valley of the West Branch of the Susquehanna.

Generally speaking, the species on the above list appear gradually to be extending their ranges—in some cases markedly. Year by year they move farther north and encroach more and more upon the highlands. The evidence for such progression is presented in detail in the discussion of each species. Moreover, the occurrence in spring of the Summer Tanager (*Piranga rubra rubra*) suggests that this southern species is also attempting to enter our region as a summer resident. This movement northward is not peculiar to western Pennsylvania biota; interpreted in conjunction with a corresponding recession of other northern forms, it signifies that life is still flowing north in the backwash of the Glacial period. That the process has sometimes been accelerated by human agency cannot be denied. As already pointed out, the displacement of the original coniferous forest of the highlands by second-growth hardwoods favors the appearance of austral bird life. There is reason to believe that under primeval conditions the ranges of the several species in the above list were not only more uniform, but also more restricted than at present.

It is worth noting that singularly enough the observable extensions of range of certain resident species have almost invariably been attendant upon the appearance of these species in new territory during the winter. It seems that the breeding ranges are being extended by wandering individuals that on the approach of the nesting season settle down wherever they chance to be. A contributing factor must be the increasing mildness of our winters in recent years. It is obvious that winter conditions rather than summer temperature must determine the ranges in all such instances. Thus we find that, while the Carolina Wren on the one hand and the Kentucky Warbler on the other have practically identical local ranges, these are undoubtedly the result of different conditions. Merriam's "laws of temperature control" break down here, as other writers have already pointed out. The fact is that we do not yet know the right formula for expressing the relation between temperature and distribution.

Next to be considered is the Alleghanian Fauna. Most of the species of birds that are supposedly limited by this fauna toward the north actually range across our entire area, although several are decidedly less common in the highlands, and there are indications that some of these are newcomers there. Deforestation has undoubtedly resulted in attracting some species that must heretofore have been absent. Among these is the Eastern Bob-white (*Colinus virginianus virginianus*), a resident species that has invaded our region from either side of the mountains, but one that has been unable to establish itself permanently over the greater part of the highlands because of the severity of the winters there. The Rough-winged Swallow (*Stelgidopteryx rufipennis serripennis*) is usually adjudged a Carolinian species, but it is more properly Alleghanian; it may have extended its former range into the latter fauna. The species presumed to be limited by the Alleghanian Fauna in their southward breeding ranges are:

Yellow-bellied Sapsucker (*Sphyrapicus varius varius*)
Least Flycatcher (*Empidonax minimus*)
Tree Swallow (*Iridoprocne bicolor*)
Black-capped Chickadee (*Penthestes atricapillus atricapillus*)
Veery (*Hylocichla fuscescens fuscescens*)
Nashville Warbler (*Vermivora ruficapilla ruficapilla*)
Black-throated Green Warbler (*Dendroica virens virens*)
Chestnut-sided Warbler (*Dendroica pensylvanica*)
Bobolink (*Dolichonyx oryzivorus*)
Rose-breasted Grosbeak (*Hedymeles ludovicianus*)
Eastern Purple Finch (*Carpodacus purpureus purpureus*)
Eastern Savannah Sparrow (*Passerculus sandwichensis savanna*)
Swamp Sparrow (*Melospiza georgiana*)

The southern breeding limits of these forms are fully as irregular as the northern limits of the several Carolinian forms already considered. In the westernmost counties, for instance, the Eastern Purple Finch is unknown south of Crawford County; the Yellow-bellied Sapsucker reaches

Butler County, and the Eastern Savannah Sparrow, Lawrence County; the Black-capped Chickadee reaches the Ohio Valley; while the Bobolink has even been found breeding in Greene County, although only rarely. The range of the Veery west of the mountains is closely complementary to that of the Carolinian species of most restricted distribution, such as the Carolina Chickadee—but the ranges of other species on the above list show varying degrees of overlapping with Carolinian forms. Similar irregularities and overlapping are shown in the ranges of these species east of the Allegheny divide. From that region there are as yet no breeding records for the Yellow-bellied Sapsucker, Nashville Warbler, and Eastern Purple Finch; the Tree Swallow and the Swamp Sparrow are rare and local. The Veery is there restricted to the Seven Mountains in Centre and Huntingdon counties and to the Allegheny foothills in Blair County. The Black-throated Green Warbler and the Chestnut-sided Warbler, on the other hand, overspread the entire ridge and valley section, where they are by no means confined to the ridges, but invade the valleys as well.

It is thus evident that the concept of the Alleghanian Fauna as a distinct zoogeographical unit, characterized by certain species of its own, is unsatisfactory. As I have previously pointed out, "Nowhere in western Pennsylvania, so far as known to the writer, does a pure Alleghanian Fauna exist, sundry species of both of the adjacent zones entering more or less into its composition everywhere. The irregular contour of the country, deforestation in recent years, and the comparative narrowness and virtually altitudinal character of the zone in this part are probably responsible for this state of affairs."[1] If the Alleghanian Fauna is to be recognized at all it must be regarded simply as applying to a transition belt of varying width between the Carolinian Fauna on the one hand and the Canadian on the other, where certain species of each meet and intermingle.

The Canadian Fauna now presents itself for analysis and discussion. We are here concerned only with those species that are limited by this fauna in their southward dispersion in the breeding season. Omitting several aquatic species the status of which is uncertain, we list the following as species of this fauna:

Eastern Goshawk (*Astur atricapillus atricapillus*)
Yellow-bellied Flycatcher (*Empidonax flaviventris*)
Alder Flycatcher (*Empidonax trailli trailli*)
Olive-sided Flycatcher (*Nuttallornis mesoleucus*)
Red-breasted Nuthatch (*Sitta canadensis*)
Brown Creeper (*Certhia familiaris americana*)
Eastern Winter Wren (*Nannus hiemalis hiemalis*)
Eastern Hermit Thrush (*Hylocichla guttata faxoni*)
Olive-backed Thrush (*Hylocichla ustulata swainsoni*)
Eastern Golden-crowned Kinglet (*Regulus satrapa satrapa*)
Blue-headed Vireo (*Vireo solitarius solitarius*)
Magnolia Warbler (*Dendroica magnolia*)
Black-throated Blue Warbler (*Dendroica caerulescens caerulescens*)
Blackburnian Warbler (*Dendroica fusca*)
Northern Water-Thrush and Grinnell's Water-Thrush (*Seiurus noveboracensis noveboracensis et notabilis*)
Mourning Warbler (*Oporornis philadelphia*)
Canada Warbler (*Wilsonia canadensis*)
Northern Pine Siskin (*Spinus pinus pinus*)
Red Crossbill (*Loxia curvirostra pusilla*)
Slate-colored Junco (*Junco hyemalis hyemalis*)
White-throated Sparrow (*Zonotrichia albicollis*)

On scanning this list we are at once impressed by the absence of certain species that are characteristic of this fauna in Canada; namely, the Canada Spruce Grouse (*Canachites canadensis canace*), Arctic Three-toed Woodpecker (*Picoides arcticus*), American Three-toed Woodpecker (*Picoides tridactylus bacatus*), Canada Jay (*Perisoreus canadensis canadensis*), Hudsonian Chickadee (*Penthestes hudsonicus hudsonicus*), and Canadian Pine Grosbeak (*Pinicola enucleator leucura*). On the above list the only species of undoubted boreal origin are the Eastern Goshawk, Red-breasted Nuthatch, Brown Creeper, Eastern Winter Wren, Eastern Golden-crowned Kinglet, Northern Pine Siskin, Red Crossbill, and possibly the Slate-colored Junco. The remaining thirteen species are clearly of austral origin, and are all migrants from the south. This reduction in true boreal forms "is not surprising when we remember that the Canadian Fauna of the Appalachian highlands is entirely isolated from the same zone in Canada by the interposition of low country in New York State."[2] Moreover, the spruce and fir forests characteristic of this zone in Canada are represented in Pennsylvania by only a few outlying communities, too small and too isolated to retain much of their original boreal avifauna. As already remarked, these trees are represented instead by white pine and hemlock, now unfortunately approaching extirpation.

[1] *Cardinal,* 1924, v. 1, no. 3, p. 6.
[2] Todd, *Cardinal,* 1924, v. 1, no. 3, p. 4.

Not only is the Canadian Fauna in Pennsylvania weak in boreal forms and diluted by the intrusion of Alleghanian species from the south, but it is also recessive in character, largely because of the passing of the coniferous forest. Some species, such as the Eastern Hermit Thrush and the Mourning Warbler, seem able to survive the destruction of their favorite habitat, while others, such as the Red-breasted Nuthatch and the Olive-backed Thrush, do not. For this very reason many of the locality records made some forty years ago and appearing on the accompanying maps could not be duplicated at the present day. But even after making all due allowance, we find wide discrepancies in the local distribution of the species attributed to this fauna, scarcely any two of which have exactly the same range. In general the Canadian Fauna is, or was, coextensive with the Allegheny Plateau in western Pennsylvania; it is found at all altitudes above two thousand feet. Some supposedly Canadian species, however, drop below one thousand feet in the Allegheny Valley wherever local conditions—deep and cool hemlock ravines—permit. But beyond a certain limit such conditions are inoperative. This fact is discussed more fully in the account of the range of the Magnolia Warbler. Certain species, such as the Olive-backed Thrush, have not yet been recorded in summer south of the West Branch of the Susquehanna in Pennsylvania; but since several of these reappear in the mountains of Maryland and West Virginia the presumption is strong that, as with most of their associates in this zone, their actual breeding ranges are, or were, continuous throughout the highlands of Cambria and Somerset counties.

While the Allegheny divide sharply limits the respective ranges of most of our Canadian species on the east, a few—the Blue-headed Vireo, Black-throated Blue Warbler, and Blackburnian Warbler—extend across the ridge and valley section, where they are not necessarily confined to the higher elevations. The Magnolia Warbler and the Canada Warbler, on the other hand, invade this section only toward the north. On the line between Centre and Huntingdon counties there is a complex mountain mass called the Seven Mountains, large and high enough to attract some species of Canadian birds. Bear Meadows, a wooded swamp once covered by a stand of spruce and fir, lies in this region and must formerly have been the home of still other northern birds, which have since disappeared with the removal of these trees. Another boreal island, faunally considered, is what remains of Pymatuning Swamp in Crawford County. There are signs, however, that several species of the Canadian Fauna may once have ranged entirely across Crawford and southern Erie counties, following a westward extension from the highlands of the original hemlock–white pine forest, which is now reduced to only a few remnants in these counties.

A summary of the facts which pertain to the distribution of the western Pennsylvania avifauna follows:

Less than half (forty-one per cent) of the breeding birds on our list are found throughout the area, although not all are evenly or impartially distributed at the present time. These species are for the most part those having a wide range that includes our area.

Current ecological conditions virtually restrict certain species of aquatic and paludicoline habitat to the northwestern part of the state.

Omitting those species that are rare and little known, there remain fifty-four, the local distribution of which apparently depends upon temperature and which are, therefore, significant as life-zone indicators.

The species of the so-called Carolinian Fauna enter from the south to occupy separated areas on either side of the Allegheny Plateau. In a few cases, however, the range is apparently continuous across the southern part of the plateau.

The local ranges of the several species of the Carolinian Fauna vary through wide latitudinal and altitudinal limits.

There is evidence that some if not all the Carolinian birds are extending their respective ranges, in some instances as the result of winter wandering.

Resident species of the Carolinian Fauna are governed by winter and not by summer climatic conditions; their occasional agreement in range with certain summer-resident species is fortuitous.

With but two exceptions, the species supposed to be limited by the Alleghanian Fauna in their northward range have a wide local distribution, while those similarly limited in their southward range irregularly overlap the ranges of the Carolinian species. No pure Alleghanian Fauna is known to exist in western Pennsylvania.

The Canadian Fauna of the Appalachian highlands is weak in truly boreal forms and is diluted by the intrusion of Alleghanian species from the south. It is therefore mainly characterized by the number of migrant species of austral derivation that breed within its confines. The species representing the Canadian Fauna have also widely varying latitudinal and altitudinal range-limits. Moreover, largely because of changes brought about in forest conditions, the Canadian element is receding and is being replaced by a more austral type.

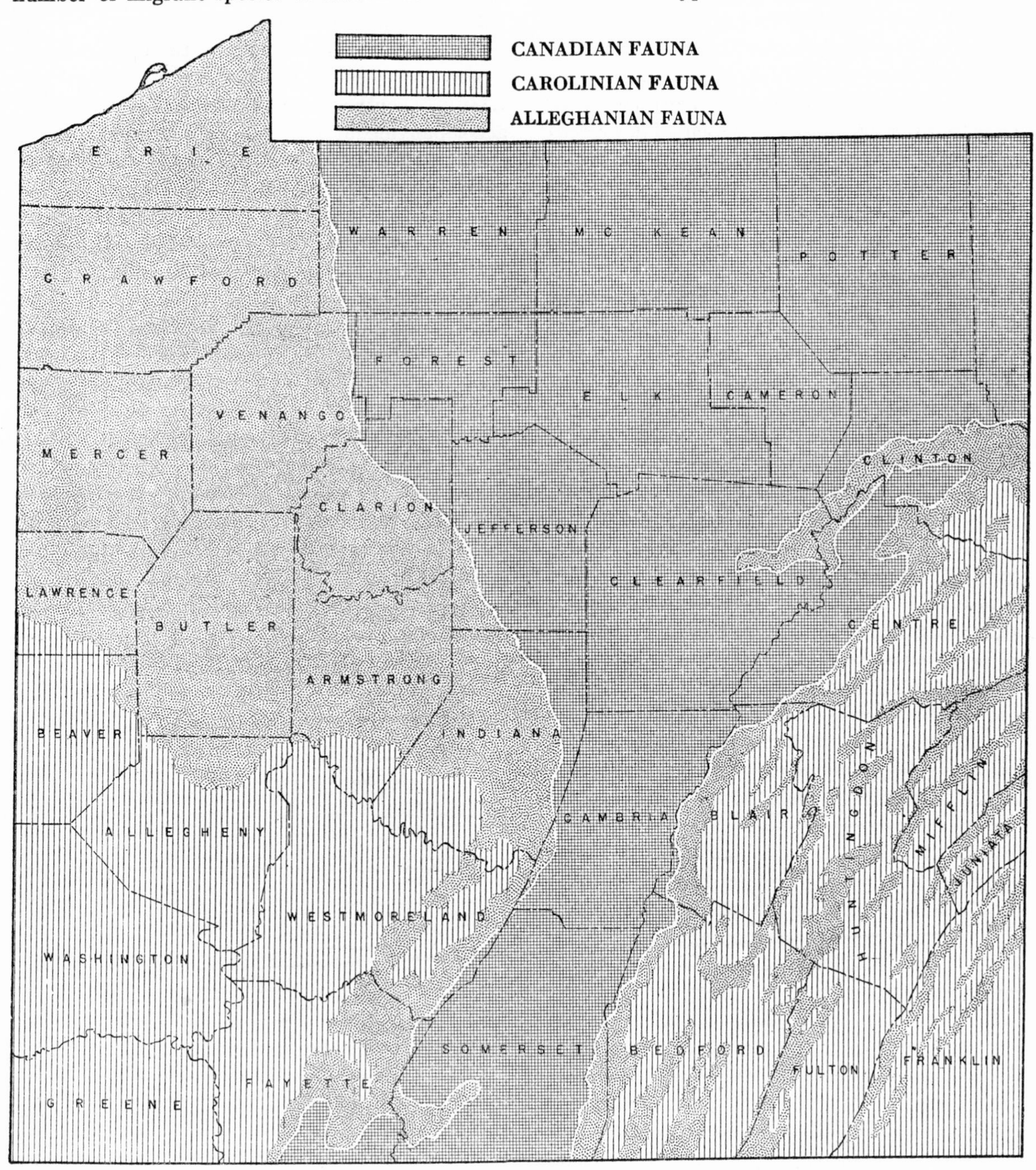

PROVISIONAL LIFE-ZONE MAP OF WESTERN PENNSYLVANIA

Local conditions may suffice to attract certain species of the Canadian Fauna to isolated spots or areas far beyond their main confines.

Conclusion—The faunal differences between the Ohio Valley and the highlands of Potter County are perfectly obvious, but the attempt to express these differences in terms of the current life-zone divisions is unsatisfactory and confusing. The mere allocation of one locality to the Carolinian Fauna and the other to the Canadian, without explanations or reservations, is inadequate. The fact is that these faunas, as represented in western Pennsylvania, share the variations shown in the corresponding life areas in other parts of the country. If our local distribution studies prove anything, it is that no such close correlation exists between the respective ranges of many species as we have been wont to believe. Every species is more or less a law unto itself insofar as its actual and potential distribution is concerned. One has only to examine and compare the distribution maps presented herewith to realize the irregularity and variability of the ranges of even the several species attributed to the same fauna. Between the ranges of species attributed to different faunas, moreover, there is so much overlapping that the faunal disposition of these transition belts is necessarily indeterminate.

Omitting from consideration species indiscriminately distributed throughout, and thus without real significance here, the true faunal picture of our area that thereupon emerges shows two distinct elements, or faunal groups of species, approaching from opposite directions to meet and commingle. The austral element, entering from the south, seems gradually to be increasing in numbers and enlarging its occupied territory, while the element entering from the north, on the other hand, is diminishing and retreating. The component species of both groups, however, vary widely in their responsiveness to changing environmental conditions, so that their respective range-limits show correspondingly wide divergencies. As a result, scarcely any two species of either group have identical ranges, and the kinds and degrees of overlapping between the two groups are inconstant. The progressive weakening and dilution of the boreal element in the Appalachians, although partially offset by increasing elevation toward the south, challenges the integrity of the Canadian Fauna as commonly understood. Certainly this fauna is by no means a homogeneous assemblage from north to south, and the propriety of considering it as such is questionable.

Where western Pennsylvania is concerned, the Alleghanian Fauna is likewise unrecognizable, since it has no species of its own. It is possible, however, with some degree of accuracy, and by using the method of averages, to delimit the zone of overlapping between the relatively northern and the relatively southern elements in the avifauna. The accompanying life-zone map represents an approximation to the facts in this regard and gives a fairly correct picture of the faunal areas of our region as determined by their bird life. In general, the northern element prevails over the Allegheny Plateau, from an elevation of two thousand feet upward, but it drops to lower elevations in the northern counties. Pymatuning Swamp is an outlying island where the northern element is dominant, as it is also in the Seven Mountains region of Centre and Huntingdon counties. The southern element prevails from the upper Ohio and lower Allegheny valleys southward; thence eastward to the foot of Chestnut Ridge; also in the Ligonier Valley; and in the extreme southeastern corner of our region, in Franklin County. Elsewhere, through the ridge and valley section generally, and across a wide belt in the western counties north of the Ohio and lower Allegheny valleys, the northern and southern elements mingle and overlap to a confusing extent.

Purely as a matter of convenience, these respective faunal areas are referred to in the body of this work as the Canadian, Carolinian, and Alleghanian faunas, but these designations are misleading in a broader sense, as we discover when we try to correlate the areas in question with the schematic divisions called by these names. While faunal zones have a certain objective reality, as all experienced field workers know, they are not fixed quantities but variables. In the East especially, the ranges of many species have greatly changed since primeval times, and faunal conditions are still in a state of flux. Belts of transition are wide and variable, and the whole life-zone picture is blurred and inconsistent. It is perhaps not too much to say that the facts of the distribution of birds, in western Pennsylvania at least, do not readily lend themselves to interpretation on the basis of the life-zone concept as it is currently understood. This concept will have to be considerably modified if it is to be accepted. Even so, the indications are that the primary faunal divisions of North America are not life zones, since the latter play only a secondary part in determining distribution. This thesis we hope to develop another time, and pause here only to add that the faunal allocation of any given locality on the basis of a relatively small percentage of its whole fauna is misleading and unscientific.

PRESENT STATUS OF BIRD LIFE

In early times bird life in western Pennsylvania, as elsewhere, must have been incredibly more abundant than it is today. The advent of the white settler with his ax and gun doomed the wilderness and much of its wild life. Unfortunately we are without trustworthy records of primitive conditions so far as birds are concerned; even Wilson and Audubon, who arrived on the scene before great changes had come to pass, are virtually silent on this phase of the subject. It is not hard, however, to reconstruct the picture. Forest species must have predominated. There could have been few if any such birds as the Bob-white, Prairie Horned Lark, Bobolink, Meadowlark, Vesper Sparrow, Savannah Sparrow, and Grasshopper Sparrow—all of which must have come in after the forest had been cleared. They probably approached from the Mississippi Valley—precisely as we believe certain other species, such as the Lark Sparrow, have done in more recent years. We have already discussed the effects of deforestation in changing the climate and in furthering the advance of austral species at the expense of boreal forms. It is equally obvious that the actual number of individuals of strictly woodland species has decreased with the passing of the virgin forests. This decrease has been offset somewhat by an increase in the numbers of more adaptable species that now tenant our orchards and gardens and of still others that prefer second growth and bushy thickets rather than the deep forest.

Two especially favored species, the Robin and the House Wren, have increased beyond normal bounds in the past forty or fifty years, as has also the Cardinal. Nevertheless, taken by and large, the small Passerine and Picarian birds have certainly decreased numerically during this period—some more than others. This is the considered judgment of the writer, based on his own experience and that of such reputable local observers as Harry C. Kirkpatrick, Ralph B. Simpson, J. Warren Jacobs, and Bayard H. Christy. Even the winter birds seem to be less numerous than formerly. Over wide areas some species, such as the Blue Jay and the Rose-breasted Grosbeak, have almost disappeared from their former haunts. The cause of this general recession can be laid to man's interference in one way or another, either within or, in the case of migratory species, beyond the limits of our region. Among contributing causes may be suggested the following: the progressive reduction of suitable habitat, as country and suburban building grows apace; the building of automobile roads; some activities of the Civilian Conservation Corps; the spraying of orchards; the pollution of streams and consequent destruction of insect and aquatic life; the grievous increase of the parasitic Cowbird; intensified competition from such imported pests as the English Sparrow and the European Starling; and direct action by enemies such as the Crow and the Red Squirrel, formerly held in check by predators. Nor can the domestic cat be overlooked, although most of the harm it does is confined to a few species.

If the encroachments of civilization have thus operated to change and restrict the distribution of the small members of the bird fauna, how much more have they affected the larger and more conspicuous birds! Birds of prey in particular have suffered such ruthless persecution that over most of the state they have been reduced to a tithe of their former numbers. Ignorance and stupidity could have gone no further than the legal sanction given to their senseless slaughter! There is a class of gunners—I refuse to call them sportsmen—to whom all sizable birds are objects of pursuit, and these men are largely to blame for the comparative scarcity of hawks, owls, herons, gulls, loons, and grebes. Nor have the game birds been spared. The Wild Turkey was long ago exterminated over the greater part of our area, although it still persists in the mountainous counties. The Ruffed Grouse is sadly depleted, and holds its own only where it enjoys absolute protection. Waterfowl are the worst sufferers from the shooting mania, as well as from stream pollution. There was a time when ducks were regular and fairly common on the Ohio River, where now they are sufficiently rare to excite remark. On the other hand, ducks and other waterfowl are far more numerous today on the waters of Erie Bay and Presque Isle than they were in 1900—not because they have increased in general (the contrary is true), but because of the present immunity afforded them there. Pymatuning Lake has also served to attract water birds in large numbers, and the most astonishing development has been the increasing number of species that breed there. The maintenance of a state sanctuary covering the best part of the area naturally favors this development. Authorities are agreed that excessive shooting is chiefly responsible for the present deplorable state of waterfowl in the country at large.

Shore birds, never very common anywhere in western Pennsylvania except at Erie, have certainly not become more abundant in recent years. The Woodcock in particular is now alarmingly scarce, and Wilson's Snipe is much less common than formerly. The Passenger Pigeon, which once nested by the million in the northern counties, was virtually exterminated before the close of the last century, and its near relative, the useful and pretty Mourning Dove, is now only about one-fiftieth as plentiful as it then was. It is most encouraging, therefore, to find the latter bird removed from the game list by a recent legislative act, at the behest of interested conservationists. The Pennsylvania Game Commission, sponsor of the act, is to be highly commended, too, for its about-face in the matter of hawk and owl destruction. What is needed in Pennsylvania, however, is a conservation commission with a broad outlook and wide powers—one that could be depended upon for a constructive, correlated, and continuing policy, based on scientific principles, to protect the forests, streams, and wild life of the state.

HISTORICAL REVIEW OF WESTERN PENNSYLVANIA ORNITHOLOGY

THE EARLIEST references to the birds of western Pennsylvania are merely incidental ones in certain old books of travel. Alexander Wilson, the first author to publish any scientific information on the subject (1811), mentions very briefly only five species. Edwin James's account of Major Stephen H. Long's expedition to the Rocky Mountains in 1819–20 contains a few desultory observations on the bird life along the Ohio River. Audubon, in the five volumes of his *Ornithological Biography* (1831–39), refers to localities in western Pennsylvania in connection with birds only seven times. Yet both Wilson and Audubon had unparalleled opportunities to study the bird life of the Allegheny Mountains, which they repeatedly crossed; and the latter once journeyed from Lake Erie to Pittsburgh by way of Meadville. Ornithological records made in the mountains at this early period, when conditions were still virtually primitive, would have been invaluable for comparison; but this field was neglected in the haste to reach the supposedly more interesting and productive regions beyond. Jared P. Kirtland, who wrote on the birds of Ohio in 1838, casually includes two extralimital records from Beaver County, Pennsylvania, one of which, however, is admittedly doubtful. Maximilian, Prince of Wied, refers in 1839 to a few species observed in the Allegheny Mountains, probably near Ebensburg. R. M. S. Jackson's list of birds in his book *The Mountain* (1860) is worthless. Between 1877 and 1882 just seven brief notes appeared in ornithological journals; among the authors were included such well-known authorities as George B. Sennett and Charles H. Townsend.

In 1882 and 1883 the first local lists for our region were published: one on the birds of Bradford, McKean County, by James A. Teulon; the other on the birds of Westmoreland County, primarily Latrobe and Chestnut Ridge, by Dr. Townsend. In the next few years appeared more notes and articles, of no great importance. W. T. Warrick added a few notes on the birds of Washington County. George P. Elliott wrote of certain birds observed at Mercer. Walter Van Fleet's first and only printed note was published in 1884, the same year that Harry C. Kirkpatrick, the veteran ornithologist of Meadville, published his first short article. In 1886 appeared the first article by an observer and collector whose long-continued work in Greene County has made him the acknowledged authority on the birds of that section—J. Warren Jacobs. Between 1886 and 1890 he wrote no less than twenty-one articles, mostly on the nesting of various species, for "amateur" ornithological serials, now unfortunately rare and hard to locate.

Thus it appears that until 1890 western Pennsylvania, from an ornithological point of view, was practically an unworked and unknown field, although by then the bird life of the adjoining states (West Virginia excepted) had become fairly well known. The publication in 1890 of the second edition of B. H. Warren's *Report on the Birds of Pennsylvania* marked an era in the ornithological history of the state and stimulated numerous local amateur observers to make studies of its birds. The merits and demerits of Warren's work are discussed in the Bibliography. Despite all its faults, it afforded the first real hint of the ornithological riches of the mountains and of the western part of the state generally. One effect of its publication was to stimulate in the next few years the output of papers and notes on local birds, among which were some by the present writer. Jonathan Dwight's "Summer Birds of the Crest of the Pennsylvania Alleghanies" (1892) was shortly followed by Todd's "Summer Birds of Indiana and Clearfield Counties" (1893), Jacobs' "Summer Birds of Greene County" (1893), and William L. Baily's "Summer Birds of Northern Elk County" (1896). These local lists were actually the first papers dealing faunally with western Pennsylvania birds. In the meantime the present writer, impressed by the need and importance of working this field, had begun a systematic survey of the summer avifauna of western Pennsylvania as a whole—a project which engaged his time and attention for several successive seasons until 1899, as explained below. The next year, 1900, he made an intensive study of the bird life of Erie and Presque Isle, the best region for water birds in the western half of the state. The results of this study were published in 1904, preceding the general report (the present work) for which they were originally intended.

Many of the titles in the Bibliography for the years from 1891 to 1910 are technical monographs and other papers of wide scope that deal only incidentally with western Pennsylvania. In 1903 Wells W. Cooke, for instance, began a series of articles in *Bird-Lore* on "The Migration of Warblers," a series that was extended to include other families of birds and has been continued since 1917 by Harry C. Oberholser. These articles contain data supplied by several observers in our region and are therefore pertinent. Among the more noteworthy faunal papers of this period (after 1901) may be mentioned Francis R. Cope's "Observations on the Summer Birds of Parts of Clinton and Potter Counties" (1902), Todd's "Mammal and Bird Fauna of Beaver County" (1904), Thomas D. Keim's "Summer Birds of Port Alleghany" (1905), and Witmer Stone's "June Birds of Fulton County" (1906)—the latter paper obviously brought out without knowledge of the present writer's previous explorations in that particular area. Valuable studies of certain species were contributed by Thomas H. Jackson (on the Mourning Warbler) and by Mr. Jacobs (on the Yellow-throated Vireo, Purple Martin, Golden-winged Warbler, and Grasshopper Sparrow).

About 1910 the literature dealing with the birds of western Pennsylvania began to develop, and it has been growing ever since. This increase in interest was due in the first instance to the appearance in the field of four observers and collectors whose contributions in print bulk large in the total: Ralph B. Simpson, Richard C. Harlow, Thomas D. Burleigh, and Samuel S. Dickey. Mr. Simpson's first printed note appeared in 1890, and by 1909 he was writing freely in the *Oölogist* of his experiences in Warren County. He was the first to discover the Goshawk and other northern birds nesting in this region, and his articles have been copiously used in the preparation of the present report. Mr. Harlow began to write at about the same time, and has made some notable contributions. Being primarily an oölogist, however, he has too often been purposely vague as to the exact localities of his valuable finds, a practice that seriously detracts from the scientific value of his published work. Most of his collecting in western Pennsylvania was done in Centre and Huntingdon counties, but he worked also in other parts of the state. His formal attempt to correlate these scattered activities, however, is rather unfortunate, as elsewhere pointed out. His last article, "The Breeding Habits of the Northern Raven in Pennsylvania" (1922), is his best. Beginning in 1910, Mr. Burleigh has written extensively on the bird life of Allegheny, Centre, and Fayette counties; he has published a résumé of his observations in the form of fully annotated local lists, one for each county. Dr. Dickey's initial contributions appeared in 1909 and at first referred wholly to Greene County; but he soon extended his field of operations to other counties. Some of his work was carried on in Centre and Huntingdon counties in collaboration with Messrs. Harlow and Burleigh, as we learn by a comparison of the records of all three observers. Dr. Dickey, too, is often indefinite as to localities, but his manuscript notes supply most of the missing data. His outstanding accomplishments are his discoveries of Henslow's Sparrow nesting in Huntingdon County and of Bachman's Sparrow nesting in Greene County.

The founding of the Western Pennsylvania Audubon Society in 1916 gave impetus to the study of birds in Allegheny County and disclosed interest and resources previously unsuspected. The local lists in the annual "Christmas Census" of *Bird-Lore* increased to such an extent that their publication has had to be curtailed. "The Season" reports, in the same periodical, were begun in 1923 and were compiled for two years by George M. Sutton; from 1925 to 1927 by Sidney K. Eastwood; and in 1928 by Rudyerd Boulton. Based on sight observations by persons of widely varying degrees of experience, these records must be received with caution. An effort has been made to evaluate them for the purposes of the present work, as indicated in the text and in the Bibliography. The establishment of the *Cardinal* in 1923 as the official organ of the Sewickley Valley Audubon Society, under the editorship of Bayard H. Christy, has supplied a medium of publication for the members of both regional societies. At first many of the shorter notes and articles in this semiannual serial were untitled and unsigned, but lately a higher standard has prevailed. For the past fifteen years the *Cardinal* has been publishing more material on western Pennsylvania birds than all other ornithological serials combined. While there has been the usual modicum of inconsequential items, the number of articles of serious intent and wide general interest has so increased that the place of the *Cardinal* as an ornithological serial is now fully assured—even beyond the local field.

Among the numerous articles from Mr. Christy's pen which deserve special mention are those on the Whistling Swan at Erie, the nesting of the Turkey Vulture, the Sparrow Hawk in Pittsburgh, the Upland Plover, and the Goshawk bounty law. In collaboration with Dr. Sutton he has also brought out two extremely valuable papers—on the Bobwhite and on the Wild Turkey in Pennsylvania—and a list of the birds of Cook Forest. Dr. Sutton's own contributions number forty-two titles, many of which are of great interest and value both from a local and from a general standpoint. He has made carefully prepared and well-written studies of such interesting species as the Goshawk, Wilson's Snipe, Prairie Horned Lark, Chimney Swift, and Northern Pileated Woodpecker. His longest paper, dealing with the birds of Pymatuning Swamp and Conneaut Lake (1928), is the best local list from western Pennsylvania. In connection with it should be read Ruth Trimble's résumé of the results of later field work in the same region (1937). Dr. Sutton has also published *An Introduction to the Birds of Pennsylvania* (1928), which merits high praise and is indeed the first attempt to deal with the birds of the state at large since Warren's *Report.*

The random notes and field lists, mainly from Erie and the Pymatuning region, that have been appearing lately in various serial publications, are of dubious scientific value. Based wholly on sight identifications, in some cases by observers who did not know what to expect, these records must be scrutinized with care. Many are of no particular importance, while those referring to rare or unusual species are often compiled in a suspiciously offhand fashion. Higher scientific standards should prevail in recording further additions to our knowledge of the birds of western Pennsylvania.

FIELD WORK

Although I first became actively interested in the study of birds in 1886, it was not until a year later that I undertook to make a systematic record of my observations, and began to collect eggs in sets with full data. Handicapped by the lack not only of a suitable book of reference but also of any means of securing specimens for identification, my progress for two years was slow indeed. In 1889, however, I acquired a shotgun as well as a copy of Elliott Coues's *Key to North American Birds*, and thereafter my local list increased by leaps and bounds. Seldom did I find it necessary to shoot a second specimen of the same kind for identification. It was at this time that I began to send migration reports to the Division of Economic Ornithology and Mammalogy (later the Bureau of Biological Survey) of the United States Department of Agriculture; this proved a most helpful connection, which eventually led to my appointment late in 1891 as an assistant in that office, and brought my local field work to an end for the time being. My journal for the five years from 1887 to 1891, dealing with 155 species of birds, is really the nucleus of the present volume and moreover contains numerous notes and observations which, because of changed conditions, could not now be duplicated. All my field work during this period was done in Beaver County, with my home of Beaver as a center, save for a month—May 15 to June 14, 1889—spent in the Buffalo Creek region of Armstrong and Butler counties.

Incidentally, it was this 1889 excursion that revealed unexpected differences between the respective avifaunas of two localities only forty miles apart and suggested the need for similar studies in adjoining regions heretofore neglected. The bird life of the mountains in particular, and of the highlands in general, was almost entirely uninvestigated. True, Warren had in 1890 published some desultory information on the birds of these areas, but in such an inexact fashion that it left much to be desired. Dwight's "Summer Birds of the Crest of the Pennsylvania Alleghanies," which appeared in 1892, led me to consider a plan by which I might connect his work there with my own farther west, in the upper Ohio and lower Allegheny valleys. Thus it came about that I utilized part of my vacation in June, 1892, to make a study of the summer bird life of two intermediate stations, in Indiana and Clearfield counties respectively.[1]

These studies were so fruitful that I determined to undertake an exhaustive ornithological survey of western Pennsylvania, and to do here for myself what the government was then doing in other parts of the country. C. Hart Merriam, then chief of the division, took sufficient interest in the proposed work to grant me a month's leave of absence during June and early July in several successive years, excluding 1896. During these periods I traveled over the state, according to a carefully prearranged schedule, and made collections and observations at various strategic points. During the seasons of 1893, 1895, and 1898 I also utilized the services of others toward the same end. Thus I succeeded in covering western Pennsylvania fairly well and in amassing a great store of data on its breeding birds and their local distribution. My last excursion of this particular kind was in 1899, after I had become associated with the Carnegie Museum. Of the 1,926 specimens of birds collected from 1892 to 1899, inclusive, 1,092 are in the Biological Survey collection, and 834 are in the Carnegie Museum. In labeling these specimens I indicated the localities with meticulous exactness. Since these several expeditions actually supplied the bulk of the distributional data for the present work, the itinerary for each is here presented:

1892—June 22–25: Two Lick, Indiana County, from Two Lick and Yellow creeks to the summit of Chestnut Ridge; 65 species. June 28: Cresson, Cambria County (between trains); 15 species. June 28–July 2: East of Coalport, Clearfield County; 55 species. (Lists published.)

1893—June 12–17: Traveled on foot, with gun and knapsack, from Ebensburg, Cambria County, to Punxsutawney, Jefferson County, to determine the western limit of the predominance of conifers (hemlock and white pine) and of the birds that inhabit this association. At this time the western part of Cambria County was still largely virgin forest, rich in northern bird life but hard to penetrate. In Indiana County the country became

[1]Published in the *Auk*, 1893, 10:35–46.

more civilized. My route took me from Ebensburg into the valley of the south branch of Blacklick Creek and thence along the highway to a point about three and one-half miles east of Belsano. On June 13 I followed the highway another mile to the west, struck off into the forest in a northerly direction for about three miles, and then veered to the northwest, crossing the main Blacklick Creek and its north branch, and stopping for the night at a point near the mouth of Dutch Run. On June 14 I proceeded north for a while and then turned to the west along the first road encountered, crossed Dutch Run a second time, and shortly thereafter entered opener country in Indiana County. Up to this point, 51 species of birds were recorded, including many attributed to the Canadian Fauna. From here to Pine Flats this element was less in evidence, while, conversely, several open-country species became prominent. On this part of the trip, and at Pine Flats on June 15, I listed a total of 36 species. During the afternoon of that day I continued northward to Richmond (Rochester Mills post office). The pines gradually disappeared near Purchase Line, and beyond that point what little remained of the forest growth was almost wholly deciduous. On June 16 I listed 32 species between Richmond and Punxsutawney, and on the next day, 5 additional species at the latter place.

On June 19 I traveled from Beaver to "Pine Grove," near Industry, in company with Edward A. Preble. June 20: By rail to Foxburg, Clarion County. June 21–22: Clarion Junction to Clarion, Clarion County; 45 species. June 23–24: Buffalo Creek region, Armstrong and Butler counties.

From June 2 to July 15 Edward A. Preble collected birds for me. His itinerary follows: June 2–5: New Paris and Chestnut Ridge, Bedford County; 57 species. June 6–12: Crumb, Somerset County, on the western slope of the Alleghenies proper; 55 species. June 14: Hooversville, Somerset County; 45 species. June 15–17: Somerset (south to Kimberlen's Run), Somerset County; 56 species. June 18–19: Beaver to "Pine Grove," near Industry. June 20–21: By rail to Stoyestown, Somerset County. June 22–24: On foot across Laurel Hill to Laughlintown, Westmoreland County, by way of Jennerstown, Somerset County; 57 species. June 26–29: Chestnut Ridge, southwest of Idlewild, Westmoreland County; 51 species. June 29–July 3: About two miles east of Mount Pleasant, Westmoreland County; 54 species. July 5–6: Chestnut Ridge near Jumonville, Fayette County; 31 species. July 7–8: Ohiopyle, Fayette County; 36 species. July 8–11: Confluence to Sugarloaf Mountain, Fayette County; 48 species. July 12–13: Rockwood to Negro Mountain, Somerset County; 38 species. July 14–15: Meyersdale and Keystone Junction, on the western slope of the Alleghenies, Somerset County; 49 species.

During this season Fred LeRoy Homer also investigated three localities on the upper Allegheny River in my behalf: June 30–July 5: Tidioute, Warren County; 54 species. July 5–8: Tionesta, Forest County; 52 species. July 10–14: Franklin, Venango County; 50 species.

To the above record must be added the note of a brief trip I made to Erie from August 28 to 30.

1894—June 9: From Freeport north along Buffalo Creek, Armstrong County; 35 species. June 10–11: Buffalo Creek region, Armstrong and Butler counties, as far as Boggsville. June 12: Clarion Junction, Clarion County. June 12–13: Kane, McKean County, to a woods along the Philadelphia and Erie Railroad three miles west; 29 species. June 14: Ridgway, Elk County (south of the town); 36 species. June 14–15: Maysville (now Mayport), Clarion County, 44 species. June 15–16: Redbank, Clarion County; 37 species. June 18–19: Beaver. June 20–21: Weedville, Elk County; 49 species. June 22–23: Driftwood, Cameron County; 47 species. June 25–26: Keating, Clinton County, including a trip up Burns Run to the summit of Beech Creek Mountain; 47 species. June 27: Renovo, and up Drury Run, Clinton County. June 28: On foot from Renovo to Tamarack Swamp, Clinton County. June 28–29: Tamarack Swamp; 47 species. June 30: Conemaugh Furnace, Westmoreland County; 29 species. July 1–4: Beaver.

1895—From June 8 to 11 I hiked across parts of Mifflin, Huntingdon, and Centre counties. Leaving the railroad at McVeytown, Mifflin County, I followed the road leading north over Jacks Mountain to Belleville, and recorded 43 species of birds on the way. On June 10 I continued across Standing Stone Mountain to Greenwood Furnace, Huntingdon County, and thence across the western flank of Broad Mountain to the valley of

Standing Stone Creek, which I followed to a point about a mile beyond the mouth of Detweiler Run. Over this part of the route 37 species were observed. On June 11 I retraced my route for two miles, and then took a trail that led up the mountain into Bear Meadows, Centre County, of which I made a cursory examination. Thence a tramroad guided me down the north side of the mountain, and I presently reached Boalsburg and finally State College. I listed 40 species on the way.

On June 12 I observed 23 species at State College, and at the Pine Barrens west of the town. June 13: Howard, Centre County, to summit of Bald Eagle Mountain; 29 species. June 14: Renovo, Clinton County, to Tamarack Swamp (up Drury Run). June 14–15: Tamarack Swamp; 48 species. June 16: Cross Fork, Potter County; 15 species. June 17: Cross Fork Junction, Potter County; 20 species. June 18: Clermont, McKean County, to Katrine Swamp. June 19: Katrine Swamp to Mount Jewett, by way of Hazelhurst; 43 species. June 20: Cranberry Swamp, near Tiona, Warren County; 43 species. June 20, evening: Warren, Warren County, with R. B. Simpson; 12 species. June 21: On foot from Waterford to Lake Pleasant, Erie County, returning on June 22; 43 species. June 23–24: Meadville, Crawford County, with Fred LeRoy Homer. June 25: Hartstown, Mud Lake, and Pymatuning Swamp, Crawford County; 34 species. June 26: Harrisville, Butler County, to Pine Swamp, Mercer County; 36 species. June 27: Buffalo Creek region, Armstrong and Butler counties. June 28–July 1: Beaver. July 1: By rail to Portage, Cambria County. July 2: On foot from Portage up Trout Run and across the crest of the Alleghenies to a point on the western flank of Blue Knob; 35 species. July 3: To the summit of Blue Knob, thence to Blue Knob village, East Freedom, and McKee Gap, Blair County; 39 species. July 4: Martinsburg, Blair County; 20 species.

From July 1 to 20 Mr. Homer investigated a number of localities in the northwestern counties for me: July 1: Half Moon Swamp, Mercer County; 35 species. July 2–3: Sandy Lake and Stoneboro, Mercer County; 45 species. July 3–4: Sugar Lake, Crawford County; 46 species. July 6: Waterford and Lake Le Bœuf, Erie County; 41 species. July 15–16: Hartstown and Mud Lake, Crawford County; 45 species. July 17–18: Tamarack Swamp, Erie County; 43 species. July 19–20: Edinboro and Conneauttee Lake; 56 species.

From June 19 to July 19, William H. Phelps traversed on foot Franklin, Fulton, and Bedford counties, close to our southern boundary, after which he worked the southern part of Huntingdon County in similar fashion, concluding his trip in extreme southern Mifflin County. His written report on this trip is a model of neatness and precision; his route traced on the county maps shows the exact place where each individual specimen was collected. On June 19 and 20, starting from Mercersburg, Franklin County, he covered the country between the West Branch of Conococheague Creek to the foot of Cove Mountain; 46 species were listed. June 20–22: Little Cove, Franklin County, and the west slope of Cove Mountain and the east slope of Tuscarora Mountain; 50 species. June 24–25: Licking Creek, two miles east of Needmore, and the western slope of Scrub Ridge, Fulton County; 52 species. June 26–27: Whips Cove north of Locust Grove, and Town Hill to a point east of Emmaville, Fulton County; 53 species. June 28–29: Shavers Creek east of Clearville, Bedford County; 45 species. July 1–3: From Charlesville, Bedford County, as headquarters, the valley of Cove Creek was worked, and the west slope of Tussey Mountain southeast of Springville, north to a point within two miles of Everett, and south to beyond Rainsburg. Martin Hill was also explored. Here 66 species were listed. July 4–6: Newburg (Trough Creek post office); including Trough Creek, Tatman Run, Broad Top Mountain, and Round Mountain; 58 species. July 8–9: Hares Valley, Huntingdon County, and Jacks Mountain north to Butler Knob; 53 species. July 10–12: Black Log Valley, east of Orbisonia, Huntingdon County, and thence to Black Log and Shade mountains; 43 species. July 12–16: Shade Valley, two miles south of Shade Gap, Huntingdon County, and thence east to Tuscarora Mountain and west to Shade Mountain; 46 species. July 16–19: Newton Hamilton, Mifflin County, northwest to Long Hollow and Jacks Mountain, and east to Sugar Valley, Blue Mountain, and Licking Creek; 66 species.

From August 27 to September 3, Paul W. Roth collected specimens at Conneauttee Lake, near Edinboro, Erie County.

1896—No special trip was undertaken, but the next year work was resumed.

1897—June 7 found me at Mapleton, Huntingdon County, where I began a trip on foot across country to Marklesburg. My route lay up Smith Run, thence along the road across Sideling Hill and down Trough Creek Valley, through Colfax and Calvin to a point about two miles west of Cassville. On this part of the route, 49 species were observed. The next day I crossed the Tussey Mountain Barrens to Great Trough Creek, following down its valley and crossing the Raystown Branch of the Juniata River to reach Marklesburg by the direct road; 34 species were listed. June 9: Spruce Creek, Huntingdon County, and Tyrone, Blair County. June 10: Port Matilda, Centre County, to the crest of the Alleghenies; 44 species. June 11: "Sang Hollow," Cambria County, to the summit of Laurel Hill and thence to Nineveh (now Seward), Westmoreland County; 31 species. June 12: Along the railroad from Bolivar to Blairsville Intersection (now Torrance), Westmoreland County; 30 species. June 13–14: Beaver. June 15: Volant to Black Swamp, Lawrence County, and return; 38 species. June 15: Mercer, Mercer County (between trains); 6 species. June 16: Linesville and Pymatuning Swamp, Crawford County; 38 species. June 17: Presque Isle, Erie County; 17 species. June 18: Spartansburg and Mill Pond, Crawford County; 38 species. June 19: Sheffield Junction, Forest County; 28 species. June 20–21: Renovo, Clinton County (on the south bank of the river); 27 species. June 22–23: Tamarack Swamp, Clinton County; 44 species. June 24: By rail to Lock Haven, and thence to Vail, Blair County, and to Woodland, Clearfield County. June 25: Woodland; 36 species. June 26: Sandy Ridge, Centre County; 18 species. June 28–July 3: Buffalo Creek region, Armstrong and Butler counties. July 5: Beaver.

1898—June 7: Flowing Spring, Blair County, to summit of Lock Mountain; 47 species. June 8: Gallitzin, Cambria County, east and south to Sugar Run, Blair County; 28 species. June 9–10: Dunlo, Cambria County; 37 species. June 11: Blairsville Intersection, Westmoreland County, east along the gap through Chestnut Ridge; 35 species. June 12–14: Beaver. June 15: Pulaski, Lawrence County; 48 species. June 16: Hartstown and Pymatuning Swamp, Crawford County; 36 species. June 17: Conneaut Lake, Crawford County (south of the town); 38 species. June 18–20: Bear Lake, Warren County; 52 species. June 21: Port Allegany, McKean County; 34 species. June 22: Coudersport, Potter County; 37 species. June 23: On foot along the highway from Sweden Valley to Cherry Spring, Potter County; 40 species. June 24–25: Tamarack Swamp, Clinton County; 35 species. June 26–27: Renovo. June 28: Vail, Blair County; 21 species. June 29–30: Kingston, Westmoreland County, to the summit of Chestnut Ridge south of the Loyalhanna Gap; 57 species. July 1–2: Buffalo Creek region, Armstrong and Butler counties.

Percy W. Shufeldt accompanied me as assistant on my 1898 trip. After I left he continued work in the Buffalo Creek region until July 14; and later (July 21–23) went to Casselman, Somerset County.

Thaddeus Surber also collected for me from June 1 to 15, at the following localities: June 1: Hyndman, Bedford County, to summit of Wills Mountain; 54 species. June 2: Riddlesburg, Bedford County, and the ridge to the west; 45 species. June 3–4: Entriken, Huntingdon County, west to Tussey Mountain and southeast to Tatman Run, where it breaks through Terrace Mountain; 70 species. June 5–6: Spruce Creek and Tussey Mountain, Huntingdon County; 52 species. June 7–8: Lloydville, Cambria County; 44 species. June 8–10: Snow Shoe to Moshannon to Pine Glen, Centre County; 56 species. June 13–14: Tamarack Swamp, Clinton County; 56 species. June 15: Rathbun, Elk County. Since it is questionable whether or not the specimens marked as taken at the last-named place were actually collected there, none of the records has been used.

1899—On April 13 I resumed regular field work at Beaver. In June I undertook another trip, starting at Ohiopyle, Fayette County, on June 3, whence I ascended to the summit of Sugarloaf Mountain; 42 species were listed. June 4–5: New Lexington, Somerset County, with H. D. Moore; 34 species. June 6–8: I crossed northern Fulton County by conveyance and on foot, and covered a considerable area unexplored in previous seasons. My route on June 6 was from Richmond Furnace, Franklin County, into Fulton County by way of Cowan Gap, across Cove Mountain to Knobsville, Hustontown; on June 7, from West Dublin, across Sideling Hill to Wells Tannery; and on

June 8, to Hopewell, Bedford County. Thirty-seven species were noted on the first day; 31 on the second; and 23 on the third. June 9: By conveyance from Clearfield, Clearfield County, up Moose Creek to the summit of the divide to the northward, to a point now known as Anderson Creek. June 10: On a lumber train to Winterburn, Clearfield County. Thirty-four species were recorded during these two days. June 11–12: Renovo, Clinton County, with A. K. Pierce. June 13–14: Tamarack Swamp, Clinton County; 31 species (23 along Drury Run). June 15: Cherry Spring, Potter County; 41 species. June 16: Newfield Junction, Potter County; 32 species. June 17: Gold, Potter County; 42 species. June 18–20: Renovo, to the summit of Beech Creek Mountain, Clinton County; 29 species. June 21: Croyland, Elk County; 18 species. June 21–22: On foot from Hallton, Elk County, up Spring Creek to Parrish, Forest County. Sixteen species were recorded from Hallton to a point just beyond the Forest County line, and 21 species from this point to Parrish, where the road ran through virgin forest; on June 22 I listed 26 species, some of which had also been seen the day before. June 23: Centerville to Lakeville, Crawford County; 10 species. June 23–24: Oil Creek Lake (now called Canadohta Lake), Crawford County; 36 species. June 26–27: Presque Isle, Erie County; 28 species. June 28: Hartstown and Pymatuning Swamp, Crawford County; 27 species. June 29: Callery, Butler County; 26 species. June 30–July 3: Buffalo Creek region, Armstrong and Butler counties.

1900—The spring and fall months were spent in studying and collecting the birds of Erie and Presque Isle, Erie County, in collaboration with Willis W. Worthington. A full report of this study was published in 1904. On June 26 I went to Warren, Warren County, and on June 28 drove thence across country to a point about three miles southeast of Thompson (now Althom) in quest of the Olive-sided Flycatcher; I returned to Thompson on June 30. Upon concluding the work at Erie I visited Round Island, Clinton County, on November 23 and 24, and Mount Union, Huntingdon County, from November 28 to December 1. At the latter place I worked over both slopes of Jacks Mountain, north to Mill Creek and south to Singers Gap, in quest of wild turkeys, which were located but not secured.

Satisfied that I had covered the area fully enough for the purposes of my report, I made no other extended tours in western Pennsylvania after 1900. I continued, however, to make further observations at Beaver, where for a number of seasons, spring and fall, I spent considerable time afield, added a number of species to my earlier list, and accumulated a long series of migration records for many species. These records have been invaluable in compiling the present report and in comparing the results of observers in other sections. In recent years, however, my local field work has necessarily been desultory. Sundry short trips, however, have been made from time to time in the interest of western Pennsylvania ornithology, often in company with other members of the Carnegie Museum staff. We have been going more or less regularly to Erie and Presque Isle, to Pymatuning Swamp and Lake, to Waynesburg, and to the Buffalo Creek region. Visits to certain other places, taken in company with various interested companions, may be briefly outlined, as follows:

November 29–December 2, 1902: Mount Union, Huntingdon County, covering the same ground as in 1901. December 4, 1902: Renovo to Tamarack Swamp, Clinton County, by way of Drury Run, and return. May 9, 1903: Along the Beaver River from Wampum to Mahoningtown, Lawrence County, and return. May 24–25, 1905: Beaver to Frankfort Springs, Beaver County. June 26, 1909: Douthett, Butler County. April 20, 1921: On foot from Huntingdon to the summit of Jacks Mountain, opposite McConnellstown, Huntingdon County. June 9–10, 1927: A reconnaissance by automobile through Westmoreland, Indiana, Jefferson, Clarion, and Armstrong counties, with J. B. Semple and B. H. Christy. Our route on June 9 was from Pittsburgh to New Alexandria, Westmoreland County, thence to Saltsburg, Indiana County, and by a roundabout way through northern Indiana County to Gastown and Elderton, Armstrong County. Thence we traveled southward to Idaho, and then northward to Greendale, Pine Creek (near Oscar), and Putneyville, all in the same county, and to New Bethlehem, Jefferson County. On the return trip on June 10 we passed through Climax and Dee, Armstrong County, and reached the Allegheny River at Templeton. May 6–7, 1933: "Jumbo

Woods," Crawford County. May 12, 1933: Little Deer Creek, south of Rural Ridge, Allegheny County. June 6, 1933: Woodlawn, Beaver County. June 10, 1933: New Castle to Gardner Swamp, Lawrence County. January 27, 1934: "Patton's Point," Beaver County. April 28, 1934: Hollidaysburg, Blair County. June 7–9, 1934: Benson Swamp, Tamarack Swamp, and Bear Lake, Warren County. June 12–13, 1934: By automobile to the highlands of Somerset County—Buckstown, Berlin, Salisbury, Springs, thence to Negro Mountain (3,320 feet), Glade Run marsh, and Big Spring—returning by way of Lake Seaton, Fayette County.

CONTRIBUTORS

Without the active co-operation of local observers in western Pennsylvania the present work would be far from complete. It is a pleasure to acknowledge their contributions, whether consisting of a few notes or of exhaustive faunal lists. Nearly all the manuscripts utilized in the preparation of the present report have been deposited in the Carnegie Museum, where they will be available for future reference if desired. Included in this mass of material are the writer's own notes and journals, beginning with 1887, and the reports submitted by his several field assistants. The subjoined list of correspondents includes those who supplied data at the writer's request. His thanks are especially due to the following:

*D. A. Atkinson, Pittsburgh, for a full and carefully prepared list of the birds of Allegheny County, compiled from his field notes. This manuscript has been used extensively in writing the present work; it includes some species not encountered by later workers in this county. For the rarer species exact particulars are given. Dr. Atkinson's work was done mainly in the period from 1889 to 1899, with his former home of Wilkinsburg as a center; the migration dates he cites are assumed to refer to this place. His collection of birds' eggs, presented to the Carnegie Museum many years ago, has been invaluable as a source of local nesting data.

*Samuel E. Bacon, Erie, for a list of the birds of Erie, utilized by this writer in preparing his 1904 report on the birds of that locality. This manuscript includes also a few notes and records made in other parts of Erie County, such as Lake Pleasant, Cherryhill, and Albion.

*Annie E. Berg, Hollidaysburg, for a list of the birds of Hollidaysburg and vicinity, and for particulars on some of the rarer species. Her migration reports to the Biological Survey have also been consulted.

Rudyerd Boulton, Chicago, Illinois, for the use of his field notes made at Beaver and at various other places.

Albert T. Buckhout, for a list made in 1901, of the birds of State College and vicinity.

Thomas D. Burleigh, Gulfport, Mississippi, for the use of his field notes of 1909–19 covering Allegheny, Centre, northern Huntingdon, and Fayette counties. These notes often give precise localities that supplement his published records on the birds of these counties. His collection of birds' eggs made during this period is now in the Carnegie Museum.

Elsie D. Canan, Johnstown, for a list of the birds of Johnstown and vicinity.

Bayard H. Christy, Sewickley, for the use of his notebooks of 1885–1932, referring mainly to the birds of the Sewickley region but including many interesting records from outlying localities. These notebooks often amplify the records published by this observer.

Samuel S. Dickey, Waynesburg, for a transcript of his notes on certain species and lists from certain localities. These have been invaluable in supplementing his published records. Moreover, Dr. Dickey has generously placed at this writer's disposal accounts of several species of which he has made especial study, and these have been freely utilized in the present work.

W. E. Dilley, Erie, for notes on certain species observed at Erie and in the Pymatuning region.

H. H. Elliott, Forest Hills, for a list of birds observed near Jamisonville, Butler County, and for sundry records from other localities.

*Deceased.

Ruskin S. Freer, Lynchburg, Virginia, for a nominal list of birds observed at Johnstown and on Laurel Hill, and for comments on certain species of special interest.

Reinhold L. Fricke, Pittsburgh, for data on the birds of the Pymatuning region in particular, and on his local field work in general. His collections have yielded numerous distributional records for the present work.

H. L. Gans, for a partial list of the birds of Washington compiled from records made during the years 1894–97.

W. M. Guynes, Erie, for his notes on the birds of Erie, including a transcript of migration records for the period from 1932 to 1934.

Richard C. Harlow, Cambridge, Massachusetts, for a nominal list, abstracted from his notebooks, of his principal finds of nests and of unusual migration records. Through this list it has been possible to supply many localities and dates omitted from his published records.

Lawrence E. Hicks, Columbus, Ohio, for notes on birds observed along Lake Erie, on the Pennsylvania side of Pymatuning Swamp, at Heart's Content, Warren County, and at a few other places.

*Fred LeRoy Homer, New Hamburg, for a list of the birds of his locality. His notebooks and journals are in the Carnegie Museum.

J. Warren Jacobs, Waynesburg, for much written and verbal information on the birds of Greene County; for data supplied from the mounted specimens in his collection; for the opportunity to consult his splendid collection of birds' eggs; and for the loan of files of certain ornithological journals.

*A. D. Johnston, Pittsburgh, for a list of species observed at Allegheny in 1893, and at Freeport and Boggsville, Armstrong County, in 1894.

*R. L. Keesler, Forestville, for a list of the birds of northwestern Butler County, with incidental records from adjoining counties.

Harry C. Kirkpatrick, Meadville, for a fully annotated list of the birds of Crawford County, based on his experience there since 1880, and for supplementary notes sent to this writer. Much of this information has already been utilized by George M. Sutton in his 1928 report on the birds of that region.

Harry A. McGraw, Altoona, for a list, with dates and localities, of species observed by him in Blair County, with Altoona as a center; and for critical comment on other records from this region.

Howard M. McQuiston, Sharon, for lists of the birds of his locality and of those observed at Big Bend, northwest of Mercer, in the summer of 1935 and in Elk County in the summer of 1934.

Oliver P. Medsger, State College, for a nominal list of the birds observed at Jacobs Creek and Scottdale, Westmoreland County, up to 1904.

Ansel B. Miller, Springs, for an annotated list of the birds of extreme southern Somerset County, including Negro Mountain, with migration dates for many species.

George Montgomery, for an annotated list of the birds of Washington and vicinity, based on observations made up to 1897.

Ralph V. Mostoller, Stoyestown, for the use of his original notebooks on the birds of Somerset and Cambria counties.

John K. Musgrave, Pittsburgh, for a list of the birds of Centre County made in 1909 and presented as a thesis in partial fulfillment of the requirements for the degree of bachelor of science at The Pennsylvania State College.

*James S. Nease, Washington, for a list of the birds of Washington County, based on his observations up to 1897.

J. Elmer Perry, Erie, for notes on various birds from the Erie region and in particular on the nesting of the Bald Eagle and Common Tern.

*Albert K. Pierce, Renovo, for an immense mass of data on the birds of Clinton and McKean counties, with scattered notes from Cameron and Elk counties. He was a freight conductor on the route between Renovo and Kane, and most of his work was done near these two places. He amassed a collection of birds (mounted specimens and skins), nests, and eggs from that region; some of these have been acquired by the Carnegie Museum. He was the first to take the eggs of the Duck Hawk and the Raven in Pennsylvania. He kept voluminous records, and regularly sent to the Biological Survey full migration reports, which were highly valued by Wells W. Cooke. These reports have been copied and freely utilized in the preparation of the present work. It is, however, an open question whether or not all these migration records

*Deceased.

actually refer to Renovo. Through the courtesy of Mr. Pierce's daughter, Mrs. J. A. C. King of Lansdowne, permission was given to examine his collection and to read his journals and notebooks, which have proved invaluable and have yielded many records of interest.

Edward C. Raney, Ithaca, New York, for a nominal list of the birds around New Castle; for migration dates from Slippery Rock, Butler County; and for miscellaneous observations made in Mercer County, all supplied in 1933.

Samuel N. Rhoads, Haddonfield, New Jersey, for his original notes on birds observed in 1896 at Round Island, Clinton County, and in 1898 at Beaver, at Laughlintown, Westmoreland County, and at Cresson and Summit, Cambria County.

Samuel S. Ristich, Aliquippa, for notes on certain species of his locality.

Paul W. Roth, Milwaukee, Wisconsin, for correspondence on certain species observed at Butler up to 1895. His migration schedules in the Biological Survey have also been examined.

Lloyd Scherer, Jr., Port Allegany, for a seasonal list made in 1938 of the birds of his locality, with notes on certain species.

Stanley J. Seiple, Grove City, for a list of the birds of Greenville and vicinity, with dates of observation, and for numerous additional notes on the birds of the Pymatuning region.

Ralph B. Simpson, Warren, for the most complete and carefully prepared list of birds from any locality in western Pennsylvania. This list is a full résumé of his work in Warren County from 1890 to 1903, and it has been kept up to date by material supplied in correspondence. Some of the information included in this manuscript has since been published in the *Oölogist*. Mr. Simpson has an extensive private collection of nests, eggs, and mounted birds, which it has been the privilege of this author to examine. Lately his interest has inclined more to photography, and he has supplied some excellent pictures of nests and eggs taken by Harry Granquist and himself.

Merit B. Skaggs, Cleveland, Ohio, for lists of birds and for notes on observations made during his visits to Erie and Presque Isle and to the Pymatuning region in 1936 and 1937.

George M. Sutton, Bethany, West Virginia, for the use of his notes on western Pennsylvania birds made during his connection with the Carnegie Museum and later with the Pennsylvania Game Commission.

Ruth Trimble, Greensburg, for a list of birds made during a visit to Indiana County in June, 1935; for sundry observations of interest made in Westmoreland County; and for records from the Pymatuning region and Canadohta Lake, Crawford County.

H. T. Van Ostrand, for a list of birds observed at Morganza, Washington County, between June and October, 1896.

*Hurlburt H. Wickham, Beaver, for his notes of 1887–90 on the birds of Beaver County. A few records of later date have been abstracted from letters.

Notes and data on various species have also been contributed by the following: Mrs. F. G. Andrews, Erie; Clark S. Beardslee, Kenmore, New York; C. A. Bergstrom, Conneaut Lake; Helen M. Blair, Pittsburgh; Grant M. Cook, Youngstown, Ohio; J. Glenn Crumb, Linesville; W. M. Dippold, Kittanning; Maximilian Duman, O.S.B., Latrobe; Sidney K. Eastwood, Pittsburgh; Ralph M. Edeburn, Beaver; C. W. G. Eifrig, River Forest, Illinois; Norman W. Franke, Pittsburgh; *Ludwig von Fuehrer, Verona; G. W. Gordon, Uniontown; Harry P. Hays, Altoona; W. D. Hunter, Racine; Robert Irons, Linesville; O. E. Jennings, Pittsburgh; P. P. Malley, Homestead; C. W. Mason, Pittsburgh; *S. S. Miller, Springs; Ralph O'Reilly, Jr., Cleveland Heights, Ohio; Burt L. Oudette, Linesville; Walter C. Paul, East Liverpool, Ohio; *William G. Pitcairn, Pittsburgh; H. Justin Roddy, Lancaster; Thomas Smyth, Indiana; Dwight E. Sollberger, Indiana; J. Kenneth Terres, Bath, New York; Harry Van Cleve, Harrisburg; Harwood Werkheiser, New Kensington; Arthur J. Woodward, Erie.

Thanks are also due to the Bureau of Biological Survey, through Harry C. Oberholser and Frederick C. Lincoln, for permission to copy migration schedules; for a copy of a list of the breeding birds of DuBois, Clearfield County, by Walter Van Fleet; and for another list from the same locality by L. D. Balliet. The Pennsylvania Game Commission has courteously supplied a report on the number of upland game birds killed by licensed hunters in the several counties of western Pennsylvania from 1928 to 1932 inclusive.

*Deceased.

Part Two

BIRDS

OF

WESTERN

PENNSYLVANIA

EXPLANATORY NOTE

THE SYSTEMATIC arrangement of the species and the common and scientific names are those used in the 1931 edition of the American Ornithologists' Union *Check-List of North American Birds*. Ordinal groups have been omitted and the various species are arranged by families. As a guide to the problems of classification, distribution, and identification, each family group is introduced by a short discussion of its salient features and characteristics; in these accounts brief mention is made also of certain species that might conceivably be observed in western Pennsylvania but for which there are as yet no acceptable records. Introduced species, such as the Ring-necked Pheasant, the European Starling, and the so-called English Sparrow, have been omitted.

The species are discussed under several headings, as follows:

The "Descriptions" are primarily "field" descriptions, intended to facilitate the identification of birds in life. Technical terms have been avoided where possible, and emphasis has been given to general features rather than to details of coloration. Size has been treated as a relative matter, and comparisons are with well-known species.

Under "Range," the distribution of the species as a whole is indicated in general terms and is then correlated with the local range as determined by prevailing climatic, topographic, and ecological conditions. Distribution is often discussed in terms of life zones as they are currently understood, but the attempt to fit the facts to the theory has not been very successful, as has been pointed out in the Introduction. It is but fair to say that this conclusion was not reached until after all the species-biographies had been written. Extralimital records are introduced only where it is desirable to justify or explain those from local sources. The main theme of the book deals with the problems of general and local distribution; discussions of taxonomic and systematic questions have been avoided.

"Migration" is treated partly from the general but mostly from the local standpoint; the object has been to indicate the seasonal movements of the various species and their periodic fluctuations in numbers. Dates are cited freely (we hope not tediously) in order to illustrate the extremes and the mean of the migration period at given points, and unusual seasonal occurrences are also included. The paragraphs on the subject of migration are intended to guard the inexperienced student against potential errors in identifying birds in the field. Extensive series of records of seasonal migration at Beaver, Sewickley, Warren, and Renovo, and shorter series from Wilkinsburg, Pittsburgh, Waynesburg, Springs, Hollidaysburg, State College, Erie, and the Pymatuning region, together with scattered observations from other places, have supplied the data pertinent to the discussion.

The paragraphs on "Habits" are designed to present a pen picture of the bird in life, rather than an exhaustive life-history. Species that are rare or accidental are accordingly treated briefly in comparison with those that are common and more characteristic; no effort has been made to describe the nesting habits of those that do not breed within the limits of western Pennsylvania. The accounts are based mainly on local sources and written from local experience; extraneous material has been utilized only in a few cases where local information was not available. Others who have written about the avifauna of this region have been freely quoted, both verbatim and in substance. Moreover, twenty-seven accounts have been contributed especially for this work by other writers. A consistent attempt has been made to preserve local color.

Throughout this volume, the English names of birds appear in capital letters only when the reference is clearly to the species. In quoted matter, a manuscript source is implied when no publication date accompanies the name of the authority. Quotations from published sources have been followed exactly. Initials, rather than forenames, are used in nearly all instances (full names may be found in the Bibliography or in the list of contributors in the Introduction); certain well-known authorities, such as B. H. Warren, George B. Sennett, and Walter Van Fleet, are mentioned by surname only.

Where names of well-known places, including those of all county seats, appear in the text, the county is not specified. Names of smaller and obscurer places, however, appear with the name of the county in which they are located. For information on localities the reader is referred to the Gazetteer and to the map accompanying this volume.

Published references are, with some exceptions, arranged chronologically, according to the names ascribed to the various species by the authors cited. The year of issue follows the title of the publication; and the volume number, if any, precedes the page number and is separated from it by a colon. The page numbers referred to are those on which the name of the species occurs. Slight differences in spelling of scientific names have been ignored in compiling these references. It is believed that the citations, with their résumés of the status of each species at the localities specified, will be found useful as a guide. On the other hand, limitations of space forbade the inclusion of all published references. The choice of entries has been determined largely by their historical value and by their usefulness in working out the local distribution and seasonal abundance of a given species, in determining the time of its migration, or in illustrating some phase of its life-history. Duplicate references of the same general import, or from the same locality, have not been included; "etc." signifies identical references of later date. Names of localities in the references appear in corrected form; quotation marks used therewith indicate a mistake on the part of the author cited, and in such instances the correct locality follows in square brackets. A question mark enclosed in parentheses is used at the beginning of a citation when the authenticity of the record is doubted by the present author. *Fide*, as here used, indicates "on the authority of." The titles of books and periodicals, abbreviated in the references, have been listed in complete form in the Bibliography, under the name of the authority cited.

"Additional Records" are authenticated unpublished records that tend to supplement the published notices. To cite all the available manuscript records for species having zonal significance, however, has been deemed unnecessary, since the distribution maps graphically and concisely convey this information.

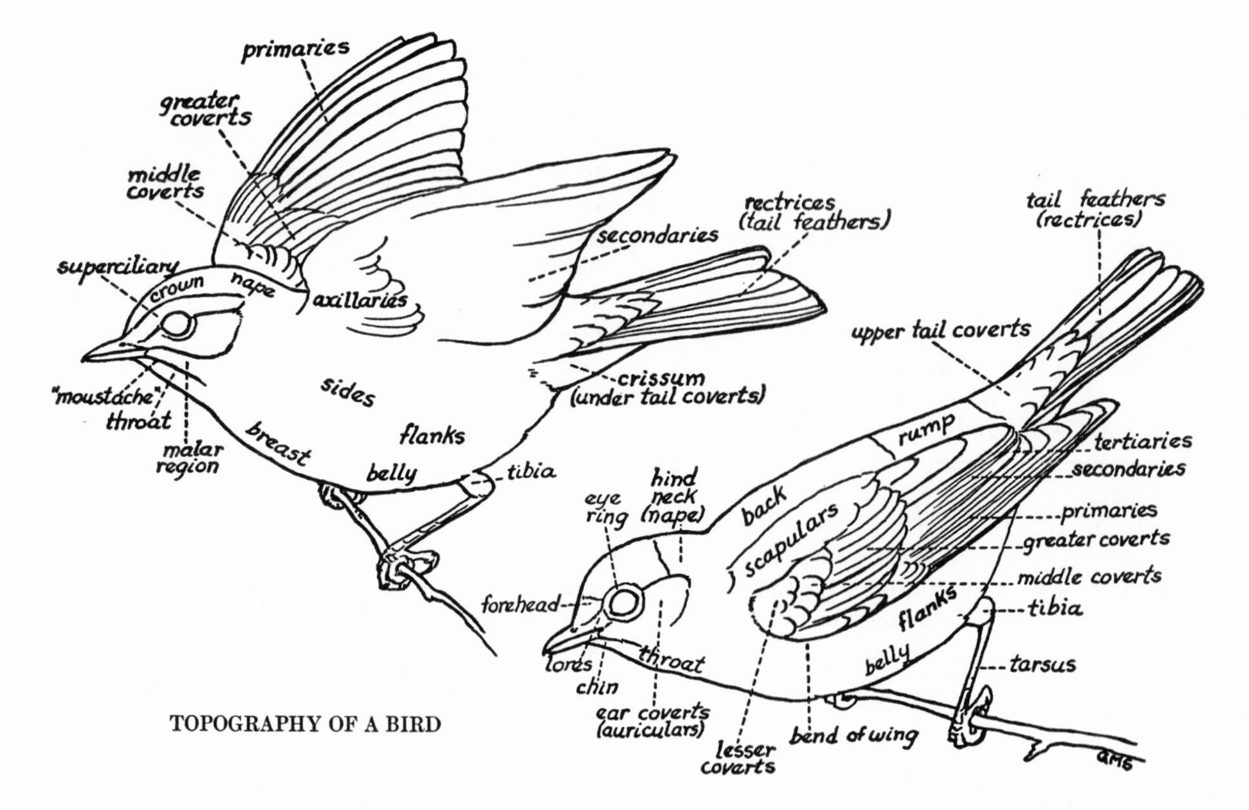

TOPOGRAPHY OF A BIRD

LOONS

FAMILY GAVIIDAE

THE LOONS are a small and compact group of four species, with an arctic and circumboreal distribution. They are large, powerful, and strictly aquatic birds, specially equipped for diving. The plumage is compact and water resistant; the body is long and streamlined; and the webbed feet, placed very far back, are strongly muscled. On the water a loon is the perfection of grace and power; on land it is well-nigh helpless. The neck is heavy; the bill is strong and spearlike; and the tail, although short, is well developed. The brown-spotted eggs are two in number, and are laid in a depression at the very edge of the water. The young are able to swim about as soon as they are hatched. Loons feed almost wholly upon fish, which they capture by direct pursuit under water. Two species occur in western Pennsylvania; a third, the Pacific Loon (*Gavia arctica pacifica*), would be of only accidental occurrence.

COMMON LOON

GAVIA IMMER IMMER (Brünnich)

Description—A large, black and white water bird with a long, pointed bill. *Adult in spring: head and neck black*, with a slight greenish gloss (bluish on the neck); a *band of short white stripes across the middle of the throat*, and another wider band of similar stripes on either side of the neck; *upperparts in general and sides of body, black, spotted with white*, the spots on the upper back large and squarish; wings and tail black; plain white below, the sides of the breast with black stripes; bill and feet dark; iris red. *Adult in fall and winter, and immature:* above (including wings and tail) dusky, *without spots*, but with indistinct paler mottling; head and neck also dusky, but the throat whitish; sides of body dusky, and underparts white. Spring birds emerging into adult plumage are variously intermediate between the two stages here described, but this species may always be known by its relatively large size as compared with the Red-throated Loon.

Range—The Loon is a species of boreal affinities, and inhabits the northern parts of North America and western Europe. Its breeding range in America does not regularly extend south of the Canadian Life Zone, at least at the present time. It may formerly have bred, however, on some of the waters in our region where now it is known only as a transient visitant, more or less regular, but common only under exceptional circumstances. Erie Bay, a stopping place for many migrating waterfowl, is of course a favorite resort, as are Conneaut and Pymatuning lakes. The Loon must occur at intervals, too, on the other smaller lakes in the northwestern part of the state. There are definite records for all the counties of the western tier and for many of the others as well, except those lying between the Allegheny River and the main divide—but this gap is certainly not significant. The species has been rare of late years on the Ohio River, because of the foul condition of its waters and the depletion of its aquatic life. The Loon is now oftener observed on the smaller and less polluted streams, where more food is available.

Migration—The spring movement of this species usually begins in March, as soon as areas of open water appear on the lakes and the first waterfowl start to move northward. February 28 (1895) is an exceptionally early spring migration date reported by D. A. Atkinson for Davis Island, Allegheny County; all his other arrival records for this season lie between March 14 (1899) and March 31 (1902). March 23, 1896 (Wickham) is the earliest spring record for Beaver County; March 25, 1913 (Sutton), for Conneaut Lake; and March 15, 1936 (Brooks), for Erie Bay. A long series of migration records made at Renovo by A. K. Pierce shows much irregularity; March 24 (1907) is the earliest date. R. B. Simpson, who has had considerable experience with this species at Warren, has observed it there as early as March 20. He states that the majority of loons pass through in April, and that in some seasons they are very numerous. He has given an interesting account of a flight of loons that took place on April 19, 1901, when many were seen and shot on the river at Warren during a heavy snowstorm. No doubt these were migrating birds that had been driven back by the unusually severe weather of the period.

By the end of April most of the loons have passed northward, but there are always some that linger into May, even until the end of the month; and a few stay until June. Since it often happens that loons do not lay their eggs until late in June or early in July, these laggards would still have ample time to reach their regular breeding grounds. Occasional birds may not go north at all. A pair was noted at Conneaut Lake, according to S. J. Seiple, through the entire summer of 1925, and one bird was seen during July and August of 1926. On July 4, 1931, a loon in winter plumage was seen by B. H. Christy on Canadohta Lake, Crawford County; according to F. A. Hegner it stayed there for several weeks. These must have been nonbreeding birds, for there is absolutely no proof that the Loon ever nests in our region.[1]

Returning in the fall, this species usually appears in October (October 6, 1900—Erie; October 18, 1904—Renovo) and remains for about two months; it leaves only when the ice begins to interfere with its fishing. I have taken it on the Ohio River as late as November 30 (1899), and there are a few December records from other places, but none for the month of January so far as we know. Hence it can scarcely be classed as a winter resident.

Habits—The Loon is a rather solitary bird in our region, and a number together have a common interest rather than a sociable disposition. In the spring, however, presumably mated pairs may sometimes be encountered, and on one occasion (May 1, 1932), Professor Seiple saw as many as twelve together on Conneaut Lake. Migration seems to take place mostly at night, since it is usual to find the birds established in the early morning on the feeding grounds of their choice, where they may remain for several days if undisturbed. When pursued they will almost always seek to escape by diving, at which they are wonderfully adept. A loon on the water is a graceful, powerful bird, the perfection of adaptation, but on the land it is awkwardness itself. Its feet are set so far back and at such an angle with the body that it can move on land only by a sort of stum-

bling shuffle, falling forward at every step; but this very arrangement makes it astonishingly efficient in the water, which is its natural element. I once watched a loon disporting and feeding in the waters of the Ohio River, and saw it dive repeatedly against the swift current with the greatest ease and reappear after a brief interval two or three hundred feet upstream. Mr. Simpson has watched loons from a bridge over the Allegheny River when the water was so clear that they could be plainly seen below. He says that in diving the bird uses both the wings and the feet,[2] and that this combination makes progress very rapid. The birds have been observed by Professor Seiple to remain under water as long as thirty-three seconds. Their food is all secured in this way. It consists mainly of fish of various kinds. These are always swallowed whole, sometimes before the bird comes to the surface. The size of the fish they can swallow is remarkably large, but occasionally one is captured that proves unmanageable. A loon that

[1]Compare, however, R. C. Harlow, *Auk*, 1908, 25:471.
[2]Some authorities disagree with this statement.

I watched on one occasion at Dollar Lake, Pymatuning Swamp, was certainly having a hard time disposing of its finny catch. G. M. Sutton has reported a case of a loon being strangled when it tried to swallow a fifteen-inch pike, which became firmly wedged in its throat. Loons are occasionally caught in the fishermen's nets on Lake Erie, and this fact shows that they are able to descend to a considerable depth. W. M. Guynes writes that he has seen loons battering captured crayfish on the water before swallowing them.

The call of the Loon is a familiar sound in the north country, but it is seldom heard in this latitude. While camped on Presque Isle in the fall of 1900, "a gunner picked up a [wounded] Loon on the shore of Misery Bay near our house-boat, and brought it to us alive. It was practically helpless on the flat surface, but quite vicious, striking savagely with its powerful beak when teased, and uttering its peculiar reverberating cry" (Todd, 1904). This cry has been described as a sort of maniacal laugh, with the *oo* sound prominent; it has a wild, wolf-like quality, and can be heard at a long distance. Another cry is a prolonged loud whoop that dies slowly away.

The flight of the Loon is strong, direct, and sustained. With such relatively small wings, it is unable to rise into the air without pattering along the surface of the water for a considerable distance, unless facing a strong wind, but once aloft it is soon under terrific headway. If it finds itself in too small a pool of water it is virtually marooned, and if it is forced to the ground it is similarly helpless. Several reports tell of loons having been found dead at some distance from the water. Such individuals have most likely been obliged to make forced landings and have starved to death. It is a matter of regret that this interesting and picturesque bird suffers to such an extent at the hands of gunners that its numbers are diminishing year by year. Although not fit for food, it offers such a tempting mark that few of the shooting fraternity can resist a trial shot. It is a difficult bird to kill, however, and even when wounded often escapes by diving.

Colymbus torquatus Townsend, *Proc. Acad. Nat. Sci. Philadelphia*, 1883, 68 (Latrobe, Westmoreland Co., transient).

Urinator imber Warren, *Birds Pa.*, ed. 2, 1890, 6 (Clinton Co., winter; Allegheny River, Warren Co., spring).

Gavia imber Todd, *Ann. Carnegie Mus.*, 1904, 2:500 (Erie Bay, Erie Co., transient)—Todd, in Bausman, *Hist. Beaver Co., Pa.*, 1904, 2:1198 (Beaver Co., transient)—Forrest, *Oölogist*, 1911, 28:115 (Washington, Washington Co., May).

"Loon" Simpson, *Oölogist*, 1911, 28:41 (Warren, Warren Co., migration)—Editor, *Cassinia*, 1923, 24:54 (Greencastle, Franklin Co., *fide* Ziegler)—Sutton, *Bird-Lore*, 1924, 26:267 (Sandy Lake, Mercer Co., May–June, *fide* Homer; "Sewickley" [Clifton], Allegheny Co., June, *fide* Christy)—Brooks, *Redstart*, 1936, 3:49 (Erie Bay, Erie Co., March).

Gavia immer Burleigh, *Wilson Bull.*, 1923, 35:81 (Highland Park, Allegheny Co., spring transient); 1924, 36:74 (State College, Centre Co., October)—Lincoln, *U.S. Dept. Agric. Bull.* no. 1268, 1924, 6 ("Altoona" [Lakemont], Blair Co., April, banding record)—Christy, *Cardinal*, 1940, 5:68 (Versailles, Allegheny Co., April).

Gavia immer immer Christy, *Cardinal*, 1923, v. 1, no. 1, [p. 1] (Sewickley, Allegheny Co., spring transient)—Sutton, *Wilson Bull.*, 1927, 39:39 (Erie Bay, Erie Co.; food, *fide* Nagle)—Sutton, *Ann. Carnegie Mus.*, 1928, 18:52 (Crawford Co. records and references; Sharon, Mercer Co., December, *fide* Fair).

RED-THROATED LOON

GAVIA STELLATA (Pontoppidan)

Description—Smaller than the Common Loon. *Spring plumage:* dusky above, with a little white mottling; white below; *head and neck gray;* the nape, back of the neck, and upper sides of the breast, striped with black and white; lower throat with a *prominent triangular patch of rich chestnut,* broadest on its lower edge. *Winter plumage:* dusky above, *with small white spots;* white below, the neck and sides of the head with more or less dusky mottling or clouding.

Range and migration—This species is found in both Eurasia and North America. Its breeding grounds in America lie north of the United States; it is, if anything, more northerly in its range than the Common Loon. In the winter it favors the seacoast, but is occasional also on the Great Lakes. It was taken at Erie Bay on February 16 and 25, 1904, and at Warren on February 12 of the same year. R. B. Simpson, who is responsible for the Warren record, remarks on the severity of the weather at the time, and it is altogether likely that the birds had been driven southward by the closing of the waters of Lake Erie. One bird was noted in open water on the Shenango River at Greenville on February 20, 1936, by S. J. Seiple.

April is the month when the spring migration takes place, and specimens shot then are usually in fine breeding plumage. Mr. Simpson has a specimen taken at Warren on April 9, 1913, and G. M. Sutton quotes several records for Conneaut Lake between April 6 (1926) and April 30 (1925). A. K. Pierce has noted this bird at Renovo, on the West Branch of the Susquehanna River, as late as May 7 (1901); his only other spring record is for April 30, 1895. Like the Common Loon, this species has occasionally been found in summer far south of its usual breeding grounds. Such a case is reported by Ludwig von Fuehrer, who writes that he saw two individuals during the month of June, 1933, on Oneida Lake, Butler County. As they were still in winter plumage, they must have been nonbreeding birds. In the fall this loon is a late migrant; the earliest date of its appearance is October 23 (1900) at Erie, and the latest, December 5 (1912) at Conneaut Lake. Mr. Pierce has also taken it at Renovo on October 25 (1906). A crippled bird was found in Noblestown, Allegheny County, on November 17, 1939 (Christy, 1940). Two undated specimens in Pennsylvania State College are marked as having been taken at Boalsburg, Centre County (Musgrave). There are no records available for other counties, although the species probably occurs as a rare and irregular transient throughout the region. In general habits and behavior it closely resembles the Common Loon, but its ordinary call is quite different and suggests the quacking note of a duck.

Urinator lumme Warren, *Birds Pa.*, 1888, 230 (Lake Erie, Erie Co., fall); ed. 2, 1890, 8 (Lake Erie, Erie Co., and Clinton Co., transient).

Gavia lumme Todd, *Ann. Carnegie Mus.*, 1904, 2:500 (Erie Bay, Erie Co., transient).

"Red-throated Loon" Simpson, *Oölogist*, 1911, 28:33, 42 (Erie, Erie Co., and Warren, Warren Co., February)—Wood, *Wilson Bull.*, 1932, 44:238 ("State College" [Boalsburg], Centre Co., *fide* Musgrave)—Bergner, *Redstart*, 1938, 5:45 (Pymatuning Lake, Crawford Co., April).

Gavia stellata Sutton, *Ann. Carnegie Mus.*, 1928, 18:53 (Conneaut Lake, Crawford Co., migration)—Christy, *Cardinal*, 1940, 5:68 (Noblestown, Allegheny Co., November).

GREBES

FAMILY COLYMBIDAE

THE GREBES are a cosmopolitan group of five genera and about eighteen species. They resemble the Loons in that their strongly muscled feet are placed very far back on the body and thus give the bird the benefit of a powerful stroke; but the toes are lobate (provided with lobes or flaps), not webbed. The plumage has a peculiar silky texture, and the tail is rudimentary. In the Grebes as well as in the Loons the tarsi are much compressed and thus offer less resistance to the water. The range of size in the family is considerable; certain extralimital species are much smaller than any of our local forms. Grebes are excellent divers and can disappear under water in a flash, but they are able as well to sink quietly beneath the surface and swim along with only the tip of the bill showing. When pursued they always try to escape by diving rather than by flying. They build floating nests of aquatic plants, and lay from four to eight dull bluish-white eggs, from which emerge curiously streaked and spotted young.

HOLBOELL'S GREBE

COLYMBUS GRISEGENA HOLBOELLI (Reinhardt)

Description—A large grebe, twice the size of the Horned Grebe, and with a relatively *longer and heavier bill* (as long as the head); crest longer on either side, giving the head a triangular aspect from in front. *Spring plumage:* head above, nape, back of the neck, and upperparts in general, dusky black; wings also dusky, with a large white patch (more or less concealed); silky white below, with indistinct dark mottling and dusky shading on the sides; throat, cheeks, and sides of the head, grayish, with a whitish line above, passing through the eyes; neck (in front and on the sides) and breast, rufous chestnut; iris red. *Fall and winter:* throat whitish, and neck washed with dusky brown; the head lacks a definite color pattern and is merely dusky above and on the sides; the crest is less developed. Otherwise much as in the spring plumage.

Range—Holboell's Grebe is the American counterpart of the Red-necked Grebe of Eurasia. It seems to be commoner, or at least better known, in the western part of its general breeding range—in Alaska, western Canada, and parts of the northwestern states. In the winter it prefers the seacoast, but sometimes remains on the Great Lakes. In our region it occurs most frequently as a transient in spring and fall and less often as an irregular winter visitant, but it is not a common species at any time. From Erie Bay, where it might be expected regularly, there are to date but eight known records. From Crawford County there are five records (Sutton, 1928), only one of which is unsupported by a specimen. R. B. Simpson, whose experience at Warren covers many years, seems to have encountered this grebe oftener than has any other observer. He has no less than twenty-four records, all of which were made in the late winter and spring. At Renovo, according to A. K. Pierce, it is "fairly common," and there are a few specimens in his collection; one taken as early as February 8 (1908) suggests that the species may winter there also. For the counties other than Erie and Crawford in the western tier there are only a few scattered records, and none whatever from the interior counties except those above specified.

Migration—There are February records for this grebe from Erie, Warren, Clinton, Armstrong, and Washington counties. If not pertaining to birds that were actually wintering where they were found, these records must indicate a considerable wandering at certain times from a presumed winter habitat elsewhere, probably Lake Erie. This explanation is suggested by the fact that Mr. Simpson has on several occasions found this grebe at Warren early in February, during blizzards. Some were picked up in an exhausted condition, due apparently to lack of food. The regular northward movement, signalized by the appearance of migrants from the south, begins very early and is under way during March and April. Some laggards remain until May. It is a curious fact that many individuals seen and shot during the spring migration, even as late as April 10, were in winter plumage. Late spring dates recorded are: Erie, April 26, 1928 (Sutton, *fide* Langdon); Warren, May 3, 1904 (Simpson); Renovo, May 7, 1902 (Pierce); Crystal Lake, Crawford County, May 13, 1922 (Sutton).

T. D. Burleigh reports having seen a Holboell's grebe on Deer Creek, Allegheny County, on September 13, 1913; and E. W. Arthur, another at "Montgomery Mill," Mercer County, on September 27, 1925. Both dates seem much too early for such a "cold-weather" bird as this species is known to be. It has been noted at Renovo, however, as early as September 25 (1902) and October 9 (1907). At Erie Bay it has not been observed earlier in the fall than October 14 (1934), nor later than December 25 (1931). An individual seen there in January and February, 1934, was doubtless a winter resident.

Habits—In its general habits this species is much like the Horned Grebe. It is a good swimmer and diver, and not easy to shoot. When pursued it remains under water with only the tip of its bill showing. On land it is virtually helpless, and when so marooned may perish of starvation. In full breeding dress it is a handsome bird, although unprovided with the flaring ruffs that adorn its smaller relative.

Colymbus holboellii Warren, *Birds Pa.*, ed. 2, 1890, 2 (Washington, Washington Co., *fide* Nease)—Rhoads, *Auk*, 1899, 16:309 ([Homestead], Allegheny Co., March, *fide* Atkinson)—Todd, *Ann. Carnegie Mus.*, 1904, 2:498 (Erie Bay, Erie Co., transient)—Burleigh, *Wilson Bull.*, 1923, 35:81 (Deer Creek, Allegheny Co., September)—Sutton, *Ann. Carnegie Mus.*, 1928, 18:50 (Crawford Co. records and references).

"Holboell's Grebe" Simpson, *Oölogist*, 1907, 24:87; 1910, 27:100; 1911, 28:33, 42; 1912, 29:370 (Warren, Warren Co., February–April)—Arthur, *Cardinal*, 1926, v. 1, no. 7, p. 25 ("Montgomery Mill," Mercer Co., September)—Eastwood, *Bird-Lore*, 1927, 29:197 ([Highland Park Reservoir], Allegheny Co., April, *fide* Jones and Elliott)—Savage, *Bird-Lore*, 1932, 34:44 (Erie Bay, Erie Co., December).

Additional records: Buffalo Creek, near Iron Bridge, Armstrong Co., February 16, 1901 (F. Myers; specimen in Carnegie Museum)—Cooks Run, Clinton Co., October 24, 1899, *fide* J. C. Kelly; and Howards, Cameron Co., February 13, 1899 (Pierce)—Waynesburg, Greene Co., transient (Jacobs)—Washington, Washington Co., February 25, 1885, and Buffalo Township, Washington Co., winter (Nease).

HORNED GREBE

COLYMBUS AURITUS Linnaeus

Description—Size of a small duck or teal. Bill *slender, shorter than the head. Spring plumage:* head black, with a broad band of rusty buff (paler behind) on either side from the base of the bill through the eyes to the sides of the nape; the head feathers very full, forming a *flaring ruff all around; neck in front, breast, and sides of the body, chestnut; rest of underparts silky white;* hindneck, back, and wings, dusky black, the latter having a *large white spot* (mostly concealed); iris red; bill dark, with pale tip. The *female* resembles the male, but is rather paler and duller, with the ruffs not so long. *Fall and winter:* upperparts in general, wings, and hindneck, *dusky* (the wings with a white spot as in spring); *throat and sides of the head silky white*, in strong contrast with the dusky crown and nape; ruffs not in evidence; sides more or less dusky; rest of underparts silky white.

Range—The Horned Grebe is circumboreal, inhabiting both Eurasia and North America. In the latter continent it breeds mostly north of the United States, and retires for the winter to the seacoast, as far as the Gulf of Mexico. It is occasional inland and farther north at that season, however, particularly in the region of the Great Lakes. Throughout the northern United States in general, and in our area in particular, it is known mainly as a transient visitant during migration. Although of fairly regular occurrence along our rivers, it cannot justly be considered a common bird except upon the larger bodies of water, such as Conneaut and Pymatuning lakes, Erie Bay, and Lake Erie itself. R. B. Simpson writes that there have been times when it has been exceedingly numerous on the upper Allegheny River at Warren, but this does not happen every year. My experience at Beaver would lead me to believe that the species is not a winter resident along the Ohio River, for even in exceptionally mild and dry winters, when conditions were seemingly favorable for its occurrence, careful search failed to reveal it. It might be expected to winter at Erie, if anywhere in our region, but there is only a little evidence to show that it does. The species was reported from there in *Bird-Lore*'s "Christmas Census" lists for 1932 and 1935. Specimens were taken on January 10, 1901, and February 6, 1904 (Bacon), and single birds were observed on February 7, 1932; January 29, 1933; and February 10, 1934 (Guynes). One was killed by a dog at Sharon on January 19, 1935 (McQuiston). Mr. Simpson reports the taking of individuals at Warren on January 18, 1901, and on February 8, 1904; in the latter instance the bird was found frozen fast in the ice. This grebe was also reported from Braddock Reservoir, Allegheny County, on February 7, 1923, by J. L. Jones. S. S. Dickey states that on January 16, 1915, he examined a living horned grebe that had been captured south of Waynesburg. These records, however, are all exceptional and scarcely affect the general status of the species as a migrant in our region. It has been recorded oftenest from the western tier of counties, but has been reported also from the ridge and valley section, and regularly from the West Branch of the Susquehanna River at Renovo.

Migration—The Horned Grebe comes and goes at the same time as the other waterfowl, and like them is more or less irregular in its movements. I have seen it along the Ohio River as early as February 22 (1904), but this is unusual, and a date a month later (March 23, 1889) is probably nearer the normal average for its arrival in spring. Some early arrival dates are as follows: Erie Bay, March 15, 1936 (Brooks); Conneaut Lake, March 25, 1913, and March 20, 1925 (Sutton); Warren, March 26, 1900 and 1904 (Simpson). At the latter place the greatest numbers appear during the month of April, according to Mr. Simpson, who adds that a remarkable flight occurred on April 25, 1893, when large flocks appeared on the Allegheny River. Other extensive flights were observed there on April 16, 1891; April 24, 1892; and April 12, 1899. In some seasons a few birds linger until the first or second week in May. G. M. Sutton says that at Conneaut Lake this grebe may remain even later and cites a record of June 6, 1925. W. M. Guynes has two summer records for Erie: June 28 and July 3, 1933. There is always the possibility that these late-staying birds were wounded earlier in the season, but such dates may not be unusual in the case of a species which does not always begin nesting before the latter part of June.

In the fall migration the Horned Grebe does not usually appear until sometime in October. A bird of this species, found helpless on a wet highway, was brought to Frick Park, on the outskirts of Pittsburgh, on September 13, 1936, and was identified by Miss Ruth Trimble. I myself saw one at Beaver on September 23, 1890. These, however, are exceptionally early records. The earliest fall date for Erie Bay is October 6, 1904 (Simpson); for Conneaut Lake, October 29, 1917 (Kirkpatrick); for Davis Island, Allegheny County, October 24, 1898 (Atkinson); for Renovo, October 24, 1911 (Pierce). At this season the birds are most abundant during November, and even at Erie Bay and Conneaut Lake some individuals linger until December, when the waters usually freeze over. This grebe has also been observed during December along the rivers and smaller streams in other parts of our region, but such late occurrences do not necessarily imply wintering. The Horned Grebe seems to be hardier than the Pied-billed, but when trapped by the freezing over of its favorite haunts it may perish miserably.

Habits—Every gunner is familiar with the "Dipper," that elusive water bird which appears when the ducks arrive, but which, because its flesh is rank and fishy in flavor, is not worth shooting for the table. As a diver it is most adept, and with amazing suddenness disappears under water at the first alarm, usually to come up out of gunshot. I have repeatedly seen a single grebe "dive at the flash" quickly enough to escape unscathed amid a shower of shot; if surprised at rest or when feeding, however, it is not hard to kill. The dive is executed by a convulsive kick of the feet, with the head plunged under water at the same instant; but the bird is equally able to sink quietly beneath the surface, leaving only the tip of its bill visible as it swims along in this inconspicuous fashion to reach suitable cover. Its food, which consists of small fish, tadpoles, and other forms of aquatic life, is mainly procured on its diving excursions, and it is able to remain under water a half minute or more at a time. It never comes to shore of its own choice, and its movements when placed on land are awkward in the extreme. On the water, however, it is thoroughly at home, and when pursued will try to escape by diving rather than by flying.

The Horned Grebe does not flock with ducks or other waterfowl, and according to my experience is generally found singly, or perhaps in twos, feeding in the eddies and quiet pools of the river, usually not far from the shore. Once in April, 1935, I found hundreds of these grebes at Conneaut Lake, scattered over the surface of the water in loose formation; and on one other occasion I observed a true flock on Erie Bay. But even in the fall migration at this latter place, when the species was much in evidence and the birds were unusually tame, those in sight were never seen to gather into a compact flock, and in their actions when feeding or when pursued they seemed to be entirely independent of one another. Sometimes in the spring there are days of great movement when the Horned Grebe appears in flocks numbering several hundred individuals. Mr. Simpson has given a vivid description of one of these enormous flights which he witnessed at Warren on April 25, 1893.

A northeast wind had been blowing, and the day was cold, with frequent showers. Flock after flock came up the Allegheny River; sometimes there were four or five groups in sight at once. Here and there they floated together downstream, and one could not walk any distance along the shore without seeing whole droves piling out of the willows just ahead. Flocks gathered at a stretch of quiet water which was a favorite feeding ground, decoying other flying flocks, just as ducks are accustomed to do. At times three or four hundred grebes were in sight—a wonderful picture. With the grebes there were a good many Bonaparte's gulls, and an occasional herring gull. It appears that this flight was general all along the Allegheny River from Pittsburgh to Olean, New York, and many hundreds were killed by gunners at various points. At Warren the shooting sounded like a Fourth-of-July celebration, and a large number of birds were killed. Most of the grebes were in full spring dress, but a few were still in winter plumage, and many were in transition from one to the other. The next day they had almost all gone.

Similar flights have been observed at Conneaut Lake, Meadville, and Renovo—always in April. A. K. Pierce writes that on April 14, 1902, the Susquehanna River at the latter place was "literally alive" with horned grebes, many of which were wantonly shot by gunners and left to rot along the shore.

Podicipes cornutus Townsend, *Proc. Acad. Nat. Sci. Philadelphia*, 1883, 68 (Loyalhanna Creek [Latrobe], Westmoreland Co.).

"Horned Grebe" Warrick, *Ornithologist and Oölogist*, 1883, 8:31 (Washington, Washington Co., December)—Simpson, *Oölogist*, 1911, 28:42 (Warren, Warren Co., April); 1913, 30:149 (Erie, Erie Co., October); 1914, 31:210 (Warren, Warren Co., and Oil City, Venango Co., migration)—Sutton, *Bird-Lore*, 1923, 25:132 (Braddock, Allegheny Co., February, *fide* Jones); (?)1924, 26:418 (Erie, Erie Co., September, *fide* Allen)—Eastwood, *Bird-Lore*, 1926, 28:208 (Highland Park, Allegheny Co., April, *fide* Jones); 1927, 29:197 ([Highland Park and Braddock] reservoirs, Allegheny Co., April, *fide* Jones and Elliott)—Savage, *Bird-Lore*, 1932, 34:44; and Upson, *et al.*, *Bird-Lore*, 1935, 37:47 (Erie Bay, Erie Co., December)—Brooks, *Redstart*, 1936, 3:49 (Erie Bay, Erie Co., March)—Oudette, *Cardinal*, 1939, 5:48 (Pymatuning Lake, near Linesville, Crawford Co., March).

Colymbus auritus Warren, *Birds Pa.*, ed. 2, 1890, 3 (Renovo, Clinton Co., spring, *fide* Van Fleet and Ferguson)—Todd, *Ann. Carnegie Mus.*, 1904, 2:498 (Erie Bay, and region, Erie Co., transient)—Todd, in Bausman, *Hist. Beaver Co., Pa.*, 1904, 2:1198 (Beaver Co., transient)—Stone, *Cassinia*, 1915, 18:50 (State College, Centre Co., May, *fide* Mason); 1919, 22:28 ("Altoona" [Lakemont], Blair Co., April, *fide* McGraw); 1920, 23:29 (Chambersburg, Franklin Co., May, *fide* Mahy; Newton Hamilton, Mifflin Co., April, *fide* McGraw)—Christy, *Cardinal*, 1923, v. 1, no. 1, [p. 1] (Clinton Pond, Allegheny Co., transient)—Burleigh, *Wilson Bull.*, 1923, 35:81 (Highland Park, Allegheny Co., spring transient); 1924, 36:74 ("State College" [Oak Hall and Scotia], Centre Co., spring transient)—Sutton, *Ann. Carnegie Mus.*, 1928, 18:51 (Crawford Co. records and references)—Christy, *Cardinal*, 1940, 5:68 (Pymatuning Lake [Linesville], Crawford Co., November).

WESTERN GREBE

AECHMOPHORUS OCCIDENTALIS (Lawrence)

Description—A large grebe, with a *long, slender neck*, and *long, spearlike bill* (about two and a half inches). No ruffs or crests; plumage plain dusky above (blackish on the head) and pure white below; these colors strongly contrasted on the head and neck. In general the Western Grebe resembles the Loon in immature plumage, but it is considerably smaller.

Range and local status—As suggested by its vernacular name, this grebe is properly a western species, and is merely accidental in the East. A specimen in the Carnegie Museum was shot at Youngstown, Ohio, just across our western border.[1] The species' place in our list rests on the authority of a mounted specimen preserved in the collection of St. Vincent College, near Latrobe, Westmoreland County, and said to have been taken on the Greensburg Reservoir southeast of the town sometime between 1898 and 1906. Although the specimen in question bears no original label, the circumstance of its capture is vouched for by one of the former members of the St. Vincent community, the Reverend Wenceslaus Sholar, O.S.B., in a letter to the Reverend Maximilian Duman, O.S.B., through whom the information was transmitted to me.

[1]Compare G. L. Fordyce, *Auk*, 1914, 31:243.

PIED-BILLED GREBE

PODILYMBUS PODICEPS PODICEPS (Linnaeus)

Description—Size of a small duck or teal; *bill relatively stout*, much shorter than the head. *Spring plumage:* upperparts and wings dusky brown; top and back of the head dusky black; *sharply defined black throat-patch*, contrasting with the grayish-brown sides of the head and neck; neck in front also grayish brown; underparts dull white, with dark mottling showing through from beneath the surface of the feathers and shading the breast and sides of the body; bill bluish or yellowish white, with a *broad black band* across the middle. *Young in fall:* head above and behind, neck above, and upperparts in general (including wings), dusky brown; throat and underparts white; sides of head and neck, foreneck, breast, and sides of the body, washed with light brown; bill dull brown, without any dark band. The *short, thick bill*, and the *lack of any white on the wings* will serve to distinguish this species in any plumage from the Horned Grebe, which is about the same size. *Downy young:* dusky above, whitish below, the head and back marked with whitish stripes and spots.

Range—The Pied-billed Grebe is strictly an American species and is remarkable for its extensive breeding range, which covers the greater part of both continents. A resident as far south as Chile and Argentina, it has been found nesting as far north as Great Slave Lake in the Canadian territory of Mackenzie—localities separated by ninety-five degrees of latitude. In eastern North America, however, it does not go nearly so far north, normally not beyond Quebec and New Brunswick. The species is migratory throughout the northern part of its range; and even in the southern United States, where this grebe is found the year round, the summer population may move southward for the winter, and be replaced by migrants from the north. In some parts of the country the species is a regular and fairly common summer resident, but in our region generally it is rare and local as such, because of the comparative scarcity of suitable nesting haunts. Until 1931 there were but five authentic cases on record of its having nested within our limits—or six if we count a second nesting by the same pair of birds, as reported by R. C. Harlow and T. D. Burleigh from Scotia, Centre County, during the season of 1917. These observers supposed that their nesting record was the first from western Pennsylvania, but as a matter of fact D. A. Atkinson had collected a set of six eggs (now in the Carnegie Museum) along the Allegheny River above Verona,

Allegheny County, on May 9, 1893. Moreover, Van Fleet recorded the species as breeding at DuBois and added that he saw young in June, 1883. R. L. Keesler found a nest on June 1, 1925, in a pond about a mile east of Forestville, Butler County. The ponds on Presque Isle would certainly seem to be good nesting grounds for this grebe, but thus far it has not been found breeding there, although one bird was seen on June 18, 1933 (Guynes). In 1928 G. M. Sutton could cite no certain breeding records from the Pymatuning region, but since the flooding of this area the species has found condi-

tions so much to its liking that it now breeds there every season in considerable numbers.

Elsewhere in our region the Pied-billed Grebe is merely a transient visitant in spring and fall. There are only two places, aside from Pymatuning Lake, where it can be considered common and regular at these seasons: Erie Bay and Conneaut Lake. It has been noted at irregular intervals along the Ohio River in Beaver and Allegheny counties, but according to my experience is not nearly so common as the Horned Grebe. Even at Warren, on the upper Allegheny River, it is not common, according to R. B. Simpson. It is likely to be found anywhere, however; and it appears in the manuscript lists of several other observers from widely separated localities.

Migration—The northward movement begins in March (March 5, 1900—Renovo; March 10, 1892—Verona, Allegheny County; March 10, 1918—Lakemont, Blair County; March 11, 1939—Pymatuning Lake; March 18, 1934—Erie; March 20, 1921—Spruce Creek, Huntingdon County), but the majority of birds do not appear until April; and most of the recorded dates of arrival fall in the first half of that month. By the first of May these grebes have nearly all departed, but the fact that some may linger a week or two longer suggests the possibility that under favorable conditions they might even remain to nest. Since eggs were taken at Verona on May 9, 1893, as already noted, such a possibility should always be borne in mind. A bird seen on the Allegheny River near Warren on June 7, 1923, by S. S. Dickey, must have been a late straggler or a breeding bird. Some of the records for the first return movement in the fall, which begins in August, also indicate that the birds may breed in the region. Thus, P. W. Roth took three young birds at the north end of Conneauttee Lake, Crawford County, between August 28 and September 3, 1895; these may have been reared in the immediate neighborhood. I myself have shot a specimen at the mouth of the Beaver River in Beaver County as early as August 28 (1893). This must have been an early migrant, however, since there is no suitable nesting ground in the vicinity. S. E. Bacon observed the species at Erie on August 8, 1903, and Dr. Sutton quotes two early August records for Crawford County. It is always commoner in the fall than in the spring, and was "exceedingly abundant" (for a grebe) on Erie Bay during the last week in September, 1900; it was even observed there until November 14 of that year. During the exceptionally mild and open season of 1931–32, it was seen on the bay as late as December 25 (Savage, 1932). At Conneaut Lake it was noted on November 17, 1921 (Keesler), and at Raccoon Creek, Beaver County, on December 4, 1899 (Wickham). The only actual winter record is of a bird caught alive in Meadville on January 13, 1912; this occurrence was doubtless purely accidental, since the species does not ordinarily pass the cold season quite so far north (at least west of the mountains).

Habits—During migration the Pied-billed Grebe is likely to be found on the still waters of pools or skulking along the weedy or brushy shores of streams, where the current is sluggish and where it finds protection from observation. When discovered it seeks to escape by diving rather than by flying, and reappears usually well out of reach, or comes up under cover of the aquatic vegetation, among which it can easily hide. Again it may sink quietly beneath the water, leaving only its bill and the top of its head above the surface. It seems to be of even more solitary habit than the Horned Grebe; when several birds congregate it is more because of a common interest in a particular resort than from a truly gregarious disposition. At Erie Bay, where I found the species common in 1900, it did not appear in flocks, although several birds might be in sight at one time. They kept mostly in the shallower parts of the bay, wherever there was an abundant growth of aquatic plants, and on the various ponds. None were ever noted on the main lake. Most of the birds seen in the fall months were young of the year, unsophisticated and not at all shy, but in the spring the old birds were watchful and not easily approached.

The nest of this species is a shapeless mass of decayed aquatic grasses and other plants mixed with some mud; it floats on the surface of the water and is held in place by leaves of the surrounding rushes or bushy growth, which are woven into the structure of the nest. It is not effectively concealed and may be built close to the shore. It is so inconspicuous, however, that it would not ordinarily be recognized as a nest at all, since when the female leaves she hides the eggs by pulling some of the nesting material over them. Most of the nests that were found at various times at Pymatuning were built in the cattail areas, in comparatively shallow water. It is very hard to catch the bird on the nest, as she slips quietly into the water at the least alarm. According to my experience, full sets of eggs vary from five to eight, six being a common number. When fresh they are said to be dull bluish white, but they soon become stained to a buffy or even a brownish hue. They average 1.72 by 1.20 inches. The usual nesting time at Pymatuning, as indicated by the records, is from the middle to the end of May. Early in July (on June 1 in 1935) the females may be found with their broods of young, swimming leisurely about in the quiet pools covered with aquatic plants. The young seem to feed mostly on the surface, and snatch at their food with quick stabbing motions. S. J. Seiple once watched a female catch a small frog, crush it, and then feed it to one of her young; she was alert and restless while overseeing her charges.

Except in the breeding season the Pied-billed Grebe is silent. In May and June, at Pymatuning, I have repeatedly heard a loud, sonorous, prolonged, cuckoo-like call that I assumed was the mating song of the male.

Podilymbus podicipes Townsend, *Proc. Acad. Nat. Sci. Philadelphia*, 1883, 68 (Latrobe, Westmoreland Co., "resident").

Podilymbus podiceps Warren, *Birds Pa.*, ed. 2, 1890, 4 (Crawford and Erie Co., transient, *fide* Sennett)—Rhoads, *Auk*, 1899, 16:309 (Six-mile Island, Allegheny River, Allegheny Co., August)—Todd, *Ann. Carnegie Mus.*, 1904, 2:499 (Erie Bay and Presque Isle, Erie Co., transient)—Todd, in Bausman, *Hist. Beaver Co., Pa.*, 1904, 2:1198 (Beaver Co., transient)—Harlow, *Auk*, 1918, 35:19 (Franklin Co., summer; Scotia, Centre Co., nesting)—Burleigh, *Auk*, 1918, 35:218 (Scotia, Centre Co., nesting)—Stone, *Cassinia*, 1919, 22:28; 1920, 23:29 ("Altoona" [Lakemont], Blair Co., migration, *fide* McGraw)—Christy, *Cardinal*, 1923, v. 1, no. 1, [p. 1] (Sewickley and Clinton Pond, Allegheny Co., transient)—Burleigh, *Wilson Bull.*, 1923, 35:81 (Highland Park, Allegheny Co., October); 1924, 36:70 (State College, Centre Co., migration).

"Pied-billed Grebe" Warrick, *Ornithologist and Oölogist*, 1883, 8:32 (Washington, Washington Co.)—Christy, *Cardinal*, 1923, v. 1, no. 2, [p. 13] (Clinton Pond, Allegheny Co., spring)—Eastwood, *Bird-Lore*, 1926, 28:403 (Clinton region, Allegheny Co., October)—Boulton, *Bird-Lore*, 1928, 30:13 (Cook Forest, Clarion Co., October)—Christy, *Cardinal*, 1931, 3:43 (McDonald Reservoir, Washington Co., May)—Savage, *Bird-Lore*, 1932, 34:44 (Erie Bay, etc., Erie Co., December)—Trimble, *Cardinal*, 1937, 4:105 (Pymatuning Lake, Crawford Co., nesting)—Oudette, *Cardinal*, 1939, 5:47 (Pymatuning Lake, near Linesville, Crawford Co., March).

Podilymbus podiceps podiceps Sutton, *Ann. Carnegie Mus.*, 1928, 18:52 (Crawford Co. records and references; Mill Run, near Meadville, Crawford Co., winter, *fide* Kirkpatrick)—Burleigh, *Cardinal*, 1932, 3:74 (Lake Seaton, Fayette Co., August).

STORM PETRELS

FAMILY HYDROBATIDAE

THE MEMBERS of this family are pelagic and most of them are confined to southern oceans. They seldom come to land except to nest, and their occurrence inland is purely fortuitous, as a result of storm conditions. Petrels are of small size; the feet are webbed, but too frail as a rule to support the weight of the body; the plumage is soft but dense. The bill is weak but decidedly hooked, while the nostrils (as in other Tubinares) are the characteristic feature, and open at the end of short tubes. Petrels spend most of their time in the air or resting on the water; on the wing they are exceedingly graceful and are suggestive of giant moths. The two species recorded in our region are both waifs from the Atlantic.

MADEIRA PETREL

OCEANODROMA CASTRO CASTRO (Harcourt)

Description—Sooty, or brownish black, with a conspicuous white spot at the base of the tail above, and some white below also, on the sides of the crissum. It can be distinguished from Leach's Petrel (*O. leucorhoa*) only by the less deeply forked tail and by the greater extent of the white on the flanks and crissum. Smaller than the Robin.

Range and local status—This pelagic species is properly a bird of the other side of the Atlantic Ocean, where it breeds on the Cape Verde Islands and on the Azores, and its occurrence here is purely accidental. It has been recorded from Indiana and the District of Columbia, while the most recent record is that concerning a specimen in the collection of Frank S. Flack, taken at Chambersburg, Franklin County, on the extreme eastern border of our region. "The specimen was brought to Mr. Flack on April 15, 1912, by Mr. William Lippey, who had found the bird dead along one of the streets of Chambersburg. Mr. Flack does not remember that any considerable storm preceded this date, but according to the records of the Weather Bureau an unusually constant easterly and northeasterly wind had been blowing over Pennsylvania on April 13, 14, and 15 of that year. While this wind was not of high velocity in Franklin County, it may have been sufficiently strong to account for the presence of this maritime bird so far inland. It is possible that the street lights lured the wandering bird to the environs of the town" (Sutton, 1927). The example in question agrees well with authentic specimens in the collection of the Carnegie Museum.

The allocation here of the petrel recorded by Warren from Elk County (Williamsville), on the authority of the late Captain A. A. Clay, is conjectural. The specimen is not extant, and there is no way of fixing its identity. Captain Clay told me that the bird was killed during a flight of small gulls (Bonaparte's Gull?) in the fall (October?), about the year 1884.

(?)*Oceanodroma leucorhoa* WARREN, *Birds Pa.*, ed. 2, 1890, 26 ([Williamsville], Elk Co., *fide* Clay).

Oceanodroma castro SUTTON, *Auk*, 1927, 44:556 (Chambersburg, Franklin Co., *fide* Flack).

WILSON'S PETREL

OCEANITES OCEANICUS (Kuhl)

Description—Sooty, or brownish black, darker above, duller below; upper tail coverts, flanks, and lateral under tail coverts, white; wing coverts with some grayish or whitish edgings. Tail nearly even; *feet long and slender* (tarsus one and one-fourth inches). Smaller than the Robin.

Range and local status—Wilson's Petrel is a bird of the Atlantic Ocean, breeding mainly in the Antarctic, and migrating northward in the summer months. Its occurrence inland is entirely fortuitous. There is a mounted specimen in the collection of St. Vincent College, near Latrobe, Westmoreland County, which, according to information received from the Reverend Maximilian Duman, O.S.B., the curator of the collection, was taken on the Greensburg Reservoir sometime between 1898 and 1906. The circumstance of its capture is vouched for by a former member of the St. Vincent faculty, who mounted the bird, although it bears no original label.

PELICANS

FAMILY PELECANIDAE

THE PELICANS are a small but highly specialized group of eight species, which are confined principally to the tropical and subtropical regions of both hemispheres. They are birds of large size, with short legs, totipalmate feet (all four toes webbed), ungainly wings, and enormous bills. The lower mandible is expanded into a pouch capable of holding a large quantity of food (which is primarily fish).

The supposed occurrence of the Brown Pelican (*Pelecanus occidentalis occidentalis*) on the Ohio River, as recorded by Maximilian, Prince of Wied, in 1859, is too highly improbable to be given credence.

WHITE PELICAN

PELECANUS ERYTHRORHYNCHOS Gmelin

Description—A large white bird, exceeding the Whistling Swan in size, with black wings and an enormous reddish-yellow bill and pouch.

Range and local status—The White Pelican is properly an inhabitant of the lake regions of the western interior; but it has appeared at odd times during migration far to the eastward of its breeding range, and there are several records for western Pennsylvania. "On October 13, 1898, three of these birds appeared on Conneaut Lake. One was shot on the morning of that day by William Foust; later in the day another was secured by Douglas Stewart and Arthur W. Bell. Mr. Stewart secured the specimen shot by Mr. Foust and had both specimens mounted by Ward's Natural Science Establishment, and presented them to the Carnegie Museum, where they now are" (Holland, 1901). G. M. Sutton (1928) contributes two records: one for Conneaut Lake, and one for Pymatuning Swamp. A recent record for the latter region (cited below) concerns a bird that remained on Pymatuning Lake for five days (June 19–23, 1936), and was seen by several observers independently. Warren cites a record for Keating, Clinton County, based on a specimen taken there "three or four years ago" (about 1886), and quotes Sennett to the effect that the species occurred at Erie between 1870 and 1875. Even if specimens are not actually secured one can scarcely mistake this bird for any other; afloat or awing it is easily identified.

Pelecanus erythrorhynchos WARREN, *Birds Pa.*, 1888, 232 (Erie, Erie Co., *fide* Sennett); ed. 2, 1890, 29 (Erie, Erie Co., *fide* Sennett; Keating, Clinton Co., *fide* Van Fleet)—HOLLAND, *Ann. Carnegie Mus.*, 1901, 1:3 (Conneaut Lake, Crawford Co.)—SUTTON, *Ann. Carnegie Mus.*, 1928, 18:60 (Pymatuning Swamp and Conneaut Lake, Crawford Co., transient)—OUDETTE, *Cardinal*, 1937, 4:121 (Pymatuning Lake [Linesville], Crawford Co., June).

CORMORANTS

FAMILY PHALACROCORACIDAE

THE CORMORANTS are a group of ancient origin, wide distribution, and aquatic habits. They are fish-eating diving birds with very short tarsi, totipalmate feet (all four toes webbed), relatively long tails, and stout, strongly hooked bills, without external nostrils. The family has only one representative in our region.

DOUBLE-CRESTED CORMORANT

PHALACROCORAX AURITUS AURITUS (Lesson)

Description—A large, dark water bird with a long neck and long tail. *Spring adult:* black; a tuft of curly black feathers on each side of the head; pouch and bare space around the eyes orange-yellow. *Fall and winter adult:* similar, but without crest. *Immature:* brown, duller and paler below; no crest; pouch dull yellow.

Range and migration—In the eastern part of its range, the Double-crested Cormorant is rather northerly in the breeding season. In former years it is said to have bred in northern Ohio, but there are no recent records to that effect, nor indeed any from the lower Great Lakes. In our region it is a transient, rare in the spring, and only occasional in the fall. As might be expected, it has been met with oftener at Erie Bay and Conneaut Lake than elsewhere; records from other localities are few in number. At Erie Bay it has been noted at infrequent intervals, oftenest in the fall and early winter, the exact dates ranging from September 25 (1930) to December 14 (1901). During the unprecedentedly mild winter of 1931–32, when the bay did not freeze over, a few birds of this species must have remained through the entire cold season, since they were observed at intervals from December to February. Again, in 1934 a single bird was seen in January and February, and in 1935 one on February 17. In 1932 the species was noted there as late as April 10 (Simpson) and in 1933 on April 23 (Guynes). From Conneaut Lake we have a number of records supplied by various observers, ranging from April 15 (1926) to May 30 (1913) in the spring, and from August 26 (1926) to November 2 (1884) in the fall. R. L. Fricke reports seeing one bird on Pymatuning Lake on June 20, 1936, and five on May 25, 1937. These late spring dates can have no breeding significance, however. R. B. Simpson noted the species at Warren but once (May 1, 1903), when he saw a full-plumaged male on the Allegheny River. He has examined a mounted specimen said to have been shot at Glade Run in the eighties. An early record for the Ohio River is that made by Major Stephen H. Long's expedition in 1819, cited below. I have seen the species on the Ohio but once (November 16, 1889) —a single bird at the mouth of the Beaver River; and H. H. Wickham saw another on April 16, 1890, at the same place. There is one record from Mercer County, but for the larger part of our region there are as yet none.

Habits—This is the only inland species of cormorant in North America, and its large size and dark coloration render it unmistakable, either when swimming or when flying. Its flight is direct but rather heavy, like that of the Crow, and is accomplished with comparatively slow, even strokes of the wings. Its food consists entirely of fish, which it captures by diving from the surface. S. E. Bacon speaks of having taken two ten-inch perch from the gullet of a bird that he shot at Erie, and adds that "the fishermen inform me that the birds when present often alight on the pond-net stakes."

Pelicanus carbo (error) JAMES, Long's *Exped. Pittsburgh to Rocky Mts.*, 1823, 4 (Ohio River, western Pa., May).

Phalacrocorax dilophus WARREN, *Birds Pa.*, 1888, 232; ed. 2, 1890, 28 (Lake Erie, Erie Co., transient, *fide* Sennett and

Thompson)—Todd, *Ann. Carnegie Mus.*, 1904, 2:508 (Erie Bay, and region, Erie Co., transient)—Todd, in Bausman, *Hist. Beaver Co., Pa.*, 1904, 2:1198 (Beaver Co., transient).
"Cormorant" Simpson, *Oölogist*, 1910, 27:34 (Warren, Warren Co., May)—Nicholson, *Bird-Lore*, 1918, 20:180 (Barmore Lake, Mercer Co., migration).
"Double-crested Cormorant" Christy, *Cardinal*, 1932, 3:86 (Erie Bay, Erie Co., February)—Savage, *Bird-Lore*, 1932, 34:44 (Erie Bay, Erie Co., December)—Brooks, *Redstart*, 1936, 3:49 (Erie Bay, Erie Co., March).
Phalacrocorax auritus auritus Sutton, *Ann. Carnegie Mus.*, 1928, 18:60 (Conneaut Lake, Crawford Co., transient).

The wood ibis (*Mycteria americana* Linnaeus), a tropical American species belonging to the Family Ciconiidae, is not known to breed anywhere north of the South Atlantic and Gulf states, but has been reported as a straggler in Clinton County by Warren (*Report on the Birds of Pennsylvania*, ed. 2, 1890, p. 53), on Van Fleet's authority. Although its occurrence is not intrinsically impossible, there is now no way of substantiating the record.

HERONS

FAMILY ARDEIDAE

THE HERONS are typical wading birds, equipped for living and feeding along the water's edge. They have comparatively small bodies, but long feet with widespreading toes, and long, much compressed, and extremely slender necks; the bill is usually long and spearlike. A peculiar feature is the possession of powder-down tracts —areas of skin covered by short feathers with a scurfy excretion. These tracts occur in pairs: on the lower back, on the lower belly, and on the breast. (The Bitterns lack the second pair of these.) In the breeding season some species assume long ornamental plumes on the head and back. More than 150 forms are known, arranged in about thirty genera. The group is widely distributed throughout the tropical and temperate regions of both the Old and New Worlds, and has reached its highest development in the warmer climates. The true Herons (Subfamily Ardeinae) have twelve tail feathers and three pairs of powder-down tracts; they inhabit open places, nest in trees, and lay from three to six pale blue eggs. The Bitterns (Subfamily Botaurinae) have only ten tail feathers and two pairs of powder-down tracts; they are paludicoline in habit and nesting. The family has only a few representatives in western Pennsylvania, and only five species are known to breed.

GREAT WHITE HERON

ARDEA OCCIDENTALIS Audubon

Description—A little larger than the Great Blue Heron. Pure white; bill and feet yellowish; crest feathers shorter and broader than in the Great Blue Heron.

Range and local status—This heron is a salt-water species, now confined to the Florida Keys in the breeding season. Postseason wanderings have occasionally carried it to other parts of peninsular Florida, and once as far as North Carolina. Its occurrence as far north and as far inland as northwestern Pennsylvania is truly astonishing, and would be incredible were the evidence not unassailable. The bird captured on Pymatuning Lake, near Linesville, on May 14, 1938, had been observed for several days by both B. L. Oudette and R. L. Fricke before it was finally secured by the former. It is an adult female, rather small, but within the size limit for this sex, and possessing the short crest characteristic of this species. H. C. Oberholser, who has examined and identified the specimen, thinks that the occurrence, although admittedly extraordinary, may be explained on the ground of an unusual northward wandering, perhaps due to stress of storm. Since the Great White Heron population of Florida amounts to only a few hundred individuals, the chances against even one bird finding its way to such a remote point from its home grounds would be about one million to one. The odds against a second individual turning up later at the same place are correspondingly greater. Yet this is precisely what happened in October, 1938. Furthermore, Mr. Oudette believes that a third bird was present at this time. These occurrences were probably not unrelated. It is possible that after all the Great

Blue Heron is actually a dichromatic species (like certain other herons), with its white phase localized in southern Florida but appearing rarely and fortuitously in other parts of its range. It is earnestly to be hoped that if any more great white herons come to Pymatuning they may be sedulously protected and that further developments will be carefully noted.

Ardea occidentalis Christy, *Cardinal*, 1938, 4:202 (Linesville, Crawford Co., May)—Oberholser, *Cardinal*, 1939, 5:15 (critical).

"Great White Heron" Krieble, *Cardinal*, 1939, 5:15 (Linesville, Crawford Co., October).

GREAT BLUE HERON

ARDEA HERODIAS HERODIAS Linnaeus

Description—A large heron, standing *three feet high* or more, and with a wingspread of from five to six feet. *Spring plumage:* general color *bluish gray above, the wings and tail blackish;* striped with gray and white below; throat and head whitish, with a broad black band from the base of the bill over the eye to the nape, continued as a crest of long feathers; a blackish stripe down the front of the neck; long breast plumes dull whitish; sides of breast black; thighs and bend of wing rufous; eyes yellow; bill yellowish, sometimes darker above; feet dark. *Young in summer and fall:* similar to the adult, but crest feathers and whole top of the head blackish; the upperparts and wing coverts more or less mottled with reddish brown and buff; underparts whitish, with dusky and grayish stripes; the dark neck-stripe scarcely apparent, and the breast without any long plumes; colors of the bill and feet much duller than in the adult. The crest feathers are shorter, and the underparts appear whiter than in the adult.

Range—The range of the Great Blue Heron covers practically all the North American continent from the Canadian Life Zone southward, as well as the West Indian Islands and northwestern South America; one outlying race occurs in the Galapagos Archipelago. Several subspecies are now recognized. In the northern part of its range it is truly migratory and retires southward for the winter months. It is known to breed regularly, even if not commonly, throughout its extensive range, but in many parts it is now of only local occurrence as a nesting species. Summer records for our region are sufficiently numerous, it is true, but there is no certainty that they all represent breeding individuals, and only the actual discovery of the nest can be accepted as valid evidence of breeding. Authentic records of this kind are unfortunately few. R. B. Simpson writes that until 1916 from ten to fifteen pairs nested in the virgin forest near the middle fork of Hickory Creek in Warren County, but because of lumbering they deserted that place; and while the species is still seen there in summer, he does not know where the nesting site is at present. Harry Van Cleve reports that for seven years (1917–23) a pair was located on a hardwood ridge at the head of Wildboy Run, north of Conrad, Potter County. The same observer adds that great blue herons had nested in the vicinity of Kettle Creek, Clinton County (opposite the mouth of Hammersley Fork) for fifteen years. Van Fleet includes the species without comment in his list of the breeding birds of DuBois. The Presque Isle record cited below (Boulton, 1928) is probably an error, since it has not been substantiated by other observers. There are, however, several recent and definite records for Crawford County. The first of these was contributed by L. E. Hicks, who wrote me that in 1931 there were at least nineteen nests in a heronry which he had discovered in the "Jumbo Woods," in the northwestern corner of Beaver Township, close to the Ohio line. I visited this heronry with B. H. Christy early in May, 1933. Later in the month a second and smaller colony was discovered on the edge of Pymatuning Swamp, about two miles north of Hemlock Island. The following year a colony of at least seven pairs was found established in the swamp itself, about two miles north of Hartstown, and the year after that still another group of nests was observed west of Shermansville. B. L. Oudette informs me that near Cambridge Springs there is a colony that dates from about 1927. These interesting discoveries serve to confirm the suspicions entertained by earlier writers that the Great Blue Heron nested in the region. They serve also to extend the breeding range recently worked out for the adjoining state of Ohio.

Although the breeding records just discussed are the only unquestioned ones available, it is probable that at least some May and June records of odd individuals and pairs may apply to nesting birds. Thus, in recording a specimen killed at Tambine, Elk County, on June 1, 1898, A. K. Pierce remarks that he had encountered this heron many times during the summer in that county and believed that it was breeding in some secluded spot. In addition to those shown in the published references, there are May and June records from Erie, Mercer, Butler, Greene, and Indiana counties by several observers. It is well known that birds of this species are wont to go a long way from their nesting grounds in search of food. Although repeatedly observed at Presque Isle in May, 1933 (Guynes), the Great Blue Heron almost certainly does not breed there, and those seen must come from some other section or are nonbreeding individuals. O. E. Jennings states that in the summer of that year no herons were observed on the peninsula until July 10, and by August 20 they had perceptibly decreased in numbers. On the basis of the ascertained facts and the probabilities, we are justified in the belief that there is no part of our region where the Great Blue Heron may not be regarded as a potential breeding species.

Migration—The herons as a class are rather delicate birds, but the Great Blue is a big, hardy species, able to withstand considerable cold weather without inconvenience. It arrives early in the spring and stays late in the fall. O. J. Murie saw one at Aspinwall, Allegheny County, on February 22, 1916; but this was exceptionally early. At Erie it comes during the last week in March or early in April, after most of the ice on the ponds has disappeared. What may have been a wintering individual was seen there on February 16, 1935, by Mr. Christy. J. G. Crumb reported that the birds composing the colony near his home, north of Hemlock Island, came back about March 20. Mr. Simpson gives first dates at Warren as between March 19 (1904) and April 3 (1901). March 24 (1903) is the earliest date for Renovo, and March 30 (1916) for State College. March 25 (1911) is an early date for Conneaut Lake, with other records mostly in early April. It is doubtless during this latter month that the main northward movement takes place.

The appearance of young birds in July and August, at localities distant from known nesting grounds, is of course not a true migratory movement, but rather a dispersal of the young after the breeding season. Most of the individuals noted in late summer are birds of the year. They often remain, although in diminished numbers, well into November before going south. There are even a few December and January records (Meadville, December 3, 1897; Oakdale, Allegheny County, December 1, 1922; Conneaut Lake, January 12, 1926). At least one heron remained on Presque Isle during the open winter of 1931–32, and was noted at intervals by several observers. W. M. Guynes reports one seen there in 1934 on January 7, but none again until March 31. Mr. Crumb thinks that a few herons winter almost every year at Pymatuning. So long as the birds can find food, the exigencies of the weather do not seem to affect them seriously.

Habits—The Great Blue Heron (wrongly called "Crane") is one of the few water birds that are not absolutely dependent upon lakes and marshes for cover and food. Thus it happens that the Erie-Crawford district does not enjoy a monopoly of the records for this species. The bird is likely to be seen almost anywhere in our region, along large or small streams, wading in the still water along the banks, or standing motionless in statuesque pose on an outlying bar. A wild and wary bird, ever on the alert for danger from its only enemy, man, it has survived to the present day largely because of its ability to take care of itself. Indeed, most observers agree that it is more likely to be seen at a distance, or when flying high overhead. In flight its long legs are stretched out behind and its long neck is drawn in—affording a characteristic silhouette against the sky. Small fish and other aquatic forms of animal life are its favorite prey; these it stalks in the shallow water and captures by quick thrusts of the spearlike bill. "It is a stately bird, dignified in its bearing, graceful in its movements and an artistic feature in the landscape."[1] What a pity that it often falls

[1]A. C. Bent, U. S. National Museum, *Bulletin*, no. 135, 1926, p. 101.

victim to the unprincipled gunner, for whom any large bird is a tempting target!

In the Pymatuning region the Great Blue Heron has become successfully established as a breeding species, and it is a common sight along the shores of the new lake. It is also numerous on the outside beach as well as about the ponds of Presque Isle. Small flocks have been noted there in the spring, and J. E. Perry has on several occasions in August counted from fourteen to thirty individuals in sight at one time, mostly young birds; while S. J. Seiple once saw sixty-five together at Crystal Point. On another occasion he observed two of these herons alight and swim on the water near the fish nets. Dr. Jennings remarks that their appearance along the beach always aroused considerable commotion among the common terns, which were then either brooding eggs or feeding young—a circumstance suggesting that the larger birds may not have been overparticular in their choice of food.

Like many other herons, the Great Blue tends to be gregarious in the breeding season, and a number of pairs usually nest together in some secluded spot. In the Warren County heronry, visited by Mr. Simpson, the nests were placed in the very tops of huge pines or hemlocks. A lofty site was characteristic also in the Crawford County colonies. The larger of these, the one in the "Jumbo Woods" of Beaver Township, near the little village of Wing, persisted, according to local report, for over fifteen years, but was not visited by any scientific observer until June, 1931, when Professor Hicks located it, after following the line of flight taken by the birds from the Ohio side. Of this he writes as follows: "Twenty-nine young were counted on eleven of the nests. The others either had small young or could not be seen clearly in the growing darkness. Some of the birds feed along West Branch of Conneaut Creek or to the south and east, but apparently about three-quarters of the adults climb rapidly until at a height which should mean at least a five-mile flight. These head to the northeast and probably cover the five miles to the main Conneaut Creek or the ten miles to the Lake Erie shore, as the proximity of a colony was first suspected from the number of herons found there. The colony seems well established and is in fairly good feeding territory and should prosper if unmolested by gunners and if the nesting-trees are not cut."

In 1932 twenty-one nests were occupied, according to local report. In 1933 Mr. Christy and I made a visit to this colony, and the former has at my request written the following account of our experiences:

"On May 7, 1933, Mr. Todd and I visited a nesting colony of Great Blue Herons in northwestern Pennsylvania. It was in wet woodland, near the watershed between Lake Erie and the Ohio Valley. The herons' nests were placed in the tops of the largest trees—beeches and sugar maples with boles a foot to eighteen inches through, and their tops reaching sixty to eighty feet. Uncanopied by leafage, the nests were open to heaven and accessible to free approach from the air. Built of sticks, they were three or four feet across and a foot deep; it is surprising that such large structures could continue coherent for any sufficient length of time in a wind-tossed treetop.

"Although we had been advised that a year or two ago the colony had numbered forty nests, we could discover scarcely half so many. Nearly all of these were gathered within a radius of a hundred yards, and a few more were perhaps three hundred yards distant. Frequently a single tree held more than one nest, and twice we noticed as many as four in one tree. Most of the nests were in beeches; one group of three was in a maple.

"On the evening of May 6 we had succeeded in locating an outlying group of nests. The next morning we returned to these; they afforded no other sign of life than that they were manifestly new (there were other tumble-down remains of nests of earlier years). But as we waited we heard again more clearly what we had also heard and mistaken the evening before—distant, loud, deep shouts, like the clamor of a dogfight. The sound was intermittent, and now we knew it was the croaking of herons, not the barking of dogs. Guided by these shoutings we soon were in the center of the colony, and even our quiet approach was the cause of much flapping of great pinions and loud guttural shoutings. But as we sat quietly, the birds returned to perch in their treetops and some of them to settle again on their nests. [They usually alighted a little way from the nest and approached it by walking, balancing precariously on the branch with unsteady feet and wings ready for instant use. When more than one bird attempted to alight on the same branch the first occupant would drive the other away with loud, throaty squawks. These large, water-loving birds seemed highly out of place walking on the branches in the treetops.]

"The time of egg-laying was already past. On the ground we found a few fragments of shells, and as we waited we remarked also another sound coming from the treetops, higher-pitched, weaker, and cackling—evidently the calls of young within the nests. These young were not yet large enough to stand and move about. We could see none, but we judged that in most of the nests the young were already hatched. There was no feeding in progress while we watched. The undisturbed birds had been incubating and brooding. We perceived that the loud shouts that had attracted our attention from afar were not—or were at least not always—cries of alarm; for I observed two birds face one another in a treetop, extend their necks, wave their great pinions, and utter with mutual satisfaction those same ear-splitting shouts."

Later in the season, on June 17, Professor Hicks again visited this colony and counted thirty-four nests. Some of the outlying nests were a mile away from the main group. His census showed fourteen nests in red maple trees, nine in beech, one in black ash, two in shellbark hickory, six in white elm, and two in sugar maple.

On May 20, 1933, I was one of a party to visit a newly established rookery of the Great Blue Heron on the edge of Pymatuning Swamp. The individuals composing it had nested in the swamp to the southward for several years, according to Mr. Crumb, who lived near by, and when their original nesting place was destroyed they moved northward a few miles. They were then located in a narrow tongue of woods, about a hundred yards wide, between two cultivated tracts. These woods were low and swampy, and the larger trees were rather scattered and not so high as those in use at the other colony. We counted fourteen nests, situated in the very tops of the trees. All contained young. We decided that the herons must lay their eggs about the middle of April; and accordingly we paid our next visit to this heronry on April 18, 1934. There were again fourteen occupied nests. The birds were uneasy at our intrusion, but kept at a distance; thus the eggs had probably been laid but not hatched. Louis Homer climbed to two nests in an elm tree; these held three and four eggs respectively. Later in the day we visited the "Jumbo Woods" rookery, and Mr. Homer climbed to three nests in the top of a tall beech, fully eighty feet from the ground by actual measurement. These nests were all much alike—shapeless masses of dead twigs, with a depression six inches deep for the eggs. These are clear pale bluish green in color, and measure about 2.55 by 1.80 inches, but vary somewhat in size and shape. Four eggs seem to be the usual number, although on May 4, 1934, R. L. Fricke examined a nest in the Hartstown rookery that held five.

The three interesting rookeries mentioned in the last paragraph are unfortunately no longer in existence. The one near Hartstown has been abandoned, while the one in the "Jumbo Woods" has been eliminated by the cutting of this tract of timber. Although the rookery in Pymatuning Swamp near Mr. Crumb's home had increased to over forty nests during the season of 1938, it was for no apparent reason abandoned the following year after the eggs had been laid.

In the meantime a substantial colony had developed within the Pymatuning Lake sanctuary. It was estimated with much satisfaction that fifty or more pairs of great blue herons occupied this area in 1938. They returned to the same locality in the spring of 1939, built their nests, and laid eggs, but after the young had been hatched, some unknown disturbance caused the adults to desert this site completely. An aeroplane survey of the nesting site, made by Mr. Fricke and G. B. Thorp on May 19, 1939, revealed only deserted nests. During June and July no immature birds were observed, according to Mr. Fricke, but the adults at Pymatuning Lake were still very numerous. What factor is involved in the sudden shifting of heron populations has not been determined.

Ardea herodias TOWNSEND, *Proc. Acad. Nat. Sci. Philadelphia*, 1883, 67 (Loyalhanna Creek [Latrobe], Westmoreland Co., transient)—COPE, *Cassinia*, 1902, 5:13 (Kettle Creek, Oleona, Potter Co., June)—TODD, *Ann. Carnegie Mus.*, 1904, 2:531 (Presque Isle, Erie Co., spring, summer, and fall)—TODD, in Bausman, *Hist. Beaver Co., Pa.*, 1904, 2:1198 (Beaver Co., transient)—JENNINGS, *Cardinal*, 1930, 2:185 (Presque Isle, Erie Co., September).

"Great Blue Heron" SIMPSON, *Oölogist*, 1907, 24:134; 1913, 30:50; 1914, 31:91; 1920, 37:134 (near Warren, Warren Co., spring); 1912, 29:329 (head of Tionesta Creek, Warren Co., breeding)—CHRISTY, *Cardinal*, 1923, v. 1, no. 2, [p. 15] (Clinton Pond, Allegheny Co., April); 1931, 3:43 (McDonald Reservoir, Washington Co., May)—STREET, *Cassinia*, 1923, 24:11 (Conococheague Creek, Mercersburg, Franklin Co., June)—BOULTON, *Bird-Lore*, 1928, 30:337 (Presque Isle, Erie Co., nesting[?])—EASTWOOD, *Wilson Bull.*, 1932, 44: 240 ([Boydstown], Butler Co., August)—COPE and HAWKINS, *Forest Leaves*, 1934, 24:26 (East Tionesta Forest Reserve, Warren and McKean Co., summer)—TRIMBLE, *Cardinal*, 1937, 4:106 (Pymatuning region, Crawford Co., nesting).

Ardea herodias herodias HARLOW, *Auk*, 1912, 29:477 (southern Centre Co., April)—OBERHOLSER, *Proc. U. S. Nat. Mus.*, 1912, 43:534 (Conneauttee Lake, Erie Co., September)—COOKE, *Bull. Biol. Surv.* no. 45, 1913, 33 (Renovo, Clinton Co.; migration)—HARLOW, *Auk*, 1918, 35:20 (mountains of Pa.)—CHRISTY, *Cardinal*, 1923, v. 1, no. 1, [p. 3] (Sewickley, Allegheny Co., transient)—BURLEIGH, *Wilson Bull.*, 1923, 35:83 (Deer Creek, Allegheny Co., July); 1924, 36:70 (State College, Centre Co., migration); 1931, 43:37 (Centre Co., breeding[?])—SUTTON, *Ann. Carnegie Mus.*, 1928, 18:86 (Crawford Co. localities and records)—HICKS, *Wilson Bull.*, 1933, 45:176 (Beaver Township, "Erie" [Crawford] Co., nesting).

AMERICAN EGRET

CASMERODIUS ALBUS EGRETTA (Gmelin)

Description—A large, white heron, standing about twenty-four to thirty inches high; bill yellow; legs and feet black.

Range—The Egret is a species of wide range in both the Old and New Worlds. Our bird belongs to the tropical American race, which finds its present northern breeding limit in the South Atlantic and Gulf states, although formerly it ranged farther north, well up the Mississippi Valley. Like many of the other herons, the young of this species wander widely at the close of the breeding season, and are just as likely to go north as in any other direction. Most of the reported occurrences in our region are for the latter half of the summer, and are explained on this basis. Such invasions have become increasingly marked and regular of late years, and this circumstance suggests that the species has largely recovered from the effects of the persecution to which it was formerly subjected on its breeding grounds. Forty to fifty years ago such appearances were by no means unknown, but they seem to have ceased in the nineties, and then recommenced about 1925. Of the early invasions we have only unsatisfactory accounts. Warren, writing in 1890, says that the Egret is found as a straggler "in almost every quarter of the commonwealth." C. H. Townsend records it as irregular in Westmoreland County, but gives no particulars. In Washington County, according to W. T. Warrick (1883) and J. S. Nease, several were killed from July 23 to 27, 1883, in different parts of the county, one by Mr. Nease himself near the town of Washington. H. C. Kirkpatrick writes that two birds, shot near Cambridge Springs, Crawford County, were left with him to be mounted in August of 1885. He adds: "Three were reported on the authority of Charles Harrington as having been observed at the mouth of Conneaut Outlet in the early autumn of 1891."

During the thirty-odd years that followed, the Egret did not figure in the literature or records of western Pennsylvania birds, except for a single specimen in the A. K. Pierce collection, secured at North Bend, Clinton County, on June 27, 1920. It is significant that this period covered the time when persecution by plume-hunters was actually threatening the very existence of the species. Happily this danger no longer exists, and the Egret is now coming back. In 1919–20, reports of its appearance at various points in the northern states began to come in, but not until 1925 were any received from western Pennsylvania. That year it was recorded from three separate localities: near Mount Union, Huntingdon County, on July 2 (one bird); Conneaut Lake, where three were noted from August 15 to September 12; and Presque Isle, Erie County, where one bird was seen by J. E. Perry on August 16. In 1926 one was noted at "Kidds Mill," Mercer County. During the same season one was killed at Shirleysburg, Huntingdon County (Sutton). In 1927 the species was reported from Fannettsburg, Franklin County (Sutton), and in 1929 from Warren (Simpson) and from Greene County (Jacobs). The next year, 1930, there was a considerable northward flight, extending all the way across the state of Ohio[1] and into western Pennsylvania, from Presque Isle (Hicks) south to Iron Bridge, Armstrong County (Manley, 1931).

Meanwhile S. J. Seiple had been finding the species regularly in Crawford County. He writes as follows: "I have seen the American Egret in the region of Pymatuning Swamp (Hartstown) each year since 1926. This year (1933) it has been more abundant than ever before. The greatest number that I observed at any one time was on August 5, when I saw twenty-five at Hartstown —a beautiful and unusual sight." It was my privilege to be with Professor Seiple on this particular occasion. Returning the same day, I saw an egret along the Shenango River, about three miles south of Pulaski, Lawrence County.

Reports came in from counties other than those in the northwestern part, indicating that the 1933 invasion was not local in its extent, but general and widespread. Egrets were reported from five points in Westmoreland County (United, Brinkerton, Wendel, Beatty, and Madison) by Miss Ruth Trimble and Richard Trimble—in each case at an artificial reservoir or a natural pool of water. At a reservoir near Boydstown, Butler County, as many as sixteen were seen by Ludwig von Fuehrer, and this group, or part of it, was also reported by two other observers. (The species had been seen at this same locality by S. K. Eastwood in 1932.) Other reports were from the Beaver River at Rock Point, Lawrence County, and from the Allegheny River between Franklin and Oil City. In the north the birds again reached Presque Isle, where they were repeatedly noted by several observers, including myself. There were some reports also from the eastern part of our region. One, transmitted by L. A. Luttringer, Jr., pertains to a flock of fourteen birds seen at Cross Fork, Potter County, by W. H. Jones. A single egret was seen near Reynoldsville, Jefferson County, between August 10 and 15, by W. W. Mowry (Seiple). A flock of seven was seen along the river at Renovo by C. A. West, and four were seen at a pond near Ebensburg by F. A. Hegner. The last-named observer also saw one at Juniata Crossing, Bedford County. To the above records, and to the others as listed by B. H. Christy, I am able to add a few more. R. B. Simpson writes that egrets were present at Warren during July, August, and most of September, 1933, and that they were reported from various points along the Allegheny River all the way to Salamanca, New York. H. A. McGraw states that almost every week-end in August and September of that year, while traveling by rail, he used to see single egrets at various points along the Juniata River, as far west as McVeytown, Mifflin County. J. W. Jacobs writes that several were noted in Greene County in July and August, and that one was killed about six miles north of Waynesburg—and the killer fined for his act! The 1933 invasion seems to have been the most widespread of all, but the species has been recorded every subsequent season in the Pymatuning area. The year 1937 was also a good season. On August 23 of that year R. L. Fricke saw at least one hundred egrets scattered along the shores of Pymatuning Lake. There are also several records from Erie and other points.

Migration—The appearance of the Egret in our region in late summer results from a general dispersal after the breeding season, which carries many individuals far to the northward of their nesting grounds. It can hardly be regarded as a migration in the restricted sense commonly employed by ornithologists. We do not yet know from what part of the country our egret visitors come. This question could be answered definitely only by extensive banding in the rookeries of the southern United States, but speculation is permissible. L. E. Hicks, in discussing the Ohio records, notes that the great majority are from the western half of Ohio. This would suggest that the invasion comes from the southwest and proceeds toward the northeast, the number of individuals involved varying inversely with the distance traversed, so that only a remnant reaches western Pennsylvania.

[1]Compare L. E. Hicks, *Wilson Bulletin*, 1931, 43:268–281.

Where the conditions are unusually favorable, as they are on Presque Isle and at Pymatuning Swamp, a greater concentration naturally occurs. By the same reasoning we infer that the birds seen in the eastern part of our region probably come from the southeast, up the Atlantic coast, to spread out in the drainage of the Susquehanna River. The Allegheny divide is a barrier which the Egret is probably seldom able to cross.

This post-breeding movement must begin very promptly after the young are on the wing, for the Egret often appears in the North during the first half of July. It was observed at Mount Union on July 2, 1925 (Sutton, *fide* Aukerman and others); on Presque Isle on July 11, 1930 (Hicks); at Hartstown on July 8, 1930, July 12, 1933, and July 9, 1938 (Seiple). Only at the last locality were continuous observations made during one season (1933). These show fluctuations in the number of individuals seen from day to day; one bird was seen on July 12, and twenty-five on August 5, after which a gradual decrease was noticed. A few were still present there on September 21, and the last was seen on September 23. One was seen at Espyville, only a few miles distant, however, on September 29, by another observer. In 1936 the latest record at Pymatuning was made on October 4 (Skaggs). As many as seventeen were counted at one time on Presque Isle in August, 1933. The Egret was there as late as September 25 in 1930 and September 17 in 1933. At Warren it remained in 1933 until September 21 (Simpson). Thus its stay with us at this season lasts almost three months, during which there must be a considerable wandering of individuals.

While the Egret is thus becoming a more or less regular summer visitant in our region, its occurrence in spring is difficult to explain. When our party saw an egret flying over the lake near Linesville on May 17, 1935, there was much surprise. This must have been the same bird that was seen by E. W. Arthur and others a week before. Other cases have since come to light. G. M. Cook reports seeing one bird near the same place on May 30, 1937. W. C. Paul of East Liverpool, Ohio, tells me that on April 14, 1937, he saw a single bird along the Ohio River near Industry, Beaver County. According to P. P. Malley, one was observed in Frick Park, on the outskirts of Pittsburgh, on May 18, 1934, by C. B. Shoemaker. In 1934 W. E. Dilley saw one bird near Hartstown on June 30; this may possibly have been an unusually early wanderer. One was reported from Osceola Mills, Clearfield County, on April 22, 1893, by J. L. Henderson (Bent, 1926). A single bird was seen on May 8, 1939, near Linesville (Oudette, 1939), and on June 9 and 10, R. L. Fricke saw as many as six. The significance of these records is not obvious; they evidently do not indicate breeding.

Habits—The beautiful snow-white plumage of the American Egret stands out in bold but pleasing relief against the dark green of the marshy growths where most of its waking hours are spent. It is the aristocrat of the heron tribe. If a single bird is so conspicuous, what of the impression made by a number together? Early in August, 1933, when Professor Seiple and I halted our car on the causeway crossing Pymatuning Swamp at Hartstown and looked out over its marshy expanse, we counted twenty-five individuals in a scattered company, with a few single birds at some distance. They were not shy and paid little attention to the cars that were coming and going along this much-traveled highway. They kept mostly to the open swamp, in plain view of the road, but some were feeding among the cattails and rushes, where they were more or less concealed. While the birds were looking for food their ordinary gait was graceful and rather slow, but when excited or pursuing their prey they could move rapidly enough. When one would catch a tadpole it would hold it by the tip of the bill and gradually work it backward until it could be properly swallowed. The only sound I heard from them was a sort of impatient chattering cry, given when chasing one another about. Professor Seiple, however, says that in the early morning, when birds from outside came to join those that roosted in the swamp, their squawking created considerable uproar. He noticed that one bird seemed to be the acknowledged head of the flock and acted in a very arbitrary and obstreperous manner, chasing new arrivals around and even swooping down and knocking other birds into the water. They did most of their feeding in the morning hours and from time to time shifted their feeding grounds. Tadpoles and small catfish appeared to form the bulk of their food. At one time he saw a bird eating what looked like a tuberous root.

A little later in the same month Mr. Christy

visited this spot, and he has drawn such a vivid pen picture of the egrets as he saw them that I am pleased to reproduce a portion of his account (1934):

"Scattered singly, they seem to be engaged, each in his own affairs. The sun is still an hour from setting, and the birds still are feeding. We mark one out for attention. We note his total whiteness, peat-stained only at the tip of his down-curved tail. He stands in shallow water and moves deliberately, raising a black foot clear with each advancing step. As we approach he straightens his neck stiffly, raises his great yellow beak, and for a moment fixes his pale eye upon us; but presently, reassured, he turns again to his fishing. He pauses with high shoulders and low-swung neck. Suddenly he strikes, and raises his wriggling prey—a three-inch bull-head. The heron leaps from the water, flaps slowly to a grassy islet, and there for a good many minutes is busied with the struggling fish. He loosens hold and grabs, as though bringing it to proper position between the mandibles. Once or twice he lets it fall, only to take it immediately up again. At length, bringing it to head-on position, he gulps it down.

"Yonder one bird rises and, swooping down upon a second, starts it to flight. The two start a third, and they are off in a game of running and wing-waving, of short pursuits, and wide circling flights. We hear a few weak, raucous calls; but for the most part the birds are silent. Surely they are not timid: they scarcely heed the 'gallery' along the causeway.

"The sun sinks; the green water-growths take on the translucence of emeralds; the earthy tones become lavender. Then twilight; and casually, one by one, as though it were each for himself alone, the white birds rise and flap away, to perch at length high in the bordering oak wood. There, after some shifting about, they come to rest in close company, and two or three Great Blue Herons with them."

On Presque Isle, where the egrets were also common and conspicuous during the season of 1933, they were noted about the ponds and the shores of Erie Bay, and were not hard to approach. It would be interesting to know to what extent (if any) the adults accompany the young on their summer wanderings.

Herodias egretta Townsend, *Proc. Acad. Nat. Sci. Philadelphia*, 1883, 67 (Latrobe, Westmoreland Co., irregular)—Warrick, *Ornithologist and Oölogist*, 1883, 8:80 (Washington, Washington Co., July).

Casmerodius egretta Sutton, *Auk*, 1925, 42:583 (Mount Union, Huntingdon Co., July)—Donaldson, *Auk*, 1926, 43:537 (["Kidds Mill," south of] Greenville, Mercer Co., August)—Bent, *Bull. U. S. Nat. Mus.* no. 135, 1926, 133 (Osceola Mills, Clearfield Co., April [*fide* Henderson])—Seiple, *Auk*, 1930, 47:74 (Hartstown, Crawford Co., July).

Casmerodius albus egretta Sutton, *Ann. Carnegie Mus.*, 1928, 18:87 (Conneaut Lake, Crawford Co., August–September, *fide* Welshons)—Seiple, *Auk*, 1929, 46:104 (Conneaut Lake, Crawford Co., August)—Luttringer, *Oölogist*, 1930, 47:116 (Potter Co.)—Seiple, *Auk*, 1931, 48:113 (Hartstown, Crawford Co., July–September)—Manley, *Cardinal*, 1931, 3:15 (Buffalo Creek, near Iron Bridge, Armstrong Co., July)—Eastwood, *Wilson Bull.*, 1932, 44:240 ([Boydstown], Butler Co., August)—Christy, *Cardinal*, 1934, 3:164 (western Pa. localities; habits, etc.)—Arthur, *Cardinal*, 1936, 4:95 (Linesville, Crawford Co., May)—Fricke, *Wilson Bull.*, 1937, 49:302 (Linesville, Crawford Co., August–September).

"Snowy Egret" (error) Thompson, *Bird-Lore*, 1933, 35:320 (Presque Isle, Erie Co., August–September).

"American Egret" Trimble, *Cardinal*, 1937, 4:107 (Linesville, Crawford Co., May; Hartstown, Crawford Co., July–August)—Skaggs, *Wilson Bull.*, 1937, 49:47 (Pymatuning Lake, near Linesville, Crawford Co., September)—Oudette, *Cardinal*, 1939, 5:48 (Pymatuning Lake, near Linesville, Crawford Co., May).

Egretta candidissima (error) Boggs, *Redstart*, 1937, 5:1 (Pymatuning Lake, Crawford Co., September).

SNOWY EGRET

EGRETTA THULA THULA (Molina)

Description—A rather small heron, standing about fifteen to eighteen inches high; *pure white (no dark color on wings); tarsi black, the toes yellow;* bill dark, yellowish at base. It may be distinguished from the American Egret by the much smaller size; and from the immature of the Little Blue Heron by the differently colored feet and the absence of any dark clouding on the wing tips.

Range and migration—The Snowy Egret has a wide range that covers most of South America and extends north through Middle America to the southern United States. It used to breed along the

Atlantic coast as far north as southern New Jersey, and in the Mississippi Valley to southern Indiana. Formerly common in its general range, it was so reduced in numbers through the depredations of plume-hunters that for a while its existence as a species was seriously threatened. But in recent years the effects of protection in the United States are being felt, although the total number of individuals is still considerably less than the total number of American Egrets. The Snowy Egret wanders northward in the summer after breeding, but it is a rare and infrequent visitor in our latitude. Ohio records are few in number, but there is a chance that the species may sometimes have been confused with the young of the Little Blue Heron, which it superficially resembles.

Our only records for western Pennsylvania come from the Pymatuning region. S. J. Seiple saw one individual at Hartstown, at the lower end of Pymatuning Swamp, on August 16, 1930. He writes that he approached it within seventy-five to one hundred feet, and by using his eight-power binocular was easily able to verify all its distinctive characters. Not only was there a good light at the time, but the bird was in company with an immature little blue heron, so that he could compare the two side by side. On September 27 and again on October 4, 1936, M. B. Skaggs and others saw a single individual under similarly favorable circumstances along the spillway just south of Linesville. It was studied at a distance of about fifty feet, and the diagnostic points were carefully noted. The bird was very active in its movements compared with an immature little blue heron observed at the same time. This characteristic invariably holds good in distinguishing these two species from each other in life, according to authorities familiar with both. In 1937 a number of herons attributed to this species appeared in this region and were noted by several observers. These sight identifications were duly confirmed by R. L. Fricke, who collected two immature specimens on September 13.

Egretta thula thula SEIPLE, *Auk*, 1931, 48:113 (Pymatuning Swamp, near Hartstown, Crawford Co., August)—SKAGGS, *Wilson Bull.*, 1937, 49:47 (Pymatuning Lake, near Linesville, Crawford Co., September–October)—FRICKE, *Wilson Bull.*, 1937, 49:302 (Linesville, Crawford Co., August–September)—PETERSON, *Cardinal*, 1938, 4:175 (Linesville, Crawford Co., September).

LOUISIANA HERON

HYDRANASSA TRICOLOR RUFICOLLIS (Gosse)

Description—A heron of medium size; height twenty inches; bill approximately four inches long. *Adult in breeding dress: dark slaty blue* above (including wings and tail), with the *rump white*, and the lengthened shoulder plumes dull grayish brown; head and neck darker, more blackish; crest feathers white, purplish maroon at the base; *chin and throat white*, passing into rich brown, which continues as a *stripe down the front of the neck;* breast plumes dark slaty blue like the back, but with some purplish-maroon wash; rest of underparts, and wings underneath, white; bill black and yellow; legs and feet dull greenish yellow.

Range and local status—This species was attributed to Clinton County by Warren, on the authority of Van Fleet, but without the particulars necessary to the acceptance of such an unusual record. The Louisiana Heron is not known to range north of the South Atlantic and Gulf states in the breeding season, and outlying records are singularly few.[1] A recent sight record from Centre County, however, fulfills the necessary conditions for credibility. A single bird was seen at Red Mill Pond, on the extreme eastern edge of our region, on May 24, 1933, by H. B. Curry and Dr. and Mrs. T. C. Benton, of State College. It was studied at a distance of fifty feet, and its distinctive characters remarked. The appearance of this species in our region is of course purely accidental. In this case it may have been blown north by a storm, as suggested by Mr. Curry.

(?) *Ardea tricolor ruficollis* WARREN, *Birds Pa.*, ed. 2, 1890, 61 (Renovo, Clinton Co., *fide* Van Fleet).

"Louisiana Heron" CURRY, *Auk*, 1933, 50:428 (Red Mill Pond, near Tusseyville, Centre Co., May).

[1]W. W. COOKE, U. S. Department of Agriculture, Biological Survey, *Bulletin*, no. 45, 1913, p. 51.

LITTLE BLUE HERON

FLORIDA CAERULEA CAERULEA (Linnaeus)

Description—A rather small heron, standing about eighteen inches high. *Adult: slaty blue,* with head, neck, and thin crest, *vinous chestnut;* legs black. *Young: white,* with a slight *wash of slate on the wing tips;* legs greenish yellow.

Range and local status—In its general range this heron is mainly a bird of tropical America, whence it extends northward to breed in the South Atlantic and Gulf states. In common with certain other species of the heron tribe, the young have the curious habit of wandering widely after the breeding season, and at this time they often go far north of the known breeding range. While this phenomenon is a regular occurrence, the species does not reach our latitude every season, although, judging from the records at hand from adjoining states, in recent years it is apparently increasing in numbers. R. C. Harlow, indeed, writing in 1909, even called it abundant at times in New Jersey, and said that it was "taken occasionally in the Alleghanies" in Pennsylvania. Authentic records for our region are as yet few in number. G. M. Sutton points out that the supposed records for the Snowy Heron quoted by Warren almost certainly were based on young individuals of the present species. He states that "Mr. H. C. Kirkpatrick has seen such small, white herons near Meadville in August of 1885 and during the fall of 1891," and adds that he himself saw one at Lower Lake, Pymatuning Swamp, on August 29, 1925. During that season the Little Blue Heron as well as the American Egret came north in considerable numbers. The former appeared also in Beaver and Washington counties in August. In 1926 S. J. Seiple saw one of these herons in the swamp south of Conneaut Lake on July 29.

On July 26, 1928, one bird of this species was seen near McAlevy's Fort, Huntingdon County, by Dr. Sutton. The year 1930 was one of unusual abundance and marked northward movement. The species invaded Ohio in July,[1] and six individuals were observed on Presque Isle as early as July 11 (Hicks). One was seen near Lake Erie at North Girard, Erie County, early in August by P. P. Malley. Professor Seiple saw two at Hartstown, Pymatuning Swamp, on August 1 and 16, and R. L. Fricke noted one along Loyalhanna Creek near Rector, Westmoreland County, on July 19, and on the next day saw a party of nine. In August, 1932, two or three were seen on Presque Isle by W. M. Guynes. In 1933, the year when the American Egret appeared in such surprisingly large numbers, the Little Blue Heron was unexpectedly scarce. Mr. Guynes writes that he received a report of an adult bird seen for almost two weeks that summer about a small pond some ten miles west of Erie. In 1936, according to information received from M. B. Skaggs and B. L. Oudette, the species appeared in some numbers in the Pymatuning region; the last bird was observed there on September 27. Of exceptional interest is Mr. Fricke's record at Linesville on June 9, 1939, of a little blue heron in the mottled transition stage between immature and adult plumage.

The only local specimen in the Carnegie Museum is a young bird taken at Immel Reservoir, near Lycippus, Westmoreland County, on July 12, 1921, by Audley Herrick.

Ardea candidissima (error) WARREN, *Birds Pa.*, ed. 2, 1890, 60 (Crawford and Erie Co., *fide* Sennett and Kirkpatrick; Renovo, Clinton Co., *fide* Van Fleet).

Ardea cærulea WARREN, *Birds Pa.*, ed. 2, 1890, 62 (Clinton Co., *fide* Van Fleet).

"Little Blue Heron" HARLOW, *Auk*, 1909, 26:189 ("Alleghany Mountains")—[CHRISTY], *Cardinal*, 1925, v. 1, no. 5, [p. 19] (Avella, Washington Co., August, *fide* Sutton; Big Traverse Creek, Beaver Co., August, *fide* McPherson)—SKAGGS, *Wilson Bull.*, 1937, 49:47 (Pymatuning Lake, near Linesville, Crawford Co., September).

Florida cærulea cærulea SUTTON, *Ann. Carnegie Mus.*, 1928, 18:87 (Meadville and Lower Lake, Crawford Co., August; critical)—FRICKE, *Auk*, 1930, 47:573 (Loyalhanna Creek, near Rector, Westmoreland Co., July).

Florida cærulea SEIPLE, *Auk*, 1931, 48:113 (Pymatuning Swamp, Crawford Co., July–September).

[1]Compare L. E. HICKS, *Wilson Bulletin*, 1931, 43:268–281.

EASTERN GREEN HERON

BUTORIDES VIRESCENS VIRESCENS (Linnaeus)

Description—A small dark heron, standing about a foot high. *Adult:* top of head, and long feathers of the *crest, black,* with a bottle-green gloss; throat whitish, and neck maroon-brown, with a broad whitish stripe (usually interrupted by dark spots) down the front, reaching to the breast; *upperparts* in general *deep bottle green,* with the long plumes of the back more or less grayish in tone, and the wing coverts showing slight pale (buffy) edgings; wings and tail similar but darker; underparts from the breast down, dull brownish gray, almost uniform; eyes yellow; bare skin around eyes yellowish or greenish; bill dark, paler below basally; legs and feet greenish yellow, in the breeding season tending to coral or orange. *Young:* top of head, and crest feathers, black, glossed with bottle green; throat whitish; neck streaked with two shades of brown, with a paler stripe down the front; rest of underparts buffy white, with darker (brownish) streaks; upperparts dull brownish green, the wings and tail similar but darker; wing coverts with prominent rusty and buffy edgings and streaks; iris, bill, and feet as in the adult, but generally duller.

Range—The typical form of the Green Heron inhabits the eastern United States and adjacent parts of Canada, west to the Great Plains, and south to Mexico and northern Central America. In winter it retires into the southern part of its general range, mostly beyond the Gulf of Mexico. In our section it is of course only a summer resident, and if not common throughout it is at any rate generally distributed. Those counties without definite records are few indeed, and the circumstance is without significance. Moreover, since this species does not as a rule wander far from its nest during the breeding season, it is fairly safe to consider all occurrences during the latter half of May and all of June as breeding records.

Migration—Unlike the Great Blue Heron, this species is markedly a warm-weather bird and does not ordinarily come north until after all snow and ice are gone and the streams have reached a normal stage again after the spring freshets. All observers agree that the northward movement takes place during the latter half of April and is usually completed early in May. Available dates of arrival correspond closely. The earliest date for Blair County is April 20 (McGraw); for Allegheny County, April 21 (Burleigh); for Beaver County, April 22 (Todd); for Crawford County, April 18 (Seiple); for Warren County, April 12 (Granquist); for Erie County, April 19 (Todd); for Centre County, April 24 (Burleigh); and for Clinton County, April 23 (Pierce). In Greene County J. W. Jacobs has seen this heron as early as April 14. Fall records of departure are fewer, but those that exist show that the species remains through most of September (September 25, 1907—Beaver) and even on occasion into the next month (October 10, 1900, and October 5, 1902—Warren; October 14, 1909—Renovo; October 3, 1916—State College; October 1, 1933—Erie).

Habits—The Green Heron occurs along most of the streams of any size in our region, provided that such streams are unpolluted and afford suitably secluded retreats at intervals along their courses. At some places, as for instance along Raccoon Creek, Beaver County, and its larger branches, the species used to be fairly common as a summer resident, and there are still a few there. Many of the smaller streams, too, support one or more pairs. These birds are particularly numerous in the Pymatuning Swamp area, where conditions are much to their liking, and many pairs nest there; but at Presque Isle the species is less common than might be expected. By the time the migratory movement is over, usually early in May, the pairs are mated and settled for the season. Nest-building begins shortly thereafter, but there is no uniformity in the choice of a nesting site. At Raccoon Creek I looked in vain for nests in trees along the banks, only to find in 1909 that three pairs were nesting in an orchard east of the mouth of the stream, half a mile back from the Ohio River. The nests were all in apple trees, and not far apart; they were about twenty feet up and were easy to reach. But according to T. D. Burleigh, "the nests are always in thick underbrush near water and never more than one pair of birds can be found in any one locality." Two of the nests that he found were in haw bushes; but a third was thirty feet from the ground in the top of a slender elm. B. H. Christy speaks of having found nests in hemlocks along the banks of streams, and R. B. Simpson writes that in his section the nest is often placed in a pine. In Greene County Mr. Jacobs says that the species nests "in orchards and thickets along the streams," and thus agrees with the other observers. At Pymatuning Swamp similar diversities of nesting habitat have been noted. Some nests were placed in trees far from the water, others at the water's edge. "On May 18, 1922, we discovered a fair-sized colony of Green Herons in a high stand of huckleberries, which grew in a pool of water about a mile southeast of Hartstown. This thickly upgrown spot was sheltered from the nearby road by great trees and was a spot ideally suited to the nesting activities of this species. At least eight nests were found here, one of which was only three inches above the surface of the water. Most of the nests were high in the slender bushes and rather difficult to reach" (Sutton, 1928).

The nest is a rude and shapeless affair, nothing more than a frail platform of sticks, arranged with their ends converging toward the middle. There are usually four or five eggs; occasionally, however, as many as six are laid, and sometimes only three. They are laid in May (May 12 is the earliest date on record) or early June; sets of later date doubtless belong to pairs that were disturbed in their first nesting. In color they are pale greenish blue, like the eggs of other American herons, but tend to be a more rounded oval in shape. They average 1.50 by 1.17 inches. The young birds are unattractive little creatures, covered at first with down of a brownish-gray color; they are said to remain in the nest or in the home tree for some weeks and to leave it ordinarily by the end of July, after they have acquired the streaked plumage of the juvenal stage. During August and September it is a common sight to see family groups, old and young together, stalking along the margin of the river beaches or wading leisurely about in the still pools common along the courses of our smaller streams. They were fond of the extensive tracts of semiaquatic plants (water willow—*Dianthera americana*) that used to cover considerable areas of the exposed bed of the Ohio River at low water and that offered some concealment. When the green herons are feeding they are rather deliberate and walk along slowly with the head held low, but they strike out with amazing quickness when in reach of their prey, which consists of minnows, tadpoles, and some crayfish. When alarmed the herons fly off with raucous squawks, in a slow, awkward manner, and become an easy mark for the thoughtless man with a gun. During the breeding season they often alight on trees, where they perch precariously on the upper branches, but ordinarily they are seen along the banks of streams that are sheltered but not too densely wooded.

Butorides virescens Townsend, *Proc. Acad. Nat. Sci. Philadelphia*, 1883, 67 (Latrobe, Westmoreland Co., breeding)—Todd, *Ann. Carnegie Mus.*, 1904, 2:531 (Erie and Presque Isle, Erie Co., summer)—Todd, in Bausman, *Hist. Beaver Co., Pa.*, 1904, 2:1198 (Beaver Co., summer)—Keim, *Cassinia*, 1905, 8:37 (Port Allegany, McKean Co., summer)—Christy, *Cardinal*, 1929, 2:129 (McDonald Reservoir, Washington Co., May; coloration).

"Green Heron" Jacobs, *Hawkeye Ornithologist and Oölogist*, 1888, 1:88 (Waynesburg, Greene Co., April)—Burleigh, *Oölogist*, 1911, 28:156 (Harmarville, Allegheny Co., nesting)—Simpson, *Oölogist*, 1911, 28:201 (Warren, Warren Co., nesting)—McClelland, *Am. Mid. Nat.*, 1922, 8:37 (Washington, Washington Co.)—Christy, *Cardinal*, 1923, v. 1, no. 2, [p. 15] (Clinton Pond, Allegheny Co., May)—Street, *Cassinia*, 1923, 24:11 (Conococheague Creek, Mercersburg, Franklin Co., June).

Ardea virescens Dwight, *Auk*, 1892, 9:134 (Cresson, Cambria Co., June)—Jacobs, *Summer Birds Greene Co., Pa.*, 1893, 5 (Greene Co., nesting)—Baily, *Auk*, 1896, 13:291, 292 (Williamsville, Elk Co., July)—Cope, *Cassinia*, 1902, 5:13 (Little Kettle Creek, Oleona, Potter Co., June).

Butorides virescens virescens Harlow, *Auk*, 1912, 29:468 (State College, Centre Co., nesting)—Oberholser, *Proc. U. S. Nat. Mus.*, 1912, 42:538 (McKee Gap, Blair Co., July)—Cooke, *Bull. Biol. Surv.* no. 45, 1913, 56 (Renovo, Clinton Co., Waynesburg, Greene Co., and Beaver, Beaver Co., migration)—Harlow, *Auk*, 1918, 35:21 (central and northern Pa., nesting)—Christy, *Cardinal*, 1923, v. 1, no. 1, [p. 3] (Raccoon Creek, Beaver Co., and Big Sewickley Creek, Allegheny Co., nesting)—Burleigh, *Wilson Bull.*, 1923, 35:80, 83 ([Harmarville], Allegheny Co., nesting); 1924, 36:70; 1931, 43:37 (State College, Centre Co., breeding; migration)—Christy and Sutton, *Cardinal*, 1928, 2:68 (Thom's Run, Cook Forest, Clarion Co., May)—Sutton, *Ann. Carnegie Mus.*, 1928, 18:88 (Crawford Co., nesting records)—Burleigh, *Cardinal*, 1932, 3:74 (Lake Seaton, Fayette Co., breeding).

BLACK-CROWNED NIGHT HERON

NYCTICORAX NYCTICORAX HOACTLI (Gmelin)

Description—A stocky, thick-billed heron, standing about twenty inches high. *Spring adult:* top of *head, nape, and back, black,* with a greenish gloss; two or three long, narrow, white crest feathers; *wings and tail gray;* forehead, throat, and *entire underparts, white,* the breast and sides more or less washed with gray; bill black; feet coral red in breeding season, later yellowish; iris red. *Young:* grayish brown above, *streaked and spotted with white;* white below, *streaked with grayish brown;* legs dull greenish; iris yellow.

Range—This species has an extensive range in the Old World, as well as in North and South America. The North American race breeds north to southern Manitoba and the St. Lawrence Valley in the East. In the New England states, and in southeastern Pennsylvania and New Jersey, it is a well-known bird, although somewhat locally distributed. West of the mountains in Pennsylvania, however, it is comparatively rare, and while there are a number of spring and summer records from various parts of our region (suggesting a correspondingly inclusive breeding range), the known nesting colonies are few and isolated. Van Fleet marks this species "rare" in his manuscript list of the breeding birds of DuBois (1892), without giving further particulars. Until 1934 this rather unsatisfactory breeding record was the only one available for western Pennsylvania. In the spring of that year I received word that there was a nesting colony of night herons near Hollidaysburg, in the valley east of the main Allegheny divide, and on April 28 it was my privilege to be one of a party of visitors to this colony. We found only three nests, but Miss A. E. Berg, under whose guidance the visit was made, assured us that originally the colony consisted of about fifteen pairs of birds, but that it had been "shot out" by local gunners a year or two before and reduced to a pitiful remnant. It is gratifying to be able to state (on the word of H. A. McGraw) that this particular colony has been unmolested since that time. According to local report, it had been in existence for ten years or more before it came to Miss Berg's notice. She said that formerly there was another colony west of the town, so that it is possible that, as often happens, the birds merely shifted their nesting grounds.

Probably other colonies of this heron remain to be discovered in the ridge and valley section. A June record from Franklin County (Street, 1923) is suggestive. The species has doubtless invaded this area from the east. In the western counties it has probably come in from Ohio, where there are at least nineteen colonies known, with the number of birds constantly increasing (Hicks). On May 14, 1936, R. L. Fricke discovered a newly established colony on the north shore of Pymatuning Lake, west of Linesville. I visited this colony in company with others later in the month, and it was visited still later by other observers. In 1937 this nesting ground was abandoned; the birds had apparently shifted to a spot located in the sanctuary to the east, where they were safe. In May, 1939, Mr. Fricke found a colony in an area of low bushes and trees growing in the water on the edge of the lake. Some of the nests in this colony were only a foot or two above the water. It is quite possible that night herons may have bred in the Pymatuning region before 1936 and that the site they chose remained undiscovered. Adult birds had indeed been seen at Conneaut Lake in June and July, and young birds both there and at Hartstown in August. R. B. Simpson has occasionally seen young birds at Warren in June, July, and August, but only one adult (on April 14, 1937). The young birds of this species, like those of some others of the heron family, are accustomed to wander widely after attaining the power of flight, and appear in places far distant from the breeding grounds. Several late summer records from the western counties are of old birds, a fact which indicates that this wandering propensity is not confined to the young. Whence such birds come we do not know, but May and June occurrences surely indicate breeding.

Migration—The individuals seen on Presque Isle on March 31, 1937 (Dilley) and on April 2, 1933 (Guynes); at Linesville on April 2, 1934 (Dilley); and at Clinton Pond, Allegheny County, on April 6, 1923, and April 7, 1929 (Christy), were probably early migrants. Latest dates in the fall are: Linesville, October 24, 1936 (West); and Conneaut Lake, October 30, 1916 (Kirkpatrick). A November record (exact date not specified) comes from Johnstown (Canan).

Habits—The Black-crowned Night Heron is a rather shy and retiring bird, keeping to the shelter of trees near the water during the daytime, and doing much of its feeding by night. I have on occasion, however, observed single birds working along the shores of Pymatuning Lake in the daytime. This species is of stouter, shorter build than the other herons, and its heavier bill and fuller neck give it a somewhat different, more bittern-like appearance. Fish and small aquatic animals in general constitute its food; these it captures by still-hunting or by stalking cautiously in the shallows. Young birds are often unsuspicious and easy to approach, but adults on their nesting ground are timid and watchful. Their ordinary call note is a hoarse croak or squawk, given when they are disturbed and forced to fly. At egg-laying time the birds are so quiet in daytime that the existence of a heronry would never be suspected. When approached too closely, they begin to squawk and move about among the trees, and then to fly out and circle high overhead. Firing a shot near the Linesville rookery would bring the birds boiling out in a panic-stricken company which scattered in every direction. In their manner of flight they remind one of gulls or owls rather than herons; their aerial evolutions are always executed in perfect silence. But after the young are hatched a night-heron rookery is a noisy and busy place.

The colony which we visited near Hollidaysburg in 1934 was located on a thinly wooded ridge or mound, not far from the Juniata River; the nests were near the tops of rather small trees. The reason the birds had picked such an open spot was far from obvious. The nests were merely loose masses of dead sticks, without form or pattern, and with only a shallow depression for the eggs. Only one nest was actually examined, with its set of three eggs; a second nest into which we could see with the glass from the hill above also contained three eggs. The nests in the Linesville colony were all in an area about one hundred yards square, within which almost every tree of sufficient size held at least one nest—some as low as fifteen feet from the ground. The nests varied greatly in size and position, and some of them were so frail that it was questionable whether they could withstand a storm. We avoided disturbing this colony unnecessarily, and examined but one nest, which held three eggs. Four is said to be the usual number, however; they are oval in shape, pale bluish green in color, and measure about 2.00 by 1.40 inches.

Miss Berg sends an interesting account of the colony of night herons that was formerly (about 1924) located near her home on the western outskirts of Hollidaysburg. Beside a brook fringed with saplings and grapevine tangles there was a grove of very old oak trees, which in other years had been tenanted by crows, squirrels, and green herons, but that year was pre-empted by the night herons—either because of or in spite of the fact that a number of dead cattle had been hauled there and left unburied. "This woods was dark with shade and the herons seemed to do little flying in the daytime unless one entered the woods; then there would be a great rush of wings as they left their nests, but as the tangles were so great one could not see through them. I should have judged there were not more than a dozen nests in all. The old herons were beautiful when seen at close range, but the young ones were certainly odd-looking as they perched all 'hunched up' on a dead limb. They suggested a Plymouth Rock fowl with an ensemble in brown instead of gray. One evening near sunset four of us decided to go to the river bank above the heronry and watch them come out to feed. The evening was extremely sultry and mosquitoes were almost unbearable. We sat and slapped them until the sun went down, but still no herons appeared—save one young bird sailing up the river. We finally gave it up and started back. Suddenly in the dusk we came to a place where every dead limb held a night heron. Directly they started to fly; they darted around and dashed at our heads and squawked until we fairly ran to get out of the woods."

Nycticorax nycticorax nævius Todd, *Ann. Carnegie Mus.*, 1904, 2:531 (Erie, Erie Co., summer, *fide* Bacon)—Todd, in Bausman, *Hist. Beaver Co., Pa.*, 1904, 2:1198 (Beaver Co., "transient")—Keim, *Cassinia*, 1905, 8:37 (Port Allegany, McKean Co., August, *fide* Burt)—Harlow, *Auk*, 1918, 35:21 (rare west of Alleghenies)—[Christy], *Cardinal*, 1924, v. 1, no. 3, [p. 20] (Clinton Pond, Allegheny Co., April and August)—Sutton, *Ann. Carnegie Mus.*, 1928, 18:89 (Conneaut Lake, Crawford Co., summer; October).

"Black-crowned Night Heron" CHRISTY, *Cardinal*, 1923, v. 1, no. 2, [p. 16] (Clinton Pond, Allegheny Co., April)—STREET, *Cassinia*, 1923, 24:11 (Conococheague Creek, Mercersburg, Franklin Co., June)—SUTTON, *Bird-Lore*, 1924, 26:337 (Sewickley, Allegheny Co., July, *fide* Christy)—CHRISTY, *Cardinal*, 1931, 3:43 (McDonald Reservoir, Washington Co., May)—WOOD, *Wilson Bull.*, 1932, 44:238 (Oak Hall, Centre Co., May, *fide* Curry)—CHRISTY, *Cardinal*, 1934, 3:165 (Hartstown, Crawford Co., August)—BOGGS, *Redstart*, 1936, 3:92; TRIMBLE, *Cardinal*, 1937, 4:106; and CHAPMAN, *Cardinal*, 1937, 4:108 (Linesville, Crawford Co., breeding).

Nycticorax nycticorax hoactli WEST, *Redstart*, 1936, 4:5 (Linesville, Crawford Co., October).

Additional records: Presque Isle, June 19, July 10, 1932; April 2, 1933; April 15, 1934 (Guynes)—Smith's Ferry, Beaver Co., June, 1894 (Todd, *fide* Wickham)—Renovo, May 25, 1891 (Pierce)—Washington, May 8, 1893 (Nease)—McDonald Reservoir, Washington Co., July 17, 1923 (C. E. Schinneller; specimen in Carnegie Museum)—Laughlintown, Westmoreland Co., June 26, 1898 (Rhoads)—Huntingdon, September 21, 1927 (Sutton, *fide* C. E. Woolheater)—Hartstown, August 5, 1931 (Seiple).

YELLOW-CROWNED NIGHT HERON

NYCTANASSA VIOLACEA VIOLACEA (Linnaeus)

Description—Size of the Black-crowned Night Heron, but legs relatively longer. *Adult:* streaked with black and gray above; plain bluish gray below; head black, except for a *broad white stripe on the forehead and crown*, and another on either side (beginning under the eye). *Young:* dark brown above and streaked below with brown, buff, and white; they might be mistaken for the young of the Black-crowned Night Heron, but the white spotting on the wings is very much finer and less conspicuous than in that species; and the legs are relatively longer.

Range—Compared with the Black-crowned Night Heron, this species is relatively more southern, and does not breed north of South Carolina on the coast nor regularly beyond southern Illinois in the interior. In 1928, however, it was found nesting in Ohio,[1] and there are a few outlying records of nonbreeding individuals, one of which comes from our region. The specimen upon which this particular record is based (now in the collection of J. W. Jacobs) was taken along Ten-mile Creek near Waynesburg some years ago, but the exact date was not recorded. It is an adult bird.

Nyctanassa violacea DICKEY, *Auk*, 1915, 32:236 (Ten-mile Creek, Greene Co.).

[1] C. F. WALKER, *Auk*, 1928, 45:370.

AMERICAN BITTERN

BOTAURUS LENTIGINOSUS (Montagu)

Description—A stocky, mottled and streaked heron, standing about two feet high. General color above, *brown, mottled with buff*, the wings and tail darker and more uniform; below, *buff, with broad brown streaks*, most numerous on the neck and breast; throat white, with a brownish stripe down the middle, and a prominent black stripe on either side of the upper neck; iris yellow; bill yellowish, and feet yellowish green. Sexes alike in color, the female somewhat smaller; young similar.

Range—The American Bittern occurs over North America at large, north almost to the limit of trees, and breeds southward regularly to the Middle Atlantic states in the East; in winter it retires into the southern part of its general range. It is a summer resident in our region, but because of unsuitable local conditions over most of the area its known breeding range is actually much restricted. As with other marsh-loving birds, it has been found nesting most commonly in Erie, Crawford, and Mercer counties, particularly on Presque Isle and in the Pymatuning region. R. L. Keesler reports finding a nest near Forestville, Butler County. This local breeding area has recently been discovered to extend as far south as Gardner Swamp, in Lawrence County, three miles southeast of New Castle, where the species was noted by several observers, including myself, in June, 1933. For the whole plateau country there is but one admissible breeding record: that appearing on Van Fleet's manuscript list of the breeding birds of DuBois. The same observer is quoted by Warren as authority for recording the species as breeding "occasionally and sparingly in Clinton County," and the more recent work of A. K. Pierce tends to confirm this statement. The latter observer, however, has no nestings to report, and but one late May record. It is significant that in many years' experience R. B. Simpson has found the Bittern in Warren County as a transient only; and everything indicates that its nesting in the plateau region is exceptional. In the ridge and valley section, young have been found by R. C. Harlow at Lemont, Centre County, and he has also observed the species in the breeding season at Charter Oak, northern Huntingdon County. Elsewhere in our region the Bittern is an irregular and uncommon transient in spring and fall. There are more records from the upper Ohio Valley than from other sections, but the species is one that is likely to occur anywhere, even in unexpected places.

Migration—This species is a comparatively early migrant in the spring; it follows the Great Blue Heron northward in early April. In 1907 it was seen at Renovo on March 29, but April 10 is the average time of arrival at that place. In the mountains farther south, at State College, it has been noted as early as April 3 (1917). Dates of arrival for Conneaut Lake and Erie agree well with those just given; they range from March 29 to April 17, and bring the average to about the same time—the second week in April. One bird was taken at Davis Island, Allegheny County, on March 23, 1893 (Atkinson). The earliest spring date on record is supplied by Mr. Simpson, who saw a single bird at Warren on March 21, 1893. Transient individuals have been noted at various places until the second week in May. As might be expected, the Bittern stays later in the fall than many other water birds, the Great Blue Heron not excepted. The southward movement at that season begins in September, but does not appear to get fully under way until October, and while the majority of birds have gone before the end of that month, numerous individuals linger into November. Scattered records for the fall months pertain mostly to birds seen or taken at a distance from their known nesting grounds. The latest fall date available is that of a specimen shot at Sharpsburg, Allegheny County, on December 2, 1901.

Habits—Herons as a class are conspicuous birds even if they are not brightly colored. They are fond of the company of their own kind, and may be seen in the open in broad daylight. The Bittern, however, is a shy and solitary recluse of the bog; its stripes blend so perfectly with the reeds and cattails of its chosen haunts that even the initiated is deceived; and, moreover, much of its migrating and feeding are accomplished under cover of the night. Its preference is for the larger bogs, since small tracts have little appeal for such a large bird. In 1900 the Bittern was fairly common on Presque Isle, where it found congenial haunts in the rank growth of rushes and other aquatic plants fringing the various ponds, and in bushy areas. It seemed to rely for protection more on its resemblance to its surroundings than on wariness, and would keep concealed until closely approached, when, rising with a harsh and disconcerting squawk, it would fly off heavily. A well-known ruse of this bird, which I saw practiced, is that of keeping perfectly still in an upright position, with the bill pointing straight up into the air, thus increasing the resemblance to a stub or dead reed. The habits of the Bittern are not easy to observe, because of the nature of its habitat and because it is most active under cover of night. They do not differ from those of other herons. Fish, frogs, and other aquatic animals are eaten with gusto. I once took the body of a fair-sized frog from a bittern's gullet. On April 21, 1905, a bird that was merely wing-tipped was brought to me alive (it had been taken along the Ohio River at Beaver); it was quite vicious and struck savagely with its bill when teased, at the same time flaring out its neck-ruff and uttering a peculiar growling cry.

The "booming" of the Bittern is a unique performance; it seems to correspond to the nuptial song of our smaller birds, and has given rise to the vernacular names of "Thunder-pumper" and "Stake-driver" by which the bird is often known.

The sound has been aptly likened by some writers to that made by a pump operated in a nearly dry well, and by others to the sound made by driving a stake into soggy ground. As a matter of fact, it varies with different individuals and at different times. It is a familiar and characteristic sound in the Bittern's haunts, and can be heard for a long distance, especially in the stillness of the night, and has the same peculiar resonant quality as has the "drumming" of the Ruffed Grouse. I have never had the good fortune to see the Bittern in the act of emitting this curious sound; but according to William Brewster, "He first makes a succession of low clicking or gulping sounds accompanied by quick opening and shutting of the bill and then, with abrupt contortions of the head and neck unpleasantly suggestive of those of a person afflicted by nausea, belches forth in deep, guttural tones, and with tremendous emphasis, a *pump-er-lunk* repeated from two or three to six or seven times in quick succession and suggesting the sound of an old-fashioned wooden pump."[1]

Not less curious is the nuptial display in which the male birds indulge during the season of courtship, which begins about the first of May. This is the only season when the Bittern forsakes its solitary habits and seeks out others of its kind. G. M. Sutton (1928) says that at Pymatuning Swamp, where the Bittern is common, three or four birds occasionally pursue each other about the marsh, squawking loudly or circling high in the air. Booming and plume-display, which often go together, begin, he says, almost as soon as the resident birds arrive and by May 5 are at their height. In this display the bird walks along in a crouching position, the body and neck held low, and the scapular and back plumes spread out so as to expose their light-colored bases, giving the impression of an extensive white area on these parts. Dr. Sutton further writes: "A male bird observed on May 15, 1925, was remarkably tame, as he displayed his plumes and boomed in front of us. The white shoulder plumes fell like a misty spray on his back. The queer, clicking, booming call was accompanied by fantastic bows and expansion of the neck and breast." He adds that "Bum Cluck" is the local vernacular name for this bird.

The nest is a rude, flat structure of dead cattails, rushes, flags, or any other material at hand; it is raised a few inches above the general level of the marsh, and is more or less screened from view by the surrounding vegetation. A nest found at Pymatuning Swamp by Dr. Sutton "was built in the wildest portion of the marsh and was surrounded by very high sedge grass." This nest, when collected on May 17, had three eggs, incubated a few days. On May 22, 1934, the party of which I was a member found a nest with four nearly fresh eggs in a tuft of rushes on the edge of the marsh. These cases probably indicate the normal time of nesting, which is further confirmed by the nest found by Mr. Keesler near Forestville on June 3, 1925. This nest was on a pile of dead cattails a foot above the water, which was two feet deep all around. There were five eggs, apparently near hatching, since the parent bird sat very closely. The eggs when freshly laid are a uniform buffy brown—entirely different from those of the herons—but they soon become more or less discolored from nest stains. They average 1.92 by 1.44 inches.

During migration the Bittern is often found in strange places—not from choice, but rather by accident. Migrating as it does at night, it is sometimes forced to come down for the day in situations far from ideal for its comfort. I have received several reports of bitterns captured in thickly settled districts. On one occasion (May 10, 1923) I put up a bittern from some dense shrubbery at the edge of a woods, where it probably had been overtaken by the snowstorm of the night before and had been compelled to pass the night.

Botaurus mugitans Townsend, *Proc. Acad. Nat. Sci. Philadelphia*, 1883, 67 (Latrobe, Westmoreland Co.).

Botaurus lentiginosus Warren, *Birds Pa.*, ed. 2, 1890, 55 (Presque Isle and Lake Pleasant, Erie Co., and Conneaut Lake and Oil Creek Lake, Crawford Co., breeding, *fide* Sennett; Clinton Co., breeding, *fide* Van Fleet)—Rhoads, *Auk*, 1899, 16:309 (Allegheny Co., *fide* Link; Hookstown, Beaver Co., breeding [error]; Emporium, Cameron Co., *fide* Larrabee)—Todd, *Ann. Carnegie Mus.*, 1904, 2:530 (Presque Isle, Erie Co., summer)—Harlow, *Auk*, 1912, 29:477 (Laurel Run, Huntingdon Co., June; and Center Furnace Swamp, Centre Co., May)—Miller, *In the Open*, Nov., 1912, 3:67 (Knoxville, Allegheny Co., September)—Cooke, *Bull. Biol. Surv.* no. 45, 1913, 26 (Renovo, Clinton Co., migration)—Harlow, *Auk*, 1918, 35:20 (Lemont, Centre Co., breeding; and Charter Oak, Huntingdon Co., summer)—Stone, *Cassinia*, 1920, 23:30 (Chambersburg, Franklin Co., May, *fide* Mahy)—Christy, *Cardinal*, 1923, v. 1, no. 1, [p. 2] (Sewickley, Allegheny Co., transient)—Burleigh, *Wilson Bull.*

[1] *Bird-Lore*, 1902, 4:46.

1923, 35:83 (Allegheny Co., May); 1924, 36:76 (State College, Centre Co., spring transient)—SUTTON, *Ann. Carnegie Mus.*, 1928, 18:84 (Conneaut Lake, Conneaut Marsh, and Pymatuning Swamp, Crawford Co., summer; habits).
"American Bittern" SIMPSON, *Oölogist*, 1907, 24:133 (Warren, Warren Co., May)—HARLOW, *Cassinia*, 1912, 15:20 (Center Furnace Swamp, Centre Co., spring)—THOMAS, *In the Open*, June, 1920, 10:23 (Mud Lake, Hartstown, Crawford Co., habits)—CHRISTY, *Cardinal*, 1923, v. 1, no. 2, [p. 15] (Clinton Pond, Allegheny Co., April)—Editor, *Cardinal*, 1934, 3:165 ([Pine Creek, near Wexford, Allegheny Co.], May, *fide* Auerswald)—BOGGS, *Redstart*, 1936, 3:92 (Linesville, Crawford Co., nesting)—TRIMBLE, *Cardinal*, 1937, 4:107 (Pymatuning region, Crawford Co.).

EASTERN LEAST BITTERN

IXOBRYCHUS EXILIS EXILIS (Gmelin)

Description—A small heron (about the size of a Virginia Rail), standing *not over ten inches high. Adult male:* top of head black; neck deep rufous, passing into buff in front, with the throat almost pure white, in contrast with the deep buff sides of the head; back black, with a white stripe on either side, above the wings; tail black; wings dusky at the tips, buffy on the coverts, with a broad rufous band between; underparts buff (more or less deep), with a dark spot on either side of the breast (sometimes concealed); eyes yellow; bill yellowish, with darker ridge and tip; bare skin on face light green; feet greenish to yellowish. *Adult female:* similar to the male, but back deep brown instead of black, and neck, breast, and flanks more or less streaked with dusky brown, the throat also with a dull stripe down the middle. *Young:* rich rufous brown replaces black of upperparts; larger feathers buff-tipped; top of head also rufous brown, a little darker; underparts have rich buff and dusky stripes on a whitish background.

Range—The Least Bittern is a more delicate bird than its larger cousin, and does not go nearly so far north as the other—not beyond southern Quebec in the East. The eastern race winters in the southern half of its general range, in Florida and the West Indies, and from southern Texas to Guatemala. In our region the only definite breeding records come from Erie, Crawford, Mercer, and northern Butler counties, where alone the bird is a locally common species. It has been noted in July in southern Washington County and also along the lower Allegheny River—from which circumstances its breeding at these points may also be inferred. A. K. Pierce considered it rare at Renovo; his single record was for June 10, 1917. An injured bird was captured at Conrad, Potter County, on June 14, 1925, by Ernest Hunsinger (Sutton). All other records, published and otherwise, refer to individuals which may have been migrating at the time; most of them come from the western counties.

Migration—As might be expected, migration records for this species are later in the spring and earlier in the fall than for the American Bittern. The earliest recorded date of its normal appearance is April 27 (1897), based on a specimen taken at McKeesport (Atkinson). R. B. Simpson has seen it occasionally at this season at Warren, between May 3 and 16. These dates agree with those recorded for Crawford County—May 3 (1897) to 17 (1893). I did not see it on Presque Isle in 1900 until May 21, but in 1933 W. M. Guynes noted it there as early as April 30. Thus its migration through our region must be performed mainly from the first to the third week in May. There is always the chance that individuals observed later in the month may have been intending to breed where they were found. The fall movement is accomplished in September. Mr. Simpson has taken this species at Warren on September 12 (1893), and it has been seen until September 25 in the Erie-Crawford district.

Habits—My personal acquaintance with this diminutive species has been chiefly confined to views of it on Presque Isle in the season of 1900. There it was if anything rather commoner than its larger relative but, unlike it, was never observed away from the tracts of rushes and marsh grass unless disturbed, when it would occasionally alight in the shrubbery. Thus it was most numerous at Yellow Bass and Niagara ponds, which afford the most extensive marshy areas. Mr. Simpson writes that in tramping around these two ponds in May of 1932, he flushed about a dozen individuals; the species, therefore, was apparently maintaining its numbers in more recent years. A small and secretive bird, the Least Bittern may frequently be overlooked. It lies very closely, and flushes only to alight again at a little distance, flying low, in slow, awkward fashion, head straight out and legs dangling. Like the American Bittern, it sometimes assumes a straight up-and-down pose, the more easily to blend with its surroundings in seeking to escape notice. It is said to be an expert climber among the water weeds. "I have never witnessed any courtship antics of this species, and the only sounds heard from it are hoarse, throaty squawks, resembling those of the Green Heron, but not nearly so loud" (Sutton, 1928). S. K. Eastwood, writing in 1932 of its feeding habits as observed by him at a reservoir at Boydstown, Butler County, describes an individual seen on the edge of the mud on September 5, 1931:

"When first seen, it was standing very still with the head drawn in toward the body somewhat, and the long bill parallel to the water surface. As I watched, it slowly raised one foot and put it down on the water with extreme care. There was almost no ripple on the water as the bird advanced for about eighteen inches, making no movement except that of the feet. Then the head and neck shot forward, the bill pierced the surface of the water and a four-inch fish was captured by the bill grabbing it in the center of the body. The bittern turned toward the shore and walked rapidly out of the water holding the bill with the fish pointing skyward. On shore, the fish was eaten while the tail feathers of the bird wiggled very much like the wagging of the tail of a contented dog."

The nest is a hastily built affair of dead cattails or other water plants, placed among and sheltered by the aquatic vegetation of the marsh. It is fairly well constructed even though it appears flimsy; for the supporting stems are tied together with almost as much skill as that exhibited by the Long-billed Marsh Wren or the Red-winged Blackbird. The nest is so flat, however, that a little tipping causes the eggs to roll out. Several nests found by R. L. Fricke at Pymatuning were in the cattails or spatterdocks, as were also those described by G. M. Sutton from Sandy Lake and by R. L. Keesler from Butler County. In some cases they were placed as much as a foot above the water. Four or five eggs are the usual complement; they are white, with a pale bluish or greenish cast, and average 1.25 by .93 inches. They are ordinarily laid early in June, and our July records doubtless refer to delayed second nestings. The young birds are at first covered with buffy down.

Botaurus exilis Warren, *Birds Pa.*, ed. 2, 1890, 56 (Crawford and Erie Co., breeding, *fide* Sennett)—Rhoads, *Auk*, 1899, 16:310 (Pittsburgh, Allegheny Co., *fide* Link).

"Least Bittern" Forrest, *Oölogist*, 1900, 17:58 (Ten-mile Creek, near Hackney, Washington Co., July)—Nicholson, *Bird-Lore*, 1918, 20:180 (Grove City, Mercer Co.)—Sutton, *Bird-Lore*, 1924, 26:267 (Jennerstown, Somerset Co., May; Sandy Lake, Mercer Co., nesting), 337 (Harmarville, Allegheny Co., July, *fide* Christy)—Wood, *Wilson Bull.*, 1932, 44:238 (Oak Hall, Centre Co., September, *fide* Curry)—Trimble, *Cardinal*, 1937, 4:107 (Pymatuning region, Crawford Co., breeding).

Ardetta exilis Todd, *Ann. Carnegie Mus.*, 1904, 2:530 (Presque Isle, Erie Co., summer).

Ixobrychus exilis Christy, *Cardinal*, 1923, v. 1, no. 1, [p. 2] (McDonald Reservoir, Washington Co., May)—Eastwood, *Wilson Bull.*, 1932, 44:42 ([Boydstown], Butler Co., September, habits).

Ixobrychus exilis exilis Sutton, *Ann. Carnegie Mus.*, 1928, 18:85 (Pymatuning Swamp and Conneaut Lake, Crawford Co., summer; Sandy Lake, Mercer Co., nesting; migration records).

SWANS, GEESE, DUCKS

FAMILY ANATIDAE

This is a large, important, and widely distributed family. Although varying considerably in general size and in details of form, its members all possess lamellate bills; that is, bills provided with a series of thin plates set crosswise just inside the edges of the mandibles, which act as strainers. The bills are moreover covered with a leathery membrane, and terminate in a hard, horny "nail." The plumage is dense and water resistant; the front toes are always fully webbed; and the whole structure and economy are adapted to aquatic life. The Swans are the largest of the group; they have extremely long necks and partly bare lores. In the Geese the neck is not so long, and the lores are feathered; the average size is smaller.

The Ducks differ from the Swans and Geese in their shorter necks and scutellate (instead of reticulate) tarsi, which are moreover relatively shorter—a fact which accounts for their more awkward walking-gait. An outstanding feature of the coloration of many species is the speculum, a brightly colored, usually iridescent, area on the secondary wing feathers. There are several subgroups of the Ducks proper. The "River" or "Pond" Ducks are mainly surface feeders—"dabblers," one might call them; they include the kinds most highly prized for the table, as their food is largely of a vegetable character. All Ducks of this class have the hind toe simple. The "Sea" or "Diving" Ducks, on the other hand, have the hind toe provided with a flap or lobe; they find their food (mostly of an animal nature) in deeper water; and their flesh is often decidedly fishy in flavor. The Mergansers are also set apart by reason of their piscivorous habits and their cylindrical bills with saw-tooth edges.

Our species of this family are all migratory; many of them are properly transients that breed north of our limits and winter southward. The formation of an artificial lake in the Pymatuning region of Crawford County, however, has led to new and surprising developments in the case of numerous species of Ducks, which within the past few years have adopted this area as a breeding ground. A succession of mild winters has also induced certain species to remain farther north than is usual.

Hutchins' Goose (*Branta canadensis hutchinsi*), a small race of the Canada Goose, should be expected to occur at least casually in western Pennsylvania, as should also Barrow's Golden-eye (*Glaucionetta islandica*). There are in fact two local records for the latter species,[1] but I am not disposed to accept them without confirmatory evidence. The Trumpeter Swan (*Cygnus buccinator*) is another species which may have occurred formerly[2] but for which the evidence of occurrence is likewise unsatisfactory.

[1]N. G. Nicholson, *Bird-Lore*, 1918, 20:181; G. M. Sutton, *Annals Carnegie Museum*, 1928, 18:76.
[2]Compare G. M. Sutton, *Annals Carnegie Museum*, 1928, 18:84.

WHISTLING SWAN

CYGNUS COLUMBIANUS (Ord)

Description—A very large bird; wingspread six to seven feet. *Adult pure white;* bill black, usually with a yellow spot at its base in front of the eye; feet black. (The rusty color on the feathers of the head and neck of some individuals is merely water stain.) *Young birds:* somewhat smaller; whitish, but *clouded with dull grayish brown;* the head and neck rather darker.

Range—The breeding grounds of the Whistling Swan lie in the arctic countries, to the north and west of Hudson Strait and Bay. Its regular winter range is the Atlantic coast, from Chesapeake Bay to Currituck Sound. Its migration route therefore carries it across the Great Lakes, where it is a regular visitant in spring and fall. Plotting the western Pennsylvania records on a map, we find that the great majority of the localities represented are in the northwestern counties, near Lake Erie. There are several records for the northern tier of counties, and some also for Blair County, in the ridge and valley section, but only a few for the plateau region at large. The reason apparently is that there are few suitable feeding or alighting grounds there, so that the birds are not tempted to come down until they reach the larger streams west of the mountains, and the lakes and ponds of the northwestern counties. Moreover, in crossing the mountains they probably fly fairly high as a rule, and are thus seldom observed in transit. The fact remains that in almost every part of our region this species is apt to be seen occasionally in migration, and of late years it is becoming commoner and more regular at Erie Bay and Conneaut Lake—the two localities where it has been most frequently observed. Pymatuning Lake is also attracting a fair share of migrants.

Migration—Cold weather alone does not seem to discommode swans or to discourage their northward movement, but they must have open water. Consequently they are among the first of the waterfowl to push northward in the spring. When the ice has weakened on Erie Bay and open leads show here and there, the swans may be expected. Actual first dates are March 11, 1897 (Bacon); March 22, 1925 ([reported to] Sutton); February 15, 1927 (Sutton); March 25, 1928 (Todd); March 17, 1929 (Perry); March 19, 1933, and March 3, 1934 (Guynes). Swans have been known to remain there until April 8 (1928) or 10 (1932) or 15 (1934), and in one case until May 7 (1933). At Conneaut Lake local observers report that the swans stay in the spring from March 18 to April 9. Corresponding dates for the Pymatuning region are from March 9 (1939) to April 27 (1933). R. B. Simpson gives March dates at Warren from the twentieth on, while in 1899 he saw a single bird as late as April 12. T. D. Burleigh saw one on the Highland Park Reservoir, within the city limits of Pittsburgh, on April 8, 1914. A late spring record is that of A. K. Pierce, who saw a single bird near Keating, Clinton County, on April 30, 1897. In 1935 a lone bird (probably a "pensioner") remained on Pymatuning Lake through the month of May. An exceptionally early date is supplied by H. A. McGraw, who reports that on March 4, 1906, a flock of twenty-two alighted on the Frankstown Branch of the Juniata River near Kladder, Blair County; several were killed. These exceptions aside, the migration dates from these various points are in substantial accord, and enable us to place the main northward migration of this species in our region from the middle of March to the middle of April.

As with other waterfowl, there are sometimes days of great movement, and then the swans attract much attention because of their prominence and unusual numbers. Such flights must have been common enough in the early days, but the first of which there is an authentic record took place in March, 1879, during a storm. Concerning it I quote from Sennett's account (1880): "An unusual flight of Swans occurred in Northwestern Pennsylvania, on the 22nd of last March (1879), Crawford, Mercer, Venango, and Warren Counties being the places where they were seen. On the day mentioned, as well as the previous day and night, a severe storm prevailed, the rain and snow freezing as they fell. The Swans, on their migration north, were caught in the storm, and, becoming overweighted with ice, soon grew so exhausted that they settled into the nearest ponds and streams, almost helpless. Generally a single one was seen in some mill-pond or creek; and the fowling-piece, loaded with large shot, and not unfrequently the rifle, was used to bring to bag the noble game, though, considering the plight they were in, in all probability any one might have paddled up to the birds and taken them alive. In fact, in a number of instances they were reported as thus taken alive. Large flocks were seen in some districts in the same pitiable condition. In close vicinity of Meadville only two, I believe, were taken. Titusville and Oil City, and the intervening eighteen miles up Oil Creek and its branches, seem to have been the points where they were seen in greatest number. A published report from the former place states that 'ten or twelve White Swans were captured alive' near East Titusville." Sennett then quotes a newspaper account of the annihilation of a flock of about thirty-five of these fine birds that was forced down on Cherry Run, near Plumer, during this particular flight.

More recent records from this same region are available. G. M. Sutton (1928) records several extensive flights: one of huge flocks at Meadville on March 24, 1895, reported by H. C. Kirkpatrick; one at Conneaut Lake on March 27 and another on March 29, 1926, reported by G. M. Langdon; and one of at least two hundred birds at the same place on March 30, 1925, reported by C. A. Bergstrom. At Greenville on April 3, 1934, S. J. Seiple observed a flock of about three hundred heading northwest and flying low in a V-shaped formation. Mr. Simpson writes that at least one hundred swans alighted at Tidioute, Warren County, on March 20, 1910. Again, on April 7, 1914, a storm brought to Warren a good many whistling swans, together with geese and ducks; over fifty swans were counted in a single flock. Very possibly there have been similar flights in the Ohio Valley—in fact, I have preserved a newspaper account of one in late March, 1894. In recent years there has been an increasing tendency among whistling swans to stop over in transit at certain of the artificial reservoirs in the mountain section. Thus Miss A. E. Berg writes that on April 7, 1934, she saw two at Lakemont, Blair County, and over sixty at Lake Altoona, in company with hundreds of ducks and a number of gulls. Similar occurrences have been noted at Tubmill Reservoir, Westmoreland County, on October 21, 1934 (Heard, 1935), and at Lake Seaton, Fayette County, in April, 1936 (Gordon).

Fall records for this species are neither so numerous nor so satisfactory as those for the spring; they indicate a migration period lasting from October 18 through November, and sometimes even into December. Mr. Simpson reports that on September 21, 1894, a young bird of the year, weighing eleven pounds, was shot at "Highouse's Eddy," just below Warren; this was a most unusual date.

By far the most extraordinary circumstance relating to the local status of the Whistling Swan is its wintering in numbers at several points on Lake Erie—well to the northward of its usual resorts—during the season of 1931–32. The unprecedented mildness of that winter was of course the chief factor in this development. Reports of wintering swans came that year from Kingsville, Ontario, and from Erie, Michigan, but the birds on Erie Bay attracted the most attention. They came from the north in November, but instead of leaving at the usual time they lingered, unmolested by gunners, while the waters of the bay and lake remained unfrozen. Estimates of their number varied, since the flocks were widely scattered, but there could not have been less than five hundred individuals, and possibly there were as many as eight hundred. When it became evident that they might remain all winter, the local park commissioners provided food for them, as an additional inducement, and every day until the end of their stay several bushels of grain were scattered in the shallow waters near the head of the bay. The supply was by no means enough to care for the whole number, however, so there must also have been plenty of natural food available. In due course the flocks of swans became a local attraction, and brought many visitors, including myself, to see the unique spectacle.

B. H. Christy has published (1932) a full account of this interesting visitation. In his opinion, the swans remained on Erie Bay because of freedom from molestation and because of the unusual climatic conditions. He writes: "Were the swans prescient? It is incredible that they were. And yet the temptation to suppose something of that sort would have been strong, had the winter continued mild to the end. But in the early hours of the sixth day of March a storm broke, the temperature fell, the bay was frozen over. And it remained frozen over for weeks. What then of swans? Their feeding-grounds were sealed in ice, and but for a small remnant they left the bay. Indeed, it is said that the swans departed on the day before the coming of the storm." Mr. Christy thinks that by this time the migration impulse to go southward must have passed, and that the birds dispersed to other areas.

W. M. Guynes of Erie, who has had exceptional facilities for observation, sends an account differing in a few particulars. He writes: "In the fall of 1931 there were about 750 swans here at one time. In December the flock had dwindled to about 300, but by January 10 the number had grown to 550, which remained until the northward movement on March 5. During this winter there was little or no ice on the bay until March 7, but on March 5, which was a beautiful warm day, all of the 550 swans collected in 'Swan Cove' and at about 7 A.M. started to leave. They circled upward to a great height, and approximately 400 headed northwest over the lake while some 20 scattered around the bay and 60 settled with 10 Canada geese about a mile out in the lake.

"The next day (March 6) there were 53 swans on the bay, and these stayed there during the week when the thermometer went down to 7° and the bay froze over except for three holes. On March 11 some swans came in from the south and on March 12 there were about 250 in these open holes and in open lanes on the lake near the east end of the peninsula. On March 13 there were approximately 100 in evidence; but most of these went on north when the real thaw came on March 16. The northward flight from Chesapeake Bay evidently must have started on March 10, and while the storm into which the swans ran seemed bad to us, it is probable that the weather was no more severe than that encountered every year on their migration."

No whistling swans are known to have wintered at Erie Bay during the season of 1932–33. During the following winter, however, a group of twenty or more remained through December and January. What became of them during the month of February, when the weather grew unusually severe, is unknown. Swans were reported again, however, as early as March 3, and these may have belonged to the same flock. Again in the winters of 1934–35 and 1936–37 whistling swans remained on Erie Bay through the entire cold season, in the latter year to the number of about eighty birds. (During the severe winter of 1935–36, however, none were observed.) The swans that enter western Pennsylvania thus seem to find Erie Bay increasingly attractive as a stopping place en route and as a potential wintering ground.

Habits—When I wrote my report on the "Birds of Erie and Presque Isle" in 1904, I could find but few records for the Whistling Swan. I did not see or hear of a single swan during the season of 1900. This was not surprising in view of the fact that there were then hordes of hunters in the locality. Since that time conditions have changed: now the federal law gives swans absolute protection at all seasons; spring shooting has been abolished; and Presque Isle and its adjacent waters have been made sanctuaries. Under the influence of these beneficent conditions the swans are coming back, and Erie Bay is again being favored by their visits. There, on March 25, 1928, with J. E. Perry, I had my first sight of wild swans—a flock of twenty-nine birds feeding at ease less than two hundred feet offshore. Again in 1932, on February 20 and 21, in company with Mr. Christy and others, I visited Presque Isle and watched the flocks of wintering birds. Not a bit of ice could be seen anywhere on the lake or bay —a strange contrast to the icebound conditions encountered there in March thirty-two years before. I cannot tell with what strange mingling of interest and elation I looked out over the smooth waters at the flocks of ducks and other waterfowl, in greater abundance and variety than I had ever known them in other years. Dotted here and there over the bay as far as the eye could see, and standing out as white patches on the water, were the flocks of swans, in imposing and magnificent array. Mr. Christy describes the scene as he saw it on January 2, 1932:

"Out on the gray water we could dimly see the gleaming forms of swans. Their calls were rising here, there, and afar—the waking calls, the integrating shouts, of a wide-spread host. . . .

"As light increased we began to see, close-dotted about the swans, the dark bodies of attendant ducks. And already the throng was in motion; the ducks, particularly, were springing up in large companies and departing—to distant feeding-grounds, as we supposed. The swans were not so greatly disturbed. Now and again half a dozen would rise together and, with a stretching-out of long necks, a beating of wings, and a slapping of great feet upon the water, they would get under way, and move along the shore and settle again. At length in broad daylight a line of swans was discovered offshore, extending all along the edge of the marsh and beyond our range of view on either hand.

"They were not timid—not nearly so fearful as the ducks. Though we stood within a screen of bushes, and were careful that our movements should be slow, it was manifest, by the erection of a neck, by the turning of a head, by the utterance now and again of a trumpet-note, that the eyes of the birds nearest were upon us. We caused them, perhaps, a little more shouting, a little more winging about, but not much. . . .

"We drove along the peninsula from end to end, stopping repeatedly to fix our glasses upon the swans, and we easily perceived how different was the habit of these birds from that of a migrating host. No longer were they herded, as for traveling, in a compact and restless mass. The assembly had lost coherence; it had loosened into scattered smaller companies; and these in turn had frayed out into family groups, at rest in winter quarters. Typically the birds tended to associate in groups of five or six individuals, of which two would be black-billed adults, and the others duskier, pale-billed cygnets.

"We made such estimate of numbers as we could. Standing in one place, we could count as many as three hundred; and as we moved about we judged the total to have exceeded five hundred. . . .

"On the twenty-fifth day of March we again visited Erie. We found the bay ice-coated still, but we found in the narrow leads of water opened by the winds and by navigation vast numbers of waterfowl. Spring migration had set in, and thousands of birds—birds in numbers far exceeding the winter-time census—were congregated there. . . . We found a band of twenty-seven swans still remaining. On the afternoon of the twenty-fifth most of these were standing together on the ice at the edge of an open lead, a hundred and fifty yards from shore, in which a few of their companions were floating and thrusting down their heads as though feeding."

The Whistling Swan feeds in the same manner as its European cousin, the Mute Swan, which is a well-known captive bird. Its food is mainly vegetable in character and is secured by thrusting the long neck and often almost the entire body downward to reach the bottom. Its favorite feeding grounds are thus those where the water is of the right depth for this procedure. The abundance of suitable food at Erie Bay must have been an important factor in causing the swans to winter there. Mostly they frequented the shallower parts of the bay, but occasionally they would fly out to the open lake, and sometimes even to the ponds on Presque Isle. For such heavy birds they get under way rather easily, and their flight is strong and well sustained. Flocks in migration often move in a V-shaped formation, like that of geese, but Mr. Guynes writes that those he has observed at Erie were usually in a single straight line forming a slight angle with the line of flight—one side of the "V," as it were.

Cygnus americanus Sennett, *Bull. Nuttall Orn. Club*, 1880, 5:126 (Meadville and Titusville, Crawford Co.; Oil City, Plumer, and Rouseville, Venango Co.; Warren and Mercer Co.; migration).

Cygnus columbianus Townsend, *Proc. Acad. Nat. Sci. Philadelphia*, 1883, 67 (Loyalhanna Creek, Westmoreland Co.)—Luttringer, *Oölogist*, 1928, 45:42 (Sheffield, Warren Co., March)—Sutton, *Ann. Carnegie Mus.*, 1928, 18:83 (Crawford Co. localities and records)—Perry, *Cardinal*, 1932, 3:68 (Erie Bay, Erie Co., November)—Christy, *Cardinal*, 1932, 3:87 (Erie Bay, Erie Co., winter; habits); 1935, 4:18 (Erie Bay, Erie Co., December, *fide* Perry)—Heard, *Cardinal*, 1935, 4:17 ([Tubmill Reservoir], Westmoreland Co., October)—Perry, *Cardinal*, 1938, 4:177 (Erie Bay, Erie Co., October, December)—Manley, *Cardinal*, 1938, 4:203 (Allegheny River, near Braeburn, Westmoreland Co., April).

Olor sp.? Rhoads, *Auk*, 1899, 16:309 (Keating, Clinton Co., and West Branch Susquehanna River, Clearfield Co., *fide* Nelson).

Olor columbianus Todd, *Ann. Carnegie Mus.*, 1904, 2:529 (Erie Bay and region, Erie Co., transient)—Burleigh, *Wilson Bull.*, 1923, 35:83 (Highland Park, Allegheny Co., April)—

Christy, *Cardinal*, 1926, v. 1, no. 8, p. 15 (Erie Bay, Erie Co., *fide* Perry; "Horseshoe Curve" [Kittanning Point], Blair Co., *fide* Jennings; Mount Jewett, McKean Co., *fide* Benson).

"Whistling Swan" Simpson, *Oölogist*, 1911, 28:39 (Warren, Warren Co.; Oil City, Venango Co., migration)—Savage, *Bird-Lore*, 1932, 34:44; Beal and Peterson, *Bird-Lore*, 1934, 36:33; and Upson, *et al.*, *Bird-Lore*, 1935, 37:47 (Erie Bay, Erie Co., December)—Brooks, *Redstart*, 1936, 3:49 (Erie Bay, Erie Co., March)—Oudette, *Cardinal*, 1939, 5:47 (Pymatuning Lake, near Linesville, Crawford Co., March).

Additional records: Betula, McKean Co., November 2, 1919 (Frank Oviatt; specimen in Carnegie Museum)—Trauger, Westmoreland Co., November 4, 1927 (W. L. Wright; specimen in Carnegie Museum)—Washington, Washington Co., "saw a flock about 1872. One killed on Chartiers Creek near Canonsburg, April 8, 1886" (Nease)—Jacobs Creek, Westmoreland Co., occasional migrant (Medsger)—Mount Jewett, McKean Co., April 8 and May 4, 1926, taken alive by Carl B. Benson (Sutton)—Wilcox, Elk Co., June 6, 1927, found dead by T. F. McMahon (Sutton)—Sheffield, Warren Co., March 30, 1928, crippled bird from Elmer H. Nelson (Sutton)—Keating Summit, Potter Co., May 5, 1928, found dead by Cecil Marsh (Sutton)—Indian Creek, Fayette Co., March 23, 1907, shot by Harry Linowebber (Todd)—Linesville, Crawford Co., November 26, 1904, shot by Luther Carnes (Kirkpatrick)—Lake Altoona, Blair Co., December 2, 1923, one seen; Tipton Dam, Blair Co., November 16, 1933, flock of twenty-seven seen by C. B. Tobias (McGraw)—Canonsburg Waterworks, Washington Co., March 19, 1933, one seen (Grimm)—Westport, Clinton Co., November 20, 1896, one shot by S. M. Wertz (Pierce)—Espyville-Andover Road, Crawford Co., March 27, 1933, flock of sixty seen (Dilley)—Oneida Lake, Butler Co., April 4, 1936, five seen (Mason)—Lake Seaton, Fayette Co., April, 1936, three seen (Gordon)—Homestead, Allegheny Co., November 3, 1935 (specimen in Carnegie Museum).

COMMON CANADA GOOSE

BRANTA CANADENSIS CANADENSIS (Linnaeus)

Description—About the size of the domestic goose; sexes alike, and young similar but rather smaller. *Head and neck black*, relieved by a *broad white throat-patch*, extending upward on either side to cover the cheeks; upperparts brown, with paler feather-edgings, giving a more or less barred or scaled effect; rump and tail pure black, with a broad white V-shaped band between; wings blackish; underparts dull brownish or grayish white, the sides more or less barred with darker color, and the flanks, lower abdomen, and under tail coverts, white in abrupt contrast; bill and feet black.

Range—The Canada Goose in its various geographical phases has a wide range, coextensive with the North American continent from Mexico northward. It breeds regularly from Newfoundland and Labrador west to Alaska, and southward to the mountainous parts of the western United States. There was doubtless a time when it also bred regularly farther south in the eastern part of the country, but records are wanting for most of this area in general, and for western New York and Ohio in particular. The nearest extralimital breeding station on record is a former one in the state of Indiana.[1] A number of pinioned geese, however, were released several years ago in the Pymatuning game refuge with the hope that they might breed; and, according to R. L. Fricke, some actually did breed in the season of 1937. During the breeding season the Canada Goose requires conditions that are incompatible with the settlement of the country; nevertheless it seems to be holding its own fairly well. In western Pennsylvania it is a regular transient visitant, well known and generally distributed, but like others of its family it is most frequently observed in the lake region of the northwestern counties, and in the Ohio and Allegheny valleys.

Migration—W. W. Cooke has discussed the migration of the Canada Goose at some length. He says: "This bird fulfills the popular notion of bird migration, *i. e.*, it moves northward in spring as soon as the loosening of winter's fetters offers open water and a possibility of food. It continues its progress at the same rate as spring, appearing at its most northern breeding grounds at the earliest possible moment. The isotherm of 35° F. seems to be the governing factor in the rate of spring migration of the Canada goose."[2]

In our region March is the month of greatest movement, as shown by a long array of dates from several different stations. A number of February occurrences are on record, however, and during the exceptionally mild winter of 1931–32, when

[1]A. W. Butler, *Birds of Indiana*, 1898, p. 637.
[2]U. S. Department of Agriculture, Biological Survey, *Bulletin*, no. 26, 1906, p. 72–77; no. 185, 1915, p. 41.

many whistling swans remained on Erie Bay, some Canada geese stayed over also. W. M. Guynes writes that almost every year a few geese may be found there in January or February. My own arrival records for Beaver County, covering seven different (not successive) seasons, range between February 25 (1891) and March 26 (1887); March 17 is the average. My latest spring date is April 12 (1899). For Crawford County the earliest arrival date is February 8 (1900) and the latest March 10 (1926); the species has been recorded there in migration as late as April 26 (1936). Corresponding arrival dates for Erie Bay are February 15 (1927) and March 28 (1895). S. E. Bacon says: "On April 30, 1889, I saw a flock of a dozen Geese, and on May 1, 1902, a single pair; I consider both of these very late records" (in Todd, 1904). R. B. Simpson considers his records for Warren made on March 7 (1894) and 8 (1924) very early dates indeed; he has seen Canada geese as late as April 12 (1902). S. J. Seiple writes that a flock passed over Greenville on March 8, 1934, and that a few had gone over before March 1 in 1937. From Altoona, in the eastern part of our area, we have H. A. McGraw's record for March 9, 1918. Several seasons' notes from Renovo by A. K. Pierce give March 5 (1893, 1913) to March 26 (1904, 1920) as the dates of arrival. T. D. Burleigh has seen the species at State College as early as February 26 (1917). At Hares Valley, in southern Huntingdon County, it was noted on February 19 (1887—Greene). In 1926 Miss Elizabeth Alsop saw geese in large numbers passing overhead at Ridgway on February 17 and 18.

In the fall the migrating geese usually appear during the last ten days of October. Mr. Simpson reports a flock of seventy-five birds seen at Warren on September 30, 1895, on the occasion of the first snowfall; this was of course unseasonably early. A flock passed over Beaver during the early morning hours of October 13, 1937. October 7 (1904), is the earliest recorded date of fall arrival at Renovo, while the average for fourteen years is October 20 (Pierce). Canada geese have been seen at Altoona as early as October 14 (McGraw), and at Stoyestown, Somerset County (Mostoller), and Linesville (Seiple) on the same date. Mr. Guynes's fall arrival records at Erie for the years 1932–34 are October 22, 20, and 27. November, however, appears to be the month of greatest movement at all stations, and some birds linger into the following month. Professor Seiple writes that many geese passed over Greenville on the morning of December 1, 1933. A flock was observed on December 6, 1899, at the mouth of Raccoon Creek, Beaver County (Wickham). On December 25, 1925, large flocks were seen at Conneaut Lake by C. A. Bergstrom (Sutton, 1928). Thus the entire migration of this species at this season occupies about the same length of time as it does in the spring. No given individual or flock, of course, remains at any one place during the whole period; a few days or a week at the most is the usual length of time for a stop.

Habits—Canada geese passing overhead in a V-shaped line, with an old gander in the lead, all honking back and forth, are bound to attract the attention of even the casual passer-by. Sometimes they fly so high that, although heard, they cannot be seen, and again they barely clear the treetops. Flocks are the rule, and single birds the exception; it is fair to assume that the latter have strayed away from their companions. The flocks vary in size from six birds up to one hundred or more, and on days of great movement the flocks may trail one another in loose and disconnected order. Mr. Bergstrom writes that on November 4, 1928, near Hartstown, he saw a procession of flocks that took at least twenty minutes to pass. This flight was also observed on the same day a little farther south, according to R. L. Keesler, who reports that fourteen flocks, estimated to contain at least two thousand birds, passed over Greenville. Some were also seen at Forestville, Butler County. According to the *Conneaut Lake Breeze*, Canada geese to the number of "several thousands" alighted on Conneaut Lake on November 21, 1931, and passed the night there.

Migration is by no means confined to the daytime, but is often carried on during the night, especially if there is a moon. At such times the only intimation one may have of the flight of geese is an occasional honk coming from overhead. Storm and fog sometimes interfere with nocturnal migration, and several cases have been recorded of birds becoming bewildered by city lights and forced down, sometimes to fall victims to mercenary pothunters. But ordinarily the geese are amply able to take care of themselves; they are at all times wild and wary. The common expression "silly as a goose" has no basis in fact. At Conneaut and Pymatuning lakes and at Erie Bay, where geese regularly alight, they contrive to keep well out of gunshot, and but few birds are ever taken. Under the protection now afforded at Erie Bay the geese are less wary; on March 25, 1932, the party of which I was a member saw about twenty-five resting on the shore of a sheltered cove, and without apparent concern they permitted us to drive up in an automobile within one hundred feet.

In the marshes the geese "feed on wild rice, arrowhead, sedges, marsh grasses, and various aquatic plants, eating the roots as well as the leaves and shoots. On the fall migration they again frequent the grain fields to pick up the fallen grain, pull up the stubble, and nibble at what green herbage they can find."[1] In the vicinity of Pymatuning Lake in the fall of 1936 the migrating birds caused considerable damage to fields of winter wheat. Great numbers of them were found feeding in grainfields many miles from the lake.

Bernicla canadensis Townsend, *Proc. Acad. Nat. Sci. Philadelphia*, 1883, 67 (Latrobe, Westmoreland Co., transient).

"Wild Goose" Enty, *Ornithologist and Oölogist*, 1885, 10:78 (Templeton, Armstrong Co., March)—[Christy], *Cardinal*, 1924, v. 1, no. 3, p. 9 (Pittsburgh, Allegheny Co., fall, *fide* Anderson).

"Canada Goose" Todd, *Oölogist*, 1887, 4:89 (Raccoon Creek, Beaver Co., March)—Wickham, *Oölogist*, 1888, 5:92 (Beaver, Beaver Co., March)—Simpson, *Oölogist*, 1911, 28:39 (Presque Isle, Erie Co., April)—McClelland, *Am. Mid. Nat.*, 1922, 8:37 (Washington, Washington Co., transient)—Sutton, *Bird-Lore*, 1924, 26:190 (Brookline, Allegheny Co., April, *fide* Ogden)—Eastwood, *Bird-Lore*, 1926, 28:208 (Ridgway, Elk Co., February-March, *fide* Alsop)—Boulton, *Bird-Lore*, 1928, 30:195 (Pittsburgh, Allegheny Co., March, *fide* Gordon)—Christy, *Cardinal*, 1932, 3:86 (Presque Isle, Erie Co., February)—[Christy, ed.], *Cardinal*, 1933, 3:150 (Oakmont, Allegheny Co., October, *fide* Kirk)—Oudette, *Cardinal*, 1939, 5:47 (Pymatuning Lake, near Linesville, Crawford Co., March).

Branta canadensis Todd, *Ann. Carnegie Mus.*, 1904, 2:528 (Erie Bay and Presque Isle, Erie Co., transient)—Todd, in Bausman, *Hist. Beaver Co., Pa.*, 1904, 2:1198 (Beaver Co., transient)—Cooke, *Bull. Biol. Surv.* no.26, 1906, 72 (Renovo, Clinton Co.; Hares Valley, Huntingdon Co.; migration)—Forrest, *Oölogist*, 1911, 28:115 (Washington, Washington Co., transient)—Christy, *Cardinal*, 1927, 2:11 (Clinton Pond, Allegheny Co., October).

Branta canadensis canadensis Christy, *Cardinal*, 1923, v. 1, no. 1, [p. 2] (Sewickley, Allegheny Co., transient)—Burleigh, *Wilson Bull.*, 1923, 35:83 ([Squaw Run], Allegheny Co., November); 1924, 36:76 (State College, Centre Co., migration)—Sutton, *Ann. Carnegie Mus.*, 1928, 18:82 (Crawford Co. localities and records).

[1]A. C. Bent, U. S. National Museum, *Bulletin*, no. 130, 1925, p. 213.

AMERICAN BRANT

BRANTA BERNICLA HROTA (Müller)

Description—Smaller than the Canada Goose, *Head and neck* (all around), *as far as the middle of the breast and upper back, black*, relieved by a white-striped area on either side of the neck; wings and tail black, but the flanks, lateral upper tail coverts, and under tail coverts, white; back and rump grayish brown, and underparts similar but much paler, with a suggestion of barring on the sides; bill and feet black. Easily distinguished from any of the forms of the Canada Goose by the lack of any white on the cheeks and by the continuation of the black of the neck over the upper back and breast.

Range and local status—The Brant is essentially a maritime species. In North America it ranges mainly along the Atlantic coast, winters from New Jersey to Florida, and breeds in the far North. "Brant" records from the interior, made by persons with no scientific training, are questionable, since the name is sometimes loosely applied by gunners to the small form of the Canada Goose. For this reason I would discredit the alleged Beaver

County record cited below. The Conneaut Lake records all rest on the authority of local observers, but are admitted by G. M. Sutton. The occurrences were all in late fall and early winter, and during one season (1910–11) the bird was said to be "fairly common on the deeper waters of Conneaut Lake." The appearance of this species on inland waters is unusual and irregular. It has also been identified at Pymatuning Lake, however, in the spring. B. L. Oudette, the guardian of the state game refuge near Linesville, reports that on March 15, 1936, he saw a group of four brant feeding along the shores of the lake west of the spillway. The next morning there were thirty-one. The flock remained in the vicinity of the baited area until March 20. "In flight these [geese] did not take up any flock formation, and this characteristic further identified them as Brant." Since Mr. Oudette has had previous experience with this species on the Atlantic coast, his record is accepted here. The capture of specimens will nevertheless be awaited with interest.

(?)*Branta bernicla* Warren, *Birds Pa.*, ed. 2, 1890, 51 (Beaver Co., *fide* Scroggs).

Branta bernicla glaucogastra Sutton, *Ann. Carnegie Mus.*, 1928, 18:82 (Conneaut Lake, Crawford Co., fall, *fide* Peterson, Langdon, and Welshons).

Branta bernicla hrota Oudette, *Cardinal*, 1936, 4:96 (Linesville, Crawford Co., March).

WHITE-FRONTED GOOSE

ANSER ALBIFRONS ALBIFRONS (Scopoli)

Description—Smaller than the Canada Goose. *Adult:* grayish brown above, whiter below, and with more or less *irregular black blotches from the breast downwards; face with a prominent band of white* all around the base of the pink bill; *feet yellowish. Young birds:* darker and browner, and without the white face and dark blotches on the breast; the colors of the bill and feet are said to be the same as in the adult.

Range and local status—The White-fronted Goose breeds in the arctic regions and winters mainly in the western half of the United States, southward to Mexico. East of the Mississippi River it is rare or casual. D. A. Atkinson includes it in his list of Allegheny County birds on the strength of his examination of a specimen which had been shot on the Allegheny River near Tarentum, on November 28, 1895, by W. C. Evans. G. M. Sutton (1928) gives two sight records for Conneaut Lake: "Mr. Welshons saw a small flock on the ice at Conneaut Lake on March 8, 1908, but unfortunately did not procure a specimen. Mr. Langdon saw a flock of thirteen birds on April 3, 1926. These were examined to good advantage and their yellow feet were noted. One or two hunters have secured specimens during former years but these were not preserved."

Anser albifrons gambeli (error) Rhoads, *Auk*, 1899, 16:309 ([Tarentum], Allegheny Co., *fide* Atkinson)—Sutton, *Ann. Carnegie Mus.*, 1928, 18:82 (Conneaut Lake, Crawford Co., spring, *fide* Welshons and Langdon).

LESSER SNOW GOOSE

CHEN HYPERBOREA HYPERBOREA (Pallas)

Description—Smaller than the Canada Goose. *Adult: pure white, with black primaries*, very conspicuous in life. *Young birds:* similar, but the white areas more or less *shaded with gray.*

Range and migration—For many years there has been much confusion and uncertainty about the range and status of the two forms of the Snow Goose in North America. The question has recently been re-examined by A. C. Bent[1] and by F. H. Kennard,[2] with whose conclusions I fully agree. These authorities show that the Greater Snow Goose is virtually confined to the Atlantic coast, while the records from the interior, under whatever name they appear, must all pertain to the smaller form. It is of course this latter bird that passes through western Pennsylvania. Unfortunately no local specimens have been secured, but there is no mistaking this goose in life.

[1]U. S. National Museum, *Bulletin*, no. 130, 1925, p. 173.
[2]*Proceedings New England Zoölogical Club*, 1927, 9:85–93.

On March 31, 1888, at what used to be known as Merrill, Beaver County, I saw a flock of about twenty snow geese flying quietly in V-shaped formation down the Ohio River, as if seeking an opportunity to alight. Again, over forty years later, on April 12, 1931, not far from the same place, I saw a flock of fifty passing over the land. They were flying about one hundred yards high, also in V-shaped formation, and the sun glinted on their white bodies as they swung steadily along towards the northwest, gabbling and chattering among themselves at intervals. This was at about 4:30 P.M., and no doubt by nightfall they must have reached Lake Erie. In Centre County, at State College, T. D. Burleigh saw a flock of fully seventy on November 16, 1916. G. M. Sutton (1928) gives several records for Crawford County, from Conneaut Lake and Meadville: "On March 15, 1915, and March 24, 1924, Mr. Kirkpatrick saw immense flocks of snow-white birds passing over Meadville. Their wing-tips were black and the line of flight was different from that of the Canada Goose. 'One flock,' says Mr. Kirkpatrick, 'must have had five hundred individuals.' Among the white birds were a few dark colored ones, probably immature, or possibly Blue Geese (*Chen cærulescens*) for which we have no authentic record at present. Mr. Kirkpatrick has also noted Snow Geese in the fall, a flock of about fifty individuals having passed over Meadville on October 29, 1922." Two of Dr. Sutton's records were made by local observers during the fall migration (November 12, 1920; December 2, 1925). According to a newspaper report a flock of thirty-two geese, some of which were pure white, flew over the town of Conneaut Lake on November 22, 1936—the same day on which a large flight of Canada geese took place. B. L. Oudette reports having seen a single snow goose in early March, 1938, at Pymatuning Lake, and three on October 20, 1939, with a flock of blue geese.

At Erie Bay the Lesser Snow Goose was never recorded until the fall of 1934, when it appeared on October 28. An unwonted flight of blue geese occurred at the same time. On October 31 local observers reported approximately eighty snow geese, intermingled with a much larger number of the other species. The majority remained only a couple of days, however, and the last few birds were noted on November 4. According to I. B. Boggs, two "Snow Geese" were seen on Presque Isle on October 10, 1937.

Chen hyperborea nivalis (error) TODD, in Bausman, *Hist. Beaver Co., Pa.*, 1904, 2:1198 (Beaver Co., spring)—BURLEIGH, *Wilson Bull.*, 1924, 36:75 (State College, Centre Co., November)—SUTTON, *Ann. Carnegie Mus.*, 1928, 18:81 (Conneaut Lake and Meadville, Crawford Co., *fide* Kirkpatrick, *et al.*, transient).

Chen hyperborea hyperborea [CHRISTY, ed.], *Cardinal*, 1935, 4:18 (Erie Bay, Erie Co., October–November, *fide* Perry).

"Snow Goose" BOGGS, *Redstart*, 1937, 5:2 (Presque Isle, Erie Co., October).

Chen hyperborea OUDETTE, *Cardinal*, 1940, 5:68 (Pymatuning Lake, near Espyville, Crawford Co., October).

BLUE GOOSE

CHEN CAERULESCENS (Linnaeus)

Description—Smaller than the Canada Goose. The *adult* Blue Goose can always be identified by its *pure white head*, in contrast with the dark (bluish-gray) body. The rump, upper tail coverts, and wings (except the flight feathers) appear lighter (more grayish white) than the back. The amount of white on the underparts varies. The *young bird* in the fall is a dull *bluish gray*, with a *white spot on the chin.*

Range—The Blue Goose nests in Baffin Land and Southampton Island, and migrates along the east coast of Hudson Bay and through the Mississippi Valley to winter on the coast of Louisiana. Our region thus lies to the east of its regular route of migration. Until 1927, indeed, the sole basis for its inclusion in our list rested on the not-too-trustworthy authority of Warren, who says that one bird killed on the Ohio River near Pittsburgh in the fall of 1887 was identified by T. L. Hazzard. I heard no reports of it at Erie in 1900; but in April, 1927, J. E. Perry supplied the first authentic record from that locality. Since then so many more occurrences have been noted that this goose can now be considered a semiregular transient at Erie Bay. The largest flight took place in October, 1934. The species has even been found wintering there on more than one occasion. L. E. Hicks reports that on December 26, 1930, he observed a single blue goose on Presque Isle. This bird must have escaped the notice of the local observers, but during the memorable winter of 1931–32, when Erie Bay stayed open until March, allowing the Whistling Swan and other waterfowl to remain far north of their usual wintering grounds, a single blue goose was seen repeatedly by several persons. Again in 1934, C. S. Beardslee reported a blue goose there on January 9. It is possible that these several reports involve the same individual, which may have been following a highly abnormal vagary of its own. Two recent records from Pymatuning Lake induce the hope that this species may in due course learn to use this body of water also as a regular stopping place en route.

Migration—In the spring of 1927 the first blue geese were seen on Erie Bay on April 3, and the last (two birds) on April 17 (Perry). These dates correspond with those from outside our area, and probably mark the usual time of the spring movement in this latitude. The return movement takes place during the latter half of October and extends into November. October 20 (1936) is the earliest date for Erie Bay (Simpson), and November 20 (1934) the latest (Guynes)—excluding, of course, the wintering dates referred to above. At Pymatuning Lake the species was observed in 1936 between October 14 and 23, and in 1939 on October 20 (Oudette, 1940).

Why certain groups of blue geese have altered their migration route to include northwestern Pennsylvania has not been determined, but speculation is permissible. It is possible that small numbers were originally forced from their usual course by stress of weather, and, having found conditions to their liking, have voluntarily returned in later years. The great bulk of the species, however, has adhered to a westerly route. From the paucity of records it is obvious that the Blue Goose seldom stops between James Bay and the coast of Louisiana. Further developments will be awaited with interest.

Habits—The Blue Goose, as I know it in the north country, is a noisy bird, on the wing as well as while feeding. Besides the usual "honking" call, it has a variety of guttural, gabbling, cackling notes, hard to describe and harder still to imitate. Flocks fly in V-shaped lines, sometimes broken or irregular, as do those of Canada geese. It is believed that the old and young birds keep together in family groups even after the flocks have been formed. Flocks are not very large as a rule—from six to twenty-five or thirty birds—but sometimes great concentrations bring together many thousands. The number of birds seen together on Erie Bay on October 31, 1934, was estimated at four or five hundred. Their presence was accounted for by the prevalence of a furious northwest gale a few days before. Blue geese are vegetarians; some that Mr. Perry once watched at a distance of about fifty feet appeared to be feeding on roots at the water's edge.

Chen cœrulescens Warren, *Birds Pa.*, ed. 2, 1890, 49 (Pittsburgh, Allegheny Co., *fide* Hazzard)—[Christy], *Cardinal*, 1927, 2:42 (Erie Bay, Erie Co., April, *fide* Perry)—[Christy, ed.], *Cardinal*, 1935, 4:18 (Erie Bay, Erie Co., October–November, *fide* Perry)—Oudette, *Cardinal*, 1935, 4:121; and 1940, 5:68 (Linesville, Crawford Co., October).

"Blue Goose" Christy, *Cardinal*, 1932, 3:86 (Presque Isle, Erie Co., winter)—Savage, *Bird-Lore*, 1932, 34:44 (Presque Isle, Erie Co., December).

COMMON MALLARD (Plate 1)

ANAS PLATYRHYNCHOS PLATYRHYNCHOS Linnaeus

Description—A rather large duck, with the bill as long as the head. (The familiar green-headed duck of the barnyard.) *Adult male: head and upper neck glossy dark green;* below this a white ring around the neck; *breast dark chestnut brown,* this color running well up over the sides; rest of underparts dull white, the sides and flanks waved with fine dusky lines, giving a grayish appearance; tail whitish, the upper and under tail coverts black, in strong contrast; some of the upper coverts curled backwards; upperparts grayish brown, the lower back duskier; wings grayish, with the *speculum violet,* bordered before and behind by a black bar and then by a white one; under wing coverts white; bill greenish yellow; feet reddish orange. *Female* entirely different: above, *dusky, with buffy mottling;* below, *buffy, with dusky mottling;* head and neck buffy with dusky streaks, heaviest on the crown, lighter on the sides, leaving the chin and throat almost uniform buff; *wings as in the adult male*, but the *speculum smaller;* feet duller than in the male. The *immature male*, and the *adult male in eclipse plumage* (summer), resemble the adult female. *Downy young:* olive brown above and pure buff below, with the crown and a streak through the eye also olive brown.

Range—The Mallard has an extensive range in both Eurasia and North America; it breeds in the northern portions of both continents and retires southward for the winter. On this side of the Atlantic its main breeding grounds lie west of the Appalachian highlands from about latitude 41°, north to the Mackenzie Valley and Alaska, and southward in the mountains to New Mexico and Lower California. It has been found nesting occasionally in all the states bordering the Ohio River on the north, and it is probable that in the early days, before the country was settled, it was a regular and common summer resident in these regions. E. H. Eaton gives it as a rare breeding species in several counties in New York state.[1] That it breeds in the intervening region of western Pennsylvania is therefore not surprising. Warren quotes James Thompson to the effect that the Mallard occurred as an occasional summer resident on Presque Isle, and Mr. Thompson personally gave me the same information, but added that he did not know of any instance later than about 1892. (R. B. Simpson saw a female there in early June, 1911, but could find no nest.) In view of the demonstrated status of the species as a breeding bird in Crawford County to the south, I think that Mr. Thompson's record, despite the lack of details, should be accepted at its face value. The first intimation that the Mallard was breeding in Crawford County came from H. C. Kirkpatrick, who reported that about 1898 a few pairs had been found nesting at Conneaut Outlet. He said that his report "was based on a nest found there by Mr. William Powers, near where the 'Mercer Pike' bridge spans the Outlet. At the time of its discovery the parent bird was on the nest, which contained nine eggs."

That this was not a sporadic occurrence is attested by the further evidence collected and published by G. M. Sutton (1928), from his own observations and those of other reliable persons. Even in those days the Mallard must have bred regularly in the region of Conneaut and Pymatuning swamps; and since the transformation in 1934 of the greater part of the latter swamp into a lake, the breeding population there has increased tremendously. The Mallard is now one of the commonest ducks in the breeding season, and its nests along the shores of the lake are no longer a novelty.

That the Mallard breeds also at some of the smaller lakes in the northwestern counties is virtually certain. On May 19, 1937, I flushed a pair in the marsh at the head of Conneauttee (Edinboro) Lake, and on June 9, 1934, I encountered several pairs in the small lakes west and south of Tamarack Swamp, Warren County, and was assured by a farmer that a brood of young had been seen in the vicinity. S. S. Dickey writes that during April, May, and June, 1926, a half-dozen mallards were present on Lake Le Bœuf, in southern Erie County. In the past few years, as a result of special care and protection, mallards and other ducks have come every season to Franklin, on the Allegheny River, and some of these have remained to breed. It is unlikely, however, that the Mallard's local breeding range extends beyond the northwestern counties, where alone there are lakes and swamps of any consequence. Even there it is best known as a transient, common and regular in the season of migration, and occasionally remaining through the winter. It is somewhat irregular at Warren, and even more so farther south, along the Ohio and lower Allegheny rivers, so that it is probable that most of the southbound migrants pass over these regions without stopping. There are sundry records, however, for the plateau region and the ridge and valley section, which suggest that some individuals must stop there on their way to and from their main wintering grounds on the Atlantic coast of Virginia and the Carolinas.

Migration—The Mallard is a hardy duck, capable of withstanding severe cold if it can get plenty of food. It was one of several species that remained on Erie Bay during the winter season of 1931–32, and since then a wintering tendency has been remarked, although the number of individuals has been smaller. At Pymatuning Swamp in 1931 it lingered until December 23, when ice began to form (Bergstrom), and in 1936, at least until December 27 (Christy, 1937). Mr. Kirkpatrick has

[1]*Birds of New York*, 1910, 1:184.

found it near Meadville in December, and "Mr. Langdon and Mr. Bergstrom have known it to winter customarily, though always in small numbers, in the sheltered open stretches of water about Pymatuning [Swamp]" (Sutton, 1928). Even from Warren, where the winters are colder than in Crawford County, Mr. Simpson reports it as occasional during mild seasons and sometimes in quite severe weather. At any rate, "with the breaking up of the ice in March along the borders of the lakes, marshes, and streams, we look for the coming of the wild ducks, and should there be a few days with warm, southerly winds, and a warm rain, they are certain to make their appearance, the Mallard among the first" (Kirkpatrick). For Erie Bay the earliest recorded arrival date is February 23 (1891), but this is exceptional. S. E. Bacon recorded the Mallard's arrival there on March 2 (1902), March 8 (1898), and March 11 (1897). Records made in later years lie within these limits. For Conneaut Lake and Pymatuning Swamp the arrival dates correspond in general with those from Erie Bay. March 9 (1904) is the earliest date for Renovo, according to A. K. Pierce. H. H. Wickham, who has met with this species in Beaver County much oftener than I have, says that it comes usually by the middle of March. April is the month of greatest movement, however, and some migrating flocks remain until May.

The earliest migrants in the fall appear about the middle of September, and by October and November the movement is in full swing. Mr. Simpson has remarked the abundance of mallards in November at Warren; and in 1900 I observed many during the same month on Presque Isle. In 1901, according to Mr. Bacon, an unprecedented flight occurred at the latter place from October 17 to 19. Large numbers now come to Pymatuning Lake every spring and fall. I have noted the Mallard in Beaver County, near the mouth of Raccoon Creek, as late as November 22 (1899). For the past several years the species has been found on Erie Bay by various observers during the last week in December.

Habits—The Mallard is the original stock of the domestic duck. It is a popular and well-known game bird. In the wild state it is usually found in flocks, which may vary from twenty-five to several thousand birds. A flock of about five thousand was seen at Shaw's Landing, Crawford County, on April 18, 1926; and in recent years great numbers have appeared at Pymatuning Lake. The Mallard often associates with other species of similar haunts and habits, the Black Duck in particular. At Warren it prefers overflowed meadows, coves, ponds, quiet places along shore, and the dead water at the foot of islands; it is seldom seen in running water. The ponds on Presque Isle are a favorite resort, but the ducks arrive even before the ponds are open in the spring, and keep out on the bay, along the edge of the ice.

All late spring records show that as the season advances the flocks break up into mated pairs. While some pairs nest in April, May is the more usual month. Of the many nests found at Pymatuning Lake almost all were in open places, but concealed from above. Tufts of rushes and marsh grasses along the shore are favorite nesting sites, but some females choose "low stumps just above the level of the water in the shallow areas; others resort to marshy pasture fields, away from the shore" (Trimble, 1937). Nests with incomplete sets of eggs have been found as early as April 8; and broods of young have been noted on May 21, although dates two weeks later are the rule. The nests are depressions lined with any bits of dry material at hand, and with down from the breast of the female. The eggs number from nine to fourteen; they are precisely like those of the domestic bird—elliptical ovate, averaging 2.30 by 1.63 inches, and of a greenish or grayish-buff color.

The young are cared for by the female parent until they are fairly well grown and able to fly. Once, at Pymatuning, I encountered a female with a brood of nineteen. On another occasion I was interested in watching the maneuvers of an old bird as she led her brood through the tall grass and hurried them into the water just ahead of me. After the eggs are all laid, and while the young are growing up, the males forgather by themselves and assume what is known as the "eclipse" plumage, which is very like the plumage of the female. By the time the young are on the wing, however, the old males have reassumed their distinctive dress, and old and young assemble for their southward journey. At Presque Isle in the fall of 1900, the flocks consisted of males alone; thus there seems to be a tendency at this season for the sexes to travel in separate flocks. The maneuvers of the birds when seeking a place to alight are interesting. At Presque Isle they "would sweep low over the waters of a pond, then rise and disappear over a wooded ridge half a mile away, returning to repeat the movement until satisfied that the coast was clear, when they would settle in some shallow spot and begin to feed, remaining in one place for hours at a time, if not disturbed" (Todd, 1904).

The food of this species is largely of a vegetable nature, and is obtained along the edges of the pools, or below the surface in shallow water. In flight the Mallard is swift and strong, and wherever it is subjected to much hunting it is wild and wary. It prefers to fly over the water, for the sake of safety. I once saw a flock flying up Raccoon Creek, following the windings of the stream closely, although the birds were certainly high enough to see across from one bend to another.

Donald Glenn details the history of a female mallard that in the fall of 1924 made its headquarters on a small island above the bridge across French Creek, near Franklin. Passers-by fed the duck, which became very tame and remained in the vicinity all winter. The next spring a mate appeared, and in the winter of 1925–26 there were eight ducks. Each subsequent year the mallard population increased, and at the time of Mr. Glenn's writing (January, 1930), about fifty ducks had become "pensioners" of the Franklin residents. They were continually fed by the public, and became so tame that they paid no attention to the traffic on the bridge about twenty feet above them. Apparently these ducks nested on the island and along the banks of French Creek, where, in flood season, nests and many young, too, were doubtless destroyed.

Mallard eggs hatched by hens or by domestic ducks produce birds that are tame from the start and show no fear of man. For several years B. L. Oudette had a flock of these semidomesticated ducks about his home near Linesville. They were perfectly tame, and the females nested in all sorts of places around the buildings. There is another such flock on Presque Isle, living on a small pond that is kept open through the winter by artificial heat. With the necessary food supplied, these birds show no disposition to migrate as do their wild brethren; in fact, they soon become so fat that it is hard for them to fly! Wherever there are tame mallards about, caution is necessary in recording the migratory movements of this species.

Anas boschas Townsend, *Proc. Acad. Nat. Sci. Philadelphia*, 1883, 67 (Latrobe, Westmoreland Co., *fide* Beckwith)—Warren, *Birds Pa.*, ed. 2, 1890, 35 (Erie Bay and Presque Isle, Erie Co., transient; breeding, *fide* Thompson)—Todd, *Ann. Carnegie Mus.*, 1904, 2:512 (Erie Bay and Presque Isle, Erie Co., transient)—Todd, in Bausman, *Hist. Beaver Co., Pa.*, 1904, 2:1198 (Beaver Co., transient).

"Mallard" Simpson, *Oölogist*, 1912, 29:350 (Presque Isle, Erie Co., June), 370 (Warren, Warren Co., March)—Harlow, *Cassinia*, 1912, 15:20 (Center Furnace Swamp, Centre Co., spring)—Miller, *In the Open*, Aug., 1913, 4:34 (Pymatuning Swamp, Crawford Co.)—Simpson, *Oölogist*, 1913, 30:51; 1914, 31:210 (Warren, Warren Co., March–April)—Christy, *Cardinal*, 1932, 3:86 (Presque Isle, Erie Co., February)—Savage, *Bird-Lore*, 1932, 34:44; Upson, *et al.*, *Bird-Lore*, 1933, 35:47; and Beal and Peterson, *Bird-Lore*, 1934, 36:33 (Erie Bay, Erie Co., December)—Trimble, *Cardinal*, 1937, 4:104 (Pymatuning region, Crawford Co., nesting)—Christy, *et al.*, *Bird-Lore*, 1937, 39:44 (Pymatuning Lake, Crawford Co., December)—Oudette, *Cardinal*, 1939, 5:47 (Pymatuning Lake, near Linesville, Crawford Co., February).

Anas platyrhynchos Christy, *Cardinal*, 1923, v. 1, no. 1, [p. 2] (Clinton Pond, Allegheny Co., and Beaver River, Beaver Co., April)—Burleigh, *Wilson Bull.*, 1924, 36:75 (Scotia, Centre Co., fall)—Fricke, *Cardinal*, 1931, 3:42 (Pymatuning Swamp, Crawford Co.).

Anas platyrhynchos platyrhynchos Sutton, *Ann. Carnegie Mus.*, 1928, 18:63 (Pymatuning Swamp, Crawford Co., nesting; Crawford Co. records)—Sutton, *Cardinal*, 1929, 2:121 (Shermansville, Crawford Co., nesting, *fide* Thompson and Graham)—Bergstrom, *Cardinal*, 1930, 2:186 (Conneaut Lake, Crawford Co., nesting, *fide* Keene).

RED-LEGGED BLACK DUCK

ANAS RUBRIPES RUBRIPES Brewster

COMMON BLACK DUCK (Plate 1)

ANAS RUBRIPES TRISTIS Brewster

Description—A fairly large duck, almost as big as the Mallard; sexes alike. General coloration *dark brown*, with paler feather-edgings, more prominent below; *wing-speculum dark violet to greenish, with a black border; lining of wings white;* head dark brown above, the sides of the head and the throat buff, with dusky streaks, the chin paler, usually unspotted; bill yellowish (in *rubripes*) to dull dark greenish (in *tristis*); feet brownish or dull reddish (in *tristis*), or coral red (in *rubripes*).

The color of the legs and feet is considered to distinguish the two supposed races of the Black Duck. The Red-legged race also averages larger and generally darker, with the dark markings on the head and neck coarser. Some authors believe, however, that the characters distinguishing the two alleged races are merely those due to age, the red-legged birds being adult, the brown-legged ones immature. The last word is yet to be said on this question; in granting recognition here to both races, I have followed the American Ornithologists' Union *Check-List*.

Range—The region east of Hudson Bay and the Mississippi River constitutes the main range of this species, which is commonest east of the Appalachian highlands, in New England, New York, and the Maritime Provinces of Canada, just where the Mallard is rare. It is known to breed locally south to Long Island, New Jersey, and the northern parts of Ohio, Indiana, and Illinois, and to winter along the Atlantic and Gulf coasts, from New England southward. During the winter it is not nearly so common in the interior as on the coast, yet it has been found at that season as far north as the states bordering on Lakes Erie and Michigan.

A supposed northern form (*rubripes*), said to be characterized by its relatively large size, red legs, and generally darker coloration, has been described, but the evidence for its establishment as a separate form is contradictory and inconclusive. It is not feasible in any case to try to separate all the records for the two supposed forms, because of the difficulty of distinguishing the living birds and because of the scarcity of information on the colors of the soft parts in preserved specimens; hence for the purposes of this work they will be considered together. If there really are two races, then the breeding records for this region should refer to *tristis*, while most of the wintering records, on the other hand, should pertain to *rubripes*. But the local observers at Erie all insist that both kinds sometimes winter there, as alleged in the annual "Christmas Census" list. The red-legged birds, at any rate, were certainly abundant on Erie Bay during the open winter of 1931–32, and again in the winter of 1933–34.

As a local breeding bird the Black Duck occupies virtually the same ground as the Mallard, and some outlying stations in addition. Conneaut Outlet and more particularly the Pymatuning area in Crawford County are its principal local nesting grounds. G. M. Sutton's intensive study of this interesting region brought out the fact that the Black Duck nested there occasionally before 1927. At least one nest with eggs had been found, and young broods had been observed repeatedly. The clearing and flooding of the greater part of the swamp, however, had an immediate effect in increasing the numbers of pairs breeding there. Since 1934 the Black Duck has rivaled the Mallard in abundance, and its nests are no longer objects of special note.

The conditions on Presque Isle are, or were, similarly favorable for breeding; indeed, the Black Duck has been noted there through the summer months by several different observers, and W. M. Guynes has supplied conclusive evidence of its nesting. He writes that he discovered a female bird with nine young (about three days old) on Fox Pond on May 24, 1934; and on June 17 of the same year he found a nest with eggs (doubtless a delayed nesting). He reports that the parent of these eggs was a brown-legged bird, while the parent of the ducklings was just as clearly a red-legged bird. What little information we have on the identity of the black ducks that breed at Pymatuning is similarly contradictory.

Actual and potential breeding records from other parts of our region are also available. R. B. Simpson once saw two birds in a pond at the upper end of Cranberry Swamp, Warren County, late in May. He also reported that during the season of 1893 a black duck spent the summer around the mouth of Conewango Creek. "It was not a cripple, and could fly well, but had no mate." His only positive breeding record is that of a pair that must have nested on Mead Island in the Allegheny River, just above the mouth of Grunder Run, in 1925 and 1926; in this case the young ducklings were repeatedly observed. S. S. Dickey has found a few black ducks near Cambridge Springs, Crawford County, several times during the latter half of May; and H. M. McQuiston has seen young near Sharon, Mercer County. Very suggestive is T. D. Burleigh's observation of two birds swimming about at the edge of the reeds at Lake

Seaton, Fayette County, on August 1, 1914. On August 10 of the following year he saw fifteen at the same place. Since the dates are too early for fall migrants, the presumption is that these birds were reared there. According to H. J. Roddy, the Black Duck used to nest in certain marshy places along Laurel Run in northern Huntingdon County, about two miles west of Bear Meadows, Centre County. Dr. Sutton supplies a breeding record for the extreme southeastern corner of our district, in Franklin County: about the middle of May, 1924, Ray Dunkle and others found a nest with eggs near Chambersburg, across the railroad tracks from the Wilson College campus, in the grass and willows bordering a pond. J. F. Street (1923) also saw this species along the Conococheague Creek near Mercersburg, in the same county, on June 18, 1920.

Migration—While the Black Duck is thus a potential summer resident in our section wherever favorable local conditions obtain, it is much better known as a transient visitant in spring and fall, and is commonest on Erie Bay and at Conneaut and Pymatuning lakes. Winter records, such as those for Erie Bay, Meadville, Pymatuning Swamp, and Warren, are assumed to refer to the red-legged form, which is a hardier and more northern bird. It comes earlier in the spring and stays later in the fall than the other, although their migrations overlap to a considerable extent. The earliest migrants usually appear in March, soon after the breaking up of the ice. In 1893 the species was first noted at Warren on March 4. Presumably these early comers belong to the red-legged form. A specimen shot by A. K. Pierce at Renovo on March 15, 1908, looks like *rubripes*, but the vast majority of sight records cannot well be checked. In 1936 the Black Duck was first observed at Pymatuning Lake on February 29, and in 1939 on February 18 (Oudette). In 1937 three of these ducks were seen on the Beaver River at College, Beaver County (Malley). The first migrants reached Erie Bay in 1933 on March 12 (Guynes), and this is probably an average date. I saw a number along the Ohio River at Industry, Beaver County, on March 18 (1923). The height of the northward movement is reached in April, and some birds remain until May. Mated pairs noted after about May 10 may be belated migrants, but are more likely potential breeding birds.

Just when the fall movement actually begins is uncertain. August records are indecisive, as already intimated. Three individuals seen in a pond near North East, Erie County, on September 3, 1930, by C. S. Beardslee, may have been reared in the vicinity. According to S. E. Bacon's observations, the species does not generally reappear at Presque Isle until about the middle of September. In 1900, however, September 7 was the recorded date, but the black ducks did not become at all numerous until November, and, although they unquestionably remained considerably later, were last observed on November 17. Presumably this later flight consisted largely of the red-legged race, while the September birds were of the other race. At Conneaut Lake and Pymatuning Swamp the species is "apparently not common until late October and November" (Sutton, 1928). It was once found by H. H. Wickham along the Ohio River, at Bellowsville, as late as December 14 (1899), and was seen by B. H. Christy at Clinton Pond, Allegheny County, on October 30 (1928). W. D. Hunter has a mounted bird which was taken on the Beaver River near Racine on December 20, 1915. A red-legged specimen was shot on November 4, 1925, at Shade Gap, Huntingdon County, by S. H. Price (Sutton). Mr. Burleigh records the Black Duck from Centre County during both spring and fall migration; at the latter season between September 25 and November 2. In the Pittsburgh region he has noted it as early as September 3 (1914) at Harmarville, and as late as October 26 (1913) at Highland Park.

Through the bird-banding carried on by officials of the Canadian government, some light has been thrown on the movements of this species. A good many birds banded at Lake Scugog, Ontario, in the past few years, have been recovered at various points in the eastern United States and Canada. Two recoveries were from Erie Bay: one four years after the date of banding; the other the same fall.

Habits—"Dusky Duck" is a better name for this species, since it is not black, in the sense that the Scoters are, for instance. In general habits it resembles the Mallard, with which, indeed, it often flocks and feeds on the most amicable terms. Upon their arrival at Erie Bay in the spring the birds are found only on the waters of the bay, but as soon as the ice leaves the ponds on Presque Isle these become their chosen resting places and feeding resorts. Throughout April they are, or were, fairly "common in such situations, usually in flocks of from five to fifteen individuals, feeding mainly on the seeds of wild rice, with which the gullets and stomachs of the specimens secured were crammed. Towards the end of April it was usual to find these ducks in pairs, apparently mated for the season" (Todd, 1904). In recent years flocks numbering thousands have been observed at Erie Bay and at Pymatuning Lake during days of great movement in April and October.

Like all pond ducks, these birds are essentially non-divers and work mostly in shallow water, where they can reach their food by thrusting the head and neck below the surface. During the winter months they have been observed at Erie Bay attending the whistling swans and diving ducks, ready to poach on the food supplies brought up by their neighbors' industry. They are in general shy birds, quick to take alarm at the slightest noise of breaking branches or approaching footsteps, and are often suspicious of decoys. When badly wounded they have been known to lie quietly on the water, to all appearances dead, but only waiting a chance to dive away into the brush and weeds. They differ from most ducks in their preference for brushy places and wooded sloughs, where they seek concealment. In flight this species may readily be distinguished by the white patch under the wing, which is a good field mark at a considerable distance.

At Pymatuning, I have observed black ducks in pairs as early as April 7 (1937). In general, the Black Duck nests earlier than the Mallard. In May the sets of eggs of the former are usually well advanced in incubation, while those of the latter are still fresh or incomplete. A brood of young was once noted as early as May 12 (1931); in this case all the eggs must have been laid by the middle of April. Nests are more likely to be concealed in the tree growth or brush back a little from the water's edge, where there is more cover, rather than situated in the open; but at Pymatuning several nests were found built in the rotting stumps of trees in the flooded area, exposed from above. The nests are of the usual duck type—a depression lined with bits of dry vegetable debris and a liberal layer of down from the breast of the female. I have never found more than eleven eggs in a nest, while sets of seven, eight, and nine are more usual. The eggs closely resemble those of the Mallard in color and size. The downy young, too, are scarcely distinguishable from those of that species, although the general coloration averages darker. The young are cared for by the female parent until they are well able to fly, after which old and young gather into flocks preparatory to the fall migration.

Anas obscura Townsend, *Proc. Acad. Nat. Sci. Philadelphia*, 1883, 67 (Latrobe, Westmoreland Co., *fide* Beckwith)—Rhoads, *Auk*, 1899, 16:309 (Cameron Co., *fide* Larrabee)—Todd, *Ann. Carnegie Mus.*, 1904, 2:513 (Erie Bay and Presque Isle, Erie Co., transient and winter resident)—Todd, in Bausman, *Hist. Beaver Co., Pa.*, 1904, 2:1198 (Beaver Co., fall).

"Black Duck" Simpson, *Oölogist*, 1911, 28:41; 1913, 30:50; 1914, 31:210 (Warren, Warren Co., March–April)—Christy, *Cardinal*, 1923, v.1, no.2, [p.14] (McDonald Reservoir, Washington Co., May)—Street, *Cassinia*, 1923, 24:11 (Conococheague Creek, Mercersburg, Franklin Co., June)—Sutton, *Bird-Lore*, 1923, 25:194 ("Beaver" [Industry], Beaver Co., March, *fide* Todd); 1924, 26:190 (Highland Park, Allegheny Co., April, *fide* Jones)—Boulton, *Bird-Lore*, 1928, 30:13 (Clinton Pond, Beaver Co., October, *fide* Christy), 401 (Presque Isle, Erie Co., August)—Christy, *Cardinal*, 1928, 2:104 (Clinton Pond, Allegheny Co., October)—National Parks of Canada Branch, *Canadian Field-Nat.*, 1928, 42:108, 157 (Erie Bay, Erie Co., winter; banding records)—Seiple, *Auk*, 1931, 48:113 (Pymatuning Swamp, Crawford Co., August)—Christy, *Cardinal*, 1932, 3:86, 90 (Presque Isle, Erie Co., February–March)—Savage, *Bird-Lore*, 1932, 34:44; Beal and Peterson, *Bird-Lore*, 1934, 36:33; and Upson, *et al.*, *Bird-Lore*, 1935, 37:47 (Presque Isle, Erie Co., December)—Trimble, *Cardinal*, 1937, 4:104 (Pymatuning region, Crawford Co., nesting)—Malley and Shoemaker, *Redstart*, 1937, 4:70 (Beaver River, Beaver Co., migration)—Oudette, *Cardinal*, 1939, 5:47 (Pymatuning Lake, near Linesville, Crawford Co., February).

"Black Mallard" Simpson, *Oölogist*, 1912, 29:248 (Warren, Warren Co., February); 1920, 37:142 ([Cranberry Swamp], Tionesta Creek, Warren Co., May).

Anas rubripes Burleigh, *Wilson Bull.*, 1923, 35:82 ([Harmarville and Highland Park], Allegheny Co., transient); 1924, 36:75 (State College, etc., Centre Co., migration)—Christy, *Cardinal*, 1926, v. 1, no. 8, p. 15 (Clinton Pond, Allegheny Co., April)—Fricke, *Cardinal*, 1931, 3:42 (near Linesville, Crawford Co., breeding).

Anas rubripes rubripes Sutton, *Ann. Carnegie Mus.*, 1928, 18:65 (Pymatuning Swamp, Meadville, and Conneaut Lake, Crawford Co., fall and winter).

Anas rubripes tristis Sutton, *Ann. Carnegie Mus.*, 1928, 18:66 (Crawford Co. nesting and migration records)—Burleigh, *Cardinal*, 1932, 3:74 (Lake Seaton, Fayette Co., breeding?).

"Red-legged Black Duck" Upson, *et al.*, *Bird-Lore*, 1933, 35:27; 1935, 37:47; and Beal and Peterson, *Bird-Lore*, 1934, 36:33 (Erie Bay, Erie Co., December).

GADWALL

CHAULELASMUS STREPERUS (Linnaeus)

Description—A medium-sized duck, with the bill about two inches long. *Male in spring:* upperparts, breast, and sides waved with dusky and white lines (coarsest on the breast); head brown above, buff below, with fine dusky spotting; wings with a chestnut area on the coverts, succeeded by black, and this followed by a white spot (speculum) on the secondaries; under surface of wings white; upper and under tail coverts black; underparts, from the breast down, white, or waved with fine dusky lines, contrasting with the black under tail coverts; feet yellow. *Female:* mottled brown and buff above; whitish below; breast mottled like the back; the wings show a black area followed by a gray spot. *Young:* similar to the female, but the underparts display some dusky spotting. Easily distinguished from the Baldpate by the longer bill (equal to the head), and by the smaller amount of white on the wing.

Range—The Gadwall inhabits both Eurasia and North America. In the latter continent its main breeding area lies in the western United States and adjoining British provinces. East of the Mississippi it is accounted uncommon even during the season of migration, and it is certainly one of the rarest ducks in western Pennsylvania at large. Although reported from Erie Bay on the authority of Sennett (very possibly by mistake), it had never been seen there by S. E. Bacon, nor did I find it during the season of 1900; it was included in my Erie list (1904) mainly on the basis of a fall record supplied by R. B. Simpson. In November, 1909, the Carnegie Museum received a fine pair from F. G. Lynch of Erie; these are the only local specimens in the collection.

Since 1930, however, the Erie observers have been finding a few gadwalls every spring, and the species seems to be growing more regular there if not commoner. There are also a few records for Conneaut Lake (Sutton, 1928), French Creek below Meadville (Kirkpatrick), and Warren (Simpson). This duck has been observed in the Pymatuning region every year since 1934, although only in limited numbers. A remarkable development is that a few pairs remain to breed there—far short of their usual nesting grounds. Outside the northwestern counties the Gadwall is almost unknown. One was seen at close range at Saint Marys, Elk County, on September 29, 1926 (Sutton). W. D. Hunter has taken three fall specimens on the Beaver River at Racine, Beaver County, and D. A. Atkinson examined two taken by G. E. Hodge on the Monongahela River near Braddock.

Migration—The Gadwall is not a markedly early migrant in the spring, although it was observed at Erie Bay on March 15, 1936 (Brooks, 1936), and at Pymatuning Lake on March 19 of the same year (Oudette). For Warren the earliest dates are March 12 (1894) and 20 (1890). The great majority of the observed spring occurrences are in April and May, even up to the end of the month, while in 1932 a flock of fifteen was reported from Erie as late as June 11 (Guynes). May records from Pymatuning Lake, however, probably pertain to breeding birds in some cases. In the fall movement the species reappears in September, and may remain until November. H. C. Kirkpatrick writes that on September 17, 1936, he observed a flock of about forty baldpates and gadwalls in French Creek about two miles below Meadville. This flock remained until the middle of October. The Beaver River specimens mentioned above were taken by Mr. Hunter on September 28, 1929, and October 2, 1914. November 17 (1897) was the date on which Mr. Hodge took his specimens on the Monongahela River; and there are a few other records for that month for Erie, Warren, and Conneaut Lake.

Habits—My personal acquaintance with this duck in Pennsylvania has been limited to a few observations made at Pymatuning Lake in May. In general appearance and behavior it resembles the Baldpate; indeed, it frequently associates with that species, and the females of the two forms are at times hard to tell apart. On May 22, 1934, R. L. Fricke conducted several of us to a nest which he had found five days before, and from which he had flushed a female gadwall. This was on the south side of Pymatuning Lake, in newly flooded territory. The nest was built in plain sight on a little island mound surrounding a stump. At the time of our visit the brood had departed, leaving behind two unhatched eggs, which we appropriated. On May 27 of the following year Mr. Fricke discovered a female with three young. In 1938, on May 22, I. B. Boggs saw a brood of four near the same place; and B. L. Oudette reported to Mr. Fricke the finding of a nest with eleven eggs on June 23, 1939. A few pairs undoubtedly breed in this locality every season.

Anas strepera WARREN, *Birds Pa.*, ed.2, 1890, 36 (Erie Bay, Erie Co., transient).

Chaulelasmus streperus TODD, *Ann. Carnegie Mus.*, 1904, 2:514 (Presque Isle, Erie Co., rare transient)—SUTTON, *Ann. Carnegie Mus.*, 1928, 18:67 (Conneaut Lake, Crawford Co., spring and fall, rare).

"Gadwall" SIMPSON, *Oölogist*, 1911, 28:33 (Warren, Warren Co., March)—SUTTON, *Bird-Lore*, 1924, 26:123 (Warren, Warren Co., October, *fide* Simpson)—(?)EASTWOOD, *Bird-Lore*, 1926, 28:273 (Hartstown, Crawford Co., May, *fide* Blair)—BROOKS, *Redstart*, 1936, 3:49 (Erie Bay, Erie Co., March)—TRIMBLE, *Cardinal*, 1937, 4:105 (Pymatuning region, Crawford Co., nesting)—BOGGS, *Cardinal*, 1939, 5:19 (Pymatuning Lake, Crawford Co., breeding).

EUROPEAN WIDGEON

MARECA PENELOPE (Linnaeus)

Description—Similar in size, form, and general pattern of coloration to the Baldpate (*Mareca americana*), from which it may readily be distinguished, in the male sex, by the rich *chestnut color of the head and neck;* only the crown is whitish or buff-colored. The *female* is practically indistinguishable in life from the female of the American species, although the head and neck are more or less shaded with buff, rather than with gray.

Range and local status—This European duck was at one time thought to be of merely accidental occurrence on this side of the Atlantic, but in recent years so many American records have appeared that the latest authority is inclined to think that it may breed somewhere in our north country.[1] At any rate, it seems to be more or less regular in fall and winter on the Atlantic coast, and there are also numerous records for the interior. Captain A. A. Clay assured me that he once killed a bird of this species on his place near Williamsville, Elk County. This specimen was identified by John Krider, and is probably the one referred to by that writer as having been sent to him in 1875.[2] The Presque Isle record cited below refers to a male seen on March 26, 1933, and studied with binoculars by two persons independently. C. S. Beardslee saw a single bird on Presque Isle on April 29, 1932; W. M. Guynes saw another on March 31, 1934; and Fred Ralph says that a few years ago he killed one while hunting on Erie Bay. These records come from reliable observers, and are acceptable. Hence the occasional occurrence of the species at this locality seems established.

G. M. Sutton (1928) mentions some unverified reports of this widgeon from Conneaut Lake. Entirely credible, however, is W. E. Dilley's record of a single bird in the swamp just south of the lake on April 12, 1937. During 1936 and 1937 an unusual influx of the species at Pymatuning Lake was remarked by several different observers. In 1936 one widgeon was observed on April 26 (Seiple), and one on October 23 (Trimble, and others). In 1937 the species was first noted there on March 27 (Skaggs). A party from the Carnegie Museum saw four together, as well as several single birds, near Linesville on April 6. At Hartstown, on April 10 of the same year, one bird was present (Dilley), and on April 11 there were five (Cook). According to Lloyd Scherer, Jr., four were observed on the Allegheny River at Port Allegany, McKean County, on March 27. Although these are all sight records and although locally collected specimens are still to be taken, there is no doubt of the accuracy of the identifications. Close watch should be kept in the future to determine whether these appearances are merely sporadic or an indication of increasing regularity.

Mareca penelope (?)SUTTON, *Ann. Carnegie Mus.*, 1928, 18:67 (Conneaut Lake, Crawford Co., doubtful)—WOODWARD, *Cardinal*, 1933, 3:147 (Presque Isle, Erie Co., March)—WEST, *Redstart*, 1936, 4:4 (Pymatuning Lake [Linesville], Crawford Co., October).

[1] J. C. PHILLIPS, *A Natural History of the Ducks*, 1923, 2:176.
[2] *Forty Years Notes of a Field Ornithologist*, 1879, p. 73.

BALDPATE (Plate 3)

MARECA AMERICANA (Gmelin)

Description—A medium-sized duck, with extensively white underparts and much white on the wings. *Adult male: top of head white;* a dark green patch on the nape, extending forward on either side to include the eyes; sides of head (otherwise) and of neck whitish, with fine dusky spotting; throat more or less blackish in the center; upperparts finely waved with vinaceous-brown and dusky lines; *wing coverts white,* followed by a black spot surrounding another of dark green; inner secondaries black, with a white outer edge; *breast and sides vinaceous;* under tail coverts black; rest of underparts white; feet dull bluish. *Female* and *young* very different from the male: head and neck with white and dusky streaks; upperparts mottled with dull brown; breast and sides light brown; wings with a *small white patch* formed by the tips of the greater coverts, followed by a dark spot.

Range—In summer this duck inhabits the interior of North America, from the western shores of Hudson Bay to the upper Mississippi Valley, while its regular winter home is from the western United States and Mexico east to the Atlantic coast, and north to Chesapeake Bay. Its migration route to and from this latter region thus lies across western Pennsylvania. Although it is regular in certain favored localities, where in recent years it has apparently increased in numbers, it can scarcely be considered a common duck in the sense that the Mallard and the Black Duck are common.

Our records are mainly from the counties in the western tier, with a few scattered observations from Warren County (five records only) and Centre County. As a pond duck, the Baldpate is naturally more partial to the Erie-Crawford district, where conditions are to its liking. It is one of the ducks that have been attracted to Pymatuning Lake in goodly numbers in spring and fall. Surprisingly, a few pairs have remained to breed there, as attested by my observations in June and July, 1936, and in May, 1937 and 1938, although no nests have yet been found. This recent development involves a considerable extension of the previously known breeding range. There are no comparable summer records from Erie Bay and Presque Isle, where, however, the Baldpate stays quite late in the spring and returns correspondingly early in the fall. It is certainly far commoner there now than under the conditions that prevailed about forty years ago. During the unprecedentedly mild winter of 1931–32, when the waters of Lake Erie and of Erie Bay remained open, the baldpates were among the ducks that lingered through the cold season, although not in large numbers. A few also remained during the winter of 1932–33 (Guynes).

Migration—The fact that the Baldpate occasionally winters in our region indicates that it is a hardy duck—a conclusion borne out by its early arrival in normal seasons. It usually follows the Black Duck in the spring. At Erie Bay its arrival has been observed between March 15 (1936) and 25 (1901); the majority of birds usually pass through toward the end of the month. For two or three weeks in April the species is also much in evidence, and in 1933 it was noted until May 21 (Guynes). At Conneaut Lake it has been found as early as March 18 (1913), and as late as May 15 (1925). Its arrival at Pymatuning Lake has been recorded on February 27 (1939), although a later date is more usual (Oudette, 1939). Other dates for this season are: May 11, Lake Pleasant, Erie County (1875—Sennett); March 14, Warren (1901—Simpson); March 10, Ben Avon, Allegheny County (1899—Atkinson); March 15, Boalsburg, Centre County (1909—Musgrave); May 14, State College (1932—Wood).

In the fall migration this is sometimes one of the first ducks to arrive. It has been noted at Presque Isle as early as August 25 (1928—Boulton); and on August 30, 1890, I surprised a flock of five in a quiet pool of water along the Ohio River at the mouth of the Beaver. Usually, however, the Baldpate comes after the middle of September, is most abundant in October, and disappears toward the end of that month or in November. One was seen near Erie on December 5, 1901 (Bacon), and one was shot at Sandy Creek, Allegheny County, on November 25, 1898 (Atkinson), but these dates were extremely late. When its shallow feeding grounds freeze over, this duck is necessarily forced southward; otherwise it might habitually remain all winter, as in 1931–32.

Habits—At Presque Isle in 1900 I found the Baldpate confined almost wholly to the ponds. It was usually in pairs or small flocks, but was sometimes associated with kindred species, particularly the Black Duck. Like that species it is a surface feeder, and likes to work through the aquatic plant growth near the shore in its search for food. It is noticeably quicker and more active than the diving ducks, with which it was observed on Erie Bay in February and March, 1932. In recent years it has appeared on the bay in larger flocks than formerly, and seems to be coming back to some extent in that particular locality. The gunners there call it "Speckle-head." Large flocks have also been noted at Pymatuning Lake; on April 11, 1937, fully two thousand were observed there (Seiple); and on October 11 of the same year, I. B. Boggs "saw, at conservative estimate, 5,000 Baldpates, in two major flocks." Our party from the Carnegie Museum found mated pairs there as early as the first week in April, and through May and June. This duck has a distinctive musical call note that is uttered in flight as well as on the water.

Anas americana Warren, *Birds Pa.*, ed. 2, 1890, 37 (Erie Bay, Erie Co., transient).

Mareca americana Todd, *Ann. Carnegie Mus.*, 1904, 2:514 (Presque Isle, Erie Co., transient)—Todd, in Bausman, *Hist. Beaver Co., Pa.*, 1904, 2:1198 (Beaver Co., transient)—Cooke, *Bull. Biol. Surv.* no. 26, 1906, 28 (Beaver, Beaver Co., migration)—Burleigh, *Wilson Bull.*, 1923, 35:82 (Highland Park, Allegheny Co., April)—Sutton, *Ann. Carnegie Mus.*, 1928, 18:67 (Crawford Co. localities, transient)—Woodward, *Cardinal*, 1933, 3:147 (Presque Isle, Erie Co., March).

"Baldpate" Boulton, *Bird-Lore*, 1928, 30:401 (Presque Isle, Erie Co., August)—Wood, *Wilson Bull.*, 1932, 44:239 (State College, Centre Co., spring)—Christy, *Cardinal*, 1932, 3:86 (Erie Bay, Erie Co., February)—Brooks, *Redstart*, 1936, 3:49 (Erie Bay, Erie Co., March)—Boggs, *Redstart*, 1937, 5:2 (Pymatuning Lake, Crawford Co., October)—Oudette, *Cardinal*, 1939, 5:47 (Pymatuning Lake, near Linesville, Crawford Co., February).

Additional records: Lake Pleasant and Waterford, Erie Co., April–May, 1875 (Sennett Collection)—Waynesburg (3 miles west), Greene Co., April 1, 1915, one shot (Dickey)—"Chambers Dam," Washington Co., April 3, 1890, one killed by gunner (Nease)—Beaver, Beaver Co., April 13, 1889, one killed by gunner (Todd)—Racine, Beaver Co., November 4, 1925, one taken (collection W. D. Hunter).

AMERICAN PINTAIL

DAFILA ACUTA TZITZIHOA (Vieillot)

Description—A duck of medium size, with a *long, slender neck* and an elongated body. *Male:* upperparts and sides of body finely waved with black and white, producing a *gray appearance; head brown;* underparts white, this color running up in a stripe on either side of the neck, and enclosing a black area on the back of the neck; wings gray, with the speculum dark green, between a rusty-buff bar in front and a white one behind, and some of the inner wing feathers broadly marked with black; *middle tail feathers long and pointed*, black; under tail coverts black, in strong contrast with the conspicuous white of the flanks and underparts generally; bill and feet grayish. Some males in fall plumage lack the elongated tail feathers. *Female* entirely different: dusky above, with pale feather-edgings, giving a veiled or mottled appearance; head and neck show fine dusky streaks on a buffy background, darker above, paler on the throat; underparts buff, with dusky mottling; wings much as in the male; tail dusky, mottled with white, and without elongated feathers. *Young males and adult males in eclipse plumage* (summer) resemble the adult females. Males emerging from the eclipse plumage are variously intermediate in coloration between the adult male described above and the adult female. *Downy young:* grayish brown above, with some whitish markings; below, dull whitish; sides of head whitish, with two brownish stripes, one through the eye and the other below, with a paler stripe between; lores more or less brownish.

Range—The Pintail as a species is common to the northern portions of both the Old and the New Worlds, and migrates southward in the winter. The North American race, *tzitzihoa*, breeds in Canada and the northern United States, commonly in the western parts, but only casually in the East. A record of the Pintail breeding on the north shore of Lake Erie some years ago was considered unusual, but since 1934 it has been a regular summer resident in the Pymatuning region of Crawford County. In our section it is mainly a transient in spring and fall, common only in the lake regions of Erie and Crawford counties, and rare elsewhere. There are scattered migration records for Allegheny, Beaver, Washington, and Westmoreland counties in the west, and for Blair and Centre counties in the mountains. This duck is not included in the bird lists of A. K. Pierce from Renovo, and according to R. B. Simpson it is rare at Warren. It is one of the ducks that as a result of overshooting have greatly decreased in numbers in recent years, not only in this state but throughout the country in general.

Migration—Together with certain other waterfowl, pintails remained in some numbers on Erie Bay through the remarkably open winter of 1931–32, and they manifest a tendency to remain every year as long as open water prevails. They were also noted during the winter months at Pymatuning Swamp, although never in large numbers; and they usually associated there with the wintering black ducks and mallards. These observations are noteworthy, as they are among the few on record from northern localities.

The Pintail is one of the earliest ducks to push north in the spring, and arrives with or before the Black Duck. S. E. Bacon's earliest record for Erie is February 23 (1891), with March 11 as the average date of arrival; dates for later years accord with these. The Pintail reaches Conneaut and Pymatuning lakes also at just about this time. In 1912 Mr. Simpson saw a male at Warren as early as February 15; and T. D. Burleigh saw single birds at Oak Hall, Centre County, on February 4 and 8, 1917. The large flights take place in March. H. C. Kirkpatrick speaks of "prolonged flights . . . in early March back in the late eighties along the French Creek Valley in the Meadville region," and G. M. Langdon reported "tremendous flocks" everywhere about Pymatuning Swamp and Conneaut Lake on March 20, 1925 (in Sutton, 1928). The day for such spectacular occurrences, however, is probably past. They were no doubt due to some fortuitous circumstance of weather. No similar flights have ever been observed in other parts of our region, although flocks numbering three hundred have been seen in recent years on Erie Bay (Guynes). The Pintail ordinarily remains through April at this latter locality, and exceptionally as late as May 14 (1932), but in 1934 it was not noted after April 2. At Pymatuning the transients leave by the middle of April, while the summer residents remain behind. Although not nearly so common there in summer as the Mallard, Black Duck, and Blue-winged Teal, the Pintail is nevertheless present in fair numbers every season.

In the fall, too, the Pintail is one of the first of the waterfowl to appear, and one of the last to leave. It arrives early in September (September 6, 1893—Erie; September 3, 1912, and September 4, 1928—Conneaut Lake), and is most abundant in October. Late records at this season are: December 3, 1903—Erie; December 1, 1917—Conneaut Marsh; December 12, 1908—Scotia, Centre County; December 18, 1929—Racine, Beaver County.

Habits—At Erie the large flocks of this species keep to the bay, while single birds or small groups are the rule in the ponds of Presque Isle. Pintails are wary and hard to approach, but will come to decoys, over which most of those taken by the local gunners are shot. As they migrate early in the spring, they often arrive before the lakes and ponds are fully open and then they may be seen sitting around on the edge of the ice. On the water the Pintail is one of the most graceful of the ducks; the male's long neck and uptilted tail, with its long and pointed middle feathers, are good field marks at a considerable distance. This duck feeds by dipping its head, but is able to dive if necessary, and when wounded will often attempt to escape by this means or by scrambling to shore and making for the bushes.

At Pymatuning, pintails have been observed in pairs as early as the first week in April. I have repeatedly watched the remarkable courting-flight, when the duck, pursued by one or more drakes, executes a series of curious evolutions in mid-air, at an amazing rate of speed, to the accompaniment of a characteristic guttural, frog-like rattle. The nest is similar to that of other ducks—a depression lined with bits of dry grass, stems, and down from the female. Of three nests found by R. L. Fricke, two were built on small hummocks in the marsh, surrounded by water, while one was in the high grass near the shore line of one of the islands. To judge from the condition of the sets examined, incubation begins by the middle of May. The eggs are eight, nine, or ten in number, pale olive buff in color, and measure about 2.26 by 1.50 inches.

Dafila acuta Townsend, *Proc. Acad. Nat. Sci. Philadelphia*, 1883, 68 (Latrobe, Westmoreland Co., *fide* Beckwith)—Todd, *Ann. Carnegie Mus.*, 1904, 2:517 (Erie Bay and Presque Isle, Erie Co., transient)—Burleigh, *Wilson Bull.*, 1924, 36:75 ("State College" [Oak Hall, "Thompson's Spring," and Scotia], Centre Co., spring transient)—Fricke, *Cardinal*, 1931, 3:42 (Linesville, Crawford Co., May).

"Pintail" Harlow, *Cassinia*, 1912, 15:20 (Center Furnace Swamp, Centre Co., spring)—Christy, *Cardinal*, 1923, v. 1, no. 2, [p. 14] (Clinton Pond, Allegheny Co., March)—Beal and Peterson, *Bird-Lore*, 1934, 36:33 (Presque Isle, Erie Co., December)—Trimble, *Cardinal*, 1937, 4:105 (Pymatuning region, Crawford Co., nesting).

Dafila acuta tzitzihoa Sutton, *Ann. Carnegie Mus.*, 1928, 18:70 (Crawford Co. localities, transient and winter resident)—Sutton, *Cardinal*, 1929, 2:121 (Conneaut Lake, Crawford Co., September).

"American Pintail" Christy, *Cardinal*, 1932, 3:86 (Presque Isle, Erie Co., February)—Savage, *Bird-Lore*, 1932, 34:44 (Presque Isle, Erie Co., December).

GREEN-WINGED TEAL

NETTION CAROLINENSE (Gmelin)

Description—One of the smallest ducks. *Male: head rufous chestnut, with a broad, dark green band on either side*, running up as far as the eye; slight crest black; chin dusky; upperparts finely waved with dusky and white lines, giving a general grayish appearance; sides of the breast with a more or less concealed white crescent; *breast buffy, with round dusky spots*, partly concealed; rest of underparts white, the sides grayish; under tail coverts black and white; wings gray, with the speculum partly dark green and partly black, between two whitish or buffy bands; some black also on the sides of the back, and on the upper tail coverts; bill black; feet grayish. *Female:* upperparts dusky, spotted with buff; wing-speculum as in the adult male; underparts (including throat) buffy white, the breast mottled with brown.

Range—The breeding range of the Green-winged Teal extends across the continent of North America, from the tree limit south to the northern tier of states and still farther southward in the mountainous regions of the West. The species is not at all common as a breeding bird in the East, although it has been found as such in western New York and southern Ontario. There are no actual breeding records for the Erie region, and if individuals were captured at Erie Bay "during the early summer months," as stated by Warren (no authority given), they were probably "pensioners." Until 1934 there was little ground for suspecting that the Green-winged Teal might breed in the Pymatuning region, but, attracted by the lake, it has now become established there as a regular although far from common summer resident.

In the winter this species migrates as far south as Mexico and the West Indies, but many individuals remain in the United States, wherever they can find open water. It seems to have wintered on Erie Bay in the season of 1931–32, when many other waterfowl remained; at any rate, B. H. Christy and I noted a few there on February 20 and 21, long before the migration had started. Ordinarily, however, the species is a transient in spring and fall, common and regular only in the Erie-Crawford district. Even at Warren R. B. Simpson considers it rare, and A. K. Pierce has recorded it but once at Renovo. W. D. Hunter took two specimens at Racine, Beaver County, and there are a few scattered records for Allegheny, Westmoreland, and Washington counties. R. C. Harlow has noted it near State College, and A. B. Miller, at Springs, Somerset County; these reports show that it crosses the mountains on occasion. But the paucity of records from these sections is an indication that the great majority of the birds that pass through the Erie-Crawford district either do not stop until they reach country where the local conditions are suited to their needs, or they avoid these parts entirely and swing over to the westward through Ohio.

Migration—The Green-winged Teal is one of the earlier migrants, and moves northward in March. It has appeared at Erie Bay as early as March 12 (1898), and as late as March 28 (1895). In 1936 it arrived in the Pymatuning region on March 13 (Oudette). H. C. Kirkpatrick took a specimen at Meadville on March 25 in 1895. The spring movement continues into April; the latest date for Erie is April 17 (1932—Guynes). In the fall this teal is one of the first ducks to appear, and this fact suggests that some of its breeding grounds cannot be far away. September 1 (1894) is the earliest definite fall date for the Erie region, and arrival dates for Conneaut Lake have been recorded at about the same time. One specimen was taken at Wilkinsburg on September 6 in 1896 (Atkinson). Although its arrival at this season coincides fairly well with that of the Blue-winged Teal, the present species is hardier, and remains somewhat later than the other, or into November, for which month there are many records. Late dates from Erie recorded by W. M. Guynes are November 20 (1932) and December 4 (1934). One of the few specimens Mr. Simpson has taken at Warren was shot on November 27, 1899. Another, which he secured on January 17, 1901, constitutes the only winter record for our region, aside from those from Erie Bay. Mr. Harlow saw a flock of six late migrants along Spring Creek near State College on December 5, 1908.

Habits—Like most of the pond ducks, the Green-winged Teal usually moves in flocks, sometimes in company with other species of similar haunts and habits. At Erie it is occasionally found on the open waters of the bay, but is more partial to the ponds on Presque Isle, and sometimes alights on marshy pools on the mainland. It feeds mostly in shallow water, like the other pond ducks, and takes both vegetable and animal food. In flight it is one of the swiftest of the ducks, and is capable of a speed of over one hundred miles per hour, so that it is necessary for the gunner to hold well ahead when shooting on the wing.

At Pymatuning Lake on May 22, 1934, I examined a nest of this species that had been found by R. L. Fricke a week previously, at which time it had contained three eggs. No more eggs had been added, and the nest had been deserted. It was of the usual duck type, and was built under a fallen tree stump in the newly flooded area, in thick brush. The eggs of the Green-winged Teal are similar to those of the Blue-winged; the full set usually numbers ten to twelve—sometimes more. On May 21 and 22, 1937, a few mated pairs of green-winged teal were observed in the sanctuary at Pymatuning, but no nests were located. This teal is far less numerous, even during migration, than the Blue-winged, and is sorely in need of special protection.

Querquedula carolinensis Townsend, *Proc. Acad. Nat. Sci. Philadelphia*, 1883, 68 (Latrobe, Westmoreland Co., transient).

Anas carolinensis Warren, *Birds Pa.*, ed. 2, 1890, 37 (Erie Bay, Erie Co., transient)—Rhoads, *Auk*, 1899, 16:309 (Cameron Co., *fide* Larrabee).[1]

Nettion carolinensis Todd, *Ann. Carnegie Mus.*, 1904, 2:515 (Erie and Presque Isle, Erie Co., transient).

Nettion carolinense Christy, *Cardinal*, 1926, v. 1, no. 7, p. 25, 28 (Clinton Pond, Allegheny Co., September)—Sutton, *Ann. Carnegie Mus.*, 1928, 18:68 (Crawford Co. records and references).

"Green-winged Teal" Harlow, *Cassinia*, 1912, 15:20 (Center Furnace Swamp, Centre Co., spring)—Wood, *Wilson Bull.*, 1932, 44:238 (State College, Centre Co., *fide* Musgrave)—Christy, *Cardinal*, 1932, 3:86 (Presque Isle, Erie Co., February)—Trimble, *Cardinal*, 1937, 4:104 (Pymatuning region, Crawford Co., nesting).

[1]The record for Homestead, Allegheny County (*fide* Atkinson), is an error.

BLUE-WINGED TEAL (Plate 2)

QUERQUEDULA DISCORS (Linnaeus)

Description—A small duck, the size of the Green-winged Teal. *Adult male:* head generally dark gray, with a slight purplish sheen in certain lights, the whole crown black, and the chin and upper throat also black; a *broad white crescent-shaped band on the sides of the head*, between the bill and the eye; upperparts dusky greenish, with buffy, wavelike markings on the upper back; underparts with dusky mottling on a buffy background, which is more or less washed with vinous color; flanks white, and under tail coverts black; *wings* with the lesser coverts pale blue, showing as a *large blue patch*, and some of the inner secondaries also blue; wing-speculum deep green, separated from this blue area by a white bar; bill bluish black; feet dull yellowish. *Female:* an obscure-looking duck, dusky above, with paler feather-edgings; dull buffy white below, with dusky mottling, the throat unspotted; *wings with a blue patch* on the coverts as in the male, bounded outwardly by a white band. *Young males* resemble the adult female. The blue patch on the wing is the best field mark in both sexes.

Range—Although this duck ranges across the continent of North America from east to west, it is far less common coastwise than in the interior of the country. Its main breeding range covers the territory lying between the Rocky Mountains on the west and the Great Lakes on the east, north to the Canadian province of Saskatchewan. In winter it goes far southward, even to South America, but some individuals spend this season in the southern half of the United States. It has been found nesting in Brooke County, northern West Virginia (Sutton); at several points in northern and eastern Ohio (Hicks); and in the lake region of central New York (Eaton). A growing suspicion that it might also breed in the Erie–Crawford district of western Pennsylvania was finally confirmed by the finding of a nest on Presque Isle on May 30, 1932 (Guynes). In the same month R. L. Fricke reported seeing at least two pairs in the Pymatuning region near Linesville. The females of these pairs later disappeared, and were probably on their nests. During the two following years I saw ducks of this species under similar circumstances at Pymatuning, and in 1935 Mr. Fricke found the first nests. Every season since has witnessed the finding of more nests, as the numbers of breeding pairs have steadily increased, until now only the Mallard and Black Duck are more numerous. Blue-winged teal have also been noted on Conneaut Lake during the summer months by several observers, and the early date (August 28) on which young birds have been found suggests that they may have been locally reared. On Presque Isle, according to W. M. Guynes, two or more pairs usually remain to breed every summer.

Only in this same general region (Erie and Crawford counties) is the Blue-winged Teal at all common and regular as a transient. It is in fact rather more numerous there than the Green-winged species. At Warren, on the upper Allegheny River, it is irregular, and elsewhere in western Pennsylvania it is rare. There are a few odd records for some of the southwestern counties; and that this teal crosses the mountains in its migration is attested by records from Springs, Somerset County (Miller); State College (Burleigh); Lakemont, Blair County (McGraw); and Renovo (Pierce).

Migration—The Blue-winged Teal is not so hardy as the Green-winged; it comes earlier in the fall, and as a rule later in the spring. August 28 (1901) is the earliest fall migration date for Presque Isle and likewise (1925) for Conneaut Marsh. Three blue-winged teal were observed near North East, Erie County, on September 3, 1930, by C. S. Beardslee. These early fall dates may possibly refer to individuals that had summered in the vicinity, but this is unlikely in the case of similar records from farther south. Thus, B. H. Christy saw a blue-wing at Clinton Pond, Allegheny County, on August 27, 1922, and H. A. McGraw found four at Lakemont, Blair County, on August 25, 1919. Most of our fall arrival dates, however, are in September, which appears to be the month of most marked movement. A specimen in the collection of W. D. Hunter was taken at Racine, Beaver County, on September 3, 1926. By the middle, or at the latest the end, of October almost all have passed through. Some dates of "last seen" at this season are: October 15, Renovo (1909); October 18, Conneaut Lake (1926); October 21, Oak Hall, Centre County (1916); November 1, Wilkinsburg (1894); and November 6, Erie (1932 and 1934).

Arrival of this species in the spring was noted once at Pymatuning Lake as early as March 4 (1936—Oudette), but this date is highly exceptional; other early dates for the same general region range from March 15 (1925) to 30 (1926). At Erie Bay the earliest date of record at this season is March 27 (1898). The month of April covers the period of greatest movement in the spring, and May 5 (1892) is the latest date on which individuals assumed to be migrants have been observed there. At Renovo, according to A. K. Pierce, the species has been noted in the spring only three times: on April 9, 1907; April 10, 1910; and May 12, 1914.

Habits—During the season of 1900 the Blue-winged Teal was often found feeding in the ponds of Presque Isle, and in recent years it has also been observed along the shores of Erie Bay. In the Pymatuning region it keeps more to the shallow bays and marshy areas and avoids the open waters of the main lake. Usually it arrives in small flocks, sometimes intermingled with other species of surface-feeding ducks, all on friendly terms. A flock estimated at one thousand birds, seen on Conneaut Lake on April 18, 1926, by G. M. Langdon, must have been an impressive sight. Towards the close of the spring sojourn, mated pairs are the rule. A little later in the season, when only males are in evidence, it is fair to assume that the females are incubating.

In their choice of nesting sites the birds are not overly fastidious, and any natural depression or recess not too far from water may be used. At Pymatuning Lake nests were found in the tall grass in an old orchard, in shorter grass on one of the small islands in the lake, in a clump of rushes in a small marshy pond, and in an open field, with scarcely any protection from above. When the first eggs are laid the nest is a sketchy affair, and not until the female has finished laying and is ready to incubate is the full lining of down added. Full sets are to be looked for during the third week in May; according to my experience they vary from eight to twelve. The higher number has been found more than once. The eggs are very pale creamy buff in color; they average 1.85 by 1.30 inches.

Mr. Guynes sends the following account of the nest that he discovered on Presque Isle in 1932: "The nest was placed deep down in a hummock of the tall marsh grass. When found on May 30 it contained twelve eggs, which hatched during the afternoon of June 23—just twenty-four days later. The following morning I took pictures of the young, but by evening they had left the nest and we did not encounter them again until August 7, when we saw them on Niagara Pond. It was gratifying to find that all twelve had been raised and were now able to fly. They were quite tame and circled around us within ten feet many times as we watched."

Migrating flocks in the fall number from twenty to thirty birds, both adults and young of the year. This teal seems to prefer smaller bodies of water—overflowed meadows, coves, ponds, or other quiet places where it can find the tender aquatic plants that are its main food. I have frequently seen it working along the muddy, weedy shores in such situations. In flight it is almost as swift as the Green-winged Teal. Both species have been sadly reduced in numbers by excessive shooting in the past thirty years.

Querquedula discors Townsend, *Proc. Acad. Nat. Sci. Philadelphia*, 1883, 68 (Latrobe, Westmoreland Co., transient)—Teulon, *Jour. Boston Zoöl. Soc.*, 1883, 2:11 (Bradford, McKean Co., fall)—Todd, *Ann. Carnegie Mus.*, 1904, 2:516 (Presque Isle, Erie Co., transient)—Christy, *Cardinal*, 1923, v.1, no.1, [p.2], and 1926, v.1, no.8, p.15 (Clinton Pond, Allegheny Co., April, August)—Burleigh, *Wilson Bull.*, 1924, 36:75 (State College and Oak Hall, Centre Co., transient)—Sutton, *Ann. Carnegie Mus.*, 1928, 18:68 (Crawford Co. records and references)—Sutton, *Cardinal*, 1929, 2:121 (Conneaut Lake, Crawford Co., summer, *fide* Cross)—Fricke, *Cardinal*, 1931, 3:42 (Linesville, Crawford Co., May).

"Blue-winged Teal" Simpson, *Oölogist*, 1914, 31:210 (Warren, Warren Co., April)—Seiple, *Auk*, 1931, 48:113 (Pymatuning Swamp, Crawford Co., August)—Boggs, *Redstart*, 1936, 3:92; and Trimble, *Cardinal*, 1937, 4:104 (Pymatuning region, Crawford Co., nesting).

SHOVELLER (Plate 2)

SPATULA CLYPEATA (Linnaeus)

Description—A rather small duck, with the bill longer than the head and much expanded at the tip. *Male in full plumage: head and neck black* (all around) *with dark green reflections;* middle of the back dusky; sides of the back and entire breast white; under tail coverts black; *rest of underparts rich vinaceous brown; wing coverts pale blue;* wing-speculum dark green, bordered with white in front; inner secondaries pale blue; feet orange. *Female* very different from the male: above, dusky brown with pale buffy feather-edgings, producing a scaly appearance; below, dull buffy, the breast with a little dusky mottling; wings resembling those of the male, but the colors duller and the green area restricted. *Younger males and adults in eclipse plumage* are more or less intermediate in coloration between the adult male and the adult female. *Downy young:* deep olive brown above, with buffy spots on the sides and flanks; top of head dusky black; a buffy stripe over the eye and a dusky stripe through the eye; another elongated dusky stripe on the ear coverts; underparts dull buff, interrupted on the sides by wide bars of olive brown.

Range—In North America the Shoveller is now mainly confined in the breeding season to the prairie region of the interior and is rare to the eastward. W. W. Cooke says it has been known to nest at Long Point on the Canadian shore of Lake Erie;[1] and L. E. Hicks cites breeding records from the Sandusky region, on the southern shore of the same lake.[2] There was no suspicion of its nesting within the limits of our region until the spring of 1935, when the presence of mated pairs on Pymatuning Lake late in May prompted a successful search for a nest. The number of breeding pairs there has gradually increased, although the species remains comparatively rare. It is far from common even during migration, and is scarcely known outside the Erie-Crawford district. Its migration route takes it diagonally across our region in spring and fall between its main breeding grounds in the interior and its wintering stations on the south Atlantic coast.

Migration—The records available from Conneaut Lake show that the Shoveller moves northward on occasion as early as the middle of March. An exceptionally early report from Pymatuning Lake is for March 4 (1936—Oudette); another from Wilkinsburg, for March 3 (1896), is based on the capture of a specimen, now in the Carnegie Museum. The migratory movement is in full swing during April, and most of the reported occurrences fall in that month. April 30 is the latest spring migration date on record for both Conneaut Lake and Erie. Spring records from other parts of our region are few. B. H. Christy saw a pair at Clinton Pond, Allegheny County, on April 18, 1926. Two were shot at Greencastle, Franklin County, in the extreme southeastern corner of our region, on April 10, 1920, by G. F. Ziegler, Jr.

Fall arrival dates for Erie lie between September 6 (1893) and 11 (1904). On September 3, 1930, a shoveller was found on a small pond west of Findlay Lake, New York (Beardslee). The movement continues through September and most of October, if the weather then is not too severe. At Conneaut Lake the species has been taken as late in the season as November 24 (1922), and along French Creek (near Meadville) on December 1 (1917). Other late dates are: November 20, Racine, Beaver County (1925—Hunter); December 2, Erie (1934—Guynes); and December 18, Sandy Creek, Allegheny County (1898—Atkinson). The only suggestion that this species ever winters in our region comes from J. E. Perry, who writes that a young shoveller remained with a flock of tame mallards on Presque Isle during the winter of 1937.

Habits—The Shoveller usually travels in small flocks that seldom exceed forty or fifty birds, and often there are only a few together. It avoids running water and prefers instead shallow pools and quiet bays, where it takes its food from the surface or scoops up the soft bottom ooze that contains an abundance of minute vegetable and animal life. The huge, shovel-like bill, from which this duck derives its name, is well adapted to surface feeding, and the Shoveller is more strictly a dabbler than any other duck. The lamellae or comb-like projections on the bills of ducks are highly developed in this species. Water and soft mud are strained through these rows of tooth-like structures and the particles of food are sieved out and retained. The Shoveller paddles briskly along, sometimes with its head half submerged, and seldom tips up, mallard-fashion, in feeding. Both vegetable and animal food are taken; the latter consists of small aquatic forms.

Shovellers have been observed in mated pairs at Pymatuning as early as the first week in April. When in 1935 they were present after the middle of May, it was suspected that they might be breeding. Finally a nest was found by R. L. Fricke on May 27. Here a peculiar state of affairs existed, since the female parent had laid in the nest of a Ring-necked Pheasant, and there were eight eggs of each species. Ducks not infrequently lay in each other's nests, but to find them imposing upon a bird of a different family is unusual. Another nest with ten fresh eggs was discovered near Pymatuning Lake on May 27, 1936; it was built in a tussock

[1] U. S. Department of Agriculture, Biological Survey, *Bulletin*, no. 26, 1906, p. 36.
[2] *Ohio State University Studies*, 1935, 40:143.

of high grass in a marshy area of an open field, some distance north of the lake. This nest was of the usual duck type—a down-lined depression partially rounded out with dry grasses and weed stalks. The eggs are pale buffy white, like those of the Mallard, but much smaller, averaging 2.06 by 1.45 inches. The young are hatched toward the end of June. The eclipse plumage of the adult male is usually not doffed until October or even later.

Spatula clypeata TODD, *Ann. Carnegie Mus.*, 1904, 2:516 (Erie Bay and Presque Isle, Erie Co., transient)—STONE, *Cassinia*, 1923, 24:25 (Greencastle, Franklin Co., April, *fide* Ziegler)—CHRISTY, *Cardinal*, 1926, v. 1, no. 8, p. 15 (Clinton Pond, Allegheny Co., April)—SUTTON, *Ann. Carnegie Mus.*, 1928, 18:69 (Crawford Co., transient; records and references).

"Shoveller" TRIMBLE, *Cardinal*, 1937, 4:105 (Pymatuning region, Crawford Co., nesting)—OUDETTE, *Cardinal*, 1939, 5:47 (Pymatuning Lake, near Linesville, Crawford Co., March).

WOOD DUCK

AIX SPONSA (Linnaeus)

Description—A duck of medium size, with the bill shorter than the head. *Adult male* with a full *decumbent crest*, the head varied with dark green and dark purple, and with a white line from the base of the bill to the tip of the crest feathers, and another from behind the eye to either side of the crest; throat pure white, this color running up on the sides of the head and neck as two white wedges or bars; upperparts dusky green, the sides of the back darker, appearing black; wings grayish toward the tips, and with a narrow white bar on the tips of the secondaries; *breast rich purplish chestnut*, with whitish spots; on either side of the breast a white bar followed by a black one; under tail coverts dusky; rest of underparts white, the sides buffy, and the flanks crossed by several black and white bars; bill blackish; feet orange-red. *Adult female* very different: dusky greenish above, the wings with some purple and greenish wash, and with a white bar as in the male; crest not so full as that of the male, plain dusky green; sides of the head dull dusky, with a large spot of white that includes the eye; throat whitish; breast and sides dull brownish, with faint paler spotting; rest of underparts whitish. *Males in eclipse plumage* and young birds more or less resemble the adult female. *Young in the down* are brownish above and grayish white below; the sides of the head are buffy, and there is a dark stripe through the eye as in some other species.

Range—This is a strictly North American species of duck, and one of the few that breed more commonly in the United States than in Canada. It ranges across the continent, and nests wherever the local conditions permit. In the southern half of its range it is a permanent resident, and its numbers are augmented in the winter by birds that have come from the north. Judging from the wide range of the records now in hand, it is fair to assume that in the early days the Wood Duck must have bred throughout western Pennsylvania. At any rate, it is not restricted during the breeding season to swampy or lake country, since it is satisfied with slow-running water and woodland conditions. Nevertheless, Pymatuning and Conneaut swamps supply ideal environment for feeding and nesting. Considered by G. M. Sutton as "a regular and common summer resident" at Pymatuning, it has steadily increased in numbers there since 1933. Presque Isle is another known breeding station, where broods have been found accompanied by the female parent, even during recent years (Guynes). I myself have never seen the Wood Duck in Beaver County, but J. S. Nease wrote that it probably bred in Washington County, as he shot one near Washington on July 23, 1883. C. H. Townsend (1883) gives it as a summer resident near Latrobe. R. B. Simpson says that at Warren it is known only as an irregular migrant, but he adds that it has been reported to breed at the headwaters of Tionesta Creek, Warren County. In the adjoining county of McKean it has been observed in June in Katrine Swamp (Scherer). It is noted as "common" in Van Fleet's list of the breeding birds of DuBois, but this list was compiled more than forty years ago.

For the ridge and valley section there are only R. C. Harlow's breeding record for Bedford County, the exact locality for which he has not divulged, and a more recent one for northern Huntingdon County by Dr. Sutton, who noted a female duck, apparently with young, on July 27, 1928, at the

State College Nature Study Camp. Miss A. E. Berg writes that for eleven consecutive years (1922–32) a pair nested near her home in Hollidaysburg. While the records are thus few and far between, they tend to show that the potential breeding range of this duck covers our entire region. The encroachments of civilization are alone responsible for the actual curtailment of the breeding area of this species and for the diminution in its numbers.

Migration—Even in localities where the Wood Duck is known to breed it is far more numerous during migration than at any other time. In Crawford County, according to Dr. Sutton (1928), it is "common, and sometimes during recent years, abundant as a migrant." This report is encouraging, in view of the special difficulties besetting this species in the effort to hold its own. It also indicates that the majority of birds must breed farther north. The Wood Duck arrives somewhat later than the Mallard, Pintail, and Black Duck—usually late in March (March 27, 1932, at Erie—Guynes). The only other series of arrival dates available are Mr. Simpson's for Warren; they are mostly in April, with March 28 (1904) the earliest. He has seen this duck as late as May 14 (1892), and by that date there should be nests with eggs. It has been noted by B. H. Christy at Clinton Pond, Allegheny County, where it certainly does not nest, on April 24 (1921), and this date is probably near the usual tail end of the spring migration.

In the fall movement actual migrants from the north are easily confused with locally reared young birds and their parents. August occurrences almost certainly belong to the latter category, since at that time the old birds have not yet completed the molt and the young are not fully grown. By October, however, an influx from the north apparently takes place, and by the end of that month the migration is almost complete. An occasional bird may linger into November, and there are a few records for December (December 2, 1889—Warren; December 7 and 28, 1931—Hartstown), but none that would certainly indicate wintering.

Habits—The rich and varied coloration of the adult male Wood Duck makes it one of the most beautiful of the family. Its flowing crest, with two white stripes on either side, its white-spotted chestnut breast, and its barred flanks, are conspicuous field marks. The male Hooded Merganser has an equally conspicuous crest, but of a very different shape. The drake Wood Duck is fond of displaying its ornamental plumes as it swims along with its mate in the nuptial season. Small flocks are the rule early in the spring, but these soon break up into pairs, which begin almost at once to seek nesting sites. The Wood Duck gets its name from its preference for wooded swamps, overflowed forest in bottomlands, and sluggish streams passing through woodland, where its gaudy plumage is a fitting complement to the play of sun and shade on the water.

H. C. Kirkpatrick contributes the following note on this species: "In early years, particularly in September and October, 1884, the Wood Duck was tolerably common on French Creek, about four miles below Meadville, where it came to feed on the acorns and beechnuts so abundant there. It is wary and difficult of approach when an enemy is known to be near, as I learned on one occasion when hunting along Conneaut Outlet in September. I had unexpectedly come upon a flock of wood ducks, which flew upstream perhaps a quarter of a mile before alighting. While yet far out of range I saw what I took to be an old male scramble off the high bank into the water, whereupon the whole flock took wing. This maneuver was several times repeated, until I at last reluctantly gave up the chase, being unable to get near enough for a shot before the bird on guard gave the alarm."

The nest of this duck is placed in a natural cavity of a tree or sometimes in an old nest-hole of the Pileated Woodpecker; it consists merely of a quantity of down supplied by the female parent. In the Pymatuning region W. W. Andrews (quoted by Dr. Sutton, 1928) "often found the nests in the very tops of the dead stubs, sometimes in a more or less exposed situation." A nest found by Edgar Huidekoper was in a huge sycamore. Three nests found by R. L. Fricke in May, 1935, near Linesville, were all in natural cavities in beech trees, and one was not more than ten feet from the ground. Some variation exists in the time of egg laying, since one nest found on May 22 held twelve fresh eggs, while in another examined the same day there were two newly hatched young. A set has from ten to fifteen eggs; they are pale creamy white—lighter in color than the eggs of our other ducks—and measure about 2.00 by 1.53 inches.

During July and August, broods of young in company with the female parent are a common sight in the Pymatuning region. S. J. Seiple writes that he has noted very young birds and others almost fully grown on the same date (July 22), an observation that confirms the variation in nesting time already mentioned. Ordinarily, however, the young do not attain their full growth until September; their full winter plumage is acquired still later. "In the fall the locally-reared young congregate, seemingly by themselves, and the single males and females, or small groups of the adults, wander about aimlessly, resting on the ponds or walking along the banks. On October 1, 1925, Mr. Langdon saw at least a hundred young birds in one pond near Shaw's Landing, where each evening the family flocks came in to rest, and probably to spend the night" (Sutton, 1928).

Aix sponsa Townsend, *Proc. Acad. Nat. Sci. Philadelphia*, 1883, 68 (Latrobe, Westmoreland Co., breeding)—Todd, *Ann. Carnegie Mus.*, 1904, 2:517 (Presque Isle, Erie Co., breeding)—Harlow, *Auk*, 1918, 35:20 (Bedford Co.)—Christy, *Cardinal*, 1923, v.1, no.1, [p.2] (Clinton Pond, Allegheny Co., April)—Sutton, *Ann. Carnegie Mus.*, 1928, 18:70 (Pymatuning Swamp, Crawford Co., nesting; Crawford Co. records and references).

"Wood Duck" Simpson, *Oölogist*, 1912, 29:370; 1913, 30:51; and 1914, 31:210 (Warren, Warren Co., March and April)—Miller, *In the Open*, August, 1913, 4:34 (Pymatuning Swamp, Crawford Co.)—Wood, *Wilson Bull.*, 1932, 44:238 (Alan Seeger Forest, "Centre Co." [northern Huntingdon Co.], *fide* Sutton)—Editor, *Cardinal*, 1933, 3:150 ([Sandy Lake, Mercer Co., October], food, *fide* Fricke)—Christy, *Cardinal*, 1934, 3:165 (Hartstown, Crawford Co., August)—Trimble, *Cardinal*, 1937, 4:104 (Pymatuning region, Crawford Co., nesting).

REDHEAD (Plate 3)

NYROCA AMERICANA (Eyton)

Description—A rather large duck, with a general resemblance to the Canvas-back, but with the *bill* forming a *decided angle where it meets the forehead. Male:* head and neck rich rufous chestnut; fore part of the body (all around) black, gradually passing below into the white of the rest of the underparts; back, wings, and sides of the body, gray, becoming dusky on the lower back; under tail coverts also dusky; under wing coverts white; bill very dark bluish, with the tip black. *Female:* an obscure-looking duck, without any definite markings anywhere, except the gray wing-speculum; upperparts in general, and sides of the body, dull brown; breast brownish white, passing into the white of the rest of the underparts; the feathers around the base of the bill often buffy whitish, but not abruptly so. The female of this species is practically indistinguishable in life from the same sex of the Ring-necked Duck. *Downy young:* light brownish olive above, with buffy spots on the sides of the back; plain creamy buff below; head rich buff (chamois color), the crown-patch brownish olive in abrupt contrast.

Range—Like certain other ducks that breed mainly in the central and western parts of North America and winter far to the eastward, even to the Atlantic coast, the Redhead presumably crosses our region in a diagonal direction in the spring and fall. It seldom stops, however, save on the larger bodies of water. Conneaut and Pymatuning lakes and Erie Bay are thus the only places where it is of regular occurrence as a transient. Once one of the commoner ducks, it has been sadly depleted in numbers in late years by excessive shooting and by drought. Whether or not belated legal protection will suffice to save it from virtual extermination remains to be seen. It is one of the few ducks said to be more numerous at Conneaut Lake than at Erie Bay, at least in the spring migration. At the latter locality it has repeatedly been found in the winter months also, whenever there is open water. Outlying records are comparatively few.

At Warren the Redhead is a rare visitor. My Beaver County record of 1904 was based on a bird shot by a local gunner near the mouth of the Beaver River on March 21. W. D. Hunter has two specimens taken at Racine, Beaver County, on November 14, 1918, and November 6, 1928. The Redhead has been reported also from Allegheny, Washington, Greene, Westmoreland, Cameron, Centre, Blair, and Clinton counties, but is rare and casual everywhere in these sections.

The addition of the Redhead to the list of ducks breeding at Pymatuning came as a great surprise in 1936, since there are only a few sporadic breeding records for the East. In both 1936 and 1937, within the sanctuary limits there must have been fifteen or twenty pairs, most of which succeeded in raising young. Thus the Redhead seems likely to become established as a regular summer resident there, despite its instinctive predilections for the prairie sloughs and marshes of the West. It would be interesting to know whence came the particular individuals that now breed at Pymatuning, and just what induced them to adopt a new summer home.

Migration—The Redhead is one of the first ducks to push north in the spring, and sometimes arrives before all the ice is gone. The earliest date available for this season is February 29 (1936) for Pymatuning Lake (Oudette). Other spring dates are March 8, Washington (1897); March 15, Conneaut Lake (1925); and March 18, Warren (1899). Arrival records at Erie Bay are confused with possible wintering records, but correspond to those just cited. The last week in March and the first week or ten days in April are the periods of greatest abundance, and most of the records from outlying localities fall within these limits. S. J. Seiple reported an unusually large flight at Pymatuning Lake on March 28, 1937, and I found the species still common there on April 6. The Redhead has been noted at Renovo on April 20 (1896), at Conneaut Lake until April 24 (1925), at Erie Bay until April 30 (1933), and at Warren as late as May 2 (1892).

Soon after the first of October the Redhead returns with the first flight of deepwater ducks. At Erie Bay its arrival has been noted as follows: October 1 (1934); October 3 (1901); October 6 (1894); October 13 (1900). At Conneaut Lake it has been observed at about the same time (on October 3 in 1909). It remains through most or all of November, depending on the severity of the season and the prevalence of open water. It was one of the ducks that stayed on Erie Bay through the open winter of 1931–32, and in subsequent years it has been repeatedly observed during the last week in December—a fact which shows that it has a decided tendency to winter. At Pymatuning it has been known to remain until November 17 (1935—Skaggs). Two birds were seen at Warren on October 24, 1891 (Simpson), and there is a specimen in the Carnegie Museum that was shot on Greensburg Reservoir, Westmoreland County, on November 4, 1921.

Habits—The Redhead usually appears in flocks, sometimes by itself, but often mingling with the Scaups (both kinds), the Ring-necked Duck, and the Canvas-back. Like these it is a typical diving duck and seeks its food by plunging beneath the surface, sometimes descending to a considerable depth in search of the aquatic plants and animals which constitute its fare. It prefers to feed in large, open bodies of water such as Erie Bay, and seldom enters the ponds of Presque Isle. Flocks have been known to come to feed week after week at the western end of the bay, but they were so wary that only an occasional bird could be killed by the gunners. On Conneaut Lake the species appears under much the same conditions.

At Pymatuning Lake it is rather common during the migration season, but it was a surprise to find mated pairs still present in May and June of 1936. No nests were found that season, but in late June R. L. Fricke encountered young broods that seemed to be either redheads or ring-necked ducks. I went to Linesville early in July and with the assistance of B. L. Oudette collected a few ducklings from some of these broods; these verified our suspicions that both species were represented. These ducks kept out in the deep water; and females with broods of young were always some distance from shore. It was interesting to watch the behavior of the birds as they sensed danger. The old one would flutter off in one direction with a great splashing of water, while the young scattered in the opposite direction and dived when closely pressed. They were rediscovered hiding among the aquatic vegetation, keeping beneath the water with only the tips of their bills exposed. The Pymatuning population of breeding Redheads has continued to maintain itself ever since 1936; at least fifteen or twenty pairs are present each summer.

Fuligula ferina americana TOWNSEND, *Proc. Acad. Nat. Sci. Philadelphia*, 1883, 68 (Latrobe, Westmoreland Co., transient).

Aythya americana WARREN, *Birds Pa.*, ed. 2, 1890, 41 (Erie Bay, Erie Co., transient)—RHOADS, *Auk*, 1899, 16:309 (Emporium, Cameron Co., *fide* Larrabee)—TODD, *Ann. Carnegie Mus.*, 1904, 2:518 (Erie Bay, etc., Erie Co., transient)—TODD, in Bausman, *Hist. Beaver Co., Pa.*, 1904, 2:1198 (Beaver Co., transient).

Marila americana BURLEIGH, *Wilson Bull.*, 1924, 36:75 (Oak Hall, Centre Co., March).

Nyroca americana SUTTON, *Ann. Carnegie Mus.*, 1928, 18:72 (Conneaut Lake and Meadville, Crawford Co., transient).

"Redhead" CHRISTY, *Cardinal*, 1932, 3:86 (Erie Bay, Erie Co., February)—SAVAGE, *Bird-Lore*, 1932, 34:44; BEAL and PETERSON, *Bird-Lore*, 1934, 36:33; and UPSON, *et al.*, *Bird-Lore*, 1935, 37:47 (Erie Bay, Erie Co., December)—TODD, *Auk*, 1936, 53:440; and TRIMBLE, *Cardinal*, 1937, 4:105 (Pymatuning region, Crawford Co., breeding).

Additional records: Verona and Neville Island, Allegheny Co., shot by gunners (Atkinson)—Duncansville, Blair Co., April 12, 1928, one reported by Robert Mutzabaugh (Sutton)—Waynesburg, transient (Jacobs).

RING-NECKED DUCK (Plate 4)

NYROCA COLLARIS (Donovan)

Description—This duck resembles the Lesser Scaup in size and general proportions. *Male: head, neck, breast, and entire upperparts, black*, the head with a slight purplish sheen in certain lights, and the neck with a chestnut collar (seldom conspicuous); wings like the back, and with a gray speculum; underparts white from the breast down, this color appearing to run up in a *wedge between the black of the breast and that of the back;* under tail coverts blackish; bill grayish blue with a narrow whitish base and a paler band near the tip. *Female:* not certainly distinguishable in life from the female Redhead, but averaging rather darker in color and somewhat smaller in size, with a whitish ring around the eye and more or less white at the base of the bill. *Downy young:* above, olive brown to clove brown, with buffy spots on the sides of the breast and flanks, and a small buffy spot on the middle of the back; top of head olive brown like the back; front and sides of the head buff, as are the underparts.

Range—The defined breeding range of the Ring-necked Duck is in the interior and western parts of North America; the upper Mississippi Valley marks its regular eastern limit. In the winter, however, it comes east to the Atlantic coast, but until lately it has been considered rare to the northward.[1] All precedents were broken by the discovery in 1936 that this species is not merely a transient in northwestern Pennsylvania but also a summer resident and, on occasion, a winter resident as well. Elsewhere in our region it is rare, and apparently passes over without stopping, precisely as do the Redhead and certain other ducks. R. B. Simpson has only six records for Warren, while from farther south there are only a few odd sight records for Allegheny and Westmoreland counties. The breeding of the Ring-necked Duck at Pymatuning was definitely established in 1936 by the capture of young; its wintering on Erie Bay during the exceptionally mild and open season of 1931–32 was attested by repeated observation. Since then it has been noted at the latter locality several times during the winter months, and its tendency to remain seems to be growing. The species, however, is obviously decreasing in numbers.

Migration—The Ring-necked Duck comes and goes with the Lesser Scaup. There are several February records for Erie Bay, but these possibly refer to wintering birds. An influx of birds from the south takes place there in March, sometimes as early as the first week of that month. The movement continues through April, and laggards bringing up the rear carry it into the first week in May. In 1932 this species was observed there as late as May 21 (Guynes). The dates for Conneaut Lake substantially correspond: belated migrants have been reported there on May 15 (1925), and on May 28 (1926). H. C. Kirkpatrick has seen this species at Meadville on March 15 (1899). In 1934 it was first noted at Pymatuning Lake on March 7 (Dilley), and in 1939 on March 10 (Oudette, 1939).

[1] Recently this species has been found breeding in Maine and New Brunswick, and seems to be increasing in numbers in New England. Compare H. L. MENDALL, *Auk*, 1938, 55:401–404, and LUDLOW GRISCOM, *Auk*, 1939, 56:134–137.

In 1923 five ring-necked ducks were seen on Braddock Reservoir, Allegheny County, on March 14; they were reported to have come on March 9 (Sutton, 1923). Our other Allegheny County spring records were made between March 25 and April 9. Miss Ruth Trimble saw a single bird at Darlington, Westmoreland County, on April 21, 1935. There is one early May record for State College.

In the fall this duck seems to be less common than in the spring. It arrives in October (October 10, 1889, and October 22, 1933—Erie Bay; October 15, 1926—Conneaut Lake), and lingers well into November. It has been observed in December at Erie Bay, and has occasionally remained through the entire winter. Two late dates at this season are: November 25, Warren (1914—Simpson); and November 26, Conneaut Lake (1925—Langdon).

Habits—The Ring-necked Duck is a frequent associate of the Lesser Scaup, which it resembles in general habits and behavior. Both species are good divers and are lively and active in their movements on the water. The Ring-neck "flies mostly in small flocks of open formation, rather than in close bunches or lines, so that it does not offer such tempting shots as the other bluebills. While on its feeding grounds it is also usually more scattered and more often flushed singly or in pairs."[1] The adult male may easily be distinguished from the Lesser Scaup by the black back and gray speculum, and in particular by the wedge-shaped white bar on the sides of the breast. In breeding dress the white line at the base of the bill and the dark ring around it are also conspicuous at close range. Moreover, the profile of the head shows a peculiar and characteristic triangular outline. The female is hard to distinguish from the same sex of the Redhead, unless one is close enough to descry the dark band on the bill.

During the first week in April, 1937, this duck was more numerous than any other in the Pymatuning sanctuary. Large numbers were attracted by the grain that had been scattered along the shores at one point near a blind, where I spent considerable time watching their courting antics. The males outnumbered the females on an average of three to one. They would swim along in a group by themselves, passing and crossing in front of a female in the effort to attract her attention. It was the presence of mated pairs in May, 1935, that first suggested the possibility that this species might be breeding there. The suspicion was confirmed by the capture of one of a brood of seven ducklings in early July, 1936. The female parent fluttered off in one direction with a great splashing, while the brood paddled away in another, diving when closely approached. I estimate that there were possibly fifteen pairs of ring-necked ducks nesting in this area in 1936, and equally as many in 1937 and later. No nests or eggs have yet been discovered there.

Aythya collaris Warren, *Birds Pa.*, ed. 2, 1890, 44 (Erie Bay, Erie Co., transient).

Fuligula collaris Todd, *Ann. Carnegie Mus.*, 1904, 2:521 (Erie Bay, Erie Co., transient).

"Ring-necked Duck" Simpson, *Oölogist*, 1913, 30:50 (Warren, Warren Co., March)—Christy, *Cardinal*, 1923, v. 1, no. 2, [p. 15] (Clinton Pond, Allegheny Co., March)—Sutton, *Bird-Lore*, 1923, 25:194 (Braddock Reservoir, etc., Allegheny Co., March); (?)1924, 26:190 (Deer Creek, Allegheny Co., spring, *fide* Elliott, *et al.*)—Wood, *Wilson Bull.*, 1932, 44:238 (State College, Centre Co., spring, *fide* Benton)—Savage, *Bird-Lore*, 1932, 34:44 (Erie Bay, Erie Co., December)—Todd, *Auk*, 1936, 53:440; and Trimble, *Cardinal*, 1937, 4:105 (Pymatuning region, Crawford Co., breeding)—Oudette, *Cardinal*, 1939, 5:47 (Pymatuning Lake, near Linesville, Crawford Co., March).

Perissonetta collaris Sutton, *Ann. Carnegie Mus.*, 1928, 18:74 (Conneaut Lake and Meadville, Crawford Co., transient).

[1] A. C. Bent, U. S. National Museum, *Bulletin*, no. 126, 1923, p. 228.

CANVAS-BACK

NYROCA VALISINERIA (Wilson)

Description—A fairly large duck, resembling the Redhead in size and coloration, but with a longer and differently shaped *bill*, the base of which *runs up on the forehead without an angle. Male:* head dark chestnut (tending toward black above), and neck the same; fore part of body (all around) black; back white, with fine wavy dark lines, giving a grayish cast; rump black, underparts otherwise white, the under tail coverts dusky; wings grayish, whitish beneath; bill dark. *Female:*

head and neck brown, the throat more buffy; fore part of body also brown, almost uniform with the head; back grayish, with fine wavy dark lines, the rump browner; underparts (except as aforesaid) dull whitish.

Range—The winter range of the Canvas-back extends far to the eastward of its summer home. In the breeding season the species is confined to the interior of the country, with Minnesota its present eastern limit. In winter it is a common duck on Chesapeake Bay. The Great Lakes lie along its path of migration between these two regions. Erie Bay attracts its share of the transients during the season of migration, and beyond question this species is far more numerous there now than it was in 1900—not, perhaps, because of any actual increase in the numbers of the species at large, but simply because of the better protection now afforded in that locality. Almost every winter a few canvas-backs remain on Erie Bay, and during the winter of 1931–32 the species was actually common. At Conneaut Lake, too, it is a regular and common transient—at times it is even more numerous than the Redhead. Pymatuning Lake also attracts its quota of visitants.

Elsewhere in our region the Canvas-back is rare. Like certain other species of waterfowl, it probably passes over the smaller waterways and covers the distance from Conneaut Lake to the Lower Susquehanna River in one flight. Thus, R. B. Simpson has but three records for Warren; H. C. Kirkpatrick but one for French Creek, near Meadville; and D. A. Atkinson only one for Allegheny County (specimen taken at Tarentum on November 26, 1893). Ducks of this species were also noted on Braddock Reservoir, Allegheny County, on November 5, 1923 (Elliott), and on Oneida Lake, Butler County, on April 3, 1935 (von Fuehrer). There is one occurrence recorded for Centre County, and one for Clinton County (Renovo, March 30, 1899—Pierce).

Migration—At Erie Bay the Canvas-back is pre-eminently a "cold-weather" duck and is the last of the family to appear in the fall. It arrives late in October (October 21–29 by the record) and sometimes remains all winter. It reaches Conneaut Lake at about the same time and stays almost until the time of the freezing of the deepest waters. At Pymatuning Lake it has been observed as late in the fall as November 17 (1935—Skaggs) and as early in the spring as March 6 (1936—Oudette). According to G. M. Sutton (1928), it returns to Conneaut Lake with the Redhead in mid-March (March 17, 1912 and 1913). He adds: "Mr. Bergstrom did not record it in 1925 until March 30, on which date he saw flocks of a thousand or more at Conneaut Lake. From this date on they were seen daily, and were present in multitudes until April 9 and 10. Thereafter the flocks diminished, although a few lingered about as late as May 29 (Langdon), and June 5 or 6 (Langdon and Bergstrom). The last date is unusual, and it may be that the few birds seen were non-breeding individuals." The spring sojourn on Erie Bay covers approximately the same period as at Conneaut Lake. Actual dates of supposed first appearance there are March 13, 1902, and March 12, 1933. In 1927 the last canvas-back was seen on April 17 (Perry), and in 1934, on April 23 (Guynes). Three were seen on Pymatuning Lake on April 26, 1936, by M. B. Skaggs. Mr. Simpson saw one at Warren on March 18, another on April 4, 1934, and one on April 21, 1929. A flock of six was seen by Dr. Sutton on the Ohio River at Emsworth, Allegheny County, on April 15, 1923.

Habits—The Canvas-back, famed by epicures for the flavor of its flesh, is much overrated in this respect. Under ordinary circumstances it is little if any better than the Scaups, and is rather inferior to the Redhead. Only when it has been feeding extensively upon the wild celery (*Vallisneria spiralis*) does its flesh become permeated with the peculiar flavor of that plant, which is supposed to render it unusually palatable. This plant grows in Erie Bay at certain places, and must be a great attraction to this duck. In the old days, however, the Canvas-back was so persistently hunted that it evidently had little chance to feed in peace, and it became so wild that it was seldom brought to bag. Now it appears to be coming back, and every year flocks may be seen offshore at the proper season. W. M. Guynes writes that there is a beautiful show of these ducks in the spring, when they come to feed in the west end of the bay, just south of the police cabin.

"The canvasback is essentially a diving duck and one of the most expert at it; it swims low in the water like a grebe and dives quickly, swimming for long distances under water, using its wings for this purpose; if pursued it comes to the surface only for an instant, diving again promptly and swimming away so far and so swiftly as to distance its pursuer; it hardly pays gunners to chase the crippled birds, as they are tough and hard to kill, as well as skillful divers; well-trained retrievers have been taught that it is useless to attempt to catch them. The canvasback can dive to great depths and is said to be able to obtain its food at a depth of from 20 to 25 feet."[1]

Aythya vallisneria RHOADS, *Auk*, 1899, 16:309 (Tarentum, Allegheny Co., *fide* Atkinson)—TODD, *Ann. Carnegie Mus.*, 1904, 2:518 (Erie Bay, Erie Co., transient).

"Canvasback" [CHRISTY], *Cardinal*, 1923, v. 1, no. 2, [p. 8] (Emsworth, Allegheny Co., April [*fide* Sutton])—BOULTON, *Bird-Lore*, 1928, 30:271 (Presque Isle, Erie Co., May, *fide* Reiter, *et al.*)—WOOD, *Wilson Bull.*, 1932, 44:238 (State College, Centre Co., November)—CHRISTY, *Cardinal*, 1932, 3:86 (Erie Bay, Erie Co., February)—SAVAGE, *Bird-Lore*, 1932, 34:44; BEAL and PETERSON, *Bird-Lore*, 1934, 36:34; and UPSON, *et al.*, *Bird-Lore*, 1935, 37:47 (Erie Bay, Erie Co., December).

Aristonetta valisineria SUTTON, *Ann. Carnegie Mus.*, 1928, 18:72 (Conneaut Lake and Meadville, Crawford Co., transient).

Nyroca valisineria PERRY, *Cardinal*, 1938, 4:177 (Erie Bay, Erie Co., December).

[1]A. C. BENT, U. S. National Museum, *Bulletin*, no. 126, 1923, p. 196.

GREATER SCAUP DUCK

NYROCA MARILA (Linnaeus)

Description—A fairly large duck, with a bluish-gray bill about as long as the head. *Male: head, neck, and fore part of body, black,* the head showing a greenish sheen in certain lights; *upper back appearing dull whitish* (white with fine wavy black barring); rump and tail dusky; wings dusky, with a conspicuous *white speculum; underparts,* from the breast down, *white,* becoming dusky or blackish on the under tail coverts, in strong contrast with the white flanks; eyes yellow. *Female* very different: head, neck, back, breast, and sides, dull brown, the region around the base of the bill abruptly white, giving the effect of a *white face* when viewed from the front; *wings* darker brown, with a *white spot* as in the male; underparts (except the breast) mostly white, shaded with brown toward the tail. *Young males* in the fall and winter are variously intermediate between the adult male and the adult female. In *young females* the white face is not clearly defined, and the colors are more or less blended.

Range—This duck is a native of both Eurasia and North America. In summer it is distributed through the interior of the latter continent from Alaska and British Columbia east to Manitoba and Hudson Bay; and there are a few sporadic or outlying breeding records from farther east, even as far as New Brunswick. In winter the species is abundant along the Atlantic coast, and is occasional also on the Great Lakes. Its migration route trends in general from southeast to northwest and vice versa, and carries it directly across our region. Since it usually avoids running water, it is a regular visitant with us only at Erie Bay and Conneaut Lake.

Records for this scaup not based on the actual capture of specimens are inevitably open to question, since it is difficult or impossible to distinguish it in life from the Lesser Scaup, which is much commoner and more generally distributed during migration. For this reason most of the available records may justifiably be placed under the head of the Lesser Scaup, and some of the remainder may be questioned. R. B. Simpson lists the species as an irregular spring transient at Warren; H. C. Kirkpatrick has taken it in March along French Creek at Meadville; and D. A. Atkinson reports one bird shot at Davis Island dam, Allegheny County, on March 12, 1892. These are the only absolutely certain records from elsewhere than Erie Bay and Conneaut Lake. There is a probability, however, that some of the scaups reported in February by sundry observers may have belonged to this species, which is in general the hardier of the two and the likelier to remain during cold weather. It has been taken on Erie Bay in December and January, and like the Canvas-back seems to be more or less regular in the winter, even in severe seasons. As nearly as I could tell with the help of a good glass, the scaups I watched feeding and disporting in the open water at the Erie docks on February

5, 1934, belonged to this species—and they were seen by other observers both before and after this date. During the mild and open winter of 1931–32 they remained there in large numbers.

Migration—During the season of migration the Greater Scaup is obviously less common than the other on Erie Bay,[1] although the relative numbers of the two species would be difficult to estimate. As the Greater Scaup is hardier, it seems to leave earlier in the spring (April 13, 1900; April 14, 1903; April 17, 1927) and to return later in the fall (November 8, 1900). At Conneaut Lake it was noted in 1913 as early as March 17, and in 1910 as late as April 20. In the fall of 1925 it was first taken on November 10. Mr. Simpson has spring specimens taken at Warren between March 19 (1894) and April 24 (1903). B. H. Christy feels certain that the individuals he saw at Clinton Pond, Allegheny County, on April 8 and 14, 1923, and on March 28, 1926, were of the larger species. H. A. McGraw saw two scaups at Lakemont, Blair County, on April 14, 1917, and two at Spruce Creek, Huntingdon County, on April 8, 1928, all of which he considered to be the Greater. These various dates correspond fairly well and indicate that the spring movement of this species takes place mainly during the latter half of March and the first two or three weeks of April. Later dates probably pertain to the other species. Some other questionable references appear under the head of that form.

Habits—The general habits and behavior of this duck are essentially the same as those of the Lesser Scaup. Both kinds are known as "Bluebills" to the gunners. Mr. Guynes writes of it at Erie: "This is a hardy, open-lake duck and can be considered a winter resident here, for when the bay and lake are frozen almost solid some will stay in the east slip of the public dock and live on small fish, of which there are millions. In the fall it is a wonderful sight to see the 'raft' which forms in the lake east of the bay and north of the Hammermill Paper Company's plant. I have seen such a 'raft' at least one mile long by an eighth of a mile wide, which I estimated to hold at least ten thousand ducks."

Fuligula marila Todd, *Ann. Carnegie Mus.*, 1904, 2:519 (Erie Bay, Erie Co., transient).

"American Scaup Duck" (?)Sutton, *Bird-Lore*, 1923, 25:194 (Clinton Pond, Allegheny Co., April, *fide* Christy).

Marila marila (?)Burleigh, *Wilson Bull.*, 1923, 35:82 (Highland Park, Allegheny Co., transient); (?)1924, 36:75, part ("State College" [Scotia, etc.], Centre Co., spring transient).

"Greater Scaup Duck" (?)Christy, *Cardinal*, 1923, v. 1, no. 2, [p. 14] (Clinton Pond, Allegheny Co., April)—Savage, *Bird-Lore*, 1932, 34:44; and Upson, *et al.*, *Bird-Lore*, 1935, 37:47 (Erie Bay, Erie Co., December).

Fulix marila nearctica Sutton, *Ann. Carnegie Mus.*, 1928, 18:73, part (Crawford Co. localities and records).

"Scaup Duck" (?)Christy, *Cardinal*, 1932, 3:86 (Erie Bay, Erie Co., February).

[1]W. M. Guynes, for whose opinion I have great respect, disagrees with this statement. There is only one satisfactory test: to secure specimens taken at various times and under various circumstances.

LESSER SCAUP DUCK (Plate 4)

NYROCA AFFINIS (Eyton)

Description—Smaller than the Greater Scaup Duck; similar in coloration, but gloss of head of adult male purplish rather than greenish, and white area on wings less extended.

Range—The main breeding grounds of this duck lie in the region west of the Great Lakes and Hudson Bay and extend south to the northwestern United States. In addition, there are sporadic but apparently authentic breeding records for northern Ohio, Indiana, and Iowa. It is quite possible that crippled birds may breed in regions far removed from the normal and regular breeding range, as John C. Phillips suggests.[2] At any rate, the species has been found summering at several points in our region, but thus far there has been no real proof of its breeding. At Lake Pleasant, Erie County, on June 22, 1895, I shot a female lesser scaup, whose gonads showed no signs of activity. There was a male bird there too, and although I was assured by the local residents that the pair was nesting, I could not believe it. Again, on June 16, 1898, I shot a female at Crystal Lake, near Hartstown. It was alone, and showed no actual indications of breeding. R. B. Simpson saw a female at Warren on June 10, 1910. One

[2]*A Natural History of the Ducks*, 1925, 3:273.

was seen on the Raystown Branch of the Juniata River, east of Entriken, Huntingdon County, early in June, 1898, by Thaddeus Surber. "Mr. [G. M.] Langdon observed a flock of twelve birds throughout the month of June, 1926, at Conneaut Lake. These were no doubt non-breeding birds" (Sutton, 1928).

At Erie Bay, where this species is abundant in migration and lingers late in the spring, there is a hearsay report of its having bred on one occasion in recent years, but the evidence is not quite satisfactory. "The presence of this duck thus late in the season is a regular occurrence every year, as is evident from the statements of local gunners and from Mr. [S. E.] Bacon's notes. He says: 'I am certain that this species does not breed here, but it occurs in numbers all through the spring and well into the summer months. Early in June of every year there is always a fair-sized flock feeding on the bay. Thus on June 21, 1901, I saw about fifty birds, both males and females, in one flock, and on July 9, 1892, I saw a party of eight; this latter date is, however, my latest summer record.' In further support of this statement may be recorded a party of five seen by the writer on June 17, 1897, off the mouth of Mill Creek. The most reasonable explanation of these facts would seem to be that such late staying birds are those which for some reason have not the ability or inclination to breed, some of them at least being 'pensioners,' but just why these should be the only ducks known to regularly spend the summer here without breeding it is difficult to say, unless it be that their abundance brings them into more prominence" (Todd, 1904). The very fact that the species was found in flocks at this season would argue that it could not be breeding at the time. Similar reports come from neighboring states.

Pymatuning Lake, however, is one place in our region where this duck very probably breeds, as do certain other species of similar haunts and habits. It is common there until mid-May, and a few mated pairs remain still later. Although neither nests nor young broods have been found as yet, they may be expected.

In winter the Lesser Scaup is common in the South Atlantic states; thence it ranges south to the West Indies and west to the Pacific coast. Its line of flight in spring and fall carries it across the Great Lakes. At the present time it is probably the commonest duck of all, not only on Erie Bay and on Conneaut Lake, but also throughout our region in general. Once very numerous on the Ohio River, but far less so now because of pollution of the waters, it still is seen in small numbers almost every season. At Warren, on the upper Allegheny River, Mr. Simpson calls it "the commonest wild duck found here." At Renovo it is a fairly regular migrant in the spring, but not so numerous in the fall (Pierce). Although several inland observers seem to think that it must occasionally winter, the only positive evidence that I can present is that based on an individual picked up exhausted at Lakemont, Blair County, on January 6, 1918, by H. A. McGraw. Mr. Simpson saw a Lesser Scaup at Warren on January 1, 1890, and during the winter of 1931–32 both species of scaup were reported as plentiful on Erie Bay. This was probably correct, but generally speaking, any scaups seen in winter are likely to be the larger species.

Migration[1]—The Lesser Scaup Duck moves north very early in the season. I have seen it along the Ohio River as early as February 26 (1890), and T. D. Burleigh's earliest spring date for Pittsburgh is February 22 (1914). It appears at Conneaut Lake and Erie Bay shortly after the ice breaks up, usually about the middle of March, and soon becomes common. Mr. Simpson cites dates of arrival at Warren for ten years, from March 8 (1899) to 29 (1902). March 11 (1904) is the earliest date for Renovo given by A. K. Pierce; the fact that most of his records are for April suggests a later average migration in the mountain section. The movement continues unabated through April, and not until the end of that month does it perceptibly diminish. Stragglers often remain until the end of May, and nonbreeding birds even later. As the Lesser Scaup is a rather late nester, the individuals thus lingering could still reach their breeding grounds in time to lay their eggs and rear their young.

[1]Collation of data under this head has been complicated by the uncertainty as to which species is meant in many cases. It is probable that the ducks which Audubon wrote of having seen at Pittsburgh years ago were the Lesser and not the Greater Scaup, and the same conclusion applies to other references that have been questioned in the list on pages 104 and 105. Quite possibly, February dates (including my own) may refer to the Greater Scaup. That the latter species remains beyond April is also highly improbable. The paragraph must be read with due allowance for possible error.

On its return in the fall this duck appears at Erie Bay about the middle of October (October 7, 1904; October 14, 1900), is most abundant during the cold and stormy weather of November, and remains well into December, doubtless as long as there is open water. "Mr. Bacon contributes the following interesting account of the migration of this species: 'On one occasion I saw, as I believed, all the Lesser Scaups in this neighborhood start for the south. The bay had frozen over a few nights before, and on this particular afternoon a large flock of these ducks kept circling over the lake, sometimes high in the air, again dropping swiftly to the surface and skimming along for a mile or so. Finally, having evidently gathered into one flock all the birds of the vicinity, they rose to a great height, and starting southward, were soon lost to view' " (Todd, 1904). Very few actual dates of arrival and departure in the fall migration are available for other points. I have seen this duck along the Ohio River only between November 15 (1889) and 27 (1890), but there are October records for several other localities.

Habits—My personal acquaintance with the Lesser Scaup dates back to March 25, 1889, when after a difficult stalk across the mud and through the willow growth at the mouth of the Beaver River, I held in my hand a beautiful male bird, the first duck of any kind I had ever shot. Since that time I have observed thousands of these ducks but have tried to avoid shooting any more for identification. The risk of confusing the Lesser with the Greater Scaup is considerable, however, so that all sight records must be received with caution. In the nineties flocks of this species used to alight on the Ohio only rarely, and usually passed over just out of gunshot, but single birds were quite often found loitering along the shore, concealed from the casual observer by the rank growth of willows. In recent years there are by comparison only a few ducks, but now it is not unusual for a flock to remain in the same vicinity for several days at a time, if undisturbed. It is not easy to say what they find to eat, especially in the turbid and more or less polluted river waters, but they spend much of their time in diving to the bottom, evidently with some result, or they would not stay so long in the same place. A flock of these ducks swimming at ease on the sunlit waters of the river is a beautiful sight. They are active birds, almost nervous in their quick turns and odd jockeyings. Flocks on the wing fly very swiftly but often in erratic fashion, swerving suddenly in their course unaccountably.

Nowhere in our region is the Lesser Scaup commoner than at Erie Bay. "At the time of our arrival in the spring of 1900 (March 23) they were already numerous, and with the breaking up and final disappearance of the ice the flocks were augmented by fresh accessions from the south. They were rarely observed on the lake, and only occasionally on the ponds, the bay being their chosen haunt. Here they were found in flocks numbering sometimes hundreds of individuals, often associated with other species of sea-ducks, but always outnumbering them. These flocks were wild and could not be approached in a boat within one hundred yards, but refused to leave the bay, rising merely to settle in another part until again disturbed. However, many were killed over decoys set out at various points, even in the open bay during foggy weather, when a boat could be anchored at the proper distance. A favorite feeding-ground, to which the birds persisted in returning despite constant persecution, lay between one hundred and three hundred yards off the mouth of Mill Creek, where the water was only a few feet deep" (Todd, 1904).

Mr. Simpson writes of the Lesser Scaup at Warren: "Whenever we have a big duck day in the spring this species is sure to be plentiful; I have at such times seen flocks of as many as sixty birds, and flocks of twenty-five or thirty are not uncommon at any time in this season. They are not particular where they alight, and are just as apt to be seen floating about in midstream as along shore, or in ponds or other quiet water. I have even seen them in little pools left by the receding waters after a flood."

Fuligula marila (error) (?)AUDUBON, *Orn. Biog.*, 1835, 3:225 (Pittsburgh, Allegheny Co.)—(?)TOWNSEND, *Proc. Acad. Nat. Sci. Philadelphia*, 1883, 68 (Latrobe, Westmoreland Co., transient).

Aythya affinis WARREN, *Birds Pa.*, ed. 2, 1890, 44 (Erie Bay, Erie Co., transient)—RIVES, *Auk*, 1898, 15:134 (western Pa., summer, *fide* Todd).

Aythya marila nearctica (error) (?)[DWIGHT], *Abstr. Proc. Linnæan Soc. New York*, no. 4, 1892, 2 (Erie, Erie Co., *fide* Bacon).

Fuligula affinis TODD, *Ann. Carnegie Mus.*, 1904, 2:520 (Erie Bay, etc., Erie Co., transient)—TODD, in Bausman, *Hist. Beaver Co., Pa.*, 1904, 2:1198 (Beaver Co., transient).

"Lesser Scaup Duck" SIMPSON, *Oölogist*, 1907, 24:133; 1909, 26:86; 1911, 28:41, 44; and 1914, 31:210 (Warren, Warren Co., April–May); 1912, 29:250 (Erie, Erie Co., June)—CHRISTY, *Cardinal*, 1923, v. 1, no. 2, [p. 14] (Clinton Pond, Allegheny Co., spring)—SUTTON, *Bird-Lore*, 1924, 26:190 (Deer Creek, Allegheny Co., April, *fide* Elliott, *et al.*)—EASTWOOD, *Bird-Lore*, 1926, 28:273 (Ridgway, Elk Co. May, *fide* Alsop)—BOULTON, *Bird-Lore*, 1928, 30:13 (Clinton. Pond, Allegheny Co., October, *fide* Christy)—WOOD, *Wilson Bull.*, 1932, 44:238 (State College, Centre Co., transient)—SAVAGE, *Bird-Lore*, 1932, 34:44; and (?)UPSON, *et al.*, *Bird-Lore*, 1933, 35:27; and 1935, 37:47 (Erie Bay, Erie Co., December)—OUDETTE, *Cardinal*, 1939, 5:47 (Pymatuning Lake, near Linesville, Crawford Co., March).

Marila affinis STONE, *Cassinia*, 1919, 22:29 ("Altoona" [Lakemont], Blair Co., April, *fide* McGraw)—CHRISTY, *Cardinal*, 1923, v. 1, no. 1, [p. 2] (Sewickley and Clinton Pond, Allegheny Co., transient)—BURLEIGH, *Wilson Bull.*, 1923, 35:82 (Highland Park, Allegheny Co., transient).

Marila marila (error) BURLEIGH, *Wilson Bull.*, 1924, 36:75, part ("State College" [Scotia and Oak Hall], Centre Co., spring transient).

"Greater Scaup Duck" (error) EASTWOOD, *Bird-Lore*, 1926, 28:274 (Sandy Lake, Mercer Co., May, *fide* Squier, *et al.*).

Fulix affinis SUTTON, *Ann. Carnegie Mus.*, 1928, 18:74 (Crawford Co. localities and records)—FRICKE, *Cardinal*, 1931, 3:42 (Hartstown, Crawford Co., May).

Fulix marila nearctica (error) SUTTON, *Ann. Carnegie Mus.*, 1928, 18:73, part (Crystal Lake, etc., Crawford Co., transient).

"Scaup" BOGGS, *Redstart*, 1936, 3:92 (Pymatuning region, Crawford Co., June).

AMERICAN GOLDEN-EYE

GLAUCIONETTA CLANGULA AMERICANA (Bonaparte)

Description—A stocky duck of medium size, with a short neck, a bill about one and one-half inches long, and yellow eyes. Feathers of the head somewhat long, giving it a puffy appearance. *Adult male:* head (all around) black, with a greenish sheen in certain lights, and with a *rounded white spot at the base of the bill* above; neck (all around) and entire underparts pure white; back black, with a white stripe on either side, and tail dusky; wings also black, but with the coverts and secondaries extensively white, showing as a large white area when they are folded; under surface of wings dusky; bill blackish; feet yellow-orange, the webs dusky. *Adult female:* head (all around) deep brown (without any white spot); upperparts in general, breast (paler), sides, flanks, tail, and wings, dusky; the last with a large white spot, crossed diagonally by a black bar; bill dusky; feet brownish yellow. *Young male:* similar in general to the adult female, but head usually blacker, and with an *indication of the white spot* at the base of the bill; the white of the underparts tends to replace the gray of the breast and to run up on the neck; there is also more white on the wings and scapulars.

Range—Two races of the Golden-eye are recognized. One has an extensive distribution in Eurasia; the other is confined to North America. The latter breeds in the Canadian and Hudsonian life zones from the Gulf of St. Lawrence through Canada to Alaska, and winters in the United States as far north as the New England states on the coast and the Great Lakes in the interior. Its presence on Lake Erie in the winter is attested by Warren, presumably on Sennett's authority, and by me, on information received from S. E. Bacon: "Whenever the bay opens up a little a few Golden-eyes find the open holes, so that it would seem that they are always present on the lake in winter." During the mild winter of 1931–32 this was one of the ducks that stayed on Erie Bay in considerable numbers. Since that memorable season, the Erie observers have found it regularly every winter, even during severe weather, about the docks at the foot of State Street, where the water remains open. R. B. Simpson writes that it is rare at Warren during mild winters, but that during severe winters it comes to open holes in the ice and is at times rather common. This would suggest that the ice conditions on Lake Erie may govern the dispersal of this and other hardy species of waterfowl in our region during the winter. The Golden-eye is far more numerous, however, as a spring and fall transient at both these stations, as well as at Conneaut and Pymatuning lakes. I have seen and taken it in April and November on the Ohio River at Beaver, and there are also a few records for Allegheny County. There is only one wintering record for the plateau section (Port Allegany, McKean County, 1935–36—Scherer), and in the mountains the species has been noted only in Blair, Centre, and Clinton counties, where it is rare and irregular.

Migration—The Golden-eye is a "cold-weather"

duck; in fact it is one of the first to appear in the spring and among the last to leave in the fall. March and November are accordingly the months of greatest movement. Since Erie Bay is more or less a regular wintering station, it is not always easy to determine just when the first transient individuals arrive there, although W. M. Guynes gives March 5 as the arrival date in 1933. The same difficulty applies to records from Warren, where, however, the arrival of this species in 1928 was recorded on March 17 (Granquist). Conneaut Lake is another locality where the Golden-eye seems to be common. It arrives there as soon as the winter ice breaks up; the earliest date on record is March 15 (1925—Sutton). An early date for the Pymatuning region is February 4 (Oudette, 1939). S. J. Seiple reports a flock of twenty-five birds between Jamestown and Pymatuning Dam on March 5, 1934, and W. E. Dilley reports another south of Linesville on the same date. The movement continues into April, and even in May a few belated birds may occasionally be encountered. May 21 (1933) is a late date for Erie Bay (Guynes), and May 27 (1936) is one for Pymatuning Lake (Seiple; Fricke). Mr. Simpson gives last dates at Warren as May 5 (1902) and 6 (1892, 1901); and at Conneaut Lake, according to G. M. Sutton, they are as late as May 15 (1925) or 25 (1926). Last dates at Renovo, based on the observations made during ten years (not consecutive), lie between April 7 and May 21 (Pierce).

Fall migration at Erie Bay starts late in October (October 22, 1934; October 29, 1889) and continues through November. The latest fall date on record for Conneaut Lake is November 29 (1912). I shot one bird at the mouth of the Beaver River on November 22 in 1899, and a specimen in the collection of W. D. Hunter was taken on December 6 in 1929, at Racine, Beaver County. One was captured alive near Altoona in December, 1931 (McGraw).

Habits—The Golden-eye is commonly called "Whistler" because of the peculiar whistling made by its wings in flight—a characteristic sound which may be heard at a considerable distance, sometimes before the bird itself comes clearly in sight. This is a deepwater duck, which prefers the lakes and larger rivers and avoids the shallower waters. Its food is obtained by diving, at which it is expert. At Erie, these ducks "prefer the open lake for a feeding ground, but they are commonly found on the bay also, and occasionally even in the ponds. As a rule they go in flocks by themselves, but sometimes occur in the company of other ducks, the Lesser Scaup in particular" (Todd, 1904). Such flocks are usually not large, seldom exceeding twenty-five or thirty individuals, although in recent years flocks numbering over two hundred have been observed during the spring movement. "Mr. Kirkpatrick observed some prolonged flights of this species, of two or three hours' duration, during late March and early April, about thirty-five years ago. Small flocks, passing at varying intervals, were seen migrating up the French Creek valley" (Sutton, 1928). Mr. Simpson writes that in 1895 during March, which was a severe month, golden-eyes were quite plentiful on the Allegheny River between Warren and Oil City. He has often found them with American mergansers—a species of much the same haunts and habits—in the winter, at open holes in the ice of the river. They are hard to kill, and when wounded will often escape by diving, as I have learned by repeated experience. Moreover, their flesh is usually so rank and fishy in flavor that they are really worthless as food.

Glaucionetta clangula americana Warren, *Birds Pa.*, ed. 2, 1890, 44 (Lake Erie, Erie Co., winter)—Sutton, *Ann. Carnegie Mus.*, 1928, 18:75 (Crawford Co. localities and records).

Clangula clangula americana Todd, *Ann. Carnegie Mus.*, 1904, 2:522 (Erie Bay, etc., Erie Co., transient and winter visitant)—Todd, in Bausman, *Hist. Beaver Co., Pa.*, 1904, 2:1198 (Beaver Co., transient)—Burleigh, *Wilson Bull.*, 1923, 35:83 ([Highland Park], Allegheny Co., spring transient); 1924, 36:75 ("State College" [Scotia], Centre Co., spring transient).

"Golden-eye" Simpson, *Oölogist*, 1907, 24:87; 1910, 27:100; 1912, 29:248; and 1921, 38:135 (Warren, Warren Co., winter)—Sutton, *Bird-Lore*, 1924, 26:56 (Grove City, Mercer Co., November, *fide* Nicholson)—Beal and Peterson, *Bird-Lore*, 1934, 36:33 (Presque Isle, Erie Co., December).

"Whistler" Simpson, *Oölogist*, 1911, 28:41; 1912, 29:370; and 1914, 31:210 (Warren, Warren Co., March and April).

"American Golden-eye" Christy, *Cardinal*, 1932, 3:86 (Erie Bay, Erie Co., February)—Savage, *Bird-Lore*, 1932, 34:44; and Upson, *et al.*, *Bird-Lore*, 1933, 35:27; and 1935, 37:47 (Erie Bay, Erie Co., December)—Oudette, *Cardinal*, 1939, 5:47 (Pymatuning Lake, near Linesville, Crawford Co., February).

Additional records: McKees Rocks, Allegheny Co., one shot by John Watson, March 23, 1890 (Atkinson)—Duquesne, Allegheny Co., March 26, 1923, one seen (Sutton)—Lake Pleasant, Erie Co., May 1, 1875 (specimen in the American Museum—Sennett)—Forestville, Butler Co., spring and fall; Barmore Lake, Mercer Co., one seen May 7, 1926 (Keesler).

BUFFLE-HEAD (Plate 5)

CHARITONETTA ALBEOLA (Linnaeus)

Description—A small duck, with extensively white underparts, a short neck, and a stubby bill shorter than the head. *Adult male: head* very fully feathered, giving it a rounded or puffy appearance, black, strongly glossed with purple, steel blue, and bottle green, and with a *broad white area* extending from the nape forward as far as the eyes on either side; back black, with some white on the scapulars, becoming grayish on the upper tail coverts and dusky on the tail; wings black, with the coverts and secondaries mostly white, very prominent either when closed or extended; neck (all around) and underparts white, the latter slightly washed with gray toward the tail; bill dark; feet pinkish or flesh-colored. *Female* much smaller, and differently colored: dusky above, white below, the sides and flanks light dusky; wings with a small white spot on the secondaries, and head with an elongated white spot, poorly defined, below and behind the eye on either side. *Young males* in first winter plumage resemble the adult female in general coloration, but the white patch on the head is usually more extensive; the size also is larger.

Range—This is a strictly North American species, which breeds in the wooded region from Hudson Bay to Alaska, and occasionally, or sporadically, farther south. Its winter home is in the United States, where it ranges from one coast to the other. On the Atlantic side, the coast of Maine marks its usual northward limit at that season, but it is much commoner farther south. According to W. W. Cooke and others, it winters regularly as far north in the interior as the Great Lakes, but only within the last few years has any positive evidence to this effect been secured from our region. During the unusually mild winter of 1931–32, all records were broken, and the Buffle-head was one of the many ducks that remained on Erie Bay in large numbers from January to April. In the following winter one individual was seen late in December; and in 1933–34, according to my observations and those of others, a few remained through the entire cold season. They frequented the open water at the public docks after the bay proper had frozen over. Ten birds were seen there on January 20, 1936 (Dilley). Thus perhaps this duck is becoming a regular winter resident.

Elsewhere in our region the Buffle-head is known only as a transient in spring and fall. At Erie Bay it used to be one of the common kinds during migration, and R. B. Simpson writes that with the exception of the Lesser Scaup it was formerly the commonest duck at Warren. In recent years, however, there has been a marked diminution in its numbers, so that shooting it for game was for a time forbidden. Conneaut Lake is another favorite resort, as might be expected, but the Buffle-head is by no means confined to the larger bodies of water, and often alights in small lakes, reservoirs, ice ponds, rivers, and creeks. Most of the known records, it is true, come from the western counties, but the species is a regular and common migrant at Renovo on the upper Susquehanna River, and there is probably no part of our region where it could not be expected to occur.

Migration—As a rule the spring movement of this species is under way by the middle of March. March 9 (1939) is the earliest spring arrival date for Pymatuning Lake; March 11 (1899), for Erie Bay; March 16 (1912), for Conneaut Lake; March 19 (1901), for Warren; and March 19 (1891), for Beaver. March 18 is the average date of arrival at Renovo, and February 29 (1904), the earliest date in a series of observations covering twenty years. The migration usually reaches its height during the first and second weeks in April, after which there is a gradual decrease in numbers; and by the end of the first week in May the flight is almost completed. Mr. Simpson records a great flight of ducks, mostly of this species, on April 23, 1903; and on April 28, 1906, it was "the most abundant species present at Conneaut Lake" (Sutton, *fide* Langdon, 1928). J. K. Musgrave saw a female at "Thompson's Spring," near State College, Centre County, as late as May 15, in 1909. There are several late dates (May 28 in 1899) among the A. K. Pierce records for Renovo, but they cannot indicate breeding.

Fall migration does not begin as a rule until the latter part of October, according to data from several observers; and the southward movement is often not completed until December. Mr. Simpson saw one bird at Warren as late as December 20 in 1898, and another was taken on the Ohio River at Beaver on December 6, 1899. The species appears regularly in the recent "Christmas Census" reports from Erie Bay.

Habits—At Erie Bay in the season of 1900, buffle-heads "were found usually in small parties by themselves, although during the earlier part of their sojourn they were often met with in larger numbers associated with the flocks of Scaup Ducks. Sometimes, too, they were noted in the ponds with other ducks, but the bay seemed to be their favorite resort, and many were killed here over decoys, as well as shot from a boat, they appearing less wild than most ducks" (Todd, 1904). My experience at the same place in 1932 in general confirmed these impressions. Other observers have also remarked the Buffle-head's aloofness and comparative tameness. Flocks of this species rarely exceed forty in number; they fly compactly, not "stringing out" as do so many ducks. During the latter part of the spring migration the males are often busy with their courting activities, and toward the end of the season probably most of the birds are already mated. Buffle-heads feed largely upon animal matter, which they obtain by diving; their flesh thus acquires a fishy rankness that makes it unsuitable for table use.

Clangula albeola Townsend, *Proc. Acad. Nat. Sci. Philadelphia*, 1883, 68 (Latrobe, Westmoreland Co., transient).

Charitonetta albeola Todd, *Ann. Carnegie Mus.*, 1904, 2:522 (Erie Bay and Presque Isle, Erie Co., transient)—Todd, in Bausman, *Hist. Beaver Co., Pa.*, 1904, 2:1198 (Beaver Co., transient)—Cooke, *Bull. Biol. Surv.* no. 26, 1906, 51 (Renovo, Clinton Co., migration)—Christy, *Cardinal*, 1923, v. 1, no. 1, [p. 2] (Clinton Pond, Allegheny Co., April)—Burleigh, *Wilson Bull.*, 1923, 35:83 (Highland Park, Allegheny Co., April); 1924, 36:75 ("State College" [Oak Hall and Scotia], Centre Co., migration)—Sutton, *Ann. Carnegie Mus.*, 1928, 18:76 (Crawford Co. localities and records).

"Bufflehead" Simpson, *Oölogist*, 1911, 28:41, 44; 1912, 29:370; and 1914, 31:210 (Warren, Warren Co., migration)—Christy, *Cardinal*, 1923, v. 1, no. 2, [p. 15] (Clinton Pond, Allegheny Co., spring)—Eastwood, *Bird-Lore*, 1926, 28:208 (Sandy Lake, Mercer Co., April, *fide* Elliott; Edgewood, Allegheny Co., April, *fide* Jones); 1927, 29:197 ([Highland Park and Braddock] reservoirs, Allegheny Co., April, *fide* Jones and Elliott)—Christy, *Cardinal*, 1932, 3:86 (Erie Bay, Erie Co., February)—Savage, *Bird-Lore*, 1932, 34:44; Upson, *et al.*, *Bird-Lore*, 1933, 35:27; and 1935, 37:47; and Beal and Peterson, *Bird-Lore*, 1934, 36:33 (Erie Bay, Erie Co., December)—Oudette, *Cardinal*, 1939, 5:47 (Pymatuning Lake, near Linesville, Crawford Co., March).

OLD-SQUAW (Plate 5)

CLANGULA HYEMALIS (Linnaeus)

Description—A rather small duck, with a very short, stubby bill only an inch long. Sexes unlike, the *male with a long and pointed tail. Adult male in winter plumage:* head white except for the grayish cheeks; on the sides of the neck a large black spot which narrows down and fades into a brownish-yellow wash; neck otherwise white, this color reaching the upper back and breast, where it is abruptly replaced by black, in strong contrast; wings and rest of upperparts black except for the long white scapulars, which give the effect of a broad white stripe on either side of the back; tail mostly black, the outer feathers with some white, the two middle feathers very narrow and extending four to six inches beyond the rest; *sides of body* (except in front), flanks, and abdomen, *white*, in *abrupt contrast with the black breast;* bill black, with a broad pinkish band near the tip; feet bluish gray. *Adult male in spring:* similar to the winter dress, but head and neck (all around) black, with only the sides of the head grayish; and upper back and scapulars variegated or streaked with buff instead of being pure white. *Female in winter plumage:* smaller than the male, and without the long tail; dusky, gray, and brown mottling on the back; the wings and tail dusky; white below, the breast shaded with gray; head white, the throat, crown, nape, and a large spot on the lower sides of the neck, dusky; or else head dusky, with the cheeks and eye-region white in varying degree, and the neck-band white. The *female in breeding dress* has the upperparts more or less variegated with brown or buff. *Young males* at first resemble the adult female, and later show an intermediate stage.

Range—In the breeding season this duck is truly arctic and its range is circumpolar. In North America it is known to nest only in the northern part of the continent and on the arctic islands beyond. Its winter range in the East is along the Atlantic coast from the Gulf of St. Lawrence south to North Carolina. The Great Lakes, too, are frequented at this season; the regularity with which the species appears there depends on the prevalence of open water. The evidence indicates that old-squaws must once have been very common offshore on Lake Erie during migration, and under favorable conditions a certain proportion of migrating individuals doubtless remained through the winter. At any rate, specimens that constitute valid winter records have been taken on Erie Bay in January and February. When I wrote my report on the "Birds of Erie and Presque Isle" in 1904, the Old-squaw was one of the commonest ducks there, but now it is one of the rarest. Thus, during the exceptionally mild and open winter of 1931–32, when no ice appeared on Erie Bay until March, this species was conspicuous by its absence, although several other kinds of ducks were unexpectedly common. One might suppose that the birds elected to stay farther north, or that they remained far out on the lake, in deep water. But in view of the present extreme scarcity of the species at all seasons it is impossible to escape the conclusion that the former wintering population of old-squaws on Lake Erie has been exterminated—sacrificed to the fishing industry, as described below.

In this connection R. B. Simpson's observations at Warren are significant. There, as at Erie Bay, the status of the Old-squaw was that of a regular transient, most numerous in the spring (April and May); but on two different occasions (1895 and 1899), during blizzards in February, some of these ducks were observed with the flocks of American golden-eyes and American mergansers. This would suggest that they might have been driven south from some other wintering resort, such as Lake Erie, by the exigencies of the weather. Very possibly the other February records might be explained on the same basis; in fact, several of these were made under similar circumstances. Conneaut Lake and Renovo are the only other places in our region where the Old-squaw has ever been found with any regularity, although there are a number of odd records from Beaver, Allegheny, Westmoreland, Centre, and Blair counties. A transappalachian movement in spring and fall is thus indicated.

Migration—As stated above, the February records for the Old-squaw probably refer to winter wanderers rather than to true migrants. These records are as follows: Erie Bay, February 10 and 25, 1934 (Guynes and Perry); Conneaut Lake, February 19, 1900 (Kirkpatrick); Renovo, February 7, 1891, February 28, 1901, and February 12, 1904 (Pierce); Beaver, February 24, 1905 (Todd), February 7, 1915 (Boulton); Latrobe, February 5, 1881 (Townsend); Monongahela River near Pittsburgh, February 2, 1937 (Malley); Waynesburg, "middle of February," 1899 (Jacobs); and Tarentum, February 26, 1897 (Atkinson).

According to W. W. Cooke, the spring movement does not get under way until April—a statement which appears to be borne out by the fact that most of the dates for our region occur in that month. The average date of arrival in fifteen years' observations at Renovo, where this species is said to be sometimes "very common," is April 11 (Pierce). March 28 was the date of its first observed appearance on Erie Bay in 1900, and it was common there during the first half of April. In 1932 it was first seen at that place on March 13, and in 1933, on March 5 (Guynes). In former years it was very common at times on Conneaut Lake also. March 8, 1908, was a day of great abundance there, but the date seems too early for a true migratory movement. A single bird was observed on Pymatuning Lake on April 6, 1937. Many individuals linger well into May before finally going north.

The fall movement usually begins in October (October 15, 1934, and October 18, 1900—Erie Bay); it is in full swing in November, and lasts almost to the end of the month. For some reason this species appears to be less numerous in the fall than in the spring. There is but one fall record for Renovo (October 13, 1909). Three birds were taken at Racine, Beaver County, on December 9, 1919 (Hunter), and the species was noted on Braddock Reservoir, Allegheny County, on November 11, 1923 (Elliott).

Habits—The Old-squaw is properly a deepwater

duck, and while it may and does occasionally alight on our rivers and smaller streams, it is more at home on the larger bodies of water. At Erie Bay in 1900, it was found usually in small parties, or in flocks of moderate size. "Although all which were thus recorded were seen on the bay, it is evident that this species must be far more numerous on the waters of the open lake, miles off the shore. Here the birds, in diving for their food, get entangled in the immense gill-nets set by the fishermen, and perish by drowning. In lifting the nets their bodies are removed, and as a rule thrown overboard, being little esteemed as food, when they eventually drift to shore, to be devoured by Crows and Bald Eagles. Many thousands are thus destroyed annually, but, singularly enough, no other species of duck seems to suffer similarly, unless it be the various species of Scoters, but the proportion of these thus taken is inconsiderable. Such wholesale destruction as this involves has necessarily operated to reduce their numbers materially. Eight or ten years ago [1890] these birds were a pest to the fishermen of Lake Erie, particularly in the fall" (Todd, 1904).

S. E. Bacon, writing in 1892, cited evidence to show that most of these ducks were caught when the nets were set in fifteen fathoms of water, a few were taken in eighteen or twenty fathoms, and one duck was caught in twenty-seven fathoms —a remarkable proof of their diving powers. "Feeding as they do mainly on the lake, and flying into the bay at dusk to spend the night, they are seldom killed by gunners in any numbers, and, indeed they are not worth the ammunition, as they are too fishy for table use. The species is called 'Pintail' or 'Coween' by the local gunners, and exhibits a great variety of plumages in the transition from the winter to the summer dress, and *vice versa.* Many individuals attain a practically complete breeding plumage before their departure in the spring, which does not finally take place until about the first of June, a few lingering until that date almost every season" (Todd, 1904). At Conneaut Lake the species "is seen, along with the Scoters, only in the deepest water" (Sutton, 1928). At Warren, according to Mr. Simpson, it is commonest in April, when sometimes after severe storms, flocks of as many as forty birds may be found floating on the Allegheny River, keeping in midstream rather than in the quieter water or in ponds. In the spring of the year the Old-squaw is a voluble duck—the males have a variety of odd, sonorous call notes that can be heard for a long distance and that when given in chorus have a very pleasing effect.

Harelda glacialis TOWNSEND, *Bull. Nuttall Orn. Club,* 1882, 7:251; *Proc. Acad. Nat. Sci. Philadelphia,* 1883, 68 (Latrobe, Westmoreland Co., February).

Clangula hyemalis WARREN, *Birds Pa.,* ed. 2, 1890, 46 (Erie Bay, Erie Co., transient)—TODD, *Auk,* 1891, 8:240 (Beaver, Beaver Co., April)—BACON, *Ornithologist and Oölogist,* 1892, 17:45 (Lake Erie, Erie Co., fall)—SUTTON, *Ann. Carnegie Mus.,* 1928, 18:77 (Crawford Co. localities and records).

"Long-tailed Duck" KIRKPATRICK, *Auk,* 1895, 12:310 (Meadville, Crawford Co.)—SIMPSON, *Oölogist,* 1910, 27:34; 1911, 28:44; and 1914, 31:210 (Warren, Warren Co., migration).

"Old Squaw" [Secretary], *Abstr. Proc. Delaware Valley Orn. Club,* 1900, 3:14 (Waynesburg, Greene Co., February, *fide* Jacobs)—BOULTON, *Bird-Lore,* 1916, 18:123 (Beaver, Beaver Co., migration)—WOOD, *Wilson Bull.,* 1932, 44:239 (Oak Hall, Centre Co., April)—BROOKS, *Redstart,* 1936, 3:49 (Erie Bay, Erie Co., March).

Harelda hyemalis TODD, *Ann. Carnegie Mus.,* 1904, 2:523 (Erie Bay and Lake Erie, Erie Co., transient)—TODD, in Bausman, *Hist. Beaver Co., Pa.,* 1904, 2:1198 (Beaver Co., spring transient)—BURLEIGH, *Wilson Bull.,* 1923, 35:83 (Highland Park, Allegheny Co., April); 1924, 36:75 (State College, Centre Co., April).

KING EIDER

SOMATERIA SPECTABILIS (Linnaeus)

Description—Immature bird in fall and winter: a large dark duck, with a large head, rather short neck, and comparatively short, swollen bill. The general color is brown, mottled with buff, the upperparts darker. In some males the pattern of the adult may be more or less indicated. There is a white patch under the wings, formed by the axillaries. *Adult female:* similar, but the upperparts mottled with rusty color. This species may be distinguished from the American Eider in the same stage by the *pattern of the feathers on the forehead, which extend to the hinder edge of the nostrils.*

Range and migration—In the breeding season the King Eider is strictly confined to the Arctic Life Zone, but in winter it comes south regularly to the Gulf of St. Lawrence, and occasionally to the Great Lakes, following the same route no doubt as sundry other species of otherwise marine predilections. It has been recorded from Erie Bay on at least seven occasions, in the months of November, December, and January, and is to be regarded as a casual winter visitant at that place. A flock of fifteen or twenty appeared on the bay on November 30, 1889, after a two days' storm, and seven of these came into the possession of Sennett and Warren. "They are all in varieties of immature plumage, none appearing in anything like the breeding condition. The nearest approach to it was one male that showed pearl-gray mixed with dark on top of head; he also had a distinct black V-shaped mark on the white throat. The other males had browner heads and fainter black V-shaped throat-markings. Of the seven, six are males, and one a female in good typical plumage" (Sennett, 1890). Sennett later mentioned a flock of this species observed on Erie Bay in January, 1890. S. E. Bacon has supplied two additional records, which I have already published, based on specimens shot on November 13, 1894, and December 30, 1900, respectively. F. G. Lynch sent to the Carnegie Museum three specimens which he killed on the bay on November 27, 1904, and R. B. Simpson has a single bird shot by a local gunner on the outside beach of Presque Isle on December 22 of the same year. The most recent record refers to a female found in a dying condition on the ice on December 27, 1933.

Habits—The King Eider is a deepwater duck and secures its living mostly from the bottom. The young birds composing the bulk of the wintering flocks appear fearless or stupid, and are thus easy targets. Their flesh is said to be unpalatable.

Somateria spectabilis Sennett, *Auk*, 1890, 7:88 (Erie Bay, Erie Co., November)—[Dwight], *Abstr. No. 2 Proc. Linnæan Soc. New York*, 1890, 10 (Erie Bay, Erie Co., January, *fide* Sennett)—Warren, *Birds Pa.*, ed.2, 1890, 46 (Erie Bay, Erie Co., November)—Todd, *Ann. Carnegie Mus.*, 1904, 2:525 (Erie Bay, Erie Co., records and references).

"King Eider" Simpson, *Oölogist*, 1911, 28:33 ([Presque Isle], Erie Co., December)—Beal and Peterson, *Bird-Lore*, 1934, 36:33 (Erie Bay, Erie Co., December)

WHITE-WINGED SCOTER

MELANITTA DEGLANDI (Bonaparte)

Description—A large duck, the size of the Mallard. *Male: black*, with a small *white spot behind the eye* and a *conspicuous white patch on the wings;* feathering of the forehead and cheeks reaching forward to cover the base of the swollen bill, almost to the nostrils; flat part of bill mostly orange. *Female:* similar to the male, but much duller (browner); head with two conspicuous white spots, on the *cheeks and sides* respectively; bill not so swollen, and without bright colors, but with the feather pattern similar. *Young:* similar to the female, but still duller; white patches on the head less conspicuous and underparts dull whitish, with a brownish wash or mottling. The *white spot on the wings* distinguishes this species from the other scoters in any plumage.

Range and migration—The White-winged Scoter is the best known of the three North American species of this group. It ranges in summer from the Gulf of St. Lawrence to Alaska and even to Siberia, and south to North Dakota in the interior. It winters on both coasts, and in the interior on the Great Lakes. At Erie Bay and on Lake Erie, during the period from October 9 to November 19, 1900, it was the commonest of the three scoters; together with the Surf Scoter, with which it was found in mixed flocks, it frequented the waters of the main lake. An occasional bird would come into the bay, but the large flocks were all seen off the outside shore, resting or feeding on the surface or flying back and forth. No doubt they regularly remain through the winter months in areas of open water far out on the lake, and thus seldom come under the notice of observers. There are records, however, from Erie Bay for late December as well as for February and March, and even for as late in the spring as April 29 (1932—Beardslee).

Scoters are deepwater ducks, and obtain their food by diving; rough water does not seem to hamper their operations. At Conneaut Lake G. M. Sutton found this scoter fairly common during migration and occasional in winter, although the latest fall date he quotes—December 1 (1917)—would scarcely suffice to prove a wintering status. This species appears there usually in late October (October 18, 1926), with September 11 (1910) the earliest record. Spring records range from March 20 (1925) to as late as May 28 (1926). Individuals found thus late are in fine fresh breeding dress, but in the fall movement old males are scarce.

This scoter is the only one that has ever been found in western Pennsylvania away from Lake Erie and Conneaut Lake. A specimen in the Sennett collection was secured at Edinboro, Erie County, on October 6, 1877. H. C. Kirkpatrick has taken it at Sugar Lake, in Venango County, and noted it along French Creek at Meadville in the late fall. R. B. Simpson has seen and shot a few at Warren in April and May, and once as late as June 5 (1917), but he has only two fall records—December 6, 1900, and October 30, 1923. A few sight records have been published for Mercer and Allegheny counties. In 1897 I examined a mounted male in the collection of M. M. Larrabee, said to have been killed near Emporium, Cameron County. The records of A. K. Pierce show that at Renovo this species is an irregular spring transient between April 13 (1899) and May 19 (1904); for the fall there is but one record—October 24, 1915. W. D. Hunter took this scoter at Racine, Beaver County, on October 28, 1925. A recent record for Pymatuning Lake refers to a flock of seven seen there on May 16, 1936 (Chapman, 1937). H. A. McGraw writes that he saw a pair at Lakemont, Blair County, on May 10, 1936.

Oidemia deglandi Warren, *Birds Pa.*, 1888, 233; and ed. 2, 1890, 47 (Erie Bay, Erie Co., fall and winter)—Todd, *Ann. Carnegie Mus.*, 1904, 2:526 (Erie Bay, etc., Erie Co., transient and winter resident)—Burleigh, *Wilson Bull.*, 1923, 35:83 (Highland Park, Allegheny Co., May)—Sutton, *Ann. Carnegie Mus.*, 1928, 18:79 (Crawford Co. localities and records)—Sutton, *Cardinal*, 1929, 2:121 (Crystal Lake, Crawford Co., fall, *fide* Kiskadden).

"White-winged Scoter" Simpson, *Oölogist*, 1911, 28:33; 1914, 31:210 (Warren, Warren Co., April, May)—Sutton, *Bird-Lore*, 1924, 26:123 (Warren, Warren Co., October, *fide* Simpson)—Eastwood, *Bird-Lore*, 1926, 28:274 (Sandy Lake, Mercer Co., May, *fide* Squier)—Savage, *Bird-Lore*, 1932, 34:44; Beal and Peterson, *Bird-Lore*, 1934, 36:33; and Upson, *et al.*, *Bird-Lore*, 1935, 37:47 (Erie Bay, Erie Co., December)—Chapman, *Cardinal*, 1937, 4:108 (Pymatuning Lake, Crawford Co., May).

SURF SCOTER

MELANITTA PERSPICILLATA (Linnaeus)

Description—Intermediate in size between the White-winged Scoter and the American Scoter; feathers of the forehead extended far forward over the bill, but those of the cheeks cut squarely off. *Male:* black, with a *white spot on the top of the head* (even with the eyes) and *another on the nape;* bill much swollen, mostly reddish, white at the base, with a large spot of black. *Female and young:* similar in general to the White-winged Scoter, except for the white patch on the wing, and the different feather pattern at the base of the bill.

Range and migration—The Surf Scoter is a northern-breeding bird, summering from Alaska and the arctic coast to Greenland and Newfoundland. In winter it passes southward along both coasts, and in the interior to the Great Lakes and beyond. In western Pennsylvania it is unknown except at Lake Erie and Conneaut Lake, and from the latter place it has been reported on only a few occasions in October and November. At Erie it occurs regularly and rather commonly during the same two months, associated with the White-winged Scoter in flocks on the open lake. October 9 was the earliest date in 1900. A surf scoter was seen by W. M. Guynes on March 5, 1933—our only spring record. As proof of its wintering there, Warren's remark that he secured a specimen from a gunner in January may be cited. All three species of scoters are known locally as "Boobies," and are little esteemed as food.

Oidemia perspicillata Warren, *Birds Pa.*, ed. 2, 1890, 48 (Erie Bay, etc., Erie Co., transient and winter resident)—Todd, *Ann. Carnegie Mus.*, 1904, 2:527 (Erie Bay, etc., Erie Co., fall transient).

Melanitta perspicillata Sutton, *Ann. Carnegie Mus.*, 1928, 18:79 (Conneaut Lake, Crawford Co., fall transient).

AMERICAN SCOTER

OIDEMIA AMERICANA Swainson

Description—The smallest of the scoters; a duck of medium size. *Male: pure black;* bill black, with swollen basal part bright yellowish orange, the *feather outline of the forehead cut squarely off. Female:* dull dark brown, with faint lighter mottling above; top of head uniform with the back, contrasting with the paler throat and sides of the head. *Young:* similar to the adult female, but lighter brown, the underparts finely mottled with brown and white. In any plumage the species may be recognized by the configuration of the feathering of the forehead, which does not extend forward over the bill.

Range and migration—The summer range of the American Scoter is imperfectly known. Very few actual breeding records have been published, and these are from such widely separated stations as Alaska and Labrador. In the winter the species is abundant along the Atlantic coast from Newfoundland to New Jersey, and it is occasional still farther south. It is also more or less regular at that season on the Great Lakes, although it is more numerous during migration, particularly in the fall. In the vicinity of Erie it is the least common of the three species of scoters, and the few dates that certainly apply to this species all fall in November and December. At Conneaut Lake it is considered by G. M. Sutton (1928) "a rare but fairly regular migrant, which may occasionally occur in winter, when the deep water is free from ice." The spring dates he quotes run from March 21 (1912) to April 22 (1926), and his fall date is November 9 (1925). There are no records whatever from any other part of our region, since this is a species that avoids the rivers and all running water.

Oidemia americana Warren, *Birds Pa.*, ed. 2, 1890, 47 (Erie Bay, Erie Co., transient)—Todd, *Ann. Carnegie Mus.*, 1904, 2:526 (Erie Bay, etc., Erie Co., fall transient)—Sutton, *Ann. Carnegie Mus.*, 1928, 18:78 (Conneaut Lake, Crawford Co., transient).

"American Black Scoter" Bacon, *Ornithologist and Oölogist*, 1892, 17:45 (near Erie, Erie Co., fall).

"American Scoter" Savage, *Bird-Lore*, 1932, 34:44 (Erie Bay, Erie Co., December).

RUDDY DUCK

ERISMATURA JAMAICENSIS RUBIDA (Wilson)

Description—A small, chunky duck, with a short neck; bill as long as the head and much flattened toward the tip. *Adult male in breeding dress:* general color above, *rich rufous chestnut,* this color extending to the throat, upper breast, sides, and flanks; *top of the head and the nape black;* an extensive *white patch on the sides of the head,* reaching from the eye to the chin; wings and tail dusky; chestnut of upper breast passing into the dull grayish white of the rest of the underparts; under tail coverts white; *bill brilliant blue;* feet dusky bluish. *Adult male in fall and winter dress:* brown above, the top of the head darker, more blackish, and the sides of the head and the chin white, as in summer; underparts grayish white, the throat, breast, and sides more or less shaded with brown; wings and tail dusky; bill dull blue; feet dark. *Adult female:* similar in general to the winter male, but duller; head dull brown to just below the eyes; sides of head and chin whitish, with a dark stripe from the gape to the side of the nape; upperparts, wings, and tail, dull brown; underparts dull grayish white, the throat, sides, and flanks washed with brown. *Immature birds* in the fall resemble the adult female in general.

Range—The main breeding area of the Ruddy Duck lies in the western United States and western Canada, but there are on record from outlying regions so many cases of its nesting that no general statement covers them all. Thus, it has been found breeding in the New England states, New York, and Michigan—to mention only those localities closest to our section. The significance of these scattered breeding colonies is not understood; they may be the relicts of a once more extensive range, or an indication of a tendency toward expansion in the present range. While odd individuals and small flocks have been observed on Erie Bay in summer (a statement made by Warren, doubtless on Sennett's authority, and confirmed by S. E. Bacon), there is no evidence that the species has ever bred there. The same remark applies to the birds observed at Conneaut Lake in June and to the female (now in the collection of the Biological Survey) that was shot at Sugar Lake, Crawford County, on July 3, 1895, by F. L. Homer. But when in late May, 1934, our party from the Carnegie Museum saw several mated pairs on Pymatuning Lake, we began to suspect that they might be breeding there—a suspicion that was confirmed the next year when we encountered females leading young broods. The number of pairs breeding at this favored spot has slowly but steadily increased in the past few years.

Elsewhere in our region the species is a transient visitant in migration and a sporadic winter resident. Our records come mostly from the western tier of counties. In the Erie-Crawford district, where alone the Ruddy Duck is of fairly regular occurrence at the present time, it is said to be commoner in the fall than in the spring. But R. B. Simpson reports that he has never seen it at Warren in the fall and that it is irregular even in the spring. Similarly, A. K. Pierce has encountered it during migration at Renovo only six times in the spring and only once in the fall. It has been recorded from Centre County on a few occasions by T. D. Burleigh, but the greater part of our region is at present without definite records. Writing some forty years ago, I referred to the Ruddy as one of the best-known and most abundant ducks on the Ohio River in Beaver County. Then one of the commonest ducks in that locality, it is now one of the rarest; in fact, I have not seen it there since 1904. Evidence from elsewhere in the region supports the conclusion that its numbers have greatly decreased in recent years. Winter records are as follows: Brilliant, Allegheny County, three seen and one shot, on January 17, 1896 (Atkinson); Warren, one seen on February 23, 1894 (Simpson); Erie Bay, one seen on January 30, 1936 (Dilley).

Migration—The ruddy ducks that pass through western Pennsylvania in migration probably winter on the Atlantic coast; their general course, like that of so many in this family, takes them across the Great Lakes in a northwesterly direction in the spring and in a southeasterly direction in the fall. The van arrives sometime in March (March 6, 1932, and March 19, 1933—Erie Bay; March 9, 1918, and March 15, 1925—Crystal Lake, Crawford County; March 25, 1895—Warren; March 25, 1913—Conneaut Lake), while the bulk passes through in April, and the rear guard and stragglers carry the migration far into the following month. Probably even the members of flocks which remain until June reach their usual nesting grounds in plenty of time to lay their eggs and rear their young, since this species is well known to be a late nester. Four ducks noted at Conneaut Lake on August 3, and again on September 16, 1926, must have been either nonbreeding birds or young birds that could have come from no great distance. The fall movement begins about October 1, with September 27 (1893) the earliest date for Erie Bay, and one record as early as September 14 (1892) from Beaver (Wickham). The movement continues through October and until about the middle of November, and some laggards do not get away until near the end of that month. Warren's statement that the Ruddy Duck is a winter resident in Pennsylvania is certainly not generally applicable to the western part of the state.

Habits—The Ruddy Duck is the sole North American representative of a subfamily the members of which differ sharply from all other ducks in certain important respects. The most obvious external peculiarity is the tail, which is composed of eighteen feathers with long, stiff shafts, exposed to their bases. When the duck is swimming, the tail is ordinarily held up stiffly at an angle with the body; and in diving it serves as a rudder. The Ruddy Duck is a more expert diver than some of its allies; in fact, its behavior in general suggests that of a grebe, and like a grebe it can sink under the surface quietly. Moreover, it is as a rule less wary than most other ducks, especially in the fall of the year when the flocks are composed largely of young and unsophisticated birds. This tameness has led to its destruction in large numbers by gunners, and at one time the very existence of the species was threatened. In the old days, when ruddy ducks were common along the Ohio, I used to find them from the end of March until about the middle of April. "Singly and in twos and threes, or more commonly in flocks of a dozen or more, they rarely miss the opportunity to alight which the smooth water at the mouth of the Beaver affords, there to feed, rest, and recruit for the next stage of their long journey. Many a time before sunrise on a frosty March morning, peering out from my hiding-place among the willows, or sitting motionless in the stern of a drifting boat, have I watched a group of these Ducks disporting in the shallow water, swimming about from place to place, and raising themselves in the water to flap their wings" (Todd, 1892).

Spring shooting of ducks has happily been abolished. The troubles of the migrating birds are not thereby at an end, however; let me quote again from my article written in 1892: "Apropos of ducks being driven back by storms, I would say that on April 6, 1889, occurred the most notable instance of this kind that has come under my observation. That was the greatest day for Ducks I ever saw. We had had comparatively pleasant weather for a week or so previous[ly], so that the bulk had left, but the night before it grew very cold and stormy, and about two inches of snow fell. No doubt the storm was more severely felt farther to the northward, for that morning the Ohio was literally crowded with Ducks. Flock after flock came down the Beaver, circled around for a short time and then settled. It is perhaps needless to add that the whole shooting fraternity was very busy that day, but still the Ducks kept coming, until it almost seemed there could not be room for more. It is a noteworthy fact that the Ohio marked the limit of their southward movement, for a visit to Raccoon Creek failed to discover a single individual. Nor did the Ducks alone suffer from the storm; other water-fowl accompanied them, and some migrating land birds were also driven back. As the afternoon wore away, the sun coming out warm, they began to go north again, until by evening but a very few of that mighty host remained."

On the wing the Ruddy Duck may easily be recognized by its rapid, buzzing flight, usually rather low, suggesting that of certain small sparrows. It prefers to migrate by night, and is a silent bird except in the courting season. It rather avoids other ducks, but sometimes associates with the American Coot. As it feeds very largely on vegetable matter, its flesh is usually well flavored, and while not so delicate as that of the pond ducks, is still desirable for table use. It is one of the few ducks that have a distinctive summer dress; and the spring molt takes place during its sojourn in our region. "Trim and jaunty of form, and tastefully yet modestly clad in a suit of warm, brownish red, it is without doubt a beautiful bird. In the fall, however, its plumage is not so bright as at the other season" (Todd, 1892).

R. L. Fricke contributes the following observations on the breeding of this duck at Pymatuning Lake: "On May 29, 1934, about a mile southeast of Linesville, in the area now included in the game refuge, I discovered two males and one female ruddy duck engaged in courting antics. They were swimming about a quarter of a mile from shore, where the water was at least six feet deep. Keeping behind a natural screen of cattails, red osiers, and other shrubbery, I managed to approach rather closely. The males with tails up-tilted and fully spread, kept circling the female, bobbing and nodding their heads and uttering guttural quacks. At intervals one male would pursue the other in an attempt to drive him away, but for the most part both males centered their attentions on the female. If she dived they followed, and upon returning to the surface always kept near her. I watched this interesting performance for about ten minutes and then halted the competition of suitors by collecting one of the males. Both were in full nuptial dress, with bright sky-blue bills.

"On June 19, 1936, in the same area, I located a well-hidden nest of the Ruddy Duck with four eggs. It was built in a clump of bur reeds, green stems of which were interwoven with dry material of the same plant to form a platform about six inches above the surface of the water, which here was about eighteen inches deep. There was no lining of down at this time, but when I again visited the nest on June 22 some had been added, as well as three more eggs—a full set. The eggs are remarkably large for the size of the bird (2.46 by 1.80 inches), and chalky white in color, but they soon become nest-stained."

Erismatura rubida Townsend, *Proc. Acad. Nat. Sci. Philadelphia*, 1883, 68 (Latrobe, Westmoreland Co., transient)—Warren, *Birds Pa.*, ed. 2, 1890, 48 (Erie Bay, Erie Co., summer)—Todd, *Ornithologist and Oölogist*, 1892, 17:61 (Beaver, Beaver Co., transient; habits)—Rhoads, *Auk*, 1899, 16:309 (Emporium, Cameron Co., *fide* Larrabee).

Erismatura jamaicensis Todd, *Ann. Carnegie Mus.*, 1904, 2:527 (Erie Bay, Erie Co., transient)—Todd, in Bausman, *Hist. Beaver Co., Pa.*, 1904, 2:1198 (Beaver Co., transient)—Christy, *Cardinal*, 1923, v. 1, no. 1, [p. 2] ([Clinton Pond], Allegheny Co., April)—Burleigh, *Wilson Bull.*, 1923, 35:83 (Highland Park, Allegheny Co., May); 1924, 36:75 ("State

College" [Scotia and Oak Hall], Centre Co., migration)—SUTTON, *Ann. Carnegie Mus.*, 1928, 18:80 (Crawford Co. localities and records).

"Ruddy Duck" SIMPSON, *Oölogist*, 1911, 28:41, 44; and 1914, 31:210 (Warren, Warren Co., migration)—SUTTON, *Bird-Lore*, 1923, 25:194 (Clinton Pond, Allegheny Co., April, *fide* Christy)—EASTWOOD, *Bird-Lore*, 1926, 28:208 (Sandy Lake, Mercer Co., April, *fide* Elliott; Highland Park, Allegheny Co., April, *fide* Jones)—TRIMBLE, *Cardinal*, 1937, 4:105 (Pymatuning region, Crawford Co., nesting).

HOODED MERGANSER

LOPHODYTES CUCULLATUS (Linnaeus)

Description—The smallest of our three mergansers; in size about equal to the Buffle-head. Bill shorter than the head. *Adult male:* head black, ornamented with a *large compressed crest*, semicircular in outline, *white in color*, with a *black border all around;* back black, with a wedge-shaped bar of the same color running down over either side of the breast; wings dusky, with a white speculum, crossed by two black bars; tail dusky; underparts white, this color reaching well up on the sides of the breast, behind the black of the neck; sides brownish gray to rufous, with fine wavy crossbands, producing a dull effect; bill black; feet brownish. *Female:* head and neck dull brownish, the throat paler; *crest plain brown*, and very much smaller than in the male; upperparts dusky, the wings with a small white spot; dusky shading on breast and sides; rest of underparts white. The young bird in the fall resembles the adult female, but has a smaller crest.

Range—This is the most southerly of the three mergansers. It breeds as far south as Florida on the Atlantic coast, to Tennessee and Arkansas in the interior, and thence to Alaska and Great Slave Lake. Western Pennsylvania comes well within its general breeding range, and the species is a potential summer resident wherever the local conditions permit. In our section, however, the conditions are largely unfavorable; hence the Hooded Merganser is known to most observers only as a transient. Our only acceptable breeding record comes from Clearfield County, where Van Fleet lists the species as a rare summer resident at DuBois, adding that he had taken newly hatched young. His observations were made a good many years ago (1892), when that section was more of a wilderness. It may well be that in the early days this species, like many others, was not so rare and local as it is now.

There are indications that the Hooded Merganser may still nest in other counties in our district. G. M. Sutton remarks (1928) that "some parts of Pymatuning [Swamp] are so admirably suited to the nesting of this species that I believe we may reasonably expect it to be recorded as a breeding bird. Mr. Langdon noted a pair on the extremely late date of June 17, 1926, at Conneaut Lake." Near Linesville H. L. McQuiston saw a female fly from a hollow tree, which, however, contained no nest. R. B. Simpson writes that he has seen the Hooded Merganser at Warren several times in June and July and that old residents say that it formerly bred along the Allegheny River. On June 28, 1895, he shot a bird that was evidently a young of the year, raised not far away. There is a female specimen in the Carnegie Museum that was shot on Buffalo Creek, near Iron Bridge, Armstrong County, on June 10, 1902, by Frank Myers; and S. S. Dickey writes that some years ago a male remained for some time during the summer along Ten-mile Creek near Waynesburg. Such occurrences as these, however, do not necessarily imply that the individuals in question were breeding at the time; they could have been wounded or nonbreeding birds. Eggs of this merganser have been found in this latitude, however, as early as the latter part of April. The finding of a nest or the capture of young birds with the parent is the only incontrovertible evidence of breeding. Winter records are discussed beyond.

Migration—Migration records for this merganser are rather few in number and are fairly well scattered. Most of them come from Erie, Crawford, and Warren counties, where the species seems to be commoner and more regular than elsewhere. In the spring it usually arrives in March, sometimes as early as the first or second week, the exact date depending on the opening of the rivers and lakes. H. C. Kirkpatrick once saw it near the mouth of Conneaut Outlet, Crawford County, as early as February 21 (1897), but this must have been exceptional. March 7 (1934) is an early arrival date for Pymatuning Lake (Seiple). The northward movement lasts for a month or six weeks, and May records are not unusual. All my spring records for the Ohio River were made in April, and several records for Washington County fall in the same month. On the other hand, C. W. G. Eifrig once saw the species at Confluence, Somerset County, on March 11 (1900), and B. H. Christy has observed it at Clinton Pond, Allegheny County, as early as March 24 (1929) and as late as May 30 (about 1919). A. K. Pierce says that at Renovo, in the upper Susquehanna Valley, it is common as a transient; his spring dates lie between March 20 and May 13. Miss A. E. Berg observed a pair near Hollidaysburg on March 19, 1922.

Unlike the other mergansers, this species seems to be almost as common in the fall as in the spring. It reappears about the last of October, and sometimes remains until fairly late in the season if the water keeps open. Even at Warren it has been observed as late as December 10 (1899), and at Meadville, on December 14 (1897). For Renovo, December 7 (1899) is the latest fall date. At Beaver and along Raccoon Creek I have observed it at this season from November 1 until December 6. Late in December it was present in some numbers on Erie Bay during the open winter of 1931–32, and in subsequent years has been repeatedly noted there. Miss Berg saw one bird at Hollidaysburg on February 8, 1928.

Habits—The Hooded Merganser differs from the other two species in shunning deep or running water; it prefers coves, ponds, overflowed meadows, and quiet water along the shore. On Presque Isle it was oftenest seen on the ponds, feeding in company with coots and pied-billed grebes—whence came the name "Pond Fisher" that was used by the local gunners. It is as much a "wood" duck as the Wood Duck itself, and is at home in wooded swamps, where, inconspicuous amid the shadows, it floats along among the snags, dead trees, and partly submerged timber. It feeds mainly on small fish and other forms of aquatic life, but is known at times to take vegetable food also. As a rule it appears in small flocks during migration, but occasionally in smaller groups or singly. Its flight is very swift, and good marksmanship is necessary to bring it down on the wing. Its flesh, although not so rank and fishy as that of other mergansers, cannot be compared with that of the true pond ducks.

Mergus cucullatus Townsend, *Proc. Acad. Nat. Sci. Philadelphia*, 1883, 68 (Latrobe, Westmoreland Co., transient).

Lophodytes cucullatus Todd, *Ann. Carnegie Mus.*, 1904, 2:511 (Erie and Presque Isle, Erie Co., transient)—Todd, in Bausman, *Hist. Beaver Co., Pa.*, 1904, 2:1198 (Beaver Co., transient)—Christy, *Cardinal*, 1923, v.1, no.1, [p.2] (Clinton Pond, Allegheny Co., May)—Burleigh, *Wilson Bull.*, 1924, 36:75 ("State College" [Oak Hall and Scotia], Centre Co., transient)—Sutton, *Ann. Carnegie Mus.*, 1928, 18:62 (Crawford Co. records)—Fricke, *Cardinal*, 1931, 3:42 (Hidden Lake, near Hartstown, Crawford Co., May).

"Hooded Merganser" Simpson, *Oölogist*, 1912, 29:370; and 1913, 30:50 (Warren, Warren Co., March)—Christy, *Cardinal*, 1923, v. 1, no. 2, [p. 13] (Clinton Pond, Allegheny Co., April)—Eastwood, *Bird-Lore*, 1926, 28:273 (Ridgway, Elk Co., May, *fide* Alsop)—Christy, *Cardinal*, 1932, 3:86 (Erie Bay, Erie Co., February)—Savage, *Bird-Lore*, 1932, 34:44; Beal and Peterson, *Bird-Lore*, 1934, 36:33; and Upson, *et al.*, *Bird-Lore*, 1935, 37:47 (Erie Bay, Erie Co., December)—Oudette, *Cardinal*, 1939, 5:47 (Pymatuning Lake, near Linesville, Crawford Co., February).

AMERICAN MERGANSER

MERGUS MERGANSER AMERICANUS Cassin

Description—The largest of the mergansers, equal in size to the Mallard. Head with a slight crest, more pronounced in the female. Bill as long as the head, the nostrils near the middle. *Adult male:* head and neck black with a greenish gloss; underparts white, tinged with salmon pink; black of back separated from the black of the head by a band of white (continuous with the white of the breast); wings dusky, but the *secondaries* white (showing as a *large white area*), *with a black bar across the coverts;* tail gray; bill and feet deep red. *Adult female: head and neck rufous chestnut*, but the chin and upper throat whitish; *upperparts in general, and tail, gray;* primaries dusky, and *secondaries* gray, with a *white area, crossed by a black bar;* underparts white, more or less tinged with salmon buff, the sides shaded with gray. The immature male closely resembles the adult female.

Range—The breeding range of the American Merganser (now regarded as a race of the European form) stretches from the Atlantic to the Pacific coasts, across Canada and the northern United States, and southward in the Rocky Mountains. In the East this merganser has nested in the Adirondacks, and even near Buffalo and in the Montezuma marshes in New York state. Thomas Nuttall wrote that he encountered a female with a brood of young along the Susquehanna River in Pennsylvania, in May, 1832; and Warren quotes several other breeding records for the same general region, including one from Clinton County by Van Fleet. The American Merganser is classed as rare in Van Fleet's manuscript list of the breeding birds of DuBois. While there is nothing to show that the species has nested in our section in recent years, it must have done so formerly when the conditions were more primitive. W. M. Guynes, indeed, writes: "On July 9, 1933, I found three young American Mergansers on 'Thompson's Bay' [Presque Isle] that could not fly. They grew up here, but I never saw an adult with them. They may have been hatched on Long Point or somewhere east of here, and blown in by one of the hard storms from the East not long before I discovered them." At the present time the species is known only as a transient and a winter visitant along our rivers and larger streams and at Erie Bay and Pymatuning and Conneaut lakes.

Migration—The American Merganser is a cold-weather species and arrives late in the fall, as a rule not before November (November 7, 1900; November 13, 1932; November 17, 1934—Erie Bay). The earliest date on record is October 21 (1926), when one bird was shot at Racine, Beaver County, by W. D. Hunter. This merganser seems to be a regular winter resident on Lake Erie; for it always comes to any open water on Erie Bay, and during the mild winter of 1931–32 was much in evidence. R. B. Simpson writes that at Warren, on the upper Allegheny River, it is scarce during mild winters, but in severe winters, when the river is icebound, it is at times common in the open holes. It seldom appears there before December, and females and birds in immature dress always come first; males in full plumage are not common at any time. It leaves for the North very early. In 1894 none were seen at Warren after March 3, but ordinarily the species remains until near the end of that month (in 1895 until April 2). Farther up the river, at Port Allegany, McKean County, the American Merganser appeared during the severe winter of 1935–36, and kept to the spots of swift open water (Scherer). February 10 is an early arrival record for Pymatuning Lake (Oudette, 1939). Many American mergansers were still noted there during the first week in April in 1937; and a flock of one hundred or more was observed as late as April 24 in 1938 (Trimble). Dates of record from French Creek and Conneaut Lake, as quoted by G. M. Sutton (1928), are all in March with one exception (April 9, 1926). In 1932, 1933, and 1934 the species was observed on Erie Bay until April 23 (Guynes). It was very common on the Ohio River at Beaver during the severe weather of February, 1895, when the river was frozen over except for a few open holes where the birds congregated (Wickham). A similar visitation occurred during February, 1936. In 1916 I encountered a single bird as late as May 13 at Raccoon Creek, Beaver County; it was unable to fly, and must have been wounded.

Occasionally the American Merganser visits small lakes and ponds. Dr. Sutton reports a flock of twenty-eight observed at Braddock Reservoir, Allegheny County, on March 11, 1923. J. W. Jacobs has a specimen in his collection that was taken on Ten-mile Creek, near Waynesburg, on February 17, 1898. On the upper Susquehanna, at Renovo, the species seems to be somewhat irregular in its occurrence, judging from A. K. Pierce's records, which lie between February 12 (1904) and April 25 (1901). H. A. McGraw saw a single bird at Lakemont, Blair County, on April 26, 1934.

Habits—My personal experience with the American Merganser has been limited, but I quote from my journal for February 14, 1936: "The coldest winter in many years is now drawing to a close. The Ohio River has been frozen over for several weeks, with a few open holes here and there. For about a month a flock of American Mergansers has been frequenting one such hole a little above the railroad station at Beaver. This morning I counted twelve birds, sleeping at the edge of the ice or swimming and diving in the water. With them were a few Herring Gulls. I am told that there are flocks of ducks, presumably of this species, at other open holes downriver." When the ice broke up a few days later the mergansers disappeared. Other observers record similar experiences. Mr. Simpson, who has studied waterfowl at Warren for a good many years, has had exceptional opportunities for observation. In midwinter, when the Allegheny River has been mostly frozen over, he has seen American mergansers in flocks of greater or less size in the open holes. They are wary and difficult to capture under such circumstances and do not permit a close approach. He says: "Although unfit for food, they are hunted a great deal for sport, and during hard winters a good many are shot. On picking them out of the water after shooting, I have often found mullets and suckers six to eight inches long in their throats, and a fine male that I once shot had a partly digested sucker eleven inches long in its gullet."

Mergansers are almost as expert divers as loons and grebes. H. C. Kirkpatrick, referring to a flock of these birds that he watched along French Creek on one occasion in January, says: "When one of their number caught a fish the others tried to get it, and in their endeavor to do so would shoot over the surface of the water with great speed and much splashing. Both wings and feet were used in propelling themselves forward. After they tired of fishing they crawled out on the ice that lined the shore. Some dressed their plumage; others laid their heads and necks on their backs as though sleeping, and some acted as sentinels on lookout for danger. While fishing they worked against the current" (in Sutton, 1928).

Mergus merganser Townsend, *Proc. Acad. Nat. Sci. Philadelphia*, 1883, 68 (Latrobe, Westmoreland Co., transient).

Merganser americanus Warren, *Birds Pa.*, ed. 2, 1890, 31 (Clinton Co., breeding, *fide* Van Fleet)—Todd, *Ann. Carnegie Mus.*, 1904, 2:509 (Erie Bay and Presque Isle, Erie Co., transient).

"American Merganser" Simpson, *Oölogist*, 1907, 24:87; 1910, 27:100; 1912, 29:248; 1914, 31:53; and 1921, 38:135 (Warren, Warren Co., winter)—Harlow, *Cassinia*, 1912, 15:20 (Center Furnace Swamp, Centre Co., spring)—Eastwood, *Bird-Lore*, 1926, 28:208 (Sandy Lake, Mercer Co., April, *fide* Elliott)—(?)Boulton, *Bird-Lore*, 1928, 30:271 (Presque Isle, Erie Co., May, *fide* Reiter, *et al.*)—Wood, *Wilson Bull.*, 1932, 44:238 (State College, Centre Co., April)—Christy, *Cardinal*, 1932, 3:86 (Presque Isle, Erie Co., February)—Savage, *Bird-Lore*, 1932, 34:44; Upson, *et al.*, *Bird-Lore*, 1933, 35:27; 1935, 37:47; and Beal and Peterson, *Bird-Lore*, 1934, 36:33 (Erie Bay, Erie Co., December)—[?]Boggs, *Redstart*, 1936, 3:92 (Pymatuning region, Crawford Co., June)—Oudette, *Cardinal*, 1939, 5:47 (Pymatuning Lake, near Linesville, Crawford Co., February).

"Merganser" Sutton, *Bird-Lore*, 1923, 25:132 (Raccoon Creek, Beaver Co., December).

Mergus merganser americanus Sutton, *Ann. Carnegie Mus.*, 1928, 18:61 (Crawford Co. localities and records).

Mergus americanus Christy, *Cardinal*, 1923, v. 1, no. 1, [p. 2] (Beaver, Beaver Co., February).

RED-BREASTED MERGANSER

MERGUS SERRATOR Linnaeus

Description—A duck of medium size (smaller than the American Merganser); head with a long, pointed, double crest, less conspicuous in the young; bill as long as the head, the nostrils in the basal third. *Adult male:* head black (all around), with a slight greenish gloss, the neck white in strong contrast, and the *breast rufescent buff with dusky speckling*, this buffy area extending up over the sides; back black, also the inner feathers of the wings; wings with primaries dusky and *secondaries* extensively white, *crossed by two black bars;* tail dusky; underparts from the breast down, white, the sides shaded with wavy black lines, giving a grayish appearance; bill red; feet reddish orange. *Adult female, and young:* grayish above; wings dusky grayish, with a white area on the secondaries, crossed by a black bar; underparts white, the sides grayish; head rufescent buff, browner on the crown, and whiter on the throat; bill and feet dull red.

Range—The Red-breasted Merganser has a wide distribution in both Eurasia and North America; it ranges over the greater part of both continents, breeds northward, and in winter migrates southward. Its breeding range in eastern North America is even more extensive than that of the American Merganser. It does not come any farther south, but it goes much farther north, to Greenland and Baffin Land. Nevertheless, its seasonal status in our section is not exactly the same as that of the other species; it is a transient, rather than a winter visitant.

At Warren R. B. Simpson states that it is a migrant, regular in the spring, occasional in the fall, and rare in mild winters (one was shot on December 29, 1896). H. H. Wickham reported a good-sized flock on December 27, 1889, at a point about five miles up Raccoon Creek, in Beaver County. This species is known to remain very late in the fall at Erie Bay, so late indeed that it has appeared on the "Christmas Census" reports from that locality for several years. I saw a few there on February 5, 1934, in the open water at the city docks. These are the only unquestionable winter records now available. Otherwise the few observers who have noted this species list it as a transient. It is certainly a common migrant on Lake Erie and Erie Bay in both spring and fall,

and is somewhat less common at Conneaut and Pymatuning lakes. Farther south, however, it is scarce. W. D. Hunter has a specimen in his collection that was taken at Racine, Beaver County, on November 14, 1918. I have never observed this merganser along the Ohio River, although I examined a bird killed there on November 25, 1901. D. A. Atkinson records another taken at Tarentum, Allegheny County, on April 4, 1895. B. H. Christy has also seen the species at Clinton Pond, Allegheny County. Oddly enough, although A. K. Pierce found the American Merganser at Renovo on various occasions, he sent in but one migration record for the present form (April 10, 1910). With this exception, there are no records for the Red-breasted Merganser from the mountain or plateau region of western Pennsylvania, and it seems either to avoid this section or to have escaped observation. In view of its comparative abundance in the northwestern part of the state, this scarcity is worthy of remark.

Migration—Our knowledge of the migratory movements of this species is derived in the main from observations made at Erie Bay, Conneaut and Pymatuning lakes, and Warren. In these localities it usually arrives in the latter part of March. February 21 is an exceptionally early record for Pymatuning Lake (Oudette, 1939); and March 15 (1901) is the earliest record for Warren. When the season is backward this merganser may not make its appearance before April, but in any event this is the month when the majority of birds pass through on their way north. Some may linger into the following month; and flocks have been observed even as late as May 25 and 30. Thus the spring migration covers a period of two months. A single bird (no doubt injured) was noted at Clinton Pond, Allegheny County, on June 4, 1923, by B. H. Christy and G. M. Sutton.

It often happens that wounded ducks and other waterfowl, so-called "pensioners," remain behind after the rest of the species has left for the north, so that discretion must be used concerning summer records of this merganser, lest a wrong impression result. Two pairs were noted at Conneaut Lake between June 1 and 15, 1926, by G. M. Langdon; and Dr. Sutton remarks (1928): "These records are so late for migration that we are led to believe that this species may nest in the region." Mr. Simpson saw a female merganser flying up the Conewango on June 11, 1903. Significance is given to these potential breeding records by S. E. Bacon's observations made at Erie. He says: "I have several times seen young mergansers on the bay in July and August, and on one occasion (July 27, 1893) I shot one. All of these birds I am quite certain were of this species, although since I have regretted not having made the identification more positive. On September 6, 1900, I killed an old bird of this species, although it is well into October before the mergansers are expected. Taking all these facts into consideration, I think they breed here occasionally" (in Todd, 1904). As the only other species with which the present one could be confused is the American Merganser, and as Mr. Bacon, who was a keen observer and familiar with both species, could scarcely have made such a mistake, I feel that his statement should be accepted at its face value. C. S. Beardslee reports having seen two red-breasted mergansers at Erie on August 31, 1933. The few arrival records for the fall migration are mostly for Erie Bay, and run from October 17 (1900) to October 29 (1932).

Habits—The name "Fish Duck," by which this merganser is commonly known to local gunners, alludes to the character of its food and to the flavor of its flesh, which is scarcely fit for table use. Mr. Simpson writes that the species is never very common at Warren and usually appears singly or in pairs, sometimes in small parties of a half-dozen or so, and only occasionally in flocks of as many as twenty. In general it prefers the open river and running water. At Erie, however, while "single individuals and small parties were often met with, it was usually found in larger flocks on the bay, being detected but once on the ponds. In the fall it was first noted on October 17, soon becoming numerous, and thus continued up to the time of our departure [November 20]. At this season it was one of the few ducks that frequented the lake proper, and there were occasions when a number of flocks were visible at one time from the outside beach. It was also one of the species which was readily decoyed, and was thus the source of much annoyance to gunners who were in quest of more edible kinds. As a diver it is most expert, and the writer has repeatedly seen an entire flock while engaged in feeding disappear beneath the surface simultaneously. It is said to remain in the fall until the bay freezes over" (Todd, 1904).

W. M. Guynes contributes the following notes made at the same place: "The spring migration of the old males is surely a great sight. I have been fortunate in seeing them come through on two different occasions. At this time there is usually only one female to about fifty males; and they stay on the bay. Later on, the females and young males appear on the main lake in 'rafts' of from one to two hundred birds each—also a wonderful sight. Last of all come the mated pairs, which keep to themselves and leave us quite late in the spring (in 1932 some were seen on June 11)."

Mergus serrator Townsend, *Proc. Acad. Nat. Sci. Philadelphia*, 1883, 68 (Latrobe, Westmoreland Co., transient)—Burleigh, *Wilson Bull.*, 1923, 35:82 (Highland Park, Allegheny Co., transient)—Sutton, *Ann. Carnegie Mus.*, 1928, 18:62 (Crawford Co. records and references)—Fricke, *Cardinal*, 1931, 3:42 (Linesville, Crawford Co., May).

Merganser serrator Todd, *Ann. Carnegie Mus.*, 1904, 2:510 (Erie Bay, etc., Erie Co., transient)—Todd, in Bausman, *Hist. Beaver Co., Pa.*, 1904, 2:1198 (Beaver Co., transient; occasional in winter).

"Red-breasted Merganser" Simpson, *Oölogist*, 1911, 28:44; 1912, 29:370; 1913, 30:50; and 1914, 31:210 (Warren, Warren Co., March and April)—Sutton, *Bird-Lore*, 1923, 25:260 (Clinton Pond, Allegheny Co., May, *fide* Christy)—Christy, *Cardinal*, 1923, v. 1, no. 2 [p. 13] (Clinton Pond, Allegheny Co., spring)—Savage, *Bird-Lore*, 1932, 34:44; and Beal and Peterson, *Bird-Lore*, 1934, 36:33 (Erie Bay, Erie Co., December)—Brooks, *Redstart*, 1936, 3:49 (Erie Bay, Erie Co., March)—Boggs, *Redstart*, 1936, 3:92 (Pymatuning region, Crawford Co., June)—Malley and Shoemaker, *Redstart*, 1937, 4:70 (Beaver River, Beaver Co., migration)—Oudette, *Cardinal*, 1939, 5:47 (Pymatuning Lake, near Linesville, Crawford Co., February).

AMERICAN VULTURES

FAMILY CATHARTIDAE

This is a small but well-defined family, which is centered in the American tropics. Vultures (not to be confused with the Old World birds of the same name) are degenerate raptorial birds. Their heads are almost completely unfeathered; their nostrils are large and open; and their feet resemble those of a fowl rather than those of a hawk. When on the ground they move with a walking gait. They feed on dead or dying animals, and thus perform a useful service as scavengers. During much of the time they circle about high in the air; their flight is extremely graceful, easy, and often indefinitely protracted. The Condor of the Andes (*Vultur gryphus*) and the California Condor (*Gymnogyps californianus*) are among the largest of flying birds. The Black Vulture (*Coragyps atratus atratus*), a characteristic species of the southern states, has been taken repeatedly in our latitude, and should be looked for in western Pennsylvania. Plate 23 illustrates the flight patterns of the Turkey Vulture and the Black Vulture.

TURKEY VULTURE

CATHARTES AURA SEPTENTRIONALIS Wied

Description—A large black bird, with a wingspread of from five and a half to six feet; *tail rounded.* General color black, the back and upper wings with some brown mottling; *head* and upper neck bare of feathers, and *deep red* in color, with the bill whitish; shafts of primaries and of rectrices showing white. *Immature birds* have the head much darker or blackish. *Young* in the downy stage are white.

Range—The North American Turkey Vulture has an extensive east-and-west distribution; it ranges from the Atlantic to the Pacific coasts, but like many other forms of tropical origin and affinities it does not go very far north, and is much commoner southward. When J. A. Allen brought out his memorable paper on the faunal areas of eastern North America in 1871,[1] he listed the species among those whose northward ranges were limited by the Carolinian Fauna. At that time such an allocation was doubtless correct; but the Turkey Vulture, like certain other birds of this fauna, seems to have extended its range considerably in recent years. Hence some distinction needs to be made between actual nesting records and mere occurrences in spring and summer. There are records of the latter class from every one of the New England states, but not a single record of breeding. In central New York the same condition obtains. The birds observed there in late summer and fall may be irregular wanderers in a post-breeding dispersal, while those noted in spring may have overpassed the usual limits in migration. The range-extension of the species may thus have been achieved by such individuals remaining to breed.

In western Pennsylvania there are two main areas where the Turkey Vulture breeds regularly and from which it seems to be spreading into adjacent territory. One of these areas is the ridge and valley section, east of the main Allegheny divide, in the Potomac and Susquehanna drainage. In the counties of Franklin, Fulton, and

[1] *Bulletin Museum Comparative Zoölogy*, 1871, 2:375–425.

Bedford, and in the southern part of Huntingdon County, this bird is not uncommon—as large birds go—in June and July. In Blair County, however, it is reported "not common" (McGraw). So far as we know, nests have not been found in this section, but presumably they are located in the many rocky exposures on the mountainsides. At any rate, the Turkey Vulture may often be seen soaring over the tops of the ridges as well as across the valleys. Farther north, in Centre County, it has been observed repeatedly in summer in the mountains along the Centre-Huntingdon line, and its nest has been found at least once. The Turkey Vulture must thus be listed as one of the birds characteristic of the region east of the main Allegheny Mountains.

The upper Ohio Valley is the other center of dispersion. More than a hundred years ago—in May, 1819—the Turkey Vulture was observed by Major Stephen H. Long's expedition on its way down the Ohio River—perhaps at the very spot where I had my first glimpse of this species on some overhanging cliffs along the south bank of the river, almost opposite the town of Beaver. This was on April 25, 1891, and since that date other turkey vultures have been seen near the same place. On May 25, 1899, no less than eleven were sailing about the steep, wooded hillside along Raccoon Creek, a mile or so from its mouth. I inferred that they were probably nesting not far away. Farther up this stream, in the valley of its principal tributary, Big Traverse Creek, B. H. Christy had also seen the Turkey Vulture; but E. G. Holt was the first to discover a nest in this region. The exact locality of his find, in 1926, was about a mile and a half southwest of Frankfort Springs, Beaver County. A second nest was discovered by Mr. Christy in the spring of 1929, not far from the same spot, and has been in use every year since. There is one nesting record (1931) for the extreme northwestern corner of Allegheny County, at a point directly east of the village of Wall Rose, Beaver County. J. W. Jacobs and S. S. Dickey list the species from Greene County, but they have not found any nests there. From Fayette, Westmoreland, and Washington counties there are a few scattered summer records.

In the northern section the Turkey Vulture is common locally about Pymatuning Swamp, where several nests have been found. Another nesting record comes from Reed's Furnace, Mercer County. R. L. Keesler considers the species a regular summer resident at several points in the neighboring county of Venango (Polk, Raymilton, Pearl, Wesley). Oddly enough, however, it has not been reported as yet from Erie County, save for one July record from the extreme southeastern corner (Guynes). Although Warren quotes Sennett to the effect that it is unknown at Erie, his statement may be discounted by the fact that in Ohio its range extends to the shore of Lake Erie.[1]

It is improbable that in early times the Turkey Vulture ranged across the plateau region. The omission of the species from Van Fleet's list of the breeding birds of DuBois seems significant. In his long experience in Warren County, R. B. Simpson has recorded it but once—in July, 1903—when a group of ten birds was seen at "Smith Hill," near Youngsville, and one was captured alive. There is but one record (July 28, 1897) for Clinton County in the notes of A. K. Pierce. In recent years, however, there has been an unquestionable invasion of the plateau region, and the birds have appeared in considerable numbers where they had never been seen before. The evidence for this extension of range has been aptly summarized by G. M. Sutton in his paper on this species (1928). The reason advanced—the presence of a dependable food supply in the form of deer carcasses—is probably the correct one, rather than any change in climatic conditions. Nests have actually been found near Clearfield and DuBois, while the birds have also appeared farther north, in McKean, Potter, Cameron, and Elk counties. Toward the south the invasion has reached the Cambria–Somerset district. R. V. Mostoller tells me that within recent years the Vulture has appeared on Laurel Hill, southeast of Johnstown, and in 1933 was fairly common there. A. B. Miller reports that it is an uncommon summer resident, not yet known to breed, at Springs, Somerset County. It remains to be seen whether the advent of the Turkey Vulture in the plateau region of western Pennsylvania is of a permanent character.

Migration—As elsewhere near the northern limit of its range, the Turkey Vulture in this region is normally a summer resident only. Thus far there is

[1]Lynds Jones, *Birds of Ohio*, 1903, p. 87.

nothing to show that it ever winters in the ridge and valley section. The only available winter record from anywhere within our limits is that supplied by O. C. Reiter and P. F. Squier, who reported seeing two individuals near the mouth of Raccoon Creek, Beaver County, on December 26, 1926. The Vulture is nevertheless among the early migrants in the spring and appears in the western counties during the latter part of March or early in April. Only a few actual dates of record are available, however. Mr. Christy saw one bird at Clinton Pond, Allegheny County, on March 25, 1928. The earliest date for the Pymatuning area is March 25 (1934—Dilley). In the eastern part of our region it comes even earlier: Dr. Sutton observed it at Mill Creek, Huntingdon County, as early as March 18 in 1921, while T. D. Burleigh supplies arrival dates for State College and vicinity ranging from March 4 (1919) to 26 (1916). Fall records of departure are even scarcer; they are mostly in October, and the latest is November 2 (1916) for State College (Burleigh).

Habits—A bird of sordid coloration, ungainly mien, disgusting feeding habits, and generally unsavory reputation, the Turkey Vulture is scarcely an attractive subject for discussion. It fills an important place in the economy of nature, however, and in warm and tropical countries its services as a scavenger are highly valued. But in the North, where the disposal of dead domestic animals is accomplished by more sanitary methods, one wonders how the Vulture manages to exist, especially when there are a number together. In Pymatuning Swamp, northwest of Linesville, there is a roost of turkey vultures, the source of whose subsistence remains a puzzle. The fact that an overabundance of deer has served to attract this bird to new territory has already been mentioned; whether or not it is similarly dependent upon the native fauna in other sections where it is common and well known has not been determined. Each bird evidently covers a wide range of country in its daily search for food; this conclusion is suggested by the sudden appearance of vultures in places remote from their usual and known haunts. Mr. Simpson cites a case in point: early in July, 1903, a farmer living at "Smith Hill," near Youngsville, Warren County, left a dead calf unburied in a field. This carcass attracted four large birds. A trap was set, and the next morning a fine male vulture was found fast, and nine others were feasting on the calf's remains. After being chased away, the flock vanished completely. The captive was kept in a pen for some time, where it was viewed as a great curiosity. Mr. Simpson later purchased and mounted it. In the farmer's long-time residence in that locality he had never seen a vulture before.

A wing-tipped bird of this species secured between Keating and Karthaus, Clinton County, was once brought to A. K. Pierce, who kept it for several years. It had the freedom of the premises, and made an interesting but mischievous pet, dragging off everything it could hold in its bill. It fed greedily upon meat scraps and offal, but preferred fresh meat to putrid matter. When given a snake (dead or alive) it invariably would spread its wings and tail to their fullest extent, and would then circle its prey for half an hour or more, stamping its feet at intervals, before finally pouncing upon and devouring the reptile. It was friendly with a captive ruffed grouse but had an antipathy for cats and dogs, and took great delight in teasing the dog and in scattering the flock of domestic pigeons by suddenly jumping into their midst.

Whether the Vulture is guided to its food by sight or by scent is a question that has been much discussed. Earlier observations and experiments were inconclusive and unsatisfactory, because more or less contradictory, but the consensus of later research shows that the Vulture hunts by both sight and smell. Moreover, some uncanny method of intercommunication must account for the amazing quickness with which a company of vultures forgathers.

The Vulture at close range is not an attractive object, but seen soaring in the distance it excites interest and admiration because of its wonderful powers of flight. From the ground it rises heavily and with some apparent difficulty, but once clear of trees and other obstructions it sets its wings and mounts upward in a wide, sweeping spiral, soaring around and around, seemingly without effort, and with but a momentary flapping or readjustment of its pinions. Just how all this is accomplished is a problem in aerodynamics—one that man has but lately begun to solve in his mechanical glider. It involves taking advantage of the upward currents of air that are constantly arising from the surface of the earth. The Vulture soars high overhead for hours at a time, seemingly as much at home as when perched on some tall dead tree or gormandizing with its fellows over an unsavory repast.

Nests of this species were not reported from our region until recent years, but there are now several accounts available. The nest found by Mr. Holt near Frankfort Springs, Beaver County, was described (1926) as "merely the natural litter at the ground level inside the hollow shell of an old oak standing in a small patch of woods at the back of the farm. The snag was about four feet in diameter inside and 16 or 17 feet high, but was torn down each side by a wide cleft," through which the bird gained entrance. On June 6 this nest contained one young bird a few days old and one addled egg. In 1930 Mr. Christy published an interesting account of the nest with two eggs which he had discovered on May 5 of the previous year in the same general locality. This nest was in a peculiar location—a natural tunnel beneath a great block of sandstone that had broken off from the slope above. The female parent left the nest and flapped heavily away as Mr. Christy peered in at one end of the tunnel:

"Her cave within was dry. Midway its length lay her two great eggs, as large as a turkey's, of pale clay color, as seemed in the dim light, sparsely though boldly blotched with chocolate brown. They were of opaque appearance, indicating that incubation was well advanced [?]. They lay within a rude rim formed of fragments of rotten bark. These the bird herself must have brought, and manifestly they served as the wall of a nest, to confine the nurturing warmth of her body. Near by, though beyond the ring of bark, lay a long white goose-quill. The dead leaves littering the floor were, from the entrance inward, slightly fouled; otherwise the place was quite clean. A disgusting smell, as of swill, seemed rather to have been left by the bird than to rise from any defilement.

"Particularly we were impressed by the secrecy of it all. While we searched the ravine, no vulture had appeared. The rock was to all appearance an outcrop merely; the existence of the chamber beneath it could hardly have been suspected. The forest had recently been cut; undergrowth screened, and fallen tree-tops obstructed approach. Discovery could only have been by accident." Although the surroundings have altered since the finding of this nesting site, it has been in use every year since, as it probably had been for many previous years. The vultures have clung tenaciously to their home.

A nest found by E. W. Arthur at Reed's Furnace, Mercer County, on June 11, 1927, was located on a rocky outcrop along a stream. He writes (1927): "We found the two eggs lying upon the bare surface, over which at a height of 15 or 18 inches extended a heavy overhang of rock surmounted by trees. The eggs were about three feet back from the edge of a shelf." Dr. Sutton (1928) described two nests from Crawford County; both were in hollow logs. In one instance "the parent bird (probably the female) refused to leave the nest when the young were being brought out for inspection. She feigned death ably and offered no resistance as she was dragged from the nesting cavity." This artifice is often used by the Vulture under such circumstances.

The nest found in northwestern Allegheny County was at the bottom of a burned hollow stump, in a place similar to the one described by Mr. Holt. On July 28 a party from the Carnegie Museum examined this nest, which then held two young birds. A set of eggs taken by R. L. Fricke near Linesville, Crawford County, on May 10, 1935, was about one-fourth incubated. The nest was under the root end of a fallen tree and consisted of merely a few small sticks and bits of bark. Data from present sources indicate that in our region the eggs of this species are laid about the first week in May. Two are the usual number; they measure 2.84 by 1.92 inches.

The difficulty of finding the nest of the Turkey Vulture is described by Mr. Christy: "We tramped the wooded hills, but without success. And let him who supposes it should be a simple matter to find the nest of so large a bird, try it. He will find that it is not. To be sure they are large birds, but they are few—so few that, were they sparrows, they would be counted the greatest of rarities. They build no nest, they carry no food in beak or claw, they make no sound. They scale the sky in great spirals until, attaining a desired elevation, or perhaps a desired air stream, they set their pinions and actually fly out of sight. With a keenness of vision surpassing all, they are unapproachable. The only way to find a nest, we concluded, is to find it by no way, but by accident."

"Turkey Vulture" JAMES, Long's *Exped. Pittsburgh to Rocky Mts.*, 1823, 4 (Ohio River, western Pa., May)—STONE, *Cassinia*, 1906, 9:43 (McConnellsburg, Fulton Co., June)—SIMPSON, *Oölogist*, 1910, 27:35 (["Smith Hill," near Youngsville], Warren Co., July)—SUTTON, *Bird-Lore*, 1923, 25:194 (Mill Creek, Huntingdon Co., April)—STREET, *Cassinia*, 1923, 24:12 (Greencastle to Ft. Loudon, Franklin Co., June)—CHRISTY, *Cardinal*, 1924, v. 1, no. 4, p. 10 (Big Traverse Valley, Beaver Co., June)—REITER and SQUIER, *Bird-Lore*, 1927, 29:28 (Raccoon Creek, Beaver Co., December)—SUTTON, *Cardinal*, 1927, 2:44 (near Harmonsburg, Crawford Co., nesting)—EASTWOOD, *Bird-Lore*, 1927, 29:196 (Raccoon Creek, Beaver Co., spring).

Cathartes aura KIRTLAND, *Second Ann. Rept. Geol. Survey Ohio*, 1838, 177 (Little Beaver Creek, Beaver Co., nesting)—TOWNSEND, *Proc. Acad. Nat. Sci. Philadelphia*, 1883, 66 (Latrobe, Westmoreland Co.)—WARREN, *Birds Pa.*, ed. 2, 1890, 115 (distribution by counties)—JACOBS, *Summer Birds Greene Co., Pa.*, 1893, 5 (Greene Co., summer)—RHOADS, *Auk*, 1899, 16:310 (Beaver, Beaver Co.; Round Island, Clinton Co., *fide* Nelson)—TODD, in Bausman, *Hist. Beaver Co., Pa.*, 1904, 2:1199 (Beaver Co., summer)—SURFACE, *Ninth Ann. Report Pa. Dept. Agric., for 1903*, 1904, 178 (State College, Centre Co., summer).

"Turkey Buzzard" SCOVILLE, *Atlantic Monthly*, 1920, 126:36 (Seven Mountains, Centre Co., nesting)—EASTWOOD, *Bird-Lore*, 1926, 28:343 (Kane, McKean Co., July, *fide* Alsop).

Cathartes aura septentrionalis HARLOW, *Auk*, 1912, 29:470 (Bald Knob, Tussey Valley, Shingletown Gap, Centre Co., summer)—CHRISTY, *Cardinal*, 1923, v. 1, no. 1, [p. 4] (Sewickley, Allegheny Co., summer)—BURLEIGH, *Wilson Bull.*, 1924, 36:70; 1931, 43:39 (State College, Centre Co., migration; summer)—HOLT, *Auk*, 1926, 43:542 (Frankfort Springs, Beaver Co., nesting)—CHRISTY, *Cardinal*, 1927, 2:13 (Frankfort Springs, Beaver Co., June)—ARTHUR, *Cardinal*, 1927, 2:43 (Reed's Furnace, Mercer Co., nesting)—CHRISTY and SUTTON, *Cardinal*, 1928, 2:69 (Cook Forest, Clarion Co., June)—SUTTON, *Ann. Carnegie Mus.*, 1928, 18:121 (Crawford Co., migration and nesting records)—SUTTON, *Auk*, 1928, 45:501 (Clearfield, Elk, Cameron, Potter, and Clinton Co., nesting; extension of range)—CHRISTY, *Cardinal*, 1930, 2:192 (near Frankfort Springs, Beaver Co., nesting)—BURLEIGH, *Cardinal*, 1932, 3:74 (Chestnut Ridge, near Uniontown, Fayette Co., summer)—HEGNER, *Cardinal*, 1934, 3:172 ([Frankfort Springs, Beaver Co.], nesting habits).

HAWKS

FAMILY ACCIPITRIDAE

THIS FAMILY includes all the diurnal birds of prey except the Falcons, Caracaras, and their allies. The Kites, true Hawks, Eagles, Buzzards, and Old World Vultures are members of this group. Although there is great diversity in the structural details of these birds, the essentially raptorial characters of the bill and feet are common to all; the bill is strongly hooked, and the feet are provided with sharp, curved, contractile claws. A tough membrane, the *cere*, covers the base of the upper mandible.

The family is cosmopolitan in its distribution and includes numerous species that are large in size as well as several that are remarkably small. The predatory habits of its members have aroused the prejudice of the unthinking and have given the hawks a bad name as a class, but scientific investigation has conclusively demonstrated the economic value of all but a very few species. The services of predators in controlling the undue increase of noxious rodents and other injurious forms of life have come to be recognized. Predators are a necessary factor in Nature's scheme of checks and balances; their wanton destruction may have unexpected results. Thus, Cooper's Hawk and the Sharp-shinned Hawk are generally regarded as harmful species, to be destroyed at every opportunity; but their decrease has permitted the Red Squirrel to increase, at the expense of the various forest birds whose eggs and young are eaten by the latter. The near extermination of these and other hawks has thus indirectly had an effect precisely opposite to that desired.

I believe that the killing of predatory birds (and animals) is justifiable only when the predators interfere directly with man's interests—as they do when they destroy domestic fowls. Otherwise they should enjoy full legal protection and actual immunity. But not for a moment do I admit that the killing of so-called "game" birds by their natural enemies is an invasion of human rights. The hunters do not own the game; it belongs to the people at large, as does all the wild life. Birds of prey have just as much right to exist as have game birds, and no sound and scientific conservation policy would conceivably discriminate against one in favor of the other. Through study and experiment it has been proved that predators actually benefit (within certain limits) the species on which they prey, by weeding out the weak and unfit and thus keeping the stock strong and virile. To my knowledge no species has ever been exterminated by native predators, but many, alas, have been exterminated by human agency.

The notorious "Scalp Act" of 1885, which placed a bounty on the head of every hawk and owl killed in Pennsylvania, was a vicious piece of legislation, conceived in ignorance and prejudice. This act cost the state a large sum of money and the lives of thousands of its feathered benefactors before it was finally repealed, largely through the efforts of B. H. Warren, whose investigations were set forth with convincing effect in his *Report on the Birds of Pennsylvania.* For some years afterwards, hawks and owls, with certain specified exceptions, enjoyed protection under the law. But in course of time there arose in Pennsylvania a new generation, which knew not Warren, and there came a new demand for discriminatory legislation. This demand was aided and abetted by the sportsmen's organizations and periodicals, which took up the hue and cry for the extermination of "vermin." Consequently, nearly all hawks and owls were removed from the protected class, and a bounty act was also passed directed at one species, the Goshawk, which was blamed for the growing scarcity of the Ruffed Grouse in Pennsylvania. The results of this act were precisely those that its sponsors had hoped for: it cost the state very little, since comparatively few goshawks were actually killed; but large numbers of other species were sent in by those who knew no better. The Pennsylvania Game Commission has recently reversed its former antagonistic position, but nothing save a campaign of education in behalf of these unjustly maligned birds will suffice to save them from virtual extermination everywhere. In the accounts that follow, a great deal of space has been given to a presentation of facts and arguments in their favor.

The Swallow-tailed Kite (*Elanoides forficatus forficatus*) is included in Warren's *Report* (edition 2, 1890, p. 118) on the basis of its occurrence in Allegheny County as alleged by one of his correspondents. I have ascertained that this correspondent kept no written records and left no collection; and under the circumstances I can find no valid reason for admitting the species to the present work.

For flight patterns of certain species, see Plate 23.

EASTERN GOSHAWK

ASTUR ATRICAPILLUS ATRICAPILLUS (Wilson)

Description—One of the larger hawks, with a relatively long tail, and a wingspread of from three and a half to four feet. *Adult:* general color of upperparts, wings, and tail, *slaty gray,* the head blackish, with a whitish stripe over the eye, and the tail with several darker bars; *underparts* white, with fine blackish stripes and dusky cross-bars, giving a *mottled grayish appearance;* under tail coverts unmarked white; eyes red (sometimes orange or yellow); feet yellowish or greenish yellow. *Immature plumage* very different: mottled above with dusky brown and buff; *heavily streaked below with brownish black on a buffy background;* tail marked with grayish and dusky bars; eyes yellow. *Nestling* covered with white down.

Range—The range of the American Goshawk (both races collectively) extends across the continent from coast to coast. It is a species of boreal origin and affinities and is closely related to the Eurasian *Astur gentilis.* The American bird is a characteristic breeding species of the Hudsonian and Canadian life zones, and as such it tends to follow these zones southward along the Rocky Mountains and the Appalachian highlands. Breeding records for New England and New York state, however, are surprisingly few, and as far as I know there are none that would serve to connect our Pennsylvania records with others from the Adirondacks. There are no such records from the Catskills. Audubon, however, speaks of finding the Goshawk breeding in the "Great Pine Swamp" in Pennsylvania, and Warren (1890) quotes Otto Behr concerning its breeding in Sullivan County. Both these localities are beyond our limits, but

Warren also casually remarks, without giving his exact authority, that the species was stated to have "bred regularly" in Cameron, Warren, Elk, Potter, Forest, and McKean counties "fifteen or twenty years ago"—between 1870 and 1875. He suggests that this was in the days when the Wild Pigeon was abundant in these parts, and that since the passing of the Pigeon the Goshawk has also disappeared as a breeding species. In a later publication Warren adds that he himself had seen the Goshawk in June and July in Clinton and Centre counties (exact localities not specified), where he suspected that it was nesting. For Centre County there is also the report of H. J. Roddy, who saw the species there in the summer of 1889 and judged it to be breeding. He tells me that the exact locality was in the Seven Mountains, about two miles west of Bear Meadows. This is the only (presumed) breeding record for our region outside the plateau section.

To R. B. Simpson of Warren belongs the credit for validating the status of the Goshawk as a breeding bird in western Pennsylvania. On May 25, 1906, near Tyler, Clearfield County, he shot a large adult female that was obviously breeding. This circumstance led him to suspect that the species might breed near Warren also, and in the spring of 1909 this suspicion was verified by the finding of a nest. Mr. Simpson examined no less than fifteen nests in all, from 1909 to 1925 inclusive, and has published full accounts of his observations in the several articles cited below. All these nests were found south of the Allegheny River—one of them only two miles south of Warren, the others farther away. One was located at the head of the West Branch of Hickory Creek, about three miles east and a little south of Cobham, while several were found on high ground between two and three miles east and north of Tiona. Mr. Simpson tells me, however, that the persecution to which this hawk has been subjected in recent years and the lumbering over of its chosen haunts have so depleted its numbers that there is now no assurance of finding any nests there.

The Goshawk has been seen by G. M. Sutton at Newmansville, in the extreme northern part of Clarion County, in July, under circumstances that would indicate its nesting. This record would imply that it was breeding in Forest County as well. In 1925 Dr. Sutton published a full account of the nesting habits of this species as studied by him in Potter County. The nest he describes was found near Conrad, but he refers also to other authenticated cases of nesting—at Roulette and in the extreme southeastern corner of the county. An instance of breeding (based on the taking of some young birds) at Firstfork, in Cameron County, is reported by L. A. Luttringer, Jr. (1930). W. M. Dippold writes that in the years 1930–35 he and his brothers found more than forty nests in Jones and Benzinger townships, Elk County, and he has also supplied some additional records from Cameron and Potter counties. While as yet there are no breeding records from McKean and Jefferson counties, it is fair to infer that the breeding range of this species is, or at least was, continuous across the whole of this intervening region, where the topographic, climatic, and forest conditions are uniform throughout. There are at present no breeding records from the plateau region south of the northern part of Clearfield County; but it can be reasoned by analogy that the Goshawk, like other species limited in their southward range by the Canadian Life Zone, must be a potential if not an actual breeding bird much farther south, through the area covered by this zone in Clearfield, Cambria, and Somerset counties. Intensive field work in these sections may confirm this prediction, which is further justified by a nesting that occurred in 1901 near Jennings, Garrett County, Maryland, a few miles south of the Pennsylvania line.[1]

Elsewhere in western Pennsylvania—and in fact over much of the recognized breeding range as well—the Goshawk is a winter visitor only. It is rare or casual as a rule—so rare indeed that I have never yet seen a single living bird in Beaver County. In fact until lately there were only a few scattered records for some of the other counties, and the species is not included at all on most of the local lists. Like some of our other erratic winter visitors, goshawks appear at certain times in unwonted numbers; they come down from the North and spread over our entire territory. Such flights took place during the winters of 1896–97, 1906–7, and 1916–17, but unfortunately only a few actual records for our region can be cited.

[1]Herman Behr, *Auk*, 1914, 31:548.

For the invasions of 1926–27 and of 1927–28, however, we have unusually full records, thanks to Dr. Sutton's interest in accumulating data for the specimens and reports that came to his notice. The most recent flights were those of 1935–36 and 1936–37—the latter perhaps the greatest of all, although the record of it is imperfect. Every county in western Pennsylvania was entered in the course of these invasions, and several hundred goshawks were killed. It is indeed well that these great southward incursions do not take place every season; otherwise this species would soon be doomed.

Migration—Whether or not the goshawks that breed in northern Pennsylvania move southward for the winter has not been determined. Probably they wander more or less at that season, and this explanation may account for the individuals that occasionally appear here and there almost every year. Mr. Simpson has often observed the birds during the winter in Warren County, and he has found pairs near the nest as early even as February 22—a circumstance which suggests that they are sedentary after all. In any event the resident birds could be only an insignificant fraction of the total goshawk population during seasons of relative abundance. Analysis of the records secured on such occasions indicates that these invasions come from the northeast and proceed toward the west and the south. In his paper on the distribution of the Goshawk (1931) Dr. Sutton points out that the species occurs regularly every fall at Blue Mountain, near Drehersville, Schuylkill County, in eastern central Pennsylvania, and from there spreads out westward and southward. During seasons of special invasion its numbers are naturally greatly augmented.

While there are a few September records for both 1926 and 1927 it is entirely possible that these may pertain to birds that did not have far to come from their breeding grounds. The real movement did not get under way until late October, and was at its height during November. Allowance must of course be made for the fact that more birds were killed during the latter month because of the hunters then in the field. The movement continued through December and January, but in February there was a perceptible falling off in numbers. In 1927 the latest date recorded was February 27, from Osceola Mills, Clearfield County. For 1928 there are several March records, the latest for March 4, when single goshawks were shot near Erie and at Philipsburg. Presumably the remnants of the goshawk hosts retreat to the northward during the month of March, but the only available records are those from W. M. Guynes, who reported that he saw goshawks at Erie on March 17, 1934, and on April 23, 1933. The latter is certainly a very late date.

Habits—Among our birds of prey the Goshawk has long been famed for its boldness, its ferocity, and its powers of flight. Its large size and great strength enable it to kill and carry off prey almost as heavy as itself. No other hawk, save the Duck Hawk, has more dash and courage, or habitually preys on such large game. In the north country, where the Goshawk is widely distributed even if not abundant, its usual quarry is hare and ptarmigan. For reasons not yet well understood there are recurrent periods when both these species become very scarce. Deprived at these times of their accustomed source of food, the hawks turn southward and eventually enter our borders. This is undoubtedly the explanation for the several incursions that have taken place in the last forty years. A curious circumstance is that certain of these invasions seemed, contrary to the rule in the migrations of most species, to consist almost exclusively of adult birds. This was true of all the later invasions, and also of that in 1896–97, so far at least as southern Ontario was concerned.[1] E. H. Forbush suggests in explanation that during periods of scarcity of food the hawks rear practically no young.[2]

The Goshawk is properly a forest-ranger; it likes to live and hunt in the "big woods." Little wonder, then, that the wooded slopes of the Pennsylvania mountains and the timbered areas of some of the western counties are favorite hunting grounds in these enforced southern excursions. In our region the Goshawk preys on cottontail rabbits instead of hares, and in place of ptarmigan it takes ruffed grouse and ring-necked pheasants. When pressed by hunger it comes out into the open country and makes inroads upon the farmer's poultry. So little does it fear man that often it does not hesitate to strike and carry off full-grown fowls under his very eyes. The economic status

[1]J. H. Fleming, *Auk*, 1907, 24:72.
[2]*Birds of Massachusetts*, 1927, 2:119.

of this species, as determined by its food, has been investigated by several competent authorities, whose observations agree. Two recent investigations applying to the state of Pennsylvania at large will be examined here. Dr. Sutton (1931) says:

"Of the 266 stomachs examined, sixty-one were empty. In the 205 stomachs and crops which contained food, some of them holding the remains of two or more creatures, were found flesh, feathers, fur, or bones of the following: 81 Ruffed Grouse (*Bonasa umbellus*); 55 cottontail rabbits (*Sylvilagus floridanus*); 29 domestic chickens, including several White Leghorns, a Rhode Island Red hen, and a Barred Plymouth Rock rooster; 16 Bob-Whites (*Colinus virginianus*); 13 Ring-necked Pheasants (*Phasianus colchicus*); 10 gray squirrels (*Sciurus carolinensis*), one of the black phase; 3 red squirrels (*Sciurus hudsonicus*); 2 Chipmunks (*Tamias striatus*); 2 white-footed mice (*Peromyscus* sp.); 1 domestic pigeon; 1 Meadowlark (*Sturnella magna*); 1 Cardinal (*Richmondena cardinalis*); 1 Song Sparrow (*Melospiza melodia*); and 8 small birds the species of which were not determined. Three contained unidentifiable flesh and fur. Three stomachs each held the remains of two Ruffed Grouse; one, a Bob-White and a cottontail; one, a chicken and a cottontail, and so on. Six birds which were killed while attacking poultry, or pursuing prey, had much food in their stomachs. Eight birds were killed while chasing or killing poultry, two while killing grouse, and two while chasing squirrels. Three birds were killed while carrying prey a few feet above the ground: one, a female, was carrying a large Rhode Island Red hen; one, a full grown cottontail; one, a young cottontail; one, a grouse. Many of the birds which had eaten grouse and Bob-Whites had swallowed the feet *entire*, and mandibles were also found in almost every case. Not many feathers were found in the stomachs—evidence that Goshawks pluck their prey rather carefully before eating it. The crop alone of one individual held over twelve ounces of grouse flesh. One male, shot by Mr. Charles Mack, on February 14, 1928, at Slatington, Lehigh County, is thought to have killed twelve hens before it was captured."

Merrill Wood announces the following results of an examination of the stomach contents of 294 goshawks killed during the last great flight (1936–37): "Ruffed Grouse, 40; Northern Flicker, 2; Eastern Crow, 1; Domestic Fowl, 45; Domestic Pigeon, 1; unidentified birds, 13; total birds, 102. Cottontail rabbit, 23; deer mouse, 1; chipmunk, 1; red squirrel, 4; gray squirrel, 19; shrew, 4; unidentified mammals, 8; total mammals, 60. Contained food, 156; empty, 138."[1] These figures are in substantial accord with Dr. Sutton's.

Were the Goshawk common in settled districts —as common even as some of the smaller hawks, such as the Sharp-shinned Hawk—it might become a menace to the raising of poultry. But it comes only at infrequent intervals, and its depredations in the aggregate cannot equal those committed by other enemies of the barnyard. Every resident should of course have the right to protect his property by shooting any hawk attempting to molest it.

The chief count against the Goshawk, however, comes not from the farmer, but from the sportsman, and arises from the fact that the Goshawk destroys much game. The contention of the sportsman that all predatory animals and birds that kill "game" are "vermin" and should be exterminated, is a grave misconception. It arises from the assumption that the sportsman, or hunter, has the sole vested interest in the wild game, that it virtually belongs to him, and that he alone has the right to kill it. This assumption is clearly false from a scientific and economic standpoint, and even from a purely legal standpoint. The wild predators have precisely the same right to exist as has anything else. They have their place in Nature's scheme of things, and they have their function to perform in maintaining a proper balance among living beings. It is well known to those who have made a study of the subject that predatory animals and birds actually benefit the species on which they prey, by weeding out the weak and the unfit. It is only when these predators turn from their wild prey to domestic animals and fowls that man is justified in interfering with their activities. The act placing a bounty on the Goshawk was a legislative mistake—an ill-considered law that is indefensible from any point of view. It would be far better for the state to compensate the farmer for the comparatively few domestic

[1] *Auk*, 1938, 55:123.

fowls he may lose than to forfeit the services of the birds of prey in general.

It is inevitable that during a widespread invasion by this species the numbers of grouse will noticeably decrease; but wild birds are amply able to hold their own against their natural enemies. In an article on the Goshawk law, published not long ago, B. H. Christy tried to show that on an average each goshawk kills one ruffed grouse in a week.[1] This estimate is probably much too low, but does anyone suppose that all the grouse killed by goshawks in Pennsylvania during the 1927–28 invasion would amount to more than a fraction of the 150,000 killed by licensed hunters during the same season?

It is even questionable whether ruffed grouse suffer seriously from our nesting goshawks. The pair nesting in Potter County, described by Dr. Sutton, had been living largely on chipmunks and squirrels; no grouse remains whatever were in sight. Mr. Simpson says that about the tree in which he found a nest were many remains of victims, mostly red squirrels and chipmunks, but no signs of grouse or rabbits; and he adds that only a few yards from the nest he came upon an old grouse and her brood of large young. Mr. Dippold, however, found conditions somewhat different in Elk County; his experience will be recounted later.

The Goshawk is said by some writers to have preyed extensively on wild pigeons on their nesting grounds, and Audubon relates that he once saw a goshawk attacking a flock of bronzed grackles passing over the Ohio River. Probably the species does not bother the smaller birds to any appreciable extent. In one instance (reported by Mr. Simpson) a blue-headed vireo was building its nest in a low hemlock just under a goshawk's nest; again, a pair of slate-colored juncos were neighbors of a hawk. Imagine such happenings had the hawk been a sharp-shin instead! The Goshawk in action is a good example of the typical bird of prey. Like other hawks that hunt through the forest, it captures its quarry by a sudden lunge—a surprise attack such as is made by the members of the cat tribe among mammals—rather than by a sustained pursuit. Sometimes it dives from its perch in a tree, or turns aside from leisurely flight through the forest, to fasten on its prey with amazing quickness, striking with its powerful talons and holding its victim with a terrible death grip until life is extinct. The swiftness and precision of its attack are such that often its intended victim may have no warning whatever. The method is described by Dr. Sutton (1925), in an account of his own experience with a pair of goshawks at their nest:

"The most memorable thing about the day's experience was the method of attack of the female bird, which has partly explained to me the ease with which some of these birds capture their prey. When the Goshawk left her perch to strike at me her set wings and slim body were for several seconds almost invisible and the only actual movement perceptible was the increase in the size of her body as she swiftly approached. Three times at least I was looking directly at the approaching bird *and did not see her at all* because the lines of her wings and body so completely harmonized with the surroundings, and the front view was comparatively so small.

"In alighting the bird struck heavily and often the dead branches were completely broken off. Her every movement combined power, grace, and swiftness to an amazing degree, and only once, as she sped by me did I succeed in whacking her with a stick. She seemed so surprised at my ability to fight back that after my clumsy victory she was quiet for over ten minutes and viewed me pensively from the top of a distant tree!"

The nest to which Dr. Sutton alludes was built in a beech tree, about thirty-five feet from the ground. "It was a great bulky affair, about three and one-half feet across, and three feet in depth, and rather beautifully designed for so large a structure." The lining was of fine hemlock twigs. At the time of his visit (May 19) the two young were almost ready to leave the nest, and one actually did leave when he climbed up. The male parent eventually appeared on the scene, but was not so bold and vicious as its mate, which repeatedly swooped at the intruders and screaming savagely tried to drive them off.

Mr. Simpson's experience has been similar. He has found mated pairs (in the latter part of February) guarding their nesting territory by screaming and dashing about overhead in the usual hawk fashion. He has found nests in four

[1]*Cardinal*, 1930, 2:220–232.

different kinds of trees—beech, oak, pine, and hemlock, but always in "big timber" and in remote and unfrequented locations. The nests are large, coarse structures made of sticks; they are placed anywhere from forty to seventy-five feet up, and are often hard to reach. The birds use the same nest for several successive seasons, but add a new lining of leaves and hemlock sprigs every year. The eggs are laid late in March or early in April; they vary from two to four in number, and are pale blue or greenish blue, unmarked. They average 2.31 by 1.78 inches. Securing the eggs always involves more or less risk, as the female parent is often quite savage. For further interesting details concerning the finding of goshawk nests the reader is referred to the series of articles by Mr. Simpson, cited in the references below.

Mr. Dippold's manuscript account of his wide experience with this hawk in Elk County deserves extensive quotation. He writes as follows:

"It was about six years ago [1930] that I became more than casually interested in the Goshawk. My interest was aroused by the accidental discovery of a nest containing three young birds that were undergoing the change from the downy feathers of the nestling to the brown-streaked first plumage.

"Examination of the ground under the nest-tree disclosed a large number of grouse bones and gave me a profound respect for the Goshawk as a hunter. Since then I have made it a practice to search for the remains of birds and animals near hawk nests, and it has always seemed to me that there was a direct ratio between the relative abundance of grouse in the hawks' territory (say within two or three miles of the nests) and the quantity of grouse bones at the nests. Thus, if grouse were plentiful, virtually all the bones found in the nests and on the ground near by would be those of grouse. Several times during the winter I have come upon piles of grouse feathers on the snow and all the signs pointed to goshawks as the killers. Twice I have surprised goshawks on the ground in the act of stripping grouse they had killed.

"The nesting habits of the Goshawk seem to be so fixed and its selection of a certain type of woodland for a nesting site so constant that one familiar with its habits has very little trouble in locating most of the nests within a given favorable area. The nests are usually built in beech trees in remote, little-disturbed stands of large timber, at elevations between twenty and sixty feet, or occasionally even higher. All but three of the nests I have found were in beeches, built in three-pronged forks; the exceptions were in large maples and one in a black birch. Almost always in the vicinity of an occupied nest could be found one or more old nests. Sometimes old nests are refurbished and used again. I have found five nests, one new and the others in various stages of disrepair, on an acre of woodland that was peculiarly suitable."

Two sets of three eggs each, collected on April 6 and 21, 1935, respectively, by Mr. Dippold and R. L. Fricke, are in the Carnegie Museum; they fit the description already given. The first set was fresh; the second, about one-third incubated. Concerning the latter Mr. Dippold writes: "The nest was about thirty-five feet high in a beech. Under the 'roost-tree' near the nest the ground was literally covered with grouse bones." He goes on to explain: "Almost invariably the regular perch of the male goshawk is easily identified. Usually it is a lower, horizontal limb on a large maple near the nest-tree. Anyone familiar with goshawk nesting sites can readily spot this 'roost-tree' by the droppings underneath and the bones of the kills. Sometimes a quantity of bones on and about a log or stump near the nest-tree indicate where the prey has been eaten."

The parents are often very bold in defense of their nest, Mr. Dippold says, and will fly at an intruder in a threatening manner. One female that he shot had its feet covered with porcupine quills. Very likely the animal was climbing the nest-tree and the goshawk attacked it. "When nesting goshawks are disturbed their usual cackling cry at times becomes a scream, not loud but conveying an impression of peevishness, and when the birds are circling over a nest that is being molested they give vent to a steady, long-drawn-out, wheezy whistle." Young goshawks, Mr. Dippold adds, "seem to stay close to the nest through the first five or six months of their lives."

Accipiter atricapillus Warren, *Birds Pa.*, ed. 2, 1890, 124 (distribution by counties)—Warren, *Bull. Pa. Dept. Agric.*, no. 17, 1897, 171 (Centre and Clinton Co., summer).

"Goshawk" Simpson, *Oölogist*, 1906, 23:136; 1909, 26:85 ([near Tyler], Clearfield Co., May); 1907, 24:87; 1909, 26:25, 85,

119; 1911, 28:47; 1912, 29:370; 1913, 30:32; 1915, 32:29; 1920, 37:91; and 1922, 39:36 (Warren Co., nesting, food, etc.)—JACKSON, *Oölogist*, 1911, 28:47 (Warren Co., nesting, *fide* Simpson)—BARNES, *Oölogist*, 1924, 41:37 (Port Allegany, McKean Co., February, *fide* Abbott)—[CHRISTY], *Cardinal*, 1927, 2:16 (Kennedy Tp., Allegheny Co., November)—CHRISTY, *et al.*, *Bird-Lore*, 1937, 39:44 (Pymatuning region, Crawford Co., winter).

Astur atricapillus SHARPLES, *Cassinia*, 1910, 13:25 (Warren Co., nesting; Simpson's record)—SUTTON, *Cardinal*, 1927, 2:35 (western Pa. records and references; food)—SUTTON, *Auk*, 1927, 44:563 (Newmansville, Clarion Co., July, breeding?)—CHRISTY, *Cardinal*, 1930, 2:201 ("Waggoner's Hollow," Allegheny Co., December)—LUTTRINGER, *Cardinal*, 1930, 2:220 (Firstfork, Cameron Co., nesting; food)—CHRISTY, *Cardinal*, 1931, 3:15 (Sewickley Heights, Allegheny Co., December).

Astur atricapillus atricapillus BURLEIGH, *Wilson Bull.*, 1924, 36:77 (State College [Shingletown Gap and Musser's Gap], Centre Co., migration)—SUTTON, *Wilson Bull.*, 1925, 37:193 (Conrad, Roulette, etc., Potter Co., nesting)—SUTTON, *Ann. Carnegie Mus.*, 1928, 18:126 (Conneaut Lake, "Meadville" [Guys Mill], and Hartstown, Crawford Co., winter)—Editor, *Cassinia*, 1929, 27:27 (Warren Co., nesting, *fide* Stuart)—SUTTON, *Wilson Bull.*, 1931, 43:108 (western Pa., distribution and abundance).

SHARP-SHINNED HAWK (Plate 6)

ACCIPITER VELOX VELOX (Wilson)

Description—A small hawk, of slender build, with long tarsi, and a relatively *long, even tail*, gray with dusky barring. *Male* about the size of the Northern Flicker, and with a wingspread of twenty to twenty-three inches. *Female much larger*, equaling a pigeon in size; wingspread twenty-four to twenty-seven inches. *Adult:* above (including top of head, wings externally, and tail), slate color (male) or dusky brown (female); bars on the wings and tail below, dusky and grayish-white; throat white, with narrow dusky shaft-streaks; under tail coverts white; rest of *underparts* and tibiae with *rufescent and white* barring and very narrow dusky shaft-streaks; eyes yellow to red; feet yellowish; bill black, with yellowish cere. *Immature:* above, brown, more or less varied with white about the head; *below*, whitish, with *heavy brownish streaks*, narrower on the throat, and absent on the under tail coverts; wings and tail barred as in the adult. The small size, rounded wings, and elongated and nearly even tail will always serve to identify the species.

Range—This little hawk, a representative of the European Sparrow Hawk (*Accipiter nisus*), enjoys an extensive range in North America, both in latitude and in longitude. It breeds from the Gulf of Mexico northward to Hudson Bay, but in the northern part of its range it is a summer resident only; the individuals that nest there retire southward in winter. In western Pennsylvania it is common and generally distributed throughout, although this region is evidently near the northern limit of its winter range. It is certainly much more regular in summer than in winter, but R. B. Simpson has seen it even as far north as Warren during some of the coldest weather ever known there, and W. M. Guynes once observed it at Erie in January. Although the winters in Beaver County are much milder than in some other sections, I have but one winter record from there—December 28, 1919. There are a few winter dates for Allegheny County also, and the species must occur occasionally at this season throughout our region. While it is not so common as formerly, all observers agree that it is more numerous in migration, especially in the fall, than at any other time of the year.

Migration—Some uncertainty naturally attaches to migration records for such species as this, since there is always the chance that they may refer to wintering individuals. There are no arrival dates available for any of the southwestern counties. In Crawford County the Sharp-shin has been observed at Atlantic on March 30 (1926) and at Conneaut Lake on April 8 (1914). In 1900 the first one was noted at Presque Isle, Erie County, on April 7, and from April 17 to 21 there was a considerable flight. The same year, according to A. K. Pierce, the species appeared at Renovo on March 23, although his arrival dates for other years run from April 1 to 18. B. H. Christy saw one bird at Presque Isle on March 30 in 1929. The fall movement takes place mostly in September and October. At Presque Isle this hawk was noted between September 26 and October 23 (1900), while last dates for Renovo are in September and the first week in October. Individuals were seen in 1927 at Sewickley, Allegheny County, and at

Raccoon Creek, Beaver County, on October 23 (Boulton, 1928). These dates correspond with those from adjacent regions and may therefore be accepted as representing the normal movements of this species.

Habits—Ornithologists are accustomed to use an artifice known as "squeaking"—a sound made by kissing the back of the hand—for the purpose of calling birds closer. The scheme is often very effective, particularly in the breeding season, as the sound imitates the cries made by a bird in distress. More than once, while I have stood partially hidden in thick woodland, my "squeaking" has unexpectedly called up a sharp-shinned hawk. It always comes with a rush, darting through the branches with uncanny speed and assurance to bring up suddenly in surprise on the nearest convenient perch, while all the small birds in the vicinity scatter in every direction. This species is pre-eminently a "bird hawk," fitted by form and habit for preying on small birds. These constitute its main fare, as shown both by observation in the field and by examination of stomach-contents, but upon occasion it will pick off mice and squirrels, and if hard pressed will even take insects. Once let a sharp-shinned hawk discover how easy it is to catch young poultry, and it will return again and again to the same place.

Wanting in size and strength to carry off large prey, this hawk nevertheless sometimes attacks quarry of considerable size. Mr. Simpson once effected the escape of a mourning dove that had been brought down by a sharp-shinned hawk; and on another occasion he heard a pileated woodpecker making loud outcries against a desperate attack: "The big woodpecker was on the trunk of a large tree and its only hope seemed to be to keep the trunk between itself and its enemy. Every time the hawk rushed, the woodpecker would whisk around the tree. All the time, the Pileated made the woods ring with its distressed cries." How the affair would have ended had not Mr. Simpson decided to enter the fray on behalf of the woodpecker is uncertain. Woodpeckers as a class are slow-moving birds, and as a rule are easy picking for the hawk, but that a sharp-shin should venture to attack such a large species as the Pileated seems strange. Even the Crow has been known to give way before the vicious onslaught of this bold marauder, and all the smaller birds are in terror at its appearance.

"The Sharp-shinned Hawk is remarkably swift, graceful and skilful in flight. It swings and circles through the forest aisles and even among thick branches with the greatest ease. Its usual cross-country flight consists of periods of steady flapping, with short intervals of sailing, but sometimes, especially during its migrations when hundreds may be seen passing at very considerable heights, much soaring is indulged in" (Forbush, 1927).

I have never observed any such extensive flight in Pennsylvania during migration as that described by P. A. Taverner and B. H. Swales from Point Pelee, Ontario, when several scores of sharp-shinned hawks were in sight at once, winging their way southward.[1] Migrating sharp-shins keep mostly in the open country around clearings and cultivated districts. In August and September they are in the habit of harrying the large flocks of bronzed grackles and red-winged blackbirds that gather in the grainfields, and they throw their ranks into the wildest confusion. English sparrows suffer also; they are not safe from attack even near dwellings, as the hawks, seemingly unafraid of man's presence, often extend their raids into towns and villages. So suddenly do they appear, and so swiftly do they strike, that their victim is often borne off before the interested spectator realizes what is happening. The only chance that small birds have is to dive into thick covert, where the hawk cannot follow.

In nesting time the Sharp-shinned Hawk seeks out the deep woodland, and if undisturbed returns season after season to the same spot for the purpose of raising its young. Mr. Simpson thinks that the nests he has found in Warren County were all old crow nests, built over, but all the nests I have ever examined were certainly built by the hawks themselves. The hemlock is a favorite nest-tree, since its thick, leafy branches tend to conceal the bulky structure. A grapevine tangle in a treetop is another site often chosen. A nest that I found in such a situation was built upon an old squirrel nest, and it seems that this choice is not unusual. Mr. Simpson and I have each found one nest in a beech tree.

Usually the nests are built next the tree trunk

[1] *Wilson Bulletin*, 1907, 29:92.

and rather low—seldom over forty feet from the ground—and are not hard to reach. A most unusual but not unique location is reported by D. A. Atkinson, on the authority of one Samuel Clark, who collected eggs from a nest built in a natural cavity of an oak, where a limb had broken off. The hole was lined with twigs, leaves, and some fine grasses. The typical nest, however, is a rough platform of dead twigs, about fifteen to twenty inches in diameter, and quite shallow. Sometimes there is a special lining of bark or other soft substance, but often the bed for the eggs is also made of twigs, of much smaller diameter. Five eggs are usually laid, but sometimes only four, and occasionally six. They are round ovate, average 1.46 by 1.20 inches, and in ground-color are pale bluish green, but the markings vary greatly. In a set that I collected in 1890 the blotches range from brownish black, sharply defined, in the most heavily marked specimen, to a rufescent shade, blurred in outline, in the most lightly marked. In some eggs the dark blotches coalesce and give the effect of only a few large colored areas, while in others there is only a ring of spots around the larger end. Between these two extremes there is every possible degree of intermediate coloration.

The birds do not begin building until April, when most of the other hawks already have eggs. May 20 is an average date for full sets, but Mr. Christy reports a nest that held three eggs as early as May 4. The nest is frequently betrayed by the actions of the parent birds. Long before any eggs are laid, one or both are on guard; they resent intrusion into their domain by flying back and forth, uttering their characteristic prolonged outcries. With eggs or young in the nest, they become more insistent in their protests, and will often attack a climber. The female sits very closely; but the male is always near, and his vociferations suffice to indicate where his interests lie. On June 22, 1894, I found a nest near Driftwood, Cameron County, after my attention had first been attracted by the actions of the male. The nest was in a hemlock, not over twenty feet from the ground, and the tail of the female could be seen projecting over the edge. She left when I commenced the ascent, and with her mate retired to a little distance until I had reached the nest itself. Then they both came at me with loud outcries, darting straight for my head till within a couple of feet, when they suddenly veered off in another direction, only to repeat the attack. This performance was kept up as long as I was at the nest, which was nothing but a platform of sticks and twigs resting on some smaller branches next the trunk. There were at this date one unhatched egg and three young birds, not more than a few days old and covered with yellowish-white down. They were of different sizes and evidently not of exactly the same age.

The young must require a great deal of food while growing, and it is in the midst of the breeding season that the adult hawks destroy so many of our smaller birds. Since these are on the whole beneficial species, their destruction must count against the Sharp-shinned Hawk from an economic standpoint. But so long as the hawk does not interfere with poultry, and so long as its numbers are no greater than at present, it should be left undisturbed. Some of the charm of our woods and wild lands would be gone with the passing of this spirited little bird of prey.

Astur fuscus Wied, *Journ. f. Orn.*, 1858, 6:15 (Ebensburg, Cambria Co., fall).

Accipiter fuscus Townsend, *Proc. Acad. Nat. Sci. Philadelphia*, 1883, 66 (Latrobe, Westmoreland Co.).

Accipiter velox Jacobs, *Oölogist*, 1892, 9:248 (Greene Co., nesting)—Todd, *Auk*, 1893, 10:39 (Chestnut Ridge, near Two Lick, Indiana Co., June), 44 (Coalport, Clearfield Co., June)—Jacobs, *Summer Birds Greene Co., Pa.*, 1893, 6 (Greene Co., nesting)—Fisher, *Bull. Div. Orn. and Mammal.*, no. 3, 1893, 32 (Beaver, Beaver Co.; food)—Warren, *Bull. Pa. Dept. Agric.*, no. 17, 1897, 159 (McKean Co.; food)—Cope, *Cassinia*, 1902, 5:13 (Kettle Creek Valley, Oleona, Potter Co., June)—Todd, *Ann. Carnegie Mus.*, 1904, 2:552 (Presque Isle, Erie Co., migration)—Todd, in Bausman, *Hist. Beaver Co., Pa.*, 1904, 2:1199 (Beaver Co., resident)—Keim, *Cassinia*, 1905, 8:37 (Port Allegany, McKean Co., summer)—Harlow, *Auk*, 1912, 29:477 (southern Centre Co.); 1918, 35:24 (Centre, Huntingdon, Mifflin, and Allegheny Co., summer)—McGrew, *Oölogist*, 1916, 33:72 (Pittsburgh, Allegheny Co., February)—Christy, *Cardinal*, 1923, v. 1, no. 1, [p. 4] (Sewickley, Allegheny Co.)—Burleigh, *Wilson Bull.*, 1923, 35:86 (Harmarville, Allegheny Co., nesting)—Christy and Sutton, *Cardinal*, 1928, 2:69 (Cook Forest, Clarion Co., May)—Sutton, *Ann. Carnegie Mus.*, 1928, 18:124 (Crawford Co. records and references; nesting)—Burleigh, *Wilson Bull.*, 1931, 43:40 (State College, Centre Co., nesting).

"Sharp-shinned Hawk" Stone, *Cassinia*, 1906, 9:44 (Scrub Ridge, west of McConnellsburg, Fulton Co., June)—Simpson, *Oölogist*, 1907, 24:87; 1909, 26:169; 1911, 28:54; 1920, 37:134; and 1922, 39:36 (near Warren, Warren Co., nesting); 1912, 29:329 (head of Tionesta Creek, Warren Co., summer)—McGraw and Hays, *Bird-Lore*, 1920, 22:31 (near Altoona,

Blair Co., December)—SCOVILLE, *Cassinia*, 1920, 23:19 ([Charter Oak, Huntingdon Co.], nesting)—SUTTON, *et al.*, *Bird-Lore*, 1923, 25:24, 132 (Monaca to Raccoon Creek, Beaver Co., December), 260 (Allegheny Co., nesting); 1924, 26:267 (Crafton, Allegheny Co., nesting, *fide* Walter)—BOULTON, *Bird-Lore*, 1928, 30:14 (Sewickley, Allegheny Co., October, *fide* Christy; Raccoon Creek, Beaver Co.)—COPE and HAWKINS, *Forest Leaves*, 1934, 24:26 (E. Tionesta Forest Reserve, Warren and McKean Co., summer)—JACOBS, *Oölogist*, 1936, 53:56 (Fish Creek, Greene Co., nesting).

Additional nesting records: McDonald Reservoir, Washington Co. (Sutton; specimen in Carnegie Museum)—Gayly, Allegheny Co. (C. E. Schinneller; specimen in Carnegie Museum)—Verona and Tarentum, Allegheny Co. (Atkinson; specimen in Carnegie Museum)—Sewickley Heights, Allegheny Co.; Big Traverse Valley and Frankfort Springs, Beaver Co. (Christy)—Industry, Beaver Co. (Karl D. Wilson; specimen in Carnegie Museum)—Hemlock Island, Crawford Co.; Presque Isle, Erie Co. (Hicks)—Beaver Dams, Blair Co. (McGraw)—Sharon, Mercer Co. (McQuiston)—Clarksville, Mercer Co. (Seiple)—Jamisonville, Butler Co. (Elliott)—near Gaibleton, Indiana Co. (Sutton, *fide* Terres).

COOPER'S HAWK (Plate 6)

ACCIPITER COOPERI (Bonaparte)

Description—A slender, medium-sized hawk with short wings and a relatively long, *rounded tail.* Similar to the Sharp-shinned Hawk in general form, proportions, and coloration, but differing in its larger size and in the rounded shape of its tail. A small male Cooper's hawk might easily be mistaken in life for a large female sharp-shinned hawk, except for its distinctive tail. The wingspread is from twenty-seven to thirty inches in the male, and from twenty-nine to thirty-six inches in the female.

Range and migration—The general range of this hawk is almost as extensive as that of its smaller cousin, the Sharp-shinned, but on the whole is less northerly, not reaching beyond the Gulf of St. Lawrence in the East. Like the latter species, too, Cooper's Hawk is a migrant in the northern part of its range but a permanent resident southward. It occurs throughout our region, and although it cannot now be considered a common species, a fairly widespread local distribution is suggested by the records that have come in, even from comparatively well-settled areas. The total number of birds is probably not much smaller than that of the Sharp-shinned species, but like other hawks this one is decreasing in numbers yearly, and to the next generation it will doubtless be as rare as the Goshawk is to ours. Its seasonal status is about the same as that of its smaller relative: it is a regular summer resident, semiregular in winter, and most numerous during the season of migration. Its migrations are performed in March and October, but no definite dates are available. The individuals seen in winter may possibly have come from farther north; certainly they must wander more or less at that season.

Habits—Cooper's Hawk is a large replica of the Sharp-shinned Hawk, or, conversely, the latter is a miniature of the former. In general behavior, fierce disposition, and daring spirit, the two are much alike, but the greater size of Cooper's Hawk enables it to capture larger prey. These two species are mainly responsible for the disfavor with which all hawks are generally but unjustly regarded. If they would confine their destructive propensities to wild birds and animals they could more easily be defended, but unfortunately they are likely to extend their forays to the poultry yard, with results that tend distinctly to hurt their standing. A large female Cooper's hawk can carry off a pullet almost as heavy as itself. Appearing suddenly on the scene, it swoops on its victim and bears it off before the astonished farmer realizes what is happening. If its career is not summarily ended by a charge of shot, a single bird will often return day after day for fresh victims. Sometimes, indeed, it strikes down a fowl a little too large to handle in flight; it will then proceed to devour its victim on the spot, and may even return a second time to its kill.

Under natural conditions, or away from inhabited sections, Cooper's Hawk preys mostly on birds, large and small. Some small mammals, such as squirrels and chipmunks, are taken, but very few mice. The Ruffed Grouse is a favorite prey, and the Bob-white is often hunted in open country. In referring to my first experience with this hawk, I noted that "the crops and stomachs of five young, still in the down, which were taken from a nest in the top of a tulip tree on July 8, 1891, contained among other things not identified, the remains of a brown thrasher and light-colored flesh, evidently that of a young ruffed grouse, of which there was a covey in the same woods" (in Fisher, 1893).

E. H. Forbush says that the characteristic reiterated cry of this species strikes terror into the bird population of the woods: "When the 'Cooper's' fierce 'cucks' ring through the sunny, leafy woods of June, the hush of death pervades everything. All erstwhile cheerful thrushes and warblers become still and silent. . . . The bird hunts more or less upon the wing, usually flying low near the ground or at a very moderate height above the trees, darting suddenly upon any victim taken by surprise. It gets up great speed almost immediately, and it alights on a perch with the quickness and readiness of a flycatcher. It will follow a bird into a thicket, often plunging through by sheer velocity, and so driving its victim out into the open and capturing it by its superior powers of flight, or by so terrorizing it that it becomes almost helpless from fright."[1]

Against this positive statement may be ranged G. M. Sutton's observations (1928) of a Cooper's hawk's nest at Pymatuning Swamp: "Under this nest, and plainly in view from it, were the nest and three eggs of a pair of Cerulean Warblers, yet during the two days of observation about the tree the hawks were never seen to disturb their small neighbors." Since the warblers are later comers than the hawks, their choice of a nesting site must have been a deliberate one. Dr. Sutton adds: "One difference was most noticeable in the nesting-activities of the Cooper's and Sharp-shinned Hawks. About the clump of hemlocks where the Sharp-shinned Hawks nested there were absolutely no small birds. When one entered that dark clump of evergreens one seemed to be in a lifeless spot. Without question the smaller birds had all either been captured or frightened away. About the nests of the Cooper's Hawk this was not at all the case. One might properly infer, I should say, that Cooper's Hawk hunts its prey some distance away, whereas the Sharp-shinned Hawk takes everything which occurs near its nesting-grounds."

An interesting note in the same article is contributed by H. C. Kirkpatrick: "I once observed a Cooper's Hawk near the nesting-stub of a Flicker, which [the hawk] to all appearances was waiting for the owner of the nest to leave. At any rate, no sooner had the Flicker done so, than the hawk struck and killed it, and feasted upon it at once. In spite of the fact that I walked up to within forty feet of it to shoot, it would not take wing nor relinquish its hold on its prey."

Cooper's Hawk is properly a woodland bird and seeks out a secluded spot in the forest in which to build its nest and rear its young. A beech tree is frequently chosen, from all accounts, but any large tree will answer. In the Pymatuning area R. L. Fricke has found several nests that were built in hemlocks. Sometimes an old crow nest is remodeled or used as a foundation, but oftener the hawks build an entirely new nest for themselves. Usually it is placed against the trunk, or in the crotch of a large branch, higher up in the tree than a sharp-shinned hawk would build, and in a more inaccessible position. It is a substantial structure of sticks and twigs, compactly arranged and more or less hollowed out for the eggs; the cavity is lined with finer material—leaves, grasses, or bits of bark. The eggs, three to five in number, are laid in late April (earliest date, April 19—Atkinson) or early May, and sometimes later, if the first nesting is interfered with. Ordinarily they are pale bluish white, immaculate; but sometimes they show brownish spotting, pale and poorly defined. They are more ovate in shape than the rounded eggs of the Sharp-shinned Hawk. Average measurements are 1.90 by 1.50 inches. Sometimes the parent birds are very bold in the defense of their nest and will dash at an intruder with loud and vehement outcries. Other pairs retire to a distance and utter their usual cries, which have been likened to the cackling call notes of the Pileated Woodpecker. Strange as it may seem, both crows and squirrels sometimes interfere with the nesting activities of this hawk.

Accipiter cooperi Townsend, *Proc. Acad. Nat. Sci. Philadelphia*, 1883, 66 (Latrobe, Westmoreland Co., nesting)—Jacobs, *Oölogist*, 1892, 9:247, 248 (Greene Co., nesting)—Todd, *Auk*, 1893, 10:44 (Coalport, Clearfield Co., June)—Jacobs, *Summer Birds Greene Co., Pa.*, 1893, 6 (Greene Co., nesting)—Fisher, *Bull. Div. Orn. and Mammal.*, no. 3, 1893, 38 (Beaver, Beaver Co., nesting, food, *fide* Todd)—Baily, *Auk*, 1896, 8:293 (Williamsville, Elk Co., June–July)—Cope, *Cassinia*, 1902, 5:13 (Tamarack Swamp, Clinton Co., and Kettle Creek Valley, Potter Co., June)—Todd, *Ann. Carnegie Mus.*, 1904, 2:553 (Presque Isle, Erie Co.,

[1]*Birds of Massachusetts*, 1927, 2:113.

March–April, September)—TODD, in Bausman, *Hist. Beaver Co., Pa.*, 1904, 2:1199 (Beaver Co., resident)—FORREST, *Oölogist*, 1911, 28:116 (Washington, Washington Co., breeding)—HARLOW, *Auk*, 1912, 29:470 (southern Centre Co., nesting); 1918, 35:24 (Pa.)—CHRISTY, *Cardinal*, 1923, v. 1, no. 1, [p. 5] (Sewickley, Allegheny Co., nesting; occasional in winter)—BURLEIGH, *Wilson Bull.*, 1923, 35:86 (Squaw Run, Allegheny Co., nesting); 1924, 36:69 (State College, Centre Co., resident)—SUTTON, *Ann. Carnegie Mus.*, 1928, 18:125 (Crawford Co. records and references; nesting)—LUTTRINGER, *Cardinal*, 1930, 2:220, 223 (Kennard, Mercer Co., January)—BURLEIGH, *Wilson Bull.*, 1931, 43:39 (Charter Oak, Huntingdon Co., nesting)—BURLEIGH, *Cardinal*, 1932, 3:74 (near Uniontown, Fayette Co., summer).

"Cooper's Hawk" WICKHAM, *Oölogist*, 1888, 5:92 (Beaver, Beaver Co., January)—SIMPSON, *Oölogist*, 1909, 26:169; 1920, 37:92; and 1922, 39:36 (Warren, Warren Co., nesting)—HARLOW, *Oölogist*, 1912, 29:308 (Centre Co., nesting)—BURLEIGH and MCGREW, *Bird-Lore*, 1917, 19:23 (Pittsburgh, Allegheny Co., December)—MILLER, *Oölogist*, 1919, 36:155 (Pine Grove Mills, Centre Co., nesting)—SAVAGE, *Bird-Lore*, 1923, 25:24 (McKeesport, Allegheny Co., December)—ABBOTT, *Oölogist*, 1924, 41:49 (Port Allegany, McKean Co., March)—SQUIER and ELLIOTT, *Bird-Lore*, 1925, 27:40 (Deer Creek district, Allegheny Co., December)—EASTWOOD, *Bird-Lore*, 1927, 29:126 (East Pittsburgh, Allegheny Co., December, *fide* Squier)—BOULTON, *Bird-Lore*, 1928, 30:195 (Raccoon Creek, Beaver Co., February)—BERKHEIMER, *Bird-Lore*, 1933, 35:27; etc. (near Osterburg, Bedford Co., December).

EASTERN RED-TAILED HAWK (Plate 7)

BUTEO BOREALIS BOREALIS (Gmelin)

Description—A large hawk, of robust form, with a wingspread of from forty-six to fifty-six inches, and a relatively short, nearly even tail. Underparts extensively white, with dark streaks (no bars), and wings also extensively white below. *Adult:* above, brown, varied with buff and gray; *tail conspicuously rufous*, with a narrow black bar near the whitish tip; underparts whitish, sometimes shaded with buff, and with some dark (brown or black) streaks, especially on the throat, sides of the breast, and across the middle of the abdomen, where they tend to form a band; lower abdomen, under tail coverts, and tibiae, dull buffy white; under side of wings extensively white, with some dark mottling; eyes brown; bill dark, with yellowish cere; feet yellowish. There is great individual variation in the amount and intensity of the dark markings on the underparts. *Immature:* upperparts in general similar to those of the adult, but grayer in tone; tail decidedly grayish, with narrow dusky barring (the tip paler, whitish); underparts with more white, the throat and breast often pure white medially; upper abdomen showing dusky streaks as in the adult, and tibiae often with small dusky or brownish spots; feet duller than in the adult. As the bird grows older the rufous tail appears and increases in prominence. *Downy young* are dull white.

Range and migration—The Red-tailed Hawk is a species characteristic of North America, where it ranges across the continent from east to west, and from Costa Rica northward to the forests of Canada. In the West and South it splits up into several well-marked races. The typical eastern race, to which our Pennsylvania birds belong, ranges from the Gulf states northward to Newfoundland, Quebec, and Hudson Bay. In the more northern part of this range it is migratory, but elsewhere it is sedentary. Years ago, even within my memory, it was one of the commonest and best-known hawks of our region, but its numbers are now sadly reduced, and the destruction of the big timber has moreover left it without suitable nesting sites over much of the territory it once frequented. More than forty years ago J. W. Jacobs called it "abundant" in Greene County, and his series of eggs collected then would seem to bear out this statement. Today it is probably most numerous, everything considered, in the ridge and valley section and in the plateau region, where there are still some extensive timbered areas, but there is probably no part of the region where it does not occur in greater or less numbers. It is certainly a permanent resident in the western counties, even as far north as Crawford County. Since I have seen certain pairs of birds in the same place at all seasons, it is fair to infer that they do not wander very far. In Warren County, however, R. B. Simpson declares that this hawk is to be classed as a summer resident, as it arrives late in March and occurs only occasionally in mild winter weather. Whether this holds true in the other northern counties is doubtful. S. S. Dickey writes of having seen a flock of about a dozen red-tailed hawks in migration at Waynesburg in the fall.

Habits[1]—The Red-tailed Hawk is oftenest seen wheeling high in the air above woodland. Its pattern against the sky is distinctive. The arc of the fanned-out tail lies well within the compass of the extended wings. The wings at their tips are rounded and digitated. This great circling form, once made familiar, is always recognizable. As the bird swings across the line of sight, a slight upward reach of the wings will be noted; and, at the same instant, if it be an adult, a glimpse will be gained of the clear burnt sienna of the upper surface of the pliant tail, dispelling any remaining doubt of identity. Yet another characteristic is the bird's only note, a long-drawn scream, easily imitated by whistling.

The Red-tail frequents wood-skirted wastelands, fields, and meadows, and may often be found perched in erect attitude on the branch of a dead tree, on watch for meadow mice and like prey below. When disturbed it swings its body to horizontal position, stands for a moment on straightened legs, and then flaps heavily away, with a wing motion not unlike a crow's. In still and heavy air the flight is always thus labored. The flapping may be intermitted with sailing, particularly as the bird approaches a perch. But when the air is buoyant, the bird's powers of soaring are magnificent: it easily rises to great heights; and I suspect that in summer these hawks spend much time in the sky, beyond the range of ordinary vision. On a high wind a red-tail will glide and swoop with great speed—perhaps in courtship, perhaps in play. Assailed by smaller birds—by crows, particularly—it will easily mount beyond pursuit.

The bird's food is essentially small mammals: primarily mice, occasionally a rabbit or a squirrel. Like all living creatures, it will take whatever suitable food falls to its lot, and will even seize frogs and snakes. A few of many stomach examinations have revealed traces of game birds devoured, but these birds were likely weak or sickly; for the Red-tail is too slow to capture vigorous, swift-flying grouse. In outlying places a fowl may now and then be taken, but such trespasses are the exception and scarcely deserve serious consideration. The species is, so far as human interests are concerned, a most valuable one; the ignorance with which it is persecuted to the point of extermination is most deplorable.

The Red-tail usually nests in March. I have seen birds carrying nest material as early as February 26 and as late as April 12. I have found eggs as early as March 17 and as late as the middle of April. The nest is built in a forest tree—commonly a white oak, sometimes a hickory—and usually at a height of from sixty to eighty feet. The tree ordinarily is one that stands in a continuous patch of forest; but even so, the nest is conspicuous. So large an object could hardly be concealed at a season when the trees still are bare. The tree is likely to be near the edge of the patch of woodland; or, again, the nest may be placed in a lofty treetop surmounting the forest, and in most cases is so situated that undetected approach is impossible. And, indeed, until incubation is in progress, a hawk will leave its nest while the visitor is yet a long way off.

It may be a matter of chance that by far the greater number of nests known to me have been situated on the northward-facing slopes of ravines, which, in our region, are the steeper slopes. J. W. Jacobs (1898) graphically describes the actions of a particular pair of birds on their nesting ground in Greene County. He tells of their great anxiety at his approach, which was always first discovered by the male from his favorite perch in a treetop in a small, sparsely wooded tract about three hundred yards down the hollow from the nest. With a shrill scream he would spread his wings and flap lustily to the upper woods, where his mate joined him; both would then circle higher and higher, beyond gunshot. Then by a circuitous route they would descend slowly to the lower woods, alight in the treetops, and continue their shrill screams. On only one of many occasions in my experience did a nesting bird make a threatening attack. Mounting overhead, she swooped down at great speed and with a loud rushing sound close by my head. After two or three trials, she retired.

One nest that I examined may be described as typical. The ground beneath was strewn and the bushes hung with strips of grapevine bark, the material used as lining in the nest. The nest was built of newly broken oak sticks—dead pieces, of course—almost three feet long, heaped up in the

[1]Account contributed by Bayard H. Christy.

supporting crotch to a height of about three feet. The cavity above was ten inches in diameter and four inches deep, and was lined with grapevine bark, smoothly coiled within. On the rim lay a spray of pine needles.

Invariably the nest contains such a green spray, usually of pine needles; in one instance a spray of laurel was found instead; and in yet another, the cavity of the nest was wreathed about most beautifully with many sprays of pine. Sometimes food will be found lying on the rim of the nest even before the eggs are hatched. This usually consists of mice; once, however, I found a rabbit's leg. The eggs commonly are two, sometimes three, or rarely even four, in number. The surface of the shell is dull and lusterless. The ground-color is ordinarily bluish white; and in markings there is wide variety. Sometimes the eggs are scarcely marked at all; sometimes they are heavily blotched and clouded; but ordinarily they are lightly wreathed with spots of pale brown and lilac. Average measurements are 2.36 by 1.80 inches.

Mr. Jacobs (1892) thus describes a red-tailed hawk's nest in Greene County: "After a rough walk of five or six hours . . . I came within sight of a nest from which I took a set of two eggs in 1890. Last year I was disappointed at this point as the nest was not used. But this time I had found the object of my search, for high in the air was a small speck circling against the light flying clouds, which told conclusively that the male was watching his home. The female left the nest while I was yet some distance off and joined her mate.

"The tree was a 'shellbark' hickory and very tall and slender, and rocked and jerked dangerously in the strong wind which prevailed throughout the day. The nest was placed near the top in a very small crotch ninety feet above the ground, and was extremely hard to reach, owing to the oscillating motion of the tree. The material used was sticks and twigs for the body of the nest with a lining of fine strips of bark and was rather bulky, measuring thirty-six inches in diameter and twelve inches deep, outside. While I was nearing the nest both old birds swooped down toward me several times passing quite close.

"The eggs were two in number, white with soiled bluish tint. One is marked over the entire shell with light cloudings of yellowish brown, thickest on the small end. The second . . . was marked sparingly and chiefly on the larger end."

The Great Horned Owl, which nests a month or six weeks earlier and which manifests adaptability in the choice of nesting sites, will often appropriate a red-tail's nest of the year before. For a number of years I have had under observation the nesting of a particular pair of red-tails. One spring they built for themselves a new nest, a quarter of a mile from their old one. The second nest was much more conspicuous. On that account I was somewhat anxious for the continued safety of the hawks, and I wondered what had caused them to change their residence. Later I discovered a pair of owls in possession of the old nest, and I suspected that the owls had displaced the hawks. During three successive years, however, I found on the same nesting site first a pair of red-tailed hawks, next a pair of great horned owls, and then a pair of hawks again. The owls merely occupied the nest that the hawks had built; but the hawks, when they came a second time into possession, built upon the old one an entirely new nest. More than once a hawk's nest has been found built upon a squirrel's dray as a foundation. Mr. Jacobs mentions one based on "an old dilapidated crow's nest."

Buteo borealis Townsend, *Proc. Acad. Nat. Sci. Philadelphia*, 1883, 66 (Latrobe, Westmoreland Co., breeding)—Teulon, *Jour. Boston Zoöl. Soc.*, 1883, 2:11 (Bradford, McKean Co.)—Jacobs, *Nat. Companion*, 1886, 2:4 (Waynesburg, Greene Co.; nesting)—Elliott, *Ornithologist and Oölogist*, 1886, 11:34 (Mercer, Mercer Co., habits)—Norris, *Ornithologist and Oölogist*, 1886, 11:67 (Washington, Washington Co., nesting)—Jacobs, *Oölogist*, 1892, 9:247 (Greene Co., nesting)—Todd, *Auk*, 1893, 10:39 (Chestnut Ridge, near Two Lick, Indiana Co., June)—Jacobs, *Summer Birds Greene Co., Pa.*, 1893, 6 (Greene Co., nesting)—Baily, *Auk*, 1896, 13:293 (Williamsville, Elk Co., nesting)—Jacobs, *Gleanings from Nature*, 1898, 1:5, 14, 21 (Waynesburg, Greene Co., nesting)—Cope, *Cassinia*, 1902, 5:14 (Tamarack Swamp, Clinton Co., June)—Todd, *Ann. Carnegie Mus.*, 1904, 2:553 (Erie and Presque Isle, Erie Co., resident)—Todd, in Bausman, *Hist. Beaver Co., Pa.*, 1904, 2:1199 (Beaver Co., resident)—Keim, *Cassinia*, 1905, 8:37 (Port Allegany, McKean Co., summer).

"Red-tailed Hawk" Jacobs, *West Am. Scientist*, 1887, 3:184, (Waynesburg, Greene Co., nesting)—Wickham, *Oölogist*, 1888, 5:92 (Beaver, Beaver Co., winter)—Stone, *Cassinia*, 1906, 9:42, 44 (Scrub Ridge, west of McConnellsburg, Fulton Co., nesting)—Simpson, *Oölogist*, 1907, 14:183; 1909, 26:25; 1911, 28:162; 1913, 30:32; and 1922, 39:36 (Warren, Warren Co., nesting, etc.)—Jacobs, *Oölogist*, 1910, 27:50 (Greene Co., description eggs)—Dickey, *Oölogist*, 1914, 31:28, 63 (Waynesburg, Greene Co., nesting), 171 ([Charter Oak],

Huntingdon Co., May); 1918, 35:140 (Waynesburg, Greene Co., migration)—JACOBS, *Oölogist*, 1918, 35:45; 1932, 49:110 (Waynesburg, Greene Co., nesting)—SCOVILLE, *Atlantic Monthly*, 1920, 126:37 (Treaster Valley, Centre Co., March)—CHRISTY and HEGNER, *Bird-Lore*, 1920, 22:31 (Sewickley and vicinity, Allegheny Co., December); 1924, 26:30; etc. (upper Raccoon Creek, Beaver Co., etc., December)—MILLER, *Bird-Lore*, 1922, 24:23 (Springs, Somerset Co., December)—HOFFMAN, *et al.*, *Bird-Lore*, 1923, 25:23 (Grove City, Mercer Co., December)—JONES, *et al.*, *Bird-Lore*, 1923, 25:25; etc. (Deer Creek, Allegheny Co., December)—EASTWOOD, *Bird-Lore*, 1926, 28:136 (Harmarville, Allegheny Co., winter, *fide* Squier), 213 (Rector, Westmoreland Co., May, *fide* Knauz; Deer Creek, Allegheny Co., nesting, *fide* Squier)—CHRISTY, *Cardinal*, 1931, 3:45 ([near Patton's Point], Beaver Co., May)—ELLIOTT, *Cardinal*, 1934, 3:170 (Raccoon Creek, Beaver Co., December)—COPE and HAWKINS, *Forest Leaves*, 1934, 24:26 (E. Tionesta Forest Reserve, Warren and McKean Co., summer).

Buteo borealis borealis HARLOW, *Auk*, 1912, 29:470 (Fillmore, Centre Co., *fide* Spencer); 1918, 35:24 (Greene, Washington, Warren, and Indiana Co., breeding)—CHRISTY, *Cardinal*, 1923, v. 1, no. 1, [p. 5] (Big and Little Sewickley creeks, Allegheny Co., and Big Traverse Creek, Beaver Co., resident)—BURLEIGH, *Wilson Bull.*, 1924, 36:77 (State College, Centre Co., migration)—CHRISTY and SUTTON, *Cardinal*, 1928, 2:69 (Cook Forest, Clarion Co., summer)—SUTTON, *Ann. Carnegie Mus.*, 1928, 18:127 (Crawford Co. localities, resident)—WOOD, *Wilson Bull.*, 1933, 45:79 (Bradford, McKean Co., albino).

WESTERN RED-TAILED HAWK

BUTEO BOREALIS CALURUS Cassin

Description—This hawk is extremely variable in coloration. There are both light and dark phases, with all degrees of intermediacy. The dark extreme is uniform dark sooty brown except for the rufous tail.

Range and local status—The Western Red-tailed Hawk is casual in the East during migration. Its sole claim to a place in this list rests on a specimen shot by W. D. Hunter near Racine, Beaver County, on November 18, 1912. This is a young bird in the reddish-brown phase. Herbert Friedmann of the United States National Museum, to whom it was sent for examination, has written me that it is the only specimen (of over two thousand red-tails he has handled) that he has seen in this particular plumage. Mr. Hunter has deposited the specimen in the Carnegie Museum.

HARLAN'S HAWK

BUTEO BOREALIS HARLANI (Audubon)

Description—A dark-colored race of the Red-tailed Hawk—dull sooty brown, mottled with white, and somewhat streaked on the underparts; tail often more or less rufous. The status of this form is still in dispute; it is considered by some as a distinct species.

Range—This is a bird of the Pacific Northwest; its occurrence in the East is purely accidental. The capture of a specimen near Racine, Beaver County, "in the autumn about ten years ago" (1927) therefore constitutes a noteworthy record, and adds another bird to the Pennsylvania list. The specimen was sent to P. A. Taverner of the National Museum of Canada for examination and report. He has written that it is "a juvenal *harlani* in almost complete black phase but showing suggestions of *krideri* blood in the white intermixed on the back."

NORTHERN RED-SHOULDERED HAWK (Plate 7)

BUTEO LINEATUS LINEATUS (Gmelin)

Description—A fairly large hawk, but smaller than the Red-tailed; wingspread from thirty-three to fifty inches. *Adult:* brownish dusky above, the head with indistinct paler streaks; the bend of the wing more or less rufous; wings and tail blackish, with narrow white bars; *underparts strongly shaded with light rufous color*, inclining to bars on the upper abdomen, flanks, and tibiae, and leaving only the lower abdomen and crissum unmarked whitish; wings below, white at base, with dusky bars toward the tip, the under coverts rufous like the breast; tail below showing obscure whitish bars; feet dull yellow. *Immature birds* different: above, dusky brownish, varied with rufous and buff markings; light bars on tail and wings less distinct; underparts dull buffy white, heavily streaked with brown, the tibiae more or less barred or spotted with brown. In this stage the species may be distinguished from the young Cooper's Hawk by the relatively shorter tail and generally stouter build. The rufous "shoulders" are not in evidence in the young bird, and even in the adult they are not conspicuous in life.

Range and migration—The general range of the Red-shouldered Hawk is not so extensive as that of the Red-tailed. The typical eastern race does not occur so far north as the Red-tailed, nor is it found farther west than the edge of the Great Plains. It is reported as a permanent resident in extreme western Pennsylvania, but its local distribution is somewhat uneven. Unlike the Red-tailed Hawk, which prefers high upland woods, this bird is more partial to bottomlands and swampy forest for nesting and feeding grounds. Pymatuning Swamp seems to have been perfectly suited to its needs; and this hawk was probably more numerous there than in any other section of equal size in the state. G. M. Sutton remarks (1928) that it was abundant in the wooded sections of the swamp in 1922, but that since then its numbers have been decreasing; and the destruction of the swamp in 1932 will doubtless result in reducing the hawk population to a pitiful remnant.

The species has been found breeding and wintering in other parts of Crawford County (near Cambridge Springs—Dickey), and I have taken it in June in low woods on the western shore of Oil Creek Lake. It was observed at Tamarack Swamp, Erie County, on May 13, 1925, and probably breeds there (Dickey). Nests with eggs have been taken on the high ridge behind the city of Erie; and if given a chance this hawk would breed on Presque Isle. It is known to breed at Greenville, Kennard, Sharon, and Sandy Lake, in Mercer County (Seiple, McQuiston, Elliott). South of the Erie-Crawford-Mercer district, however, and in the hill country of the upper Ohio Valley, the Red-shouldered Hawk is rare. I have never certainly identified it in Beaver County,[1] although others claim to have done so. B. H. Christy calls it rare in Allegheny County, but on one occasion he found it nesting along Little Sewickley Creek. There are at least three other valid nesting records for this county: Harmarville (Manley, 1931), Oakmont (nest with young found in 1928 by W. C. Sheaffer, *fide* Sutton), and Bridgeville (nest with eggs found in 1897 by D. A. Atkinson). Dr. Sutton writes that he has heard this hawk at Squaw Run in late June, which would imply that it breeds there also. J. W. Jacobs omits it from his list of the breeding birds of Greene County, but S. S. Dickey discovered a nest near Waynesburg some years ago.

From the mountains to the eastward a few more records have appeared. O. P. Medsger lists the species from Jacobs Creek and Scottdale, Westmoreland County, but does not say whether or not it breeds there. It was "rather common" at Latrobe, in the same county (Townsend, 1883), more than fifty years ago. It has been noted during June and July on Laurel Hill above Laughlintown, Westmoreland County (Rhoads); at Cresson, Cambria County (nest found by Dr. Dickey); at Somerset and Crumb, Somerset County (Preble); and at Springs, Somerset County (Miller). At the last locality it is reported as breeding regularly and as outnumbering the Red-tailed Hawk two to one. East of the Allegheny divide it apparently becomes rare again. The only available records from this region are: Johnsburg, Somerset County, August (Eifrig); Six Roads, Bedford County, June (Preble); Mill Creek, Huntingdon County, March (Sutton), and State College and vicinity, southern Centre County (Harlow and Burleigh [1912; 1924]). In this section the clearing of the forest in the bottomlands seems to explain the comparative scarcity of this hawk.

In the northern part of our region the species is decidedly commoner. In addition to the locality records already listed, there is one from Norwich, McKean County, based on a nest with young birds found by J. A. Santens in June, 1911, and now exhibited in the Carnegie Museum. Between 1893 and 1904 A. K. Pierce collected not less than eight sets of eggs at Kane, where at that time this hawk was apparently a regular and not uncommon breeding bird. In Clinton County, however, he evidently did not find it nesting, although several specimens were taken at intervals. I saw a red-shouldered hawk along Drury Run, a few miles from Renovo, on June 13, 1899, and inferred that the species must breed at least occasionally in that section. R. B. Simpson considers this the common hawk along the upper Allegheny River at Warren, but

[1]The record for Beaver County in my 1904 list was based on a sight identification, which I am now convinced was an error. There are Beaver County specimens, however, in the collection of W. D. Hunter of Racine.

adds that it is now much reduced in numbers. He insists that it is only a summer resident there, however, and quotes dates of arrival between March 9 (1899) and 30 (1895). His latest fall date is October 10 (1900). As yet there are no records for Potter County.

These data have been given thus in some detail to indicate the spotty character of the distribution of the Red-shouldered Hawk in western Pennsylvania. Before the country was settled the species was probably more evenly distributed. It is not so shy as the Red-tailed Hawk and has seemingly not been so well able to hold its own against the unjustified persecution of farmers and gunners; thus it is yearly growing scarcer.

Habits[1]—It is a summer morning in swampy woodland along the Shenango. Slant rays of light pierce the cool leafage, bringing to patches of cobweb and drops of dew a delicate brilliance. The sedges and alders are heavy with moisture. There is a sound of water dripping on broad leaves.

High on a stub that towers above the river and its weedy margin, and full in the sun, perches a red-shouldered hawk. He stands on one foot; the richly barred plumage of his belly is fluffed out comfortably; but he is not asleep. His head jerks as his dark eyes focus upon a rippling at the water's edge, a sudden movement among the sedges, a trembling of low leaves. The red-shoulder is hungry.

Suddenly his interest centers in a thin, checkered band that slips across the bank to a sun-bathed log. His under-plumage shrinks as his tucked-in foot opens and comes to rest upon the stub. A fierce trimness transforms him. He lifts his wings, flaps swiftly over the trees, hovers for a moment, soars out over the river, returns at lower level for closer hovering, and plunges to the grass.

There is a clutching of talons that we cannot see—a vise-like clutching of rough-edged grass as well as of prey. Then the hawk rises, a trifle heavily now, with a half-grown water snake that writhes and whips about the yellow talons that hold it. Directly he makes for and alights on a fallen tree, adjusts himself, wrenches off the reptile's head with his beak, and swallows this mouthful pensively. There is much pulling and tugging as the tough victim is torn asunder. The fore part is swallowed chunk by chunk, but the rear third is gulped greedily, all at once. The hawk wipes his bill on the bark, shakes himself, peers through the woodland, and flies to a perch amongst the tops of the slender birches.

He rests while most of his meal passes from his bulging crop on down into his stomach. Now he preens himself carefully, running his beak through his long primaries, nibbling the oil gland at the base of his tail, rubbing his head along his shoulders, and scratching his forehead with his foot.

Again he shakes himself, directs a swift glance in our direction, and with an almost owl-like lightness of flight, beats out into the sunlight again, this time mounting in wide circles to the sky. As he soars we note the rich buffy-tan tone of his underparts, and the hint of white barring that shows faintly from below through his dark tail. Suddenly he begins to scream, and the river bottom echoes with clear, rapidly repeated cries.

The adult Red-shoulder, similar though it is in many respects to the adult Red-tail, is a bird of very distinct character, with its comparatively buoyant flight and its clear screaming that has so little of the Red-tail's wheeziness; it is always a lighter-bodied, more spirited bird.

The Red-shoulder nests in the damp quiet of its hunting ground, or in a slightly drier woodland back from the river bottom. Here, in a lofty crotch of some beech, oak, maple, birch, or hemlock, the birds construct a broad platform of dead twigs, which they usually carry in their feet. Occasionally they enlarge an old crow or squirrel nest. Nests I examined at Pymatuning Swamp were all of the hawks' own building, and all but one of them had been built during the season in which they were found. All had a rather well-defined lining of leaves, small twigs, flakes and strips of bark, leaf galls, bits of down, and trim, fresh sprigs of hemlock. Such hemlock sprigs are added for their decorative quality for all I know; but they may serve some sanitary or heat- or moisture-regulating end that we do not at present understand.

The eggs are deposited in March and April. A nest with four young found near Meadville by H. C. Kirkpatrick on April 4, 1904, must have held eggs very early in March if not in late February. This date we must consider as exceptionally early for this latitude and at the same time regard it as evidence of the occasional wintering

[1]Account contributed by George M. Sutton.

of the species in Crawford County. A nest I found on March 28, 1926, near Hartstown, contained one fresh egg. Dr. Atkinson found a nest with four eggs in an oak tree in deep woods near Bridgeville, on April 7, 1897. Mr. Simpson has taken sets near Warren on April 25, 1899, and on May 5, 1890. The latter consisted of but two eggs and may conceivably have been a second set for the season.

The set usually numbers three or four eggs, though two and five are sometimes found. The eggs, when newly laid, are very pale bluish green or greenish blue, with heavy, irregular blotchings of dark brown, chiefly about the middle and larger end. Some sets have relatively few markings, and occasionally one egg of a large set is practically immaculate. As incubation progresses, the ground-color becomes less greenish blue, and the shell takes on a soiled-whitish, somewhat glossy appearance. The eggs measure about 2.13 by 1.69 inches.

The young hatch in early May (an infertile egg frequently remains in the nest with the growing brood). They are downy white, with dark eyes, at the time of hatching. The eye color lightens as time passes, so that by the time the birds leave the nest they are gray-eyed. During the following year the eyes must become dark again, for red-shoulders in mature feather, so far as I have noted, always have dark brown eyes.

Parent red-shoulders are vociferous, sometimes fiercely so, in defense of their young. Mr. Simpson tells of having been attacked by a female bird while climbing to a nest on May 24, 1893 (there must have been half-grown young in the nest) along Jackson Run, near Warren. He says: "I had reached a point just under the nest . . . and thought the female had left, when she suddenly landed squarely on top of my head, carrying my hat off twenty or thirty feet, before getting her talons loose, and leaving several sore scratches in my scalp. The blow was quite heavy."

I have climbed to several red-shoulder nests in Pennsylvania and remember hearing an almost incessant outcry from the old birds; but as I have never been attacked, I am inclined to regard Mr. Simpson's experience with this relatively mild-natured hawk as a little unusual.

The young are fed on mice and other small mammals, frogs, crayfish, insects, snakes, and occasionally small birds. Examination of the stomachs of several adult and immature individuals, and of the linings and surroundings of several nests has convinced me that the Red-shoulder is, on the whole, a desirable bird-citizen, entirely innocent as compared with the bird-destroying Cooper's Hawk, and much less likely than the Red-tail to attack rabbits, grouse, squirrels, and poultry. Mr. G. M. Langdon tells us, however, that he once was led to the nest of a red-shoulder by the squawking of tiny goslings that were being carried through the woods alive. The availability of certain items doubtless determines in large measure this species' bill of fare. Close observation on the nesting ground will convince any fair-minded person, however, that the Red-shoulder should be classed with the "good" rather than with the "bad" hawks, in spite of the fact that certain frogs and snakes are beneficial creatures and in spite of the fact that the Red-shoulder now and then captures game or poultry. The present law gives the species full protection in this state.

Buteo lineatus Townsend, *Proc. Acad. Nat. Sci. Philadelphia*, 1883, 66 (Latrobe, Westmoreland Co.)—Dwight, *Auk*, 1892, 9:135 (Cresson, Cambria Co., nesting)—Todd, *Ann. Carnegie Mus.*, 1904, 2:553 (Erie and Presque Isle, Erie Co., nesting)—Keim, *Cassinia*, 1905, 8:38 (Port Allegany, McKean Co., summer)—Manley, *Cardinal*, 1931, 3:15 (Deer Creek, near Harmarville, Allegheny Co., nesting).

"Red-shouldered Hawk" Warren, *Forest and Stream*, 1891, 37:83 (Kane, McKean Co., summer)—Simpson, *Oölogist*, 1907, 24:134, 183; 1909, 26:25, 87, 169; 1910, 27:148; and 1911, 28:162, 165, 202 (Warren, Warren Co., nesting, etc.); 1912, 29:329 (head of Tionesta Creek, Warren Co., summer)—Dickey, *Oölogist*, 1913, 30:23 (near Waynesburg, Greene Co., nesting); 1915, 32:22 (southwestern Pa.)—Simpson, *Oölogist*, 1913, 30:32; 1914, 31:91; 1920, 37:25, 134; and 1922, 39:36 (Warren, Warren Co., nesting, etc.)—Morrison, *et al.*, *Bird-Lore*, 1916, 18:28 (Sewickley, Allegheny Co., December)—Nicholson, *Bird-Lore*, 1921, 23:18, and Hoffman, *et al.*, *Bird-Lore*, 1923, 25:23 (Grove City, Mercer Co., December)—[Christy], *Cardinal*, 1923, v. 1, no. 2, [p. 8] (Little Sewickley Creek, Allegheny Co., nesting)—Sutton, *Bird-Lore*, 1924, 26:56 (Wildwood and Harmarville, Allegheny Co., fall).

Buteo lineatus lineatus Harlow, *Auk*, 1912, 29:477 (southern Centre Co.); 1918, 35:24 (distribution in Pa.)—Burleigh, *Wilson Bull.*, 1923, 35:86 (Allegheny Co., fall and winter); 1924, 36:77 (State College, Centre Co., January)—Christy and Sutton, *Cardinal*, 1928, 2:69 (Brookville, Jefferson Co., June)—Sutton, *Ann. Carnegie Mus.*, 1928, 18:128 (Crawford Co., nesting; records and references)—Burleigh, *Cardinal*, 1929, 2:117 (Deer Creek, near Harmarville, Allegheny Co., August)—Cope and Hawkins, *Forest Leaves*, 1934, 24:26 (E. Tionesta Forest Reserve, Warren and McKean Co., summer).

BROAD-WINGED HAWK (Plate 8)

BUTEO PLATYPTERUS PLATYPTERUS (Vieillot)

Description—One of the smaller hawks, about the size of the Crow, with a wingspread of thirty-two to thirty-nine inches. *Adult:* above, brownish gray or dusky, the head and neck with obscure buffy streaking, and a more or less well-defined dark "mustache" or mystacial stripe; wings blackish, plain externally; tail blackish, with pale tip and pale crossbands; underparts and tibiae with rufous bars on a whitish or buffy background, the markings on the throat more like streaks, and the under tail coverts nearly or quite pure white; wings below, extensively white, with some buffy wash and darker spotting on the coverts; tail below showing broad dusky and white bars; feet yellowish. *Immature:* above, brown, the head and neck with indistinct and broken whitish streaking; tail showing narrower brown and dusky bars above; mystacial stripe on either side brown; throat white; rest of underparts white, with broad brownish streaks and spots; wings below as in the adult; narrow dusky and white bars on tail below. From this stage on, birds exhibit plumage that is variously intermediate between that of the immature bird and that of the fully adult. This species is of about the same size as Cooper's Hawk, but its stouter build, shorter tail, and unbarred wings (below) will serve to distinguish it therefrom.

Range—The Broad-winged Hawk is essentially an eastern species. Its northern breeding range is limited by the Canadian Fauna, which it follows to the westward as far as central Alberta, but being a forest bird it naturally avoids the open prairie country immediately to the southward. It breeds also as far south as Florida, while in the Antilles it is represented by several insular races. It is decidedly migratory, and many individuals go as far as Central and South America for the winter. That it regularly winters anywhere north of Mexico and Florida may well be doubted—authors to the contrary notwithstanding. In western Pennsylvania, at any rate, it is a summer resident only; the alleged cases of its wintering (cited in the references) have been based on sight identifications, in all probability erroneous.

Although not a common species anywhere in this region and although many counties are as yet without records, this hawk appears to be generally even if somewhat locally distributed. Nests have been found in Allegheny County (Harmarville, Rural Ridge, McKeesport, and Little Sewickley Creek) by several different persons. In Beaver County I have found but one nest (near Beaver). The species is reported to be rare in Greene County, where S. S. Dickey found one nest, on the western edge of Waynesburg, in May, 1932. For Crawford County there are two nesting records: near Meadville, June, 1880 (Kirkpatrick); and Hemlock Island, Pymatuning Swamp, June, 1931 (Hicks). In Warren County, according to R. B. Simpson, the Broad-winged Hawk was formerly almost unknown, but since 1919 it has been a regular although still rare summer resident, and several nests have been discovered. Its eggs were taken by A. K. Pierce at Renovo and by R. C. Harlow, S. S. Dickey, and T. D. Burleigh in the mountains of southern Centre and northern Huntingdon counties, where it seems to be more numerous than elsewhere in our region. A nest was found near Lambertsville, Somerset County, in June, 1932 (Mostoller).

The above list comprises all the known nesting records, but the species has been identified and in some cases collected in various other sections, up to the crest of the Alleghenies at Gallitzin, Cambria County (Todd), and at Crumb, Somerset County (Preble). I shot an adult at Mayport, Clarion County, on June 15, 1894, and W. H. Phelps secured an immature specimen on the south bank of the Juniata River, in Mifflin County, about half way between Newton Hamilton and McVeytown, on July 18, 1895. There are also several sight records for Indiana, Westmoreland, Bedford, Fayette, and Greene counties. Some observers may have confused this species with the Red-shouldered Hawk or with Cooper's Hawk, but even with allowance made for misidentification, the Broad-wing appears to be much rarer than either of these. The factors that apparently have saved it from extermination are its late nesting, the nature of its habitat, and the fact that it seldom comes into the open to invite the wrath of the poultry farmer.

Migration—As already stated, this hawk is regularly migratory. All hawks have a disinclination to migrate over water and even at the Great Lakes will follow along the shores rather than fly across. The Broad-winged Hawk is believed to make the semiannual flight between its summer home in the eastern United States and its winter home in Central and northern South America by a circuitous all-land route, passing around the Gulf of Mexico instead of directly across it. This means that the individuals summering in the northeastern states must bear far to the westward in the fall movement. F. L. Burns, who has published an exhaustive monograph on this species,[1] believes that the Mississippi Valley is the main highway of migration, from which the migrating hosts diverge in the spring and toward which they converge in the fall. The Broad-wing appears in our region in April, as shown by a series of records covering twenty-three years made at Renovo by A. K. Pierce. His exact dates of arrival vary between March 22 (1894) and April 30 (1910); the average is April 20. With these the few known records from other parts agree. Mr. Burleigh observed a "distinct diurnal migration" at State College on April 20 in 1917. There is a record of a bird caught alive in a barn at "Coraopolis Heights," Allegheny County, on April 18, 1929. The only data on the fall movement are supplied by the Pierce records for Renovo, in which departure dates range from September 4 (1906) to October 6 (1900) and the average is September 25.

Habits—The accepted English name for this hawk is an unfortunate misnomer, since the species is little more "broad-winged" than any of its relatives. It is a typical *Buteo* or "Buzzard Hawk," with the same stout build, rounded wings, and short tail as the other members of this group, but much inferior to them in size. Like them, too, it has at times the habit of soaring—mounting high in the air in gradually widening spirals, with little or no apparent motion of the wings. This performance must be a pastime, as it can scarcely have anything to do with sighting prey. The ordinary flight of this hawk through the forest is rather silent, slow, and sluggish, with none of the dash of the Sharp-shin's flight or of that of Cooper's Hawk; but in pursuit of its prey it moves with ease and power. In migration it flies in scattered companies. Mr. Burleigh says of the broad-winged hawks which he observed in flight (1924) that "for several minutes early in the afternoon they soared by high overhead in a loose, straggling line; at times but one or two would be in sight, while again a fairly compact group of seven or eight would appear; in all, forty-five were counted."

Characteristically a bird of the deep and shady woods, the Broad-wing customarily perches rather low. It waits for its prey in catlike silence and captures its victim by a surprise attack. It comes out into open country only to look for snakes, frogs, and toads, in wet places, or meadow mice and shrews in the fields. It does not attack poultry or game birds and seldom touches small birds, which as a class ordinarily pay no attention to it. It catches some red squirrels, chipmunks, and young cottontail rabbits and a great many of the smaller mammals, such as mice and shrews. Salamanders and lizards are also taken. Insects—large moths, crickets, grasshoppers, cicadas, and beetles—constitute a large proportion of its fare, and even crayfish are eaten on occasion. From an economic standpoint, therefore, the work of the Broad-wing is almost all to the good, and the species deserves the same protection accorded other useful birds.

The outstanding characteristics of this hawk are its tameness and gentle disposition. Most hawks are wild and wary and can be closely approached only by accident or stratagem. Not so the Broad-winged. Several persons have reported amazing tales of striking the bird down from its perch with a pole, or even of slipping up behind it and snatching it by the feet with the bare hands! Audubon relates that his painting was made from a bird that was taken from a nest while brooding and that obligingly posed for him. The young birds in particular are easily tamed, and make attractive pets, although individuals naturally differ in disposition. On entering a woods inhabited by a pair of these hawks, one is directly apprised of their presence by their plaintive and not unmusical cries, uttered in their anxiety as they follow the intruder around. Thus they betray the proximity of their nest, which is easily located, but not always so easily examined. For nesting they are not partial to any particular kind of tree, but usually choose a fork next the trunk, from thirty to fifty feet from the ground. The

[1]*Wilson Bulletin*, 1911, 23:139–320.

nest is roughly built of sticks and twigs and is not nearly so neat as that of Cooper's Hawk, for example. Sometimes the birds remodel or build over an old crow nest, or even an abandoned nest of one of the other hawks. Almost invariably there are some sprays of fresh green leaves or blossoms in and around the nest, as if for ornament. Hemlock is often used for this purpose if available, and the whole lining is sometimes made of the leaves of this tree. Certain other hawks have the same habit, but it is especially characteristic of this one. The reason for the practice is not exactly understood.

Fresh eggs may be found during the first half of May. Three are commoner than two, and a set of four is rare. They vary greatly, both in ground-color and in markings, even in the same set. Usually they are grayish white, but not infrequently they have instead a bluish, greenish, or even a creamy tinge. Some eggs are almost immaculate, or have faint shadow markings, but oftener there are spots and blotches of various shades of brown, confluent usually around the larger end, sometimes around the smaller. Presumably the most heavily marked egg of the set is the first laid. Average measurements are 1.92 by 1.53 inches.

(?)*Buteo pennsylvanicus* Enty, *Ornithologist and Oölogist*, 1885, 10:78, 79 (Templeton, Armstrong Co., nesting). [Probably refers to *B. lineatus*.]

Buteo platypterus Todd, *Ann. Carnegie Mus.*, 1904, 2:554 (Presque Isle, Erie Co., summer?)—Burns, *Wilson Bull.*, 1911, 23:(146), 182 (western Pa. records), 227, 243, 253 (Renovo, Clinton Co., migration, nesting, *fide* Pierce)—Harlow, *Auk*, 1912, 29:470 ("Stone Valley," Huntingdon Co., Shingletown Gap, Bear Meadows, and Pine Grove Mills, Centre Co., summer); 1918, 35:24 (western Pa., nesting range)—Burleigh, *Wilson Bull.*, 1923, 35:86 (Harmarville, Allegheny Co., nesting); 1924, 36:70 (State College, Centre Co., migration); 1931, 43:40 (Charter Oak, Huntingdon Co., nesting)—Christy, *Cardinal*, 1926, v. 1, no. 8, p. 15 (Little Sewickley Creek, Allegheny Co., nesting, *fide* Arthur)—Fricke, *Cardinal*, 1927, v. 2, no. 1, p. 16 (Rural Ridge, Allegheny Co., nesting).

"Broad-winged Hawk" Simpson, *Oölogist*, 1914, 31:27 (Warren, Warren Co., nesting)—Harlow, *Oölogist*, 1915, 32:29 ([Pine Grove Mills, Centre Co.], nesting)—Dickey, *Oölogist*, 1914, 31:170; Miller, *Oölogist*, 1919, 36:155; and Scoville, *Cassinia*, 1920, 23:19 (Charter Oak, Huntingdon Co., nesting)—(?)Elliott, *et al.*, *Bird-Lore*, 1924, 26:30 (Deer Creek, Allegheny Co., December)—Christy, *Cardinal*, 1924, v. 1, no. 4, p. 11 (Big Traverse Valley, Beaver Co., May)—(?)Christy and Hegner, *Bird-Lore*, 1925, 27:41 (Sewickley, Allegheny Co., December).

Buteo platypterus platypterus Sutton, *Ann. Carnegie Mus.*, 1928, 18:129 (French Creek, Meadville, and Titusville, Crawford Co., May–June, *fide* Langdon and Kirkpatrick)—Burleigh, *Cardinal*, 1932, 3:74 ([Summit], Fayette Co., summer).

SWAINSON'S HAWK

BUTEO SWAINSONI Bonaparte

Description—About the same size as the Red-shouldered Hawk; but only three of the outer primaries are notched on the inner vane. The plumage varies greatly, from an almost uniform sooty brown to a brown-backed, white-bellied phase with a rufous band across the chest.

Range—Swainson's Hawk is primarily a western species, and its occurrence anywhere east of the Mississippi River must be regarded as merely accidental. I have examined a mounted bird that was shot by J. A. Medsger in an open field at Jacobs Creek, Westmoreland County, on September 5, 1901. This specimen is, I believe, the first known to have been taken in Pennsylvania; it has recently been deposited in the Carnegie Museum.

AMERICAN ROUGH-LEGGED HAWK

BUTEO LAGOPUS S. JOHANNIS (Gmelin)

Description—A large hawk, with the tarsi completely feathered (not obvious in life). (The Golden Eagle is the only other diurnal bird of prey in our region with feathered tarsi.) *Ordinary phase:* mottled buff and brown in variable pattern, the throat and breast whiter, and a *broad band of brown across the belly*, very conspicuous in life; wings dark above, white below, with the *base and tips of the feathers dark-colored;* tail dark-colored, with paler base and under surface. *Dark phase:*

almost uniform dark brown (*appearing black* in life); wing pattern as in the ordinary phase. There is every gradation between the two phases, but the large size, peculiar wing pattern, and feathered tarsi will always serve to identify the species.

Range and migration—This hawk breeds entirely beyond the United States, in the Hudsonian and Arctic life zones of Canada. It comes southward in the winter as far as the northern United States, but it is by no means of regular occurrence at that season, at least in western Pennsylvania, where it must be accounted rather rare. R. B. Simpson is the only local observer who has met with it in any numbers. It was particularly numerous during the early months of 1899 and 1901 in his section of Warren County. He writes that he has never seen one in the fall before November 22 (1900), and his latest spring date is April 26 (1901). An earlier fall date is that given by J. E. Perry for a bird seen on Presque Isle on October 10, 1937—the third known record for that locality. G. M. Sutton (1928) gives only three records for the Pymatuning region—all for the month of November. There are a few scattered records for Lawrence, Beaver, Allegheny, Westmoreland, Fayette, and Washington counties; and one record each for Venango, Blair, and Centre counties.

Habits—Although one of the largest of our raptorial birds, the Rough-legged Hawk is content with lowly prey. Field mice are its main food; hence the open marshes and meadows are its chosen haunts. At Warren Mr. Simpson says that it is not at all a bird of the hills, but keeps instead along the river. Mead Island, which is overrun with mice, is a favorite resort. This hawk is generally a wary bird and, as it stays in the open, is unusually hard to approach. Its flight is slow and labored; when hunting its prey it beats over the tops of the tall grasses and weeds and pounces down on the animals thus disturbed from their covert. Far too slow on the wing to capture such swiftly moving prey as living ducks, it is not averse to picking up dead or wounded birds. Mr. Simpson writes that he once trapped a rough-leg by using the skin of a black mallard as bait. The species is one of the most beneficial of hawks from an economic standpoint and deserves full protection.

Archibuteo lagopus sancti-johannis Townsend, *Proc. Acad. Nat. Sci. Philadelphia*, 1883, 66 (Latrobe, Westmoreland Co., spring)—Todd, *Ann. Carnegie Mus.*, 1904, 2:554 (Erie, Erie Co., winter)—Christy, *Cardinal*, 1923, v. 1, no. 1, [p. 5] (Sewickley, Allegheny Co., November)—Sutton, *Ann. Carnegie Mus.*, 1928, 18:129 (Conneaut Lake and Cochranton, Crawford Co., November; Greenville, Mercer Co., November).

"Rough-legged Hawk" Simpson, *Oölogist*, 1912, 29:247, 370 (Warren, Warren Co., winter)—Matuszak, *Bird-Lore*, 1926, 28:29 (Hyde Park, Westmoreland Co., December)—Wood, *Wilson Bull.*, 1932, 44:238 (State College, Centre Co., November, *fide* Curry).

Triorchis lagopus sancti-johannis Luttringer, *Cardinal*, 1931, 3:42 (Marion Township, Beaver Co., and near Vanderbilt, Fayette Co., November).

Buteo lagopus s.johannis Perry, *Cardinal*, 1938, 4:177 (Presque Isle, Erie Co., October).

Additional records: Bridgeville, Allegheny Co., December 7, 1901 (received from R. L. Walker; specimen in Carnegie Museum)—Dorseyville, Allegheny Co., December 11, 1901 (John C. Cato; specimen in Carnegie Museum)—New Castle, Lawrence Co., November 10, 1909 (W. F. Lloyd; specimen in Carnegie Museum)—Wilkinsburg, Allegheny Co., shot November 17, 1897 (Atkinson)—Washington, Washington Co., two shot January, 1884 (Nease)—Cooperstown, Venango Co., February 4, 1929, one shot by Edward Rogers (Sutton)—Georgetown, Beaver Co., one seen October 27, 1924 (Christy).

GOLDEN EAGLE

AQUILA CHRYSAËTOS CANADENSIS (Linnaeus)

Description—A large bird, with a wingspread of from six to seven and a half feet. *Tarsi feathered to the base of the toes*—a character distinguishing it from the Bald Eagle in any plumage. *Adult:* very dark brown with a purple sheen, and with paler, buffy-golden markings on the back of the neck; feet yellow. *Young:* similar, but with some white on the tail and large white patches at the base of the primaries below.

Range and local status—The Golden Eagle has a wide range both in Eurasia and in North America, but in the eastern United States it is rather rare and local. It is partial to mountainous country but is not now known to nest anywhere in our region, although it may formerly have done so. Van Fleet included it in his manuscript list of the breeding birds of DuBois (1892) and added that it "quite certainly breeds in Clearfield County."

At the present time it is merely a transient; or perhaps it would be better to call it a winter wanderer, since its appearance is irregular and apparently not governed by seasonal conditions. There are records from a number of widely scattered points, as listed below, and there are probably other occurrences that have escaped record. R. B. Simpson writes that he has noted this eagle on a few occasions at Warren, from November until April 1 (1899), but has not seen any since 1905.

Habits—A most remarkable instance of the killing of a young fawn by one of these powerful birds is reported by G. M. Sutton, on the authority of one of his correspondents, C. E. Logue. The incident took place in Clinton County in December, at "Sunnyside Park," northeast of Hyner, just outside our geographical limits. When Mr. Logue reached the scene the eagle had torn the fawn's neck open in several places and was feeding between the ribs, several of which it had already broken. The tracks of the fawn in the snow were those of an animal that had been hard pressed, and apparently the eagle had been attacking it over a distance of several hundred yards. The bird was shot.

Other observers speak of the Golden Eagle preying on poultry and game birds. An eagle shot in Elk County (listed below) had taken twenty-two fowls before it was finally brought down. Samuel Scoville, Jr., relates (1927) the following interesting incident: "One bitter winter day in a deer camp on the top of Seven Mountains in Pennsylvania, I was shown a magnificent stuffed golden eagle that had followed a flock of wild turkeys for days and weeks until he had killed almost all of them. At last he came to an ignominious end while feeding on the carcass of a deer. A trapper found him there too gorged to fly, and thinking that he was a buzzard threw his coat over him and wrung his neck." If the Golden Eagle were not so comparatively rare everywhere it might conceivably become a factor to be reckoned with from an economic standpoint.

Aquila chrysaëtus canadensis SENNETT, *Bull. Nuttall Orn. Club*, 1882, 7:58 ([Millers (Station)], Rookdale Township, Crawford Co., December).

Aquila chrysaëtos WARREN, *Birds Pa.*, ed. 2, 1890, 133 (Cameron Co., December)—WARREN, *Bull. Pa. Dept. Agric.*, no. 17, 1897, 195 (Cameron and Clinton Co.)—RHOADS, *Auk*, 1899, 16:311 (Cameron Co., March, *fide* Larrabee)—SUTTON, *Auk*, 1928, 45:375 (Mattawana, Mifflin Co. and Potter's Mills, "Huntingdon" [Centre] Co., winter).

"Golden Eagle" MUNSON, *Ornithologist and Oölogist*, 1882, 6:94 (Millers [Station], Crawford Co., December)—JACOBS, *Oölogist*, 1922, 39:123 (southern Greene Co.)—SCOVILLE, *Runaway Days*, 1927, 189 (Seven Mts., Centre Co.)—WOOD, *Wilson Bull.*, 1932, 44:238 (State College, Centre Co. [and "Stone Valley," Huntingdon Co.], *fide* Musgrave).

Aquila chrysaëtos chrysaëtos SUTTON, *Ann. Carnegie Mus.*, 1928, 18:130 (?Pymatuning Swamp, Crawford Co.)—SUTTON, *Cardinal*, 1929, 2:129 (Portersville, Butler Co., April).

Additional records: Dunkard, Greene Co., November 15, 1893; Pine Bank, Greene Co., November 11, 1917 (collection of J. W. Jacobs)—Amity, Washington Co., March 5, 1914 (H. E. McCollum; specimen in Carnegie Museum)—Jones Tp., Elk Co., October 29, 1924, one shot by George S. Stewart; Kane, McKean Co., October 3, 1924, one shot by George M. Stuart; near Bellefonte, Centre Co., one shot by Thomas Mosier, about December 10, 1926 (Sutton)—near Tidioute, Warren Co., one trapped December 4, 1891 (Simpson)—"Stone Valley," Huntingdon Co., one seen April 16, 1908 (Musgrave)—Cross Fork, Potter Co., one captured by a trapper in 1936 or 1937 (Scherer).

NORTHERN BALD EAGLE

HALIAEËTUS LEUCOCEPHALUS ALASCANUS Townsend

Description—One of our largest birds of prey, with a wingspread of from six to seven feet or more; *lower third of tarsus bare of feathers. Adult: head and neck* (all around), *and tail, white;* rest of body, and wings, deep brown, with slightly paler mottling; bill and feet dull yellow. *Immature:* wholly deep brown, with some white intermixed in the form of streaks or spots; tail dark, with some white mottling. Four years are required to reach maturity, and individuals are found in every conceivable intermediate stage during this interval. In the field, the immature Bald Eagle is hard to distinguish from the Golden Eagle; in the hand it can always be recognized by the partially (instead of wholly) feathered tarsi.

Range—This eagle is indigenous to North America, where it enjoys an extensive range both in longitude and in latitude. There is a gradual increase in individual size from south to north, and although Pennsylvania specimens are distinctly intermediate in this respect, they are accounted nearer the northern race, originally described from Alaska. To a bird such as this, whose living depends primarily on aquatic sources, large bodies of water offer peculiar attractions. Hence in the East the species is locally distributed and nests along the seacoast, the shores of the Great Lakes, and the courses of the larger rivers. But like all other large birds, the Bald Eagle is yearly decreasing in numbers in settled districts. It has long been known to breed at several places along the south shore of Lake Erie in the state of Ohio, where intensive studies of its nesting habits have been made by F. H. Herrick. This breeding area extends to the lake shore in Pennsylvania as well; it is in fact the only part of our region where the bird nested regularly until within recent years. During our ornithological survey of Presque Isle in 1900, bald eagles were seen almost daily during April and May. The locality seemed indeed to be a favorite rendezvous and feeding ground, but was not then being used for nesting. In recent years the eagles have not decreased in numbers there, and in 1938 at least two pairs were breeding—and this despite the fact that Presque Isle was made into a state park and public recreation ground. In 1933 J. E. Perry supplied a brief history of the Presque Isle eagle nestings, together with a map showing the positions of the nests:

"While the Bald Eagle has doubtless frequented Presque Isle from primeval times, breeding records prior to 1924 are very scant.

"Mr. C. K. Dickinson, a well-known sportsman and lifelong resident of Erie, recalls an incident of his young manhood that occurred about 1885. When he visited Presque Isle for the purpose of securing a load of moss for a local florist, he discovered an eagle's nest in a white pine, located at a point in the wooded section southwest of Long Pond. After great effort he succeeded in climbing to the nest, in which he found two eggs; the old birds meanwhile were flying overhead and calling in great distress.

"For recent years I have records of seven nests that have been found on Presque Isle. The first was estimated by Mr. Andrew Shaw, for twenty-six years keeper of the Presque Isle Light, to be about twenty-five years old, although I did not myself see it until 1924. It was built in a dead pine near the head of Long Pond, about sixty feet up, and looked like a bushel basket on top of a pole. It was destroyed by storms during the winter of 1924–25, and the eagles immediately built a second nest close by, in a black oak at about the same elevation. Nests no. 3 and no. 5, also in black oaks, fifty and forty feet up respectively, are small and doubtless recently built, as was also no. 6, which was destroyed either by a storm or by the cutting down of the tree. Nest no. 4 is a large nest in the top of a dead white pine, sixty feet up, in the center of a little-frequented section; it is apparently an old nest.

"The latest nest, no. 7, in a poplar tree on Long Ridge, and only about twenty-five feet up, was built this spring (1933) and abandoned soon thereafter. Our local observers are convinced that throngs of curious people in the vicinity of this nest so disturbed the eagles that they finally left. In 1932 nests no. 4 and no. 5 were occupied. In 1933 nest no. 4 was occupied; and no. 7 was occupied for a short time and then abandoned. Each new nest was farther east than the last.

"The Bald Eagle is a timid bird. It shuns human society and has been retreating year by year from its first nesting site into the more secluded parts of Presque Isle, only to have trails cut under or close to the newly chosen sites. Indeed, the whole history of the changes in nesting sites points to an unsuccessful effort to escape from publicity. Prior to the building of the main highway on Presque Isle in 1925, the section at the head of Long Pond, where nests nos. 1 and 2 were located, was a dense forest, unfrequented except by occasional hunters and hikers. After the construction of the highway, trails were cut through this forest, in some cases directly under the trees selected by the eagles for their nests. The next few years will decide whether the Bald Eagle will become accustomed to the ever increasing throngs which frequent this beautiful park or will be only a memory on Presque Isle."

The allusion to North East and Girard as breeding stations in my "Birds of Erie and Presque Isle" was based on hearsay only. R. C. Harlow, however, has written that the former locality actually was a breeding station, although it is now abandoned; and full confirmation of the status of the latter locality is also at hand. For many years, according to Professor Herrick, a pair of bald eagles had a nest at North Girard (formerly known as Miles Grove), on the western border of Erie County not far from the lake shore.

In years gone by the Bald Eagle nested at various points in the interior of the state, especially along the larger rivers. John H. Chatham, in his brochure on the subject (1919), writes: "Within the recollection of my father, who was born in 1808, the Bald Eagle nested as far west on the Bald Eagle Creek as Milesburg [Centre County], there being a nest on a large buttonwood tree on an island near the present location of the town. . . . [The eagles] nested on the West Branch of the Susquehanna as far up as the mouth of Sinnemahoning Creek." H. W. Shoemaker, in an extended introduction to this account, says that in the summer of 1918 he and Mr. Chatham "saw two immature Bald Eagles on the Sinnemahoning, near Round Island, Clinton County." Considerable weight is given this testimony by the actual capture of an immature bird at Renovo in April, 1919, as recorded by A. K. Pierce. The same observer also positively identified adult bald eagles on two other occasions in this general region: one was seen near Shawmut, Elk County, in April, 1901, and another at Ridgway, in the same county, in April, 1903. In his mounted collection there is a fine adult which was taken at Sterling Run, Cameron County, in April, 1888. It is possible that these birds were actually breeding there, and that the species persisted as a resident in this thinly settled section until recent years.

In the collection of the Carnegie Museum there is an adult specimen which was taken at Homestead Park, Allegheny County, on June 8, 1920; but it had probably not been breeding. Summer occurrences of this eagle do not necessarily imply nesting, since immature and nonbreeding birds often wander widely at that season. In his paper on the birds of the Pymatuning region (1928) G. M. Sutton cites several records of this nature. The conversion of the larger part of the swamp into a lake affording an unfailing food supply, however, has made this locality a regular rendezvous for eagles at all seasons, and it is not unusual to see a number there together. Moreover, B. L. Oudette discovered a pair nesting within the sanctuary in the spring of 1937, and again in 1938—a new and gratifying development.

Migration—In northern Ohio the bald eagles live and hunt in the vicinity of their nests almost the year around and are absent for only a few weeks in the dead of winter. The freezing over of Lake Erie makes food harder to get and must be the primary cause of their disappearance at that season. Mr. Perry writes that the same thing is true of the eagles he has observed on Presque Isle: "They are not resident, but return in March." In this connection it is significant that during the exceptionally mild winter of 1931–32, when both Erie Bay and Lake Erie itself remained open, the eagles were repeatedly noted during all the winter months (Christy). But under ordinary circumstances they must wander southward at that season, a fact that would account for the scattered records from other parts of our general region. Individuals (mostly immature birds) have been observed or taken at sundry localities in the western tier of counties, and east to Westmoreland, Cambria, and Bedford counties. At Warren R. B. Simpson has seen both adults and young irregularly from May to September.

Habits—Although the Bald Eagle is powerful in build, magnificent in appearance, haughty in mien, and strong in flight, it is a sadly overrated bird. It is scarcely more than a sublimated buzzard-hawk, an overgrown but degenerate *Buteo.* Where it excels in size, other hawks excel in spirit. In dash and courage it must give way to the Goshawk; in speed and grace, to the Duck Hawk; in fierce demeanor, to the Gyrfalcon. Strange indeed that it came to be chosen as the emblem of the American nation! Yet as we watch the eagle soaring in the blue, its effortless, majestic evolutions seem to be at once a prophecy and a pledge of attainment for man's own inmost desire and aspiration. Here indeed the celebrated bird of freedom appears at its best, as it climbs the sky in ever widening spirals, disdaining, as it were, the things of earth. Or seen perched on some tall dead stub, commanding a view of the surrounding country, it seems the embodiment of kingly dignity and power in the bird world. But our admiration lessens when we find that its powerful physique is often put to ignoble use. It is true that the Bald Eagle can and on occasion does strike down prey worthy of its powers. But it is also true that it much prefers fish to anything else, and that while it is perfectly able to capture these for itself, it often robs the Osprey. If for any reason fresh fish are not to be had, the eagle is by no means averse to picking up dead ones, and at times will stoop to feed on other carrion. The old-squaw ducks caught and drowned in the fishermen's nets on Lake Erie, and cast up on shore, are greedily devoured by the eagles of Presque Isle.

The tactics pursued by the eagle in capturing living ducks are described in a communication received from Mr. Shaw and transmitted through Mr. Perry. In substance the account is as follows: One morning in the spring of 1925 Mr. and Mrs. Shaw noticed offshore a flock of ducks that had been disturbed by the approach of an eagle. Most of them made their escape by flight, but several that had been diving found the eagle close upon them when they came up. The eagle swooped at the nearest duck, which dived and escaped by a hair's breadth. Every time the duck came to the surface the eagle would swoop and force it under before it could get its breath. This endurance contest lasted forty-five minutes before the duck finally became exhausted and lost its fight for life. The eagle seized the duck and gave it several hard blows with its beak; then it tried in vain to rise with the duck in its talons. Leaving the dead bird on the water, it flew to a tree stump on the shore for a rest, but presently returned for its prey, which it succeeded this time in carrying off and devouring.

Eagles are at all times shy, suspicious, and difficult to approach, but sometimes they unwittingly fly within range of the conscienceless gunner. Immature and inexperienced birds are naturally less wary, but adults are more discerning. They rely on size and strength rather than on speed and courage for mastery. Audubon tells of an eagle being soundly whipped by a game cock; and S. K. Eastwood relates that Frank Ellair saw one put to flight by a marsh hawk. Even the lowly kingbird has been known to drive off an eagle. On the other hand, E. H. Forbush says that H. A. McGraw once found a red fox (in Blair County) that must have been killed by a bald eagle. A wing-tipped eagle that I saw, threw itself on its back and made vicious lunges with beak and talons, while its eyes shone with a baleful glare. Ordinarily, however, the eagle has learned respect for man—its only enemy—and seldom ventures to make hostile demonstrations even at the nest.

It is believed that eagles mate for life, or until one of the pair dies, when the survivor hunts up a new mate. Professor Herrick (1934) outlines the history of the pair that nested at North Girard:

"One day in September, 1899, when I was westward bound on a railroad skirting the southern shore of Lake Erie, a large eagle's nest happened to catch my eye as I glanced from the car window. This was near Milesgrove, now known as North Girard, Pennsylvania, close to the western limits of that state. No castle on a hill could have been more conspicuous, for the nest topped a dead tree-trunk which stood alone not far from the rails. Upon learning that this great eyrie had long been a landmark in the region, my interest was aroused, and I resolved to pay it a visit.

"I found upon reaching Girard in the following June that this famous nest had crashed in a storm of the previous winter, but from photographs made and kindly given me by the late Mr. H. E. Denio . . . of Milesgrove, as it was then known, and from measurements which it was possible to make upon the ground, I am able to give its true dimensions: the eyrie was nine feet tall and had a nearly uniform diameter of six feet. According to report, it had been started in 1885 and had been occupied fifteen years without a break; and its top, as measurements showed, had stood at a height of seventy-seven feet. The main supports of the nest were two upright, nearly parallel branches, and this circumstance had led to its remarkably cylindrical form. These supports, which had been broken off at a height of six or eight feet from the top of the eyrie, had served as admirable nest-perches and lookout-points for that guard-duty which eagles perform with unremitting zeal.

"For many years the fabricators of this nest were said to have occupied a dead sycamore in the midst of woods near Milesgrove, and when this aged tree succumbed, the more famous nest just described was established in another sycamore, also dead, which lasted until January, 1900. How many predecessors of these eyries there had been in that neighborhood is not known. A third nest, however, was started in the winter or spring of 1900, not many rods from the site of the one recently destroyed, and this was also in a sycamore, but a living and sound one. This tree had a girth of twelve feet at the time of my visit, and a clean, straight bole for upwards of sixty feet without a branch; but it spread out into a number of strong arms to form an all-embracing crotch suited to hold a nest of great size.

"Upon my approaching this eyrie on the 8th of June, not a sound was heard for full twenty minutes, when suddenly an eagle appeared and, circling above my head, began to sound the alarm . . . Then, alighting on the topmost branch of a dead tree, he expressed his emotion in a manner characteristic of many birds even as remote of kin as the night-hawk: with head down and neck extended and with drooping and quivering wings, his mandibles opened and closed slowly but with the regularity of clockwork. The male eagle, as Dr. William L. Ralph has noticed, can always be recognized by his characteristic alarm call, while that of the female is harsh and more broken. The female eagle was sitting in her eyrie at the time of my approach, as became evident when she suddenly left it and, with protesting cries, joined her mate in the air. At this time there were two eaglets in dark juvenal plumage, but they were quite invisible from my position on the ground, except when one would arise and 'shoot' over the edge of the nest. . . .

"Shortly after my visit the forest around and to the north of this nest was cut over, but James H. Hall, the owner, was careful to spare the eagles' tree, and I always looked for it when passing that way by rail in after years, but in more recent times I was unable to detect it, and I wondered if it had been destroyed. . . .

"In July, 1930, thirty-one years after my first sight of the Girard nest, when I again visited that neighborhood, the old sycamore of the eagles could not be seen from the railroad. It was with difficulty that we finally found it, even under the guidance of James Hall, son of the man with whom I had talked of eagles nearly a third of a century before. I soon realized that the eagle's tree, which had stood alone in the picture so long carried in my mind's eye, was now swallowed up and completely hidden in the new forest which had grown about it. When at last we stumbled upon the object of our search, the old nest, now grown to a mighty fabric, was still there; and the sycamore, having entered the giant class, was literally in a green old age, though its heart was no longer sound: at its base was a large cavity in which two men could stand at ease. The great nest, now abandoned, had been in use for twenty-eight years (1900–1928). Its predecessor, as we have seen, was in a sycamore and had lasted fifteen years (1885–1900); and its successor was in a sycamore also, since the eagles, two years before our visit, had moved to a living representative of this seemingly favored tree on a neighboring farm, and there we found them on the 1st of July, 1930. Before leaving their neighborhood we made our way for about one-eighth of a mile through woods to the lake, and we were surprised to find so high and steep a bank, which seemed to be up seventy feet or more from the water.

"Four times these Girard eagles had successively taken up their abode in sycamores, twice in dead trees and twice in living ones. It must not be inferred, however, that the eagles chose a sycamore out of a liking for that particular kind of tree, nor have I found any good evidence that they prefer dead to living trees, as some have thought. Moreover, the evidence that the eagle's eyrie, when long used, kills the tree on which it rests, another common belief, is not at all convincing. Only eight out of the twenty-five nests of this eagle that I have examined in the Lake Erie region . . . were in trees dying or dead. . . .

"What our eagles require in establishing their castle is a lofty tree, the taller the better, or one that will give them good visibility on all sides; but, apart from this, there must be tall perches, available for guard-duty, close at hand, or a nest-perch on the tree itself, for without such lookout-posts their eggs and young are never safe. Of course, they prefer to dwell near supplies of their staple food, that is, beside waters that will provide an abundance of fish, the favored diet of the American bird; moreover, their chosen tree must present an ample crotch to underpin a castle of the kings of the air. In all such details, however, one must expect to find in eagles a certain amount of variability, which is a measure of their adaptability and intelligence. . . . No doubt it was the invading forest which had gradually hemmed in the Girard birds that finally compelled them to move to a more open site."

Since eagles add to their eyries every season, in the course of years these become immense structures. The nests built since 1924 on Presque Isle are all small by comparison with ones of longer standing. The first nest I saw there was in the top of a dead pine, while the second, shown to me in March, 1928, was in a large oak. So far as is known no sets of eagle eggs have ever been taken anywhere in our region. The usual number of eggs is two, but sometimes three are laid, and very rarely four. They are dull white in color, and measure about 2.90 by 2.27 inches. They are laid in March, and are said to require from thirty to thirty-six days for incubation.

Haliæetus leucocephalus Jacobs, *Summer Birds Greene Co., Pa.*, 1893, 6 (Dunkard Creek, Greene Co., summer straggler)—Todd, *Ann. Carnegie Mus.*, 1904, 2:554 (Presque Isle, Erie Co., summer, not nesting)—Todd, in Bausman, *Hist. Beaver Co., Pa.*, 1904, 2:1199 (Beaver Co., winter)—Herrick, *Auk*, 1924, 41:89, (213), 219 (North Springfield and Miles Grove, Erie Co., nesting)—Jennings, *Cardinal*, 1930, 2:184 (Presque Isle, Erie Co., nesting)—Oudette, *Cardinal*, 1938, 4:203 (Pymatuning region, Crawford Co., nesting).

"Bald Eagle" Simpson, *Oölogist*, 1910, 27:100; 1914, 31:91 (Warren, Warren Co., May, June)—Chatham, *Bald Eagle on Susquehanna River*, 1919, 9 (Pa. localities; habits, etc.)—[Christy], *Cardinal*, 1923, v. 1, no. 2, [p. 8] (Osborne Dam, Allegheny Co., June); 1924, v. 1, no. 3, [p. 18] (Green Garden, Beaver Co., "November" [October]); 1926, v. 1, no. 8, p. 16 (Erie, Erie Co., April, *fide* Perry)—Eastwood, *Bird-Lore*, 1925, 27:263 (Presque Isle, Erie Co., *fide* Ellair); 1927, 29:272 (Schellsburg, Bedford Co., May, *fide* Manley)—Boulton, *Bird-Lore*, 1928, 30:13 (Hillside, Westmoreland Co., October, *fide* Jennings), 196 (Ligonier, Westmoreland Co., March), 337 (Presque Isle, Erie Co., nesting)—Christy, *et al.*, *Bird-Lore*, 1937, 39:44 (Pymatuning region, Crawford Co., December).

Haliæetus leucocephalus leucocephalus Dickey, *Auk*, 1915, 32:236 (Waynesburg, Greene Co.)—Harlow, *Auk*, 1918, 35:25 ([near North East], Erie Co., nesting)—(?)Christy and Sutton, *Cardinal*, 1928, 2:69 (Thoms Run, Cook Forest, Clarion Co., July)—Sutton, *Ann. Carnegie Mus.*, 1928, 18:130 (Crawford Co. records and references)—Forbush, *Birds Massachusetts*, 1927, 2:(150), 156 (Loop Run, Blair Co., food, *fide* McGraw).

Falco leucocephalus Shoemaker, in Chatham, *Bald Eagle on Susquehanna River*, 1919, 3 (Pa. localities; habits, etc.).

"American Eagle" Herrick, *American Eagle*, 1934, 2–7, ff., (North Girard, Erie Co., nesting, etc.).

MARSH HAWK (Plate 8)

CIRCUS HUDSONIUS (Linnaeus)

Description—A hawk of moderate size and slender build, with a small bill, long wings and tail, and weak, slender legs and feet. Wingspread from forty to fifty-four inches. It can easily be recognized in any plumage by the prominent *white spot above the tail. Adult male:* general color, *bluish gray*, with some dusky shading above, the *upper tail coverts white* in abrupt contrast; wings and tail darker toward their tips; below, white, with faint brownish spotting, the throat and breast more bluish gray; wings white below, with dark tips; feet yellow. *Adult female:* above, *brown*, mottled with buff; *upper tail coverts abruptly white;* below, buffy whitish, with broad brownish streaks, heavier on the breast; wings white below, with dark barring; tail showing white and dusky bars; feet yellow. *Young:* above, *deep brown* or blackish, the head, neck, and wing coverts mottled with rusty buff; the *upper tail coverts abruptly white;* below, deep rusty buff, with brown streaks on the breast; wings, tail, and feet as in the adult female.

Range—Our Marsh Hawk is the sole North American representative of a generic group of virtually cosmopolitan distribution. It has a transcontinental range that extends north well into the Hudsonian Life Zone. In the East it breeds mostly to the northward of the Ohio and Potomac valleys, while in winter it ranges as far north as southern Michigan and southern New York. Primarily a bird of the open country, it is naturally more numerous in the prairie region of the Mississippi Valley than elsewhere, and before the clearing of the land and the opening up of extensive areas for cultivation, its local range must have been greatly restricted. Even now this species, dependent as it is upon swamplands for hunting and nesting grounds, is scarcely known outside the flat country of the northwestern counties except as a casual visitor in migration or in winter.

In our region the Marsh Hawk is probably most numerous in the vicinity of Pymatuning Swamp, where it has often been found nesting. S. S. Dickey has also found nests near Cambridge Springs, Crawford County, and in Tamarack Swamp, Erie County. I found no nests on Presque Isle in 1900, but R. B. Simpson discovered one there in 1910; and on the mainland opposite, the species has long been considered one of the commoner hawks. Although the Marsh Hawk was frequently seen in summer in the vicinity of Warren, no nests were reported until 1930, when Mr. Simpson found one with two young; in 1932 he found two more, not far from the town. These discoveries certainly suggest an extension of breeding range. Four years previously, however—in June, 1926—Dr. Dickey had found the species nesting at Bear Lake, in extreme northwestern Warren County, only a few miles from Tamarack Swamp—the spot where in May, 1934, our party from the Carnegie Museum also discovered a nest with eggs. In May, 1927, Dr. Dickey had observed the species in Benson Swamp, a few miles east of Columbus, where it was also seen by us in 1934.

The southward limit of the known local breeding area extends to Gardner Swamp, Lawrence County (Raney), and to Muddy Creek in Clay Township, Butler County (Elliott). I have never detected the Marsh Hawk along the Ohio River, although other observers claim to have done so. B. H. Christy once saw an adult bird along Big Traverse Creek, in southern Beaver County, in July, and another at Clinton Pond, Allegheny County, in May, but there is as yet no positive evidence of its breeding anywhere south of the Ohio River. In the broken, hilly country of this section the Marsh Hawk is in fact only casual at any season, although there are a number of odd records, some of which are authenticated by specimens. It is somewhat surprising, therefore, to find the species recorded by A. B. Miller as breeding in the marshes at the head of Glade Run in Somerset County, near the summit of Negro Mountain, at an altitude of twenty-five hundred feet—a report that confirms Audubon's observations made long ago.[1] Obviously, it is not the elevation of the plateau region in general, but the fact that so little suitable ground is there available, that makes this species rare over that area, even in migration. Farther north, in Somerset County, it has been seen on a few occasions by R. V. Mostoller (once in June—near Shanksville). In the ridge and valley section, it has been repeatedly noted at various times of year by T. D. Burleigh and R. C. Harlow at State College, and the latter observer writes that it breeds at Charter Oak in Huntingdon County. Transients have been seen at Schellsburg, Bedford County (Mostoller), and at Hollidaysburg (Berg).

Migration—The appearance of marsh hawks in parts where the species is not known to breed suggests migratory movements; and these seem to reach their height in March and again in October. W. M. Guynes records a flight of this hawk at Erie on March 31 (1934). At Pymatuning Swamp the bulk of the Marsh Hawk population leaves in the fall and returns in the spring, but even there, winter occurrences are so frequent that it is impossible to distinguish the movements of these transients with any degree of certainty. The numerous accumulated winter records merely indicate that western Pennsylvania is well within the recognized range of the species at this season.

Habits—The Marsh Hawk, as its name implies, eschews the woodland and frequents open, preferably marshy, country. In its low, swinging flight, as it quarters across and over the wet meadows and swampy lands, ever on the alert for prey, it reminds one of a gull—and, indeed, the adult male is strikingly like a gull in coloration. Easy and graceful on the wing, it beats back and forth in leisurely fashion over its hunting grounds, turning this way and that to examine some promising bit of marshy covert, now sailing along for a space on set pinions, and again skimming neatly over the uneven surface growth as lightly as a butterfly. Sometimes it drops directly to the ground to seize its prey, but often it pauses for a moment and hovers in mid-air, kingfisher-like, before pouncing swiftly on its victim, which is usually devoured on the spot. Seldom does the Marsh Hawk alight

[1] *Ornithological Biography*, 1838, 4:398.

elsewhere than on the ground, although in the marsh it often selects an old snag, a muskrat hill, or a mound of earth as a lookout and perch. Its hunting, however, is all done on the wing.

The long, pointed wings of this hawk, and its long tail, give an impression of size and strength which is not borne out by its comparatively small body and slight build. In particular, its small bill and its weak and slender feet unfit it for the capture of large prey. It is therefore accounted "one of the 'ignoble' hawks—a lowly mouse hunter; a 'harrier' of the marsh, hunting mainly close to the ground" (Forbush, 1927). On the other hand, its large ear parts suggest that its hearing is probably more acute than that of most hawks and that it hunts by sound as much as by sight.

Meadow mice (*Microtus*) are the staple food of the Marsh Hawk and constitute the larger part of its subsistence. Other kinds of mice are also occasionally eaten, as well as young rabbits and other rodents; and frogs, snakes, and insects are regularly taken. Small birds, of the species partial to the same haunts, are certainly a part of the hawk's fare, at least in the nesting season. G. M. Sutton (1928) writes: "If one may judge from our limited experience with the nests containing young birds [at Pymatuning Swamp], the Marsh Hawk kills a good many smaller birds as food during latter May and June. Young Red-winged Blackbirds were constantly found at the Marsh Hawk nests, and the young (chiefly) of Song and Swamp Sparrows were also found, as well as one decapitated Sora Rail." Poultry and game birds form a negligible part of the Marsh Hawk's food. Certainly the few that may be taken in the course of an average marsh hawk's lifetime are more than compensated for by the vast numbers of injurious field mice destroyed. Certain individual birds of this (and other) species which have developed the habit of preying on young chickens ought perhaps to be destroyed; but taken by and large, the Marsh Hawk is one of the most useful birds from the standpoint of the agriculturist and should never be wantonly killed, but should be carefully protected as an important factor in the control of field mice.

The breeding habits of this hawk are most interesting. Writing further of his experience at Pymatuning Swamp, Dr. Sutton says: "When we first came to the Swamp (April 27, 1922) Marsh Hawks were circling everywhere and noisily courting. From the secluded recesses of the marsh would sound the insistent Flicker-like calling of the birds as they chased each other. Often we saw the odd tumbling antics of the male bird, which always inspired wonder and comment. These performances were given in particular portions of the Swamp, and naturally our approach usually caused the drama to cease." Several authors have described this peculiar aerial courtship-flight. E. H. Forbush writes: "In warm spring days a pair may be seen soaring to a great height, when one will suddenly plunge far downward and turn a complete forward or sidelong somersault in the air. Sometimes one falling thus from a height will turn over and over again in the manner of a tumbler pigeon. As it bounds up and down in the air, it seems to move more like a rubber ball than a bird. . . . Sometimes the male flies alone across the marsh rising and falling alternately and with each fall turning a complete somersault, as if to show his larger mate what a clever and wonderful bird he really is. Again he 'carries on' in the same way while flying in her company."[1]

The Marsh Hawk's nest is built in the open marsh, without any attempt at concealment, at least from above. It is most unusual for the nest to be built near the shelter of trees, but the one found by our party from the Carnegie Museum, in Tamarack Swamp, Warren County, was thus protected, as was also another we discovered at Pymatuning Swamp in May, 1937. If placed among the cattails or rushes, the nest is usually raised above the water enough to insure a dry bed for the eggs and young. The materials of which it is composed are those at hand—dry stalks and leaves of rushes, reeds, and other aquatic plants. They are piled into a mound in which is left a slight depression, lined with finer material of the same general character. In our region, laying begins about the first of May, and sets are complete usually by the middle of the month. From four to six eggs is the usual number, but a set of seven is reported by H. C. Kirkpatrick. They are pale bluish white, often immaculate, but sometimes beautifully although lightly marked with delicate brown. They measure about 1.80 by 1.45 inches. The incubating bird sits very closely, but when

[1]*Birds of Massachusetts*, 1927, 2:102.

disturbed protests the invasion with angry outcries. "Their rather thin call-notes sounded something like those of the Duck Hawk, but were not nearly so powerful. Sometimes the males circled high in air while the females carried on the attack" (Sutton, 1928). The young are hatched sometime in June and are on the wing by August; old and young associate in family groups before moving southward for the winter months.

Circus hudsonius Warren, *Birds Pa.*, ed. 2, 1890, 119 ([?] Allegheny Co., *fide* Wrenshall, and Clinton Co., *fide* Van Fleet, nesting)—Todd, *Ann. Carnegie Mus.*, 1904, 2:552 (Erie and Presque Isle, Erie Co., summer)—Harlow, *Auk*, 1912, 29:477 (southern Centre Co., summer); 1918, 35:23 (Centre, Huntingdon, and Erie Co., breeding)—Christy, *Cardinal*, 1923, v. 1, no. 1, [p. 4] (["Patton's Point," Beaver Co.], July)—Burleigh, *Wilson Bull.*, 1923, 35:86 ([Pittsburgh and Harmarville], Allegheny Co., transient); 1924, 36:70; and 1931, 43:39 (State College, Centre Co., resident).
"Marsh Hawk" Simpson, *Oölogist*, 1912, 29:249 (Presque Isle, Erie Co., nesting)—Simpson, *Oölogist*, 1920, 37:134 (near Warren, Warren Co., May)—Sutton, *Bird-Lore*, 1923, 25: 132 (Hart's Run [near Wildwood], Allegheny Co., January) —Jones, *et al.*, *Bird-Lore*, 1926, 28:30 (Deer Creek, Allegheny Co., December)—Eastwood, *Bird-Lore*, 1926, 28:136, 207 (Pittsburgh region, Allegheny Co., March)—(?)Reiter and Squier, *Bird-Lore*, 1927, 29:28 (Monaca to Raccoon Creek, Beaver Co., December)—Boulton, *Bird-Lore*, 1928, 30:13 (Cook Forest, Clarion Co., October).
Circus cyaneus hudsonius Christy and Sutton, *Cardinal*, 1928, 2:69 (Cook Forest, Clarion Co., June)—Sutton, *Ann. Carnegie Mus.*, 1928, 18:122 (Crawford Co. migration and nesting records)—Bergstrom, *Cardinal*, 1930, 2:186 (Pymatuning Swamp, Crawford Co., winter)—Luttringer, *Cardinal*, 1930, 2:222 (New Castle, Lawrence Co., food habits).

OSPREY

PANDION HALIAËTUS CAROLINENSIS (Gmelin)

Description—A large hawk, with a wingspread of from sixty-five to seventy inches; wings long and narrow, reaching beyond the tail when folded. Above (including wings and tail), dusky black, the head more or less white, with black on the crown and a broad *black stripe behind the eye*, separating the white of the nape from that of the underparts, which are uniform except for a *broad band of brownish spots* across the breast; wings white below, with dusky spots, the tips of the feathers black, as is also a large patch just beyond the bend of the wing; tail with dusky and white barring; *feet livid bluish;* bill dark; eyes yellowish or brownish. Younger birds have less white on the head, and the upperparts are spotted with buff.

Range—Our American Fish Hawk, or Osprey, is a geographical race of the Eurasian species. It ranges over North America at large, north to the limit of trees, and winters (in the East) from the Gulf States southward; in the North it is migratory. Like the Bald Eagle, the Osprey is more numerous along the seacoast and in the vicinity of large bodies of water than it is inland, at least at the present time. In western Pennsylvania it is found not only along the shore of Lake Erie, but also along the courses of the larger rivers and of some of the smaller streams as well. But in most places it is rare and irregular and appears only as a transient visitant in spring and fall. There are several odd records for the Ohio River in Beaver and Allegheny counties, for which B. H. Christy and I are mainly responsible, but they cover a period of many years. The Osprey is equally rare in the southwestern group of counties, and thus far has not been reported at all from the plateau region. At Conneaut Lake and at Pymatuning Swamp, however, as well as at Warren, on the upper Allegheny River, it is said to be fairly regular and common. In the higher country to the eastward the species must be rare or absent, although at Renovo, on the West Branch of the Susquehanna, according to the records of A. K. Pierce, it reappears as a regular migrant. S. S. Dickey saw three ospreys together over the Juniata River at Spruce Creek, Huntingdon County, on May 2, 1919, and H. A. McGraw has several spring and fall records for the same general region.

Breeding records for our area are surprisingly few. On May 28, 1909, near the mouth of Raccoon Creek in Beaver County, an osprey alighted on a dead tree under which I was standing, and I believed that it was nesting somewhere in the vicinity. This bird may indeed have been one of the pair whose nest was found on May 30 of that year by Frank Wolf, about a mile back from the Ohio River at Legionville, Beaver County. It is entirely possible that the birds might have wandered as far as Raccoon Creek in search of food. R. C.

Harlow reports that he found a nest at Foxburg, Clarion County, on June 20, 1910. One other record, of dubious scientific value, is reported by S. N. Rhoads on hearsay evidence: an osprey "nested in the mountains near Round Island somewhere along Cook's Run," in Clinton County. The Osprey probably breeds also in Erie County, but there is no positive evidence to this effect. Special search for nests should be made in the Pymatuning region.

Migration—The Osprey moves northward in April. Eighteen seasons' records of its arrival at Renovo lie between April 4 (1903) and 25 (1898 and 1910); the average date is April 15. It has been seen at Conneaut Lake as early as April 2 (1926), and at Warren on April 1 (1891), but it usually comes a little later. The movement may last for two or three weeks or even more, but any birds seen after the first week in May are possibly breeding. Midsummer occurrences are hard to explain on any other basis. By August the young birds are on the wing and, as they appear far from their known breeding places, evidently wander widely, although probably without any set goal. By September, however, a concerted southward movement begins which continues into the following month or, in the case of stragglers, even into November. "On November 22, 1927, at Fannetsburg, Franklin Co., Mrs. J. N. Wineman killed an osprey that was destroying goldfish in a private pond" (Sutton). November 7 (1900) is the latest date given by A. K. Pierce for Renovo.

Habits—The Osprey or Fish Hawk, imposing in appearance at rest or on the wing, adds a picturesque note to the setting of any lake or stream. One of the larger hawks, with a physique equal to that of any of its peers, it yet stoops to lowly prey and seldom touches anything but fish. Its feet are large and strong, with long, curved claws and rough granulations, and the outer toe is versatile —all modifications that facilitate the holding of its slippery prey. Its fishing methods are most interesting to watch. Its ordinary flight over the water is strong and steady, with regular wingbeats, and reminds one of a gull rather than a hawk. When on the lookout for food it flies at an elevation of from thirty to one hundred feet, and its keen vision readily enables it to discover any fish swimming near the surface. Upon descrying its prey it hovers in the air for a brief moment, then closes its wings, plunges swiftly downward at an angle, and hits the water with a tremendous splash. Sometimes it entirely disappears below the surface, to emerge directly with its victim grasped firmly in its talons. It carries its quarry to its nest or to some favorite perch—often at a considerable distance—and devours it at leisure. A bald eagle sometimes interferes with this orderly procedure by a show of force, and intimidates the weaker bird into dropping its prey, which the eagle recovers in the air or just as it reaches the water. The osprey submits to such robbery by its more powerful neighbor largely as a matter of course, as it is seldom able to outwit or outdistance its pursuer. Sometimes, however, a number of ospreys combine to resist an eagle and to put it to rout.

Where the Osprey is consistently protected, as at some places along the Atlantic coast, the birds soon become tame and build their nests in suitable trees, high or low, or on telegraph poles, chimney tops, or even the ground. But in our region, where the Osprey shares in the ignorant prejudice directed against birds of prey in general, its nesting is attended with little safety. Nests in our region are few and far between. There is a nestling specimen (preserved in alcohol) in the collection of the Carnegie Museum, received from C. P. Machesney of Ambridge, which attests one of the two known breeding records from this section. In reply to an inquiry, Mr. Machesney wrote that this young bird had been taken from a nest in a high tree by a local resident on May 30, 1909. The exact locality was on the flat above "Legionville Hollow," in Beaver County, about a mile back from the Ohio River, and the nest was between fifty and sixty feet from the ground. The parent bird made "considerable fuss" when the nest was approached, but did not attack the climber.

The Osprey, like some other hawks, uses the same nest year after year if undisturbed and adds to it every season until it becomes a large and conspicuous structure of sticks and other miscellaneous materials. The eggs are sometimes only two, usually three, and rarely four, in number; they are among the handsomest and most richly marked of the entire hawk tribe. The ground-color is a creamy white, sometimes overlaid with buff, and more or less heavily marked with brown spotting of several shades; the spots are often confluent around the larger end. The eggs average 2.45 by

1.82 inches. In our latitude they are laid early in May.

The ordinary alarm-note of the Osprey is not at all like that of any other hawk; it is a weak and puny whistle, rapidly repeated, and lacking in any suggestion of ferocity. The Osprey displays no animosity toward smaller birds but is said to drive off other hawks from the vicinity of its nest. The fish that it takes as food are ordinarily species of little or no economic value.

Pandion haliaëtus TOWNSEND, *Proc. Acad. Nat. Sci. Philadelphia*, 1883, 66 (Loyalhanna Creek, near Latrobe, and Allegheny River, Westmoreland Co.).

Pandion haliaëtus carolinensis WARREN, *Birds Pa.*, ed. 2, 1890, 142 (distribution by counties)—RHOADS, *Auk*, 1899, 16:311 (Cooks Run, near Round Island, Clinton Co., nesting, *fide* Nelson)—TODD, *Ann. Carnegie Mus.*, 1904, 2:555 (Presque Isle, Erie Co., transient)—TODD, in Bausman, *Hist. Beaver Co., Pa.*, 1904, 2:1199 (Beaver Co., transient)—HARLOW, *Auk*, 1918, 35:25 (Foxburg, Clarion Co., breeding)—CHRISTY, *Cardinal*, 1923, v. 1, no. 1, [p. 5] (Sewickley, Allegheny Co., transient)—BURLEIGH, *Wilson Bull.*, 1923, 35:86 (Deer Creek, Allegheny Co., spring); 1924, 36:77 (State College, Centre Co., April)—SUTTON, *Ann. Carnegie Mus.*, 1928, 18:133 (Crawford Co. records and references).

"Osprey" SIMPSON, *Oölogist*, 1907, 24:133 (Warren, Warren Co., May)—EASTWOOD, *Bird-Lore*, 1926, 28:273 (Adams, Butler Co., May)—CHRISTY, *Cardinal*, 1931, 3:43 (McDonald Reservoir, Washington Co., May).

FALCONS

FAMILY FALCONIDAE

THE DIFFERENCES between this family and the Accipitridae are of an anatomical character, not readily observable. The true Falcons, with which alone we have to deal in this volume, however, are readily distinguished from the other diurnal birds of prey by their long, pointed wings, toothed upper mandible and notched lower mandible, and short, very powerful feet. They comprise the so-called "noble" hawks, which capture their prey by direct and sustained pursuit. The group is represented in all parts of the world. Flight patterns of the species occurring in western Pennsylvania are illustrated on Plate 23.

DUCK HAWK

FALCO PEREGRINUS ANATUM Bonaparte

Description—A medium-sized hawk, with *long, pointed wings, short tarsi,* and long, powerful talons; wingspread, thirty-eight to forty-three inches (male), and forty-three to forty-six inches (female). *Adult:* above, dark gray with blackish mottling, inclining to bars on the lower back and tail, the head and neck almost "solid" black; forehead paler; a *broad band of black below the eye* covers the cheeks; throat, sides of the neck, and breast, buffy white, unspotted; rest of *underparts* and tibiae the same color, but *spotted and barred with dusky black;* tail dusky below, with paler bars and a narrow white tip; *wings marked below with dusky and buff bars;* bill dark blue, but cere deep yellow; feet dull yellow. *Immature:* above, dusky brown, with more or less rusty-buff feather-tipping; head with much buff, but the *dark band below the eye* still prominent; *underparts* (except chin and upper throat) *heavily streaked with black* on a buffy ground; tail dusky, with conspicuous whitish tip and inconspicuous buff bars or spots; wings barred below as in the adult; soft parts much the same.

Range and migration—*Falco peregrinus* is virtually a cosmopolitan species, with representative races in different parts of its range. The North American mainland race, *F. peregrinus anatum,* is widely distributed and ranges across the continent from one ocean to the other, north to the arctic regions, and southward into northern South America in the winter. It is commoner northward, where it occurs as a summer resident only. On the Atlantic coast it breeds as far south as the Palisades of the Hudson River in New York state, but in the mountains it is known to nest as far south as Tennessee.

This hawk is fond of rough, wooded country and avoids the flat and cultivated areas; thus it is sparingly distributed as a breeding bird in the ridge and valley region of our state, east of the crest of the Alleghenies proper. In this rough and broken country, cut up by minor mountain ridges with valleys between, the Duck Hawk finds congenial territory with plenty of nesting sites on the cliffs and no dearth of suitable prey. Warren cites several nesting records from eastern Pennsylvania. He quotes T. L. Hazzard to the effect that the Duck Hawk breeds in Allegheny County, but he has no further evidence to offer. The first nest known from our region was the one discovered by A. K. Pierce near Grove Run, Clinton County, on April 21, 1894, and from which he took a set of eggs. T. D. Burleigh writes that in April, 1919, he saw a pair of duck hawks along the Susquehanna River near Hyner, in the same county. In the spring of 1921 G. M. Sutton and S. S. Dickey visited two nests, previously located by Mr. Dickey, in the mountains of Huntingdon County. Even at this late date it is not wise to disclose the exact localities of these nests, out of consideration for the birds themselves. Probably a thorough exploration of this general region would discover more nesting pairs, although they are doubtless widely scattered. O. P. Medsger writes that in May, 1914, he learned of a nest on a cliff along Jacobs Creek, in Westmoreland County, about two and a half miles above the town of the same name. From the description he was convinced that this nest belonged to a duck hawk.

Elsewhere in western Pennsylvania the Duck Hawk is known only as a casual visitant during migration, but it is rare everywhere, and has come under the notice of only a very few observers. R. B. Simpson has seen it at Warren but once—on June 6, 1912. At Presque Isle one was seen by L. E. Hicks in June, 1931, and another by W. M. Guynes on May 14, 1933. The published spring records from Crawford County are not entirely satisfactory, but R. L. Fricke saw one bird in flight near Linesville on May 24, 1935, and Miss Ruth Trimble saw another at the same place on April 24, 1938. All these records doubtless pertained to nonbreeding individuals. The species was reported at Renovo on April 4, 1894, and on April 5, 1895 (Pierce). One bird was shot at Howard, Centre County, on November 20, 1921, by a local gunner (Sutton). Whether the Duck Hawk winters in our region has not yet been determined; and much still remains to be learned about its movements in general.

Habits[1]—It has been many years now since I had my first sight of a duck hawk, but the thrill of that moment is still fresh in my mind as I recall the circumstances. Acting on a rumor that a pair of these birds was nesting on a certain cliff in Clinton County, I went to this spot on a morning in early April, and as noon approached was seated at the foot of the cliff, wondering how I had best go about my attempt to find the nest. Suddenly, without any warning, a shadow passed over my head, and as I glanced up, a duck hawk alighted on the top of an old snag close by. It realized my presence almost at once, and was gone as silently and swiftly as it had appeared, but not before I had a vivid glimpse of this undisputed sovereign of the air.

It is perhaps unfortunate that throughout all its range the Duck Hawk is a rather scarce bird, for its appearance and habits are such as to command the admiration and respect of the most prejudiced observer. In flight its speed is unequaled by that of any other hawk, and nothing that flies can escape its swift attack. There are numerous authentic records of its pursuing and overtaking with seeming ease such fast-flying species as the Blue-winged Teal; and even swallows are not immune when the hawk is sufficiently hungry to be tempted by such a small tidbit. In taking its prey the Duck Hawk strikes with such force that its victim is dead from the moment of impact. Apparently, regardless of the height from which it has dropped in its sudden plunge, it strikes with its powerful talons as it comes up from beneath the bird it has attacked and rips open its throat and breast. Only during the breeding season is its courage tempered by caution. Throughout most of the year it is utterly fearless in pursuit of its prey, and it has been said to pick up wounded ducks almost from under the feet of the hunter. In late years it has been attracted to the larger cities, where pigeons, starlings, and even English sparrows, afford a ready and unfailing food supply, and there it has been known to remain from late fall until early spring, roosting at night on the ledges of the larger buildings.

For a nesting site the Duck Hawk chooses a ledge of a cliff, preferably in the vicinity of water. In but one instance have I seen a nest that was not at least in sight of a lake or a large stream. The ledge used is frequently rather narrow, is always difficult of access from either above or below, and is invariably protected by an overhang

[1]Account contributed by Thomas D. Burleigh.

from rock fragments that might fall from above. There is never the slightest attempt to bring in any nesting material, and the eggs are laid in a slight depression in the dirt and other accumulated debris. They vary in number from two to six, although four has been the usual clutch according to my experience. They are more heavily marked than those of most hawks and are uniformly dark reddish brown in color, obscurely blotched or smeared with varying shades of brown. They average 2.07 by 1.60 inches. Breeding activities normally are well under way in late March; the few records available for this region indicate full sets of fresh eggs by the first week in April. Two nests which I personally examined in 1919, on April 18 and 20, respectively, each held four well-incubated eggs, while Dr. Sutton found four fresh eggs in a nest in Huntingdon County on April 6, 1921. Late dates, such as that for a set recorded by Dr. Sutton on May 6, 1921, are probably due to the destruction of an earlier set.

Both parents take their turn at incubating, but are so extremely wary that the nest can seldom be found save by watching for the moment when the one that has been temporarily free of domestic duties arrives to relieve the other. I have spent many hours in hiding at the foot of a cliff waiting for such an opportunity to discover the nesting ledge, and have invariably been unsuccessful. Silently, and with uncanny speed, the bird will appear overhead, veer almost at right angles as the cliff is reached, and disappear again without revealing the site of the nest.

Birds unquestionably form the bulk of the Duck Hawk's bill of fare, and the feathers that litter the foot of the cliff give a clear picture of its activities at this season of the year. Small birds are apparently rarely molested, but little discrimination is shown otherwise. Crows and blue jays are frequent victims, and, to a less extent, meadowlarks, flickers, robins, pileated woodpeckers, and domestic pigeons. On one occasion I was interested to find that a sharp-shinned hawk had been killed and brought to the nest; and there are reports that even owls have been taken.

The average person is inclined to condemn the Duck Hawk because of its apparent destructiveness; and its existence today is undoubtedly due to its preference during the breeding season for the wilder, more rugged sections of the country. The species, however, has never existed in sufficient numbers to be a serious menace to other, more beneficial birds, and its disappearance would be a cause of real regret to all familiar with its habits. Certainly no other bird has a more interesting history; for it was the European race of our American Duck Hawk that was so popular in ancient days in the sport of falconry. There is a tendency at present to revive this outdoor pastime in this country—a tendency that may result in sufficient sentiment to give the Duck Hawk the protection it well deserves.

Falco peregrinus anatum Warren, *Birds Pa.*, ed. 2, 1890, 137 (Allegheny Co., breeding[?], *fide* Hazzard).

"Duck Hawk" Simpson, *Oölogist*, 1914, 31:92; and 1922, 39:55 (Warren, Warren Co., June)—Dickey, *Oölogist*, 1919, 36:43 ([Spruce Creek, Huntingdon Co.], central Pa., nesting).

Rhynchodon peregrinus anatum Sutton, *Ann. Carnegie Mus.*, 1928, 18:131 (Conneaut Lake, Crawford Co.?)—Sutton, *Cardinal*, 1930, 2:211 (Spruce Creek, Huntingdon Co., March).

EASTERN PIGEON HAWK

FALCO COLUMBARIUS COLUMBARIUS Linnaeus

Description—A small hawk, larger than the Sparrow Hawk; about equal in size to the Sharp-shinned Hawk, from which it may be distinguished by its long, pointed wings, much shorter legs, and relatively shorter tail. *Male:* dark bluish gray with narrow black stripes; tail blackish, crossed by several paler (bluish-gray) bands; wings dusky, showing white spots below; underparts buffy or whitish with brownish streaking; feet yellowish. *Female:* similar, but much larger, and the upperparts brownish instead of bluish gray, the streaking obsolete. *Young in fall plumage:* similar in coloration to the adult female, but generally darker and richer; feet not so bright in color.

Range—The Pigeon Hawk is the New World representative of the Merlin of Eurasia and has an extensive range in North America, from the arctic countries to those bordering the Caribbean

Sea. It breeds in the northern part of its range, south (it is believed) to northern New England and New York state, but there are no nesting records for the Pennsylvania mountains, although these might be expected, particularly in the elevated parts of our northern counties. The late dates and the circumstances of two personal observations made by G. M. Sutton do, indeed, suggest breeding. On May 18, 1925, in Game Refuge 17, near Sizerville, Cameron County, a pigeon hawk was seen perched on the top of a tall dead stub, where it was struck full on the head by a barn swallow. Again the next day, at Conrad, Potter County, one was seen flying over a goshawk nest. L. E. Hicks thinks that the Pigeon Hawk probably breeds in Erie County, since he saw one in the ravine of Walnut Creek, about eight miles west of Erie, on July 1, 1928. He also saw a single hawk on Hemlock Island, Pymatuning Swamp, on June 11, 1932, and another on August 12. He believes that the species must breed across the line in Ohio, although as yet no nests have come to light.[1]

Migration—In most parts of our region the Pigeon Hawk is only a winter resident or merely a transient, decidedly irregular and uncommon. Most of the known records come from the counties in the northwestern corner of the state: Erie, Crawford, and Warren. There it appears early in September, with the advent of the smaller migrants, and may linger for about two months. In the spring movement it arrives during the latter part of March, and remains until the first few days of May. An occasional individual may winter, as indicated by H. C. Kirkpatrick's record of one noted along French Creek near Meadville, on February 22, 1926. I have never seen this bird in Beaver County, but D. A. Atkinson has observed it six times in Allegheny County: at Wilkinsburg on January 3, 1892, February 8, 1898, and February 24, 1899; at Verona on December 19, 1897; at Sandy Creek on January 4, 1899; and at Swissvale on November 12, 1900. These dates would indicate that the species winters here.

Habits—The Pigeon Hawk makes up in swiftness, dash, and general ferocity for what it lacks in size. It preys almost entirely upon small birds, which it captures by direct pursuit in open flight. It can readily outdistance most small birds, except the swallows, which at times venture to annoy it, as Dr. Sutton has observed. A bird pursued in the open has little chance, but will make for cover of some kind in order to dodge the hawk. Woodpeckers slip quickly around to the other side of a tree, but often fall victims nevertheless. The Pigeon Hawk can strike and carry off a bird the size of a flicker, as large and heavy as itself. Its sudden appearance is the signal for all the smaller birds to hunt shelter. Its flight is exceedingly graceful and suggests that of a large swallow. It is not particularly shy and will often permit a near approach without becoming alarmed.

Falco columbarius Todd, *Ann. Carnegie Mus.*, 1904, 2:555 (Presque Isle, Erie Co., transient).

"Pigeon Hawk" Simpson, *Oölogist*, 1911, 28:52 (Warren, Warren Co., September), 144 (Presque Isle, Erie Co., September)—(?)Christy and Hegner, *Bird-Lore*, 1924, 26:30 (Clinton, Allegheny Co., December)—Sutton, *Bird-Lore*, 1924, 26:267 ([?]Clinton, Allegheny Co., May, *fide* Christy; Schenley Park and Frick Park, Pittsburgh, Allegheny Co., May)—Christy, *Cardinal*, 1926, v. 1, no. 8, p. 21 (Meadville, Crawford Co., February, *fide* Kirkpatrick).

Tinnunculus columbarius columbarius Sutton, *Ann. Carnegie Mus.*, 1928, 18:131 (Crawford Co. records and references)—Bergstrom, *Cardinal*, 1930, 2:186 (Shermansville, Crawford Co., May).

[1] *Wilson Bulletin*, 1933, 45:179.

EASTERN SPARROW HAWK

FALCO SPARVERIUS SPARVERIUS Linnaeus

Description—Our smallest hawk, about the size of the Mourning Dove; wings long and pointed. *Adult male: above, rufous chestnut*, marked with black; head above, ashy blue, with a central crown-spot (of variable size) of rufous chestnut; *tail also rufous chestnut*, with a *broad black bar toward the end* and a whitish tip; wings black externally, the coverts ashy blue, spotted with black; throat and sides of head white, with a *broad black band extending downward from the eye* and a large *black spot involving the ear coverts;* underparts white, the *breast and sides* washed with *rusty buff or cinnamon* and somewhat marked with rounded or droplike spots of black, sometimes lacking on the breast; under tail coverts and tibiae unspotted white; tail and wings barred below with black and white; feet dull yellowish or greenish; cere, and bare skin around eyes, yellow. *Female:* the parts that are rufous chestnut in the male are strongly *barred with rufous and dusky brown*, as likewise are the wing coverts; the top of the head is much duller with fine dark streaking; the dark markings of the side of the head, however, are the same; the *underparts* are heavily *streaked with pale brown;* the dark bars of the under wing and tail are much narrower. *Young birds* resemble the adults of either sex.

Range—Our American Sparrow Hawk is not closely related to the Eurasian bird of the same name (which is an *Accipiter*), but is an analogue of the Kestrel. As a species it ranges over South and Middle America in general, breaking up into many geographical races, and thence over North America to but not beyond the Canadian Life Zone. In the northern part of its range it is migratory, but elsewhere it is resident. Western Pennsylvania, in the heart of its general range, is favored with a fairly large and evenly distributed population of this species. At the present time it is probably our commonest hawk. Its relatively small size and its concealed nesting sites give it an advantage over the other hawks. In Centre County, and in the Ohio Valley and the region to the southward, it is undoubtedly a permanent resident. Elsewhere, various observers claim that it is more properly a summer resident; but there are so many cases of its occurrence in the winter in all parts of the region that it should no doubt be classed as an actual or potential permanent resident throughout. Very possibly some of the individuals that are seen in the winter are migrants from the north; on the other hand, for several years in succession I have observed a pair at intervals, summer and winter alike, about the railway yards at Conway, Beaver County, and am persuaded that this particular pair of birds is certainly not migratory.

Habits[1]—The Sparrow Hawk is a bird of the open places—of fields and wastelands. It is oftenest seen perched high in some dead treetop or on a telephone pole by the roadside, and its characteristic features are its small size, its high "shoulders," round head, and long tail. When disturbed, the bird dashes from its perch with great vigor; its flight to a more distant perch is swift, and it alights and folds its wings abruptly. As it flies away it may utter its shrill, repetitive scream, suggested in the syllables *killy-killy*.

When hunting, the Sparrow Hawk moves over open ground at an elevation of about twenty feet. It pauses here and there on fluttering wings, and remains stationary in mid-air for many seconds. From such point of arrest it may at length fall like a plummet to the ground or sweep off to another station. Its food consists chiefly of mice and large insects.

A dead tree standing alone in an open field and frequented by a pair of sparrow hawks usually has a woodpecker-hole drilled high in one of its branches; and in such places the sparrow hawks commonly make their homes. On May 18 of a year long past, W. C. Miller and I examined a sparrow hawk's nest. It was in a large charred stub some fifty feet high that stood alone in an abandoned field in the river bottom. The hawks had taken possession of a flicker-hole nearly two feet deep that had been drilled in the very top of the stub. The four eggs lay on the bare wood, and a few small bones lay with them. The eggs of this species resemble those of other falcons and are very beautiful: creamy white, heavily marked and wreathed with rather fine rust-colored dots. The usual complement of eggs is five, but sometimes four or six; they measure about 1.37 by 1.14 inches.

R. C. Harlow (1917) describes a similarly situated nesting site with "a well-defined nest of grass and a few feathers." Mr. Harlow has said elsewhere (1912) that although sparrow hawks prefer woodpecker-holes, they sometimes choose natural cavities in the trunks and branches of trees.

Sparrow hawks, like other falcons, will sometimes enter cities and take up their abode in towers and lofty buildings. Looking from an office window in New York, I once saw a duck hawk strike a pigeon from a flock in mid-air. And, seated at my desk, high above the streets of Pittsburgh, I often hear the shrill calls of sparrow hawks and see the birds go dashing by my window. On one occasion, at mating time, I saw three birds engaged in the most astonishing feats of flight high

[1]Account contributed by Bayard H. Christy.

above the city buildings. One of the factors, perhaps, in this predilection for cities, is the semblance that towers and cornices of buildings have to cliffs and precipices (a factor that is of more obvious significance in the case of the Duck Hawk than in that of the Sparrow Hawk). Another factor certainly is food; for flocks of pigeons, of English sparrows, and of starlings abound in and about the cities. Even the mice, as they scurry from place to place, are exposed, without cover. It is significant that, with the almost complete disappearance of English sparrows from the city streets, the sparrow hawks too have grown rarer.

Sparrow hawks sometimes nest in the crannies of buildings, and even in birdhouses. W. F. Jacobs (1922) describes two nesting sites used year after year in the lofts of certain school buildings in Waynesburg. Of one of these he writes: "The nest was made on the rough lath and plaster of the ceiling of the room below and in the angle made by two large timbers." Access was gained through a hole that flickers had drilled through the cornice of the building, and the nest was about a foot from that opening. The nest itself, he says, "consisted only of a few sticks and [the birds'] excretions."

A nest that I discovered in the city of Pittsburgh on June 4, 1934, was situated in a boxed-in architectural recess in a façade of granite, about a hundred feet above the pavement, in the very heart of the city. The chamber was eighteen inches long, about eight inches wide, and, to the crest of the arched roof, fourteen inches high. The hawks had spread a bed of excelsior on the granite floor of the chamber. At the time of discovery the nest contained three young—two of them well grown, the third smaller—and two infertile eggs. The excelsior was littered with the feathers of the English Sparrow and a few of the Canary, and the decapitated body of a sparrow also lay on the bed.

G. M. Sutton has made the following notes upon two young sparrow hawks that were captured and sent to the office of the Pennsylvania Game Commission: "Their apparent affection for each other was noticeable. At one time the male was perched on the top of a cupboard while the female was still in the wire cage, and in answer to her cries, the male flew to the cage, grasped the wires, and seemingly attempted to find a way to release his mate. The birds seemed very nervous while kept in the cage. When released, however, they would perch at convenient places in the room in apparent contentment. The female displayed both fear and anger to a much greater degree than did the male, and her cries were louder and shriller. The male could be stroked and petted; but the female struck viciously at anyone who approached. The birds were often seen to lie on their sides, as well as on their bellies, while reclining. Their tails were frequently used as props. Because of the trouble of securing proper food for the birds, raw beefsteak was fed them most of the time. When opportunity offered, however, we gave them grasshoppers, which were consumed with evident relish. Lacking sufficient hard skin and bone to tear, the upper mandibles began to grow long and pointed. The birds loved to bathe, and would walk into the water up to their bellies, and shake water upon themselves until they were wet all over."

Falco sparverius Townsend, *Proc. Acad. Nat. Sci. Philadelphia*, 1883, 66 (Latrobe, Westmoreland Co., breeding)—Jacobs, *Summer Birds Greene Co., Pa.*, 1893, 6 (Greene Co., breeding)—Baily, *Auk*, 1896, 13:293 (Williamsville, Elk Co., June)—Todd, *Ann. Carnegie Mus.*, 1904, 2:555 (Erie and Presque Isle, Erie Co., summer)—Todd, in Bausman, *Hist. Beaver Co., Pa.*, 1904, 2:1199 (Beaver Co., resident)—Forrest, *Oölogist*, 1911, 28:116 (Washington, Washington Co., breeding)—Dickey, *Oölogist*, 1913, 30:75 (Waynesburg, Greene Co., nesting)—Christy, *Cardinal*, 1935, 4:10 (Pittsburgh, Allegheny Co., nesting).

"Sparrow Hawk" Pitcairn, *Bird-Lore*, 1908, 10:32 (West View, Allegheny Co., December)—Dickey, *Oölogist*, 1909, 26:224 (Waynesburg [9 miles north], Greene Co., nesting)—Simpson, *Oölogist*, 1910, 27:100 (Warren, Warren Co., winter)—Harlow, *Cassinia*, 1912, 15:20 (Center Furnace Swamp, Centre Co., winter)—Harlow, *Oölogist*, 1917, 34:64 (State College, Centre Co., nesting)—Simpson, *Oölogist*, 1912, 29:329 (head of Tionesta Creek, Warren Co., nesting)—Burleigh, *Bird-Lore*, 1913, 15:29 (Aspinwall, Allegheny Co., December)—McConnell, *Oölogist*, 1918, 35:150 ("Christy Park," McKeesport, Allegheny Co., breeding)—Warfield, *Bird-Lore*, 1919, 21:37 (Chambersburg, Franklin Co., December)—McGraw and Hays, *Bird-Lore*, 1920, 22:31 (Lakemont, etc., Blair Co., December)—Savage, *Bird-Lore*, 1920, 22:31 (Moon Run and vicinity, Allegheny Co., December)—Jacobs (W. F.), *Oölogist*, 1922, 39:65 (Waynesburg, Greene Co., nesting)—McClelland, *Am. Mid. Nat.*, 1922, 8:36 (Washington, Washington Co., summer; migration)—Christy and Hegner, *Bird-Lore*, 1922, 24:23 (Clinton Pond, etc., Allegheny Co., December); 1924, 26:30; and 1925, 27:41 (Raccoon Creek, etc., Beaver Co., December)—Simpson, *Oölogist*, 1922, 39:36 (Warren, Warren Co., nesting)—Hoffman, *et al.*, *Bird-Lore*, 1923, 25:23 (Grove City, Mercer Co., December)—Jones, *et al.*, *Bird-*

Lore, 1923, 25:25 (Deer Creek, Allegheny Co., December)—STREET, *Cassinia*, 1923, 24:12 (Greencastle to Ft. Loudon, Franklin Co., June)—CHRISTY, *Cardinal*, 1924, v. 1, no. 4, p. 10 (Big Traverse Valley, Beaver Co., June)—EASTWOOD, *Bird-Lore*, 1925, 27:337 ("Slack Hollow," Allegheny Co., July, *fide* Grimm), 338 (McKinley Park, Pittsburgh, Allegheny Co., breeding)—ELLIOTT, *Cardinal*, 1934, 3:170 (Raccoon Creek, Beaver Co., December)—BEAL and PETERSON, *Bird-Lore*, 1934, 36:33; and UPSON, *et al.*, *Bird-Lore*, 1935, 37:47 (Presque Isle, Erie Co., December)—CHRISTY, *et al.*, *Bird-Lore*, 1937, 39:44 (Pymatuning region, Crawford Co., December).

Falco sparverius sparverius HARLOW, *Auk*, 1912, 29:470 (Lemont and State College, Centre Co., nesting); 1918, 35:25 (southern Pa.)—CHRISTY, *Cardinal*, 1923, v. 1, no. 1, [p. 5] (Sewickley, Allegheny Co., resident)—BURLEIGH, *Wilson Bull.*, 1923, 35:86 (Allegheny Co., nesting); 1924, 36:69 (State College, Centre Co., resident)—BURLEIGH, *Cardinal*, 1932, 3:74 (near Uniontown, Fayette Co., summer).

Cerchneis sparveria sparveria CHRISTY and SUTTON, *Cardinal*, 1928, 2:69 (Clarion, Clarion Co., summer)—SUTTON, *Ann. Carnegie Mus.*, 1928, 18:132 (Crawford Co. records and references)—BURLEIGH, *Wilson Bull.*, 1931, 43:40 (State College, Centre Co., nesting).

GROUSE

FAMILY TETRAONIDAE

THE GROUSE, of which eleven genera are now recognized, are characteristic of the arctic and temperate regions of both the Old and New Worlds. They are gallinaceous (fowl-like) birds of moderate to large size, with feathered tarsi, and densely feathered nasal grooves, in which the nostrils barely show. Several of the species are remarkable for the dilatable air sacs under the skin which are displayed by the males in mating time, and for their elaborate and involved courting antics.

There is no ground for the inclusion of the Greater Prairie Chicken (*Tympanuchus cupido americanus*) as a former inhabitant of western Pennsylvania.[1]

[1]Compare TODD, *Auk*, 1938, 55:274.

EASTERN RUFFED GROUSE

BONASA UMBELLUS UMBELLUS (Linnaeus)

Description—Size of a small domestic fowl. Head slightly crested. *Adult:* upperparts brown, varied with buffy, black, grayish, and rufous markings; tail bright rufous, with narrow dusky bars and, near the end, a broad black band, bordered with grayish white; on either side of the neck a projecting ruff of black feathers; throat buffy; rest of underparts spotted or irregularly barred with brown or rufous color on a whitish ground, these dark bars being most conspicuous on the flanks. In the *female* the markings are toned down somewhat, and the neck-ruffs are reduced in size. *Downy young* are buffy rufous above, with a dark brown stripe through the eye, and whitish below.

In occasional individuals the rufous color of the tail and upperparts in general is more or less replaced by gray. These "Silver-tails," as they are called, are likelier to be found in the northern part of the state than elsewhere, and they indicate intergradation in the direction of the northern race, *Bonasa umbellus togata*.

Range—The Ruffed Grouse as a species has a wide east-and-west range that extends across the continent. It is subject, however, to considerable geographical variation. The typical and eastern race ranges through the Carolinian and Alleghanian life zones, but in the Canadian Life Zone it is replaced by the race *togata*, which is the characteristic form of Ruffed Grouse in the spruce and fir woods of the north country, as far south as the Adirondacks in New York state. It is no surprise, therefore, to find a certain proportion of the Ruffed Grouse population of our region, particularly in the northern counties, showing an approach to *togata*. In a series of nineteen specimens in the collection of the Carnegie Museum, taken in McKean and Cameron counties in the fall of 1915, the tails of several are more or less grayish-tinged, but I have yet to see a perfectly typical specimen of *togata* from Pennsylvania.[2] G. M. Sutton has seen intermediates, however, and R. B. Simpson advises me that in the years 1902–4 he saw some birds (and examined others) from various parts of Warren County that he considered to be of the northern race. He thought that these birds might have come down from the North. This is unlikely, however, since the Ruffed Grouse is a resident species that braves the severest winters without apparent inconvenience.

This grouse is generally distributed throughout our region wherever there is enough forest left to

[2]Alexander Wetmore, in the article cited in the references, does indeed refer the Ruffed Grouse of the Appalachian highlands to *togata*, but I am unable to follow him in this allocation.

meet its requirements for food and shelter. In Audubon's time it must have been incredibly common, for he speaks of buying birds in the Pittsburgh market for twelve and one-half cents a pair. Two major factors—deforestation and excessive hunting—have reduced its numbers to the present level. The Ruffed Grouse requires woods, but not necessarily woods of extensive area, since it is often found in comparatively restricted tracts. But small tracts are usually more intensively hunted over during the open season, so that any pairs established there have less chance to survive. In Beaver County there is now scarcely one pair of grouse where there were twenty-five pairs in the early nineties, and the same is true of many other counties with similarly reduced forest acreage. At the present time the species is probably more numerous, although oftener hunted, in the plateau region and in the ridge and valley section of the state, where there are still extensive tracts of woodland, than in other areas.

Fluctuations in numbers from year to year have been remarked by several observers. A cold, wet spring, such as that of 1924, may indeed seriously interfere with the hatching of the eggs and with the raising of the broods. A few good seasons with favorable conditions, however, soon make up the loss. The Ruffed Grouse is amply able to hold its own against natural conditions and enemies; it is only when it has to contend in addition with unwonted persecution that it succumbs. The idea that the scarcity of grouse is due to the depredations of birds of prey in general, and of the Goshawk in particular, cannot be seriously entertained by the unprejudiced, since in recent years these predators have unfortunately been thinned out far more, in proportion to their numbers, than have the grouse. . . . The factors outlined above, however, have rendered the latter species so scarce in some parts of Pennsylvania that the game commission has found it necessary at intervals to close certain counties to grouse-hunting, in order to give the birds time to recuperate.[1]

Habits—Not far from my home in Beaver there is a wooded ravine where I can always depend on finding one or more pairs of ruffed grouse. Year after year, summer and winter alike, and in the seasons between, they haunt this secluded spot. This particular ravine is their home, to which they are persistently attached, since they find there both food and shelter. The Ruffed Grouse, probably more than any other bird, is naturally sedentary—not disposed to wander from its adopted haunts. I believe that a given individual, if undisturbed, may spend its entire life within the confines of one restricted area. As young birds come to maturity, they are of course forced to seek new territory, and thus the area occupied by the species is gradually expanded.

Nevertheless, several observers mention having at times met with grouse in open situations away from cover of any kind. The necessity for finding suitable food may account for this wandering. Wild fruits and berries of many kinds, seeds, green leaves, and buds, bulk large in their bill of fare, while a variety of insects are also eaten in season. In the late summer and fall, when food is plentiful and easy to obtain, the grouse wax fat as they molt into fresh plumage. Mast, consisting of acorns and beechnuts, is a favorite food, and haws, wild grapes, and the red berries of the flowering dogwood, lend variety to the provender. Even in the winter all these items are still available, but sometimes the grouse feed as well on the leaves of the wintergreen, the mountain laurel, and certain kinds of ferns. Sumac and poison-ivy berries are also eaten, apparently for the pulp alone, since the seeds seem to pass through the digestive tract unscathed. A deep snow may hamper the grouse in their efforts to find food, but it does not daunt them. In the spring they are fond of nipping off the tender buds of certain trees and shrubs, but the weight of the birds prevents them from reaching the terminal branches.

The Ruffed Grouse, like other members of the family, is at home on the ground, where it walks about in easy, graceful fashion. Seldom is an observer able to approach it undetected. At the first sign of an intruder it is on the alert and will often

[1]I am of course not unmindful of the announced results of a recent study of the Ruffed Grouse in New York state, made by Gardiner Bump and published at length in the *Transactions of the Nineteenth American Game Conference*, 1933, p. 388–403. This report has justly elicited severe criticism from the friends of wild-life conservation. Its disinterestedness is not above suspicion, and the data on which it is based surely cannot claim to have been scientifically assembled. Briefly, the report undertakes to show that out of one hundred grouse eggs laid in one year no less than fifty-seven are destroyed before hatching, mainly by predators, while of those that hatch, twenty-three young die in the first three months (from inclement weather, inherent weakness, or predators), eight die from predators when adult, three are killed by hunters, and only nine live into the second year.

squat in its tracks and remain quite motionless until almost underfoot; then with a tremendous whirring of wings it suddenly leaps into the air and disappears from view. This behavior is clearly intended to alarm and disconcert the invader. More than once, while I have been seated in the woods, a grouse has flown by, just as quietly as any other bird until it happened to see me; then at once the loud whirring began as the bird veered off from fancied danger. A cool head and steady hand are needed to bring down a grouse in the second or two during which it is in sight, especially if the birds flush wild. Hunting with a dog is a great help, for then the birds lie more closely. Grouse are fond of thick covert—brush heaps, fallen timber, grapevine tangles, evergreen and laurel thickets—where the hunter is at a disadvantage.

Sometime during the winter the coveys or family groups break up, and by spring the birds are all paired. Then the males begin their "drumming"—a nuptial performance comparable with the "booming" of the Prairie Chicken and the "strutting" of the Turkey. It may be described as a peculiar, muffled, rolling sound that begins slowly, with distinct beats, but soon becomes so rapid that the ear fails to distinguish the separate strokes, which finally blend into a continuous rumble. It has a curious penetrating effect on the ear (at least on mine) and causes a pulsing sensation within that organ. Another strange acoustic quality of the sound is that its intensity does not seem to depend upon the distance of the bird from the listener (within certain limits), since it often seems just as loud when the bird is some distance away as when it is close at hand.

Although this drumming is a familiar sound to every woods-rambler during the months from March to June, I suspect that those who have actually witnessed the phenomenon at close range are few indeed. Years ago I spent the better part of an afternoon in stalking a drumming grouse. The rustling of the dry leaves scattered during the performance was so loud that I felt sure the bird could not be far away. Proceeding very cautiously and only while the drumming was in progress, and hiding behind some tree trunks, I finally came up behind the bird to a spot where I could easily watch it as it stood on a fallen log. It drummed three times while I looked on; after the last performance it walked deliberately off the log and disappeared. Whether the Ruffed Grouse drums by beating its wings together or by beating its perch or by merely beating the air has been the subject of much written discussion. My observations satisfied me that the third is the actual method, since I was particularly careful to note the arc through which the wings moved in the first few slow strokes. These observations have been fully verified by others and confirmed by motion pictures. The bird always performs on a

raised spot, such as a log or a rock, and each individual has its own favorite resort. Moreover, it is not unusual for grouse to drum in the fall months, although why they do so then is not easily explained. They have been known to perform during moonlight nights.

Sometime in April the female finds a sheltered place at the base of a tree or under a fallen branch or a drift of dry leaves on a hillside; there she hollows out a depression, which she lines with some dead leaves or any other material at hand. In this sketchy nest she lays from eight to fifteen eggs, but usually about ten or eleven. They are pale buffy white in color and as a rule unmarked, but sometimes they have a few small dark spots. April 27 (1888) is my earliest date for a full set in Beaver County, while in the adjoining county of Allegheny, B. H. Christy gives April 24 as his earliest date. Other observers have found fresh eggs until the middle of May or even later, but such late nestings were probably second attempts.

The percentage of casualties to the eggs of the grouse seems to be unusually large, to judge from the reports of various observers. One can only guess what has happened when a nest with a full set is later found with all or part of the eggs missing. The usual period of incubation is three weeks. The female grouse sits very closely and after the young are hatched is assiduous in caring for them and in defending them with spirit from their many enemies. Mr. Simpson describes a well-known action of the brooding female: "When the young have just left the nest, the old bird will allow a very close approach, and will even try her best to drive off the intruder. Often she will rush boldly at him, dragging her wings, and hissing loudly, her feathers all ruffled up. Again she will apparently make desperate efforts to escape, dragging her wings as if badly hurt—all this of course in an attempt to divert attention from the young. The little fellows are adept at hiding and disappear like magic at the mother's warning cluck, and it is an exceedingly difficult matter to find them as they lie crouched on the ground." After the birds are older and able to fly a little, they attempt to escape by flight, but even then they are hard to find.

Mr. Simpson writes further that in Warren County this species is still holding its own remarkably well, since it lives successfully in the dense second growth that springs up after the original timber has been cut away. "Foxes destroy a great many in winter, as do also owls and wildcats. When the snow is deep, the grouse sometimes burrow beneath it, leaving only a hole to mark their entrance, and at such times they fall easy victims to prowling Reynard."

Tetrao umbellus Audubon, *Orn. Biog.*, 1831, 1:211 (Pittsburgh, Allegheny Co.)—Wied, *Reise in Innere Nord-America*, 1839, 1:(127), 130 (Ebensburg, Cambria Co.).

Bonasa umbella Townsend, *Proc. Acad. Nat. Sci. Philadelphia*, 1883, 66 (Latrobe, Westmoreland Co., resident).

Bonasa umbellus Teulon, *Quart. Jour. Boston Zoöl. Soc.*, 1883, 2:11 (Bradford, McKean Co.)—Warren, *Birds Pa.*, ed. 2, 1890, 107 (distribution by counties)—Dwight, *Auk*, 1892, 9:134 (Cresson, Cambria Co., June)—Todd, *Auk*, 1893, 10:38 (Two Lick, Indiana Co., June), 44 (Coalport, Clearfield Co., June)—Jacobs, *Summer Birds Greene Co., Pa.*, 1893, 5 (Greene Co., nesting)—Baily, *Auk*, 1896, 13:292 (Williamsville, Elk Co., breeding)—Cope, *Cassinia*, 1902, 5:13 (Kettle Creek Valley, Potter Co., June)—Todd, *Ann. Carnegie Mus.*, 1904, 2:551 (Erie and Presque Isle, Erie Co., resident)—Todd, in Bausman, *Hist. Beaver Co., Pa.*, 1904, 2:1199 (Beaver Co., resident)—Keim, *Cassinia*, 1905, 8:37 (Port Allegany, McKean Co., summer)—Christy, *Cardinal*, 1927, 2:13 (near Sewickley, Allegheny Co., nesting).

"Ruffed Grouse" Simpson, *Oölogist*, 1906, 23:136 ([near Tyler], Clearfield Co., May); 1907, 24:87; and 1920, 35:26 (Warren, Warren Co.)—Stone, *Cassinia*, 1906, 9:44 (Scrub Ridge, west of McConnellsburg, Fulton Co., June)—Miller, *Bird-Lore*, 1910, 12:29; etc. (Springs, Somerset Co., December)—[Burleigh], *Oölogist*, 1911, 28:156 (Harmarville, Allegheny Co., nesting)—Morris, *Bird-Lore*, 1913, 15:29 (Eagle Rock, Venango Co., December)—Dickey, *Oölogist*, 1914, 31:170 (Charter Oak, Huntingdon Co., nesting)—McConnell, *Oölogist*, 1916, 33:114 (McKeesport, Allegheny Co.)—Nicholson, *Bird-Lore*, 1921, 23:18 (Grove City, Mercer Co., December)—McConnell, *et al.*, *Bird-Lore*, 1922, 24:22 (Emsworth, Allegheny Co., December)—Jones, *et al.*, *Bird-Lore*, 1923, 25:25 (Deer Creek region, Allegheny Co., December)—Street, *Cassinia*, 1923, 24:12 (Little Cove Creek and Ft. Loudon, Franklin Co., June)—Christy, *Cardinal*, 1924, v. 1, no. 4, p. 10 (Big Traverse Valley, Beaver Co., June)—Sutton, *Cardinal*, 1925, v. 1, no. 5, p. 17 (western Pa., present status)—Alsop, *Bird-Lore*, 1925, 27:41 (Ridgway, Elk Co., December)—Sutton, *Auk*, 1926, 43:236 (Firstfork, Cameron Co., winter)—Berkheimer, *Bird-Lore*, 1933, 35:27; etc. (near Osterburg, Bedford Co., December)—Elliott, *Cardinal*, 1934, 3:170 (Raccoon Creek, Beaver Co., December).

Bonasa umbellus umbellus Harlow, *Auk*, 1912, 29:469 (southern Centre Co., resident); 1918, 35:23 (western Pa., range)—Stone, *Cassinia*, 1920, 23:33 (Altoona, Blair Co., nesting, *fide* McGraw)—Christy, *Cardinal*, 1923, v. 1, no. 1, [p. 4] (Sewickley, Allegheny Co., resident)—Burleigh, *Wilson Bull.*, 1923, 35:85 (Allegheny Co., resident); 1924, 36:69 (State College, Centre Co., resident)—Christy and Sutton, *Cardinal*, 1928, 2:69, 75 (Cook Forest, Clarion Co., resident)—Sutton, *Ann. Carnegie Mus.*, 1928, 18:114 (Crawford Co. records and references)—Burleigh, *Wilson Bull.*, 1931, 43:38 (Charter Oak, Huntingdon Co., nesting)—Burleigh, *Cardinal*, 1932, 3:74 (Chestnut Ridge, near Uniontown, Fayette Co., summer)—Conover, *Condor*, 1935, 37:205 (Clinton, McKean, and Cameron Co.).

"Eastern Ruffed Grouse" Cope and Hawkins, *Forest Leaves*, 1934, 24:26 (E. Tionesta Forest Reserve, Warren and McKean Co., summer).

Bonasa umbellus togata Wetmore, *Proc. U.S. Nat. Mus.*, 1937, 84:407 (Johnstown[?], Cambria Co., critical).

PARTRIDGES, QUAIL

FAMILY PERDICIDAE

THIS GROUP is almost cosmopolitan; it frequents all but the colder parts of both hemispheres. (There is some question, however, as to the family allocation of the Old World genera often placed here.) The Quail are readily distinguished from the Grouse by their (generally) smaller size and by their bare tarsi. We have only one representative of the family in the eastern United States, but in the West there are a number of others. Quail, like Grouse, are ground birds; they are more or less gregarious except in the breeding season.

EASTERN BOB-WHITE

COLINUS VIRGINIANUS VIRGINIANUS (Linnaeus)

Description—General form short and stocky, with rounded wings and short tail. Head with a short crest. *Male:* upperparts rich brown, varied with black, and with lengthwise buffy stripes on the scapulars and inner secondaries; hindneck varied with black and buff; crown brown, blackish in front; over the eye a broad white stripe, which meets its fellow on the forehead and is extended behind to the sides of the neck; below this a dark stripe (brown varied with black), which is joined behind to a broad band of the same color encircling the pure white throat; breast and underparts in general are white, marked with broken and irregular bars of black (except the belly, which is pure white); the sides and flanks in addition are heavily striped with rich brown, and the under tail coverts are varied with black and brown. *Female* similar, but the eye-stripe and throat are buffy instead of white, and the black on the lower throat and underparts in general is more or less replaced by brown.

Range—The Bob-white is found throughout most of the eastern United States. It ranges west to Colorado, north to southern Maine, and across the Canadian border into southern Ontario. Peninsular Florida on the one hand, and southern Texas and northeastern Mexico on the other, are respectively occupied by well-marked geographical races. South Carolina is the accepted type-locality for the widely ranging typical eastern race. In any attempt to define the status of the species toward the northern limit of its range, however, complications are at once encountered; for human agency has so marred the original picture that it is difficult to reconstruct. In the first place, there is every reason to believe that prior to the settlement of the country the Bob-white could not have been nearly so numerous—if indeed it was present at all—over much of the territory where it occurs commonly today. It is most unlikely that this bird, which seeks the open country and avoids the woodland, should have frequented "Penn's Woods" in the early days, and there is no contemporary evidence to show that it did. In Massachusetts, however, according to E. H. Forbush, it was recorded by one writer as early as 1632.[1] But the Bob-white was not long in taking advantage of the clearing and cultivation of the country to extend its range and increase its numbers. There followed a period of excessive hunting, whereby its numbers were seriously reduced. This in turn led to attempts to re-establish it as a game bird by introducing and releasing fresh stock from other parts—a highly reprehensible practice in unscientific hands.

The original stock, at least in New England,

[1] *Birds of Massachusetts*, 1927, 2:4.

has thus been extirpated, and there are unfortunately very few specimens preserved from which to judge its characters. The history of the species has been discussed at some length by J. C. Phillips.[1] The early Massachusetts Bob-white, he finds, was slightly larger in size than the bird of today and exhibited a tendency to less barring below. It is uncertain whether early Pennsylvania examples shared these characters, for none are known to be extant. As already intimated, however, I question whether the Bob-white existed at all in our region prior to the settlement of the Ohio Valley. It must have come in first from the West, from the prairies of the Mississippi Valley, and gradually extended its range to cover the western counties. But the forests of the Allegheny Mountains and of the plateau region were still virtually intact and formed an ecological barrier against any further dispersion in that direction. Elsewhere the penetration would have proceeded in an orderly manner, had it not been complicated by the introduction of stock from other parts. B. H. Christy (1926) has supplied an interesting and circumstantial account of these introductions, the substance of which is presented here. It appears that such practices were in vogue as early as 1859. They were initiated by certain persons who desired to replenish the supply of birds for hunting. "The birds of these earliest plantings were brought from short distances, from Ohio, chiefly, and from Indiana. The aggregate effect was of a slight shifting of the Bob-white populations, not notably different from what may be understood to have occurred naturally upon the opening of the country. And there could not have been any appreciable modification of the strain."

In later years, however, various shooting clubs brought in birds from the South and the West and released them on established preserves. All these introductions were haphazard and fortuitous, and not until after the organization of the state game commission was any systematic and concerted effort made to restock the depleted covers of the state at large. "In 1906 a special appropriation enabled the Commission to purchase 4,000 Bob-white and to distribute and release them at suitable places throughout the State. These birds came from Alabama and they cost $9 a dozen." In the period from 1915 to 1925 the commission similarly imported and distributed no less than 59,653 birds. But in the meanwhile conditions had greatly changed: "No longer was it possible to obtain birds trapped in adjacent regions. All of those states where the matter was one of importance had passed laws (the justice of which needs no defense) which forbade the trapping and exporting of wild game. The Commission, therefore, was constrained to go to Mexico for its supply of Bob-white and to pay from $18 to $25 a dozen for them."

To the unscientific and uncritical eyes of the commission, concerned as it was only with the game aspect of the situation, a bob-white was a bob-white, whether it came from Mexico or from the next state. Unfortunately the zeal shown in acquiring the birds was not actuated by knowledge. Even the most elementary acquaintance with natural laws might have forewarned of the result. To pick up individuals of a given species, developed in and adapted to a semitropical climate and showing in their racial characters the cumulative effects of such an environment, and to transplant them suddenly into another region of very different climatic and ecological conditions, originally inhabited by a distinct race, is to disregard the laws governing the distribution of life forms. And even if the experiment were eventually successful, the contamination of the original stock could not be regarded as other than deplorable.

G. M. Sutton, in an appendix to Mr. Christy's article, cited above, claims that the experiment actually has been a success and that the two races, *virginianus* and *texanus*, have interbred freely and seem to be doing well. "The admixture of Mexican birds has caused a decrease in size, and sometimes a change in coloration, which is noticeable in many parts of Pennsylvania." He thinks that our original Bob-white is virtually a thing of the past. I am not in a position to dispute his statements, but I myself have yet to see a single example of the Bob-white from western Pennsylvania showing any perceptible admixture of *texanus* blood. Moreover, our local specimens are absolutely indistinguishable, so far as I can judge, from the bird of western Florida, assumed to be true *virginianus*. But as the series of local birds available for examination is limited and poorly representative of the region as a whole, I may be in error.

[1] *Auk*, 1915, 33:204–207; pl. 16.

For the same reason I am unable further to discuss the question of geographical variation within the limits of the race *virginianus* as currently recognized.[1]

One thing seems certain: the Bob-white is more numerous and more widely distributed now than it was a generation ago. Several of my correspondents remark on the fact that it was growing scarce early in the present century, and there are some published records to the same effect. Just how much of the later increase can be laid to the importation of outside stock is an open question. Mr. Christy thinks that public sentiment toward better protection has had much to do with it, and this is no doubt true. There is, however, another consideration. The Bob-white is a good example of a species the northward range of which is determined by winter conditions rather than by the temperature of the breeding season. When the winter snows are deep, especially when a hard crust forms, the birds cannot secure food and eventually perish. One heavy storm may virtually wipe out the entire Bob-white population of a given district, as has often happened. This explains why it is that the species has not become established in the northern counties or in the plateau region in general, despite the areas of open country available there. In Warren County, for instance, it occurs occasionally, but apparently is unable to get a foothold, according to R. B. Simpson; and he knows of but one positive breeding record. The winters there are too severe.

The Bob-white has been found in northern Elk County, but is very rare (Baily, 1896; McQuiston); and in western Clearfield County (DuBois) it is listed by Van Fleet as a rare breeding bird. McKean, Potter, and Cameron counties are without known records, and the species is rare even in Clinton County. There are several specimens in the collection of the Carnegie Museum, however, from southern Clearfield County (Rosebud); these are almost certainly examples of recent introductions. In Cambria County, where the records of the game commission show about twenty-one thousand birds shot by licensed hunters from 1928 to 1932, the Bob-white is obviously more numerous. Still farther south, in Somerset County, it was noted at Hooversville in June, 1893, by E. A. Preble, and in 1935 was common in the region of Stoyestown (Mostoller). A. B. Miller writes that it is also present at Springs, close to the Maryland border, but varies in abundance from year to year: "A number of years with closed seasons resulted in a great increase in this bird. Although the season was open again last fall (1926), we had a mild winter with little snow, and the birds are common this spring. With many successive open seasons and hard winters, they disappear almost entirely."

From these facts it may be concluded that the present satisfactory status of the Bob-white in our section is due, at least in part, to the series of successive mild winters with but little snowfall that have prevailed now for some years. But it does not at all follow that the Mexican importations of *texanus* would suddenly become sufficiently hardy to withstand really cold weather, and I am yet to be convinced that they have actually done so. Bringing these birds in was certainly a mistake, as every naturalist will agree, and the effect, if any, could only be to weaken the native stock.

My remarks thus far have applied only to the western counties and to the plateau region. In the valleys of the ridge and valley section of the state the Bob-white is a common resident; it advances to the base of the Allegheny Mountains and sometimes ascends even higher. Thaddeus Surber saw a few bob-whites at Lloydville, Cambria County, in June, 1898, but was told by local residents that these were the first heard of there in several years. Almost certainly, the original advance of the species into this part of the country must have been from the Atlantic slope, by way of the Susquehanna and Potomac valleys.

My conclusions concerning the status of the Bob-white in western Pennsylvania are as follows:

The Bob-white, a species of tropical antecedents and accustomed to open country, must be a comparatively recent immigrant into this region, which was originally all heavily forested.

Its advance was probably by way of the Ohio Valley in the west, and of the Potomac and Susquehanna valleys in the east.

Artificial introduction of birds from far-distant

[1]T. E. Winecoff and L. A. Luttringer, Jr., of the Pennsylvania Game Commission, have assured me very definitely that the introduction of Mexican birds was admittedly a failure. They have examined many bob-whites killed in the past few years, and among them were none showing any impress of the introduced stock. This is only negative evidence, it is true, but it confirms the surmise already set forth.

regions has partially replaced and more or less weakened the original stock.

Nevertheless, the evidence for the belief that the introduction of individuals belonging to a different subspecies (*texanus*) has left a permanent impress on the native stock is not considered satisfactory.

The distribution of the species is determined very largely by winter temperatures and conditions, which in recent years have been admittedly abnormal.

The present status of the species in the plateau region (above fifteen hundred feet) is uncertain and precarious; elsewhere the Bob-white seems to be fairly well established.

Habits—It is a long time now since I first became acquainted with the Bob-white, but the early impression is still vivid: It is a cloudless summer day; the hot June sun beats down on the fields and meadows; waves of heat shimmer over the dusty roads. From a near-by tree a meadowlark essays a song, and a bobolink flies out across the field to meet his mate, voicing his feelings in rollicking, joyous abandon. Nearer at hand a grasshopper sparrow, perched on a tall weed topping the high grass, utters from time to time his listless shrill, but the other birds are mostly silent. I pause to rest in a bit of shade, and then, all at once, the air is cut by a loud, clear whistle—*Ah, bob-white!*—coming with almost startling distinctness. Although the call comes again and again, I catch no glimpse of its author, so closely does he keep to the tall grass. At length he mounts to the topmost rail of a fence, and then I find that he is a trim, stocky bird tastefully clad in rich brown, with dark markings on the head and underparts, and a white throat. I keep very still, and he continues to call, throwing back his head with a decided motion as he gives the last and loudest note. Presently, however, becoming aware of his human auditor, he drops down and is again out of sight in the meadow grasses, but the whistling notes continue and reveal his whereabouts.

But all this is no mere summer idyll. Bob-white has real responsibilities, and he takes them seriously. He is calling to his mate where she sits on her nest, cunningly hidden away under the protection of a bush, in a fence corner, or in a dense growth of grass. Sometimes he brings her food, or relieves her at the task of incubation. If she should be accidentally killed, he would carry on and would try to rear the brood single-handed. The nest is made of dried grasses or any other material at hand; it is often partially domed over, or at least concealed from above, and an opening is left on one side through which the bird may come and go. The eggs are pure white and of a characteristic subpyriform shape. They are unbelievably numerous for such a small bird. Ten eggs constitute a small set; fifteen is the average number; and, as stated by D. A. Atkinson, as many as twenty-three have been found. The same observer adds that in Allegheny County, according to his experience, sets of fresh eggs may be found from May 18 to August 26. He claims that two broods are regularly reared and that the eggs for these are laid during the latter part of May and early in August, respectively. Other authorities assert that the later nestings follow earlier unsuccessful attempts. At any rate, there is much irregularity, although June is perhaps the usual month. During the second week in June, 1933, J. B. Semple found a nest with nineteen eggs on his estate near Sewickley.

Incubation lasts twenty-three or twenty-four days. The young leave the nest shortly after they are hatched and follow their parents—a procession of little animated brown balls of fluff, running along with many a slip and stumble at first. At the onset of danger, after a warning cluck from the parents, they disappear like magic, to squat under a leaf or in the thick grass, so closely that they will permit themselves to be trodden underfoot before making a movement. Their wings grow very rapidly, and it is not long before the birds are able to fly short distances in trying to escape. As they grow older, they make increasing use of their wings; but the Bob-white is naturally a ground bird, and most of its moving about is done on foot. It can easily outrun any of the other birds with which it associates. It has need of all its resources to elude its enemies. Stray cats and dogs stand at the head of the list, and then come foxes, minks, and weasels, in sections where these have not been radically depleted, and, with the same qualification, the Sharp-shinned Hawk and Cooper's Hawk. After having run the gantlet of all these predators, the young and their parents must face the deadliest menace of all—the gunner and his dogs. The Bob-white is so prolific that it easily holds its own against all other enemies combined, but gives way before man. One of the most popular of our game birds, it is killed by the thousands every fall, for the sport and for a few ounces of savory meat. It is well that the open season for pursuit is short and that some counties have been closed to hunting; otherwise the prospect for the Bob-white would not be encouraging.

As the summer wanes, the coveys leave the opener situations and seek cover in briery thickets, bushy tracts, the edges of the woods—any place where they can find a little shelter and the necessary supply of food. During the summer, insects form a large part of their food, and the young feed almost entirely upon them. Wild fruits and berries are also eaten. When these fail with the coming of cold weather, seeds of many kinds become the main dependence. Weed seeds constitute the bulk of these; any grain that is taken is gleaned from the fields after the harvest. All through the winter months, the coveys, composed of one or more family groups, keep together. They roost on the ground in characteristic fashion, crouched in a circle, heads pointing outward, for warmth and for ease in getting away. Once or twice in my experience, quite early in the morning, I have stumbled across a roosting covey, which thereupon exploded in all directions, like an animated bombshell. A covey encountered while feeding will usually become motionless at the first alarm, hoping thus to escape attention, but if the intruder comes too close for comfort the birds spring suddenly into the air and are off on whirring wings, to come down with set pinions beyond the next rise and perhaps run for a long distance after that. When they get up as a unit a gunner has to be quick if he expects to make a double, but they often get up in loose sequence, and he then has a better chance at a kill. If the members of a covey have become separated for any reason, they will after a while come together again; they employ at such times a loud, clear, two-part call of characteristic tone and timbre.

Winter conditions are the crucial test of the Bob-white's ability to survive. It can withstand the cold fairly well (when not too protracted) if plenty of food is available to keep up the body temperature. Long periods of heavy snowfall may make it difficult to obtain sufficient food, and sometimes a covey becomes imprisoned under a hard crust, and then all the birds perish miserably. The practice of feeding coveys during severe weather has undoubtedly saved many birds, but under normal conditions the Bob-white can shift for itself. With the coming of spring the coveys break up, and mating begins, signalized by the familiar "bob-white" call of the cock bird. The mating call of the hen, heard at this season and later on, is a four-syllabled whistle, very sweet and lovely.

The Bob-white is one of the few birds known to eat the Colorado potato beetle, the striped cucumber beetle, and other injurious insects. A farm or garden can have no more valuable asset than a covey or several coveys of these birds. They should be encouraged in every way—by planting vines and bushes for cover, by winter feeding if need be, and by posting the premises against hunters. It is indeed a question if the time has not arrived for Pennsylvania to follow Ohio in removing the Bob-white from the list of game birds altogether and in affording it the same protection that other song and insectivorous birds now enjoy. From an aesthetic as well as a purely economic point of view this would seem to be a justifiable action. The specious argument—that without the shooting of the Bob-white the coveys would not break up in the spring—sometimes offered in opposition, is too absurd to deserve serious consideration.

Ortyx virginianus Townsend, *Proc. Acad. Nat. Sci. Philadelphia*, 1883, 66 (Latrobe, Westmoreland Co., resident).

Colinus virginianus Warren, *Birds Pa.*, ed. 2, 1890, 105 (Mercer, Crawford, and Lawrence Co.)—Todd, *Auk*, 1893, 10:37, 38 (Two Lick, Indiana Co., June)—Jacobs, *Summer Birds Greene Co., Pa.*, 1893, 5 (Greene Co., nesting)—Rhoads, *Auk*, 1899, 16:310 (Round Island, Clinton Co., *fide* Nelson)—Todd, *Ann. Carnegie Mus.*, 1904, 2:551 (Erie, Erie Co., resident)—Todd, in Bausman, *Hist. Beaver Co., Pa.*, 1904, 2:1199 (Beaver Co., resident).

"Quail" Baily, *Auk*, 1896, 13:292 (Williamsville, Elk Co., rare)—Simpson, *Oölogist*, 1911, 28:202; and 1912, 29:335 (near Warren, Warren Co., June).

"Bob-white" Stone, *Cassinia*, 1906, 9:43 (McConnellsburg, Fulton Co., June)—McConnell, *Oölogist*, 1916, 33:114 (McKeesport, Allegheny Co.)—McClelland, *Am. Mid.*

Nat., 1922, 8:35 (Washington, Washington Co., resident) —Street, *Cassinia*, 1923, 24:12 (Metal, Franklin Co., June) —Warfield, *Bird-Lore*, 1923, 25:23 (Chambersburg, Franklin Co., December)—Hoffman, *et al.*, *Bird-Lore*, 1923, 25:23 (Grove City, Mercer Co., December)—[Christy], *Cardinal*, 1924, v. 1, no. 3, p. 19 (Raccoon Creek, Beaver Co., December); 1924, v. 1, no. 4, p. 10 (Big Traverse Valley, Beaver Co., June)—Squier and Elliott, *Bird-Lore*, 1925, 27:40 (Deer Creek, Allegheny Co., December)—Eastwood, *Bird-Lore*, 1925, 27:337 (Bradford Woods, Allegheny Co., August, *fide* Frederick); 1926, 28:343 (Frick Park, Pittsburgh, Allegheny Co., *fide* Blair; Dixmont, Allegheny Co., July, *fide* Auerswald)—Matuszak, *Bird-Lore*, 1926, 28:29 (Hyde Park, Westmoreland Co., December)—Portman, *et al.*, *Bird-Lore*, 1926, 28:31 (Thompsonville and vicinity, Washington Co., December)—Boulton, *Bird-Lore*, 1928, 30:13 (Pittsburgh region, Allegheny Co., status)—Miller, *Bird-Lore*, 1932, 34:47 (Springs, Somerset Co., December)—Beal and Peterson, *Bird-Lore*, 1934, 36:33 (Presque Isle, Erie Co., December)—Elliott, *Cardinal*, 1934, 3:170 (Raccoon Creek, Beaver Co., December).

Colinus virginianus virginianus Harlow, *Auk*, 1912, 29:477 (Pine Grove [Mills], and State College, Centre Co., breeding?)—Christy, *Cardinal*, 1923, v. 1, no. 1, [p. 4] (Sewickley, Allegheny Co., resident)—Burleigh, *Wilson Bull.*, 1923, 35:85 (Allegheny Co., resident)—Christy, *Cardinal*, 1926, v. 1, no. 7, p. 7 (introduction into western Pennsylvania; etc.)—Sutton, *Cardinal*, 1926, v. 1, no. 7, p. 18 (range; critical)—Christy and Sutton, *Cardinal*, 1928, 2:69, 75 (Cook Forest, Clarion Co., resident)—Sutton, *Ann. Carnegie Mus.*, 1928, 18:113 (Crawford Co., resident).

TURKEYS

FAMILY MELEAGRIDIDAE

THIS is a small and exclusively American family, which consists of but two genera, each represented by a single species. Turkeys are large birds; their heads and upper necks are naked and covered by fleshy caruncles; their feet are large and powerful; and their tails are well developed. The Eastern Turkey, which is found in western Pennsylvania, has a tuft of bristle-like feathers suspended from the breast.

EASTERN TURKEY

MELEAGRIS GALLOPAVO SILVESTRIS Vieillot

Description—Similar in general to the domestic Turkey (the bronze-colored variety), from which it differs in the smaller size of its frontal wattle and in the *deep rusty-chestnut* color of the *upper tail coverts and the tip of the tail.* General coloration deep glossy green, with bronze, coppery, and purplish iridescence in certain lights; each feather has a black tip, producing a scaly effect. *Female* much smaller and duller than the male, the breast-pendant less developed. Naked skin of the head reddish through purple to bluish; feet purplish red.

Range—There was a time when the Wild Turkey ranged extensively in what is now the eastern United States, as far north as southern Maine, and across the Canadian border into Ontario. But like most other large birds, its history has been one of persistent persecution at the hands of man, with the result that today its range is disconnected and greatly restricted. Once one of the commonest birds in New England, it was extirpated there by 1851, and it disappeared from New York about the same time. In Ohio, according to J. M. Wheaton, it persisted somewhat longer, but if there are any records since 1900 from that state I have not come across them. Even in Audubon's day the Turkey was rapidly growing scarcer along the Atlantic seaboard. At the present time it is probably more numerous, all things considered, in the region of the Appalachian highlands, from Pennsylvania southward, than in any other part of the country. There it still finds to some extent the large areas of forest and the seclusion requisite to its needs.

B. H. Christy and G. M. Sutton (1929) have made a careful study of the past and present status and the future prospects of this species in Pennsylvania. I take the liberty of quoting from it, both directly and indirectly, while adding also some information from other authors. These early records for western Pennsylvania come from various unexpected sources. In 1753 a French soldier, whose identity is indicated only by the initials "J. C. B.," described in his journal the wholesale slaughter of turkeys on Presque Isle, where they were then abundant.[1] George Washington, while traveling down the Ohio River from Pittsburgh (then Fort Pitt) in the fall of 1770, wrote of killing five turkeys between the mouth of the Beaver River and Mingo, Ohio. In May, 1775, Nicholas Cresswell noted a turkey killed by one of his party near "Magee's Fort" (McKeesport). In 1807 the birds were easy to capture along the Allegheny River, for Christian Schulz spoke of killing them with an air gun (Wright, 1914). Alexander Wilson appears to have seen none on his trip down the Ohio in 1810, but this is not necessarily significant. Much more to the point is the positive testimony of Major J. C. Anderson, who told of seeing turkeys in the 1840's at the site of the present town of Leetsdale, Allegheny County. In Crawford County, according to R. J. Ferris (quoted by Dr. Sutton), the last turkeys were

[1]*Voyage au Canada dans le nord de l'Amérique septentrionale,* edited by Henri R. Casgrain, Quebec, 1887, p. 65. (See translation in J. W. Harpster, ed., *Pen Pictures of Early Western Pennsylvania,* 1938, p. 28.)

taken in the fall of 1881 or 1882, but whether they were native birds or domesticated birds run wild remains unproved. Warren quotes G.A. Scroggs to the effect that a turkey was killed in Beaver County in 1880—a report that can be neither affirmed nor denied but the truth of which is doubtful. Certainly the species had been virtually exterminated throughout the western counties sometime before the beginning of the present century.

In the plateau country, however, and in the ridge and valley section, the Wild Turkey continues to exist—not in such abundance as in early times, it is true, but yet in considerable numbers. If anywhere, it is more numerous in the mountain counties—Huntingdon, Blair, Bedford, and Fulton—where there are still extensive forest lands on the mountain slopes. It occurs also, but not so commonly, on the crest of the Alleghenies proper, and on Laurel Hill and Chestnut Ridge, the latter marking its westward limit in Westmoreland and Indiana counties. To the north, however, its known range contracts rapidly. Clearfield County is in part fairly good turkey country; and in 1928 "three good-sized flocks" were reported near Emporium, Cameron County, by one of Dr. Sutton's correspondents (A. G. Logue). W. L. Baily lists the species from northern Elk County, but only by hearsay. Warren mentions it as a straggler in Warren County, but R. B. Simpson writes that "men who used to make most of their living by hunting and trapping forty years ago [1863] never saw one, so that it is very doubtful if the Wild Turkey ever occurred here." There are no records available from the other northern counties, nor from across the line in New York state.

It is believed that the domestic species is a descendant of the Mexican Turkey, carried by the Spaniards to Europe early in the sixteenth century. At any rate, the two forms interbreed freely, and the wild strain often shows an admixture of domestic blood. Individuals with more or less buffy-tipped tails and sometimes with dark feet are the result of such intermingling. These characters tend to disappear in successive generations of wild birds, but they are nevertheless disturbing to naturalist and sportsman alike. It is of course desirable to keep the purity of the wild strain unimpaired, but the larger the area occupied by the bird the less chance there is of so doing. The Pennsylvania Game Commission has made commendable efforts to restock certain counties with birds of good blood transplanted from other counties in the state and from the adjoining state of Maryland. These shifts might eventually be successful in restoring the Wild Turkey to many of its former haunts, provided that the hunting of the bird could be further curbed. What happens during an open season is suggested by the following quotation from the account published by Mr. Christy and Dr. Sutton:

"Prior to the season of 1927, there existed on the eastern slope of Chestnut Ridge, near Rector, and ten or twelve miles from Ligonier, a flock of eighteen or twenty birds. Shooting had since their planting been forbidden; they were fed by a game-refuge keeper, and were thriving. . . . During 1926 there was no shooting, but in 1927 an open season was established, and in two weeks' time the flock on Chestnut Ridge was dissipated or exterminated. Throughout the State 4,070 birds, by estimate 20 per cent of the Turkey population, were killed. The kill for 1928 was 2,262."[1]

The authors call attention to the fact that mingling of the two races tends to spread certain diseases from the domestic to the wild birds, with far-reaching and deadly results. In certain parts of the state the prevalence of such diseases has already made the raising of domestic birds virtually impossible, and when these maladies take hold of wild birds the resulting mortality is even greater. Thus the preservation of this interesting species in one of its last strongholds is seriously threatened. The account goes on to say:

"The presence of good food and range are, perhaps, more important in preserving the Turkey than we have supposed. The disappearance of the chestnut has deprived our ridges of a valuable turkey food. Chestnuts were formerly such an important food that the scarcity of birds in some sections has been thought to be traceable directly to the chestnut-blight. The birds, deprived of their usual food, were forced to the farms or food-shelters, and the vitiating influences of civilization led to their disappearance. The destruction of laurel and rhododendron thickets by deer has caused Turkeys in some sections, notably in Centre

[1]According to the figures courteously supplied by the Pennsylvania Game Commission, 10,807 wild turkeys were killed in the years from 1928 to 1932 in the counties covered by the present work.

County, to disappear from certain ridges. It is hoped that they have moved to near-by ridges where cover is adequate.

"Another difficulty has followed upon the necessary care bestowed upon planted birds. It is inevitable that they should become accustomed to the presence of human beings, and that they should to a great extent lose their wildness. And, finally, there remains the difficulty of controlling the kill. The discouraging experience of the past two years leaves the matter in doubt, whether under present-day conditions the Turkey can be reinstated as a game-bird. The increasing number of people who have keen interest in the preservation of wild life in all its variety of form and beauty must recognize with appreciation the endeavor which the Game Commission has made. They must recognize, too, the fact that the Game Commission's problem is that of *game;* and that if it be not possible to maintain the Turkey as a *game*-bird—if it should become necessary to forbid killing at all seasons—then another agency would have to be found to attend to the planting and culture of the Turkey."

Habits—"Noble" and "magnificent" are the adjectives commonly applied to America's justly celebrated and greatest game bird. Audubon, who had more and better opportunities to observe its habits than anyone else before or since, has left a very full account—the best perhaps that has appeared—while A. C. Bent (1932) has endeavored to bring the life history down to date. My own observations have been fragmentary and unsatisfactory. Although more than forty years have passed, I still remember the thrill of seeing my first wild turkey. It was in June, 1893, while I was traversing on foot, with gun and knapsack, the long stretch of unbroken forest that then covered western Cambria County, that a lone gobbler got up not twenty feet in front of me and sailed off through the woods. Since then I have hunted the birds in the mountains late in the fall (November and December) near Mount Union, Huntingdon County, but without success. On one occasion, hearing the sound of scratching among the dry leaves, I looked just in time to catch a glimpse of a turkey (one of a flock) on the mountain slope below me—a dark shadow running rapidly through the woods. I hid and waited, but saw no more of the flock. Two local hunters in my party said that I should have fired at once, in the hope of scattering the flock and thus gaining a chance to use the turkey call. This instrument is made from a wing bone of the bird itself and in the hands of an expert can be made to imitate the notes of the turkeys closely enough to deceive them completely and bring them within gunshot. At other times I have sought to track the birds in freshly fallen snow, and once I even had a shot at a big gobbler as he sailed down the mountain-side with a great rumble of wings, but I have never succeeded in bagging a specimen.

Turkeys will always try to escape by running rather than by flying. Their senses of sight and hearing are remarkably keen, and, as they have an instinctive fear of human beings, they are particularly sensitive to their approach. Their size relieves them (at least when fully grown) of attention from most birds of prey, but foxes and wildcats are enemies they cannot always escape. The eggs and young suffer much more in proportion. Very young turkeys have little resistance to cold and damp weather, and a high mortality rate ensues. After they are older and able to fly well enough to allow them to roost off the ground, they fare much better. Audubon relates that the turkeys used to move southward in the fall of the year, flying over the rivers with some hesitation, but no such movement is observable today. Our turkeys, although not migratory, wander widely in the fall and winter months, traveling on foot if not disturbed. They find plenty to eat in the shape of mast, berries, and seeds of various kinds. In the summer they are very fond of grasshoppers —as are also the tame birds. Commenting on their food in Pennsylvania, Mr. Christy and Dr. Sutton make the following observations:

"The summer food of the Turkey includes much succulent vegetable matter and many insects, food which is usually abundant in Pennsylvania. They are extremely fond of grasshoppers. The most serious food problems of the bird develop in winter. Where turkeys once depended almost exclusively upon chestnuts, they now eat large numbers of the acorns of various oaks. They are also fond of corn, and of berries and weed seeds, as well as of any insect food they can find. The crop of a specimen taken on November 8, 1928, near Peru Mills (along Willow Run), Juniata County, held the following food which had not passed into the gizzard: sixty-eight large acorns of the white oak, seven wild grapes, three seeds of dogwood, a few grass blades, five needles of the white pine, many seeds of the white snake-root, a small millipede, the larva of a carabid beetle, and the entire body of a large squash-bug. In many crops and gizzards berries of the jack-in-the-pulpit have been found."

The breeding habits of the Wild Turkey are like those of the domestic bird. The strutting performance and the gobbling notes of the males are the same. The species is polygamous—each gobbler consorts with several hens. May and June are the nesting months in Pennsylvania, but very likely the later dates are for birds whose earlier nestings came to nought. The hens hide their nests very cleverly, not only to protect them from natural enemies, but also to prevent them from being destroyed by the gobblers. A nest found by E. A. Preble in the pine barrens, about a mile and a half south of Crumb, Somerset County, during the second week of June, 1893, contained fourteen eggs, far advanced in incubation. It was a mere depression in the leaves, among a small bunch of laurel bushes at the edge of a chestnut woods.

A set of fourteen eggs in the collection of the Carnegie Museum, presented by G. A. Link, Sr., came from the west slope of Chestnut Ridge near Hillside, Westmoreland County, and was collected on May 23, 1906. The photographs made of this nest show it at the base of a chestnut tree in the woods, well concealed by chestnut saplings and other bushes. Dr. Sutton (1929) has described and figured a nest with eight fresh eggs (the set probably incomplete) found by him near Clearfield on May 5, 1928. This nest was more or less in the open and was not very well concealed from above, but when the hen was sitting she was hard to discern. R. C. Harlow has recorded three nests found by him, as follows: Vail, Blair County, May 17, 1912, six eggs; Greenwood Furnace, Huntingdon County, May 20, 1915, twelve eggs; Bear Meadows, Centre County, June 22, 1916, twelve eggs. The eggs are like those of the domestic bird, buffy white to pale ochraceous buff, with small spots and dots of pale brown or drab. They measure 2.50 by 1.75 inches.

The sexes gather in separate flocks in the fall and winter, the females in larger flocks than the males. Young males, avoiding the old gobblers, also flock by themselves; for while old and young males are not actually quarrelsome, they seem to have different interests. Although turkeys obtain their food from the ground, scratching about in the manner of other gallinaceous birds, they roost in trees, where they are hard to see when they keep still. Other characters of the Wild Turkey are described by Mr. Christy and Dr. Sutton: "The Turkey is virile, tenacious of territory, adaptable to the changes brought about by civilization, and, but for the eager, thoughtless, and unmeasured destruction wrought by its human pursuers, it now would be and would continue to be an abundant species. But since it is our largest gamebird, very good to eat, alert, keen-scented [?], and swift, it is pursued to extermination. . . . The question now remains whether the conservation agencies of the states can throw about it a measure of protection sufficient to compensate for the great increase in the number of hunters and the increasing ease of access which automobile highways afford."

Meleagris gallipavo americana Townsend, *Proc. Acad. Nat. Sci. Philadelphia*, 1883, 66 (Westmoreland Co., resident).

"Wild Turkey" White, *Second Geol. Surv. Pa.*, 1885, 281 (Tussey Mountain Barrens, Huntingdon Co.)—Baily, *Auk*, 1896, 13:292 (Williamsville, Elk Co., fall)—Warren, *Bull. Pa. Dept. Agric.*, no. 17, 1897, 536 (Mt. Union, Mill Creek, Barree, Huntingdon Co., and Wolfsburg, Bedford Co.)—[Editor], *Osprey*, 1900, 5:14 ("Bowman's Station" [Mance], Somerset Co.)—Stone, *Cassinia*, 1906, 9:41 (Tuscarora Mountain, Fulton Co., June; correction of Rhoads's record)—Rehn, *Cassinia*, 1906, 9:74 (Diamond Valley, Huntingdon Co.)—Wright, *Auk*, 1914, 31:(463), 470 (Allegheny River, Schultz's records); 1915, 32:(61), 73, 74 (western Pa., early records)—Harlow, *Oölogist*, 1914, 31:98 ([Charter Oak], Huntingdon Co., spring)—Scoville, *Atlantic Monthly*, 1920, 126:36 (Centre Co.)—[Christy], *Cardinal*, 1924, v. 1, no. 3, p. 8 (Sewickley and Leetsdale, Allegheny Co., *fide* Anderson)—Sutton, *Bird-Lore*, 1924, 26:337 (western Pa., status)—Boulton, *Bird-Lore*, 1928, 30:13 (western Pa., status)—Christy and Sutton, *Cardinal*, 1929, 2:109 (western Pa. records and references).

Meleagris gallopavo Warren, *Birds Pa.*, ed. 2, 1890, 109 (distribution by counties)—Todd, *Auk*, 1893, 10:39 (Two Lick, Indiana Co., breeding)—Rhoads, *Auk*, 1899, 16:310 (Keating, Clinton Co., November; "Tuscarora Mountain" [error], Fulton Co., breeding)—Judd, *Bull. Biol. Surv.* no. 24, 1905, 48 ([near Crumb], Somerset Co., nesting, *fide* Preble).

Meleagris gallopavo silvestris Harlow, *Auk*, 1912, 29:469 ([Pine] Barrens, Nittany Mountain, and Buffalo Run, Centre Co.; "Stone Valley," Huntingdon Co.); 1918, 35:23 (Vail, Blair Co., Greenwood Furnace, Huntingdon Co., Bear Meadows, Centre Co., nesting)—Burleigh, *Wilson Bull.*, 1924, 36:69; 1931, 42:39 ("State College," Centre Co., resident)—Sutton, *Ann. Carnegie Mus.*, 1928, 18:115 (Pymatuning Swamp, Crawford Co., status, *fide* Ferris)—Sutton, *Auk*, 1929, 46:326 (State Game Refuge No. 2 [near Clearfield], Clearfield Co., nesting).

Meleagris gallopavo fera Stone, *Cassinia*, 1919, 22:31 ("Beaver Dams," Blair Co., February, *fide* McGraw).

CRANES

FAMILY GRUIDAE

THE CRANES are all large, tall birds, with long legs and necks and more or less naked heads. In general structure otherwise, they resemble the Rails, not the Herons—their similarity to the latter is purely superficial. Their young are precocial, that is, able to run about soon after they are hatched, while the young of the Heron tribe are altricial—requiring the protection of the nest and nurture from the parents for some time. Cranes fly with necks extended, while Herons draw theirs into an S-curve. The species of this group are widely distributed, but only one genus reaches America.

SANDHILL CRANE

GRUS CANADENSIS TABIDA (Peters)

Description—A very large wading bird, standing over three feet high, and with a wingspread of from six to seven feet. The general color is *grayish;* the *bill and feet are black;* and the forehead and most of the crown (in the adult) are dull reddish and bare of feathers. In *young birds* the plumage is washed with brown, and the head is fully feathered. This species must not be confused with the Great Blue Heron, sometimes incorrectly called "Crane."

Range and local status—The Sandhill Crane is found mainly in the western states and in the upper Mississippi Valley, but it has been known to breed as far east as Ohio. Its occurrence in migration in extreme southwestern Pennsylvania, while of course exceptional, is understandable in view of this extension of its breeding range. A mounted specimen in the collection of J. W. Jacobs was shot "either on Tom's Run or Hoover's Run, about a mile from Dunkard Creek, in extreme southwestern Wayne Township, in the spring of 1900 or 1901—the exact date has unfortunately been mislaid." Again, in May, 1902, Mr. Jacobs saw another sandhill crane flying near Waynesburg, heading northeast: "I could not be mistaken, for the bird was close, and I am of course familiar with the Great Blue Heron, which is the only other species in this section that could possibly be mistaken for the Sandhill Crane."

Grus mexicana COOKE, *Bull. U.S. Dept. Agric.*, no. 128, 1914, 10 (Waynesburg, Greene Co., migration, *fide* Jacobs).

"Sand Hill Crane" JACOBS, *Oölogist*, 1922, 39:123 (southern Greene Co.).

Megalornis canadensis mexicanus BENT, *Bull. U.S. Nat. Mus.* no. 135, 1926, 253 (near Waynesburg, Greene Co., May, 1902 [*fide* Jacobs]).

RAILS

FAMILY RALLIDAE

THIS IS a large and important family, most highly developed in the tropics of both the Old and New Worlds. The North American representatives are comparatively few in number and give only a partial picture of the group as a whole. More than fifty genera are recognized; they vary greatly in relative size, details of structure, and general pattern of coloration. The Rails are paludicoline (marsh-inhabiting) birds, whose structure and economy admirably fit them for life in the swamp. The body is laterally compressed (hence the expression "thin as a rail") for easier progress through the thick marsh growth; the feet are strong, with long, wide-spreading toes; the tail is short; the wings are short and much rounded; and the bill is long or short, as the case may be, and has open nostrils. Although several of the species perform extensive migrations, the Rails as a class are weak fliers and always prefer when disturbed to skulk and hide in the cover of their marshy retreats rather than to take wing. The Coots (*Fulica*) are aberrant members of this family; they have lobate feet, more depressed bodies, and natatorial habits.

KING RAIL

RALLUS ELEGANS ELEGANS Audubon

Description—A *large counterpart* of the Virginia Rail, which it resembles in color; *bill long* (one and a half inches) *and slender. Adult:* upperparts light brown, streaked with dark brown (except on the top of the head); wings plain brown; throat whitish; a paler streak from the eye to the bill; underparts rich rusty cinnamon, paler (buffy) on the belly; flanks deep brown, conspicuously barred with white, and under tail coverts mottled with the same color; legs yellowish brown. *Immature:* plumage similar, but the underparts mostly dirty white, and the barring of the flanks obsolete. *Downy young* are wholly black.

Range—The King Rail breeds over much of the eastern United States and southern Canada, and is fairly limited in its northward range by the Alleghanian Fauna. While not uncommon on the Atlantic slope and in the Mississippi Valley, it avoids the intervening Appalachian highlands, and there are no breeding records from anywhere in the mountains, from Pennsylvania southward. The individuals that breed in western New York probably come in by way of the Great Lakes, to judge by analogy, and must cross our region on their way. But records for western Pennsylvania are singularly few, and those that exist come mostly from the northwestern counties, where alone there are marshes of sufficient extent to attract this bird. It has been noted occasionally in the vicinity of Erie in spring and fall, and once in July (Guynes). In Crawford County, according to G. M. Sutton, this rail has been observed repeatedly throughout the spring and summer months, and his surmise that it must breed there has been confirmed by S. S. Dickey, who reports that he saw an old bird followed by two downy young at Hartstown on June 18, 1922; and more recently by R. L. Fricke, who found a nest with eggs in May, 1935.

Migration—The King Rail moves northward in April (April 17, 1902—Erie; April 17, 1909—Conneaut Marsh; April 10, 1925—Sandy Lake). For the fall a late recorded date is November 22, 1922, for Conneaut Lake, and another is November 6, 1929, for Rector, Westmoreland County. The Carnegie Museum has a specimen shot at McKeesport, Allegheny County, on April 20, 1922, and Dr. Dickey reports one shot at Hero, Greene County, on May 7, 1915. An emaciated king rail was taken by A. K. Pierce at Renovo on May 15, 1889—the only record thus far from that locality.

Habits—In general behavior, choice of haunts, and nesting habits, this species resembles its smaller relative, the Virginia Rail. When flushed from its reedy covert it will ordinarily fly farther than that species before dropping down, according to Mr. Fricke. A nest that he found near Linesville on May 23, 1935, held nine eggs, in which incubation had begun. It was built in thick rushes, about eight inches above the ground, and was well concealed by overhanging growth. It was composed of rush stems and lined with dry grasses. The eggs are of the usual ralline type; they are pale olive buff, regularly but sparsely spotted with wood brown and duller shell-markings. They are of course much larger than the eggs of the Virginia Rail and measure about 1.69 by 1.22 inches.

Rallus elegans Warren, *Birds Pa.*, ed. 2, 1890, 67 (Erie, Erie Co., transient; Clinton Co., *fide* Van Fleet)—Todd, *Ann. Carnegie Mus.*, 1904, 2:532 (Erie, Erie Co., transient)—Fricke, *Cardinal*, 1930, 2:201 (Rector, Westmoreland Co., November).

"King Rail" Jones, *Cardinal*, 1925, v. 1, no. 6, p. 20 (Sandy Lake, Mercer Co., April)—Seiple, *Auk*, 1931, 48:113 (Pymatuning Swamp, Crawford Co., August)—Trimble, *Cardinal*, 1937, 4:107 (Pymatuning region, Crawford Co., nesting).

Rallus elegans elegans Sutton, *Ann. Carnegie Mus.*, 1928, 18:89 (Crawford Co. records and references).

VIRGINIA RAIL

RALLUS LIMICOLA LIMICOLA Vieillot

Description—Size of the Robin; *bill slender*, about one and a quarter inches long. Resembling the King Rail in form and color, but much smaller. *Adult:* upperparts black, varied with brownish olive, inconspicuous on the crown; wings brown, all the upper coverts chestnut brown in contrast; sides of head deep gray, the lores darker; a buffy spot below the eye and another above the lores; chin whitish, the white passing into rufous brown on the throat, breast, and upper belly; lower belly and under wing coverts black, barred with white; bill and feet reddish. *Young birds* in the fall are similar, but darker and duller, and the underparts are more or less varied with dusky black in irregular pattern. The *chick* is covered with black down.

Range—The Virginia Rail ranges entirely across the North American continent from east to west, and north to the southern provinces of Canada. It breeds in the northern half of this range, roughly speaking, and winters in the southern half. Our region lies well within its breeding range, but as this bird is strictly an inhabitant of the marshes it is only locally distributed. In the northwestern counties alone is it a regular summer visitant. It breeds commonly in Pymatuning Swamp and in other suitable places in Crawford County, and eggs have been found near Erie, on the mainland. It has also been noted on Presque Isle in the breeding season (Simpson), and there is a pair in the Sennett Collection taken on May 12, 1875, at Edinboro, Erie County. In Mercer County the Virginia Rail breeds at Sandy Lake (Squier), near Sharon (McQuiston), near Mercer (Raney), and probably elsewhere. R. L. Keesler reports it as breeding at Forestville, Butler County, and more recently I have traced it to Lawrence County also, for I have noted adults and downy young in June (1933) at Gardner Swamp, southeast of New Castle. This locality probably marks the normal southward limit of its breeding range in the western tier of counties. I have never seen it in Beaver County, and while there are a half-dozen records from the adjoining county of Allegheny, there are none that can be definitely classed as breeding records. T. D. Burleigh, however, thinks that it must breed at Lake Seaton in Fayette County, and C. H. Townsend gave it as a summer visitant at Latrobe in the early eighties, but it is doubtful that it occurs there today. Van Fleet included it in his manuscript list of the breeding birds of DuBois, and R. B. Simpson has noted it at Warren a few times in May. I know of no other records for the plateau region, but east of the main divide, in the valley country of Centre County, Mr. Burleigh and R. C. Harlow have found this rail nesting in certain isolated swampy areas.

Migration—This species is not an early migrant, and it is the third week in April before the van arrives in our region. Earliest dates are: Shermansville, Crawford County, April 18 (1925—Bergstrom); Erie, April 18 (1900—Bacon); near Altoona, April 21 (1918—McGraw); State College [Center Furnace?], April 19 (1916—Burleigh). B. H. Christy saw a Virginia rail at Clinton Pond, Allegheny County, on April 9, 1926; this was of course exceptionally early. On the other hand, the spring movement continues well into May, as is evidenced by the records from places where the species is not known to breed: Carnegie, Allegheny County, May 7, 1907 (Walker); Fair Oaks, Allegheny County, May 11–15, 1898 (Seager); Warren, May 5 and 23, 1903, and May 11, 1932 (Simpson). In the fall it has been noted at Erie by S. E. Bacon as late as October 28 (1893) and 25 (1901). These are probably the normal dates of departure, but C. A. Bergstrom writes that he has found it at Hartstown on November 1 and 11, 1928, and in 1931 on the remarkably late date of December 15.

Habits[1]—The Virginia Rail, a shy and elusive bird, is rather common throughout the marshes in the northwestern part of this state. Although it is rarely seen, its varied call notes betray it to the initiated bird student. During the spring months a henlike cackling may be heard at all hours of the day or night in any suitable marsh. This is evidently a mating song, indulged in by the males alone. The various low piglike grunts emitted by this rail when disturbed, however, are notes of alarm and are made by both sexes.

Near Linesville a companion and I discovered a disturbed nest of the Virginia Rail in a small cattail marsh, less than half an acre in extent and situated in pasture land. Three of the five eggs had been thrown out of the nest into the surrounding water, which was about a foot deep. Low grunts were heard near by, and we decided to try to flush the bird. Although we spent two hours in searching the marsh we caught no more than a fleeting glimpse. Even after climbing a tree, the better to watch this small area of marsh while my companion thoroughly worked through it, I failed to sight this shy bird. At intervals the grunts could be heard, coming now from this point, now from that, and serving to spur the search, which was nevertheless unavailing.

The large areas of marshland in Pymatuning Swamp have been the scene of most of my experiences with rails in Pennsylvania. There hundreds of acres of open marsh make an ideal home for many species partial to such territory. During the five seasons from 1933 to 1937 I was able to locate

numbers of nests of both the Virginia Rail and the Sora. Of the two kinds the Virginia is the more interesting to me because its behavior is so unpredictable. Often it will skulk like the bird just described, while at other times it will flush quite readily, only to drop and disappear into the thick growth after a short, weak flight. Again, too, it will run daintily about almost underfoot, flirting its short tail and nonchalantly gazing at its observer with its bright red eyes.

Most writers remark on the fact that the Virginia Rail prefers to nest in a comparatively drier spot than that chosen by the Sora. There are exceptions, however, to this rule. On May 31, 1931, about a mile south of Linesville, a Virginia rail was flushed from one of a few scattered clumps of rushes in a flooded meadow. The nest (containing five eggs) was partly in the water, with very little cover about it, while only a few yards away there were acres of drier and apparently more suitable growth.

The Virginia Rail usually leaves the nest before it is closely approached. On one occasion, while H. M. McQuiston and I were hunting through the marsh southeast of Linesville, we found a rail nest containing ten eggs. The parent bird was flushed and when collected proved to be a female Virginia rail. Presently a second bird was flushed from a nest, likewise containing ten eggs, a short distance away. When we returned to the first nest, another Virginia rail was brooding on it and would not

[1]Account contributed by Reinhold L. Fricke.

leave until pushed off. For a time this bird stalked about within a few feet, but becoming convinced that we were there for no good, it daintily dropped into the water, swam like a miniature coot across a small open stretch, and soon disappeared into the dense growth near by.

The eggs of the Virginia Rail can easily be distinguished from those of the Sora. They are light cream color, speckled with pale buff and brown, and have faint lilac shell-markings; they average about 1.25 by .97 inches. Those of the Sora are much darker and are spotted with brown and olive. As it happens, I have never found more than ten eggs in a Virginia rail's nest, whereas the Sora often lays as many as fifteen or more. Both species use whatever nest material is at hand, and their nests are so similar that, before the eggs are laid, they are difficult to distinguish. In this region, fresh eggs may be found about the middle of May, and the young hatch out about two weeks later. I believe that both birds assist in the brooding, the one taking care of the newly hatched young while the other continues to incubate the remaining eggs. At Hartstown, on May 29, 1926, I collected a male Virginia rail that was leading downy black young scarcely larger than the eggs from which they had hatched.

Rallus virginianus Townsend, *Proc. Acad. Nat. Sci. Philadelphia*, 1883, 67 (Latrobe, Westmoreland Co., summer)—Todd, *Ann. Carnegie Mus.*, 1904, 2:532 (Erie and Presque Isle, Erie Co., nesting)—Harlow, *Auk*, 1912, 29:468 (Center Furnace, Centre Co., nesting)—Cooke, *Bull. U.S. Dept. Agric.*, no. 128, 1914, 22 (DuBois, Clearfield Co., breeding; Renovo, Clinton Co., migration)—Stone, *Cassinia*, 1919, 22:29 (["Hickory Bottom Swamp," near] Altoona, Blair Co., April, *fide* McGraw)—Christy, *Cardinal*, 1923, v. 1, no. 1, [p. 3] (Sewickley, Allegheny Co., May)—Burleigh, *Wilson Bull.*, 1924, 36:70 (State College, Centre Co., migration); 1931, 43:37 (Center Furnace Swamp and Oak Hall, Centre Co., nesting)—Sutton, *Ann. Carnegie Mus.*, 1928, 18:89 (Crawford Co. nesting records).

"Virginia Rail" Bacon, *Ornithologist and Oölogist*, 1891, 15:108 (Erie, Erie Co., nesting)—Harlow, *Cassinia*, 1912, 15:21; *Oölogist*, 1912, 29:308 (Center Furnace Swamp, Centre Co., nesting)—Holt, *Cardinal*, 1925, v. 1, no. 6, p. 24 (Pymatuning Swamp, Crawford Co., nesting)—Eastwood, *Bird-Lore*, 1926, 28:274 (Sandy Lake, Mercer Co., May, *fide* Squier)—Boulton, *Bird-Lore*, 1928, 30:271 (Harmarville, Allegheny Co., May)—Trimble, *Cardinal*, 1937, 4:107 (Pymatuning region, Crawford Co., nesting).

Rallus limicola limicola Burleigh, *Cardinal*, 1932, 3:74 (Lake Seaton, Fayette Co., breeding?).

SORA

PORZANA CAROLINA (Linnaeus)

Description—Size of the Virginia Rail, but *bill shorter and stouter*, about three-fourths of an inch long. *Adult:* upperparts olive brown, varied with black and with narrow white feather-edgings, giving the appearance of streaks; *face black*, as are *also the throat* (narrowly) and a broad, lengthwise stripe on the crown; sides of head gray (except for a brownish wash behind the eye), continuous with the gray of the sides of the neck and breast; the latter sometimes extensively black, continuous with the black throat; abdomen (medially) white; the sides, flanks, and under wing coverts show white and dusky bars; under tail coverts rusty buff, the longer ones white in abrupt contrast; bill yellowish; feet yellowish green. *Young:* duller and browner above, the face and throat white, and the sides of the head brownish; breast washed with buffy brown; and under tail coverts deep buff. The size and the shape of the bill suffice to distinguish this species from the Virginia Rail.

Range—The Sora has a much more extensive latitudinal range than the Virginia Rail; it is found farther north in the breeding season and farther south in the winter. The local ranges of the two in western Pennsylvania, however, are about the same. Both species inhabit the same type of marshy country and are usually associated in the nesting season and during migration. Hence the Sora is fairly common as a summer resident in suitable situations in the western tier of counties, from Erie to Lawrence inclusive, as well as in certain isolated localities in Centre County. Elsewhere it occurs only casually during migration. There is, however, one known instance of its breeding in Allegheny County, and one in Indiana County (Cherry Run Reservoir—Trimble), and it may yet be reported from other sections. R. C. Harlow, indeed, says that it nests in Mifflin, Clearfield, and Huntingdon counties, but gives no particulars. Van Fleet lists it as a rare breeding bird at DuBois.

Wherever found, it is always most numerous during migration, especially in the fall, a fact indicating that the great majority of birds nest farther north. The species is particularly abundant in fall migration about the ponds on Presque Isle and outnumbers the Virginia Rail about ten to one.

Migration—The meager migration data available for rails in our region suggest that the Sora is a later migrant than the Virginia Rail, but a review of a long series of records for a given locality (as, for instance, Oberlin, Ohio) shows that the two species move northward at about the same time. Arrival dates for Erie run from April 27 (1895) to May 5 (1892), with one exceptional record of March 31 (1902). At Pymatuning Swamp the earliest date is May 13 (1922), but at Conneaut Lake it is May 6 (1911). For Allegheny County D. A. Atkinson reports the following: Avalon, April 11 (1894); Sandy Creek, April 14 (1896); Wilkinsburg, April 17 (1897). The Centre County (Center Furnace) dates are April 26 (1916) and May 1 (1917). Since nests with full sets of eggs may sometimes be found as early as the middle of May it is obvious that the Sora's arrival could not well take place much later than the first of the month. Some transient individuals, however, must lag behind the main body, since there are several records of odd birds being seen or taken during the second or third week in May at places where the species is not known to breed. The return movement begins early, sometimes even before the middle of August; by the first of September it is in full swing and so continues until near the end of the month. Stragglers continue to come for another month, and belated migrants are reported even in November: Rector, Westmoreland County, November 2 (1927—Fricke); Industry, Beaver County, November 7 (1904—G. R. Wilson); Shermansville, Crawford County, November 7 (1928—Bergstrom); Washington, November 29 (1883—Nease).

Habits—To the uninitiated, the bird life of the bog is largely a closed book. Indeed, the casual passer-by would not even suspect its existence were it not for the odd, mysterious cries that emanate from such regions. Among the various birds that live by choice in these recesses none is by nature more elusive in habit, more retiring in disposition, or more closely attached to its marshy haunts than is the Sora. Since it migrates by night, its very comings and goings are cloaked in mystery. One day the swamp may seem to be bare of rails; the next day their odd calls may keep coming from all sides. Their notes range from a sudden cry of alarm to a long-drawn-out cackling call, which begins slowly but is accelerated towards the end. The mating song is described by William Brewster as "a sweet, plaintive *ѐr-e*, given with a rising inflection and suggesting one of the 'scatter calls' of the Quail. . . . This note, repeated at short, regular intervals, many times in succession, is one of the most frequent as well as pleasing voices of the marsh in the early morning and just after sunset. It is also given intermittently at all hours of the day, especially in cloudy weather, while it is often continued practically without cessation, through the entire night.

"Equally characteristic of this season and even more attractive in quality is what has been termed the 'whinny' of the Carolina [Sora] Rail. It consists of a dozen or fifteen short whistles as sweet and clear in tone as a silver bell. The first eight or ten are uttered very rapidly in an evenly descending scale, the remaining ones more deliberately and in a uniform key."[1] The author states that so far as he knows, this sound is given only by the female.

To gain a closer impression of the Sora one must penetrate its haunts on foot or by boat. When flushed the bird gets up and flies off, apparently with great effort, but in straightaway fashion, just clearing the vegetation, its legs dangling awkwardly behind; some yards farther on it drops out of sight, as suddenly as if it had been shot. If marked down and followed it is seldom flushed a second time, as it will nearly always run rapidly off through the marsh the moment it alights. A rail will not fly if it can help it. It is adept at running and skulking through the thick aquatic vegetation, however, as its narrow body passes with ease between the growing stalks. If obliged to cross an open space of water, it will often swim over, as naturally and as gracefully as a duck. It can dive, too, on occasion. The habit of concealment is instinctive with rails, but if an observer remains quiet for a time at some favorable open spot he will sometimes be rewarded by seeing the bird come to the edge of the water to feed.

[1]*Bird-Lore*, 1902, 4:48.

The Sora at ease is a beautiful creature. A. C. Bent describes it "stepping daintily over the bog, flirting its short tail up and down or spreading it out in display, and nodding its head back and forth with a graceful dovelike motion. Its toes are so long and its body is so light, that it is easily supported on the lily pads or on a few floating reeds. It takes long steps when walking, but when running its tracks may be a foot apart. If alarmed by a sudden movement or sound, it runs to cover with lowered head and outstretched neck and with wings and plumage closely pressed against the narrowed body, as it slips out of sight in the narrow aisles between the reeds."[1] H. C. Kirkpatrick (in Sutton, 1928) says: "I have often seen this rail in parties of six or eight in the swamps near the course of French Creek. Here I have observed them with tails erect tripping over the debris of the shore and over the lightest driftwood in the water, pausing not a moment before an open space but dropping into the water and swimming like a duck to the next point of drift. Sometimes, when flushed from the shore, they fly into a large clump of buttonbrush and, jumping and stepping from branch to branch and bush to bush, their long toes admirably adapted to climbing and grasping the branches, they are soon out of sight in the recesses of the Swamp."

The nesting habits of the Sora are no less interesting. Little time is lost after the birds arrive on their breeding grounds before they commence their nests. These may be built in a tussock of marsh grass at the edge of the swamp, but are oftener placed in the deeper parts where the cattails grow. Wherever located they are usually well shielded from observation from above by overhanging growths. Dry leaves and dead stalks are heaped up and packed together to make a platform a few inches above the water level, surrounded and supported by the growing stalks. The nest is well hollowed out to care properly for the eggs, sometimes as many as eighteen in number, but usually from ten to twelve. A large set is often arranged in two tiers, and how the incubating bird manages to cover them is a puzzle. The eggs measure about 1.23 by .83 inches, and in color are a rich buff (the shades varying somewhat), spotted irregularly and rather sparingly with brown, the spots rather small and well defined.

Mr. Harlow (1912), writing of his experiences with the Virginia Rail and the Sora in Centre County, says: "The nests of both species are very cunningly concealed and very difficult to see, even when one stands directly above them. They [the birds] both run off when one is still some distance away, being very hard to flush. But after noting these two similarities one comes upon distinct differences. The Carolina [Sora] Rail usually places its nest directly over water in the deeper portions of the swamp, while the Virginia often choose[s] situations where the ground is barely wet. The Carolina builds its nest more compactly, concaves it more deeply, and prefers cat-tails and shreds of flags for lining, whereas the Virginia generally uses dry marsh grass. Eggs of the Carolina are much darker, being covered with brownish and olive blotches, and the shell itself is harder; the Virginia's have a lighter cream-colored background, speckled and spotted with light buff and brown. The Carolina seems to begin incubation with the first egg laid, for the reason that in a set of ten eggs some will be fresh while others will exhibit various stages of incubation. In a set of eleven they varied from a condition of freshness to that of being nearly full[y] developed. Sets of the Virginia show some variation in development, but not to so marked a degree. Each species seems to be fairly uniform in its nesting habits, so that there is little difficulty in distinguishing them.

"May 28th to May 30th is the period when the majority of both species possess fresh eggs, but it may be noticed from the dates given above, that nidification must begin in some instances as early as May 10th, hardly a week after the arrival of the birds. Like the Clapper Rail and the Florida Gallinule, both these species exhibit a tendency to construct sham nests, as a large number are never finished nor laid in. Both species are solicitous when their homes are threatened and they have some reason to be, for they have a few enemies. Crows destroy some sets, large Snapping Turtles in the deeper portions raid others, and probably the Muskrats take their share at times. On the whole, however, their natural enemies are few in number."

My own experience at Pymatuning Swamp serves to confirm these observations. Nests with partial and full complements of eggs were found there

[1]U. S. National Museum, *Bulletin*, no. 135, 1926, p. 308.

from May 18 to 23, 1933. In 1922 G. M. Sutton found newly hatched young as early as May 25. They are odd-looking little creatures, covered with black down, relieved by a chin-tuft of a reddish color. They are able to run about as soon as they are hatched, and doubtless many fall victims to snakes, bullfrogs, and turtles, as well as to certain furred or feathered enemies. If even a moderate number of the young hatched were to come to maturity, the species would soon overtax the capacity of the marsh. As it is, the birds are often amazingly abundant in the fall months. "I have seen the time when Niagara Pond seemed fairly alive with them," writes S. E. Bacon, alluding to their numbers on Presque Isle at that season. Very large bags used to be made there by gunners, but this is happily a thing of the past. The sound of a shot was always the signal for cries of alarm from every bird within hearing distance, and for a few moments the marsh would resound with their calls. The main attraction to the birds was the growth of wild rice, on the seeds of which they became very fat. Earlier in the year, however, small mollusks and aquatic insects constitute the larger part of their food.

If one may judge from the frequency of the Sora's calls, its activities are often continued far into the night, especially if there is a moon. Its migrations are performed entirely during the hours of darkness. Shy and elusive by nature, keeping to the seclusion of the overgrown and impenetrable marsh, and immensely prolific, the Sora may hold its own for a long time to come—or until its ancient haunts shall have been completely wiped out by man.

Porzana carolina Townsend, *Proc. Acad. Nat. Sci. Philadelphia*, 1883, 67 (Beatty, Westmoreland Co.; Latrobe, Westmoreland Co., *fide* Beckwith)—Warren, *Birds Pa.*, ed. 2, 1890, 70 (Erie, Erie Co., *fide* Sennett, and Clinton Co., *fide* Van Fleet, breeding)—Todd, *Ann. Carnegie Mus.*, 1904, 2:532 (Erie and Presque Isle, Erie Co., nesting)—Todd, in Bausman, *Hist. Beaver Co., Pa.*, 1904, 2:1198 (Beaver Co., transient)—Harlow, *Auk*, 1912, 29:469 (Centre Furnace, Centre Co., nesting); 1918, 35:21 (Centre, Mifflin, Clearfield, and Huntingdon Co., nesting)—Stone, *Cassinia*, 1919, 22:29 (Altoona, Blair Co., migration, *fide* McGraw)—Burleigh, *Wilson Bull.*, 1923, 35:84 (Harmarville, Allegheny Co., nesting); 1924, 36:70 (State College and region, Centre Co., migration)—Hegner, *Cardinal*, 1926, v. 1, no. 7, p. 25 (Edgeworth, Allegheny Co., October)—Sutton, *Ann. Carnegie Mus.*, 1928, 18:91 (Pymatuning Swamp, Crawford Co., nesting; Crawford Co. localities and records)—Burleigh, *Wilson Bull.*, 1931, 43:38 (Center Furnace, Centre Co., nesting)—Christy, *Cardinal*, 1931, 3:43 (McDonald Reservoir, Washington Co., May).

"Carolina Rail" [Secretary], *Auk*, 1890, 7:71 (Erie, Erie Co.; coloration).

"Sora Rail" Harlow, *Cassinia*, 1912, 15:21; and *Oölogist*, 1912, 29:308 (Center Furnace, Centre Co., nesting)—Boulton, *Bird-Lore*, 1928, 30:13 (Rector, Westmoreland Co., November, *fide* Fricke)—Fricke, *Cardinal*, 1934, v. 3, pl. opposite p. 154 (Pymatuning Swamp, Crawford Co., nesting)—Trimble, *Cardinal*, 1937, 4:107 (Pymatuning region, Crawford Co., nesting).

YELLOW RAIL

COTURNICOPS NOVEBORACENSIS (Gmelin)

Description—*Smaller than the Sora* and *much more buffy* in general coloration. Upperparts buffy brown, streaked with deep brown and black, all finely barred with white; underparts dull white, strongly shaded with buff on the breast. The wings have a white area on the secondaries (conspicuous in flight).

Range and migration—The breeding range of the Yellow Rail has been worked out only imperfectly, and, indeed, much remains to be learned of this small and elusive species, which is still unrecorded over vast areas of country. In western Pennsylvania it is known only in the Erie-Crawford region. To quote from my earlier report (1904), "the credit of adding this interesting species to the fauna of Erie belongs to Mr. Bacon, whose notes are herewith transcribed in full: 'A rather rare spring and fall migrant, not known to the local gunners, although, like myself, they must meet with it occasionally. I observed it on the Peninsula first on September 30, 1893. In the fall of 1894 I met with it on three different occasions (October 15, 17, and 19) at the mouth of Mill Creek. On September 18, 1895, I took a single specimen in the snipe grounds west of the city, and on April 27, 1896, I took another at the same place. Again, on September 20, 1900, I shot one Yellow Rail at the mouth of Mill Creek, but in the fall of 1901 I saw and secured more than in all previous seasons combined. Evidently a small bunch, perhaps a family group, stopped in the snipe grounds (before mentioned) west of the city, where I noticed them first on September 25, when I saw three and secured two. (Previously, however, on September 15, I had received an immature bird killed by a local gunner.) From this time on I never failed to start one or two Yellow Rails by hunting through this grassy spot (marsh grass, cat-tails, and wild rice), but often they rose so close at hand and flew such a short distance that it was out of the question to shoot. Eight specimens in all were secured, the last on October 29. Seldom were more than two seen at once, but they were always flushed at about the same spot, and I am inclined to think that I secured nearly all of them. The species was also met with on April 28, May 3, and October 4, 1902, September 17, 1903, and April 23, 1904.' In view of the above facts it would not be surprising if this rail should be found nesting here. Two of the specimens taken by Mr. Bacon are in the United States National Museum (Biological Survey Collection), while most of the remaining birds are preserved in the Carnegie Museum. The series exhibits considerable variation in plumage; and seems to show that the males are larger than the females. Two fall specimens, evidently immature, are very dark-colored, and have the crown and sides of the head prominently spotted with white."

R. B. Simpson has a specimen that was shot at Erie on October 4, 1908. Although the conditions at Pymatuning Swamp seem to be ideal, G. M. Sutton's exhaustive researches failed to discover the species there. L. E. Hicks, however, saw an adult yellow rail on July 2, 1928, in the Ohio portion of the bog, and a half-grown bird on August 9, 1932, close to the state line. Without doubt this rail breeds in the swamp occasionally. H. M. McQuiston reports its occurrence two miles west of Linesville, on October 6, 1934. It should be looked for also in the smaller swamps of Crawford and Mercer counties.

Porzana noveboracensis Todd, *Ann. Carnegie Mus.*, 1904, 2:533 (Erie and Presque Isle, Erie Co., transient, *fide* Bacon).
"Yellow Rail" Simpson, *Oölogist*, 1909, 26:25 (Erie, Erie Co.).
Coturnicops noveboracensis Hicks, *Wilson Bull.*, 1933, 45:181 (Pymatuning Swamp, Crawford Co., August).

BLACK RAIL

CRECISCUS JAMAICENSIS STODDARDI Coale

Description—A *very small rail*, about the size of the House Sparrow. Head (all around) and underparts dark slate color, the abdomen barred or spotted with white. Upper back rich chocolate brown, unmarked; rest of upperparts blackish, speckled with white. Eyes deep red.

Range and local status—This diminutive rail appears to have a more southern breeding range on the whole than the Yellow Rail, but, chiefly because of its shy and secretive habits, it is even less well known. Since it is regularly found as far north as Connecticut, Michigan, and northern Illinois in the breeding season, there is no intrinsic reason why it should not occur in our region also, in the marshy areas of Erie, Crawford, and Mercer counties. As yet no records for Erie have come to light, but G. M. Sutton (1928) has added the species to the list of western Pennsylvania birds on the strength of an individual seen at Pymatuning Swamp. He says that on September 7, 1925, "a Black Rail was seen at the remarkably close range of about six feet, along the southern shore of Crystal Lake. This bird was watched for several minutes. It was not collected, because it could not be frightened to a sufficient distance for shooting, and once it was behind the screen of vegetation it was lost to view. A passing crow finally frightened it away. The red-brown neck patch was a prominent mark and the bright red eyes were unmistakable." Dr. Sutton cites R. L. Keesler as authority for a record of the species near Conneaut Lake, between September 5 and 7, 1917. It may very well be that the Black Rail is far commoner than is apparent from the data available; a bird that clings so closely to its marshy covert is easily overlooked.

Creciscus jamaicensis jamaicensis Sutton, *Ann. Carnegie Mus.*, 1928, 18:92 (Crystal Lake, Crawford Co., September).

PURPLE GALLINULE

IONORNIS MARTINICA (Linnaeus)

Description—Head (all around) and underparts *deep, dull blue;* abdomen and tibiae dusky; under tail coverts pure white; back, wings, and tail, dull green; prominent frontal shield, pale blue; bill bright red, with broad yellow tip; feet yellow.

Range and local status—In North America the Purple Gallinule is virtually confined in the breeding season to the region around the Caribbean Sea and the Gulf of Mexico. On the coast it does not breed beyond South Carolina, but it occurs as a straggler far to the northward of this range-limit. Oddly enough, many of these extralimital occurrences are in the spring, and this fact suggests that some birds tend to overrun their normal range at that migration season. Warren records it without comment from Mercer County, on the authority of one of his correspondents, but since the bird mentioned is far likelier to have been a Florida Gallinule, I am not inclined to accept this report at its face value. A valid record from Washington County, however, is supplied by H. L. Gans, who writes: "On April 23, 1896, a classmate brought me a Purple Gallinule that he had killed at the athletic park in Washington. The bird had been wounded near the town and later turned loose. This man killed it with a rock." This particular specimen is now in the collection of the Carnegie Museum.

(?)*Ionornis martinica* WARREN, *Birds Pa.*, ed. 2, 1890, 73 (Mercer Co., *fide* Overmoyer).

FLORIDA GALLINULE

GALLINULA CHLOROPUS CACHINNANS Bangs

Description—Size of a Leghorn fowl; wingspread from twenty to twenty-three inches; a naked frontal shield at the base of the bill above. *Adult:* general color *slaty gray*, the head blackish, the back washed with olive brown; wings with a white outer edge; *sides with conspicuous white streaks;* under tail coverts extensively white; abdomen medially more or less whitish; *frontal shield and bill red*, the tip of the latter greenish yellow; feet greenish yellow, with the upper part next the feathers red. *Immature:* much duller and browner, especially on the head, and with more white on the underparts; frontal shield much smaller and without bright colors. Easily distinguished from the Coot at this stage by the decidedly brownish coloration above and by the lack of any white spot on the wings. *Young in the down:* greenish black above, sooty below, with bristly silvery beard; bill red.

Range—Our so-called Florida Gallinule is now held to be conspecific with the Eurasian form, which has a wide distribution in the Old World. The North American race, *cachinnans*, inhabits the continent from Panama northward to Minnesota and southern Ontario in the East, and to California in the West. It is on the whole a species of austral predilections—it does not pass north of the Alleghanian Fauna in the breeding season and is far commoner to the south. It is truly migratory in the northern part of its range but is resident in the southern part. In western Pennsylvania it is extremely local, but is said to breed fairly commonly in suitable situations in the adjoining state of Ohio. The breeding records from western Pennsylvania all come from the Pymatuning region and Edinboro and Conneaut lakes, and evidently represent an eastward extension of the Ohio breeding area into that part of our region where similar conditions prevail. As the species breeds commonly at Sandusky Bay, there seems no reason why it should not also breed on Presque Isle, but W. W. Worthington and I felt very certain that it could not have been breeding there at the time of our visit in 1900. Whether present conditions are any more favorable is still uncertain. Elsewhere in our region the Florida Gallinule is a rare and irregular migrant, and records for it are scarce.

Migration—What few spring records there are for this species indicate a migration beginning about the middle of April and lasting for about five weeks. Arrival dates for Erie and Crawford counties, however, are no earlier than April 30.

Fall records are likewise few in number but indicate a return movement in September and October. H. C. Kirkpatrick mounted one bird that was shot at Cambridge Springs, Crawford County, on September 28, 1886.

Habits—My own experience with the Florida Gallinule is limited to fragmentary observations made at Pymatuning Swamp in May from 1933 to 1937. The species is well known in other parts of the country, however, and its habits have been studied in some detail by sundry observers. Gallinules are more like coots than rails, in that they prefer the opener parts of the marsh, where the water is deeper and where the aquatic vegetation includes water lilies, pondweeds, and other low growths. Like coots, too, they swim with ease; their white under tail coverts show conspicuously as they move gracefully along over the water through the green scum that covers the surface here and there, and on into the patches of pondweed. In these thick growths the birds are well concealed when at rest. Those I watched were apparently feeding on insects. In their actions and behavior in general they reminded me not a little of domestic fowls, and the name "gallinule" (little hen) seemed strikingly appropriate. The several pairs kept more or less apart, and each seemed to respect the territory of the others. The only note uttered was guttural and froglike, or like the squawk of a heron, although at times gallinules are noisy and emit raucous, clattering cries.

The first nest of this species ever found in western Pennsylvania was discovered by G. M. Sutton on June 30, 1927, "at the very edge of the channel of the Shenango river about four miles north of Hartstown. The structure was well sheltered with cat-tail leaves and was built between cat-tail stalks about a foot above the water. The female, which was seen but once, grunted considerably in the cat-tails nearby. The [seven] eggs appeared to be quite fresh" (Sutton, 1928). These eggs were doubtless a second laying.

Two other nests were found by R. L. Fricke in the spring of 1933, near Hartstown. The first was collected on May 21, and contained eight fresh eggs. It was in a rather open spot, in plain sight from the roadway, and was discovered by chance while the swamp was being scanned from that vantage point with a glass. The nest was a dense mat of several kinds of aquatic plants—many of them pulled up by the roots—and had a slight lining of dry, broken stems of cattail. It looked very much like a grebe's nest. The body of the nest was moist, and the eggs were almost even with the water level. The second nest, found on May 26, was entirely different in appearance, situation, and composition. It was built in the dense growth of cattails near the edge of the marsh, only about fifteen feet from a railroad fill. It was much bulkier than the other and was composed wholly of coarse, dry cattail leaves, piled up a foot above the water and surrounded by the growing stems. On one side was a ramp or runway of the same material, matted down where the bird was accustomed to enter and leave. This nest held eleven eggs, which had well-developed embryos. On both occasions the parent bird flushed wild and did not again come near while the nest was being examined. A third nest containing nine eggs, about one-third incubated, was found near Linesville on May 27, 1936. It was a woven platform in the cattails about ten inches above the water, with a ramp leading to it.

The eggs of this species are typically ralline in shape and color and measure about 1.72 by 1.21 inches. The ground-color is light ochraceous buff, and the spots, which are mostly well defined and rather evenly distributed, are brownish. Young birds stay with their parents until almost fully grown. Dr. Sutton saw such a family group on September 5, 1925, at Lower Lake, and S. J. Seiple, another in the marsh south of Conneaut Lake on August 11, 1926. He writes: "The female and one young bird were on a log feeding, when a turtle crawled onto the log between them. Both birds jumped a little and seemed somewhat frightened, but soon the old one approached the turtle and ate something or other from the turtle's back."

Gallinula galeata Todd, *Ann. Carnegie Mus.*, 1904, 2:534 (Erie and Presque Isle, Erie Co., transient)—Todd, in Bausman, *Hist. Beaver Co., Pa.*, 1904, 2:1198 (Beaver Co., transient)—Cooke, *Bull. U.S. Dept. Agric.*, no. 128, 1914, 40 (Waynesburg, Greene Co., April)—Burleigh, *Wilson Bull.*, 1924, 36:76 (Oak Hall, Centre Co., May).

"Florida Gallinule" Dickey, *Auk*, 1915, 32:237 (near Waynesburg, Greene Co., April)—Seiple, *Auk*, 1931, 48:113 (Hartstown, Crawford Co., August)—Christy, *Cardinal*, 1934, 3:165 (Hartstown, Crawford Co., August)—Trimble, *Cardinal*, 1937, 4:106 (Pymatuning region, Crawford Co., nesting).

Gallinula chloropus cachinnans Sutton, *Ann. Carnegie Mus.* 1928, 18:93 (Pymatuning Swamp, Crawford Co., nesting; Crawford Co. localities and records).

Gallinula chloropus Fricke, *Cardinal*, 1931, 3:42 (Hartstown, Crawford Co., May).

Additional records: Warren, one shot May 18, 1891 (Simpson)—Prospect, Butler Co., one taken alive on or before May 1, 1907, and examined by Todd—Industry, Beaver Co., April 27, 1904, one shot by George A. Wilson (specimen in Carnegie Museum)—Glenshaw, Allegheny Co., May 22, 1927, one shot by Howard McMillan (specimen in Carnegie Museum)—Bellevue, Allegheny Co., April 14, 1895, one shot by J. Watson (Atkinson)—Washington, April 26, 1890 (Nease)—Keating, Clinton Co., one taken May 24, 1895 (Pierce)—Lawrenceville, Allegheny Co., April 20, 1934, Jerome Hines (specimen in Carnegie Museum)—Beaver River, near College Hill, Beaver Co., one noted May 17, 1932 (Malley).

AMERICAN COOT

FULICA AMERICANA AMERICANA Gmelin

Description—Size of a small duck; wingspread from twenty-three to twenty-eight inches; general form stocky. Feet have *broad lobes or flaps* on both sides of the *toes*. Bill stout, high at the base, its covering continued well up over the forehead as a conspicuous *bare shield or plate*. *Adult:* general color *slaty black*, the head darker, the underparts grayish; a *white spot on the wings* formed by the tips of the secondaries; under tail coverts also white, in V-shaped pattern; feet dull green; *bill whitish*, with a chestnut band near the tip, and the frontal shield dull red; eyes red. *Immature:* much duller, the underparts whitish; bill smaller, and frontal shield reduced. *Downy young:* blackish, with orange and yellowish down about the head and wings.

Range—The American Coot, as its name implies, is exclusively a North American bird, although it has close relatives both in South America and in the Old World. It enjoys an extensive range in this continent and goes much farther north than the Florida Gallinule. Unlike that species, however, it is almost or quite unknown as a breeding bird over much of the eastern United States. Western Pennsylvania seems to be on the very edge of its breeding range—a range which also extends to northern Ohio and western New York, where, however, the species is still local and irregular in the nesting season. As far back as 1890, Warren, on the authority of one of his correspondents, reported this species as breeding in Mercer County, but I am inclined to doubt his statement. The first authentic record of its breeding is that cited by G. M. Sutton (1928) for Pymatuning Swamp. On May 31, 1923, he found young birds in the down. In the spring of 1934 a party from the Carnegie Museum succeeded in locating several nests with eggs in the part of the swamp northwest of Linesville, on the edge of the new lake. The favorable conditions created by this development made the lake a mecca for the Coot, and until 1938 hundreds of pairs bred within the sanctuary limits. A falling off in numbers that season may have been due to the flooding out of the cattail growth in which the birds were wont to nest. The species probably breeds also in the swamps of Conneaut Outlet, but the evidence is not so conclusive.

Dr. Sutton has discussed the breeding of the Coot and of the Florida Gallinule at Pymatuning Swamp, and has remarked on the fact that these birds do not breed at Presque Isle, where the conditions are much the same. A plausible reason for this, in my opinion, is the publicity and persecution formerly prevalent at the latter locality. Now that all shooting has been stopped there, the indications are that some of the birds that were kept away are coming back. Dr. O. E. Jennings reports having seen a pair of coots there in midsummer of 1929, and feels sure that they were breeding. On the other hand, nonbreeding coots have been seen several times in certain localities during the summer months. A notable instance was reported by Robert Little (1931) from near Clinton, Allegheny County. One bird was taken at "Chambers' Dam," near Washington on July 16, 1894, by H. L. Gans.

Aside from these actual and potential breeding records, occurrences of this species have been mainly in the seasons of migration. There are some scattered records for almost all the counties in the western tier, and a few also for the ridge and valley section, but almost none for the plateau region, where there are so few suitable marshy areas. Only in the Erie-Crawford district is the Coot of regular occurrence, and only there is it known to appear in any numbers. "It sometimes occurs at Conneaut Lake in immense flocks, which almost cover the surface of the water" (Sutton,

1928). On October 16, 1935, a party of observers counted 2,479 coots on Pymatuning Lake. At Erie Bay and Presque Isle the species is also common, especially in recent years. All observers agree that it is usually more numerous in the fall than in the spring. Ordinarily the Coot goes much farther south to pass the winter, but during the remarkably mild winter of 1931–32, when Erie Bay was open throughout and tenanted by whistling swans and other waterfowl, this species, too, remained in considerable numbers. G. M. Langdon also reports the wintering of a single individual on Erie Bay in 1927–28. A wintering status at Pymatuning is suggested by a record of one bird seen there on February 3, 1935 (Skaggs), and perhaps also by a record of 139 birds observed on February 29, 1936 (Oudette).

Migration—The coots that we see in spring in the upper Ohio Valley and on the lake shore plain probably come from the Mississippi Valley. The species is an early migrant at that season; it arrives shortly after the middle of March, while the ducks are passing north, and becomes common by the end of that month. One coot taken at Iron Bridge, Armstrong County, on March 16, 1904, is in the collection of the Carnegie Museum. March 18 is the earliest spring record for Conneaut Lake, as well as for Erie. B. L. Oudette (1939) gives February 19 as an exceptionally early arrival date at Pymatuning Lake. At Renovo the Coot was once observed as early as March 5 (1900). April is a month of great movement, and many individuals linger well into May before finally leaving for the north. There is always the chance, however, that any seen after the middle of that month (when they should be nesting) may be wounded, sick, or barren birds. August records are similarly open to suspicion, as possibly referring to birds that may have bred in the vicinity; there are several such records for localities in Crawford County. The actual fall movement gets under way during the first week in September and is usually in full swing by October. It is regularly protracted into November, and in 1923 I saw a single bird near the mouth of the Beaver River as late as December 7. There are also a few December records from other places. Thus the Coot appears to be singularly hardy, for a rail, and its wintering in our region is understandable. Further reports on its movements are desirable.

Habits—The Coot may be described as a rail that has become adapted for swimming and thus for leading a more aquatic life in general. Its more depressed body, dense feather covering, and particularly its strongly lobate feet, are all modifications in this direction. The Coot is in fact as much at home on the water as any one of the pond ducks, in whose company indeed it is often found. Like the ducks, too, it often feeds by thrusting its head beneath the surface while the tail is tipped up, or even by diving to a considerable depth. On land, or on the edge of the ice floes, it is more agile than a duck and much more graceful in its movements—as it walks it nods its head like a fowl or a pigeon. Most of its food comes from the shallow ponds and the opener parts of the marsh, where, singly or in scattered parties, it skulks among the aquatic plants. It lives on small fish, tadpoles, and other aquatic creatures, when these can be found, but its main diet is vegetable and consists of the leaves, seeds, and roots of various water plants.

When disturbed the Coot will often attempt to escape by swimming or by scrambling over the surface of the water with the help of its wings, rather than by flight. When forced to fly it gets under way with apparent difficulty, patters over the surface with a great splashing of water before it can rise at all, and never flies very high, unless it is actually migrating. The large, compact flocks or "rafts" which gather at times in the spring and descend upon open bodies of water doubtless keep together for mutual protection during the entire journey. The birds sit lightly on the water, milling around irregularly, but not losing the flock formation; their whitish bills, in contrast with their black heads, are conspicuous at a distance. At such times they are much less shy than are most ducks, but they learn caution with experience.

The Coot has a variety of calls, guttural and uncouth; it is a noisy bird on its nesting grounds. Four nests were found by our party at Pymatuning Lake on May 22, 1934. They were situated among the rushes, where the water was almost eighteen inches deep, and were built up to about a foot above its level. The foundations were of good-sized sticks; on these stable platforms were placed heaps of dry rushes and cattails, the mass hollowed out to receive the eggs. Although the nests were somewhat bulky, they were not at all conspicuous at a little distance. One nest already had nine eggs, another seven, and two had but three each. On May 30 one of these nests contained a full set of twelve eggs. The next year (May 16, 1935) we examined about a dozen nests in the sanctuary—some empty, others with full or incomplete sets of eggs. Some were heaped up well above the water level, while others were lower, virtually afloat. Again, some were well made of cattail leaves, dry and brown, while others had much green material included. Wherever placed, in sparse or in thick aquatic growth, the nests were fairly inconspicuous. Sometimes as many as fifteen eggs are laid by one bird. They are buffy, with fine spots of deep brown, rather evenly distributed. Average measurements are 1.91 by 1.30 inches.

Fulica americana Townsend, *Proc. Acad. Nat. Sci. Philadelphia*, 1883, 67 (Latrobe, Westmoreland Co.)—Warren, *Birds Pa.*, ed. 2, 1890, 74 (Erie Bay, Erie Co., transient; (?)Mercer Co., breeding, *fide* Overmoyer)—Rhoads, *Auk*, 1899, 16:310 (Emporium, Cameron Co., *fide* Larrabee; Bellevue, Allegheny Co., *fide* Atkinson)—Todd, *Ann. Carnegie Mus.*, 1904, 2:534 (Presque Isle, Erie Co., transient)—Todd, in Bausman, *Hist. Beaver Co., Pa.*, 1904, 2:1198 (Beaver Co., transient)—Cooke, *Bull. U.S. Dept. Agric.*, no. 128, 1914, 43 (Renovo, Clinton Co., migration)—Christy, *Cardinal*, 1923, v. 1, no. 1, [p. 3] (Sewickley, Allegheny Co., transient)—Burleigh, *Wilson Bull.*, 1924, 36:76 ("State College" [Oak Hall and Scotia], Centre Co., migration)—Sutton, *Ann. Carnegie Mus.*, 1928, 18:94 (near Hartstown, Crawford Co., nesting; Crawford Co. localities and records)—Jennings, *Cardinal*, 1930, 2:184 (Presque Isle, Erie Co., summer)—Little, *Cardinal*, 1931, 3:16 (Clinton, Allegheny Co., summer)—Fricke, *Cardinal*, 1931, 3:42 (Hartstown, Crawford Co., May).

"Coot" (or "American Coot") Christy, *Cardinal*, 1923, v. 1, no. 2, [p. 16] (Clinton Pond, Allegheny Co., spring)—Sutton, *Bird-Lore*, 1924, 26:56 (Rochester, Beaver Co., December, *fide* Todd)—Eastwood, *Bird-Lore*, 1926, 28:403 (Clinton region, Allegheny Co., October, *fide* Squier)—Boulton, *Bird-Lore*, 1928, 30:13 (Clinton Pond, Allegheny Co., October, *fide* Christy), 271 (Sandy Lake, Mercer Co., May, *fide* Freni and Stanton)—Seiple, *Auk*, 1931, 48:113 (Pymatuning Swamp, Crawford Co., August)—Christy, *Cardinal*, 1932, 3:86 (Erie Bay, Erie Co., February)—Savage, *Bird-Lore*, 1932, 34:44; and Upson, *et al.*, *Bird-Lore*, 1935, 37:47 (Erie Bay, Erie Co., December)—Christy, *et al.*, *Bird-Lore*, 1937, 39:44 (Pymatuning Lake, Crawford Co., December)—Trimble, *Cardinal*, 1937, 4:105 (Pymatuning Lake, Crawford Co., nesting)—Oudette, *Cardinal*, 1939, 5:47 (Pymatuning Lake, near Linesville, Crawford Co., February).

PLOVERS

FAMILY CHARADRIIDAE

THE PLOVERS are shore birds with reticulate tarsi, only three toes (the hind toe missing, or at most vestigial), and rather short and peculiarly shaped bills that are constricted basally and expanded terminally. The wings are long and pointed; the neck is short and thick; and the general outline of the body is plump. The Plovers are in general more at home on dry land than are the Sandpipers; they are fast runners and have a peculiar habit of running for a short distance and coming to an abrupt halt in a characteristic upright pose. More than one hundred forms of this group are known, and they are widely dispersed over the world. The tropical species are of course sedentary, but those breeding in the arctic tundras perform remarkable migrations. Of the six species occurring in western Pennsylvania only two are known to breed.

PIPING PLOVER

CHARADRIUS MELODUS Ord

Description—Similar in size and general pattern of coloration to the Semipalmated Plover, but *upperparts* very much paler—*pale ashy white;* black band on the forehead narrower; no black on the sides of the head; legs yellow; bill black, orange-yellow at base. The *young* lack the black band on the breast, the entire underparts being pure white.

Range and migration—The Piping Plover is a relatively southern species and does not normally range north of the Gulf of St. Lawrence on the Atlantic coast, nor beyond Manitoba in the interior, but it is very local in its distribution and shuns the shores of all but large bodies of water. Sennett first took it on Presque Isle many years ago, where later it was also recorded by Warren, who, however, supposed it to be merely a transient. My own researches in this locality definitely established its status as a summer resident, of regular but not common occurrence. In recent years its numbers have increased there considerably, and nests have been found every season. In 1900 it was first noted on April 16, but not again until May 2. Other arrival dates are April 29, 1932 (Beardslee) and April 30, 1933 (Guynes). In the fall of 1900 it was not seen after September 7, but R. B. Simpson noted it as late as September 26 in 1902, and probably these various dates represent the usual times of its arrival and departure. Other than at Lake Erie there are no records except one for Meadville of September 7, 1908, cited by G. M. Sutton on the authority of H. C. Kirkpatrick; this must have been an exceptional occurrence.

Habits—About fifteen pairs of this interesting little plover nest annually on the outer shore of Presque Isle, where I have often met with it during May and June. "Its favorite haunts are wide stretches of dry, sandy beach, with which it agrees so perfectly in color that unless in motion it is difficult to distinguish. It runs very rapidly, and is rather shy and hard to approach" (Todd, 1904). Its call is a soft, plaintive, musical whistle, repeated usually two or three times as the bird moves about or seeks to decoy an unwelcome visitor from its nest or young. On May 24, 1900, I shot a female that contained an egg almost ready to be laid, and this approximate date of nesting has since been confirmed by other observers. Mr. Simpson found a nest with eggs on May 31, 1911, and three more on May 29, 1932. A party from the Carnegie Museum found three nests on May

30 and 31, 1935, containing well-incubated eggs. Two of these nests were only about fifty feet apart.

The nest of this plover is a simple affair—merely a depression in the sand on the shingle or higher part of the beach, lined with some thin, flat pebbles. The eggs, like those of shore birds in general, are four in number, and are arranged with the small ends together; they match their surroundings so well in color that they are scarcely discernible even close at hand. In their pyriform shape they resemble the eggs of the Killdeer, but are smaller, averaging 1.24 by .95 inches. The ground-color is a very pale buff, and the markings are small dark spots, uniformly and rather sparsely distributed. The nest of this plover is not easy to locate, as the incubating bird leaves it quietly while one is yet some distance away. Those we found in 1935 were discovered by intensive search over the suspected section of beach. The parents made repeated use of the broken-wing ruse in attempting to decoy us away. A set of eggs found by J. E. Perry on June 19, 1927, may have been the result of delayed nesting. Young in the downy stage are sand-colored and are hard to see as long as they remain motionless. Young of the year were taken by S. E. Bacon on July 21 and August 17.

Ægialitis meloda WARREN, *Birds Pa.*, 1888, 236; and ed. 2, 1890, 101 (Presque Isle, Erie Co., transient).

Ægialitis meloda circumcincta TODD, *Ann. Carnegie Mus.*, 1904, 2:550 (Presque Isle, Erie Co., breeding).

"Piping Plover" SIMPSON, *Oölogist*, 1909, 26:153; 1912, 29:212, 250, 350 (Presque Isle, Erie Co., nesting)—BOULTON, *Bird-Lore*, 1928, 30:337, 401 (Presque Isle, Erie Co., nesting).

Charadrius melodus SUTTON, *Ann. Carnegie Mus.*, 1928, 18:112 (French Creek, near Meadville, Crawford Co., September, *fide* Kirkpatrick).

SEMIPALMATED PLOVER

CHARADRIUS SEMIPALMATUS Bonaparte

Description—A small plover, about the size of the Spotted Sandpiper. *Spring: upperparts dull drab;* wings dusky black, with a narrow white band showing across the middle when they are spread; tail blackish towards the end, but tipped with white, the outer feathers all white; "face" black, except for a broad white band on the forehead; throat and a narrow collar around the hindneck, white; *the breast has one broad black band*, continued over the back, just behind the white collar; rest of underparts pure white; bill dull orange-yellow with black tip; feet dull orange or yellowish. *Adult in fall:* similar, but the black replaced by grayish brown. *Immature in fall:* similar to the spring adult, but much duller; the black head pattern merely indicated and the breastband dull drab like the back; the upperparts have pale buffy feather-edgings, giving a scaled or speckled appearance; the bill and feet are darker and duller.

Range—A strictly American species, breeding northward in the Arctic and Hudsonian life zones, and wintering from the Gulf States southward, the Semipalmated Plover is only a transient over the greater part of the continent. It is common and well known, especially on the Atlantic coast and about the shores of the Great Lakes. At Presque Isle it is one of the commonest of the migrating shore birds, particularly in the fall. Away from the lake shore, however, there is an amazing dearth of records for our region in general. Even in Crawford County this plover seems to be rather rare except at Pymatuning Lake. At Warren it is also irregular and has been uncommon in recent years. I used to see it quite often along the Ohio River at Beaver in the fall, but have not noted it recently. Only four occurrences have been reported for Allegheny County (Burleigh, 1923; Atkinson). The species does not appear at all in A. K. Pierce's migration records for Renovo, and our only record for the ridge and valley section is one from State College supplied by T. D. Burleigh. To most observers in our region it is apparently unknown.

Migration—In 1904, referring to the migration of the Semipalmated Plover at Erie Bay and Presque Isle, I wrote: "May is the month when its northward movement takes place. In the spring of 1900 its arrival was recorded May 8, and it was observed at intervals until as late as May 28." Subsequent experience has served to confirm this statement. In 1911 R. B. Simpson found some semipalmated plovers still present there between May 31 and June 2, and in 1934 J. E. Perry saw three birds on June 3. Crawford County spring dates (from several localities) lie between May 15 and 31. Mr. Simpson noted the species at Warren as late as June 5 in 1895. Since this plover is a rapid traveler, such laggards would still be able to reach their northern breeding grounds in time to nest. This species returns very early in the fall at Erie, sometimes by July 24 (1932) or August 1 (1928), according to the records of the local observers. It has been noted at Pymatuning Lake as early as July 30 (1937—Skaggs), and as late as October 14 (1933—Seiple). My earliest fall date for Beaver County is August 8 (1890). The species is generally common on Presque Isle through September, but is only occasional after that; in 1900, however, one bird was collected on November 2, and in 1931 one was seen on October 27 (Beardslee).

Habits—The Semipalmated Plover usually arrives in flocks of varying size, sometimes composed entirely of its own kind, but often intermixed with other shore birds. It is fond of mud flats and gravelly bars, less so of sandy beaches. Its low, mellow, plaintive note, *chir-wee*, betrays its presence as it runs along in front of the observer. In color it matches the mud of its haunts so closely that when at rest it is sometimes difficult to see (even from a front view, as the white of the underparts somewhat resembles an exposed mussel shell). A quiescent flock standing at ease in various poses, some apparently asleep, is an interesting sight. I quote from C. W. Townsend's account:

"In flight the flocks are often compact, twisting and turning as if animated by a single thought, but they also fly in loose order. On alighting they at once spread out on the sand in true plover fashion, and do not, like sandpipers, keep together and move along close to the wave line. Another plover habit which at once distinguishes them from sanderlings or other sandpipers of a similar size, is that of running about with heads up and dabbing suddenly at the ground from time to time instead of moving along with heads down diligently probing the sand. With erect figures they run about in various directions, often pausing and standing still as if in thought, occasionally jerking or bobbing their heads and necks and ever and again swiftly dabbing at some morsel of food."[1]

Ægialitis semipalmata WARREN, *Birds Pa.*, ed. 2, 1890, 100 (Erie Co., transient)—TODD, *Ann. Carnegie Mus.*, 1904, 2:549 (Erie and Presque Isle, Erie Co., transient)—TODD, in Bausman, *Hist. Beaver Co., Pa.*, 1904, 2:1199 (Beaver Co., fall transient)—BURLEIGH, *Wilson Bull.*, 1923, 35:85 (Allegheny River [Pittsburgh], Allegheny Co., September); 1924, 36:77 (State College, Centre Co., spring transient).

"Semipalmated Plover" SIMPSON, *Oölogist*, 1910, 27:32 (Warren, Warren Co., fall); 1912, 29:250, 350 (Presque Isle, Erie Co., May–June)—EASTWOOD, *Bird-Lore*, 1926, 28:273 (Hartstown, Crawford Co., May, *fide* Blair)—BOULTON, *Bird-Lore*, 1928, 30:337 (Presque Isle, Erie Co., August, *fide* Perry)—CHRISTY, *Cardinal*, 1933, 3:148 (Geneva, Crawford Co., May).

Charadrius semipalmatus SUTTON, *Ann. Carnegie Mus.*, 1928 18:11 (Crawford Co. records and references).

[1]In A. C. BENT, U. S. National Museum, *Bulletin*, no. 146, 1929, p. 223.

KILLDEER

OXYECHUS VOCIFERUS VOCIFERUS (Linnaeus)

Description—About the size of the Robin. *Adult:* upperparts (including head), dull olive brown, the *rump and upper tail coverts bright rusty buff*, presenting a strong contrast; wings dusky, with a white band across the middle, conspicuous in flight; the tail has a broad black subterminal band and conspicuous white or buffy tips to all but the middle pairs of feathers, while the outermost pair is barred with white and black; the forehead and an elongated spot over and behind the eyes are white; a broad black band from eye to eye across the fore part of the crown; a dark band from the bill to the sides of the nape; throat white, as is also a narrow band around the hindneck; underparts white, the *breast with two broad bands of black*, the upper one of which is carried over and around the hindneck, just behind the white band; bill black; feet usually pale. *Immature birds* resemble the adults, but the black breast-collars are not so sharply defined, and the back and scapulars are more or less tinged with buff. *Downy young:* the general pattern of the adult is carried out, except that there is only *one black collar* on the breast, instead of two.

Range—Although the Killdeer does not range nearly so far north as do many of the other shore birds—does not in fact enter the Arctic Life Zone at all—its general breeding range, stretching from the Atlantic to the Pacific and from Hudson Bay to Florida and Mexico, is very extensive. Two resident extralimital races are also known, from the West Indies and the coast of Peru, respectively. The Killdeer is one of the few shore birds that are not entirely dependent upon either marshy ground or extensive beach-flats for subsistence; hence it is of general distribution throughout our region (except, of course, in forested areas), and tolerably common in most sections. During the breeding season the pairs are scattered over the country, while in spring and fall the concentration that takes place gives the impression of greater numbers at these times. Beyond question the species must be commoner now than it ever was under primitive conditions, when the whole region was covered with forest. Like the Bob-white and other open-country birds, it has become a beneficiary of civilization.

Migration—The arctic-breeding shore birds are almost all late migrants in the spring—necessarily so, it would seem—but the Killdeer, coming earlier and remaining later, is hardier than any of them. In fact, there are several instances on record of its wintering in our region. Norman McClintock (1933) saw a flock near Ligonier, Westmoreland County, off and on through the winter of 1931–32. Mrs. Ella Pim tells me that a single bird wintered on her farm south of Leasuresville, Butler County, in 1930–31. B. H. Christy says that the species is occasional in winter at Sewickley, Allegheny County, and it was noted by another observer at Deer Creek, in the same county, late in December, 1922. During the unusually severe winter of 1935–36, according to S. S. Ristich, a flock of eleven birds remained in the valley of Raccoon Creek, about five miles south of Beaver. At State College the Killdeer has lingered several times throughout the winter. Even as far north as Crawford County "it may occur irregularly in rather large flocks" through the winter months (Sutton, 1928). Although I have never actually observed the Killdeer in winter in Beaver County, I have noted it in the spring movement as early as February 22 (1922). Ordinarily, however, it is in March that the first ones appear, together with the early migrants among the land birds. Exact dates for thirteen years range from March 2 to 21, the average being March 13. Records supplied by various observers for other counties also fall within these limits. R. B. Simpson saw one killdeer at Warren on February 8, 1890, during a heavy snowstorm; but perhaps this was a true winter record.

As nearly as one can judge in the case of a summer-resident species such as this, migrants from farther north begin to appear early in September. On Presque Isle, where the Killdeer was certainly not breeding during the season of 1900, an immense flight occurred that year on September 8, to the almost complete exclusion of all other shore birds. The species was common there until early October but did not finally leave until November. S. E. Bacon noted it in that locality as late as November 26 in 1891. In the Johnstown region of Cambria County, according to Miss E. D. Canan, it sometimes remains until Thanksgiving Day. Almost every year I see it regularly along the Ohio River until the first or second week of November; it therefore lingers late in the fall, even as it comes early in the spring.

Habits—Because of its relatively more southern breeding range and its preference for open, cultivated lands, the Killdeer is better known than any other plover, but it is not less interesting on that account. Conspicuous and noisy, it seems to court attention and is easily recognized by both eye and ear. When the bird is on the ground, the double black breast-collar serves to identify it, and when it is in flight, the rusty-buff rump and upper tail coverts are similarly diagnostic. Its specific appellation of *vociferus* is eminently appropriate, while its common name of Killdeer is a rendering of its ordinary call note—*kill-dee, kill-dee, kill-dee-dee-dee*. This reiterated cry, given as the birds pass overhead on their northward way, is one of the characteristic bird notes of early spring. Although often occurring singly or in pairs at this season, the Killdeer is likelier to be found in groups of from six to fifteen, generally along the margins of the rivers or smaller water-courses, or about ponds and swampy places in open fields. Sometimes it arrives on the scene before its favorite resorts are fully thawed out, but even then it contrives to subsist. Courtship commences shortly after the arrival of the summer-resident birds, and with the onset of the breeding season the flocks break up and the mated pairs betake themselves to the dry uplands for the summer months. Pasture lands, cultivated fields, and open, stony ground—resembling certain conditions in the western prairie country—are now the Killdeer's chosen haunts, and the proximity of water seems to be immaterial.

There is considerable discrepancy in the records concerning the reported time of nesting. The supplied dates vary from early April to June. It is hard to believe, judging by analogy, that more than one brood is ever raised in a season; and it is probable, therefore, that the later dates represent second or even third attempts by those pairs whose earlier nestings came to nought. In any case a nesting date before May is unusual and worthy of remark, although there are a few that are amply attested. The majority of the nests containing fresh eggs, however, have been noted in May. Finding the nest is no easy matter, although the anxiety of the parents when their haunts are invaded betrays its proximity. Upon the alarm given by its mate, the brooding bird usually leaves the nest unobserved while the intruder is yet some distance away, and runs for a space before taking wing, whereupon both parents fly around excitedly, with loud and anxious outcries. Should the intruder come too close, the parents (one or both) will try the broken-wing ruse in the effort to decoy him away and will flutter over the ground just ahead of him apparently in great distress. This ruse must be effective with a dog or other predatory animal, and its verisimilitude is both striking and appealing. Sometimes careful and exhaustive search over the suspected area will result in the discovery of the nest, but a quicker effect is obtained by retiring at once to the distance of a hundred yards or more and watching the birds through a glass. After their alarm has subsided one of them will approach the nest by easy stages and resume its duties there. But if the observer remains too close, the birds have a deceptive habit of arbitrarily squatting anywhere in the field as if on a nest. At such times they utter a long-drawn-out, distinctive trilling note.

Even with the site marked, the exact position of the nest is not easy to distinguish against its usual background. The nests that I have examined were merely slight depressions in the ground, into which a few flat pebbles, grass stems, and weed stalks had been brought and disposed at random. The very simplicity of construction thus makes for safety from discovery. But sometimes the birds go to greater pains, and a more elaborate nest results. G. M. Sutton (1928) says that one he found at Pymatuning Swamp "was a beautiful structure in spite of the fact that Killdeers are reputed not to build a nest. Bits of burnt wood and small pebbles had been selected evidently with the greatest care, and were placed in the nest with the largest pieces noticeably at the outer

edge, and the smaller ones under the eggs. There was also a suggestion of pavement about the nest, this being made of small stones of remarkably similar size, shape, and color. The broad leaves of a marsh marigold nearby offered this nest but slight protection."

Nesting as it does in an open and exposed situation, with no attempt at concealment, the Killdeer relies on the protective coloration of its eggs. So perfectly do these blend with their surroundings that they are hard to see from a few feet away. In color they are light buff, more or less irregularly spotted and scrawled with blackish brown and with lighter markings below the surface. In the more heavily marked eggs the spots tend to run together into blotches around the larger end. As with most other shore birds, four eggs are the normal set; sometimes only three are laid, and H. C. Kirkpatrick reports once finding three young and two eggs in a nest. Still more unusual was a set of seven eggs found by R. L. Fricke at Linesville on May 16, 1938. The shape of the eggs is pyriform, and they measure about 1.43 by 1.04 inches. They are usually arranged in the nest with the small ends together, to facilitate incubation, which is said to last for twenty-four or twenty-five days.

The young are precocious little creatures, able to run about shortly after being hatched. They look like balls of fluff mounted on stilts, and they are able to get over the ground very quickly. The parents use the same tactics to divert attention from the young as from the nest itself. If the young lie closely, as they often do, they are indeed hard to find. They grow very rapidly and are on the wing by the end of July, but they do not assume fully adult plumage until the following year. August finds adults and young still together, sometimes in larger parties formed by the union of several family groups. Grasshoppers are then abundant, and the birds soon grow fat. The Killdeer is in fact one of the most valuable of our birds from the farmer's standpoint. Investigations have revealed that very nearly 98 per cent of its food consists of animal matter, mainly insects, including many destructive kinds. I remember seeing flocks of killdeers some years ago in pasture land which had been laid waste by the "white grub" (the larva of the May beetle, *Lachnosterna*). The birds were feeding among the sods upturned by the hogs.

While the flocks favor the open farming country, from which they derive much of their subsistence, some return to the river beaches and mud flats, along with the other shore birds, with which they associate freely. Thus, killdeers were abundant on Presque Isle in August and September, 1900, and thronged the outside beach in large flocks, noisy, restless, and suspicious. Unlike sandpipers, which more or less keep together while feeding, a flock of killdeers scatters upon alighting. In color the birds harmonize so well with the muddy stones of the beaches that when at rest they are hard to detect. They behave like other plover and in their movements—running for a distance and then pausing for a moment—remind one of a robin. They can run very rapidly, much faster indeed than a man can walk. Their plaintive cries are often heard at night and indicate considerable activity in the dark hours.

My account of the Killdeer must not close without reference to an extraordinary performance witnessed and described by W. E. Coon (1923):

"On foot, few birds have as quick, graceful movements as the Killdeer. Quick as a flash to dart forward and as quick to come to a sudden stop, it is the trained soldier of the field-birds. Its movements may be clearly discerned in newly plowed, or in grain fields.

"In the summer of 1919, I was assisting a farmer of western Crawford County (Pa.) in the preparation of some ground which was to be planted to wheat that year. One day shortly after the plowing and harrowing had been finished, I was driving across the field when I noticed a group of young Killdeer with an old one. At first I thought nothing of it, but with a second look, I noticed that they were acting very strangely. I stopped the team and watched the birds. There were seven or eight (I believe there were seven but have not the record of that) young ones about half-grown with one old bird. At first they were apparently skipping around aimlessly. Soon the old one gave a call. Immediately, there was started a drill which would put many a crack squad to shame. The young ones separated quickly into two groups and formed in two lines facing each other at a distance of about two feet with intervals, between individuals, of five or six inches. The old bird took a position ten or twelve inches from the ends of the lines and facing them. A second call from the old Killdeer and forward the two lines moved with precision and uniformity; the individuals passed alternately; and each line with a right-about-face of each individual came into line where the other line had been previously. Again the lines were facing each other. This was repeated three or four times before I left. This exhibition took place within fifteen yards of where I sat."

Ægialites vociferus Townsend, *Proc. Acad. Nat. Sci. Philadelphia*, 1883, 67 (Latrobe, Westmoreland Co., summer).

"Killdeer" Simpson, *Ornithologist and Oölogist*, 1890, 15:63 (Warren, Warren Co., February)—Stone, *Cassinia*, 1906, 9:43 (McConnellsburg, Fulton Co., June)—Simpson, *Oölogist*, 1909, 26:153 (Presque Isle, Erie Co., July); 1910, 27:32 (Warren, Warren Co., fall)—[Burleigh], *Oölogist*, 1911, 28:156 (Harmarville, Allegheny Co., nesting)—Harlow, *Cassinia*, 1912, 15:20 (Center Furnace Swamp, Centre Co.)—Simpson, *Oölogist*, 1912, 29:247, 350 (Presque Isle, Erie Co., May–June); 1913, 30:51; and 1914, 31:91 (Warren, Warren Co., March and June)—Dickey, *Oölogist*, 1914, 31:184 (Waynesburg, Greene Co., and State College, Centre Co., nesting)—Sutton, *Oölogist*, 1915, 32:16 (Waynesburg, Greene Co., nesting, *fide* Carter)—Harlow, *Oölogist*, 1917, 34:64 (State College, Centre Co., May)—Jones, *et al.*, *Bird-Lore*, 1923, 25:25 (Deer Creek, Allegheny Co., December)—Sutton, *Bird-Lore*, 1923, 25:194 (Duquesne, Allegheny Co., March, *fide* Galloway)—Coon, *Bird-Lore*, 1923, 25:317 (western Crawford Co., summer; habits)—Christy, *Cardinal*, 1923, v. 1, no. 2, [p. 16] (Clinton Pond, Allegheny Co., spring); 1924, v. 1, no. 4, p. 10 (Big Traverse Valley, Beaver Co., June)—Sutton, *Bird-Lore*, 1924, 26:190 (Pittsburgh, Allegheny Co., March, *fide* Schrawder), 337 (Wattsburg, Erie Co., summer, *fide* Allen)—EASTWOOD, *Bird-Lore*, 1925, 27:262 (Aspinwall, Allegheny Co., and Greenville, Mercer Co., nesting, *fide* Homer); 1926, 28:402 (Allegheny Co., October)—EASTWOOD, *Bird-Lore*, 1927, 29:197 (Springs, Somerset Co., migration, *fide* Miller)—BOULTON, *Bird-Lore*, 1928, 30:195 (Beaver, Beaver Co., March, *fide* Todd), 337 (Pittsburgh, Allegheny Co., July)—CHRISTY, *Cardinal*, 1931, 3:17 (Lowrie's Run, Allegheny Co., September).

Ægialitis vocifera DWIGHT, *Auk*, 1892, 9:134 (Cresson, Cambria Co., June)—JACOBS, *Summer Birds Greene Co., Pa.*, 1893, 5 (Greene Co., nesting).

Oxyechus vociferus TODD, *Ann. Carnegie Mus.*, 1904, 2:549 (Erie and Presque Isle, Erie Co., nesting)—TODD, in Bausman, *Hist. Beaver Co., Pa.*, 1904, 2:1199 (Beaver Co., summer)—COOKE, *Bull. Biol. Surv.* no. 35, 1910, 85 (Waynesburg, Greene Co., migration)—HARLOW, *Auk*, 1912, 29:469; and 1918, 35:22 (southern Centre Co., summer)—CHRISTY, *Cardinal*, 1923, v. 1, no. 1, [p. 4] (Sewickley, Allegheny Co., nesting; occasional in winter)—BURLEIGH, *Wilson Bull.*, 1923, 35:85 (Allegheny Co., nesting); 1924, 36:70; and 1931, 43:38 (State College, Centre Co., migration; nesting)—McCLINTOCK, *Cardinal*, 1933, 3:125 (Ligonier, Westmoreland Co., nesting; winter).

Oxyechus vociferus vociferus CHRISTY and SUTTON, *Cardinal*, 1928, 2:69 (Cooksburg, Forest Co., June)—SUTTON, *Ann. Carnegie Mus.*, 1928, 18:111 (Crawford Co. localities, nesting)—BURLEIGH, *Cardinal*, 1932, 3:74 (Chalk Hill, Fayette Co., breeding).

AMERICAN GOLDEN PLOVER

PLUVIALIS DOMINICA DOMINICA (Müller)

Description—Smaller than the Black-bellied Plover, and with a much shorter bill. *Adult in spring:* crown and upperparts dark, spotted with buff and bright golden yellow; *upper tail coverts similar to the back* (*no white*); wings plain dusky black; a broad white stripe runs from the forehead over the eye and down the neck to either side of the breast; underparts black. *Adult in fall:* similar to the spring plumage, but black of underparts more or less broken and mixed with gray, particularly on the throat; color pattern less definite. *Young in fall:* much darker than the Black-bellied Plover at the same stage, with *no white on the upper tail coverts*, which are colored precisely like the back. Upperparts black, with buffy and golden yellow spots; underparts dull white, with obscure dusky shading and mottling; *axillary feathers also grayish.*

Range and migration—The American Golden Plover is the Nearctic representative of the Old World *Pluvialis apricaria*. It breeds in high latitudes and winters in South America. Through the intervening region it occurs as a transient only, following a different route in the spring and fall. In the latter season most of the birds pass southward by way of the Atlantic coast as far as Nova Scotia, whence they swing out to sea and are next heard of in Bermuda, or even the Lesser Antilles. In the spring they return by an overland migration up the Mississippi Valley. Our region thus lies off the direct route, and we get only a comparatively few birds that happen to follow an outlying course.

This species formerly came to Erie Bay and its vicinity more or less regularly, but of late years it has become rare. Concerning the Black-bellied Plover and the Golden Plover in that locality, S. E. Bacon writes: "Taking one year with another, I consider this [latter] species much the more abundant of the two. Flocks of from twenty-five to fifty birds used to be seen every season, frequenting the ploughed fields west of the city, arriving soon after September 1, and staying for a week or two. These flocks seemed to be comprised mainly of old birds, the young being found in pairs and small bunches around the lake beach. I saw two such flocks in September, 1901, the first seen to speak of in several years. The Golden Plover is seldom noted in August, but on August 20, 1896, I shot one old bird. My latest fall note is November 5 of the same year" (in Todd, 1904). In the fall of 1900, from August 27 to September 25, I saw only a few golden plover in the Erie region and took but two specimens, both young birds. R. B. Simpson saw three as late in the season as November 18 in 1902, but this was doubtless exceptional. Recent records from Presque Isle are as follows: September 30, 1932, four (Beardslee); September 13, 1933, two (Simpson); November 3, 1934, one (Dilley). S. J. Seiple reports a single bird seen near Linesville on October 8, 1938.

The only definite spring record pertains to a

bird shot by G. E. Welshons near Conneaut Lake on the unbelievably early date of March 17,[1] 1912, as recorded by G. M. Sutton, who gives also a fall date (September 16, 1926) for Conneaut Marsh. H. C. Kirkpatrick saw two birds in a plowed field just east of Meadville on May 1, 1898, which he believed were Golden Plover, but as they were not taken it is possible that they were Black-bellied Plover instead, and they are so recorded by Dr. Sutton.

Charadrius dominicus Warren, *Birds Pa.*, ed. 2, 1890, 98 (Erie, Erie Co., transient)—Todd, *Ann. Carnegie Mus.*, 1904, 2:548 (Erie and Presque Isle, Erie Co., transient).
"Golden Plover" Simpson, *Oölogist*, 1911, 28:143; and 1913, 30:150 (Presque Isle, Erie Co., fall).
Pluvialis dominica dominica Sutton, *Ann. Carnegie Mus.*, 1928, 18:110 (Conneaut Lake, Crawford Co., transient).

[1]Almost certainly an error for May 17.

BLACK-BELLIED PLOVER

SQUATAROLA SQUATAROLA (Linnaeus)

Description—A large plover, about the size of a domestic pigeon. *Adult:* upperparts grayish white, mottled and barred with black; tail also barred with black and white, but its *upper coverts nearly pure white;* wings dusky black, with a white stripe across the middle, obvious in flight; top of head mottled with gray; forehead, sides of crown, sides of neck, and a large area on the upper side of the breast, pure white; lower abdomen, flanks, and under tail coverts, pure white; rest of underparts deep black, extending to the eyes and base of the bill; *axillaries black*, but under wing coverts white; bill and feet black. *Fall adults* usually have numerous white feathers intermixed on the underparts, and some grayish feathers of the winter plumage on the upperparts. *Immature* very different: upperparts mottled with black and buff or white; the top of the head similarly marked; wings and tail much as in the adult; underparts white; forehead, sides of head, hindneck, breast, and sides, more or less streaked with gray; *axillaries black;* bill and feet black. The larger size, lighter general coloration, black axillaries (conspicuous in flight), and in particular the *white upper tail coverts* (also conspicuous in flight) are good field marks wherewith to distinguish this species from the Golden Plover.

Range—The Black-bellied Plover is an arctic-breeding species in both hemispheres, but does not go so far south in the winter as the Golden Plover; some individuals indeed do not pass beyond the Gulf coast at that season. Moreover, in migration, this species is not so closely restricted to certain routes but spreads out more evenly over the country. At the present time it is much commoner in the interior generally, particularly during the fall movement, than is the Golden Plover. With us it is rare away from the shores of the larger bodies of water, which are attractive resting and feeding grounds en route. Thus Presque Isle is naturally a favorite resort, and is one place in our region where the species is fairly common and regular, particularly in the fall. Pymatuning Lake is attracting an increasing number of shore birds every year, the Black-bellied Plover included. R. B. Simpson has but two records for Warren County. D. A. Atkinson writes that one bird was shot at Verona in Allegheny County on September 18, 1893, and another at Neville Island on April 26, 1894. I have seen the species only twice in Beaver County, on both occasions at the mouth of the Beaver River, in September. There is also a Centre County record (Harlow, 1911). The evidence shows that the birds migrating by way of Lake Erie apparently do not need to stop over anywhere else on their southward way and do so only sporadically.

Migration—When I wrote my "Birds of Erie and Presque Isle" in 1904 I could cite no certain spring records for this species from that region, but several May records (May 19–31) are now available. At Pymatuning Lake the Black-bellied Plover has been noted from May 18 to June 2 (Fricke). Other spring records are as follows: Neville Island, Allegheny County, April 26, 1894 (Atkinson); near Meadville, May 1, 1898 (Kirkpatrick); and Conneaut Lake, April 6, 1914 (Welshons). This last date is almost certainly an error in transcription, since it seems far too early.[2] Fall records are much more numerous and satis-

[2]Compare W. W. Cooke, U. S. Department of Agriculture, Biological Survey, *Bulletin*, no. 35, 1910, p. 78.

factory. The species has been known to appear at that season on Presque Isle as early as August 1 (1890), "but ordinarily it does not arrive until about the middle of the month, attaining its greatest abundance in September, and remaining often through the greater part of October, and sometimes even later (November 10, 1894)" (Todd, 1904). Earliest and latest fall dates at Pymatuning are August 20 (1935) and October 23 (1936). Mr. Simpson has noted it at Warren also in August (August 24, 1901), and at Garland, Warren County, as late as October 24 (1907). All other known records are in September.

Habits—I first became acquainted with this plover on September 7, 1891, when I luckily secured a single immature specimen along the Ohio River. On September 27, 1899, two more were taken at the same spot. The thing that impressed me most at the time was the tameness of the birds—a lack of fear that was in surprising contrast with the behavior of some of the smaller shore birds. Later on, after having observed and collected many more individuals on Presque Isle, I learned that this apparent stupidity was peculiar to the young and unsophisticated birds that had come down from the North and were encountering human beings for perhaps the first time. Sad experience would teach the survivors much, and the passing of another year would find them as shy as their older companions. I know of no warier and more unapproachable shore bird than the adult Black-bellied Plover, unless it be the Long-billed Curlew of the western plains. Living as it does on the flat, open beaches that command a wide view in every direction, it is able to descry potential danger from afar. Young birds by themselves are easily approached, but a single old bird with them, alert and uneasy, suffices to put the whole flock on its guard, and long before one can come within range they are all off in the trail of their monitor. Practically the only opportunity one has of securing adults for specimens is when they unwittingly fly past, or when decoys are used.

In its general behavior this species is typically plover-like. It is a swift, strong flier, and flocks usually spread out upon alighting. The birds when feeding run for a little distance, then stop abruptly to pick up food, and proceed as before. At rest they are dignified in mien and statuesque in pose, an entire flock sometimes remaining motionless together when suspicious of danger. On Presque Isle we used to find them on the outside beach in small groups; occasionally we would find one bird only, or a few associating with other shore birds. They have been seen also in the plowed fields of the mainland during migration. Immature birds far outnumber the adults at this season. Their usual and characteristic call is a mellow, plaintive *pee-oo-ee*, which is easy to imitate by whistling, and which has a carrying quality that reveals the presence of the birds even when they are still too far off to be seen. Occasionally by imitating this call I have induced young birds to come very close.

Charadrius squatarola WARREN, *Birds Pa.*, ed. 2, 1890, 97 (Lake Erie, Erie Co.; Clinton Co., transient, *fide* Van Fleet) —RHOADS, *Auk*, 1899, 16:310 (Neville Island, Allegheny Co., April, *fide* Atkinson).

Squatarola squatarola TODD, *Ann. Carnegie Mus.*, 1904, 2:548 (Erie and Presque Isle, Erie Co., transient)—TODD, in Bausman, *Hist. Beaver Co., Pa.*, 1904, 2:1199 (Beaver Co., fall transient)—WEST, *Redstart*, 1936, 4:4 (Pymatuning Lake, Crawford Co., October).

"Black-bellied Plover" HARLOW, *Auk*, 1911, 28:484 ([Center Furnace], Centre Co., September)—SIMPSON, *Oölogist*, 1912, 29:247 (Presque Isle, Erie Co., May)—SUTTON, *Bird-Lore*, 1924, 26:418 (Presque Isle, Erie Co., September, *fide* Allen) —BOULTON, *Bird-Lore*, 1928, 30:401 (Presque Isle, Erie Co., August).

Squatarola squatarola cynosuræ SUTTON, *Ann. Carnegie Mus.*, 1928, 18:109 (Crawford Co., transient).

RUDDY TURNSTONE

ARENARIA INTERPRES MORINELLA (Linnaeus)

Description—A stocky, short-legged shore bird with pointed bill and bright *orange-red feet;* in size a little smaller than the Killdeer. *Spring adult: upperparts* varied with *black, white, and bright rufous cinnamon;* the wings with a white band; *rump and longer upper tail coverts white, separated by a dark band;* head mostly white, but with dark streaks on the crown and a black band running up from the sides of the throat to under the eye, and thence across the forehead, leaving a *large white spot at the base of the bill;* middle of the throat white, and sides of the neck mostly white, with a black wedge joining the black area of the breast; rest of underparts white. *Adult in fall* similar, but color pattern less distinct, and rufous-cinnamon color duller. *Young in fall* similar, but rufous-cinnamon color of upperparts virtually wanting, and color pattern less sharply defined. The reddish feet and the white rump and tail coverts, with the dark band between, will serve to distinguish the species at any time or in any plumage.

Range and migration—The Ruddy Turnstone is the American representative of a well-known holarctic species. It breeds in the far North and winters from the Gulf coast to southern Brazil and Chile. During migration it prefers the sea-coast, but some individuals traverse the interior of the country and regularly visit the shores of the Great Lakes. At Erie, where it favors the outside beach of Presque Isle, the Turnstone is a regular but not common transient in the fall, and it has been observed intermittently in the spring as well. It is a late migrant at the latter season. W. M. Guynes has not seen it on Presque Isle earlier than May 15 (1932), and most of the available records from that locality occur in the last week of that month or in the early part of June. In 1932 R. B. Simpson saw five turnstones on the outside beach as late as June 10. The same observer also noted the species at Warren on May 30, 1907, and on May 24, 1925.

Spring records for Pymatuning Lake lie between May 8 and May 30; in 1937 as many as seventy-five birds were seen on May 24 (Fricke). G. M. Sutton cites a few records from Conneaut Lake between May 16 and 28. He thinks that the apparent absence of the species there in the fall may be because it passes over without stopping, while its spring flight is possibly less hurried. One would rather expect the reverse to be true. Most shore birds have a longer migration period in the fall than in the spring and are more numerous at the former season, since their numbers are then augmented by the young. This is the case with the Turnstone, which has been known to reach Presque Isle as early as August 11 (1896) or 12 (1928) and to remain as late as September 25 (1900). Corresponding dates for Pymatuning Lake are August 16 (1930) and October 9 (1933), according to S. J. Seiple. O. P. Medsger writes that the species has been noted at McClure, Fayette County, by one of his correspondents, a Mr. Templeton. It has not yet been detected along the Ohio River or elsewhere in the interior counties. Its common name is an allusion to its habit of turning over small pebbles on the beaches in its search for food.

Arenaria interpres WARREN, *Birds Pa.*, 1888, 237; and ed. 2, 1890, 103 (Erie [Presque Isle], Erie Co., transient, *fide* Sennett).

Arenaria morinella TODD, *Ann. Carnegie Mus.*, 1904, 2:550 (Presque Isle, Erie Co., transient).

"Turnstone" SIMPSON, *Oölogist*, 1907, 24:133 (Warren, Warren Co., May); 1912, 29:250, 350 (Presque Isle, Erie Co., June).

Arenaria interpres morinella SUTTON, *Ann. Carnegie Mus.* 1928, 18:112 (Conneaut Lake, Crawford Co., May, *fide* Langdon and Kirkpatrick)—CHRISTY, *Cardinal*, 1933, 3:147 (Geneva, Crawford Co., May).

"Ruddy Turnstone" SUTTON, *Bird-Lore*, 1924, 26:418 (Presque Isle, Erie Co., August and September, *fide* Allen)—SEIPLE, *Auk*, 1931, 48:113 (Pymatuning Swamp, Crawford Co., August)—BOGGS, *Redstart*, 1936, 3:92 (Presque Isle, Erie Co., June).

WOODCOCK, SNIPE, SANDPIPERS

FAMILY SCOLOPACIDAE

THE SCOLOPACIDAE are among the most widely distributed of bird families. Most of them breed in northern regions and migrate far southward in winter. With few exceptions they are rarely found far from water. They differ from their close relatives, the Charadriidae, in the characters of the bill and feet: the bill is slender and grooved; the tarsi are scutellate (except on the sides), and the hind toe is commonly present.

Twenty-five representatives of this family are recorded from western Pennsylvania, but only a few of this number breed in the area. They are most commonly observed in spring and fall, when they occur in large flocks on sandy beaches and mud flats. There they wade in shallow water and probe in the soft mud for food. The sexes, with rare exceptions, are alike in color, although the female is usually a little larger. Seasonal plumage in many species is strongly marked, the breeding dress being entirely different from that worn during the rest of the year.[1] The eggs are usually four in number, mottled, and ovate pyriform in shape. The young are covered with down and are able to run about when hatched.

Arquatella maritima, the Purple Sandpiper, which I admitted to my Erie list on the basis of Sennett's alleged record quoted by Warren, I am now satisfied should be expunged. *Numenius americanus americanus*, the Long-billed Curlew, and *Limosa haemastica*, the Hudsonian Godwit, may possibly occur as stragglers in our region.

[1]For a concise discussion of the identification of shore birds in the field see J. T. NICHOLS, *Cardinal*, 1931, 3:23–33.

AMERICAN WOODCOCK

PHILOHELA MINOR (Gmelin)

Description—Larger than the Robin; bill two and a half to three inches long; *eyes large, placed far back.* Upperparts grayish brown with black mottling; top and back of the *head black with grayish crossbars;* front and sides of the head grayish, with a dark streak from the eye to the bill and another across the ear coverts to the nape; *underparts rusty buff*, the chin whitish; wings plain dusky; tail black, the feathers with grayish or whitish tips. In fresh fall plumage the general coloration is rusty below and brownish above. *Downy young:* upperparts mottled with two shades of brown; top of head deep chocolate brown; a deep brown stripe behind the eyes and another from the eye to the bill; underparts pale dull brown.

Range—The American Woodcock is confined to the eastern United States and southern Canada. It ranges westward to the Mississippi Valley and winters in the southern part of its general range.

A bird of decidedly southern predilections, it does not invade the Canadian Life Zone to any great extent. Western Pennsylvania lies well within its general range, and there are no parts of this area where the Woodcock may not be found at one season or another, although its numbers are dwindling. Eggs or young birds have been found at such widely separated points as Presque Isle, Waynesburg, and Charter Oak in Huntingdon County. There are several nesting records, indeed, for the thickly populated county of Allegheny, and although I have never actually observed the bird in Beaver County in the breeding season I am satisfied that it must also nest there occasionally. Some hitherto unpublished breeding localities are as follows: Buffalo Creek region, Armstrong and Butler counties (Todd); Springs, Somerset County (Miller); DuBois (Van Fleet); Warren (Simpson); Wolf Creek, west of Forestville, Butler County (Keesler); New Hamburg, Mercer County (Homer); Uniontown (Gordon). Still others of a potential nature could be cited, but those given will suffice to indicate the general distribution of breeding woodcock in our region. There are certain places, however, that naturally offer peculiar attractions to the species. One of these is Pymatuning Swamp, which must always have been a favorite resort for this bog-loving bird. I found it very common there in 1895, but it is much less numerous now. During migration it is likely to be found in unexpected places, and in suitable covert is always more numerous at such times.

Migration—The Woodcock is as hardy as the Killdeer and, like it, has been known to winter in our region. J. S. Nease saw it during the winter at Washington. C. A. Bergstrom noted one bird near Shermansville, Crawford County, from January 4 to 6, 1932. W. J. Delansky wrote G. M. Sutton that several remained in eastern Centre County (along Little Beaver Run, in Woodward and Decatur townships), during the winter of 1926–27. With the mild winters that have prevailed in recent years, these instances may not be so exceptional as they might seem. At any rate, the Woodcock is one of our early migrants in the spring, appearing on the scene in March with the Killdeer and certain land birds. Early dates of its arrival are: Frick Park, Pittsburgh, March 6 (Malley); Waynesburg, March 5 (Jacobs); Latrobe, March 13 (Townsend); State College, March 9 (Harlow); Renovo, March 13 (Pierce); Conneaut Lake, March 8 (Bergstrom); Warren, March 19 (Simpson); Erie, March 23 (Bacon). In the fall some movement is apparent by August, but not until September is any true migration in progress, and the last individuals leave for the South in November. "Last-seen" dates may be quoted thus: Erie, November 14 (Bacon); Conneaut Lake, November 28 (Welshons); Raccoon Creek, Beaver County, November 28 (Todd); Rector, Westmoreland County, November 5 (Fricke); Renovo, November 8 (Pierce); Lambertsville, Somerset County, November 13 (Mostoller).

Habits—The Woodcock is an aberrant shore bird—one whose ancestors must long ago have forsaken their original habitat and taken to the woods. Such a radical change in habit and environment necessitated a change also in coloration and even in structure. As we know it today, the Woodcock is an inhabitant of alder swamps and boggy woods, where it seems perfectly adapted to its surroundings. Its long, sensitive bill, fitted for probing in the soft mud and earth; its large eyes, set far back in the head; and its dark-colored plumage, harmonizing with the dry leaves and bare ground, are all adaptive modifications of the normal limicoline type. The unusual nature of its chosen haunts, its peculiar feeding habits, and above all its remarkable aerial and vocal performances in the mating season, combine to make the Woodcock a most interesting bird.

B. H. Christy writes: "The Woodcock has been too ruthlessly hunted and is no longer a common bird. Furthermore, it is of nocturnal, or at least crepuscular, habit. For these two reasons it is seldom seen. In autumn the rural wanderer will occasionally flush one or two of these birds singly from some damp patch of bottomland in a wooded ravine. On such occasions the bird rises suddenly and swiftly on shrill, whistling wings. It springs up at a very steep angle, almost vertically, to a height greater than the undergrowth, and then darts away and is lost to view in the woods.

"In the springtime it is not difficult to see a male woodcock, or at least to hear him, in the performance of his 'sky-dance.' Search out a damp, open place near woodland, where some little spring has softened a patch of clayey soil and where grasses or sedges grow in tussocks. Near such a place, on an evening in April or May, lie in wait as the twilight fades to dusk. Presently you will hear from the darkened ground a loud, rasping note, hardly to be distinguished from the Nighthawk's familiar cry. This note, repeated at intervals of a few seconds, is now loud and again faint, as the bird turns about and faces one way and then another. After a longer period of silence than usual between calls, another sound will be heard. It will come from a greater distance, and from another quarter: a shrill, sustained note of whistling wings. You will perhaps hesitate to identify this with the bird that has been crying from the ground. The whistling rises in pitch as the flier swings toward you, and then, if your eyes are sharp, you may catch a glimpse of his chunky form and even of his long bill in silhouette against the pale sky. On he flies in a series of wide, whistling spirals, climbing as he goes. At an elevation of perhaps a hundred feet the whistling becomes discontinuous, breaks into hurried spurts, and finally ceases. And then a third and still different sound falls from the sky—a wild and yet measured chirruping. If you have succeeded in following the performer with your eye, you will see him now actually staggering in his random flight, as he pours out his simple song. It lasts only a few seconds, and then the bird comes darting and tumbling silently to earth again, there to resume his first harsh calling. This singular performance will be repeated at brief intervals well into the darkness of night."

A very similar account is given by Samuel Scoville, Jr. (1920). This observer reports a peculiar bubble-like note, "exactly like that made by pouring water out of a bottle," uttered just before the *scaap* or nighthawk-like sound. Dr. Sutton describes the same note, likening it to the gulping sound made in swallowing water. Sometimes this note is given alone. The entire performance occupies about a minute; it is repeated over and over until darkness settles down over the scene, and is resumed again in the early morning twilight. On bright moonlight nights it may even continue at intervals through the intervening hours. The "sky-dance" indicates certainly that there is a nest close at hand, whether it be easy to find or not.

Arriving early in the spring, the Woodcock loses little time in preparing for family responsibilities. Nests with eggs (already well incubated) have been found as early as April 6 (Burleigh). Most of the nestings reported have been in April, but some in May indicate a variation in the time. There is also much variation in the site, but it is usually a drier place than the feeding grounds proper, or at least above the flood level. "A favorite nesting site is a dry bushy knoll in marshy ground" (Jacobs, 1893), or at the base of a small tree.

The nest itself is a simple affair—merely a hollowed-out depression in the ground, lined with dry leaves or grasses collected near by. The parent bird sits very closely indeed, and so well does it match its surroundings that it is hard to discern even when one knows exactly where to look. As is usual among the shore birds, the eggs are four in number, but the shape is ovate rather than pyriform. They average 1.50 by 1.15 inches. In color they are pale dull buff (pale pinkish cinnamon to pale vinous buff), rather sparsely spotted with wood brown and with paler shell-markings. In some cases the ground-color is somewhat deeper in tone. The period of incubation is said to be twenty or twenty-one days. The young are odd-looking little fellows, covered with down of two shades of reddish brown; they are soon able to run about and utter a weak, peeping cry. R. B. Simpson writes of meeting a family group of these birds along Jackson Run, Warren County: "On one occasion, in the midst of a woodland tract, I came upon an old woodcock leading her four young along. They were proceeding 'Indian file,' with bills pointing down. As I rushed at them the parent bird flew a few yards, while the young disappeared like magic, and I could not find even a single one. After I had sat quietly for a little time the old one came walking back, whereupon the young seemed to spring up as if out of the ground itself, and the whole procession again moved on. When I rushed out a second time the performance was repeated, and then I left them."

Although shy by nature and shunning open spaces and the houses and cultivations of man, woodcock sometimes, in seasons of exceptional drought when their usual haunts dry up, resort to gardens and lawns in search of subsistence. They have been seen under such circumstances within the city limits of Pittsburgh. Witness the following from the pen of Norman McClintock (1931):

"I visited Mr. Kernohan's place [in Shadyside, Pittsburgh] on August 10 and saw one Woodcock feeding on the lawn at the rear of the house. This lawn is surrounded on three sides by shrubbery and flowers, and these provided a shelter and retreat for the birds. This lawn was well watered and the Woodcocks had no trouble in securing a constant supply of angleworms, which were the only food I saw them take.

"The method of locating the worms by the Woodcocks interested me greatly, and differed altogether from the method of the Robins which were at the time feeding close by. The conditions for observations were ideal, for the light was good, and I was able to watch the bird for a number of hours, at a range of about twenty-five feet, with the assistance of a pair of eight-power binoculars.

"Most of the bird's movements were very deliberate, and I gained the distinct impression that the angleworms were located by the sense of feeling, through the feet. The Woodcock, while walking slowly, threw one foot well in advance of its body and apparently pressed this foot against the ground with an alternately light and stronger pressure. The result of this peculiar pressing movement of the feet produced the well-known teetering movement of the Woodcock's body. I watched this feeding for some time on two successive days, and could not escape the conclusion that the bird first located the worms by feeling, through its feet, and then followed this by probing with its bill."

S. E. Bacon (in Todd, 1904) had this to say of this species in the Erie region: "Erie County contains some very good Woodcock ground for both summer and fall shooting. In favorable seasons a good many broods are raised in the vicinity of Erie, particularly on the Peninsula. As a rule they are well grown by the first of July, but I have seen young birds at that time scarcely able to fly. A single Woodcock may happen to be found almost anywhere, particularly during the fall migration. For instance, such places as a fence-row, cornfield, brier-patch, orchard or thicket may harbor a single bird, but to find any number together it is necessary to traverse a growth of young poplars, and if such be overrun with goldenrod it is all the more apt to prove a favorite haunt. In such a spot, during the migration, a dozen birds may be killed, apparently depopulating the place, and yet the next day there may be as many birds as ever, the result of an influx during the intervening night. In large tracts of second-growth there are often found particular spots, seemingly no better for Woodcock than a hundred other similar places, where the birds will be found with certainty day after day, unless, indeed, the ground be flooded."

Mr. Simpson states that in Warren County in the fall, if the weather is quite dry, as it often is, woodcock gather along the valley and are sometimes fairly common in the willows along the Allegheny River.

Ruthless shooting of this interesting game bird, during the migration and in its winter quarters in the southern states, has reduced its numbers to a tithe of what they once were, even within my memory. Faced with a great many natural enemies, the Woodcock deserves the benefit of complete protection until it can recuperate and perhaps regain its quondam abundance.

Philohela minor TOWNSEND, *Proc. Acad. Nat. Sci. Philadelphia*, 1883, 67 (Latrobe, Westmoreland Co.)—TEULON, *Jour. Boston Zoöl. Soc.*, 1883, 2:11 (Bradford, McKean Co., summer)—JAMISON, *Ornithologist and Oölogist*, 1888, 13:134 (Cresson, Cambria Co., June)—WARREN, *Birds Pa.*, ed. 2, 1890, 78 (Erie, Crawford, Clarion, and Venango Co.)—JACOBS, *Summer Birds Greene Co., Pa.*, 1893, 5 (Greene Co., nesting)—BAILY, *Auk*, 1896, 13:291, 292 (Williamsville, Elk Co., June–July)—COPE, *Cassinia*, 1902, 5:13 (Tamarack Swamp, Clinton Co., June)—TODD, *Ann. Carnegie Mus.*, 1904, 2:536 (Erie and Presque Isle, Erie Co., summer)—TODD, in Bausman, *Hist. Beaver Co., Pa.*, 1904, 2:1198 (Beaver Co., summer?)—KEIM, *Cassinia*, 1905, 8:37 (Port Allegany, McKean Co., summer)—COOKE, *Bull. Biol. Surv.* no. 35, 1910, 21 (Renovo, Clinton Co., migration)—HARLOW, *Auk*, 1912, 29:469 ("Stone Valley," Huntingdon Co., and Bear Meadows, Centre Co., summer); 1918, 35:22 (Charter Oak, Huntingdon Co., nesting)—STONE, *Cassinia*, 1919, 22:30; and 1920, 23:31 (Altoona, Blair Co., nesting, *fide* McGraw)—CHRISTY, *Cardinal*, 1923, v. 1, no. 1, [p. 3] (Sewickley, Allegheny Co., migrant, rare in summer)—BURLEIGH, *Wilson Bull.*, 1923, 35:84 (Oakmont and Harmarville, Allegheny Co., nesting); 1924, 36:70 (State College, Centre Co., migration); 1931, 43:38 (Charter Oak, Huntingdon Co., nesting)—PETTINGILL, *Mem. Boston Soc. Nat. Hist.*, 1936, 9:185, 225 (w. Pa. records).

"Woodcock" JACOBS, *Oölogist*, 1887, 4:74 ("Waynesboro" [Waynesburg], Greene Co., nesting)—JACOBS, *Hoosier Nat.*, 1887, 2:78 (Waynesburg, Greene Co., breeding)—STONE, *Cassinia*, 1906, 9:44 (Scrub Ridge, west of McConnellsburg,

Fulton Co., June)—SIMPSON, *Oölogist*, 1912, 29:329 (head of Tionesta Creek, Warren Co., summer)—[SANSOM], *In the Open*, May–June, 1914, 4:46 (pl.) (Oakmont, Allegheny Co., nesting, *fide* Thomas)—DICKEY, *Oölogist*, 1914, 31:171 ("Stone Valley," Huntingdon Co., nesting)—MILLER, *Oölogist*, 1919, 36:155 (Charter Oak, Huntingdon Co., nesting)—SCOVILLE, *Cassinia*, 1920, 23:20 (Charter Oak, Huntingdon Co., May; habits)—MCCLELLAND, *Am. Mid. Nat.*, 1922, 8:36 (Washington, Washington Co., May)—SUTTON, *Bird-Lore*, 1924, 26:267 (Greenville, Mercer Co., breeding, *fide* Homer)—[CHRISTY], *Cardinal*, 1924, v. 1, no. 4, p. 21 (Trafford, Westmoreland Co., nesting)—DICKEY, *Nature Mag.*, Sept., 1926, 176 (Juniata River, central Pa., nesting)—EASTWOOD, *Bird-Lore*, 1926, 28:196 ("Slack Hollow," Pittsburgh, Allegheny Co., March–April, *fide* Grimm), 274 (Sandy Lake, Mercer Co., May, *fide* Squier)—BOULTON, *Bird-Lore*, 1928, 30:14 (Rector, Westmoreland Co., November, *fide* Fricke), 196 ("Slack Hollow," Pittsburgh, Allegheny Co., April, *fide* Grimm)—HEGNER and CHRISTY, *Cardinal*, 1931, 3:22 (North Park, along "Deer" [Pine] Creek, Allegheny Co., May)—[CHRISTY, ed.], *Cardinal*, 1933, 3:150 (Wexford, Allegheny Co., nesting, *fide* Auerswald)—COPE and HAWKINS, *Forest Leaves*, 1934, 24:26 (E. Tionesta Forest Reserve, Warren and McKean Co., summer)—TRIMBLE, *Cardinal*, 1937, 4:107 (Pymatuning region, Crawford Co., breeding).

Rubicola minor BENT, *Bull. U. S. Nat. Mus.* no. 142, 1927, 61 (Pa. migration dates)—SUTTON, *Ann. Carnegie Mus.*, 1928, 18:96 (Crawford Co. records and references).

Rusticola minor CHRISTY, *Cardinal*, 1931, 3:13 (Pittsburgh and Edgeworth, Allegheny Co.; habits).

WILSON'S SNIPE

CAPELLA DELICATA (Ord)

Description—Somewhat larger than the Robin; head larger in proportion; eyes set rather far back; bill slender, straight, about two and a half inches long. *Adult:* top of head blackish, with a pale median stripe; upperparts blackish, with rusty spots and bars, and with *conspicuous lengthwise buffy stripes on the scapulars;* wings plain dusky, with pale outer edge; tail rounded, blackish, most of the feathers with broad rufous subterminal bands and buffy tips, the outer feathers barred with black and white; throat and broad stripe over the eye, plain buffy white; breast and sides of the head and neck mottled with brown on a buffy-brown background; abdomen pure white; the sides, flanks, axillaries, and under tail coverts irregularly barred with black and white; bill greenish gray, with darker tip; feet also greenish gray. In fall and winter plumage the colors are richer and deeper; the pale stripes on the scapulars are wider; and the markings on the underparts are blended. *Downy young:* upperparts rich tawny brown, mottled with black; feather-tips silvery-white; some black stripes on the head; breast tawny brown, the throat paler, the rest of the underparts duller and more buffy.

Range—Not only does Wilson's Snipe go much farther north in summer and much farther south in winter than the American Woodcock, but its range at both seasons is also transcontinental. The majority of the birds nest in the Hudsonian and Canadian life zones, but some few habitually pass the summer considerably to the southward of these limits. Whether these outlying colonies are relicts of a former general distribution that included this region, or whether they represent a comparatively recent influx from farther north, under favorable local conditions, is not clear. At any rate, the records of breeding in our region all come from the northwestern counties, to which so many other water birds on our list are virtually confined. These records are not so isolated as has been supposed, since they are approximated by others from western New York[1] and northern Ohio.[2]

During the season of migration this species is irregularly common in that part of our region lying west of the Allegheny River and Laurel Hill, and somewhat less so in the ridge and valley section. It avoids the higher elevations—not so much perhaps for topographical as for ecological reasons. Almost every year I see a few snipe in Beaver County in certain restricted spots, and other observers report them from adjacent areas. But to see snipe in any numbers one must go to the flatter country north of the terminal moraine, where the marshy conditions are more to their liking. There they pass through in spring and fall in varying abundance, and a few are likely to remain behind to breed and to winter. The credit for finding the first nest of Wilson's Snipe in this section goes to Edgar Huidekoper of Meadville, whose published account appeared in 1877. The exact locality of this find, according to H. C. Kirkpatrick, was in

[1]E. H. EATON, *Birds of New York*, 1910, 1:301.
[2]L. E. HICKS, *Wilson Bulletin*, 1933, 44:181.

Conneaut Marsh, a little west of the Erie Railroad, near Geneva, and the date was May 13, 1875. Unquestionably this was the basis for Warren's statement, attributed to Sennett, that the species had bred in Crawford County. Warren gives also a circumstantial account of a nest found near the Erie County poorhouse (three miles west of Erie), and although this record appears worthy of credence I am quite unable to follow him in his implication that the species is a summer resident in Beaver County also. In July, 1933, however, I traced it southward to Gardner Swamp, near New Castle, Lawrence County, where I suspect it must breed. So little field work has been done in the swamps of Mercer County that its breeding there can only be surmised.

With this species, as with certain other shore birds, occurrence in summer does not necessarily imply breeding. S. S. Dickey writes that on May 30, 1925, he flushed a snipe from an extensive cattail swamp near Clarendon, Warren County. Some years ago S. E. Bacon informed me that G. C. Russell had found a nest containing four eggs near Lake Pleasant, Erie County, about 1892. One would expect to find the species breeding on Presque Isle, if anywhere in Erie County, but while it has been noted there in early and late June by R. B. Simpson, there is as yet no positive breeding record. The Pymatuning Swamp area in Crawford County seems to be in peculiar favor as a nesting ground, but even there the species may fluctuate in numbers, and in dry seasons it may be entirely absent. G. M. Sutton, to whom we are indebted for an elaborate account of the nesting habits of Wilson's Snipe in this region, regards the species as extremely susceptible to local conditions.

Migration—As hardy as the Woodcock, Wilson's Snipe is but little behind that species in the spring migration; it pushes its way northward as soon as winter loosens its grip on the marshes, and areas of open water begin to appear around the edges. Often arriving before the ice has all melted, it usually finds some unfrozen ground around springheads and little sluggish streams. B. H. Christy has seen it at Clinton Pond, Allegheny County, as early as March 19 (1923) and 24 (1929). In Crawford County it has been noted at Meadville by Mr. Kirkpatrick almost as early—March 22 (1894)—and at Shermansville by C. A. Bergstrom on March 8 (1925). This latter date is early enough to pertain to a wintering individual.

Mr. Bacon (in Todd, 1904) has this to say of the spring migration in Erie County: "From my notes on the migration of this species, covering over ten years, I find that the date of its arrival on an average falls in the last week in March, March 13 (1903) being the earliest and April 10 (1896) the latest date respectively. The bulk of the birds pass through in April, and not a few linger into the following month for a week or more, or until May 7 (1892 and 1898) to May 17 (1894)." For the mountain section there are also a few scattered March dates: State College, March 18, 1911 (Harlow); Altoona, March 23, 1919 (McGraw); Renovo, March 27, 1910 (Pierce); Port Allegany, McKean County, March 21, 1924 (Abbott). Mr. Bacon's statement that at Erie the majority of birds pass through in April and that the last stragglers do not leave until May applies as well to our region in general. Latest spring dates of record are as follows: Clinton Pond, Allegheny County, May 10, 1928 (Christy); Beaver, May 19, 1899 (Todd); Warren, May 14, 1892, and May 30, 1925 (Simpson); Hollidaysburg, May 13, 1920 (Berg); State College, May 7, 1916 (Burleigh); Indiana, May 9, 1934 (Smyth). It appears, therefore, that northward migration is still in progress long after the summer residents are settled for the season.

The return movement begins in August, is in full swing by September, and does not finally cease until November. Mr. Bacon noted the first fall snipe at Erie on August 18 in 1896, and I have seen the species along the Ohio River still earlier—on August 13 (1891). P. W. Roth took one snipe at Conneauttee Lake, Erie County, on August 27, 1895. Some of the late fall records are as follows: Erie, November 21, 1899 (Bacon); Warren, November 28, 1889 (Simpson); Forestville, Butler County, November 29, 1921 (Keesler). Local observers report that snipe, weather permitting, not infrequently pass the winter at Pymatuning Swamp. They have been reported late in December from Mercer County (Homer), and in January from Harmarville, Allegheny County (Sutton). R. C. Harlow and T. D. Burleigh both record the species as wintering at State College during 1908–9 and 1916–17. As many as nine individuals together were noted there on one occasion. We do not know the origin of either the summering or the wintering birds, or whether they come from far or near. It would be interesting to learn the whereabouts of both these groups at other seasons. It is significant that some individuals of this species pass the winter in this latitude, while others go all the way to South America.

Habits—Wilson's Snipe does not associate to any extent with the other shore birds, with which indeed it has little in common. In general habits it is somewhat like the Woodcock, but it avoids the wet woodlands to which that bird is partial, as well as the sandy beaches and mud flats where the other shore birds congregate. Less secretive than the rails, but fully as mysterious, it requires cover of a sort for its operations. Thus during its sojourn with us it favors marshy meadows, muddy ditches, the weedy margins of ponds, and low, partly overflowed fields, where it finds both suitable food and the bit of shelter that it needs. In the fall I used to encounter it along the Ohio River in a tract of semiaquatic plants (water willows) on the beach.

Invasion of its haunts means a characteristic introduction to this interesting bird, whose erratic occurrences, peculiar behavior, and odd manner of flight are well worth investigation. In surroundings where a pair of killdeers could scarcely hope to escape notice, numbers of snipe might remain undetected. But if startled by the close approach of an intruder, a snipe might, with startling suddenness and a rasping, nasal cry, spring up almost from underfoot and fly away in erratic fashion, twisting and doubling in sharp and unexpected turns, to drop down suddenly in some other part of the marsh, or perhaps even to disappear from view. I have often watched a single snipe, flushed in such circumstances, rise to a great height and fly around in a wide circle, as if seeking to locate some other suitable landing point, only to return at last and pitch down within a few yards of where it had arisen. After marking the spot carefully, I have tried to approach with caution, hoping to descry the object of my interest before it would flush again, but I have always failed in the search. A snipe crouching among dry rushes or other aquatic plants is nearly invisible to human eyes, so well do its general color and stripes melt into the background. Often a snipe upon alighting will run a little way before squatting and thus give the observer a wrong impression of its position. Very little cover is required to conceal a snipe effectually, so long as it elects to remain quiet. Once it is on the wing, its zigzag flight is of course its greatest protection.

Snipe migrate by night and feed by day. They are found singly or in twos or threes, and sometimes fly in loose, straggling flocks or "wisps." They are more active in cloudy weather, and in the morning and evening, than at other times. In their movements and appearances they are most

erratic; they will be here today and gone tomorrow, all having departed during the intervening night. On the other hand, I have known what was presumably the same group to loiter in one spot for more than a week. They feed largely upon earthworms, for which they probe in the soft mud and ooze with a nervous, jerky motion of their long, sensitive bills. Beetles and other insects are also eaten, as well as some seeds and roots of aquatic plants.

The flesh of this snipe, being tender and well flavored, is much prized by epicures, so that these birds have long been an object of pursuit by sportsmen. Indeed, their manner of flight demands great skill to bring them down. When spring shooting was in vogue, good bags could sometimes be made in certain localities where snipe were most numerous, but elsewhere their pursuit has never been profitable. Mr. Bacon, who used to hunt them assiduously in Erie County, says (in Todd, 1904): "The county in general, and the lake shore plain in particular, contain much excellent snipe ground in the spring, but in the fall the fields are seldom flooded, and being very grassy, do not furnish inducements for the birds to alight. The Peninsula on the contrary is better ground in the fall than at the other season, as the close of winter finds the edges of the ponds so bare that there is no cover for even a snipe." Mr. Kirkpatrick writes that the extensive tracts of wet, grassy meadows along Conneaut Outlet (Crawford County) are favorite snipe grounds and that many birds used to be shot there in the spring. Shooting at this season is of course indefensible, and its abolition has been a step in the right direction.

The reader who wishes a full account of the courtship and nesting habits of this species should read Dr. Sutton's article (1923), of which only an abstract can be given here. His observations were made at Pymatuning Swamp, mainly in the vicinity of Hartstown, during the seasons of 1922 and 1923. From the very beginning of spring, Wilson's snipe were much in evidence, and their aerial courtship flights were observed daily during early May. A few birds could be seen indulging in these antics at almost any hour of the day, but in the evening the whole snipe population seemed to take to the air in concert, and often the performance lasted far into the night. The birds flew about in wide, irregular circles, sometimes half a mile in diameter, over the spot where their nests were presumably located. It may be that both sexes shared in the performance, to which a weird "bleating" sound was always an accompaniment. Dr. Sutton describes this sound as "sobbing," while A. C. Bent calls it "winnowing." He says, "The sound resembles the noise made by a duck's wings in rapid flight, a rapidly pulsating series of notes, *who, who, who, who, who, who, who, who*, increasing and then decreasing again in intensity."[1] It is fairly certain that these sounds are not made vocally, but by the wings or tail—perhaps by both. (They are possibly correlated with the narrowed outer tail feathers found in this and other snipes.)

Dr. Sutton also noted other peculiar flight performances, as when two individuals repeatedly sailed gracefully over the cattails with set wings, in wide, sweeping undulations—"a type of flight totally different from any previously observed." In another instance a male bird was seen to spring up and, after a few energetic, direct wingbeats, put his wings high above his body and, describing a graceful arc, drop towards the ground—his legs trailing but not touching—only to rise again to repeat the performance. This seemed to be a ruse to lure the observer away from the vicinity of the nest.

Six nests with eggs or young were found during these two seasons, besides some young that had left the nests. The earliest nest was found on May 4, 1922, when the eggs were already advanced in incubation, although other sets found the next year, on May 15 and 16 respectively, were not so far along. No two nests were in exactly similar locations. One was built in the center of a clump of dry fern stalks and another on part of an old, partly submerged stump; a third, in a small patch of aquatic weeds, gave the appearance of having been built up directly out of the water. All but one were in the open marsh and exposed from above; the exception, less conspicuous, was placed under a dead willow branch and some leaning cattail stalks. The nests varied little in appearance and composition; each was merely a loose mass of dried weed stalks and stems of aquatic plants, the coarser materials at the bottom, but without any other special attempt at arrangement. The depression for the eggs was very shallow in every case, and the height above water level varied from scarcely an inch to almost a foot. The behavior of the birds at the nest varied also—some were very solicitous over the interference, while others made little protest. The eggs were not necessarily arranged in the nest with the small ends together, as is usual with shore birds; in some instances three were placed with the small ends pointing the same way. The eggs are ovate pyriform in general shape, but vary somewhat in exact outline and dimensions. The longest one found measures 1.63 by 1.10 inches, the shortest, 1.50 by 1.12. Nor are any two sets exactly alike in color or markings. In the palest set the ground-color is deep olive buff; in the darkest it is dull yellowish olive. The spots are dull brown of two shades; in some eggs they are heavy, and confluent around the larger end; in others, lighter-colored and more evenly distributed. In one set there are blackish scrawlings in addition to the spots.

L. E. Hicks found a nest with four eggs at Hemlock Island, Pymatuning Swamp, on May 30, 1931, and saw young on four occasions. At least sixteen pairs were nesting near there in 1929, but the number varied from year to year. Our party from the Carnegie Museum saw a good many pairs in the vicinity of Linesville in the seasons of 1933 and 1934, but latterly they have been less numerous.

[1]U. S. National Museum, *Bulletin*, no. 142, 1927, p. 82.

"Wilson's Snipe" HUIDEKOPER, *Forest and Stream*, 1877, 9:326 ("Meadville" [Conneaut Marsh], Crawford Co., breeding)—SIMPSON, *Oölogist*, 1912, 29:350 (Presque Isle, Erie Co., June)—HARLOW, *Cassinia*, 1912, 15:20 (Center Furnace Swamp, Centre Co., transient)—SUTTON, *Bird-Lore*, 1923, 25:132 (Transfer, Mercer Co., December, *fide* Homer); 1924, 26:122 (Harmarville, Allegheny Co., January), 418 (Greenville, Mercer Co., October, *fide* Homer)—CHRISTY, *Cardinal*, 1923, v. 1, no. 2, [p.16] (Clinton Pond, Allegheny Co., spring)—ABBOTT, *Oölogist*, 1924, 41:49 (Port Allegany, McKean Co., March)—BOULTON, *Bird-Lore*, 1928, 30:195 (Deer Creek, Allegheny Co., March, *fide* Reiter), 271 (Clinton Pond, Allegheny Co., May, *fide* Christy).

Gallinago wilsoni TOWNSEND, *Proc. Acad. Nat. Sci. Philadelphia*, 1883, 67 (Latrobe, Westmoreland Co., summer[?]).

Gallinago delicata WARREN, *Birds Pa.*, ed. 2, 1890, 80 (Crawford Co., breeding, *fide* Sennett; Erie, Erie Co., nesting, *fide* Thompson; [?]Beaver Co., summer, *fide* Scroggs)—TODD, *Ann. Carnegie Mus.*, 1904, 2:537 (Erie and Presque Isle, Erie Co., transient; rare in summer)—TODD, in Bausman, *Hist. Beaver Co., Pa.*, 1904, 2:1198 (Beaver Co., transient)—HARLOW, *Auk*, 1909, 26:305 (near State College, Centre Co., winter)—STONE, *Cassinia*, 1915, 18:52 (State College, Centre Co., migration, *fide* Mason); 1919, 22:30 (Altoona, Blair Co., migration, *fide* McGraw); 1920, 23:31 (Altoona, Blair Co., March, and Shirleysburg, Huntingdon Co., April, *fide* McGraw; Chambersburg, Franklin Co., May, *fide* Mahy)—CHRISTY, *Cardinal*, 1923, v. 1, no. 1, [p. 3] (Sewickley and Clinton Pond, Allegheny Co., transient)—SUTTON, *Wilson Bull.*, 1923, 35:191 (Pymatuning Swamp, Crawford Co., nesting; song; habits, etc.; Mercer Co., December)—BURLEIGH, *Wilson Bull.*, 1923, 35:84 ([Harmarville], Allegheny Co., April); 1924, 36:76 (State College and region, Centre Co., migration; winter).

Capella gallinago delicata SUTTON, *Ann. Carnegie Mus.*, 1928, 18:98 (Pymatuning Swamp, Crawford Co., nesting; Crawford Co. localities and records).

HUDSONIAN CURLEW

PHAEOPUS HUDSONICUS (Latham)

Description—One of the larger shore birds (larger than the Greater Yellow-legs). *Bill two to three inches long and strongly curved downward towards the end.* Upperparts dusky brown varied with buff; outer edge of wings plain dark brown; secondaries barred with buff; crown of head dusky brown, with a more or less distinct buffy stripe down the middle; a dusky-brown stripe through the eye; underparts buffy white, the neck and breast showing fine dusky-brown stripes, and the sides indistinctly barred with the same color; legs dark; bill dark above, pale at base below.

Range and migration—The Hudsonian Curlew breeds in the Barren Grounds of northwestern Canada and Alaska, but in migration it reaches the Atlantic coast. At Erie it "occurs as a transient visitant, rare and irregular in late years, although well known to the older generation of sportsmen. It has been seen there late in the spring, but most of the reports of its occurrence are for the fall migration. Mr. [S. E.] Bacon has seen but two individuals, on August 1, 1890, and August 27, 1895. Mr. James Thompson has a mounted specimen which he says was taken in the fall, about 1892. The Carnegie Museum has an example said to have been shot in the '80's by Captain J. D. Paasch" (Todd, 1904). Single birds were seen on Presque Isle on August 3 and 16, 1926, and August 1, 1928 (Perry), and on September 5, 1934 (Dilley). G. M. Sutton records a specimen from Conneaut Lake shot on April 17, 1912—certainly an early arrival date. On May 23, 1937, G. M. Cook saw a flock of thirteen flying over Pymatuning Lake, north of Andover, Ohio. The following day R. L. Fricke counted twenty-three birds in a flock flying over the lake west of Linesville, calling vociferously. It is to be hoped that the lake may become a regular stopping place for this fine shore bird.[1]

Numenius hudsonicus TODD, *Ann. Carnegie Mus.*, 1904, 2:547 (Erie [Presque Isle], Erie Co., transient).

Phæopus hudsonicus SUTTON, *Ann. Carnegie Mus.*, 1928, 18:109 (Conneaut Lake, Crawford Co., April, *fide* Welshons; Erie Co. references).

"Hudsonian Curlew" BOULTON, *Bird-Lore*, 1928, 30:337 (Presque Isle, Erie Co., August, *fide* Perry).

[1]A record of the Hudsonian Curlew from Renovo (A. C. BENT, U. S. National Museum, *Bulletin*, no. 146, 1929, p.123) is erroneous; it arose from a clerical mistake in transcribing the data from a migration schedule sent in by A. K. Pierce.

ESKIMO CURLEW

PHAEOPUS BOREALIS (Forster)

Description—Similar to the Hudsonian Curlew, but decidedly smaller; about the size of the Greater Yellow-legs. It differs from that species in the color of the crown, which is dark brown, varied with buff (instead of solid brown, with a buffy stripe in the middle). The *wings* are also solid dark brown, *without any buffy bars* on the secondaries as in the other species, and the underlining of the wings is reddish brown.

Range and local status—The Eskimo Curlew formerly bred in the Barren Grounds of Canada in the province of Mackenzie; migrated in the fall down the coast of Labrador and thence, by way of the Lesser Antilles, to southern South America; and returned in the spring up the Mississippi Valley, by an entirely different route. Its occurrence in our region could scarcely have been more than accidental. There is but one authentic record—a specimen shot by James Thompson at Erie on September 17, 1889, and presented to Sennett. (This bird has been acquired by the Carnegie Museum.) The species is now believed to be on the verge of extinction, probably because of the encroachments of civilization upon its wintering area in Argentina.

Numenius borealis Warren, *Birds Pa.*, ed. 2, 1890, 96 (Erie, Erie Co., transient)—Todd, *Ann. Carnegie Mus.*, 1904, 2:548 (Erie, Erie Co., September).

UPLAND PLOVER

BARTRAMIA LONGICAUDA (Bechstein)

Description—A sandpiper of moderate size, larger than the Killdeer, with a bill an inch or more long. *Adult:* upperparts mottled (the scapulars barred) with brown and buff; tail rounded, medially grayish brown, externally buffy or whitish, with conspicuous black bars and paler tip; wings dusky (the outer primary with a white shaft), barred with white below, and *under wing coverts, axillaries, and flanks barred with black and white;* crown with a pale median stripe; underparts white, the breast and sides buffy and heavily mottled with brownish black, tending to streaks on the lower throat; sides of head and neck buffy white with dark streaking; bill yellowish, dusky above and at tip; feet dull greenish yellow. *Downy young:* upperparts mottled with black, brown, and grayish white, the crown marbled with interrupted brownish streaks and bars; underparts white.

Range—This exclusively American species has a peculiar breeding range. In the East it is unknown north of southern Maine, but in the West it ranges as far north as Alaska. It is especially characteristic of the Great Plains, where it doubtless originated. It has a long migration route, connecting its breeding range with the pampas of Argentina and southern Brazil, where it finds conditions somewhat resembling those in its summer home. Once common, at least in the West, it has been sadly reduced in numbers in recent years, not only by the encroachments of agriculture on its breeding grounds, but also by unremitting persecution in its winter quarters. Beyond a doubt, it must have been—in common with the Bob-white and other birds of the plains—a comparatively recent immigrant to western Pennsylvania, which it probably invaded from the west and south.

Open country is for this species a *sine qua non*, but it must be of considerable area, and the more level the better; small tracts will not do at all. There are parts of Crawford County so flat and open that while driving through them one can easily imagine oneself on the plains of Saskatchewan. Here, if anywhere, we should expect to find the Upland Plover breeding, and here indeed it is regular if not numerous. But it is extremely local, and the pairs are widely scattered, as, according to S. J. Seiple, they are also in Mercer County. He has located several nesting pairs on hilltops in the region east of Greenville, from the Crawford County line south to the Big Bend of the Shenango River. Other pairs have been noted in the region east of Sharon by H. M. McQuiston and a party from the Carnegie Museum. In Erie County the Upland Plover is mainly a transient, but it breeds occasionally along the lake shore plain (Bacon). A recent breeding record from this county comes from a point near McKean, where W. E. Dilley saw a pair with two young on June 28, 1934.

Farther south, the species has been found nesting at Slippery Rock, Butler County (Raney), and has been seen in June in the extreme southern part of the same county (Henrici, 1926). In the hilly country of Beaver County I have never seen it at all, and in Allegheny and Washington counties it is scarcely more than accidental during migration. It is likewise rare in Greene County, according to local observers, but the finding of three birds on a high knob near Garrison in July, 1928, by S. S. Dickey, would suggest that it may occasionally breed there. Because of the generally unfavorable character of the terrain in the southwestern counties, it was with considerable surprise that this species was detected during the breeding season on a flat stretch of country in Westmoreland County, just west of Youngstown, and within sight of Chestnut Ridge. The discovery was made by B. H. Christy in 1928, and during subsequent seasons has been confirmed by him and by other observers, including myself. Miss Ruth Trimble has found other pairs established at Swede Hill and at Beatty, and has succeeded in locating a nest with eggs. Moreover, the Upland Plover has become a regular summer resident at the Johnstown airport in Cambria County (Freer and Mostoller). A. B. Miller writes that there are two or three places in Elk Lick Township, southern Somerset County, where it undoubtedly breeds.

Furthermore, the species is by no means unknown as a summer resident in the ridge and valley section. R. C. Harlow and T. D. Burleigh record it from State College, Centre County; it has been noted throughout the summer months at "Ant Hills," near Hollidaysburg (McGraw); its presence west of Rocky Ridge, Huntingdon County, and in Charlesville Cove, Bedford County, in early July, is attested by W. H. Phelps; and from Greencastle, Franklin County, at the extreme eastern limit of our region, it has been recorded as breeding (Ziegler). There is much level and cleared land in the valleys of this region, to which this species, having come in probably from the southeast, has evidently been attracted.

Migration—Scattered migration records indicate the arrival of the Upland Plover sometime in April. At Erie it appears between April 11 (1896) and May 1 (1897—Bacon), and in the Pymatuning region it arrived once as early as April 9 (Dilley). It was noted at a point in Sewickley Township, Allegheny County, on April 16, 1928 (Anderson); at Altoona on April 17, 1918 (Hays); at Greencastle, Franklin County, on April 16, 1922 (Ziegler); and at State College between April 11 (1919) and 27 (1916—Burleigh). These dates accord with those published by W. W. Cooke[1] for adjoining states and may be accepted as reasonably accurate. In the fall the Upland Plover is one of the earliest migrants. Young birds begin to appear in the neighborhood of Erie about July 15 (Bacon). If not of strictly local origin, these surely cannot come from any great distance. Moreover, the species has been noted at Ridgway, Elk County, about the same time (Alsop), and also at Morganza, Washington County, during July and August (Van Ostrand). The latest recorded fall date is September 22 (1896) from Erie (Bacon). D. A. Atkinson shot one bird at Neville Island, Allegheny County, on September 6, 1896; and G. M. Sutton heard one flying over the Allegheny Observatory in Pittsburgh on the night of September 15, 1921.

Habits[2]—The Upland Plover is of course not a plover at all but a sandpiper that long ago abandoned the waterside in favor of dry, upland fields. That it occasionally reverts to type during migration is attested by a bird that was shot from a large flock of other sandpipers by Dr. Atkinson, and by one collected from a company of Bonaparte's gulls by R. B. Simpson on Presque Isle, on April 26, 1902. Generally speaking, however, the Upland Plover is addicted to wide and open spaces; the pastures of farm lands are its accepted summer home. There, with the Bobolink and the Red-wing, the Meadowlark and the Savannah, Grasshopper, and Vesper sparrows, it dwells in scattered pairs, feasting on the myriads of grasshoppers, beetles, weevils, crickets, and other insects that damage cultivated crops. Where cattle keep the grass cropped short, and where clover and dandelion flourish, are the chosen feeding grounds of this species. Against such a background the

[1] U. S. Department of Agriculture, Biological Survey, *Bulletin*, no. 35, 1910, p. 64–67.

[2] Account contributed by Ruth Trimble.

plovers are inconspicuous, but careful watching of a favored spot will reveal them.

Other characteristics of this species have been described by Mr. Christy and Rudyerd Boulton (1929): "The feeding-habits were interesting. Each bird walked deliberately, with intervals of standing still, advancing and retracting the head with

each step, after the manner of a dove. Occasionally a bird would make a quick stab forward, as though snatching a grasshopper or caterpillar from a grass stalk. The motions, though quick, were deliberately made. . . . In flight the bill is held in horizontal position; the neck is not extended. The front edge of the anterior patagium is light, almost white; the primaries and secondaries show much lighter than their coverts. This gives the appearance in flight of a dark margin to the anterior and distal part of the wing. The central part of the tail is darker than the outer part. The flight is made with stiffly set wings, after the manner of the Curlew or the Spotted Sandpiper. There is nothing reminiscent of the long sweep of wings of a flying Killdeer or Solitary Sandpiper. When the flying bird is seen from behind, the tips of the moving wings reach well below the body, while the ulnar part describes but a narrow arc. As the bird approaches the ground to alight, the wings move through an even smaller arc, until they are barely moving at all."

On the broad, rolling fields just east of Greensburg, almost at the base of Chestnut Ridge, Mr. Christy discovered in 1928 two pairs of upland plover apparently settled for the summer season. Three times he and his companions visited this area in the hope of locating the nests, but without avail. Certain it was from the actions of the birds that their nesting territory had been invaded, but the nature of the plover is such that its secret is well guarded, and young birds are so shy that the alarm of the parents causes them to crouch motionless in the shelter of thick grass. In 1930 Mr. Boulton observed the birds there again. In 1933 I began my own observations, and to my delight on April 28 found four birds in almost the same place. The following year they were seen first on April 29 in a pasture field less than two miles farther east, and there they have returned each year. It is easy to detect their presence. If they are beyond the range of vision, a long, low, trilling call floats down the wind and dies away in a drawn-out, eerie whistle. Or perhaps one may come suddenly upon a bird, trim and alert, perched on a fence post. With a nervous chuckle it may spring from its lookout and move on quivering wings to another not far away. As it alights it habitually stretches its wings upward until the tips almost meet and then slowly and deliberately furls them in a graceful fashion.

Automobiles whiz by the ordinary plover domain in such numbers that the birds are unsuspicious even of one that stops near a favorite perch, so long as the occupants remain quiet. After the first alarm, a bird will return by easy stages to a certain fence post, the constant use of which is betrayed by white splashes. But a pedestrian causes great consternation in the plover ranks and sends the birds circling aloft. If the young are hatched, the concern of the parents is increased, and they will fly and dip over the head of an interloper, coming close in their excitement and all the while uttering their nervous alarm-note, *quip-ip-ip-ip*. At Swede Hill two birds circled excitedly above us one evening (June 3, 1935) and time after time fluttered down almost within reach, calling piteously. Soon we discovered the reason for their extreme agitation. In crossing the road, a young bird had become entangled in a patch of wet asphalt and, unable to free itself, had died there. We pried up the sticky mass and carefully cleaned the specimen for the Carnegie Museum collection. It was evidently about a week old and was covered with soft down, mottled with brown, black, and buff.

Our efforts during three successive seasons to locate a nest in the plover community east of Greensburg were strenuous but unavailing and seemed doomed to failure even in the fourth. The birds were there—several pairs; we watched them feeding; we watched them courting—a male with tail cocked, wings dragging, and throat puffed out so that it appeared like a white patch. Systematically we covered the field they inhabited, even dragging it with a rope. Then, quite by accident, a farm boy who had known of our searching, startled a plover from her nest in an unused pasture field not far away. He had almost set his foot upon the incubating bird when she fluttered off. She was well concealed on the nest, and on subsequent visits it was almost necessary to lift her away. ("Her" seems to be the proper pronoun, and yet it is known that both sexes incubate, and in appearance are virtually indistinguishable.) She fluttered about, dragging her wings and crying piteously, and the mate drew closer and added his protest. The nest was merely a hollowed-out place in the long grass and contained no lining. The four eggs had well-formed embryos and were, I judge, about two-thirds incubated; the date was May 20, 1936. The eggs of the Upland Plover are larger than those of the Killdeer, measuring about 1.78 by 1.28 inches; they are also less decidedly pyriform. The ground-color varies considerably from pale buff to greenish white, and the spots are deep brown, rather small, and more or less evenly distributed. In the three seasons following the finding of the nest, the birds have returned to their old haunts and have been discovered in new areas as well. Apparently they are thriving and increasing.

Professor Seiple recounts a similar experience with a nesting pair located by Louis Homer near Transfer, Mercer County. On June 3, 1932, the incubating bird had to be lifted from the four eggs, and, killdeer-like, feigned a broken wing to lead the intruders away. This nest was "in an uncultivated field, grown over with 'poverty-grass,' creeping briers, and weeds. Nowhere did the vegetation attain any height."

The Upland Plover is fairly common in the Pymatuning region now, but Dr. Sutton (1928) was unable to locate any nests, although he found newly hatched young on June 2. In Erie County this bird is still fairly common, as it was in the nineties, according to S. E. Bacon (in Todd, 1904): "During spring migrations I scarcely ever see more than one or two pairs, but by July 15, or soon thereafter, I always find a bunch of young birds on their way south, perhaps a half a dozen, perhaps two dozen, and, if it happens to be a favorable season, their numbers are soon augmented. It would seem to be the case that a rainy summer with a luxurious growth of weeds and grasses brings but few Bartramian Sandpipers [Upland Plovers], but let it be hot and dry, with the stubble short, and grasshoppers by the million, then they may be expected in abundance. On June 20, 1897, at Miles Grove [North Girard], I saw a bird of this species which acted unmistakably the part of a female with young, flying from side to side along a road lined with grain fields, and occasionally alighting within a few yards of me. On June 25, 1899, I saw a single bird, and on May 21, 1890, I saw several, while a female taken May 9, 1900, was nearly ready to nest, so that I think an occasional brood is raised in the vicinity of Erie also."

"Field Plover" Baily, *Auk*, 1896, 13:291 (Williamsville, Elk Co., July, *fide* Reese).

Bartramia longicauda Todd, *Ann. Carnegie Mus.*, 1904, 2:546 (Erie and Presque Isle, Erie Co., transient; occasional in summer)—Harlow, *Auk*, 1918, 35:22 (Mifflin, Centre, Indiana, and Greene Co., breeding)—Stone, *Cassinia*, 1920, 23:32 ("Altoona" ["Ant Hills," near Hollidaysburg], Blair Co., May, *fide* McGraw)—Burleigh, *Wilson Bull.*, 1924, 36:70 (State College, Centre Co., migration)—[Editor], *Cassinia*, 1926, 25:28 (Greencastle, Franklin Co., breeding, *fide* Ziegler)—Sutton, *Ann. Carnegie Mus.*, 1928, 18:107 (near Pymatuning Swamp, Crawford Co., and Greenville, Mercer Co., summer)—Christy and Boulton, *Cardinal*, 1929, 2:122 (Neville I., Allegheny Co., September, *fide* Atkinson; "Von Hofen Spring," Sewickley Tp., Allegheny Co., *fide* Anderson; "Butler" [Jamisonville], Butler Co., *fide* Elliott; near Youngstown, Westmoreland Co., breeding)—Boulton, *Cardinal*, 1930, 2:233 (near Youngstown, Westmoreland Co., May)—Burleigh, *Wilson Bull.*, 1931, 43:38 (State College, Centre Co., spring).

"Bartramian Sandpiper" Harlow, *Oölogist*, 1912, 29:279 (State College, Centre Co., July)—Street, *Cassinia*, 1923, 24:12 (Greencastle, Franklin Co., June)—Eastwood, *Bird-Lore*, 1927, 29:273 (Hartstown, Crawford Co., May, *fide* Reiter and Squier).

"Upland Plover" Henrici, *Cardinal*, 1926, v. 1, no. 7, p. 25 (Plains Church, Butler Co., June)—Eastwood, *Bird-Lore*, 1926, 28:273 (Hartstown, Crawford Co., May, *fide* Blair), 343 (Ridgway, Elk Co., July, *fide* Alsop)—McClintock, *Cardinal*, 1933, 3:128 (Ligonier and Irwin, Westmoreland Co., summer).

SPOTTED SANDPIPER (Plate 9)

ACTITIS MACULARIA (Linnaeus)

Description—One of the smaller sandpipers, with a wingspread of from thirteen to fourteen inches; bill straight, about an inch long. *Adult in spring and summer:* upperparts dull grayish olive with some darker mottling; wings dusky, the primaries with a white area on their inner webs, and the secondaries tipped with white, showing as a light bar in flight; tail dark, the outer feathers barred and tipped with white; a white streak over the eye; sides of head similar to the back, with some white mottling; *underparts* pure white, with *rounded dusky spotting*, except on the chin; under wing coverts and axillaries mostly white; bill mostly flesh-colored; feet dull yellowish or greenish. *Adult in fall, and immature*, entirely different: *upperparts plain dull grayish olive*, the wing coverts with pale buffy and darker crossbarring; wings showing a white bar as in the adult, and tail similar; *underparts white, unspotted*, but the breast shaded with gray; sides of head similar to the back; eye-ring white. *Downy young:* upperparts dull grayish brown, with a black stripe down the center of the crown and down the middle of the back, and another through the eye; underparts dull white.

Range—There are but two species in the genus *Actitis*, one confined to the Old World, the other to the New. Both are wide-ranging forms. In North America, *Actitis macularia* breeds from the Gulf states and southern California north to the limit of trees and in winter ranges (in the East) from its southern breeding limit to South America. It is common and generally distributed, and is probably more numerous now than ever, as it has been able to adapt itself to changed conditions. There is no part of our region where it is not found; it is in fact our commonest and best-known shore bird.

Migration—Thirteen years' records (not consecutive) of the arrival of this species at Beaver show April 21 as the average date of its appearance, April 4 as the earliest, and May 2 as the latest. Fifteen years' records from Sewickley, Allegheny County, show April 22 as the average (Christy). Our longest series (covering twenty-six years) of arrival dates is from Renovo (Pierce); the average is again April 21. A variation from this average of a week or two, depending on a retarded or advanced season, would include nearly all the dates of record for our entire region. H. C. Kirkpatrick recorded the Spotted Sandpiper at Meadville on March 24, 1897, and A. C. Bent cites another March record from Philipsburg; these were of course unseasonably early occurrences. Transient individuals in flocks were noted at Erie between May 2 and 9 in 1900. In 1935 I saw the species there on April 19.

Fall migration dates are neither so many nor so satisfactory. During the shore-bird movements in August this species is in evidence also, and the vast majority depart for the South before the end of that month, leaving only a few stragglers to bring up the rear. Latest fall dates may be quoted as follows: Presque Isle, September 23, 1900 (Todd); Meadville, October 16, 1909 (Kirkpatrick); Warren, September 29, 1908 (Simpson); Beaver, September 23, 1899 (Todd); Renovo, October 18, 1895 (Pierce); Pittsburgh (Highland Park), September 29, 1912 (Burleigh); Wilkinsburg, October 4, 1899 (Atkinson).

Habits—Most of the shore birds on our list are arctic, or at least boreal, in the breeding season, and their sojourn with us is only brief. But the Spotted Sandpiper comes to spend the whole summer—to build its nest, lay its eggs, and rear its young—and thus affords us some insight into the domestic life of this group of birds in general. It is a common and well-nigh ubiquitous species wherever there is standing or running water. It is found not only along the beaches of the larger rivers, but also, and in perhaps even greater numbers, along the courses of the smaller streams, which the birds follow to their very sources, although avoiding the portions that traverse woodland. Small ponds are favorite resorts and usually support several pairs, while larger bodies of water, if their shores are sandy or gravelly, like those of Lake Erie and (in places) Conneaut Lake, are also frequented.

Although a typical sandpiper, this species does not ordinarily mix with the other shore birds and keeps rather aloof even in migration. Judging from my observations at Erie, it apparently moves in flocks in the spring, but ordinarily the first ones seen at that season are single birds or pairs that have come north to reoccupy their respective breeding stations. Walking beside a stream, one may catch sight of a sandpiper picking its way along the shore with teetering steps or wading through the shallows with pretty unconcern, its tail constantly bobbing up and down as though attached to a spring, and never still, even when the bird is at rest. If unduly alarmed by too close an approach, the sandpiper may run for a few feet, then take wing and fly out over the water, low down and with a peculiar skimming, quivering flight, the wings held stiffly and raised but little above the level of the back. After describing a semicircle it will come to shore a little farther on and resume its interrupted feeding. Its alarm-note at such times is a plaintive, insistent *peet-weet-weet,* repeated several times. If pressed too far, it will eventually turn and double back to its original scene of operations. This general behavior and this style of flight are characteristic of the Spotted Sandpiper when it is settled for the season; but during migration the flocks are shy and restless, and their flight is more like that of the other sandpipers—direct and sweeping.

Instances have been recorded of birds of this species, surprised at close quarters, taking to the water. I once shot and slightly wounded a spotted sandpiper that attempted to escape in this way. When I came up, it boldly entered the stream, which was only a foot or two deep, and actually flew under water to the opposite shore. When I drew near, it repeated the action, and from where I stood I could observe the use made of the wings. This ruse is sometimes adopted, it is said, when a bird is trying to escape the attack of a hawk.

Years have passed since I found my first spotted sandpiper's nest on May 20, 1887, but as I glance over the written record made at the time, the event comes back to me with all the thrill of a new discovery. It was towards evening, as I was traversing a narrow valley where a crop of rye was being developed, that I noticed a sandpiper fly up from the small stream I was following and alight well back in the field. Keeping my eye on the spot, I advanced carefully till at length the bird flushed, but even then it took some time to find the nest. It was placed in a slight hollow among the small stones with which the ground was covered, and the eggs blended so well in color with their surroundings that they were hard to discern at a distance of only a few feet. The nest was a very flimsy affair—merely a few straws and some dry leaves lining the depression—hardly enough to keep the eggs off the ground. The rye straw was near at hand, but the leaves must have been brought from the edge of the woods. Nests subsequently found conform in both situation and composition to this general type. An open place in a field of grass, grain, or stubble—away from but within easy reach of water—is the usual choice. Sometimes, however, the bird builds nearer the water; I once found a nest in the low weeds on the sandy shore of Raccoon Creek, so close to the edge that a slight rise of the water level would have swamped it. R. B. Simpson writes that he has seen a nest under an overhanging bank, in small timber, but this too was unusual. Mr. Kirkpatrick once found a nest built close to a railroad track over which trains were passing regularly.

Eggs have been found as early as April 20 (Kirkpatrick) and as late as June 20 (Atkinson), but both extremes are exceptional, and almost certainly the latter date was the second attempt of a pair whose first nest had come to grief. The third week in May is the average time for fresh eggs. These are normally four in number and are usually arranged in the nest with the small ends together to facilitate incubation. They are of the usual shore-bird type, short ovate in shape, and large for the size of the bird, measuring about 1.27 by .90 inches. The ground-color varies somewhat in tone, but tends to be light buff, spotted and blotched more or less heavily with deep brown and black, particularly toward the larger end. Incubation lasts fifteen days. Shortly after hatching, the young are led to the water's edge, where they run about in the odd, teetering fashion of their parents. They have been observed to take to the water and swim off when pursued, but often they squat motionless along the shore, where their coloration serves to protect them from discovery. By the first of August they are all on the wing, and are soon ready to undertake the southward journey. Each day for two or three weeks in August, 1933, I watched from the train some young spotted sandpipers along the Ohio River. On August 23 they were still there, but by another week they would have vanished until the next year.

Tringoides macularius Townsend, *Proc. Acad. Nat. Sci. Philadelphia*, 1883, 67 (Latrobe, Westmoreland Co., breeding).

"Spotted Sandpiper" Jacobs, *Hawkeye Ornithologist and Oölogist*, 1888, 1:88 (Waynesburg, Greene Co., April)—Harlow, *Cassinia*, 1912, 15:20 (Center Furnace Swamp, Centre Co., summer)—Simpson, *Oölogist*, 1914, 31:91 (Warren, Warren Co., nesting)—Miller, *In the Open*, June, 1920, 10:23 (Deer Creek, Allegheny Co., May)—Sutton, *Bird-Lore*, 1923, 25:260 (Pittsburgh region, Allegheny Co., April)—Street, *Cassinia*, 1923, 24:11 (Greencastle and Ft. Loudon, Franklin Co., June)—Christy, *Cardinal*, 1923, v. 1, no. 2, [p. 16] (Clinton Pond, Allegheny Co., spring)—Eastwood, *Bird-Lore*, 1926, 28:274 (Sandy Lake, Mercer Co., May, *fide* Squier)—Christy, *Cardinal*, 1931, 3:43 (McDonald Reservoir, Washington Co., May)—McClintock, *Cardinal*, 1933, 3:128 (Ligonier, Westmoreland Co., nesting).

Actitis macularia Todd, *Auk*, 1893, 10:38 (Two Lick, Indiana Co., June)—Jacobs, *Summer Birds Greene Co., Pa.*, 1893, 5 (Greene Co., nesting)—Baily, *Auk*, 1896, 13:291, 292 (Sevenmile Run, near Williamsville, Elk Co., July)—Cope, *Cassinia*, 1902, 5:13 (Clinton and Potter Co., June)—Todd, *Ann. Carnegie Mus.*, 1904, 2:547 (Erie and Presque Isle, Erie Co., nesting)—Todd, in Bausman, *Hist. Beaver Co., Pa.*, 1904, 2:1199 (Beaver Co., summer)—Keim, *Cassinia*, 1905, 8:37 (Port Allegany, McKean Co., summer)—Cooke, *Bull. Biol. Surv.* no. 35, 1910, 69 (Waynesburg, Greene Co.; Beaver, Beaver Co.; and Renovo, Clinton Co., migration)—Harlow, *Auk*, 1912, 29:469 (southern Centre Co., summer)—Christy, *Cardinal*, 1923, v. 1, no. 1, [p. 4] (Sewickley, Allegheny Co., breeding)—Burleigh, *Wilson Bull.*, 1923, 35:80, 84 (Allegheny Co., nesting); 1924, 36:70; 1931, 43:38 (State College, Centre Co., migration; breeding)—Sutton, *Auk*, 1925, 42:580 (Chambersburg, Franklin Co., habits)—Christy and Sutton, *Cardinal*, 1928, 2:68 (Thom's Run, Cook Forest, Clarion Co., summer)—Sutton, *Ann. Carnegie Mus.*, 1928, 18:108 (Crawford Co., summer; records and references)—Bent, *Bull. U. S. Nat. Mus.* no. 146, 1929, 78 (Philipsburg, Centre Co., migration)—Burleigh, *Cardinal*, 1932, 3:74 (Lake Seaton, Fayette Co., breeding).

EASTERN SOLITARY SANDPIPER (Plate 9)

TRINGA SOLITARIA SOLITARIA Wilson

Description—A sandpiper of moderate size; larger than the Spotted Sandpiper; bill straight, slender, longer than the head—about one and a fourth inches long; wingspread, fifteen to seventeen inches; folded wings reaching beyond tail. *Adult in spring:* upperparts dusky olive; head and neck streaked, and the back, scapulars, and tertiaries spotted, with white; wings otherwise plain blackish; *tail* dusky in the center, the *outer feathers white with dark bars* (conspicuous in flight); the sides of the head and a band across the breast show white and dusky streaks; eye-ring white; throat and rest of underparts pure white; *axillaries barred with black and white;* under wing coverts dusky, with white spots; bill black; feet dull greenish. *Adult in fall, and immature:* similar to the spring adult, but the upperparts brownish in tone, the spots buffy instead of white; crown of the head plain dusky gray, unspotted.

Range—The breeding range of the Solitary Sandpiper still remains to be determined with precision. All the authentic eggs thus far found have come from Alberta, but if summer records count for anything, the species must breed throughout the Hudsonian and Canadian life zones, although its southward breeding limit is admittedly uncertain. The latest author to discuss the problem even goes so far as to question all the supposed cases of breeding in the East.[1] In attempting to estimate the validity of these several instances on the basis of the facts presented, two points must be borne in mind. The first is, of course, that individuals of many species of shore birds are known to remain through the summer far south of their breeding grounds—barren, sick, or wounded birds which have failed to undertake or to complete their migration. The second is that the Solitary Sandpiper is an unusually early migrant in the fall, and undue significance must not therefore be attached to its appearance during the month of July. Leaving extralimital records out of account for the moment, let us consider the species as it occurs in western Pennsylvania. It is a common and well-known transient in spring and fall and has also been reported or assumed to breed locally. Our interest centers around these supposed instances.

The first suggestion that the Solitary Sandpiper might breed in our area was made by Warren, on the authority of Sennett, who "has several times met with this species in midsummer about streams running through woods, in the vicinity of Meadville, Crawford County; and Mr. H. C. Kirkpatrick, a taxidermist residing at Meadville, says it is occasionally found in that neighborhood as a native." Mr. Kirkpatrick elaborates this statement as follows: "I saw a sandpiper along the old channel

[1] F. C. Lincoln, in A. C. Bent, U.S. National Museum, *Bulletin*, no. 146, 1929, p. 9.

of French Creek about two miles south of Meadville on July 29, 1887; and on May 31, 1894, individuals were seen also about one and one-half miles below Meadville, along the abandoned French Creek Feeder of the old Beaver and Erie Canal. Mr. George B. Sennett told me that he has repeatedly observed it in midsummer in the 'Tamarack Swamp' three or four miles southeast of the city. These records have led me to believe that it may breed." Mr. Kirkpatrick goes on to say that while the species may breed sparingly in certain localities, he cannot state positively that this is the case. Sennett's notes (if he ever made any) are unavailable, so that we are left without any more definite clues that might bear on this question.

Warren mentions several other observers who have claimed that the species breeds in Pennsylvania, and quotes Van Fleet on its breeding in Clinton County. (In going through the manuscript notes of A. K. Pierce, of Renovo, in the same county, I find that he has recorded the species on two occasions in July. This may or may not be significant.) The late Dr. Van Fleet, whom I had the pleasure of meeting in the nineties, impressed me as a reliable observer, but there is absolutely no way of checking his records quoted at second hand, as he kept no notes and formed no collection. In his manuscript list of the breeding birds of DuBois he says of the Solitary Sandpiper: "Rare; have seen pairs in June, several summers." Like the data in the Sennett case, this is good presumptive evidence, although not absolutely conclusive.

We now come to the Beaver County record that I myself published. Beginning on May 21, 1890, I noticed a single pair of solitary sandpipers from time to time through the breeding season, frequenting a small pond and an adjacent stream (Two-mile Run) near the town of Beaver. All attempts to discover their nest proved futile, although later in the season (July) they appeared accompanied by what were presumably their young. The following year (1891), on April 28, two pairs arrived at the same place, but only one pair remained through the season. Again I spent much time and effort in trying to locate the nest, but without success. In 1892 I noted a single individual on July 4—this within a mile of the same haunt. Very possibly all these observations applied to the same pair of birds. The young when discovered were capable of flight, and while all the circumstances suggested that they were reared where they were found, there is a possibility that they were not. Hence the evidence in this case also falls short of being conclusive.

From Erie we have S. E. Bacon's records of birds noted throughout the summer; some exact dates are July 19, 1892; July 7, 1896; and July 25, 1890. "Upon this latter date two specimens were taken, both young birds," but these have not been preserved. R. B. Simpson has noted the species at Warren in mid-July, as follows: July 13, 1894 (two); July 23, 1895; and July 17, 1903. He adds that one pair remained during the summer of 1905, but did not seem to nest. In June and July of 1906 a single bird spent the season at the same place. Also, on July 27, 1923, he saw one in the woods along Tionesta Creek. Here again the possibility that these were merely early migrants must be considered. On July 15, 1895, one bird was observed by F. L. Homer "flying northward high over the lake" near Hartstown. G. M. Sutton gives several June dates for Pymatuning Swamp and Conneaut Lake, in the same county. By far the most convincing bit of evidence, in my opinion, is Dr. Sutton's circumstantial account of finding an obviously mated pair that seemed to be searching for a nesting place. But thus far the one thing needful to settle the question absolutely, that is, the actual finding of a nest or of unfledged young, remains to be accomplished. Were it almost any species but the Solitary Sandpiper, the present evidence might suffice. The problem is one that will well repay further investigation, and I predict that sooner or later the breeding of this species in our region will be settled beyond question. Extralimital records of similar nature might also be confirmed thereby.[1]

Migration—This sandpiper reaches our latitude from its winter home in South America during the latter part of April or early in May. Dates of arrival for Beaver County lie between April 26 and May 2 and average May 1 (Todd). The combined notes of three observers (Christy, Burleigh, and Atkinson) in Allegheny County yield dates that range from April 15 to May 10. Because of the scarcity of suitable feeding and resting grounds in the Ohio Valley, the movements there of this species cannot be timed so reliably as in the Erie-

[1]Compare Alexander Wilson, *American Ornithology*, 1813, 7:53; and R. C. Harlow, *Oölogist*, 1906, 23:39, 103.

Crawford district, where it is both regular and common; nevertheless, the arrival dates for the two regions in question agree surprisingly well. Earliest dates are as follows: Erie, April 27 (Bacon); Meadville, April 25 (Kirkpatrick); Warren, April 20 (Simpson); Renovo, April 30 (Pierce); State College, April 14 (Burleigh). This species is sometimes common from the day of arrival, but usually the majority of transients do not arrive for a week or more after the first ones appear. The migrants linger until late in May, but in view of the foregoing remarks on breeding, there is naturally some uncertainty as to the status of such late-staying individuals.

The southward movement begins early with this species. Some July dates have already been quoted. The Solitary Sandpiper was seen in Schenley Park, Pittsburgh (where it certainly does not breed), on July 25 in 1922 (Sutton) and at Beaver on August 1 in 1890 (Todd). B. H. Christy saw it at Coraopolis, Allegheny County, on August 3, 1921, and D. A. Atkinson quotes August 6 as his earliest fall date for Wilkinsburg in the same county. It was noted at New Hamburg, Mercer County, on August 3, 1889 (Homer), and I saw a number at Hartstown, Crawford County, on August 5, 1933. Erie County dates are not so early, but the circumstance is not significant. Many years of observation at Renovo indicate that the arrival there takes place as a rule during the first half of August, with August 3 (1904) as the earliest date. The species is still plentiful in our section, according to general report, during the first two weeks in September, while stragglers may linger into the following month. October 14 is the latest date of which we have any record; it applies to Renovo (1897 and 1898—Pierce) and also to Hartstown (Seiple).

Habits—The common name of this species is not well chosen; it could far better have been called "Wood Sandpiper," were that name not already in use for an Old World species. It is by no means a bird of solitary habit, and often travels in small flocks during migration. It is partial to secluded pools of stagnant water fringed with grasses, or to woodland ponds in out-of-the-way situations, and when it comes to the beaches with the other shore birds it probably does so from necessity rather than from choice. Ordinarily it is not shy, and oftentimes when engaged in feeding along a grassy bank it will permit a close approach. Young birds in the fall are especially trustful.

The gait of the Solitary Sandpiper, as it wades leisurely in the shallows or picks its way gingerly along the weedy margin of a pool, is as characteristic as that of the Spotted Sandpiper; the Solitary, however, keeps bobbing its head instead of its tail. If forced to take wing, it does so with a shrill, whistling cry, repeated several times as it flies rapidly out of sight. My experience has been that if the observer elects to remain quiet for a time, a bird thus disturbed will often return to the same spot after the lapse of several minutes, dropping down unexpectedly out of the sky. It flies with long, sweeping strokes of the wings—swiftly but somewhat erratically—suggesting the Nighthawk. When alighting it raises its long wings high over its back before deliberately folding them. Its migration, like that of most shore birds, seems to be performed mostly under cover of darkness, and I have repeatedly heard its unmistakable call coming from overhead at odd hours throughout the night.

Migrants on reaching suitable feeding grounds are often tempted to remain for several days before moving on. A flock of ten birds that came to a small pond near Beaver on May 15, 1890, was there for some time, and one pair presumably from this flock stayed behind during the summer, and is believed to have reared young. My published note on this circumstance attracted the attention of C. E. Bendire, who wrote me of his suspicion that this species nested in trees, as does its relative the Green Sandpiper of Europe, which uses the old nests of other birds. He asked me to look for the nest should the birds return the next season. As it happened, the pair (presumably the same) did return on April 28, 1891, and many hours were given to watching them during the month of May. The birds always called whenever they left the pond and always flew out of sight, invariably in the same direction. I judged that their nest (if any) must be at some distance, but it seemed in the circumstances quite useless to continue the search for it. Since that time it has been ascertained that Major Bendire's suspicions were well founded and that the Solitary Sandpiper does indeed use the tree nests of other birds. Our local observers should be on the alert for its nests in our region, particularly at Pymatuning Swamp.

Ryacophilus solitarius Teulon, *Jour. Boston Zoöl. Soc.*, 1883, 2:11 (Bradford, McKean Co., spring).

Totanus solitarius Warren, *Birds Pa.*, 1888, 236 (Crawford Co., breeding, *fide* Sennett); ed. 2, 1890, 90 (Meadville, Crawford Co., summer, *fide* Sennett; Clinton Co., breeding, *fide* Van Fleet)—Todd, *Auk*, 1891, 8:236 (Beaver, Beaver Co., 1890, common transient; one breeding record)—Rhoads, *Auk*, 1899, 16:310 (Beaver, Beaver Co., Todd's record).

Helodromas solitarius Todd, *Ann. Carnegie Mus.*, 1904, 2:545 (Erie and Presque Isle, Erie Co., transient; casual in summer)—Todd, in Bausman, *Hist. Beaver Co., Pa.*, 1904, 2:1199 (Beaver Co., transient, rare in summer)—Cooke, *Bull. Biol. Surv.* no. 35, 1910, 58 (Renovo, Clinton Co., migration).[1]

"Solitary Sandpiper" Simpson, *Oölogist*, 1906, 23:136 (Warren, Warren Co., summer)—Harlow, *Cassinia*, 1912, 15:20 (Center Furnace Swamp, Centre Co., transient)—Keesler, *Oölogist*, 1921, 38:170 (Harrisville, Butler Co., spring)—Christy, *Cardinal*, 1923, v. 1, no. 2, [p. 16] (Clinton Pond, Allegheny Co., May).

Helodromas solitarius solitarius Christy, *Cardinal*, 1923, v. 1, no. 1, [p. 4] (McDonald Reservoir, Washington Co.; Clinton Pond and Sewickley Reservoir, Allegheny Co., transient)—Burleigh, *Wilson Bull.*, 1923, 35:84 (Allegheny Co., transient); 1924, 36:76 (State College and region, Centre Co., migration).

Tringa solitaria solitaria Sutton, *Ann. Carnegie Mus.*, 1928, 18:106 (Crawford Co. localities and records).

Tringa solitaria Christy, *Cardinal*, 1931, 3:43 (McDonald Reservoir, Washington Co., May).

[1]The Beaver record of November 28, 1901, cited by Cooke, is an error on his part; it actually refers to the Woodcock.

WESTERN WILLET

CATOPTROPHORUS SEMIPALMATUS INORNATUS (Brewster)

Description—A large shore bird, equal in size to the Greater Yellow-legs, but with a heavier bill and *bluish-gray feet. Spring plumage:* upperparts varied with dull gray, dusky, and grayish-brown markings; the upper tail coverts are abruptly white; the *wings* have a *broad band of white across the middle*, very conspicuous in flight; underparts white, with dusky shading on the lower throat, breast, and sides. *Fall plumage:* upperparts dull grayish with faint paler markings, the upper tail coverts abruptly white; wings as in the spring plumage; underparts white, the breast and sides shaded with gray.

Range and migration—The typical race of the Willet is virtually confined to the Atlantic coast, at least in the breeding season. Records from the interior of the country, heretofore referred to this form, have proved upon investigation to pertain to the western race, *inornatus*, which is slightly larger in size and paler in coloration. This latter form, while not known to breed nearer than Iowa (according to W. W. Cooke), often wanders far eastward in migration, and has been encountered in our region on a few occasions. It was added to the western Pennsylvania list in August, 1899, when I luckily found it along the Ohio River at the mouth of the Beaver River. Three birds (one of which was taken) were seen at the river beach on August 19, and on August 22 a second bird, probably from the same group, was obtained. Both these were young of the year, and they were not at all shy.

R. B. Simpson took a pair of adults on the outside beach of Presque Isle on April 24, 1902, and there is a more recent record from the same locality by Norman McClintock and Rudyerd Boulton, who observed three individuals there on August 25, 1928. What were presumably the same birds had been noticed by J. E. Perry three days earlier, on August 22. W. M. Guynes has one record from Erie—May 8, 1932. G. M. Sutton cites a record from Conneaut Lake, based on a specimen shot by G. E. Welshons on May 12, 1911. W. D. Hunter of Racine, Beaver County, has three specimens in his collection. One of these was taken near his home about April 10, 1908; the other two were shot on the edge of Pymatuning Swamp, south of Linesville, between April 4 and 8, 1929. These dates (if correct) seem early, but are approximated by some of those quoted by Cooke[2] in discussing the migration of this species.

Habits—The Western Willet, as I first noticed it in 1899 and as I have latterly become acquainted with it in western Canada, is easily distinguished from the Greater Yellow-legs (which it resembles in size and general proportions) by its different manner of flight. It flies slowly by comparison, and with regular wingbeats, rather suggestive of

[2]U. S. Department of Agriculture, Biological Survey, *Bulletin*, no. 35, 1910, p. 62.

the Green Heron. The birds I saw in August were completely silent, but the species is very noisy on its breeding grounds. The black-and-white-banded wing is a conspicuous field mark in flight.

Symphemia semipalmata (error) Todd, *Ann. Carnegie Mus.*, 1904, 2:545 (Presque Isle, Erie Co., April, *fide* Simpson)—Todd, in Bausman, *Hist. Beaver Co., Pa.*, 1904, 2:1199 (Beaver Co., fall).

"Willet" Simpson, *Oölogist*, 1911, 28:38 (Presque Isle, Erie Co., April)—Boulton, *Bird-Lore*, 1928, 30:401 (Presque Isle, Erie Co., August).

Catoptrophorus semipalmatus inornatus Sutton, *Ann. Carnegie Mus.*, 1928, 18:107 (Conneaut Lake, Crawford Co., May, *fide* Welshons).

GREATER YELLOW-LEGS (Plate 9)

TOTANUS MELANOLEUCUS (Gmelin)

Description—One of the larger shore birds, standing about a foot high; bill slender, about twice as long as the head, and very slightly upturned in the middle; *feet yellow. Spring adult:* upperparts mottled with gray, black, and white; the head and neck (all around) showing dusky and white streaks; *rump white,* usually with some dusky markings; *tail showing dusky and white bars; wings dull dusky;* underparts white, with dusky streaks on the sides of the head and on the neck, and with more or less dusky mottling on the breast; the sides barred with the same color; under wing coverts and axillaries barred with black and white. The dark markings below vary somewhat in extent and intensity. *Fall adult and immature:* similar in general to the spring plumage, but all the markings are blended, so that the upperparts are more uniformly dusky gray, with the whitish markings smaller and less conspicuous; underparts more extensively white, with a breastband of grayish shading and streaking.

Range—Much remains to be learned about the breeding range of this otherwise well-known species; its ascertained breeding stations are still few in number. In general, however, it ranges in summer across the continent from Newfoundland and Labrador to Alaska, and in winter from the Gulf states to the southern tip of South America. In our region, as elsewhere in the eastern United States, it is a transient only, fairly regular and common in the northwestern counties, but elsewhere rather irregular. It is occasional along the Ohio River in Beaver and Allegheny counties and has also been noted at certain localities in Washington and Greene counties. It is, as might be expected, rather rare in the plateau region, and even at Renovo, in the upper Susquehanna Valley, it is most infrequent (Pierce). At State College it was reported "common during the spring migration of 1917, but rather scarce other years" (Burleigh, 1924). While the general impression seems to be that its numbers are gradually decreasing, many birds are still shot for game every year—in defiance of federal law.

Migration—The Greater Yellow-legs is rather hardy and is one of the earlier migrants among the shore birds; a little snow and ice along the route do not discourage its advance in the spring or hasten its departure in the fall. It has thus earned the name "Winter" Yellow-legs. In the spring it arrives sometimes by the end of March (Erie, March 28, 1902 [Bacon]; Meadville, March 28, 1901 [Kirkpatrick]), although such early dates are exceptional. The more usual time for it to appear is in April or early May, as is apparent from the following arrival dates: Erie, April 8, 1934 (Guynes); Linesville, April 6, 1937 (Todd); Meadville, April 13, 1901 (Kirkpatrick); Warren, April 12, 1904 (Simpson), and April 16, 1928 (Granquist); Renovo, April 14, 1916 (Pierce); State College, April 3, 1917 (Burleigh); Clinton Pond, Allegheny County, April 16, 1922 (Christy). These dates, agreeing as they do with those from neighboring states, may be accepted as representing a fair average. The movement continues for several weeks, however, and the last individuals to leave for the north do not depart until late May or even early June. Late dates recorded are as follows: Erie, May 25, 1893 (Bacon); Conneaut Marsh, Crawford County, June 2, 1925 (Langdon); Warren, June 6, 1911 (Simpson). As a rule the spring movement in our region is over by the middle of May, but nonbreeding birds have been noted through June at Pymatuning Lake (Hicks).

In the fall migration the Greater Yellow-legs comes early and stays late. It may be fairly surmised that this circumstance is related in some way to the species' unusually extensive north-and-south distribution in the winter season. Perhaps the early arrivals are the birds that travel the farthest to reach their wintering stations. However this may be, scarcely six weeks elapse between the departure of the latest migrants in the spring and the arrival of the earliest in the fall. A few always come in the van of the shore-bird movement at the latter season, in August or even before. The earliest record for Linesville is July 9 (1938—Seiple), and for Erie, July 20 (1934—Simpson). Towards the end of August the species increases in numbers, and the majority of birds pass through in September. But many individuals linger through the following month, and a few stay even later. Some late dates follow: Erie, November 18, 1902 (Simpson); Pymatuning Lake, November 7, 1937 (Trimble); Waynesburg, November 2, 1894 (Jacobs); Conneaut Lake, October 31, 1926 (Langdon); Warren, October 28, 1914, and November 4, 1895 (Simpson); Beaver, November 6, 1902, and November 2, 1907 (Todd); State College, November 14, 1916 (Burleigh); Renovo, October 27, 1914 (Pierce). Thus the fall migration of this species through our region covers a period of about three months—a remarkably long time in comparison with that required by most birds.

Habits—In a mixed flock of shore birds the Greater Yellow-legs looms as a conspicuous figure among its fellows. Larger than they, and moving with slow, easy strides, it stalks along the shore or across the mud flats with dignity and grace, although it can be nimble enough in pursuit of its prey, of which small minnows form a considerable part. It prefers, however, the marshy shores of ponds and of sluggish streams, where there is some waterside vegetation, to the open beaches and sandspits. In such places it may often be seen wading up to its belly in the shallows, or even swimming for a short distance if caught in deeper water. In its bowing, teetering movements when feeding, it reminds one of the Solitary Sandpiper. On the wing it is no less conspicuous than when on the ground. C. W. Townsend describes it thus: "Its long yellow legs are extended out behind, its long neck and bill in front, while its white rump flashes out as the bird turns or flies away. The wings, dark and pointed, are curved downward with vigorous strokes, as the bird flies and scales alternately. In alighting, it first sets its wings, sails gracefully downward, drops its long legs, and as soon as it is firmly on the ground it frequently spreads and lifts its wings straight up over its back, then folds them carefully, and after 'teetering,' in which process it moves its whole body up and down on its legs as a fulcrum, it proceeds to go about the business of the day in feeding."[1]

The Greater Yellow-legs appears in our region singly, in twos and threes, or more rarely in small flocks, sometimes composed entirely of its own kind, but often including other shore birds, particularly the Lesser Yellow-legs. When in company with other species, its superior stature enables it to detect potential danger from afar, and since it is ever wary and on the alert, it is a mentor and monitor for the entire group. Long before one can get within gunshot it is standing on guard, and at its warning cries the whole flock comes to attention, poised for flight. When the Yellow-legs finally takes off, voicing its alarm in reiterated shrill cries, the others follow its lead. The name of "Telltale" or "Tattler," by which it is known to the gunners, is in allusion to this habit. Wild and wary though it generally is, it can scarcely be considered sagacious, for it can often be called back by a whistled imitation of its piercing alarm-notes, or brought in from a long distance by the same means, especially if decoys are also used. On the other hand, there are times when its normally shy and suspicious nature seems to undergo a change, and it becomes as tame and confiding as some of its smaller associates. I recall one occasion, some years ago, when I walked unaware into the middle of a feeding flock of both greater and lesser yellow-legs; I actually shot one of the latter (the only one I had seen) before the birds took any notice of my presence.

The well-known alarm-note of this species is a high-pitched, explosive whistle, repeated very rapidly three or four times. This cry suffices to put every other bird within hearing on the alert. The species has also a variety of other calls and cries, among them a yodeling note, heard mostly when the birds are about to alight.[2]

Totanus melanoleucus WARREN, *Birds Pa.*, ed. 2, 1890, 88 (Erie, Erie Co., transient)—RHOADS, *Auk*, 1899, 16:310 (Davis Island, Allegheny Co., August, *fide* Link; Emporium, Cam-

[1]*Memoirs Nuttall Ornithological Club*, no. 3, 1905, p. 182.
[2]Compare J. T. NICHOLS, *Auk*, 1920, 37:529–530.

eron Co., *fide* Larrabee)—TODD, *Ann. Carnegie Mus.*, 1904, 2:543 (Erie and Presque Isle, Erie Co., transient)—TODD, in Bausman, *Hist. Beaver Co., Pa.*, 1904, 2:1199 (Beaver Co., transient)—STONE, *Cassinia*, 1919, 22:30 (Altoona, Blair Co., May, *fide* McGraw)—CHRISTY, *Cardinal*, 1923, v. 1, no. 1, [p. 3] (Clinton Pond, Allegheny Co., April)—BURLEIGH, *Wilson Bull.*, 1924, 36:76 (State College [and region], Centre Co., migration)—BENT, *Bull. U. S. Nat. Mus.* no. 142, 1927, 321 (Beaver, Beaver Co., November)—SUTTON, *Ann. Carnegie Mus.*, 1928, 18:104 (Crawford Co. localities and records).

"Greater Yellow-legs" SIMPSON, *Oölogist*, 1920, 37:134 (Warren, Warren Co., May)—CHRISTY, *Cardinal*, 1923, v. 1, no. 2, [p. 16] (Clinton Pond, Allegheny Co., spring)—EASTWOOD, *Bird-Lore*, 1925, 27:262 (Clinton Pond, Allegheny Co., May, *fide* Jones)—SEIPLE, *Auk*, 1931, 48:113 (Hartstown, Crawford Co., August).

Totanus flavipes (error) BENT, *Bull. U. S. Nat. Mus.* no. 142, 1927, 349, part (Waynesburg, Greene Co., November).

LESSER YELLOW-LEGS (Plate 9)

TOTANUS FLAVIPES (Gmelin)

Description—Similar to the Greater Yellow-legs in color, but *much smaller*, standing only about eight or nine inches high; bill not over one and a half inches long.

Range—The Barren Grounds of Canada are the principal summer home of this species, but it has been known to breed sporadically much farther south, and once in west-central New York. Its principal winter home, on the other hand, is in the southern half of South America, but it is said also to be locally common in winter in Florida. In our region it is of course a transient only; it favors in general the same localities as the Greater Yellow-legs, but if anything is rather more numerous than that species. R. B. Simpson is the only observer who reports the contrary; he considers it rare at Warren. As a matter of fact, the locality records for the Lesser Yellow-legs are mostly from the western tier of counties, Erie and Crawford in particular. Its history in our region goes back to 1819, when the species was noted along the Ohio River by Major Long's expedition—unless, indeed, this observation pertained to the Greater Yellow-legs. R. C. Harlow supposed at one time that it was rare in Centre County, but T. D. Burleigh's later observations establish it as common. Oddly enough, it does not appear in A. K. Pierce's notes for Renovo.

Migration—Spring arrival dates for this species in our region average later than do those for the Greater Yellow-legs and thus confirm the general impression that it is a later migrant than the other at that season. In the vicinity of Erie it makes its appearance usually during the last week in April (April 23, 1900; April 26, 1902; April 27, 1932), and the majority of birds pass through during the first half of May. At Meadville it has been noted as early as April 26 (1895); at Linesville, on April 27 (1929); and at New Castle, on April 30 (1933). Otherwise the spring dates for the western counties all fall in May. Early April dates reported from Centre County appear suspiciously applicable to the Greater Yellow-legs. Late spring dates are: Conneaut Outlet, Crawford County, June 2, 1925 (Langdon); Erie, May 24, 1893 (Bacon); State College, May 17, 1916 (Burleigh); Clinton Pond, Allegheny County, May 17, 1923 (Christy).

Because this species habitually reappears in July on its way south, it has earned the name "Summer" Yellow-legs. At Williamsville, Elk County, it was reported from July 25 to 27, 1894 (Reese); at Erie it was noted on July 24, 1932 (Guynes); and at Linesville, on July 30, 1937 (Skaggs); but at State College it has not been seen before August 1 (1920—Burleigh). The great migratory movements occur during September, and the last individuals do not leave until sometime in October: Erie, October 14, 1893 (Bacon); Linesville, October 14, 1933 (Seiple); Scotia, Centre County, October 28, 1916 (Burleigh); Beaver, October 15, 1921 (Boulton). Taken by and large, however, the Lesser Yellow-legs is not so hardy as its larger cousin, and its migration is usually completed earlier.

Habits—This species is in appearance merely a smaller counterpart of the Greater Yellow-legs, which it also closely resembles in habits. Both are fond of the same type of habitat and indeed are often found associated. When seen thus together they are of course distinguishable by the marked difference in size, but when seen separately it is easy to mistake one for the other, so closely do they resemble each other in appearance, behavior, and calls. In general, however, the Lesser Yellow-legs is not so shy and suspicious as the larger species, at least during the fall migration, when many of the birds encountered are unsophisticated young. It is also likelier to occur in flocks. At Erie in the spring of 1900, it was more plentiful, perhaps, than any other shore bird of equal size. The marshes and mud flats at the mouth of Mill Creek were a favorite feeding ground. "Flocks of this species seldom aggregate two dozen birds, which, unlike those of the larger kind, are as a rule quite unsuspicious, so that it is comparatively easy to secure specimens" (Todd, 1904). In the account of the Greater Yellow-legs, I have already described the calm behavior of the smaller species when I walked unwittingly into the midst of a mixed flock, and Mr. Burleigh in his notes speaks of having trouble in persuading a lesser yellow-legs to fly. William Brewster's pen picture of this species may well be quoted in this connection:

"The Summer Yellow-leg[s] seems an exact counterpart of the Winter in respect to general appearance and behavior. It has the same firm, measured step, when walking about in quest of food; the same perfection of form and outlines, and grace of position, when standing erect and watchful; the same habit of tilting its body and alternately lengthening and shortening its neck with a bobbing motion, when suspicious of danger and about to take wing. Its flight, also, is essentially similar to that of its big cousin, but somewhat slower and more buoyant, and hence not so suggestive of momentum as that of the larger, heavier-bodied bird. Less vociferous and loud-voiced than *T. melanoleucus*, *T. flavipes* has a more subdued and mellow call, uttered frequently on the ground, and still oftener on wing, and consisting ordinarily of no more than two whistles, both given in the same key and pitched lower in the scale than the first two notes of the four-syllabled call of *melanoleucus*."[1]

(?)"Tell-tale Sandpiper" JAMES, Long's *Exped. Pittsburgh to Rocky Mts.*, 1823, 4 (Ohio River, western Pa., May).

Totanus flavipes WARREN, *Birds Pa.*, ed. 2, 1890, 89 (Erie, Erie Co., transient)—RHOADS, *Auk*, 1899, 16:310 (Neville Island, Allegheny Co., September, *fide* Atkinson)—TODD, *Ann. Carnegie Mus.*, 1904, 2:544 (Erie and Presque Isle, Erie Co., transient)—TODD, in Bausman, *Hist. Beaver Co., Pa.*, 1904, 2:1199 (Beaver Co., transient)—HARLOW, *Auk*, 1909, 26:305 (State College, Centre Co., April)—CHRISTY, *Cardinal*, 1923, v. 1, no. 1, [p. 3] (Clinton Pond, Allegheny Co., transient)—BURLEIGH, *Wilson Bull.*, 1924, 36:76 (State College [and region], Centre Co., migration)—SUTTON, *Ann. Carnegie Mus.*, 1928, 18:105 (Crawford Co. localities and records).

"Summer Yellow-legs" BAILY, *Auk*, 1896, 13:291 (Williamsville, Elk Co., July, *fide* Reese).

"Yellow-legs" CHRISTY, *Cardinal*, 1923, v. 1, no. 2, [p. 16] (Clinton Pond, Allegheny Co., May).

"Lesser Yellow-legs" FRICKE, *Auk*, 1930, 47:573 (Linesville, Crawford Co., May).

[1]*Bulletin Museum Comparative Zoölogy*, 1925, 66:259.

AMERICAN KNOT

CALIDRIS CANUTUS RUFUS (Wilson)

Description—A rather large, stocky sandpiper, with relatively short legs and a straight bill, about 1.25 inches long. *Spring adult:* crown and upperparts with gray, black, and rufous mottling; *upper tail coverts barred with black and white; sides of head and the underparts rufous*, the abdomen more or less white; a dark streak through the eye and dark spots and bars on the sides. *Fall plumage: upperparts gray*, with narrow black and white edgings, producing a *scaled effect; upper tail coverts white, barred with black;* underparts white, the breast and sides speckled with gray. (Not to be confused with the Black-bellied Plover in immature dress.)

Range and migration—The Knot goes so far north to breed that its eggs are still exceedingly rare in collections. Its migration is chiefly coastwise, but a few individuals traverse the interior of the country, following the Mississippi Valley for the most part. In western Pennsylvania the Knot has been found only in Erie and Crawford counties. "Although given by Dr. Warren . . . as a regular and somewhat common visitor at this locality [Erie] in spring and fall, this species has been rarely observed of late years. A pair, shot on the Peninsula September 17, 1875, are all that are in Mr. Sennett's collection. On August 27, 1895, Mr. Bacon took a single bird on the outside beach, and on August 30 of the same year examined two others which had been shot on the beach near the 'Head.' One other was secured August 29, 1896. Mr. Simpson killed a single bird from a flock of Killdeer Plover on September 10, 1900, also on the outside beach. These are all the available positive records of the occurrence of the species" (Todd, 1904).

More recently, however, on September 4, 1933, and again on September 3, 1934, a party of observers (of which I was one) identified several knots in a mixed flock of shore birds on the Soldiers' Home grounds, along the breakwater, and the species was reported from there also in September and October, 1937. L. E. Hicks writes that on September 12, 1936, on Presque Isle he saw a group of twenty-six birds—one of the largest flocks he had ever encountered. These records show that the Knot is still an occasional visitor in the Erie region. G. M. Sutton has published records for Conneaut Marsh (October 11, 1906) and for Conneaut Lake (November 22 and 28, 1912), in Crawford County. The only known record for the spring migration refers to a single bird seen on Presque Isle on June 2, 1936 (Boggs, 1936).

Tringa canutus Warren, *Birds Pa.*, ed. 2, 1890, 83 (Erie, Erie Co., transient)—Todd, *Ann. Carnegie Mus.*, 1904, 2:538 (Presque Isle, Erie Co., transient).

"Knot" Simpson, *Oölogist*, 1911, 28:142 (Presque Isle, Erie Co., September)—Boggs, *Redstart*, 1936, 3:92; 1937, 5:2 (Presque Isle, Erie Co., June and September).

Calidris canutus rufus Sutton, *Ann. Carnegie Mus.*, 1928, 18:100 (Conneaut Lake and Marsh, Crawford Co., fall, *fide* Welshons and Kirkpatrick).

Calidris canutus Christy, *Cardinal*, 1934, 3:173 (Erie, Erie Co., September).

PECTORAL SANDPIPER (Plate 9)

PISOBIA MELANOTOS (Vieillot)

Description—A sandpiper of moderate size, about as big as the Solitary; bill nearly straight, a little over one inch long; general form stocky. *Adult in spring:* upperparts streaked and mottled with black, buff, and some white; superciliaries paler but not well marked; *rump and upper tail coverts black*, bordered on either side with white, showing in flight; tail black in the middle, grayish on the sides; wings dark-colored; underparts white, the breast with dense dusky streaks on a pale grayish background (sharply set off from the whitish abdomen), and the sides showing a few dusky streaks; axillaries and under wing coverts mainly white; feet dull greenish yellow. *Adult in fall, and immature:* similar to the spring plumage, but general coloration much deeper, with more rusty buff on the upperparts, and with white spots on the scapulars; breast strongly washed with buff, and the streaking veiled, less distinct. There is much sexual variation in size, the male being considerably larger than the female. The toes are without webs and are almost as long as the tarsi.

Range—The breeding range of this sandpiper is in the far North, along the arctic coast from eastern Siberia to Southampton Island, with the center of abundance in northwestern Alaska. It goes to South America for the winter, as far as Argentina and Chile. Its migration route carries it obliquely across the country, so that it is common in spring and fall along the Atlantic coast and in the Mississippi Valley, and correspondingly rare on the Pacific side. It occurs in our region at both seasons, but is little known outside the northwestern counties, since the ecological conditions elsewhere are generally unsuitable. I used to find it occasionally in Beaver County, but have not seen it in recent years. Some unpublished records are: Washington, "one taken along Chartiers Creek, April 6, 1885" (Nease); Jacobs Creek and Scottdale, Westmoreland County, common (Medsger); Wilkinsburg, April 14, 1893 (Atkinson); Warren, a rare visitor (Simpson). Like many other shore birds, it probably crosses the mountains in a nonstop flight, and so passes unobserved.

Migration—The Pectoral Sandpiper is but little behind Wilson's Snipe in making its vernal appearance. A Washington County record for April 6 (1885) has already been listed. Three seasons' notes from Beaver give its arrival as follows: April 1, 1890; April 8, 1891; April 3, 1902. At Erie it is irregular, but is apt to be most numerous during April. In 1895 it was observed there as early as March 23 (Bacon). Crawford County (Linesville) dates are no earlier, however, than April 6 (1937—Todd). R. B. Simpson reports it from Warren on April 10, 1905, and on April 9 and 14, 1912. April 12 (1917) is the earliest arrival date for State College (Burleigh). Most birds of this species leave for the north by the end of April, but some are still present in early May, and a few stragglers stay even later. Flocks have been noted near Conneaut Lake, it is said, as late as May 28 and 29, and again on June 18, in 1926 (Langdon). These (if correctly identified) must have been nonbreeding birds, for eggs have been taken earlier than that in Alaska.

In the return movement this Sandpiper regularly arrives in our region in August, rarely earlier —July 19, 1933, Cherry Run Reservoir, Indiana County (Smyth); July 30, 1937, Pymatuning Lake (Skaggs). During the season of 1890 the species was rather common along the Ohio River at Beaver from August 6 to 20. I saw it at Hartstown on August 5, 1933. At Erie it was noted in 1897 on July 31, but this was exceptionally early; other arrival dates range from August 20 to September 4 (Bacon). Most of the birds have gone by the middle of October, but some are slow in leaving. "Last-seen" dates are as follows: Erie, October 31, 1895, and November 3, 1894 (Bacon); Warren, November 11, 1898 (Simpson); State College, October 13, 1908 (Harlow); Linesville, October 23, 1936 (West).

Habits—As already intimated, my own experience with the Pectoral Sandpiper in western Pennsylvania has been limited; and it seems to have come under the notice of only a few others. As it happened, I saw very few of these sandpipers on Presque Isle during the season of 1900, but, according to S. E. Bacon, that particular season must have been a poor one. He writes (in Todd, 1904): "The Pectoral Sandpiper is a transient visitor, irregular, but sometimes fairly common in the spring, more abundant and regular in the fall. At the former season, if found at all, it occurs in flocks numbering from twenty to forty or fifty birds, feeding in wet places in the fields." In the fall, however, "it is found in flocks seldom exceeding a dozen birds, frequenting the edges of the ponds, and the marsh at the mouth of Mill Creek in particular. It does not take to cover like the Wilson's Snipe, but stands so still and quiet that it is seldom seen until it flushes. It is a hard flier and single birds afford good sport." H. C. Kirkpatrick, referring to a flock observed on April 13, 1901, writes (in Sutton, 1928): "Some twenty-five or thirty of these sandpipers were seen on the muddy shore of a pond that lay in the open meadow bordering French Creek south of Meadville. The sun was just rising above the hills, giving promise of a warm spring day. The birds, perhaps having arrived during the night, were busily engaged in taking an early morning bath, dressing and preening their plumage and running about on the muddy shore. As the bright sunlight fell upon the scene it painted a picture sparkling with colors which I shall never forget."

"Grass Snipe," a name by which this species is known to gunners, is expressive of its fondness for overflowed fields; wet, grassy meadows; and shallow, partly overgrown pools or mud flats, where the water grasses afford some cover but are not dense or high enough to interfere with free movement. Elliott Coues says that "it never flocks on the beaches with the smaller sandpipers,"[1] but there are exceptions to this rule; for it was fairly common during one season along the exposed beaches of the Ohio River, and it associated freely with other shore birds and behaved as they did. The few spring birds I have seen have all been in wet fields; they resembled snipe in their general behavior, and flushed wild. The name "Pectoral" applies to the nuptial display of the male, in which the skin of the throat is puffed out and hangs down over the breast. The ordinary alarm-note of the species is a "loud reedy 'kerr' " (Nichols, 1931).

Actodromas maculata Todd, *Ann. Carnegie Mus.*, 1904, 2:539 (Erie and Presque Isle, Erie Co., transient)—Todd, in Bausman, *Hist. Beaver Co., Pa.*, 1904, 2:1198 (Beaver Co., transient).

Pisobia maculata Cooke, *Bull. Biol. Surv.* no. 35, 1910, 35 (Beaver, Beaver Co., migration)—Burleigh, *Wilson Bull.*, 1924, 36:76 (State College, Centre Co., spring transient)—Sutton, *Ann. Carnegie Mus.*, 1928, 18:100 (Crawford Co. localities and records).

"Pectoral Sandpiper" Harlow, *Cassinia*, 1912, 15:20 (Center Furnace Swamp, Centre Co., spring)—Sutton, *Bird-Lore*, 1924, 26:418 (Presque Isle, Erie Co., August and September, *fide* Allen)—Eastwood, *Bird-Lore*, 1925, 27:262 (Clinton Pond, Allegheny Co., May, *fide* Jones); 1926, 28:274 (Sandy Lake, Mercer Co., May, *fide* Squier)—Seiple, *Auk*, 1931, 48:113 ([Hartstown], Crawford Co., August).

Pisobia melanotos Christy, *Cardinal*, 1934, 3:173 (Erie, Erie Co., September)—West, *Redstart*, 1936, 4:4 (Pymatuning Lake, Crawford Co., October).

[1] *Key to North American Birds*, ed. 4, 1894, p. 627.

WHITE-RUMPED SANDPIPER

PISOBIA FUSCICOLLIS (Vieillot)

Description—Intermediate in size between the Pectoral and the Least Sandpiper, much *grayer* than either of these, and with the *upper tail coverts more extensively white*, showing conspicuously when in flight. *Fall plumage:* upperparts gray, more or less varied with black and rust color; a whitish line over the eye; underparts white, the breast and sides with gray shading and dusky streaking; legs and feet dusky green. *Spring plumage* is similar, but the upperparts and crown are much rustier.

Range and migration—This is another sandpiper that breeds in the arctic regions and goes to southern South America for the winter. For a bird that is very abundant during migration in the north country, at least along the coast, it is singularly rare at that time in western Pennsylvania; and even in the Erie region, where alone it seems to appear with great frequency, it is one of the rarer shore birds. On only one occasion—the great storm of August 29, 1893—did I ever find it common there, and this is the earliest date known for its appearance in the fall. Most of the other records are in October, with October 29 (1889) the latest. L. E. Hicks reports seeing several of these birds on Presque Isle on September 3, 1931—an arrival date comparable with the August record just cited. There is but one spring record for that locality, based on specimens in the Sennett Collection which were shot on the remarkably late spring date of June 4 (1875). G. M. Sutton refers to specimens taken on May 26 and 30, 1926, in the vicinity of Conneaut Lake. R. L. Fricke collected one near Linesville on May 8, 1929. Aside from the above, there remain only my Beaver County records made during the fall migration of 1899 at the mouth of the Beaver River. Two specimens were secured on September 20 and 30, respectively. The latter was a bird that had been hurt or wounded, since one wing was stiff, the plumage was dirty, and the body was emaciated. Unable to fly, it would eventually have perished. It was accompanied by a second bird (not secured), while two more were seen on October 9. According to my experience, the White-rumped Sandpiper is tame and unsuspicious. Its manner of flight is different from the swift, wayward movement of Baird's Sandpiper, and it need never be confused with that species, although it is of about the same size.

Actodromas fuscicollis Todd, *Ann. Carnegie Mus.*, 1904, 2:540 (Erie and Presque Isle, Erie Co., transient)—Todd, in Bausman, *Hist. Beaver Co., Pa.*, 1904, 2:1198 (Beaver Co., fall transient).

Pisobia fuscicollis Sutton, *Ann. Carnegie Mus.*, 1928, 18:101 (near Conneaut Lake, Crawford Co., May, *fide* Langdon)—Boggs, *Redstart*, 1937, 5:2 (Erie, Erie Co., September).

BAIRD'S SANDPIPER

PISOBIA BAIRDI (Coues)

Description—Intermediate in size between the Pectoral and the Least Sandpiper, and closely resembling them in coloration, but the white edgings of the feathers of the upperparts are generally more conspicuous, *producing a scaled appearance;* the *breast is not so heavily streaked;* and the *feet are black.* Easily distinguished from the White-rumped Sandpiper, with which it corresponds in size, by the *brown and buffy* (instead of grayish) *upperparts and breast.*

Range and migration—This sandpiper is a little-known species, and was not described until 1861. Its summer home lies north of the Arctic Circle, and in winter it migrates to southern South America. Like certain other shore birds, it seems to move north in the spring by the direct route up the Mississippi Valley, while in the return movement it swings off more to the eastward and follows the Atlantic coast. It was first added to the Pennsylvania list on September 16, 1889, when I collected a single bird on the beach at the mouth of the Beaver River in Beaver County. Two were seen at the same place on August 22, 1899, and one was secured; another was noted on September 20 of that year. No more were seen there until August 21, 1907, when a few were identified in a small mixed flock of shore birds which stayed about for a few days. In the meantime the species had been found on Presque Isle as a moderately common fall transient during the month of September, 1900, while S. E. Bacon's records, ranging in date from August 22 (1902) to October 5 (1894), indicated that it was presumably of regular occurrence. Arrival dates there for recent years are: August 19, 1931 (Beardslee), and August 21, 1937 (Trimble). The latest fall date from that locality is October 7, 1904 (Simpson). Other than these records, there are two from Allegheny County, supplied by D. A. Atkinson, which pertain to birds shot at Sandy Creek on September 14, 1896, and at Edgeworth on April 23, 1898. I have not examined the specimens on which these two records are based, and there is a possibility of misidentification. L. E. Hicks reports three birds seen on Presque Isle on June 1, 1931; this is a valid spring record.

Habits—Baird's Sandpiper is not as a rule shy, and with a little caution may be approached closely, especially if by itself. But when in the company of other and warier kinds, it seems to share their alarm and flies off with a jerky, erratic movement, uttering its distinctive notes, which are louder in volume and yet softer in tone than those of the Least Sandpiper. At Erie I saw it only on the outside beach of Presque Isle and in the muck near the breakwater. Along the Ohio River it is fond of the muddy, bouldery flats.

Tringa bairdii TODD, *Auk*, 1891, 8:240 (Beaver, Beaver Co., September).

Actodromas bairdii TODD, *Ann. Carnegie Mus.*, 1904, 2:540 (Presque Isle, Erie Co., fall transient)—TODD, in Bausman, *Hist. Beaver Co., Pa.*, 1904, 2:1198 (Beaver Co., fall transient).

"Baird Sandpiper" SIMPSON, *Oölogist*, 1911, 28:142, 143; and 1913, 30:150 (Presque Isle, Erie Co., September).

Pisobia bairdi BENT, *Bull. U. S. Nat. Mus.* no. 142, 1927, 193 (Beaver, Beaver Co., migration)—BOGGS, *Redstart*, 1937, 5:2 (Erie, Erie Co., September).

LEAST SANDPIPER (Plate 9)

PISOBIA MINUTILLA (Vieillot)

Description—Smallest of our shore birds—much smaller than the Spotted Sandpiper; bill *slender, black*, three-quarters of an inch long; *feet greenish. Adult in spring:* upperparts black, mottled and streaked with white and buff; *rump and upper tail coverts blackish, with a white streak on either side;* tail blackish in the middle, grayish on the sides; a whitish streak over the eye; fine dusky streaks on the sides of the head in general; underparts white, the breast shaded with gray and showing fine dusky streaks; wings dusky. *Adult and young in fall:* in general similar to the spring plumage, but much more rufescent, the feathers edged and tipped with rufous buff, especially prominent on the scapulars and tertiaries; the breast washed with buff, and the streaking faint, except sometimes on the sides. The small size, darker, *more rufescent upperparts, greenish feet* (the toes unwebbed), and slender bill, will serve to distinguish this species from the Semipalmated Sandpiper. In the latter the bill is heavier, the feet are black and partly webbed, and the coloration of the upperparts is grayish rather than rufescent.

Range—The Least Sandpiper breeds in the Hudsonian and southern Arctic life zones from Newfoundland and Labrador to Alaska. It winters from the Gulf coast and southern California to South America, as far as central Patagonia. Throughout most of the United States it is therefore a transient only. Although hardly to be classed as abundant, it is nevertheless a fairly common and regular migrant through our region, at least in those parts where the conditions are suitable. I used to see it in Beaver County every spring about small ponds and every fall on the beaches along the Ohio River. Although it is likely to occur almost anywhere, it is probably most numerous and regular along the shores of Lake Erie and in the flat, swampy areas of the northwestern counties. As yet, however, there are no records for the plateau region, and it probably seldom stops there in transit.

Migration—One of the later migrants among the shore birds, the Least Sandpiper does not reach our region as a rule until the first or second week in May, by which time many of its allies have passed through. The arrival date, April 18, cited for some point in Mercer County (Bent, 1927), is very doubtful. The next earliest date is April 27, for Butler (Roth), but even this is exceptional. More usual and acceptable dates are the following: Erie, May 8, 1900 (Todd); Hartstown, May 13, 1922 (Sutton); Cherry Run Reservoir, Indiana County, May 10, 1933 (Smyth); McKees Rocks, Allegheny County, May 6, 1899 (Eifrig); Chambersburg, May 7, 1925 (Sutton); State College, May 2, 1917 (Burleigh); Hollidaysburg, May 9, 1923 (Berg). "Last-seen" dates are: Erie, May 24, 1893 (Bacon); Conneaut Marsh, June 2, 1925 (Langdon); Beaver, May 28, 1891 (Todd); Warren, May 23, 1893 (Simpson); Wilkinsburg, June 11, 1896 (Atkinson); State College, May 26, 1916 (Burleigh); Sandy Lake, Mercer County, May 23, 1926 (Squier). The species is thus among the very last of the transients to pass northward.

It is wonderful that these little creatures, migrating so late in the season, can reach their northern breeding grounds, lay their eggs and rear their young, and reappear so soon; for in the return movement they often arrive in July, and never later than the second week in August. G. M. Sutton quotes G. M. Langdon to the effect that birds of this species were noted during June and July, 1926, at Conneaut Marsh, and H. C. Kirkpatrick took specimens at Meadville on July 25, 1895. Dr. Sutton saw one bird at "Rolling Rock," near Rector, Westmoreland County, on July 27, 1922. I saw a small flock on the Soldiers' Home grounds at Erie on July 19, 1910, and R. B. Simpson saw a few on Presque Isle on July 20, 1934. It is of course possible that at least some of these may have been nonbreeding individuals that had failed to complete their migration. No such doubt attaches to August dates, however, of which the following may be cited: Renovo, August 3, 1917 (Pierce); Erie, August 7, 1932 (Guynes); Linesville, August 5, 1935 (Hicks); Warren, August 8, 1893 (Simpson); Beaver, August 11, 1891 (Todd); Highland Park, Pittsburgh, August 15, 1912 (Burleigh). The stay of this species in the fall seldom extends beyond September, and there are only a few departure dates on record: Erie, October 3, 1895 (Bacon); near Meadville, September 7, 1908 (Kirkpatrick); Beaver, September 7, 1891 (Todd); Wilkinsburg, September 19, 1893 (Atkinson); Linesville, October 14, 1933 (Seiple; Dilley).

Habits—This diminutive sandpiper sometimes appears singly, but oftener in flocks of from five to twenty or occasionally more. It is fond of the society of other shore birds, especially during the fall movement, and mixed flocks are usually the rule at that season—at least when the birds are feeding. No more unsuspicious and confiding little creature than the Least Sandpiper—unless it be the Semipalmated Sandpiper—is to be found. Many a time on the beaches I have walked into the midst of a feeding flock without disturbing its members as they continued unconcernedly their busy search for food; often in their pretty ramblings they came so close that I might have touched them with my extended gun barrel had I been so disposed. A gunshot causes only momentary indecision in their feeding activities, for its significance does not seem to be understood. This species once shared in the persecution to which the larger shore birds were subjected by hunters and market-gunners, but since its removal from the game list it is maintaining its numbers fairly well. Fond as it is of the open beaches, mud flats, and the oozy margins of ponds, during the spring movement it will also often invade the grassy places favored by the Pectoral Sandpiper. Even a roadside puddle, or a pool in an open field, may tempt an occasional bird to alight. When flushed, this sandpiper rises with a reedy alarm-note and flies off swiftly, but rather erratically, to realight at a little distance. At some real or fancied alarm a flock will leap into the air simultaneously, with startling suddenness, assume a compact formation, and fly off with many a wheeling and sharp turning, then drift down again—perhaps at the same spot—to resume its feeding as before. While so engaged these birds are active, graceful little creatures, and the muddy flats where they have paused to rest and feed are often covered by the prints of their tiny feet.

Tringa minutilla Warren, *Birds Pa.*, ed. 2, 1890, 85 (Erie, Erie Co., transient)—Rhoads, *Auk*, 1899, 16:310 (Ohio River, Allegheny County, *fide* Link; [?]Pittsburgh, Allegheny Co., May)—Todd, *Ann. Carnegie Mus.*, 1904, 2:540 (Erie and Presque Isle, Erie Co., transient)—Todd, in Bausman, *Hist. Beaver Co., Pa.*, 1904, 2:1199 (Beaver Co., transient).

"Least Sandpiper" Simpson, *Oölogist*, 1910, 27:32 (Warren, Warren Co., fall)—Harlow, *Cassinia*, 1912, 15:20 (Center Furnace Swamp, Centre Co., spring)—Christy, *Cardinal*, 1923, v. 1, no. 2, [p. 16] (Clinton Pond, Allegheny Co., May)—Eastwood, *Bird-Lore*, 1926, 28:274 (Sandy Lake, Mercer Co., May, *fide* Squier).

Pisobia minutilla Christy, *Cardinal*, 1923, v. 1, no. 1, [p. 3] (Clinton Pond, Allegheny Co., spring transient)—Burleigh, *Wilson Bull.*, 1923, 35:84 (Highland Park, Allegheny Co., May and August); 1924, 36:76 (State College, Centre Co., spring transient)—Bent, *Bull. U. S. Nat. Mus.* no. 142, 1927, 202 (Mercer Co.; Butler, Butler Co.; Cataract, Clinton Co.; Beaver, Beaver Co.; and Renovo, Clinton Co., migration)—Sutton, *Ann. Carnegie Mus.*, 1928, 18:102 (Crawford Co. records and references)—Burleigh, *Cardinal*, 1929, 2:117 (Allegheny River, Allegheny Co., August).

RED-BACKED SANDPIPER

PELIDNA ALPINA SAKHALINA (Vieillot)

Description—About the size of the Solitary Sandpiper, but with much shorter legs; *bill* longer than the head, *perceptibly decurved toward the tip. Spring plumage: crown and upperparts* generally, *strongly rufous, varied with black;* wings dusky gray, with white on the secondaries showing in flight; throat and breast white, with dusky spots or streaks; *abdomen* with a *large patch of black*, more or less varied with white, and the under tail coverts white; bill and feet blackish. *Fall plumage:* upperparts gray; underparts white, the *breast and sides shaded or spotted with gray;* wings dusky, showing a little white on the coverts.

Range and migration—The Red-backed Sandpiper breeds in the arctic regions from eastern Siberia to Hudson Bay (at least), but does not go so far south in winter as do many of the other shore birds, and remains mostly within the United States. Its principal migration route in the East is by way of the Great Lakes. In the Erie region it is (or was) a common transient in the fall, but rare in the spring. It is a hardy species and migrates through that locality later in the fall than most of the other shore birds. September 5 (1937) and November 9 (1894) are the earliest and latest dates at that season, but the majority of birds pass through in October. In 1900 I encountered flocks of considerable size on October 25 and 26. Two birds that had previously been wounded were shot on November 15 and 16.

S. E. Bacon's notes (in Todd, 1904) on this species are pertinent: "In former years extensive flights [of sandpipers] took place about the first of November, upon which occasions bushels of them are said to have fallen to a single gun. During these great flights the flocks were accustomed to follow the outside beach of the Peninsula (having presumably come directly across the lake) to its southeastern extremity, thence crossing over to the sand-beach east of the mouth of Mill Creek, where, after having been sadly depleted by dozens of guns, they would finally rise high in the air and pass southward over the mainland, flock following flock all day long. I know this by hearsay only, but am positive that this is the bird that used to arrive in such numbers late in the fall. On October 29, 1897, I killed fifty-three of these birds out of two flocks, comprising in all perhaps as many more, and this is the nearest approach to a flight that has occurred of late years. Every season, however, numerous small flocks are found, appearing sometimes as early as the first week in October (October 2, 1894; October 3, 1895; October 6, 1891), but more commonly toward the latter part of the month. November 9, 1894, is my latest fall record. The spring records are few indeed. I took a specimen May 16, 1892, and on May 19, 1896, I saw a flock of perhaps forty birds, and with the sun glistening now on their red backs, and then on their black breasts, as they circled back and forth after the manner of Golden Plover, it was a sight not soon to be forgotten. On April 21, 1900, I saw one of these birds which had been killed in the fields; aside from this I have never known them to be met with away from the lake. Their flesh I consider very far from being a delicacy, tasting very fishy in fact."

Other spring dates for Erie are in the latter half of May and later: June 1, 1931, a flock of twenty-one (Hicks); and June 2, 1911 (Simpson). Dates from Crawford County correspond: M. B. Skaggs saw the species at Linesville as early as May 8 in 1937, and I also saw a small flock there on May 20. On November 2, 1930, S. J. Seiple saw a single bird at Conneaut Lake. I have never seen this sandpiper along the Ohio River, and R. B. Simpson has only two records for Warren (May 27, 1904, and May 20, 1919). The record for Clinton Pond, Allegheny County, cited below, rests on a sight identification of a single bird that was observed on May 3, 1925. Thomas Smyth recorded the species at Cherry Run Reservoir, Indiana County, on May 12, 1933. The vast majority of birds probably traverse the distance from the Great Lakes to the bays and estuaries of the Atlantic coast in one flight, without stopping en route; at any rate the species seems not to favor running water and to be attracted only by lakes and pools of some size and extent.

Tringa alpina pacifica WARREN, *Birds Pa.*, 1888, 235; and ed. 2, 1890, 86 (Erie, Erie Co., transient).

Pelidna alpina sakhalina TODD, *Ann. Carnegie Mus.*, 1904, 2:541 (Erie and Presque Isle, Erie Co., transient)—WEST, *Redstart*, 1936, 4:5 (Pymatuning Lake, Crawford Co., October)—BOGGS, *Redstart*, 1937, 5:2 (Erie, Erie Co., September -October).

"Dunlin" SIMPSON, *Oölogist*, 1911, 28:97 (Warren, Warren Co., May); 1912, 29:250, 350; and 1913, 30:149 (Presque Isle, Erie Co., June and October)—EASTWOOD, *Bird-Lore*, 1925, 27:262 (Clinton Pond, Allegheny Co., May, *fide* Jones).

Pelidna alpina pacifica SUTTON, *Ann. Carnegie Mus.*, 1928, 18:102 (Crawford Co. records and references).

"Red-backed Sandpiper" SEIPLE, *Auk*, 1931, 18:113 (Conneaut Lake, Crawford Co., November).

EASTERN DOWITCHER

LIMNODROMUS GRISEUS GRISEUS (Gmelin)

Description—Similar to Wilson's Snipe, from which it may be distinguished by its conspicuously *barred* (with black and white) *rump and upper tail coverts*. Bill more than two inches long—much longer than that of the Lesser Yellow-legs, in which the rump and upper tail coverts are also barred. The upperparts are varied with black and buff; the *underparts* in the adult are washed with *rufous cinnamon* and have *small dark spots*, which become bars on the sides and flanks. *Young birds* are paler below, sometimes almost white.

Range and migration—The breeding range of the Dowitcher is still imperfectly known. In migration it occurs chiefly along the Atlantic coast and occasionally in the interior of the country. With the exception of one record from Indiana County, it has been reported in our region only from the Erie-Crawford district. Writing in 1904 concerning its occurrence at Erie, I accounted it "a rare transient visitant, being mentioned by Dr. Warren as having been taken here (*Birds of Pennsylvania*, 1890, 83), doubtless on Mr. Sennett's authority, although there is no specimen in the Sennett collection. Concerning the single specimen in the Carnegie Museum [from Erie] Mr. Bacon speaks as follows: 'While hunting in the fields west of the city July 19, 1892, a single shore-bird whose note was unfamiliar to me flew by and alighted perhaps a mile away. Following up I came upon it again at the edge of a pool, and was successful in securing the bird, which proved to be of the present species. Since that time I have seen one or two individuals, believed to have been of this species, at the mouth of Mill Creek.' " The specimen in question is an adult. To this record of the species' occurrence at Erie several more can now be added. On September 4, 1933, I saw six dowitchers in a mixed flock of shore birds on the Soldiers' Home grounds, east of the breakwater. They were probing in the mud with their long bills. On September 7, 1936, J. E. Perry and I saw two at the same place; and on August 21, 1937, Miss Ruth Trimble saw one bird there. On October 10, 1934, one bird had been noted by W. E. Dilley. This is the latest fall record. An extraordinarily early record—July 9 (1933)—is supplied by W. M. Guynes. L. E. Hicks reports seeing a flock of six dowitchers on Presque Isle on June 1, 1931 (the only spring record for this locality), and another group of three on August 11, 1922. The species is also listed among the shore birds seen there on September 5 and October 10, 1937 (Boggs, 1937).

The creation of Pymatuning Lake is bringing about conditions that favor various species of aquatic birds, among them the Dowitcher. R. L. Fricke (1930) thus recounts his experience there with this species:

"On May 20 in a flooded field one mile south of Linesville, Crawford County, Pennsylvania, I saw three birds resembling Wilson's Snipe feeding with a flock of Lesser Yellow-legs. As I approached, the Yellow-legs flew off, but the other birds remained. Looking them over with an eight-power glass and getting to within a hundred feet of them I saw that they were Dowitchers. They became alarmed upon my approach and flew away, joining the Yellow-legs circling over the field. They circled close over head and I was fortunate enough to drop one from the flock, making identification certain. The bird was a female Dowitcher (*Limnodromus griseus griseus*), ovaries small, throat and breast bright reddish brown. This bird is the second specimen of the Dowitcher from western Pennsylvania in the Carnegie Museum."

S. J. Seiple reports seeing three birds of this species (possibly the same ones) at Hartstown three days earlier (May 17). In 1932 he saw a single bird at the same place on May 12, and in 1933, four at Linesville on May 15. There must have been a general movement about this time, for the next day Mr. Fricke counted fully a dozen dowitchers near the spillway at Linesville, and one at Hartstown on May 24. In 1934 and 1936 several were seen at Pymatuning in mid-May. Professor Seiple saw a single bird at Hartstown on August 1, 1930. It is interesting to note that the Pymatuning records are nearly all in the spring, on dates that correspond closely, while the Erie occurrences, on the other hand, are mostly for the fall migration. Thomas Smyth reports this species from Cherry Run Reservoir, Indiana County, on May 12, 1933—the earliest spring date available.

Macrorhamphus griseus WARREN, *Birds Pa.*, ed. 2, 1890, 82 (Erie Co., transient)—TODD, *Ann. Carnegie Mus.*, 1904, 2:538 (Erie, Erie Co., transient, *fide* Bacon).

Limnodromus griseus griseus FRICKE, *Auk*, 1930, 47:573 (Linesville, Crawford Co., May)—CHRISTY, *Cardinal*, 1934, 3:173 (Erie, Erie Co., September)—BOGGS, *Redstart*, 1937, 5:2 (Erie, Erie Co., September–October).

STILT SANDPIPER

MICROPALAMA HIMANTOPUS (Bonaparte)

Description—A little larger than the Solitary Sandpiper, but with *much longer bill and legs. In breeding dress* the upperparts are black, varied with buff, with some rufous shading on the head; the rump and upper tail coverts are barred with black and white (but not the tail itself); and the entire underparts are *mottled and barred with dusky markings on a buffy-white ground.* In *winter plumage* the colors are entirely different: *plain gray above*, with the *rump and upper tail coverts white*, with some dusky spotting; underparts white, the breast and sides showing obscure grayish streaks—almost exactly as in the Lesser Yellow-legs. Early in the season, individuals are variously intermediate between the two plumages above described, but the general proportions of the bird as compared with allied species, and particularly the relatively long, slender legs, give a peculiar appropriateness to its name of "Stilt" Sandpiper.

Range and migration—This is one of the rarer arctic-breeding shore birds, the exact distribution of which has not yet been fully worked out. It is probably confined in the summer, however, to the region west of Hudson Bay, and migrates through the interior as well as along the Atlantic coast (at least in the fall). It has been certainly identified in our region only at Erie, where, to quote from my 1904 report, it "must be listed as an irregular visitant in the fall. It may, indeed, occur every season, but gunners would scarcely distinguish it from the Lesser Yellow-legs, with which it is often found associated. It was first observed in this locality by Mr. Bacon and the writer at the time of the great storm of August 29, 1893, on which date five specimens were taken from a small flock at the mouth of Mill Creek. On September 13 of the same year Mr. Bacon secured a single bird, and another on the day following. It was not again met with until August 31, 1895, when he shot eight specimens out of a flock of forty birds, at least half of which were Lesser Yellow-legs. These were all obtained at the mouth of Mill Creek. Since that time, however, it has been detected on the Peninsula also, about the ponds, where one specimen was taken August 7, 1901, and a second, an adult bird still retaining much of the summer plumage, on August 20 of the same year." W. M. Guynes sends an Erie record for July 9, 1933; and on September 4 of the same year, B. H. Christy and I saw a considerable number of these birds on the mud flats along the breakwater that runs out from the Soldiers' Home grounds. There we watched them for some time. These are thus far the only certain records for our region.

Micropalama himantopus (?)WARREN, *Birds Pa.*, ed. 2, 1890, 83 (Clinton Co., *fide* Van Fleet)—TODD, *Ann. Carnegie Mus.*, 1904, 2:538 (Erie, Erie Co., fall transient)—CHRISTY, *Cardinal*, 1934, 3:173 (Erie, Erie Co., September).

SEMIPALMATED SANDPIPER (Plate 9)

EREUNETES PUSILLUS (Linnaeus)

Description—A small sandpiper, very little larger than the Least Sandpiper, from which it may be distinguished by its *grayer*, less rufescent, upperparts and by its *stouter bill* and *blackish feet*, with the front toes webbed at the base. *Adult in spring:* grayish, mottled and streaked with black; tail dark in the middle, grayish laterally; rump and upper tail coverts blackish in the middle, with white edges; the coverts have a white bar; wings dark; a pale line over the eye, and dusky streaks on the sides of the head; underparts white, the breast showing grayish and dusky streaks. *Adult and young in fall:* similar to the spring adult, but upperparts show more rusty-buff and whitish mottling, and underparts are usually without distinct streaks on the breast, which is more or less shaded with buff.

Range—The distribution of this species is comparable with that of the Least Sandpiper, its frequent associate at all seasons. The Semipalmated, however, ranges somewhat farther north in the summer than the Least, and it also occurs farther east at that season. Both winter mainly in South America and thence north to the Gulf coast. In our region the Semipalmated Sandpiper is of course only a transient, rather rare in the spring but common during the fall migration. This holds true at least for the vicinity of Erie; for elsewhere the species can scarcely be considered common. As a matter of fact, it has escaped the notice of most observers outside the Erie-Crawford district, or else has been confused with the Least Sandpiper. I used to see a few birds almost every fall along the Ohio River in Beaver County, but none in the spring. D. A. Atkinson took one at Sandy Creek, Allegheny County, on August 12, 1896; and B. H. Christy has observed the species at Clinton Pond, in the same county, in May, and also near Youngstown, Westmoreland County. R. B. Simpson considers it irregular at Warren, but rather commoner than the Least Sandpiper. Crawford County records (mainly from the Pymatuning region) show that it is irregular there also, but sporadically common.

Migration—Spring records for this sandpiper are few in number, but those that exist indicate that the northward movement of the species takes place at about the same time as that of the Least Sandpiper. Mr. Simpson shot one bird at Warren on April 22 (1901)—a very early date—and another on May 7 (1892). That the movement continues to the end of May or even beyond is the inference from the following records: Warren, May 23, 1893 (Simpson); near Youngstown, Westmoreland County, May 30, 1928 (Christy); Conneaut Lake, June 1, 1926 (Langdon); Erie, June 3, 1934 (Perry), and June 4, 1875 (Sennett). The fall movement begins very early, for in 1933 the species was noted at Erie as early as July 16 (Guynes), and was plentiful in 1934 on July 20 (Simpson). Near Linesville it was observed in 1937 on July 30 (Skaggs), and in 1938, on July 9 (Seiple). I have seen it at Hartstown on August 5 (1933) and at Beaver on August 6 (1890). The migration lasts about two months at any one place. Some late dates are as follows: Presque Isle, October 10, 1937 (Boggs); Linesville, October 14, 1933 (Seiple, Dilley); Beaver, October 3, 1902 (Todd).

Habits—This species and the Least Sandpiper resemble each other closely in size, coloration, and general habits; both have been given the name of "Peep." They are naturally tame and unsuspecting birds when by themselves, but in company with some of the larger shore birds, particularly the Yellow-legs (both species), they tend to share the wariness of their associates. Single birds or small groups are the rule at most places, but on Presque Isle and on the mud flats of the mainland opposite, the semipalmated sandpipers regularly come in large flocks. They often mix amicably with other species on the shore, but usually fly by themselves. They execute all their maneuvers on the wing—sudden twists and turns and starts and stops—as one bird. According to A. C. Bent (1927), "semipalmated sandpipers are fascinating birds to watch. When feeding on the beaches, they run along in a scattered flock just above the waveline, retreating rapidly as the wave advances, but sometimes being forced to flutter above it, all the time eagerly seeking for choice morsels. With head down, not held up as is the case with its companions the semipalmated plovers, it runs along dabbling here and there irregularly, and occasionally probing with its bill in the sand. These probings are not so deep nor so systematic as those of the sanderling, which makes a series of six to a dozen holes in succession throwing up the sand on either side. In its greediness the semipalmated sandpiper sometimes attempts to swallow too large a morsel for its small round mouth, which is much out of proportion to the stretch of the end of the bill, and many shakings of the head are needed to get a large morsel past the sticking point."

Ereunetes pusillus Rhoads, *Auk*, 1899, 16:310 (Vanport, Beaver Co., *fide* Link)—Todd, *Ann. Carnegie Mus.*, 1904, 2:542 (Erie and Presque Isle, Erie Co., transient)—Todd, in Bausman, *Hist. Beaver Co., Pa.*, 1904, 2:1199 (Beaver Co. transient)—Cooke, *Bull. Biol. Surv.* no. 35, 1910, 46 (Beaver, Beaver Co., migration)—Christy, *Cardinal*, 1923, v. 1, no. 1, [p. 3] (Clinton Pond, Allegheny Co., spring transient)—Bent, *Bull. U. S. Nat. Mus.* no. 142, 1927, 244 (Grove City, Mercer Co.; Beaver, Beaver Co.; and Warren, Warren Co., migration)—Sutton, *Ann. Carnegie Mus.*, 1928, 18:103 (Crawford Co. localities and records)—Boggs, *Redstart*, 1937, 5:2 (Erie, Erie Co., September–October).

"Semipalmated Sandpiper" Simpson, *Oölogist*, 1910, 27:32 (Warren, Warren Co., fall); and 1912, 29:250, 350 (Presque Isle, Erie Co., May–June)—Christy, *Cardinal*, 1923, v. 1, no. 2, [p. 16] (Clinton Pond, Allegheny Co., May)—Boulton, *Bird-Lore*, 1928, 30:271 (Pittsburgh, Allegheny Co., May, *fide* McClintock; Youngstown, Westmoreland Co., May, and Sewickley, Allegheny Co., May, *fide* Christy), 337 (Presque Isle, Erie Co., August, *fide* Perry)—Christy, *Cardinal*, 1933, 3:148 (Geneva, Crawford Co., May).

WESTERN SANDPIPER

EREUNETES MAURII Cabanis

Description—Similar in size and in coloration (at least in fall plumage) to the Semipalmated Sandpiper, but bill relatively longer, usually longer than the head (at least in females), and more tapering; scapulars usually rusty, contrasting with the gray of the upperparts generally.

Range and migration—Alaska (along the shores of the Bering Sea) is the summer home of this sandpiper, but it appears on the Atlantic coast regularly during the fall months, and thus, for a shore bird, has a remarkable and unique migration route. W. W. Cooke[1] says that records for the intervening region in the interior of North America are few and far between. I failed to find this bird at Erie in 1900, although its relative, the Semipalmated Sandpiper, was exceedingly abundant there during August and September of that year. My records from western Pennsylvania, heretofore unpublished, are therefore of peculiar interest. On August 21, 1907, I observed through a glass a single individual of this species in a mixed flock of semipalmated, least, and Baird's sandpipers, along the beach of the Ohio River at Beaver, and was presently successful in securing it. The much longer bill is a conspicuous feature in life, and it readily served to distinguish the bird from the semipalmated sandpipers that composed the bulk of the flock. This specimen is now in the Carnegie Museum exhibition of local birds.

More recently, L. E. Hicks reports seeing a small flock of this species on Presque Isle on August 11, 1928, and again on September 8, 1931. He considers it not rare in Ohio during migration. C. S. Beardslee sends an Erie record for August 31, 1933, and R. T. Peterson supplies one for September 5, 1937. I. B. Boggs claims to have seen the species there as late as October 10, 1937. Mr. Peterson, writing to confirm his identification, adds that "aside from the character of the longer bill, the bird has a subtle, but distinctly different carriage in life. It works more in deeper water than the other smaller 'Peeps,' often wading to its belly. Its bill is pointed at a steeper angle toward the mud when feeding. The bird is slightly larger than the Semipalmated, and in the early fall is usually two-toned in color, the rusty in the scapulars contrasting noticeably at close range with the grayer coloration of the rest of the upperparts."

Ereunetes mauri Boggs, *Redstart*, 1937, 5:2 (Erie, Erie Co., September–October).

[1] U. S. Department of Agriculture, Biological Survey, *Bulletin*, no. 35, 1910, p. 47.

BUFF-BREASTED SANDPIPER

TRYNGITES SUBRUFICOLLIS (Vieillot)

Description—Equal in size to the Solitary Sandpiper, but bill much smaller (*shorter than the head*), and general coloration very different. Upperparts buff, varied with black; flight feathers marbled with black on their inner webs, showing on the under side; *underparts dull buff*, the breast and sides sometimes marked with a few black spots; legs yellowish. No sign of white on the upper tail coverts.

Range and migration—The Buff-breasted Sandpiper is one of the rarer shore birds, at least in the eastern part of its migration range. It breeds in high northern latitudes, migrates mainly through the Mississippi Valley, and winters in southern South America. E. H. Eaton quotes several records for western New York in his work on the birds of that state, but there are no recent published records from Ohio, nor is the species included in Warren's list. It appears in the present work on the strength of two reports only. A single specimen was shot near Chambersburg, Franklin County, on May 31, 1899, by John Fahnestock, and is now preserved in the collection of F. S. Flack, a taxidermist of that place, where it has been examined by G. M. Sutton. L. E. Hicks reports seeing two individuals on Presque Isle on September 1, 1928.

MARBLED GODWIT

LIMOSA FEDOA (Linnaeus)

Description—A large shore bird with a *decidedly upturned bill*, nearly four inches long. Upperparts varied with black and buff; *wings cinnamon buff*, with the outer edge black. The adult is narrowly barred below on a pale clay-colored background; the young bird lacks the barring. Decidedly larger than the Greater Yellow-legs.

Range and migration—The summer home of the Marbled Godwit extends from the upper Mississippi Valley to southern Saskatchewan, but its breeding range is now greatly restricted. In migration it at one time regularly reached the Atlantic coast, where it is now almost unknown. This peculiar east-and-west movement would account for the Pennsylvania occurrences here cited. Warren's loose statement, on Sennett's authority, that the species is a straggler in Crawford and Erie counties is too indefinite, but it may have been based on a specimen known to have been taken by one W. G. Sargent in the spring, late in the 1870's, at Conneaut Marsh, as related by G. M. Sutton. D. G. Elliot (1895) also quotes Sennett as authority for the statement that the species breeds in our region—a report that seems wildly improbable. A specimen shot by J. E. Reynolds at Edinboro, Erie County, on October 21, 1898, and presented to Dr. Sutton, who in turn gave it to the Carnegie Museum, constitutes the second valid record for our region. That the species is still an occasional visitant here is indicated by some recent occurrences. W. D. Hunter of Racine has two mounted specimens that were taken on the south side of Pymatuning Swamp, southwest of Linesville, on October 2, 1929. J. E. Perry states that on October 1, 1934, he saw and satisfactorily identified a single marbled godwit on the shores of Presque Isle Bay, near the Soldiers' Home grounds. It was studied at a distance of less than forty feet. W. M. Guynes saw one (perhaps the same bird) there on September 23 of that year.

Limosa fedoa (?)WARREN, *Birds Pa.*, ed. 2, 1890, 88 (Crawford and Erie Co., *fide* Sennett)—(?)ELLIOT, *N. Am. Shore Birds*, 1895, 105 (western Pa., breeding, *fide* Sennett)—SUTTON, *Ann. Carnegie Mus.*, 1928, 18:104 (Conneaut Marsh, Crawford Co., spring, *fide* Sargent; Edinboro Lake, Erie Co., October, *fide* Reynolds)—CHRISTY, *Cardinal*, 1935, 4:18; and PERRY, *Cardinal*, 1935, 4:49 (Erie, Erie Co., October).

SANDERLING

CROCETHIA ALBA (Pallas)

Description—A little larger than the Spotted Sandpiper, with a straight bill as long as the head, and *black feet*, with only three toes (the hind toe wanting). *Spring:* upperparts varied with rufous, black, and (sometimes) ashy-gray markings, the wings dusky black, with a white bar on the coverts; the *sides of the head*, also the *throat and breast, varied with dusky and rufous* markings on a whitish ground; rest of *underparts pure white*. *Fall adult:* similar to the spring adult, but with little or no rufous tint, the upperparts being varied with gray and black, and the spotting below reduced. *Young in fall:* crown and back black, spotted with grayish white, these areas separated from each other by a paler, grayish band on the nape; wings as in the adult; throat and entire underparts pure white, with sometimes a faint tinge of buff on the throat.

Range and migration—The Sanderling has a wide range in both hemispheres; it breeds in high latitudes and migrates in winter to Malaysia, Africa, and South America. It is thus virtually cosmopolitan in its distribution. At Presque Isle and in the Lake Erie region, where it is (or was) the most abundant of the transient shore birds during the fall migration, it arrives early in the season, never later than August, and sometimes even earlier (July 16, 1933 [Guynes]; July 27, 1900 [Bacon]). It remains well into October, and a few birds may linger into November. Oddly enough, there is but one spring record for Erie: two individuals observed on June 1, 1931, by L. E. Hicks. The only other spring occurrence of this species within our region is attested by D. A. Atkinson, who shot a specimen at Davis Island, Allegheny County, on April 2, 1894. These dates are extremes. B. H. Christy saw one bird in the fall along the Ohio River near Dixmont, Allegheny County, on September 2, 1931. The species is rare away from Lake Erie. Indeed, there are only two other records for the interior of western Pennsylvania. One of these is based on a specimen taken at Conneaut Lake on November 1, 1909 (Sutton, 1928); the other is that of a bird identified at the Greensburg Reservoir on August 21, 1937, by Miss Ruth Trimble. The Sanderling is a species that tends to avoid the stagnant pools and running waters where so many of the other shore birds are at home; hence it probably passes directly from the shores of Lake Erie to the Atlantic coast in one flight.

Habits—During the season of 1900 the Sanderling, to quote from my 1904 report, "was met with exclusively on the outside beach [of Presque Isle], and there were not a few days when it was the only shore-bird seen there. Single birds, or two or three together, were often found, but as a rule it was observed in flocks of a dozen or thereabouts, keeping close to the edge of the water, running down and back again with the recession and advance of the waves, ceaseless in activity and graceful in every movement. The flocks of old birds met with earlier in the season were sometimes difficult to approach, but the young, which alone were found after the first of September, were usually quite unsuspicious, and would often come within a few yards if the observer remained perfectly still. A flock of about two dozen birds was seen on the mud-flats at the Soldiers' Home grounds during a brief visit made there by the writer on August 22, 1903, this being the only time the bird was ever noted away from a sandy beach." Sanderlings come regularly to this feeding ground; they have often been observed there in recent years.

Calidris arenaria Warren, *Birds Pa.*, ed. 2, 1890, 87 (Erie, Erie Co., transient)—Rhoads, *Auk*, 1899, 16:310 (Davis Island, Allegheny Co., *fide* Atkinson)—Todd, *Ann. Carnegie Mus.*, 1904, 2:542 (Presque Isle, Erie Co., transient).

"Sanderling" Simpson, *Oölogist*, 1911, 28:142, 143; and 1913, 30:149 (Presque Isle, Erie Co., fall)—Sutton, *Bird-Lore*, 1924, 26:418 (Presque Isle, Erie Co., August and September, *fide* Allen)—Boulton, *Bird-Lore*, 1928, 30:337, 401 (Presque Isle, Erie Co., August, *fide* Perry).

Crocethia alba Sutton, *Ann. Carnegie Mus.*, 1928, 18:103 (Conneaut Lake, Crawford Co., November, *fide* Welshons)—Christy, *Cardinal*, 1931, 3:16 (Dixmont, Allegheny Co., September).

AVOCETS, STILTS

FAMILY RECURVIROSTRIDAE

THE MEMBERS of this family may readily be distinguished from other shore birds by their larger size, their extremely long legs, and their long, slender, upcurved bills. They wade and feed in shallow water, and swim easily if necessary. The family consists of only a few species, and these inhabit the warmer parts of the world. The Avocet, of which there are but two records for our region, is a western species that occurs only rarely in the East.

AVOCET

RECURVIROSTRA AMERICANA Gmelin

Description—A large, conspicuous shore bird with an *upcurved bill* from three to four inches long. The general color is *white;* the wings (in part) and the scapular feathers are dusky black. In breeding plumage the head, neck, and breast are more or less shaded with cinnamon buff.

Range—The Avocet as a breeding bird is principally confined to the central western United States and adjacent Canadian provinces, although a few instances of its breeding have been recorded from as far east as Wisconsin. There are numerous spring and fall migration records, however, from some of the states adjoining Pennsylvania, so that its occurrence in our region might have been anticipated. G. M. Sutton (1928) writes that "Mr. Welshons took an adult on May 16, 1905, at the head of Conneaut Lake. The bird was alone; it was secured early on a misty morning. This specimen, which is mounted, is at present in Detroit, Michigan." A more recent record is supplied by L. E. Hicks, who reports that on September 12, 1936, he saw a single avocet in a large flock of shore birds at the eastern end of Presque Isle.

Recurvirostra americana SUTTON, *Ann. Carnegie Mus.*, 1928, 18:96 (Conneaut Lake, Crawford Co., May, *fide* Welshons)—HICKS, *Auk*, 1937, 54:538 (Presque Isle, Erie Co., September).

PHALAROPES

FAMILY PHALAROPODIDAE

THE PHALAROPES have been called "swimming sandpipers." They differ from sandpipers mainly in the structure of their feet, the toes of which are margined with a lobed or scalloped membrane; the tarsi are also much compressed. The plumage of the breast and belly is thick like that of gulls. There are but three species of Phalaropes, each representing a separate genus. Two (the Northern and the Red Phalarope) are pelagic and breed in the northern regions of both the Old and the New World, and migrate far southward in the winter. A third species (Wilson's Phalarope) is confined to the interior of North America. All three are rare transients in western Pennsylvania.

The females in this family are larger and more brightly colored than the males. They also take the lead in courtship activities and in selection of the nesting site. The incubation of the eggs and care of the young are left to the males.

RED PHALAROPE

PHALAROPUS FULICARIUS (Linnaeus)

Description—Fall and winter plumage: upperparts dark gray, sometimes more or less varied with brown because of feathers left over from the summer plumage; wings and tail dusky black, the former with a prominent white bar on the greater coverts; head white in front, dusky brown behind; a white stripe behind the eyes, and below this a dark stripe; throat and rest of underparts white, the sides with some grayish shading. Decidedly larger than the Northern Phalarope, with a much *broader, heavier bill.*

Range and migration—In the breeding season the Red Phalarope is strictly confined to the far North, and its range is circumpolar. During the fall migration it is exceedingly abundant in the Gulf of St. Lawrence, where I have seen it in the month of October in flocks and in smaller groups. In the interior of the country, however, it is only an accidental visitant. My 1904 report states that "it occurs at Erie as a very rare transient. In Mr. Sennett's collection there is a female in winter plumage shot October 10, 1899 [1889] by Mr. James Thompson. Just six years later, on October 10, 1895, Mr. Bacon secured another specimen at the mouth of Mill Creek, which bird is now in the Carnegie Museum. These examples appear to constitute the first authentic records for Pennsylvania, although the species has been noted from both sides, at Cleveland and Buffalo (Wheaton, *Birds of Ohio*, 1882, 467, and Savage, *Auk*, 12, 1895, 313)."

G. M. Cook sends a sight record of a single bird that was identified by a party of three observers at Erie Bay on November 11, 1934. The record for Beaver County, cited in the references below, refers to a specimen that I collected on October 3, 1902, along the Ohio River at Beaver. When first observed this bird was with a mixed group of killdeers and semipalmated sandpipers, which were feeding along the beach. It stayed a little farther out than the others and kept swimming about in the shallow water, and it was not particularly shy. These few records thus correspond in date with those cited by A. C. Bent[1] for the fall migration along the coast, and with those for the western Lake Erie region listed by L. W. Campbell.[2] There are no local spring records for this phalarope.

Crymophilus fulicarius TODD, *Ann. Carnegie Mus.*, 1904, 2:535 (Erie, Erie Co., October)—TODD, in Bausman, *Hist. Beaver Co., Pa.*, 1904, 2:1198 ([Beaver], Beaver Co., fall).

[1] U. S. National Museum, *Bulletin*, no. 142, 1927, p. 15.
[2] *Auk*, 1938, 55:89.

WILSON'S PHALAROPE

STEGANOPUS TRICOLOR Vieillot

Description—The largest of the phalaropes (only a little smaller than the Lesser Yellow-legs), with a very slender black bill, one and a quarter inches long. *Adult in spring:* upperparts varied with gray and chestnut (in longitudinal pattern); wings plain dusky; tail gray, the outer feathers (partly) and the upper coverts, white; crown pale gray, fading into white on the hindneck; a broad black band through the eye, passing into chestnut on the sides of the neck; eyelids white; underparts white, the breast more or less shaded with rufous buff. *Fall plumage:* crown and upperparts generally grayish, but the rump whitish; the forehead, sides of head, and entire underparts, white; a slight grayish line underneath the eye. The upperparts are colored much as in the Dunlin in the same plumage, but the bill is of course differently shaped.

Range and migration—Wilson's Phalarope is properly a Mississippi Valley species, which in migration sometimes reaches the Atlantic coast. Warren says that "at Erie bay small flocks of these phalaropes are sometimes to be seen in the fall swimming in the water like ducks." On the basis of this statement alone I included the present species in my 1904 Erie list, but I now believe that it should have been relegated to the hypothetical category so far as that particular locality is concerned. A recent record for Crawford County, however, places the species on the state list. R. L. Fricke secured a fine adult specimen near Linesville on May 15, 1934; it is now on exhibition in the Carnegie Museum. The species may yet be found breeding in the Pymatuning region.

(?)*Phalaropus tricolor* WARREN, *Birds Pa.*, ed. 2, 1890, 76 (Erie, Erie Co., transient).

(?)*Steganopus tricolor* TODD, *Ann. Carnegie Mus.*, 1904, 2:536 (Erie, Erie Co., fall, Warren's record).

NORTHERN PHALAROPE

LOBIPES LOBATUS (Linnaeus)

Description—The smallest of the phalaropes, about the size of the Spotted Sandpiper. *Fall plumage:* upperparts *blackish*, more or less *varied with buffy stripes;* wings and tail black, the latter with a broad white band on the greater coverts; top of head dusky; forehead and sides of the head white, with a blackish stripe just behind the eye; entire underparts white, with sometimes a little grayish shading or striping on the sides. The *bill* is about four-fifths of an inch long and *very slender*.

Range and migration—The Northern Phalarope, like the Red Phalarope, is an arctic-breeding species of circumpolar range. It does not go so far north as the other, however, and during migration it occurs regularly in the interior of the country, although it is not nearly so common there as it is along the coast. All the records for our region come from the westernmost counties and pertain to the fall movement, which takes place from August to October. From Erie, where, if anywhere, the species might be expected to occur, there are but three positive records. These were listed in my 1904 report: "Two specimens, females, taken September 29, 1888, and October 10, 1889, are in Mr. Sennett's collection, while a third specimen was secured by the writer at the mouth of Mill Creek on the occasion of the great storm of August 29, 1893, and is now deposited in the U. S. National Museum (Biological Survey Collection)." In the same collection is a specimen taken by P. W. Roth at Conneauttee Lake, Erie County, on September 3, 1895. I shot one bird at Beaver on September 26, 1890, in a marshy spot close to the Ohio River; this specimen is now preserved in the U. S. National Museum. G. M. Sutton gives three fall records for Conneaut Lake, ranging in date from August 29 (1926) to September 24 (1909). The Northern Phalarope, according to my experience, is singularly incautious during the fall season and may be closely approached without any difficulty.

Phalaropus lobatus WARREN, *Birds Pa.*, ed. 2, 1890, 76 (Erie, Erie Co., transient)—TODD, *Auk*, 1891, 8:240 (Beaver, Beaver Co., September)—TODD, *Ann. Carnegie Mus.*, 1904, 2:535 (Erie, Erie Co., fall transient)—TODD, in Bausman, *Hist. Beaver Co., Pa.*, 1904, 2:1198 (Beaver Co., fall).

Lobipes lobatus SUTTON, *Ann. Carnegie Mus.*, 1928, 18:96 (Conneaut Lake, Crawford Co., fall records)—MITCHELL, *Cardinal*, 1940, 5:71 (Pymatuning Lake, Linesville, Crawford Co., October).

JAEGERS, SKUAS

FAMILY STERCORARIIDAE

THE JAEGERS are aquatic birds of prey that habitually attack terns and smaller gulls, forcing them to disgorge their food. In appearance they are gull-like, but are darker in color than most gulls, and their central tail feathers are more or less elongated. The bill is more prominently hooked and bears a large, horny cere at its base; the claws on the toes are large and sharp. The members of this family are inhabitants mainly of the seacoast—the Jaegers in the arctic, and the Skuas in both the arctic and the antarctic, regions. Occasionally they appear inland on the larger lakes and water-courses. Three species of Jaegers are known, one of which is sporadic within our limits. The occurrence of the Pomarine Jaeger in western Pennsylvania is questionable.[1]

[1]B. H. WARREN, *Report on the Birds of Pennsylvania*, ed. 2, 1890, p. 11.

PARASITIC JAEGER

STERCORARIUS PARASITICUS (Linnaeus)

Description—A little smaller than the Ring-billed Gull; tail more or less wedge-shaped, the two central feathers projecting. *Young in fall plumage:* dusky brown, varied with buff, the under surface of the wings showing a whitish patch or bar at the base of the flight feathers. The head is perceptibly paler (with more buffy mottling) than the back, and the wing coverts (upper and under) and tail coverts are coarsely marked with buff. (Description from a Pennsylvania specimen.)

Range and local status—In the breeding season the Parasitic Jaeger is confined to the Arctic Life Zone of both Eurasia and America. It winters to the southward, migrating mainly coastwise, but it is not common on the Atlantic side and is rare in the interior. It has been noted at intervals on Lake Erie and Lake Ontario, however, and two locality records fall within the limits of our region. On October 14 (not 15), 1874, a certain Merrick Low shot a young parasitic jaeger at the head of Erie Bay, and the specimen came into the possession of Sennett, as reported by Warren (1890). A bird believed to be of this species was seen in the same locality on May 22, 1904, by S. E. Bacon, who wrote that "it was a handsome, spirited bird, falcon-like in its movements, and when noted was pursuing a Common Tern" (in Todd, 1904). Warren also cites Van Fleet as his authority for stating that the Parasitic Jaeger has occurred in Clinton County, but no evidence is given. There is a more recent and perfectly well-authenticated record from this county, however, cited by W. W. Cooke (1915). It is based on a female specimen formerly in the collection of A. K. Pierce, which was captured at Shintown, near Renovo, on June 18, 1911. This specimen was identified at the Bureau of Biological Survey. The late date of its capture would suggest that it was a nonbreeding bird that had failed to migrate. Both the Pierce and the Sennett specimens are now preserved in the Carnegie Museum. The species was also observed and identified on Presque Isle by A. J. Woodward and W. M. Guynes in the fall of 1934, on September 30 (two) and October 7 (three). These birds were engaged in chasing gulls at the time.

Stercorarius parasiticus WARREN, *Birds Pa.*, ed. 2, 1890, 12 (Erie Bay, Erie Co., *fide* Sennett; [?]Clinton Co., *fide* Van Fleet)—TODD, *Ann. Carnegie Mus.*, 1904, 2:502, 596 (Erie Bay, Erie Co.; Sennett's record)—COOKE, *Bull. U. S. Dept. Agric.*, no. 292, 1915, 9 (Renovo, Clinton Co., and Erie, Erie Co., migration).

GULLS, TERNS

FAMILY LARIDAE

GULLS AND TERNS inhabit the seacoasts, lakes, and larger watercourses throughout the world and are most numerous in the Northern Hemisphere. They are long-winged swimming birds, graceful and powerful in flight. Their feet have the anterior toes more or less fully webbed; the hind toe is small and elevated, sometimes rudimentary or nearly obsolete. The legs are placed near the middle of the body, and the birds, therefore, assume a nearly horizontal position in standing or perching.

The Gulls, Subfamily Larinae, are larger, heavier-bodied birds than the Terns and possess more or less hooked bills, square or rounded tails, and less pointed wings. The Terns, Subfamily Sterninae, have straight, pointed bills, forked tails, and narrow, pointed wings. They are more graceful in flight and hold their bills downward in readiness for capturing food, for which they plunge from considerable heights. Gulls, as a rule, pick their food up from the surface of the water. Both groups are economically important as scavengers; they also feed extensively on insects, fish, and other marine animals.

Both Gulls and Terns nest in scattered colonies near the water. The young are covered with soft, mottled down. They are able to run about and take to the water soon after they are hatched, but until nearly grown are cared for by the parents.

Most Gulls require at least three years to attain adult plumage, and in immature stages are often difficult to identify satisfactorily in life. The necessarily brief descriptions in these pages may be of some help to the student, but they are far from definitive. Caution is needed in attempting to name birds of this group.

Warren's records for three species of Terns (Roseate, Least, and Sooty) are not considered satisfactory insofar as they apply to western Pennsylvania.

GLAUCOUS GULL

LARUS HYPERBOREUS Gunnerus

Description—Similar to the Herring Gull, but considerably *larger*. In the adult the upperparts and wings are a pale pearl gray, and the *wings* are *uniform without any black tips*. *Young birds* are shaded and mottled with gray and buff but are much lighter-colored than the young of the Herring Gull, and the wings appear uniform; the primaries are lighter (if anything) than the mantle, never darker as in the other species.

Range and local status—This large gull is properly a bird of the arctic countries, but in winter it comes south regularly, although in small numbers, to the Great Lakes. The species was included in my hypothetical list of the birds of Erie (1904), but R. B. Simpson has supplied the first actual record from our region. While at Erie on February 22, 1908, he observed a single large gull in a flock of some twenty-five or thirty herring gulls, about the open water at the mouth of Mill Creek. The other gulls frequently came within shotgun range, but the glaucous gull stayed a little too far out. Mr. Simpson took advantage of the opportunity to compare the two kinds in life, however, and is confident of the identity of this particular bird; indeed, it could scarcely have been of any other species.

Since that time, W. M. Guynes has produced additional evidence of the occurrence of this gull. He writes that since 1932 he has repeatedly observed individuals in the early spring months about the open water in and near the city docks at Erie, where he has been able to study them and to compare them with the herring gulls that were always present. In 1932 one bird was noted on March 18 and remained for about two weeks. Mr. Guynes says, "It did not have the fighting disposition of either the Herring or the Ring-billed Gulls, as both kinds whipped it more than once while I was watching." On March 19, 1933, he saw three birds; from February 10 to March 25, 1934, several more; and in February, 1935, two. The species has also been identified there in January by C. S. Beardslee and in December and February by J. E. Perry.

"Glaucous Gull" SIMPSON, *Oölogist*, 1911, 28:33 (Erie Bay, Erie Co., February)—BROOKS, *Redstart*, 1936, 3:49 (Erie Bay, Erie Co., March)—PERRY, *Cardinal*, 1938, 4:178 (Erie Bay, Erie Co., December).

ICELAND GULL

LARUS LEUCOPTERUS Vieillot

Description—Similar to the Glaucous Gull in general coloration, but *much smaller* (smaller even than the Herring Gull). *Wings* (adult) *light-colored, without any black*, but usually showing some dull grayish outer edgings near their tips. Immature birds are clouded and mottled with gray, but the wings appear uniform or nearly so.

Range and local status—This gull breeds in the arctic regions on both sides of the North Atlantic, and moves southward in the winter, on our side to the coasts of New England and Long Island, and in the interior to the Great Lakes, where, however, it is comparatively rare. Moreover, it is scarcely distinguishable in life from Kumlien's Gull (*Larus kumlieni*), a form which some authorities rank as a hybrid and which is therefore omitted from the American Ornithologists' Union *Check-List*. The Iceland Gull has been noted occasionally in winter by local observers at Buffalo, and there are also a few Ohio records. W. M. Guynes claims that a gull he saw at Erie on March 24, 1934, must have been of this species. It was observed while feeding in the open water at the foot of State Street with a flock of herring gulls, from which it was readily distinguished by its smaller size and different coloration. It was not particularly shy, and was repeatedly approached within fifty feet. L. E. Hicks writes that on April 3, 1937, an adult gull of this species was identified on Presque Isle by F. B. Chapman and himself. I think that under the circumstances both these records are acceptable—so long at least as Kumlien's Gull is not recognized as distinct.

GREAT BLACK-BACKED GULL

LARUS MARINUS Linnaeus

Description—The largest of our gulls, much larger than the Herring Gull. In the adult the *back and wings are sooty black;* the rest of the plumage is white. Young birds resemble in general the corresponding stages of the Herring Gull, but are decidedly larger and are usually darker above, with coarser markings, but paler below. The dark-colored primaries will invariably suffice to distinguish this species from the Glaucous Gull, the only other large gull with which it might be confused.

Range and local status—In North America this magnificent gull is strictly confined to the north Atlantic coast during the breeding season and does not come farther south than Nova Scotia. It is particularly abundant in the Gulf of St. Lawrence, whence come the individuals that stray to the

Great Lakes in winter. I saw a gull at Erie in the fall of 1900 that I suspected was of this species, and it was described to me by fishermen as being encountered in early winter far out on the lake, where the nets are set. Its occurrence on Erie Bay has lately been verified by three observers independently. Maurice Brooks includes this species in his list of birds noted there on March 15, 1936. In 1937 M. B. Skaggs saw a single bird on February 20, and on the next day J. E. Perry saw four.

That this gull is not necessarily confined to the large bodies of water, however, is indicated by several records. R. B. Simpson writes from Warren: "In February, 1895, we had a blizzard, lasting from the fourth of the month to the eleventh, during which time the thermometer stayed from zero to twenty-five degrees below, with high northwest winds and snow. It was a severe winter anyway; the snow lay deep and the river was icebound. When the blizzard was over, I took a trip down the river and saw a gull that answered the description of the Black-backed species, its back and wings being black, the rest white. It did not stop, but was flying slowly against the wind and snow."

More recently, G. E. Welshons has been quoted by G. M. Sutton (1928) to the effect that this species has occurred in Crawford County: "During late winter and early spring in 1904 he [Mr. Welshons] repeatedly saw several Black-backed Gulls on the ice in the middle of Conneaut Lake. He states that, even at a distance, they appeared much larger than the numerous Herring Gulls. On November 4, 1926, he noted it again at Conneaut Lake." I believe that these sight records should be credited, since the species (in the adult stage) could scarcely be confused with any other.

Larus marinus Sutton, *Ann. Carnegie Mus.*, 1928, 18:54 (Conneaut Lake, Crawford Co., winter and spring, *fide* Welshons).
"Great Black-backed Gull" Brooks, *Redstart*, 1936, 3:49 (Erie Bay, Erie Co., March)—Skaggs, *Wilson Bull.*, 1937, 49:294 (Erie Bay, Erie Co., February).

HERRING GULL

LARUS ARGENTATUS SMITHSONIANUS Coues

Description—One of the larger gulls, with a *wing-spread* of almost *five feet*. *Adult:* head, neck, underparts, rump, and tail, pure white; back pale pearl gray; *wings* pearl gray above, white below, *black towards the tip, with a white spot*, and each feather with a narrow white tip; bill dull yellow, with an orange-red spot near the tip of the lower mandible; feet pale flesh color. *Young:* mottled with dusky brown and white, both above and below, the wings and tail nearly uniform brown; bill without bright colors. At a later stage the bird more nearly resembles the adult, but the head and neck are marked with dusky streaks, and the tail retains some of its brown coloring.

Range and migration—The Herring Gull as a species is almost circumboreal. Four races are recognized, two of which occur in North America. Of these, *smithsonianus* breeds locally from southern Alaska and British Columbia eastward to Maine and Labrador, throughout the Canadian and Hudsonian life zones. It is by no means confined to the coast, however, or even to the shores of the Great Lakes, and while it prefers the larger bodies of water as nesting and feeding places, it is likely to occur along the rivers and on the smaller lakes as well. In our region, Lake Erie seems to be a favorite and regular resort, and probably most of the herring gulls seen elsewhere at odd times are on their way to or from this body of water. There are no large nesting colonies there, although a few pairs breed irregularly on some of the islands in the western end of the lake. The Herring Gull is an abundant and characteristic species at Erie Bay during the season of migration, and remains in considerable numbers throughout the winter. In recent years that locality has become also a regular rendezvous and feeding ground for nonbreeding and immature herring gulls through the summer months, so that the species is resident. Conneaut Lake is another spot where it is of regular and fairly common occurrence, and Pymatuning Lake is lately being favored by its presence. It is found along the Ohio River also, but is far less common and regular there, at least recently.

In most parts of our region this gull is not seen so often in the depth of winter as during the migration season. It appears very early in the spring, however, usually in February, sometimes even before the Robin, and remains as a rule until the first weeks in April and sometimes still later (May 2, 1923). At Erie, J. E. Perry saw "thousands" on February 25, 1934. At Pymatuning the species was noted as late as May 21 in 1936 (Todd), and at Conneaut Lake, on June 6, 1925 (Langdon). R. B. Simpson reports that at Warren it is a migrant, regular in the spring and occasional in the fall, and is sometimes also seen in the winter during severe weather. His spring dates lie between February 1 (1904) and May 20 (1894). It is difficult to distinguish between the earliest true migrants of this species and winter wanderers—birds that have in all probability been forced southward from Lake Erie by unusual weather conditions and the consequent failure of the food supply. B. H. Christy (1923) says: "Doubtless as winter snows deepen and ice accumulates along the lake shore, these scavenger birds are driven to search more and more widely for food, until crossing the watershed they reach the headwaters of the Beaver River, and thence easily make their way along the stream."

Migration dates from Renovo, in the upper Susquehanna Valley, correspond closely to those from the western tier of counties. The average date of arrival in seven years' records at that locality is February 17, with February 5 (1911) the earliest. April 20 is the average date of departure, and May 16 (1907), the latest. For the larger part of western Pennsylvania, east of the Allegheny and Monongahela rivers, recorded occurrences of this gull are surprisingly few. The smaller watercourses there offer fewer attractions, it is true, but the apparent scarcity of the species must be attributed to lack of observations at the right season. The Herring Gull is likely to appear anywhere. R. V. Mostoller reports seeing a dozen birds near Stoyestown, Somerset County, on April 13, 1935. They were feeding in a plowed field.

Although some nonbreeding birds stay through the summer months, the earliest fall migrants appear at Erie Bay sometime in August, and by the middle of the following month the species has become common. At this season the immature birds far outnumber the adults. A clue to the origin of some of these young birds is supplied by the banding returns published by F. C. Lincoln. From a large number of young gulls banded on the Beaver Islands, Michigan, in July, 1925, two were recovered the following winter in western Pennsylvania—one at Erie, and the other at Holbrook, Greene County. During their first year the young birds seem to wander widely, as do the young of the heron tribe.

Habits—The Herring Gull occurs in greater or less numbers along the Ohio River every spring from the time of the first freshets until well along in April. Whenever two or three days of pleasant weather have melted the snow so that the river rises, and even before the ducks have begun to push northward, the gulls are fairly sure to make their appearance, singly or in twos and threes, flying well out over the middle of the stream. At rare intervals they come in flocks. An interesting and beautiful sight is that of a score of these gulls above the roiled waters of the river in floodtime, careening about from one side to the other, now mounting on graceful pinions high above the swift current, and again descending and skimming so low over its surface that their silvery-white bodies are washed by the spray from the waves. Later on, when the waterfowl migration is at its height, they occasionally become rather common. Oftentimes when out duck-hunting, chancing to glance upward, I have observed several herring gulls sailing around, hawklike, in graceful, majestic circles hundreds of feet overhead, and have followed them with my eye until, receding in the distance, they were lost to view against the clouds beyond.

To become thoroughly acquainted with this gull, however, one must visit Lake Erie and Erie Bay, where it is a familiar sight for eight months of the year. Through the winter the bay is usually frozen over, but there is always some open water at the mouth of Mill Creek or around the docks to the west (which are alive with small fish), and here the gulls are wont to congregate. They are the scavengers of the harbor and thus perform a useful service. Swooping to the surface, they pick up any floating refuse with unerring precision. They vie among themselves for the possession of a choice morsel with loud outcries and a great flapping of pinions. They are exceedingly graceful in their movements, both on the wing and on the water, and rest on the surface as lightly as feathers. The advance of the season finds their numbers increased by accessions from the south, and then they appear in scattered companies, feeding in the waters of the bay or resting on the edge of the ice. A large proportion of the birds found thus early in the spring are adults, but later these become scarce, and virtually all late stayers are immature birds in mottled plumage. In the fall there are more young birds than old ones; moreover, the species is far more numerous at this season—at least this was the case in 1900, when the following observations were made: "Although commonly found on the bay, immense flocks frequented the open lake as well, standing in more or less close order on the sandy outside shore, flying out to alight in the water when disturbed. They were at all times shy, but once or twice, during heavy storms, it became possible to approach within gunshot. They were accustomed to follow in the wake of the numerous fishing tugs as they came in the harbor with their catch of fish, ready to pick up what was thrown overboard" (Todd, 1904). The eastern extremity of Presque Isle—a sandy flat—is a favorite resort at all seasons, and large numbers of gulls sometimes roost there.

Larus argentatus smithsonianus Warren, *Birds Pa.*, 1888, 231; and ed. 2, 1890, 14 (Erie, Erie Co., transient)—Rhoads, *Auk*, 1899, 16:309 (Pittsburgh, Allegheny Co., *fide* Link; Sinnemahoning Creek, Clinton Co. and Emporium, Cameron Co., *fide* Nelson and Larrabee)—Eifrig, *Auk*, 1902, 19:75 (Confluence, Somerset Co., April)—Malley, *Wilson Bull.*, 1936, 48:310 (Dravosburg and Braddock, Allegheny Co., March).

Larus argentatus Todd, *Ann. Carnegie Mus.*, 1904, 2:503 (Erie Bay and Presque Isle, Erie Co., winter)—Todd, in Bausman, *Hist. Beaver Co., Pa.*, 1904, 2:1198 (Beaver Co., transient)—Cooke, *Bull. U. S. Dept. Agric.*, no. 292, 1915, 36 (Beaver, Beaver Co.; Erie, Erie Co.; and Renovo, Clinton Co., migration)—Christy, *Cardinal*, 1923, v. 1, no. 1, [p. 1] (Sewickley, Allegheny Co., winter)—Burleigh, *Wilson Bull.*, 1923, 35:82 (Highland Park and Allegheny River, Allegheny Co., spring transient); 1924, 36:74 (Scotia, Centre Co., April)—Lincoln, *Auk*, 1928, 45:51, 52 (Presque Isle, Erie Co., and Holbrook, Greene Co., banding records).

"Herring Gull" Simpson, *Oölogist*, 1911, 28:41; 1912, 29:370; and 1914, 31:53, 210 (Warren, Warren Co., seasonal occurrence)—Christy, *Bull. Audubon Soc. W. Pa.*, 1923, 1:12 (Allegheny Co.; Beaver River, Beaver Co., winter)—Christy, *Cardinal*, 1923, v. 1, no. 2, [p. 13] (Clinton Pond, Allegheny Co., March)—Sutton, *Bird-Lore*, 1923, 25:132 (Ohio River, Beaver Co., February, *fide* Boulton), 260 (Allegheny Co., spring); 1924, 26:122 (Ohio River, Allegheny Co., January, *fide* Christy), 123 (Warren, Warren Co., February, *fide* Simpson)—Christy, *Cardinal*, 1926, v. 1, no. 8, p. 21 (Erie Bay, Erie Co., winter, *fide* Perry; Foxburg, Clarion Co., February)—Savage, *et al.*, *Bird-Lore*, 1930, 32:36 (McKeesport, Allegheny Co., December)—Christy, *Cardinal*, 1932, 3:86 (Erie Bay, Erie Co., January–March)—Elliott, *Cardinal*, 1934, 3:170 (Raccoon Creek, Beaver Co., December)—Boggs, *Redstart*, 1936, 3:92 (Presque Isle, Erie Co., June).

Larus argentatus argentatus Sutton, *Ann. Carnegie Mus.*, 1928, 18:55 (Conneaut Lake, Pymatuning Swamp and region, Crawford Co., migration).

RING-BILLED GULL (Plate 10)

LARUS DELAWARENSIS Ord

Description—Similar in general coloration to the Herring Gull, but *smaller;* feet pale greenish yellow; the *bill* (in the adult) has a *broad dusky band* near the tip. In the *young bird* (in the mottled gray plumage) the terminal half of the bill is mostly black, contrasting with the pale base; and the tail has a well-defined dusky band near the tip.

Range—Although this species does not go so far north as the American Herring Gull, its east-and-west range is more extensive. In the East it breeds chiefly north of the United States, from Labrador to Ontario, and winters mostly on the Atlantic coast, from Chesapeake Bay to Florida. It has also been found in winter (in smaller numbers) on the Great Lakes, in the neighborhood of Chicago, Detroit, and Buffalo; but at Erie during that season it seems to have escaped the notice of observers until rather recently—or else its presence is a new development, induced by changed weather conditions. When I published my report on the "Birds of Erie and Presque Isle" in 1904 I could find no winter records there for the Ring-billed Gull, although now it is a regular winter resident, as I can testify from personal observations and from those of others. Not so numerous, perhaps, as the Herring Gull, it is nevertheless a common species, and sometimes appears in flocks of considerable size. During the unprecedentedly mild winter of 1931–32 it was much in evidence. Its numbers there are augmented during the seasons of migration, and at these times it visits other localities in western Pennsylvania as well. It comes regularly to Conneaut Lake, and I have found it very common every spring since 1935 on Pymatuning Lake at Linesville. Some nonbreeding birds also remain there, as well as on Presque Isle, through the summer. R. B. Simpson reports this gull as a regular but rare spring transient at Warren. I saw it once along the Ohio River (near Merrill, Beaver County) in May, and there are also a few scattered records (listed in the references below) from other parts of our region.

Migration—Judging by the records from adjoining states, the few birds of this species seen on Presque Isle on August 25, 1928 (Boulton, 1928), were probably the van of the fall migrants. On September 4, 1933, our party from the Carnegie Museum saw an immense flock at the same place. They were molting and were in ragged plumage —a fact which suggests that they may have been local nonbreeding birds rather than early migrants. Some were seen there also on September 2, 1934, and on September 5, 1936. These dates are significantly early as compared with those recorded in 1900, which ranged from October 17 to November 15, and with Mr. Simpson's dates for 1902 and 1903, which were all in November. In recent years the species has been more or less common at Erie Bay through the fall and winter and until the latter part of April, and a few birds have remained still later. At Warren this gull has been observed in the spring between February 22 (1903) and May 11 (1930—Simpson), and at Conneaut Lake, from April 9 to June 6 (Langdon). The latter date is exceptionally late. The species has been seen along the Ohio River as late as May 13 (1923—Reiter, and others).

Habits—The Ring-billed Gull often associates with the Herring Gull, which it resembles in general behavior and habits. Its ordinary call note is perhaps a little shriller than that of the other species. In migration it flies in scattered companies, but on Presque Isle it is often encountered in compact flocks of considerable size, resting on the sand bars or on the sheltered waters adjoining.

Larus delawarensis Townsend, *Proc. Acad. Nat. Sci. Philadelphia*, 1883, 68 (Latrobe, Westmoreland Co., May)—Warren, *Birds Pa.*, ed. 2, 1890, 14 ("Allegheny and Ohio Rivers;" Erie, Erie Co., transient)—(?)Rhoads, *Auk*, 1899, 16:309 (western Pa.)—Todd, *Ann. Carnegie Mus.*, 1904, 2:504 (Erie Bay, Erie Co., transient)—Burleigh, *Wilson Bull.*, 1924, 36:74 (Oak Hall, Centre Co., May)—Christy, *Cardinal*, 1927, 2:11 (Dixmont, Allegheny Co., September) —Sutton, *Ann. Carnegie Mus.*, 1928, 18:56 (Conneaut Lake, Crawford Co., transient).

"Ring-billed Gull" Simpson, *Oölogist*, 1911, 28:39 (Erie Bay, Erie Co., April)—Sutton, *Bird-Lore*, 1923, 25:260 (Beaver, Beaver Co., May; Monaca, Beaver Co., May, *fide* Reiter, *et al.*)—Christy, *Cardinal*, 1926, v. 1, no. 8, p. 21 (Erie Bay, Erie Co., winter, *fide* Perry)—Boulton, *Bird-Lore*, 1928, 30:400 (Presque Isle, Erie Co., August)—Christy, *Cardinal*, 1932, 3:86 (Presque Isle, Erie Co., January–March) —Savage, *Bird-Lore*, 1932, 34:44; Upson, *et al.*, *Bird-Lore*, 1933, 35:27; and Beal and Peterson, *Bird-Lore*, 1934, 36:33 (Erie Bay, Erie Co., December)—Elliott, *Cardinal*, 1934, 3:170 (Raccoon Creek, Beaver Co., December)—Boggs, *Redstart*, 1936, 3:92 (Presque Isle, Erie Co., June).

LAUGHING GULL

LARUS ATRICILLA Linnaeus

Description—One of the smaller gulls; the *adult in breeding plumage* has a black hood, dark gray back, pure white tail, plain black wings (with very narrow white tips to the flight feathers), and a reddish bill. The *fall and winter plumage* is similar, but the black hood is wanting—only the nape and the area behind the eyes are dusky gray—and the bill is dark-colored. *Young birds* have more or less black on the tail. The mantle and wings are a *darker gray* than are those of the Ring-billed Gull, which is about the same size.

Range and local status—The Laughing Gull nests in colonies at various points along the Atlantic and Gulf coasts, and southward through the Lesser Antilles to South America. It is thus a relatively southern species, and is not known to range beyond Maine at the present time. Its occurrence at any season in the interior, away from salt water, is of course purely accidental, but several such instances are on record. A. K. Pierce is the only observer who has ever encountered the species in our region. He secured a specimen in Clinton County on April 27, and another on October 14, 1893 (the latter is now in the Carnegie Museum collection); and he saw a third laughing gull on April 19, 1901. The October 14 specimen (an adult female) was shot by a local gunner along the Susquehanna River about twelve miles west of Renovo. These records are the only authentic ones for western Pennsylvania, since the Keim record, cited below, is admittedly conjectural.

(?)*Larus atricilla* Keim, *Cassinia*, 1905, 8:37 (Port Allegany, McKean Co., fall).

FRANKLIN'S GULL

LARUS PIPIXCAN (Wagler)

Description—Similar to Bonaparte's Gull, but a little larger; bill heavier and differently colored; upperparts darker gray, and wing pattern different. *Breeding plumage:* bill claret brown; head black (all around), the eyelids white; neck (all around), tail, and underparts, white, the latter rosy-tinted; upperparts deep gray; wings externally gray like the back, the *primaries* with *white tips* and *black subterminal bands*, the inner primaries and secondaries also white-tipped. In *winter dress* the black hood is wanting and the head is white, with dark shading on the nape and behind the eyes; the wings usually show more black.

Range and local status—Franklin's Gull breeds in the plains region from Iowa north to Manitoba and Alberta, and winters on the Pacific coast of South America. During migration it occasionally wanders far to the eastward of its regular route, as do certain other species of the western interior. L. E. Hicks writes that he secured a bird of this species at Ashtabula, Ohio, on September 13, 1937. The same day he drove to Presque Isle and discovered a second bird there. It was feeding along the shore of a small pond and allowed a close approach. Several times it stretched its wings in the air, affording an opportunity to check their color pattern. It was an adult in transition from breeding to winter plumage. Professor Hicks surmises that certain supposed records of the Laughing Gull from western New York really pertain to this species instead.

BONAPARTE'S GULL (Plate 10)

LARUS PHILADELPHIA (Ord)

Description—A small gull, little larger than the Common Tern, but with a square tail (not forked). *Adult in spring:* neck (all around) and underparts, entirely white (showing a delicate rosy blush); the entire head black; back pearl gray, and wings similar, except the *outer quills*, which are *white* with *black tips;* bill black; feet orange-red. *Adult in fall and winter:* similar to the spring plumage, but the black hood is wanting and only the hind crown and sides of the neck are clouded with dusky shading, usually showing as a dark *spot on either side of the head. Young in spring and fall:* similar to the adult at the same seasons, but the *tail* has a *broad band of black at the tip*, and the wing coverts are marked with dusky brown.

Range and migration—This gull has been found nesting only in northwestern North America—in the valleys of the Yukon and the Mackenzie rivers and thence southward to British Columbia and eastward to Hudson Bay—but it has been found in summer far to the southward, even around some of the Great Lakes, and its actual breeding range must be considerably more extensive. While its winter range includes both coasts, it comes in greater numbers to the Atlantic side, where it occurs from Long Island to Florida. Thus the Great Lakes lie on the main path of migration between its summer and winter homes and attract it in large numbers during its passage in spring and fall. Erie Bay seems to be one of its favorite stopping places, as are also Pymatuning and Conneaut lakes. Other records come from the upper Allegheny and Ohio rivers and their tributaries, and there are scattered records also for the ridge and valley section, as well as for the high country to the westward. At times this gull is common on the West Branch of the Susquehanna River at Renovo. The birds undoubtedly cross the mountains, which there lie directly in their path to and from their winter home, but they do not loiter by the way, and only in the lake region of the northwestern part of the state do they pause for any length of time. Bonaparte's Gull is more at home on lakes than on rivers, and when seen on the latter it is actually migrating and not resting en route. All observers have remarked that it is commoner in spring than in fall. At Warren, where it is fairly regular at the former season, R. B. Simpson has observed several good-sized flights in the month of April, during or just after stormy weather. April 3 (1904) is his earliest date, and May 13 (1904), his latest.

At Renovo this gull has been seen between April 8 and May 5 (Pierce). H. C. Kirkpatrick also speaks of it as a regular and tolerably common spring visitor in the neighborhood of Meadville. He writes: "Many of these gulls leave French Creek at the mouth of Conneaut Outlet and follow up this latter stream to Conneaut Lake, where they are commoner than elsewhere. Here, too, a few remain quite late in the season, although they are of course not known to breed. The latest date on which I have thus recorded them is June 28 (1897). The latest for the valley of French Creek is May 15 (1896)." Bonaparte's Gull has been noted occasionally along the Ohio River, but only once in large numbers; this was on April 21, 1901, when the river was in flood. Of special interest, as showing that such appearances are apt to occur almost anywhere, is the record of a flock of about one hundred birds seen about a lake near Wilson College, Chambersburg, on May 6, 1925, by R. O. Dunkle and others. Thomas Smyth reports this species from Cherry Run Reservoir, Indiana County, on May 10 and June 14, 1933—the latter certainly a late date.

At Conneaut Lake, where it is a regular and sometimes abundant spring transient, Bonaparte's Gull has been noted as early as March 25 (1913), but the large flocks come in April and May. Some birds may linger into June (June 12, 1931—Seiple) before finally going north, and there are several records of single birds for July. These must have been immature or nonbreeding individuals that had failed to migrate. According to my experience at Erie Bay in 1900, the birds encountered early in the season were all in fully adult plumage, with the black hood complete, while later on, immature birds preponderated. G. M. Sutton's experience at Conneaut Lake was much the same. He writes (1928) that "the prenuptial moult is completed earlier in the season in full adults than it is in younger birds," and notes that the immature birds "were usually observed together, in flocks separate from the adults." The first fall records for the species apparently refer to young birds, which sometimes arrive at Erie Bay as early as August 1 (1928), according to J. E. Perry. Adults have been noted at Conneaut Lake, however, on August 30 (1925). The records for the fall migration are scarcely sufficient to justify any general statement. We did not find this gull common at Erie Bay until November 1 in 1900, and it was still numerous when we left on November 17. It now winters there regularly, and it was particularly abundant during the open winter of 1931–32.

Habits—This beautiful little gull makes up in grace and freedom of movement for what it lacks in size and strength. Whenever it appears in numbers along our watercourses it is sufficiently conspicuous to excite remark. Mr. Kirkpatrick, writing of the species as he has observed it along French Creek, says: "It is indeed a pretty sight: a flock of these gulls gracefully following the windings of the stream, one minute high in the air, and the next nearly touching the surface of the water. In migrating the birds do not fly in a compact body, but are scattered out so that a flock covers a great deal of territory. On April 9, 1897, I saw two large flocks flying up French Creek in the face of a severe northwest snowstorm, which seemed greatly to impede their passage, as they kept close to the surface of the water and were frequently alighting."

At Erie Bay, to quote from my 1904 report, "our experience with this gull in the spring of 1900 was that it was usually found in loose flocks of from twenty to a hundred individuals, coursing up and down the bay, feeding, or occasionally on the outside beach, resting on a sand-bar. However, on the few comparatively calm days during the season more or less compact flocks were met with resting on the smooth water, their light color rendering them conspicuous at a long distance. At such times it was difficult or impossible to approach within range, and far better chances of securing specimens were afforded by remaining quietly in the boat as the birds came by on their course and picking off such as ventured too close. A single bird flung out as a decoy would almost always bring others within reach, and on one occasion the cries of a wounded bird brought an entire flock headed *en masse* towards the sound." Mr. Perry speaks of having seen hundreds, or possibly thousands, on April 17, 1926.

The ordinary food of this gull consists of small fish, which it captures by dropping lightly to the surface of the water while in flight; pausing only long enough to pick them up, it resumes its graceful evolutions. B. H. Christy writes: "The wing motion of this species is more rapid than that of the larger gulls and forms a greater arc; a gathering of Bonaparte's gulls always suggests to me a bevy of butterflies." The call note of this species is not unlike that of the Common Tern.

Larus philadelphia WARREN, *Birds Pa.*, 1888, 231; and ed. 2, 1890, 16 (Erie, Erie Co., transient)—RHOADS, *Auk*, 1899, 16:309 (Sinnemahoning Creek, Cameron Co., *fide* Larrabee)—EIFRIG, *Auk*, 1902, 19:75 (Confluence, Somerset Co., April)—TODD, *Ann. Carnegie Mus.*, 1904, 2:504 (Erie Bay, Erie Co., transient)—TODD, in Bausman, *Hist. Beaver Co., Pa.*, 1904, 2:1198 (Beaver Co., transient)—CHRISTY, *Cardinal*, 1923, v. 1, no. 1, [p. 1] (Sewickley, Allegheny Co., spring transient)—BURLEIGH, *Wilson Bull.*, 1924, 36:74 (Oak Hall and Scotia, Centre Co., spring).

(?)*Sterna dougalli* (error) WARREN, *Birds Pa.*, ed. 2, 1890, 21 (DuBois, Clearfield Co., *fide* Balliet).

"Bonaparte's Gull" SIMPSON, *Oölogist*, 1909, 26:153 (Presque Isle, Erie Co., July); 1911, 28:41; and 1914, 31:210 (Warren, Warren Co., migration)—SUTTON, *Bird-Lore*, 1923, 25:260 (Pittsburgh region, Allegheny Co., April)—EASTWOOD, *Bird-Lore*, 1926, 28:274 (Sandy Lake, Mercer Co., May)—BOULTON, *Bird-Lore*, 1928, 30:337 (Presque Isle, Erie Co., August, *fide* Perry), 401 (Sandy Lake, Mercer Co., September, *fide* Freni)—CHRISTY, *Cardinal*, 1932, 3:86 (Erie Bay, Erie Co., January–March)—SAVAGE, *Bird-Lore*, 1932, 34:44; BEAL and PETERSON, *Bird-Lore*, 1934, 36:33; and UPSON, *et al.*, *Bird-Lore*, 1935, 37:47 (Erie Bay, Erie Co., December).

Chroicocephalus philadelphia SUTTON, *Ann. Carnegie Mus.*, 1928, 18:56 (Conneaut Lake, Pymatuning Swamp, Meadville, etc., Crawford Co., transient).

LITTLE GULL

LARUS MINUTUS Pallas

Description—Similar to Bonaparte's Gull, but smaller; *wings dark-colored beneath, pearl gray above*, uniform with the back, the *primaries with white tips.*

Range and local status—This is an Old World gull of arctic breeding range, and is merely accidental on this side of the Atlantic, where it occurs mostly along the coast. It is admitted to this list on the basis of the record cited below, which refers to a single bird seen on December 27, 1933, by C. M. Beal and R. T. Peterson (1934): "The Little Gull was discovered among Bonaparte's Gulls at the foot of State Street in Erie. All the diagnostic features were carefully noted—the smaller size, the uniformly gray mantle with white spots at the tips of the wings, and, most important of all, the conspicuous blackish wing-linings. We believe it is the first record for Pennsylvania." Under the circumstances there could have been little possibility of misidentification, but the occurrence of this European waif so far inland is of peculiar interest.

"European Little Gull" BEAL and PETERSON, *Bird-Lore*, 1934, 36:33 (Erie, Erie Co., December).

ATLANTIC KITTIWAKE

RISSA TRIDACTYLA TRIDACTYLA (Linnaeus)

Description—A rather small gull, with pearl-gray back, black-tipped wings, and dark-colored legs and feet. The *adult in fall and winter* has a pale greenish bill, a pure white tail and underparts, and a white head, with a suggestion of a black spot on either side behind the eye, as well as some dark color around the eye itself. The *young bird* at the same season differs in having the tail broadly tipped with black and in having more or less *black on the upper wing coverts* and on the upper back, usually in the form of a band; the bill is black. In hand the Kittiwake may always be identified by the rudimentary hind toe.

Range and local status—In the breeding season the Kittiwake is strictly maritime in its distribution, and while it goes very far north on both sides of the Atlantic, there are several nesting colonies in the Gulf of St. Lawrence. Although the species is most numerous in winter on the coast of New England, some birds find their way at that season to the Great Lakes, probably by way of the St. Lawrence River. On October 17 in 1900, W. W. Worthington saw and positively identified a single individual off the outside beach of Presque Isle, but was unable to secure it. A still earlier record for our region is based on a mounted specimen in the collection of the Carnegie Museum, purporting to have been shot at McKees Rocks, Allegheny County, on January 15, 1891, by a gunner, who presented it to G. A. Link, Sr. At Warren during the blizzard of February, 1899, R. B. Simpson saw what he thought was a kittiwake, but he was too far away to shoot the bird.

Rissa tridactyla TODD, *Ann. Carnegie Mus.*, 1904, 2:502 (Presque Isle, Erie Co., October).

COMMON TERN (Plate 11)

STERNA HIRUNDO HIRUNDO Linnaeus

Description—A tern of moderate size, with a wingspread of about thirty inches. *Adult in spring:* whole cap black; back and wings pearl gray; rump, tail, and under tail coverts, white; rest of underparts light pearl gray; bill red, with *dark tip;* tail deeply forked. *Young in fall plumage:* similar to the adult, but bill darker, tail less deeply forked, underparts nearly white, black cap incomplete, the fore part of the crown whitish, and the upperparts showing more or less dusky mottling or indistinct dusky bars.

Range—The Common Tern is a native of both Eurasia and America; it breeds in the northern part of its general range and winters southward. In the interior of North America it breeds regularly south to the Great Lakes, although at only a few points on Lake Erie. When writing my "Birds of Erie and Presque Isle" (1904), I thought it probable that this species might formerly have bred on Presque Isle, since all conditions, with the exception of sufficient protection, seemed to be favorable. I could find, however, no record of any breeding colony nearer than Big Chicken Island, off Put-in-Bay, Ohio. Since then I have encountered this tern in July at Long Point, Ontario (directly opposite Erie), where its breeding has now been definitely established.[1] It has long been known in the Erie region as a common spring and fall transient, but until 1926 it had never been found breeding there. On August 1 of that year, J. E. Perry discovered a number of terns gathered at the eastern end of a newly formed sandspit on Presque Isle. They were behaving in an unusual manner—screaming and swooping at a marsh hawk and at Mr. Perry, too, who found himself on debatable ground. He noticed two young terns at the edge of the beach. This was the first intimation he had had that the terns might be breeding. The following year he revisited the spot early in June, and estimated that about twenty-five pairs of terns were nesting there. When this fact was made known, steps were taken by various interested persons to secure protection for this colony, and the state park commissioners were induced to declare the occupied ground a sanctuary for the terns. As a consequence the colony increased in size until in 1937 it numbered about two hundred pairs.

O. E. Jennings (1930), in commenting on the establishment of this colony, ventures the opinion that it became possible by reason of the formation of new land suitable for the purpose, and that it will be abandoned whenever the present conditions change. He may be right in this conjecture, but I prefer to believe that the prohibition of hunting on Presque Isle, which came into effect in 1926 when the area was set aside as a state park, had more influence than anything else in inducing the terns to remain for the summer. Certainly, since the colony has been afforded protection it has thrived in a way that otherwise would have been impossible.

This species has been frequently observed in June and July at Conneaut Lake, where it is also common and regular as a transient. It has been seen in other parts of the state as well, under similar conditions. On June 10, 1903, I saw a flock of a half-dozen terns at the mouth of the Beaver River in Beaver County—my first record for that locality. R. B. Simpson noted a single bird at Warren on June 20 of that year, and another on July 3, 1922. Thomas Smyth reported the species at Cherry Run Reservoir, Indiana County, on June 28, 1934. Had these individuals been belated migrants they would have been hurrying through instead of loitering by the way. It is likelier that they were summer wanderers that were not intending to breed that season. The status of the terns summering at Pymatuning Lake (every season since 1934) has not been determined. My impression is that they must be breeding there, although the nesting ground has not yet been discovered.

Migration—Except at Erie, Pymatuning Lake, and Conneaut Lake, the Common Tern is not at all common in our region. At the latter place transients have been observed from April 4 (an exceptionally early date) to May 19. Another early record comes from Linesville—April 9, 1934 (Dilley). At Erie the species was observed from May 7 to 29 in 1900, although it usually arrives a week or two earlier (April 24, 1932—Guynes). At Warren Mr. Simpson has noted it occasionally between May 16 (1909) and 20 (1907 and 1917). All but one of the

[1] L. L. Snyder and E. B. S. Logier, *Transactions Royal Canadian Institute*, 1931, 18:150.

spring records for the Ohio Valley are also in May. On May 11, 1916, I observed a flock of perhaps twenty-five birds resting on a sand bar at the mouth of the Beaver River (where I had seen the species in June, 1903), and on the same day I saw a half-dozen near the head of Neville Island, in Allegheny County. B. H. Christy saw a flock of eight near Clinton Pond, in the same county, on May 17, 1923, and T. D. Burleigh saw four at Highland Park Reservoir, Pittsburgh, on April 20, 1914. The only record from the plateau section comes from Springs, Somerset County, where A. B. Miller reports seeing a flock of ten or twelve on May 21, 1924. From the ridge and valley section there is a record of two birds seen at Lakemont, Blair County, on May 6, 1917, by H. A. McGraw.

In the fall migration this tern has appeared in early August (August 3, 1891—Corydon, Warren County [Simpson]; August 3, 1924—Conneaut Lake [Seiple]; August 12, 1932—Meadville [Kirkpatrick]), but it is quite possible that such records apply to summer wanderers rather than to true migrants. The real migration seems not to begin until the latter part of August, and continues through September. The latest fall record for our region is October 8, 1892, when D. A. Atkinson shot a single specimen (now in the Carnegie Museum) on the Allegheny River near Verona, Allegheny County.

Habits—During our study of the bird life of the Erie region in 1900, W. W. Worthington and I first met with this species on May 7, when, to quote from my 1904 report, "a few were observed with the Bonaparte's Gulls on the bay, and at least fifty individuals were seen in a flock by themselves. For about two weeks thereafter they were very common indeed, and a number were noted as late as May 29. While the Bonaparte's Gulls remained, the terns were frequently found in their company, and both could be decoyed by throwing over a dead bird and imitating their cry. When shot at the terns presently mounted high in the air above their dead companions, while the gulls dispersed or passed on. Later in the season the terns were often found scattered over the bay resting by preference on pieces of floating driftwood. . . . We did not meet with it in the fall of 1900 until August 28, when a flock of about thirty was noticed on the bay. It was found in greater or less numbers from that date until September 26, but no very large flocks, such as were met with in the spring, were observed. At this season it frequented the main lake as well as Erie Bay, and was often found associated with the Black Tern during the period of abundance of the latter species."

In 1932 Mrs. A. A. Andrews of Erie sent me an interesting account of the Presque Isle nesting colony:

"For the past five or six years the Common Tern has been nesting in considerable numbers on a newly formed sand bar at the eastern end of Presque Isle. The original colony occupied an area about a quarter of a mile long and not over five or six hundred feet wide, but during the season of 1931 it moved west about a quarter of a mile, encroaching thus on the public bathing beach. The greater part of the colony, however, stayed on the original settlement.

"On June 1, 1930, I was able through the courtesy of the Park Commission to investigate this colony. Walking up one side of the sand bar and down the other with a companion, we counted one hundred and twenty-nine nests in about twenty minutes. There were probably more, but as the entire colony rose on wing at our approach with plaintive cries, and dived down almost into our faces, we thought it best not to disturb them further, as the nesting had just nicely begun.

"The nests were simple depressions in the sand and were usually protected by a sunken log or a piece of driftwood. Few of them had any lining whatever. Some had two eggs, some three, and a few four. Egg-laying must have been going on for at least a week. The ground-color of the eggs varied from buff to sand color, while a few were pale green. All were heavily marked with chocolate-colored spots. [They average 1.64 by 1.17 inches.] As nearly as we could tell without again invading the colony the laying continued until about the middle of June, with incubation also going on during that period.

"The season of 1931 proved to be a most trying one for the terns, since, as already stated, not content with the area set aside for them, they moved out where bathers were coming and going at frequent intervals. The park was officially opened to the public on May 30 (when the guards are first on duty), and the newly extended colony was doomed from the start, for people were constantly walking about among the nests, and oftentimes actually stepped on the eggs before realizing it. At length some misguided person marked all the nests with a ring of upright stones, which aroused the birds' suspicions and caused most of them to desert their eggs, thus defeating the purpose of the design. A few pairs that were bolder than the rest hatched their eggs in spite of interruptions; for up until noon the bathing beach was comparatively deserted. The parents, however, had a hard time keeping their young supplied with food, as they were prevented from feeding them except during the quiet morning hours. The birds that were raised to maturity were mostly in the original colony on the sand bar, and their number, too, was greatly diminished this year."

A party from the Carnegie Museum visited this colony on May 30, 1935, and found it prospering. We located about fifty nests and must have passed by many more. Either the nesting period is unduly long, or some pairs are delayed beyond the regular time, for incubated eggs were found as late as July 20 and August 2 in 1934 (Simpson; Dilley).

The food of the Common Tern consists almost entirely of small fish, which it captures by swooping to the surface from above and sometimes diving a short distance. While in search of its prey it will often hang poised in the air in one spot on flapping pinions, with the bill pointed downward, like a kingfisher, and then suddenly drop to the water with closed wings, to emerge in a moment with a fish in its bill. In picking off a fish near the surface it is truly expert—it touches the water for an instant as lightly as a feather, and again takes wing. Its easy and graceful flight has earned for it the vernacular name of "Sea Swallow." It is a noisy bird at times, and its shrill cries are constant whenever food is abundant. It seldom flies over the land, unless to cross from one body of water to another; on such occasions it usually mounts to a considerable height.

Sterna hirundo Warren, *Birds Pa.*, ed. 2, 1890, 20 (Erie, Erie Co., *fide* Sennett; Clinton Co., *fide* Van Fleet; Franklin, Venango Co., *fide* Robertson, transient)—Rhoads, *Auk*, 1899, 16:309 ([Verona], Allegheny Co., *fide* Atkinson)—Todd, *Ann. Carnegie Mus.*, 1904, 2:506 (Erie Bay and region, Erie Co., transient)—Todd, in Bausman, *Hist. Beaver Co., Pa.*, 1904, 2:1198 (Beaver Co., transient)—Burleigh, *Wilson Bull.*, 1923, 35:82 (Highland Park, Allegheny Co., April)—[Christy], *Cardinal*, 1927, 2:42 (Presque Isle, Erie Co., nesting, *fide* Perry)—Sutton, *Ann. Carnegie Mus.*, 1928, 18:58 (Conneaut and Crystal lakes, Crawford Co., transient)—Sutton, *Cardinal*, 1929, 2:121 (Conneaut Lake, Crawford Co., September)—Jennings, *Cardinal*, 1930, 2:182 (Presque Isle, Erie Co., nesting).

"Common Tern" Simpson, *Oölogist*, 1907, 24:87 (Warren, Warren Co., May)—Christy, *Cardinal*, 1923, v. 2, no. 2, [p. 13] (Clinton, Allegheny Co., May)—Boulton, *Bird-Lore*, 1928, 30:337, 401 (Presque Isle, Erie Co., nesting)—Jennings, *Carnegie Mag.*, 1930, 4:174 (Presque Isle, Erie Co., nesting)—Trimble, *Cardinal*, 1937, 4:106 (Pymatuning Lake, Crawford Co., summer).

LEAST TERN

STERNA ANTILLARUM ANTILLARUM (Lesson)

Description—This tern may be recognized by its *small size;* it is even smaller than the Black Tern. The coloration is almost the same as that of the Common Tern, but the *bill and feet are yellowish*, and the *forehead is white*.

Range—In North America this diminutive tern breeds mainly along the Atlantic coast, from Massachusetts to the Gulf of Mexico and to the shores of the Caribbean Sea, but it also invades the interior in the Mississippi Valley. Its occurrence in our region, however, can scarcely be regarded as more than accidental. The record cited below is based on a specimen shot by G. E. Welshons on April 10, 1912, at Conneaut Lake. The only other recorded occurrence is that of two birds seen along the Raystown Branch of the Juniata River at Ardenheim, Huntingdon County, on August 16, 1929, by H. A. McGraw. They were watched at close range, and the observer is confident that they were correctly identified.

Sternula albifrons antillarum Sutton, *Ann. Carnegie Mus.*, 1928, 18:59 (Conneaut Lake, Crawford Co., April, *fide* Welshons).

CASPIAN TERN

HYDROPROGNE CASPIA IMPERATOR (Coues)

Description—A large tern, almost as big as the Ring-billed Gull; tail decidedly, but not conspicuously, forked. In the *adult* the whole cap is black, the upperparts and wings are light pearl gray, the tail and underparts are pure white, and the bill is bright coral red. *Young birds* have a yellowish-orange bill; the cap is much mottled with white; and the upperparts and tail show dusky marks and bars.

Range—The Caspian Tern has a wide range in both the Old and the New World, but shows only slight geographic variation. It is not an especially northern-breeding species but is partial to the shores of large bodies of water. At one time it was rather common in summer on the Great Lakes, but most of the former nesting colonies there have ceased to exist. In July, 1907, I saw a few Caspian terns at Long Point, Ontario, on the north shore of Lake Erie, where I suspected that they might be breeding, but L. L. Snyder and E. B. S. Logier have been unable to confirm this suspicion.[1] The discovery of a nest on Presque Isle in the season of 1924, as detailed below by T. W. Weiseman, is therefore of peculiar interest. This tern had previously been known in the Erie region as a transient only, and it has thus been recorded also from Conneaut and Pymatuning lakes and from Warren.

Migration—In the fall of 1900 I found the Caspian Tern rather common on Presque Isle from September 4 until October 3, while the latest fall date on record (October 6, 1892—Bacon) tends to confirm my own. My record of arrival, however, must be a late one, since J. E. Perry reports seeing this species on August 16, 1926, and on August 12, 1928; and C. S. Beardslee saw seven birds on August 19, 1931. I have not encountered it at Erie in the spring, but it has been observed there at that season by others, at dates varying from April 26 to May 23. At Pymatuning Lake it first appeared in the spring of 1936; the earliest and latest dates were April 26 (Skaggs) and May 21 (Todd). R. B. Simpson saw three birds along the Allegheny River at Warren on May 7, 1908—his only record for that locality. On May 5, 1925, a specimen was shot at Conneaut Lake by G. M. Langdon. These dates correspond with those from adjoining states. S. J. Seiple noted one Caspian tern at Pymatuning Lake on July 9, 1938; the significance of this record is not yet apparent.

Habits—This large, handsome tern was one of the conspicuous water birds about Presque Isle and Erie Bay in the fall of 1900. In my 1904 report I wrote: "Although occasionally met with by itself, singly, or in small companies, it was more frequently found associated with the Herring Gull, both on the bay and lake, and like that species was rather shy. The large flock of gulls on the outside beach included a number of Caspian Terns, which could easily be distinguished, if adults, by their bright red bills. The adults had a harsh, rasping cry, which was very distinctive, while the note of the immature birds was more musical." Fish constitute the chief food of this species; these are captured by a quick dash from the air into the water. On shore the birds move around very little.

Concerning the nesting of this tern on Presque Isle, I quote the following from a manuscript account by Mr. Weiseman:

"In June, 1924, I noted several large terns about Presque Isle. During the early part of the month they frequently congregated on a sand bar at the 'Head'—the western end of Erie Bay. At intervals a pair would separate from the main body, soar about in the air, and then alight on the leeward shore of the peninsula, where they would run back and forth, opening and folding their wings in an odd manner and acting otherwise in a way that convinced me that they must be mating.

"Several opportunities to observe the birds at close range with a powerful glass and to note the glossy black crest, forked tail, red bill, and extensive spread of wings, served to confirm their identification as Caspian terns.

"As the month advanced, I became interested in the activities of other birds that were nesting in the vicinity, and when later on I found time to visit the sand bar it was occupied solely by gulls. On July 6, however, while traversing the outside beach of the peninsula, a Caspian tern arose from the sand a short distance ahead, soared a hundred yards eastward along the beach, and then circled

[1] *Transactions Royal Canadian Institute*, 1931, 18:150.

lakeward and westward to pass me, about fifty yards offshore. Flying to a point west of where I stood, it again turned toward the shore and circled about directly overhead, in a suspicious way.

"A careful search of that part of the beach where the bird was first noted disclosed two grayish-colored, brown-splotched eggs, measuring about 2.75 by 1.50 inches, resting in a shallow depression in the sand. Two photographs of the nest were forthwith secured. While I was examining and photographing, another tern, evidently the male, appeared on the scene, and both birds flew around overhead in wide circles, occasionally uttering cries of alarm and protest.

"Some five hundred feet from the nesting site a clump of low bushes was utilized as a place of concealment, and when the bird returned to incubate, an eight-power glass enabled me to study to advantage the black feet and crest, forked tail, red bill, and other characters. But when I returned three days later, hoping to make a motion-picture record, I could find no trace of the eggs or the birds. The nest was probably destroyed by a violent storm that raged in the interim, or else by the gulls. At any rate, the terns were seen no more."

Sterna tschegrava DWIGHT, *Auk*, 1889, 6:198 (Erie, Erie Co., *fide* Sennett)—WARREN, *Birds Pa.*, ed. 2, 1890, 18 (Erie Bay, Erie Co., fall transient).

Sterna caspia TODD, *Ann. Carnegie Mus.*, 1904, 2:506 (Erie Bay and Presque Isle, Erie Co., transient).

"Caspian Tern" SIMPSON, *Oölogist*, 1911, 28:33 (Presque Isle, Erie Co., September; Warren, Warren Co., May)—BOULTON, *Bird-Lore*, 1928, 30:400 (Presque Isle, Erie Co., August)—CHRISTY, *Cardinal*, 1934, 3:173 (Erie Bay, Erie Co. September).

Hydroprogne caspia imperator SUTTON, *Ann. Carnegie Mus.*, 1928, 18:58 (Conneaut Lake, Crawford Co., May, *fide* Langdon; near Erie, Erie Co., nesting, *fide* Weiseman).

BLACK TERN (Plate 11)

CHLIDONIAS NIGRA SURINAMENSIS (Gmelin)

Description—Much smaller than the Common Tern; tail not deeply forked. *Adult in spring:* upperparts, tail, and wings, slaty gray; *head and neck* (all around) *and underparts, black* (except for the white under tail coverts); bill black. *Adult in fall:* upperparts light slaty gray; head with a dark-colored cap from the nape to the eyes; the forehead and neck white; *entire underparts white. Young in fall* are similar to the adults at that season but are darker above, with a tendency to brownish barring on the back and wings.

Range—The Black Tern, a close relative of the Old World species of the same name, is essentially a fresh-water tern. In the breeding season it frequents the interior of North America rather than the coast, and in the winter it retires to the region around the Gulf of Mexico. In the West it has an extensive summer range, from Great Slave Lake to southern California, but in the East its range at that season is greatly restricted and forms an inverted triangle with the apex in west-central New York (Cayuga Lake). There are a few breeding colonies on Lake Erie; the one nearest our region is at Long Point, on the Canadian shore directly opposite Erie. Warren quotes J. W. Detwiller as his authority for the statement that this tern has bred at Erie, and it may indeed have done so in former years, but Dr. Detwiller's reputation as a reliable observer is questionable. At the present time the status of the species there is that of an irregular transient, most numerous in the fall. At Conneaut Lake, where it is reported by G. M. Sutton as a fairly regular and sometimes abundant transient, two nests were actually found by G. E. Welshons about 1910, and several birds that were seen more recently through June and July may have been breeding at the time. A single bird seen at Sandy Lake, Mercer County, on June 1, 1924, by F. L. Homer and Dr. Sutton, may also possibly have been breeding. The exhaustive researches of the latter observer in the Pymatuning Swamp area, however, failed to disclose this species as a breeding bird. The changes in environment that have been effected there in the past few years have altered the status of this tern, together with that of other species of aquatic habit. A nesting colony was discovered in a part of Pymatuning Lake, northwest of Linesville, in the season of 1934, by a party from the Carnegie Museum, and for the past several seasons there has been a rapidly increasing influx in the sanctuary.

Elsewhere in our region the Black Tern is a rare

visitor during the season of migration. I have never seen it along the Ohio River, although there is a specimen in the Carnegie Museum that was shot at Shields, Allegheny County, on September 2, 1908, by W. G. Pitcairn. R. B. Simpson has noted the species at Warren on eight different occasions, and has collected a few specimens. There are also scattered records for other counties, as listed in the references below. It is extremely unlikely that the Least Tern and especially the Sooty Tern have occurred at Franklin, as stated by Warren on the authority of a local observer. These alleged records probably represent misidentifications of the Black Tern.

Migration—April 10 (1912) is the earliest spring arrival date for this species at Conneaut Lake, and April 27 (1902) is the earliest and the only spring record at Erie. At Warren, Mr. Simpson recorded it on April 24 in 1892 and again on May 30 in 1895; these are his only spring dates. The majority of birds evidently move northward in May, for most of the records fall in that month. In the Pymatuning region this tern was noted in 1937 on May 8 (Skaggs), and Dr. Sutton speaks of seeing about fifty birds on May 15, 1922, at Crystal Lake. B. H. Christy saw the species once in the spring (May 18, 1924) at Clinton Pond, Allegheny County, and once near Youngstown, Westmoreland County, as late as May 30 (1928). It was noted at Jennerstown, Somerset County, on May 25, 1924, and at Loretto, Cambria County, on May 20, 1924 (Sutton); also at Oak Hall and Scotia, Centre County, on May 17, 1915, and on May 7, 1917 (Burleigh). The fall movement begins early, apparently soon after the young birds are on the wing. Mr. Simpson has several August records from Warren, one as early as August 5 (1904); and according to Dr. Sutton, the species was noted at Conneaut Lake by a local observer on August 10 (1925). T. D. Burleigh supplies a record of four birds seen at Lake Seaton, Fayette County, on August 21, 1915, and another of two seen on August 23. September, however, is the month of greatest movement, judging from my observations at Erie in 1900. Mr. Christy has one fall record for Clinton Pond, Allegheny County (September 3, 1925), and another for Dixmont, in the same county (September 2, 1930).

Habits—In the breeding season the Black Tern inhabits the marshes rather than the open beaches; indeed, even during migration it seems more partial to lakes, ponds, and quiet bodies of water in general, than to flowing streams. Fully as graceful in its movements as the Common Tern, it is by comparison quiet, not given to quarreling with its own kind or other birds, and not shy. Its behavior, as observed at Erie in the fall of 1900, is described in my 1904 report: "Several small flocks were seen on the main lake September 12, after the most severe storm of the season. On September 15 two [birds] were seen on the bay, one of which was secured. On the evening of September 16 the species suddenly became very prominent on the bay about Crystal Point, and on the following day, which dawned stormy and threatening, with frequent gusts of rain and a strong northwest wind, it was exceedingly abundant, swarming on both the bay and lake, far outnumbering the Common Terns, which were flying at the same time. The birds were perfectly tame, silent, and very fearless, repeatedly coming within a yard of the observer in their flight. They would beat up against the wind for a distance and then drift down before it, occasionally stopping over the water to pick up food, and on the outside beach flying over the land and the ponds back of the shore, without discrimination. Individuals in the postnuptial moult, showing a black and white spotted plumage, occurred with the birds in immature and full winter dress in the proportion of about one to one hundred. The day after this great flight comparatively few birds were seen, and these mainly on Erie Bay alone. Such were almost always more or less closely associated with Common Terns, and like them were often found resting on pieces of floating driftwood. The last was recorded September 24."

On May 22, 1934, a party from the Carnegie Museum, including myself, found a colony of perhaps twenty-five pairs of black terns apparently settled for the season in a part of Pymatuning Lake, northwest of Linesville—near a place where coots were nesting. The water was about a foot and a half deep and was more or less choked with aquatic vegetation. The birds were congregated in a scattered flock and hovered over the water or perched on floating drift; when their haunts were invaded they would come to meet the intruder with cries of alarm and protest. Several beginnings of nests were found. On May 30, when R. L. Fricke again visited this colony, he found one full set of eggs. The nest is merely a shapeless heap of dead reeds and grasses, floating in the water, and anchored to surrounding stems. It is raised above the surface just enough to keep the eggs from the water. Three eggs are a full set; they are brownish buff, more or less heavily marked with deep brown, and rather closely resemble the eggs of certain shore birds. The average size is 1.32 by .97 inches. Other nests and eggs found in subsequent seasons in the sanctuary are of the same type. By the end of July some young are on the wing.

Hydrochelidon nigra surinamensis WARREN, *Birds Pa.*, 1888, 232 (Erie Co.); ed. 2, 1890, 23 (Erie, Erie Co., nesting(?), *fide* Detwiller and Sennett; Venango Co., *fide* Robertson; Mercer Co., *fide* Overmoyer, transient)—TODD, *Ann. Carnegie Mus.*, 1904, 2:507 (Erie Bay and Presque Isle, Erie Co., transient)—BURLEIGH, *Wilson Bull.*, 1924, 36:75 (Oak Hall and Scotia, Centre Co., May)—CHRISTY, *Cardinal*, 1926, v. 1, no. 7, p. 25, 28 (Clinton Pond, Allegheny Co., fall).

(?)*Sterna antillarum* (error) WARREN, *Birds Pa.*, ed. 2, 1890, 22 (Venango Co., *fide* Robertson).

(?)*Sterna fuliginosa* (error) WARREN, *Birds Pa.*, ed. 2, 1890, 22 (Venango Co., transient, *fide* Robertson).

"Black Tern" SIMPSON, *Oölogist*, 1911, 28:76 (Warren, Warren Co., August–September)—SUTTON, *Bird-Lore*, 1924, 26:267 (Jennerstown, Somerset Co., May; Sandy Lake, Mercer Co., May, *fide* Homer)—CHRISTY, *Cardinal*, 1924, v. 1, no. 4, p. 12 (Clinton Pond, Allegheny Co., May; Loretto, Cambria Co., and Pymatuning Swamp, Crawford Co., May, *fide* Sutton)—SUTTON, *Bird-Lore*, 1924, 26:418 (Gordon Lake, near Bedford, Bedford Co., August, *fide* Lazear)—BOULTON, *Bird-Lore*, 1928, 30:271 (near Youngstown, Westmoreland Co., May), 401 (Butler, Butler Co., September, *fide* von Fuehrer)—TRIMBLE, *Cardinal*, 1937, 4:106 (Pymatuning Lake, Crawford Co., nesting).

Chlidonias nigra surinamensis SUTTON, *Ann. Carnegie Mus.*, 1928, 18:59 (Crawford Co. localities, transient; Conneaut Lake, nesting, *fide* Welshons)—CHRISTY, *Cardinal*, 1931, 3:16 (Dixmont, Allegheny Co., September).

AUKS, MURRES, PUFFINS

FAMILY ALCIDAE

The members of this family are exclusively maritime and visit the land only during the short nesting period. Occasionally in migration they reach the interior, as have the several Brünnich's murres that account for the inclusion of this family in the western Pennsylvania list. These birds occur only in the northern parts of the Northern Hemisphere, nesting on rocky shores in large communities. The eggs, usually single but occasionally as many as three, are laid on the bare rock. The young, down-covered when hatched, are fed by the parents until able to fly. All species swim and dive with ease. They sit in an upright position because of the posterior placement of the legs; the feet are webbed and the hind toe is wanting.

Although the various members of this family are similar in essential respects, they show wide differences in the form of the bill. In some species it is slender and pointed; in others it is higher than it is wide, much compressed, and sometimes adorned with horny protuberances and brilliant colors.

BRÜNNICH'S MURRE

URIA LOMVIA LOMVIA (Linnaeus)

Description—About as large as a medium-sized duck (the Baldpate). *Winter plumage:* upperparts black; wings black above, white below, and with narrow white tips to the secondaries; underparts white, the black of the upperparts encroaching somewhat on the sides of the lower throat.

Range—Brünnich's Murre is an arctic and marine species, and its occurrence away from salt water is fortuitous. I quote from my 1904 report: "The month of December, 1896, was memorable for the appearance of this maritime species at many points far inland, as far west as Michigan and Indiana. The flight seems to have followed the basin of the Great Lakes, along which there are numerous records.[1] . . . With these occurrences the Erie records, here published for the first time, are in close accord. Mr. Bacon states that several [murres] were shot on the bay in December, 1896, and although he quotes no dates, the time of their capture is fairly well indicated by a specimen (labelled a female) in Mr. James Thompson's possession that is marked 'December 18, 1896,' by the party who mounted it. At least one other specimen from this flight was mounted by a local taxidermist, which bird is now in the Carnegie Museum [No. 3856]. The species was not met with again until November 20, 1899, when a single bird was killed on the bay by a gunner, this specimen also eventually coming to the Carnegie Museum. In 1900 specimens were taken by gunners on November 27 and December 2, from which flight two specimens are known to have been preserved, one now in Mr. Bacon's collection, and the other in that of the Carnegie Museum [No. 7153]. All the gunners who have met with birds of this species agree in stating that they were easily approached and killed."

The breeding station nearest our region is Bird Rock, in the Gulf of St. Lawrence. But J. H. Fleming, in analyzing the several migration flights of this species that have occurred over a period of years, thinks that the birds involved must have

[1]For a complete list, compare J. H. Fleming, *Ornis*, 1907, 16:528–543.

come, not from the Gulf of St. Lawrence, but from Hudson Bay, whence they were driven southward by failure of their usual food supply. There are no further records from Erie, but from Conneaut Lake there is one of a bird captured on December 3, 1907. A specimen (No. 8286) in the Carnegie Museum, said by G. A. Link, Sr., to have been received on September 9, 1889, from a local gunner, is supposed to have been taken in Allegheny County. The ascribed date is so far out of accord with the dates of the other records that it suggests doubt of the authenticity of the locality. Concerning the only other inland record from our region, A. T. Buckhout writes: "In the fall of 1895 a male of this species was caught alive in the 'Barrens' and came into my possession after it died. The plumage was perfect, but the body was exceedingly thin, and the stomach contained nothing." This specimen is now preserved in the museum of The Pennsylvania State College; it is the one mentioned by Merrill Wood (1932).

Uria lomvia Todd, *Ann. Carnegie Mus.*, 1904, 2:501 (Erie Bay, Erie Co., November–December).

"Brunnich Murre" Simpson, *Oölogist*, 1911, 28:33 (Erie Bay, Erie Co., November)—Wood, *Wilson Bull.*, 1932, 44:238 (near State College, Centre Co., winter, *fide* Musgrave).

Uria lomvia lomvia Sutton, *Ann. Carnegie Mus.*, 1928, 18:54 (Conneaut Lake, Crawford Co., December).

PIGEONS, DOVES

FAMILY COLUMBIDAE

THE COLUMBIDAE are widely distributed throughout the temperate and tropical regions of the world and are especially abundant in the East Indian region and in Australia. Between five and six hundred forms have been described. Since the extermination of the Passenger Pigeon there is only a single representative of this family in western Pennsylvania.

The bill is a prominent character of the Pigeons and Doves; it has a swollen, horny tip and, at the base of the upper mandible, a fleshy membrane in which the nostrils are situated. These birds have short legs, and feet with four toes all on the same level, which adapt them both for walking and perching. They have two rather peculiar habits not shared by other birds: in drinking they keep the bill immersed in the water instead of tipping the head backward; and they feed the young on regurgitated "pigeon milk" which is secreted in the crop. Their nests are crudely built of twigs. Two eggs usually comprise a set, and incubation is shared by both parents.

EASTERN MOURNING DOVE

ZENAIDURA MACROURA CAROLINENSIS (Linnaeus)

Description—A dove of medium size, a little larger than the Robin; grayish brown above, the wings darker, with black spots on the tertiaries; a bronzy-purple iridescence on the sides of the neck; a small black spot behind and below the eye; tail sharply graduated, all the lateral feathers with broad white tips and a subterminal black band; underparts pale vinous color, which becomes buffy on the abdomen and under tail coverts; bill black; feet reddish. *Young birds* are similar but duller, with pale, scalelike markings on the wings and breast.

Range—This is a species of austral origin and affinities that has spread northward as far as the Transition Life Zone, beyond which it is rather infrequent. Its east-and-west range is transcontinental, and the western birds constitute a slightly differentiated subspecies. More than forty years ago this dove was one of the most abundant birds in western Pennsylvania, but where there may once have been fifty pairs there is probably not one now. Shooting the species for game in the southern states has very likely been the main cause of this decrease. There is little likelihood, however, that the Mourning Dove will ever disappear, as has the Wild Pigeon, since it does not breed in communities. Probably it is even now far more numerous than it was in the days when our whole section was one vast primeval forest. While there are not many actual records from the northern part of the plateau region, the species may be said to be fairly common throughout. Evidently the climatic conditions in the higher parts do not totally prevent it from breeding there. It is a regular summer resident wherever found, and most observers in the western counties, as well as some in the ridge and valley section, report that it occasionally remains throughout the winter months. In fact, the Mourning Dove may almost be said to occur fairly regularly during the winter in many parts, as far north at least as Crawford County; and it is occasional even in Erie County. Every year it is reported by sundry observers in the "Christmas Census," published in *Bird-Lore*, but that its presence in winter is not a new development is attested by similar records made previous to 1900.

Migration—Because this species often winters in our region, it is not always easy to say just when true migrants from the South really appear. Everything considered, however, the northward movement seems to begin in March; in any case the Mourning Dove is one of the earlier spring birds to arrive. It comes with the Red-winged Blackbird, the Meadowlark, the Field Sparrow, and the Chipping Sparrow. Some average arrival dates are as follows: Sewickley, March 18 (earliest March 8, 1890); Beaver, March 17 (earliest March 12, 1887 and 1921); Erie, March 21 (earliest March 18, 1898); State College, March 20 (earliest March 12, 1917); Renovo, March 29 (earliest March 17, 1914); Springs, Somerset County, March 31 (earliest March 19, 1913); Warren, earliest April 1, 1899. From these records it would seem that the migration of this species across the plateau region is retarded. The available records for the fall movements are scanty and irregular and complicated by the inclusion of references to possible winter residents. The species is common enough through September, however, and often in early October as well, but a decrease in its numbers is usually evident during the second week of the latter month, and by the first of November practically all the migratory birds have gone, and only those that intend to remain for the winter are left. These indeed may have come from farther north.

Habits—Unlike the fruit pigeons of the Oriental region, some of which are among the most beautiful birds in the world, the Mourning Dove can claim no special distinction; yet it is by no means an unattractive bird. Modestly garbed in dun-colored plumage, inconspicuous against the soil of the open fields where it spends much of its time, mild and gentle, rather retiring in its disposition, and inoffensive in its relations with other species, it is not without character. It is, moreover, the sole living representative in western Pennsylvania of a large and important group of birds. On the ground, like others of its family, it has a walking gait and carries itself gracefully, nodding its head back and forth with each step. On the wing it flies swiftly and directly, with a peculiar whirring or whistling sound. It arrives in our region during the first mild, sunny days of mid-March, and its soft, mournful, cooing notes are one of the most pleasing and welcome voices of the spring. It always comes in pairs, and so remains until after the young are on the wing. All through the spring and early summer the fields and orchards resound with its mating song, as the pairs go about the task of rearing their broods. The male will usually be found perched in an exposed position, with his mate close beside him or not far away. They fly and perch together and are most devoted to each other and to their progeny.

Occasionally a pair nests in the woodland—the original habitat of the species—but the great majority of birds have adopted a more civilized way of life, so to speak, and have taken up their residences in the orchard and shade trees. Evergreen trees are always in special favor as nesting sites. Years ago, before the Norway spruce trees were removed, the Beaver cemetery (just west of the town) was inhabited by hundreds of pairs of mourning doves; the nests were built on the lower, flatter branches, while the tops of the trees were occupied by bronzed grackles. Almost every tree of sufficient size contained at least one nest and frequently also the dilapidated remains of those of previous seasons. Sometimes the nest is built next the trunk, but it is oftener placed well out on a horizontal branch. It is seldom at a greater elevation than fifteen to twenty-five feet and is sometimes much lower. I once found a nest in a dense grove of small hemlocks, within a yard of the ground; and in May, 1933, I found one at Pymatuning Swamp in a fallen dead tree in the woods, only five feet up. H. C. Kirkpatrick found a nest in a similar situation; he writes also that he has found several nests built on limbs overhanging small streams. Odd nesting sites reported by other observers include a coal tipple, old stumps, the top rail of a fence, and a piece of bark caught on a small tree. Ground-nestings are unusual but have been reported by two observers. I have often found mourning doves' nests built on old robin nests—a well-known practice of this bird everywhere. One writer (Elliott, 1884) tells of a mourning dove actually laying its eggs in an occupied nest of a robin.

Wherever placed, the nest itself is always a carelessly built, untidy structure, composed in the main of dry twigs laid loosely together to form a frail platform and lined with some finer material—rootlets, weed stalks, and dry grasses. A nest that is eight inches across is a large one, and there is never more than a slight depression for the eggs. Like most birds of this family, the Mourning Dove normally lays only two eggs, but sets of three are not unknown. Both J. W. Jacobs and R. L. Keesler report finding nests with three eggs, and two further instances have come to my personal notice: On April 20, 1887, I collected a set of three in the Beaver cemetery; and on June 13, 1909, near Ekastown, Butler County, I found a nest containing three nearly fledged young. The usual egg of this species is elliptical oval in outline and measures about 1.15 by .84 inches, but in the set of three that I found the eggs were much smaller and more spherical in shape. The color is always pure white.

Nesting begins very early, and some pairs are building and laying even before the northward migration of the species at any given place is complete. S. S. Dickey writes of finding a nest with slightly incubated eggs at Waynesburg as early as April 4 (1904), while my own earliest record for Beaver is April 6 (1888). A still earlier date—March 31 (1920)—is cited by G. M. Sutton for Hartstown, on the authority of a local observer. But there is much irregularity in the time, and there are many pairs that do not commence nesting until late in April or even until May. Moreover, each pair probably raises two broods in a season, and perhaps sometimes three. I base this suggestion on the finding of a nest containing callow young as late as September. This gives the Mourning Dove an unusually long breeding season in any one locality.

I have never known a mourning dove to resent an intruder at its nest, but I once came upon a sitting bird that flew off feigning a broken wing, scrambling and fluttering over the ground in an attempt to divert my attention from her nest. Too frequent visits to a nest with eggs are very likely to cause the birds to desert, but after the eggs are hatched, the parents are not so easily discouraged. The young are unlovely little creatures; a whitish down is their only covering. They are perfectly helpless and are at first fed by regurgitation of partially digested food, in the manner of all pigeons. As they get older they receive increasing amounts of solid food. After they are on the wing and able to care for themselves they collect in small flocks, and in July and August they may often be found feeding in grainfields, but the damage they do there is trifling. In October again, old and young frequent fields where corn has been cut and shocked, which, however, they in nowise injure; the stomachs of birds shot in such places and elsewhere are found to be gorged with weed seeds, particularly those of the ragweed (*Ambrosia*). Weed seeds, indeed, are the chief food of this species at all seasons, and the grain taken consists mostly of waste kernels left after the harvest and picked up from the ground; since the stalks are never broken down it is evident that no attempt is made to get at the ripe heads. The Mourning Dove is therefore a valuable asset to the agriculturist and deserves protection, for economic as well as aesthetic reasons.

Zenaidura carolinensis TOWNSEND, *Proc. Acad. Nat. Sci. Philadelphia*, 1883, 66 (Latrobe, Westmoreland Co., breeding).

"Turtle Dove" ELLIOTT, *Young Oölogist*, 1884, 1:113 (Mercer, Mercer Co., nesting).

"Carolina Dove" ENTY, *Ornithologist and Oölogist*, 1885, 10:78 (Templeton, Armstrong Co., migration).

"Mourning Dove" JACOBS, *Nat. Companion*, 1886, 2:59 (Waynesburg, Greene Co., November)—JACOBS, *Hoosier Nat.*, 1887, 2:78 (Waynesburg, Greene Co., occasional in winter)—TODD, *Oölogist*, 1887, 4:89 (Beaver, Beaver Co., nesting)—WICKHAM, *Oölogist*, 1888, 5:92 (Beaver, Beaver Co., February)—VAN OSTRAND, *Osprey*, 1896, 1:38 (Morganza, Washington Co., fall; food)—STONE, *Cassinia*, 1906, 9:43 (McConnellsburg, Fulton Co., June)—PITCAIRN, *Bird-Lore*, 1907, 9:155 (Riverview Park, Allegheny Co., nesting)—SIMPSON, *Oölogist*, 1911, 28:54 (Warren, Warren Co.)—BURLEIGH, *Oölogist*, 1911, 28:156, 180 (Harmarville, Allegheny Co., nesting)—MCCONNELL, *Oölogist*, 1918, 35:150 (McKeesport, Allegheny Co.)—DICKEY, *Oölogist*, 1919, 36:67 (Waynesburg, Greene Co., nesting)—MILLER, *Oölogist*, 1919, 36:155 (Lemont, Centre Co., nesting)—MCCLELLAND, *Am. Mid. Nat.*, 1922, 8:36 (Washington, Washington Co., summer)—SUTTON, *et al.*, *Bird-Lore*, 1923, 25:24 (Monaca to Raccoon Creek, Beaver Co., December)—SUTTON, *Bird-Lore*, 1923, 25:132, 194; and 1924, 26:56, 190 (Pittsburgh region, Allegheny Co., winter)—ELLIOTT, *et al.*, *Bird-Lore*, 1924, 26:30 (Denny Pond to Deer Creek, Allegheny Co., December)—CHRISTY, *Cardinal*, 1924, v. 1, no. 4, p. 10 (Big Traverse Valley, Beaver Co., June)—EASTWOOD, *Bird-Lore*, 1926, 28:136 (Harmarville, Allegheny Co., January, *fide* Squier)—REITER and SQUIER, *Bird-Lore*, 1927, 29:196, 197 (Pittsburgh region, Allegheny Co., migration)—MCCLINTOCK, *Cardinal*, 1933, 3:128 (Ligonier, Westmoreland Co., June)—ELLIOTT, *Cardinal*, 1934, 3:170 (Raccoon Creek, Beaver Co., December)—COPE and HAWKINS, *Forest Leaves*, 1934, 24:26 (E. Tionesta Forest Reserve, Warren and McKean Co., summer).

Zenaidura macroura DWIGHT, *Auk*, 1892, 9:135 (Cresson, Cambria Co., June)—JACOBS, *Summer Birds Greene Co., Pa.* 1893, 5 (Greene Co., nesting)—TODD, *Auk*, 1893, 10:39

(Two Lick, Indiana Co., June), 44 (Coalport, Clearfield Co., June)—JACOBS, *Bull. 17 Wilson Orn. Chapt. Agassiz Assoc.*, 1897, 71 (Waynesburg, Greene Co., nesting)—TODD, *Ann. Carnegie Mus.*, 1904, 2:552 (Erie, Erie Co., summer)—TODD, in Bausman, *Hist. Beaver Co., Pa.*, 1904, 2:1199 (Beaver Co., summer)—KEIM, *Cassinia*, 1905, 8:37 (Port Allegany, McKean Co., summer)—DICKEY, *Oölogist*, 1909, 26:224 (Waynesburg, Greene Co., nesting)—CHRISTY, *Cardinal*, 1930, 2:201 (Little Sewickley Creek, Allegheny Co., nesting); 1939, 5:45 (near Murdocksville, Allegheny Co., winter)—RANEY, *Auk*, 1939, 56:337 (New Castle, Lawrence Co., nesting with robin).

Zenaidura macroura carolinensis HARLOW, *Auk*, 1912, 29:469 (southern Centre Co., nesting)—CHRISTY, *Cardinal*, 1923, v. 1, no. 1, [p. 4] (Sewickley, Allegheny Co., nesting; occasional in winter)—BURLEIGH, *Wilson Bull.*, 1923, 35:85 (Allegheny Co., nesting); 1924, 36:70; 1931, 43:39 (State College, Centre Co., migration; nesting)—CHRISTY and SUTTON, *Cardinal*, 1928, 2:69 (Cook Forest, Clarion Co., nesting)—SUTTON, *Ann. Carnegie Mus.*, 1928, 18:120 (Crawford Co. localities; migration; nesting)—BURLEIGH, *Cardinal*, 1929, 2:117 (Allegheny Co., August nesting)—CHRISTY, *Cardinal*, 1929, 2:129 (Murdocksville, Washington Co., December; Little Sewickley Creek, Allegheny Co., February)—BURLEIGH, *Cardinal*, 1932, 3:74 (Chestnut Ridge, near Uniontown, Fayette Co., summer).

"Dove" STREET, *Cassinia*, 1923, 24:12 (Greencastle to Ft. Loudon, Franklin Co., June).

PASSENGER PIGEON

ECTOPISTES MIGRATORIUS (Linnaeus)

Description—Similar in form and proportions to the Mourning Dove, but *much larger*, with a wingspread of about two feet. *Male:* head (all around), bluish gray; upperparts in general, dull bluish gray, the neck with a greenish or purplish sheen; wing coverts bluish gray like the back, with more or less brownish wash; wings dusky brown, the primaries edged with buff, the tertiaries and scapulars brownish, with some black spotting; tail long and pointed, dull white, the middle pair of feathers dark-colored; lower throat, sides of the neck, and breast, rich vinaceous brown, which becomes paler posteriorly and almost white on the under tail coverts; bill dark; feet purplish red; iris red. *Female:* similar to the male, but smaller and much duller in general coloration; the upperparts are more shaded with brown, and the underparts are soiled white, without any solid vinaceous color; the breast is washed with brown. *Young birds* resemble the adult female, but are more or less spotted with buffy scalelike feather-edgings above and on the breast.

Range—The Passenger Pigeon is now believed to be extinct. Its one-time breeding range comprised southern Canada and the northern United States as far west as the edge of the Great Plains and as far south as Virginia, Kentucky, and eastern Kansas. Its winter range has not been so satisfactorily determined but was probably mainly within the southern states, although in mild and open seasons it extended irregularly farther north. The great nestings that have been recorded were in Kentucky, Minnesota, Wisconsin, Michigan, New York, and Pennsylvania. In our own region no trained ornithologist has ever had the chance to make any extended study of this bird, and we have only the random and desultory observations handed down by pigeon hunters and other interested persons. From these it would appear that the "pigeon country" comprised the northern counties, from Warren to Potter inclusive, and Forest, northern Jefferson, Elk, and Cameron counties to the south. This was the region where the beech tree flourished most extensively and insured a plentiful supply of food for the birds. There is no satisfactory proof that the pigeons ever nested along the mountains farther south, however, although several "roosts" were located there.[1] Smaller nestings have occurred in Pymatuning Swamp, Crawford County, but none have been reported from any of the counties to the southward, where the species appeared only as a transient. As late as 1890 Sennett was quoted by Warren to the effect that the Pigeon bred "very sparingly in a few localities in Crawford and Erie Counties," but no circumstantial evidence in support of this statement is adduced. It was to be expected that scattered pairs should have bred in various parts of their former range after the great nestings were broken up; such breeding is recorded by one of Warren's correspondents (M. M. Larrabee) from Cameron County.

Migration—According to one writer (A. L.

[1]H. A. McGraw has supplied data concerning one such roost which was discovered in Homer's Gap, north of Altoona, in 1873. According to his informant, T. S. Davis, the pigeons were present in vast numbers during May, June, and July, but were not breeding.

Hench, quoted by French), pigeons wintered during 1875–76 in enormous numbers in the Allegheny Mountains, where Cambria and Somerset counties meet. Considering the altitude of this region, this was a most unusual and surprising circumstance, but the statement is borne out by evidence from another source. S. S. Miller, of Springs, Somerset County, sent me the following information, quoted from the diary of his father, S. J. Miller, for January 1, 1876: "Thermometer at 62° at 7 A. M., and at noon about 72°; it has been so for some days. Wheat and the grass on the lawn have grown considerably. Immense clouds of wild pigeons moved north in the morning and returned in the evening." Mr. Miller further stated that although he was only a boy at the time, he remembered this flight very well: "There was something entirely abnormal about the behavior of the birds; they did not alight anywhere to feed, and seemed to be demoralized. I had never seen them here before at that time of the year, and I never saw them in such immense uncountable numbers; there were literally millions of them. I am thoroughly convinced that those pigeons perished en masse that winter, because that was about the last that we saw of the Wild Pigeon here. My recollection is that I saw one or two small flocks of perhaps a half-dozen each the following fall, but not one since." During the previous fall they had been exceedingly plentiful, but left as usual when snow and cold weather came. That they should have returned again in the middle of the winter is very strange, although the unseasonably mild weather may have lured them northward ahead of time. Much more understandable is the statement attributed to J. C. Anderson that in the early days some pigeons remained in Sewickley throughout the year.

Pigeons used to appear in March, before all the snow was off the ground, but actual records of arrival are few. In 1876 Sennett wrote in his journal that on March 11 "the weather was very mild and the air was full of Wild Pigeons." He shot a specimen on March 13 and another on April 11. In 1875 he collected one on April 3 and another on April 14, at Erie. In C. W. Townsend's article on this species (in Bent, 1932) there are two other arrival dates for our region: Chambersburg, February 13, 1884;[1] and Ridgway, March 22, 1886.[2] The fall movement seems to have taken place in September and October, but here again, exact dates are scarce. H. H. Wickham saw about ten pigeons near Beaver on October 16, 1888.

Habits[3]—The Passenger Pigeon is a bird that I have never seen alive, but I recall that during my boyhood, in the early eighties, birds of this species were used for trapshooting one year at the Beaver Fairgrounds and that the practice evoked considerable protest from the townspeople. At that time no one suspected that the species was on the verge of extinction, yet in a dozen years it had become so rare that single specimens were at a premium. Many thought then that it would continue to exist in isolated pairs and small flocks, but this was not to be. So quickly, indeed, did it pass out of the picture that no ornithologist of the recent school had an opportunity to make detailed studies of its life history, and what information there is comes mainly from Wilson and Audubon, whose observations were made early in the nineteenth century.

Reading the accounts of these authors, one is imbued with a sense of the irreparable loss suffered by the naturalists of the country in the passing of the Pigeon. Undoubtedly it was one of the most abundant birds (if not indeed the most abundant) on the American continent in the early days. The unbelievably vast numbers in which it was wont to appear; the extent of its daily flights; the enormous area, the unusual density, and in particular the shifting character, of its communal roosting and nesting places, were features of its life history that were unique. Here was a species so perfectly fitted to its environment and to existing conditions that, although a pair laid but a single egg at a setting, or two at most, and although its enemies were legion, it had increased in the course of time

[1]From the manuscript of Davison Greenawalt, in the Bureau of Biological Survey.

[2]"X. Tempore," in *Forest and Stream*, 1886, 26:182.

[3]Compiled before the publication of Louis Scherer's article on this subject (1939).

to such an extent that it bade fair to overrun the continent by sheer force of numbers. The story of its passing is a shameful record of human cruelty, avarice, and indifference—a story one wishes had never been told.

Audubon begins his account of the Pigeon by describing its manner of flight, on which (as he truly says) its whole economy depended. It was a strong and rapid flier, easily capable of making a mile in a minute, or sixty miles in an hour. (One writer has claimed for it a flying speed of one hundred miles an hour.) This speed enabled it to seek its food in places far from its nesting grounds; otherwise both adults and young would have perished miserably, for, obviously, the food resources of the immediate environs of a breeding colony would quickly have been exhausted by the demands of such a vast population. But with the territory within a radius of one hundred miles or more from the nesting grounds available to the birds in their daily flights, the problem of subsistence for a colony was readily solved. C. W. Townsend writes: "The immense forests of North America, before they were devastated and wasted by the ax and fire of the white settlers, furnished an inexhaustible supply of food to the enormous hosts of wild pigeons. The principal food was mast—acorns, beechnuts, and chestnuts—and also the fruit or nuts of any of the forest trees, as well as wild berries and fruits, such as cherries, raspberries, blueberries, currants, pokeberries (also called pigeon berries), and strawberries, grain, seeds of weeds, and grasses. . . . During the nesting season insects were largely eaten, especially earthworms, grubs, and grasshoppers. The pigeons were fond of salt and frequented natural salt licks as well as grounds baited with salt" (in Bent, 1932).

Vivid pen pictures of pigeon flights and pigeon "cities" have been transmitted from early sources. Audubon describes a flight that he witnessed in the fall of 1813, at Louisville, Kentucky, which required three days to pass: "The air was literally filled with pigeons; the light of noonday was obscured as by an eclipse; the dung fell in spots, not unlike melting flakes of snow; and the continued buzz of wings had a tendency to lull my senses to repose." Except near the Ohio River, the birds were flying high, beyond gunshot. Audubon undertook to estimate the number of individuals represented in a "column one mile in breadth, which is far below the average size," supposing it to require three hours to pass, and found it to contain 1,150,136,000 birds! The amount of food consumed by such a flock would be 8,712,000 bushels daily. Wilson's estimate of a flock seen by him in the same state was even greater, yet must have been conservative. From our own region there is corroborative evidence of a sort, dealing not with the true migration of the pigeons, but with their daily flights to and from their nesting colonies. At Pymatuning Swamp, according to one W. G. Hayes (quoted by G. M. Sutton, 1928), in the days when the pigeons were numerous, "the flights generally took place in the early morning or toward evening as the birds moved from or into their usual roosting quarter. Imagine a sheet of birds from one to one and one-half miles in width, passing continuously for over an hour in such numbers as to give the appearance and shadow of a cloud between the earth and sun, and some idea of the vast numbers of these birds may be formed. Usually they flew ten or twelve feet from the ground. They rose in waves to pass over fences and trees but sometimes they flew from thirty to fifty feet in the air without the undulating motion. It was often necessary to station men in the fields of late grain to keep the birds from destroying the crops."

In his book, *The Passenger Pigeon in Pennsylvania* (1919), J. C. French presents a great deal of historical data bearing on the occurrence of the species in this state, together with numerous first-hand accounts of its nesting and feeding habits and of the methods of its capture, gleaned from old inhabitants. While his treatment is disjointed, unscientific, and altogether uncritical, and while considerable extraneous matter is included, he has succeeded in rescuing from oblivion much information of interest and value concerning this bird and its extermination. The same remarks apply to a pamphlet by W. W. Thompson, of Coudersport, Potter County. *The Passenger Pigeon* (1907), by W. B. Mershon, is another work of a similar, but more general, character. Limitations of space forbid extensive quotations from these and other authors and necessitate condensing and combining certain of their accounts. A report of pigeons from our region in 1810 is probably the earliest authentic record. In the spring of that year, according to Mr. French, one John Lyman descended the Allegheny River from Coudersport to Warren—a distance of one hundred miles—to secure seeds for replanting crops that had been killed by a severe frost. He returned with the seeds and with a wild tale of twenty colonies of pigeons which he had seen along the river and which he estimated contained a million individuals each. "The pioneers of Potter county were incredulous of John Lyman's report in 1805 [1810]. They could not believe that twenty millions of the birds existed along a hundred miles of the upper Allegheny at that time. To them it was only a romance, for five years, until they returned, and experts reported that it was history and conservative."

Whether the pigeons nested annually on such a scale is not clear; the inference is that they shifted their nesting grounds in accordance with the varying abundance of mast from year to year. One writer (C. W. Dickinson, quoted by French) positively declares that pigeons never nested in Pennsylvania except in seasons following good beechnut years. "Under no other conditions could such a body of birds possibly live for a period long enough to raise their young." Several writers insist that they did not "use the same nesting place a second time in one season, the entire colony always moving from twenty to one hundred miles after the appearance of each brood of young."[1] Others, on the contrary, state just as positively that the second laying was in the same nest as the first and before the young squab had left it. All agree, however, that two or more broods were reared in a season, and Mr. French thinks it probable that there were four broods, each raised successively farther north. All this information is exceedingly interesting if true, and the lack of precise scientific data on this score is greatly to be deplored. Unfortunately there are many gaps in the records of the Pennsylvania nestings. Mr. French refers (incidentally and at length) to nestings in the years 1810 (earliest), 1830, 1855, 1860, 1861, 1866, 1870, 1874, 1878, 1880, and 1886 (last). The 1870 nesting in McKean and Potter counties, "which was the largest in this locality since 1830, was from one-half mile wide to two miles wide and about forty miles long, running through an unbroken forest. The direction of the line was nearly east and west, a zigzag line to keep near the main range of mountains that divides the waters of the Allegheny and the Susquehanna rivers."

The method by which these nesting grounds were originally chosen is not known. The pigeon hunters believed that the selection was made by scouting parties of birds sent out in advance, but how such information was relayed to the main body was never apparent. It was observed that the appearance of a few small flocks circling over a given territory was frequently the forerunner of immense flocks a day or two later. They seemed to come all at once, with an overwhelming rush. At sunrise some morning not a pigeon could be seen or heard; all was quiet in the forest. But, according to Mr. French, "soon from the west there came a sound like that of an approaching tempest, or a roar of a distant cataract; swish! The pigeons had come. Streaming through the forest with such speed that one could catch a sight of only a glint of flapping wings. Flock followed flock, sitting in the tops of the trees or lighting on the ground, and moving forward still, as if impelled by the momentum gained in their flight. Hopping, tumbling, flitting over one another, in the eagerness of each one to keep in the front rank." After satisfying their hunger, the birds lost no time in pairing off and beginning their nests. These were simple, frail structures, composed of a few dry twigs fashioned into a crude platform in the trees, with a slight hollow for the eggs. The actual building was done by the female, while the male brought the material. One or two days sufficed to complete the nest. Birds of the pigeon tribe habitually lay two eggs, but there is much difference of opinion regarding the Passenger Pigeon—some writers claim that one egg was the full set; others, that two were laid. Probably both estimates are correct. The eggs were pure white, and measured 1.50 by 1.07 inches. Two weeks' incubation was required for hatching. The young were fed by regurgitation, grew very rapidly, and were ready to leave the nest in about two weeks. They became very fat and weighed almost as much as the old birds, but by the time they were able to fly well they had grown lean.

Within the confines of a pigeon "city" every tree would be loaded with nests, placed in all available situations. The larger the tree, the more nests it contained. A tree such as a hemlock would naturally hold more nests than a hardwood. A hundred nests have been counted on a single tree. One who has not actually seen such a nesting can have no

[1]William Brewster (*fide* Stevens), *Auk*, 1889, 6:288.

real conception of the vast multitude of birds involved, and many writers have felt called upon to excuse their seeming overstatements. A curious character of these pigeon cities was their sharp delimitation—so sharp, indeed, that branches of nesting trees projecting beyond the invisible boundary line would be left unoccupied. The noise and confusion must have been inconceivable. Both sexes incubated and tended the young, relieving each other at regular intervals, the free birds going off together in flocks (the sexes separately) to feed at some distant point. These daily flights to and from the nesting grounds were remarkable phenomena. Mr. French tells of his observations near Roulette, Potter County, in 1866 and 1870: "On each morning the valley, a mile wide, between the hills, was filled, strata above strata, eight courses deep at times, for about an hour, with the multitude of birds flowing westward, at the rate of about a mile a minute, going after food. The roar of wings was like a tornado in the treetops and the morning was darkened as by a heavy thunder shower."

One writer declares that when the pigeons arrived at their chosen nesting site they began stripping the ground of beechnuts, of which there must have been thousands of bushels. Other writers aver that they always sought their food at a distance and left for the young birds whatever might be found at the nesting site. It was further claimed that the young, once they had gained the full use of their wings, followed the old birds to their new nesting grounds. One may be excused for doubting many of these unscientific observations. There are some excellent accounts, however, of the pigeons' feeding habits. Audubon writes that after some preliminary evolutions they would presently descend to the ground. "When alighted, they are seen industriously throwing up the withered leaves in quest of the fallen mast. The rear ranks are continually rising, passing over the main body, and alighting in front, in such rapid succession, that the whole flock seems still on the wing. The quantity of ground thus swept is astonishing, and so completely has it been cleared, that the gleaner who might follow in their rear would find his labor completely lost. Whilst feeding, their avidity is at times so great that in attempting to swallow a large acorn or nut, they are seen gasping for a long while, as if in agonies of suffocation." When pigeons alighted in newly sown grainfields they caused great havoc, stripping them completely of seed. Thus at a very early time they came to be regarded as a pest by the farmers, and this attitude contributed to their final annihilation.

Extermination—Audubon, who described the great devastation wrought in the ranks of the pigeons by the hunters of his day, gave it as his considered opinion that "nothing but the gradual diminution of our forests can accomplish their decrease, as they not infrequently quadruple their numbers yearly, and always at least double it." He failed to foresee the development of pigeon hunting on a commercial scale, the building of railroads into the territory the birds occupied, and the wholesale methods of slaughter that were devised. As it turned out, the forest mostly survived the pigeons. The birds were netted in enormous numbers on their way to and from their nesting grounds by the use of living birds as decoys; they were shot, suffocated by sulphur fumes, and whipped to death with long poles. Trees in their "cities" were felled in such a way as to bring down as many others as possible, and all the squabs they contained would fall to destruction. Thousands of barrels of dead birds were shipped in a season to the markets of the large cities, while live birds were sent to gun clubs for use in trapshooting. The professional "pigeoners," as they were called, of which there were as many as five thousand at one time, followed the birds around the country, summer and winter, persecuting them unremittingly at all seasons.

Between 1870 and 1880 this destruction was at its height, and the pigeons were reduced to a tithe of their former numbers. Had a measure of protection been afforded at the close of this period it might have sufficed to save the Pigeon for the benefit of future generations, or at least to have stabilized its numbers. But the cupidity of the commercial interests knew no bounds and in another decade had defeated its own object. The big nestings were all wiped out, and only a few pitiful remnants of the once vast pigeon population remained, in isolated bands and small flocks. It was at first thought that these would survive and save the species from extinction, but as the reports of their appearance became fewer, it was realized that the birds' doom was near. In 1912 a belated effort to save the Passenger Pigeon by offering a reward for locating a living pair, failed completely.

It is significant that there have been no reports of the killing of any passenger pigeons for more than twenty years. There is but a slight chance that a few wild birds still survive.

The last large nesting, or attempted nesting, in Pennsylvania was in 1886. The beechnut crop of the previous year had been very large, and the birds came in April to establish a "city" in their old haunts in Potter County. They were met with the usual reception from the inhabitants. "Thirty or forty men and boys went into the roosting with guns. . . . At 9 P. M. they began shooting into the treetops . . . as long as they could hear a bird fly among the branches. Then, gathering into small groups, they made camp-fires and waited for day-light, so they could find the dead and crippled birds under the trees. That was the death-blow to pigeons in Pennsylvania. They left in the night, which was clear, with a full moon; so the birds could see where to go, in a northerly direction." Such was the testimony of an eyewitness (C. W. Dickinson, as quoted by French). Mr. French gives his personal account as follows: "During my youthful years I was familiar with the passenger pigeons and their nesting cities in McKean and Potter Counties, in Pennsylvania. When they returned, in the spring of 1886, I saw many scouting flocks and, upon hearing that they were gathering along Pine Creek and the Kettle Creek tributaries, I went to observe them and make a careful investigation. From Coudersport I drove over the hills, before dawn of day, and reached the forest they had selected, about 8 o'clock on the morning of their disappearance. There was not a live bird to be seen, along my route of thirty miles; but young men were coming from the woods with bags full of dead birds."

The pigeon hunters believed that the birds had gone into the wilds of Canada to nest there and that eventually they would return. But this was virtually the end of the story; the later chronicles for our region are brief: A few "scout" birds flying about Sheffield, Pa., in March, 1888—J. V. Barnett. A flock of nine or ten seen at Pymatuning Swamp about 1888 by W. G. Hayes—G. M. Sutton. A flock of ten seen near Beaver on October 16, 1888—H. H. Wickham. "Last year (summer, 1889) I saw a number of single pairs and their nests in Lake, Ross, and Fairmount townships in this county" (Cameron)—M. M. Larrabee. Two shot, on June 9 and July 18, 1890, respectively, near Erie—S. E. Bacon. One shot at Washington, September 20, 1890—J. S. Nease. Three seen flying over at Warren, September 21, 1890—R. B. Simpson. One seen flying past (within two hundred feet) at Kinzua, Warren County, August 8, 1891—R. B. Simpson. A "few single individuals or pairs seen" at Kane, McKean County, summer of 1891—B. H. Warren. "Adolphe Shurr, formerly a woodsman, states that there was a small nesting of pigeons in the big hemlocks at the head of Young Woman's Creek, in Clinton County, when he peeled bark there in the spring of 1892"—H. W. Shoemaker. "In 1892 three flocks seen in Potter County"—Seth Nelson, Jr. One seen along the Allegheny River near Warren, with a flock of mourning doves, May 20, 1893; very wild—R. B. Simpson. Three small flocks (thirty to forty birds) seen on one of the tributaries of Pine Creek, Potter County, about October 25, 1897, by A. C. Kimball—A. H. Wood. Two seen at Cross Fork, Potter County, in the fall of 1897, by D. R. McCoy—A. H. Wood. A flock of thirteen seen at Pymatuning Swamp in 1899 by Nelson Gehr—G. M. Sutton. One shot at Roulette, Potter County, in 1899, by Dr. McGrannon—T. D. Keim. One seen on Grant's Run, near Grantonia, Elk County, in June, 1901—J. C. French. A flock of five birds passed over Waynesburg on September 30, 1902 (seen also by Mr. Jacobs, Sr., and John Reese); another flock of nine birds passed over on November 12, 1902—J. W. Jacobs. One shot in McKean County in 1902, preserved and exhibited—H. A. Surface. A flock of about one hundred birds seen in McKean County in September, 1905, and one lone bird in 1906—C. W. Dickinson. Five seen at Roulette, Potter County, in 1906, by William Hazen—J. C. French.

The record does not end here, but these instances are the only ones in which full confidence can be placed. It is not impossible that some few individuals may have survived until the present date, but it is most unlikely. So many reports of supposed occurrence of the Passenger Pigeon in recent years have been found on investigation to pertain to the Mourning Dove that all are open to suspicion. At any rate, no reputable ornithologist has seen a passenger pigeon anywhere in this country since 1907.

Sic transiit Ectopistes migratorius, a bird that was

once as common as the grasshoppers of the field, whose spectacular flights filled the early American settlers with awe, whose prodigious numbers astounded Wilson and Audubon, and whose vast nesting colonies covered hundreds of square miles of territory. What happened to the thousands that composed the last attempted nesting in 1886 will probably never be known; they may have perished in the north country by stress of weather. The pigeoners refused to believe that their operations had anything to do with the final debacle and offered diverse and fantastic explanations to account for the final disappearance of the birds. These explanations, and the arguments against all proposed measures for protection, sound suspiciously like those advanced by the hunters of today against further restrictions on waterfowl shooting.

The Passenger Pigeon became extinct because it was a species the well-being and very existence of which depended upon the communal habit, and because it was unable to adapt itself to new conditions of living. It must be admitted that had it survived in its quondam numbers it would have been a terrible pest to the agriculturist, judging from what is known of its fondness for grain of all kinds. Again, even if no birds had been killed, the passing of our great forests would eventually have entailed the passing of the Pigeon, or at least a tremendous reduction in its numbers. Even so, its extermination at the hands of the pigeoners, aided and abetted by the commercial interests that stood to profit by such wholesale slaughter, with the connivance of an indifferent and unthinking public, is a blot on our civilization that can never be erased. The Passenger Pigeon has gone; will the wildfowl and the birds of prey go, too? May the present generation be wiser than its forebears.

Columba migratoria WIED, *Reise in Innere Nord-America*, 1839, 1:131 (near Ebensburg, Cambria Co., September).

Ectopistes migratorius TOWNSEND (C. H.), *Proc. Acad. Nat. Sci. Philadelphia*, 1883, 66 (Latrobe, Westmoreland Co., transient)—TEULON, *Jour. Boston Zoöl. Soc.*, 1883, 2:11 (Bradford, McKean Co.)—WARREN, *Birds Pa.*, ed. 2, 1890, 111 (distribution by counties)—BAILY, *Auk*, 1896, 13:290, 291, 292 (Williamsville, Elk Co., *fide* Clay)—RHOADS, *Auk*, 1899, 16:310 (Washington and Erie Co., *fide* Sennett; Potter Co., and Round Island, Clinton Co., *fide* Nelson; Cameron and McKean Co., nesting, *fide* Larrabee)—TODD, *Ann. Carnegie Mus.*, 1904, 2:551 (Erie, Erie Co., breeding[?], *fide* Bacon and Sennett)—KEIM, *Cassinia*, 1905, 8:37 (Roulette, Potter Co., *fide* McGrannon)—CHRISTY, *Cardinal*, 1923, v. 1, no. 1, [p. 4] (Sewickley, Allegheny Co., March, 1886)—TOWNSEND (C. W.), in Bent, *Bull. U. S. Nat. Mus.* no. 162, 1932, 379 (Chambersburg, Franklin Co., and Ridgway, Elk Co.; migration).

"Wild Pigeon" WARREN, *Forest and Stream*, 1891, 37:83 (Kane, McKean Co., summer)—PUTNAM, *Forest and Stream*, 1906, 67:450 (Pymatuning Swamp, Crawford Co.)—"J. N. C.," *Forest and Stream*, 1907, 69:811 (Chestnut Ridge, Fayette Co., fall)—SIMPSON, *Oölogist*, 1909, 26:85 (Warren Co.)—"Anon.," *Cassinia*, 1913, 16:21 (Spring Creek, Forest and "Warren" Co., nesting)—PIERCE, *In the Open*, March, 1920, 10:29 (10 mi. west of Pittsburgh, Allegheny Co., 1874)—DEANE, *Auk*, 1923, 40:628, 629 (Erie, Erie Co., March–April, *fide* Sennett).

"Passenger Pigeon" [CRISPIN, *Oölogist*, 1907, 24:155 (Potter Co., nesting, *fide* Lyon—error—*cf.* BURNS, *Wilson Bull.*, 1910, 17:47)]—WRIGHT, *Auk*, 1910, 27:428, 437 (western Pa.; Ashe's records)—NEWTON, *Forest and Stream*, 1910, 74:934 (Coudersport, Potter Co., nesting)—FISCHER, *Bird-Lore*, 1913, 15:84 (Sheffield, Warren Co., nesting)—FRENCH, *Passenger Pigeon in Pa.*, 1919, 7–257 (Pa., habits, etc.)—[CHRISTY], *Cardinal*, 1924, v. 1, no. 3, p. 7 (Sewickley, Allegheny Co., *fide* Anderson, Miller, and Shields), 18 (Hickory, Washington Co., October, 1877)—TOWNSEND (C. H.), *Condor*, 1927, 29:224 (Westmoreland Co.; habits, etc.)—[CHRISTY], *Cardinal*, 1931, 3:19 (Pittsburgh, Allegheny Co., Oct. 16, 1857, *fide* McClintock)—SCHERER, *Cardinal*, 1939, 5:25 (McKean and Potter Co., habits, etc., *fide* Oviatt).

Ectopistes canadensis SUTTON, *Ann. Carnegie Mus.*, 1928, 18:117 (Pymatuning Swamp, Crawford Co., records and references).

THE CAROLINA PAROQUET (*Conuropsis carolinensis* [Linnaeus]), a representative of the Family Psittacidae, must have reached western Pennsylvania at one time, as it did also Ohio and New York. The only known records, however, are unsatisfactory (J. P. KIRTLAND, in *Second Annual Report Geological Survey of the State of Ohio*, 1838, p. 179; EZEKIEL HOLMES, in *Report U.S. Patent Office, Agriculture, for 1856*, 1857, p. 147) and are for that reason disregarded.

CUCKOOS

FAMILY CUCULIDAE

Cuckoos, of which there are more than two hundred forms, occur in almost all parts of the world, but are more numerous in tropical regions. They differ widely in appearance and in habits. All have "yoke-toed" or zygodactylous feet (two toes in front and two behind, the fourth toe being reversed). Some of the Old World species are strikingly colored, but the typical cuckoos, to which group our two species belong, are dun-colored, long-tailed birds of medium size. They are inhabitants of the woodland and are not gregarious. They have exceedingly beneficial food habits, since they consume large quantities of insects of all kinds and are particularly fond of caterpillars, which are distasteful to most birds. The American Cuckoos build rude nests and hatch their own eggs, although many of the Old World forms parasitize other species. The young are naked when hatched.

YELLOW-BILLED CUCKOO (Plate 13)

COCCYZUS AMERICANUS AMERICANUS (Linnaeus)

Description—About the size of the Robin, but of slender build; *tail* long and graduated, black beneath, *with broad white tips* to the lateral feathers; general color of upperparts (including head), hair brown ("Quaker-color"), with a faint greenish gloss; *wings* similar, with a *rufous wash on the primaries* externally, and the inner webs of the feathers deep rufous, showing conspicuously in flight; underparts white with a faint grayish shading; bill black above, *yellow below*.

Range—This species has a transcontinental range, extending north to southern Canada in the Transition Life Zone. (The Pacific coast race is scarcely separable.) It winters in South America. It is in general more southern in its predilections than the Black-billed Cuckoo and, according to my observations, outnumbers that species five to one in the Carolinian Fauna of western Pennsylvania. In the higher parts of the state, however, the other is commoner. In the northern part of the plateau region, indeed, the Yellow-billed is rare enough to suggest that it must be a comparatively recent immigrant there. G. M. Sutton supplies one spring record (a sight identification) for Potter County (Keating Summit, May 5, 1928), but as yet there are no records for McKean, Forest, Elk, and Cameron counties. R. B. Simpson reports that in Warren County, at the western edge of the plateau region, the Yellow-billed Cuckoo is far less common than the Black-billed and seems to prefer the Allegheny River Valley to the hill country.[1] Van Fleet records it as breeding at DuBois, but "not very common." It is common and regular, however, at Renovo, on the West Branch of the Susquehanna River (Pierce), and is similarly reported from Springs, Somerset County, in high country close to the Maryland line (Miller), as well as from farther north in the same county and from the Johnstown region of Cambria County (Mostoller).

Migration—Like many other species with a long migration route, the Yellow-billed Cuckoo is one of the later migrants in the spring; it seldom reaches our region before the second week in May and often not until the third week. Seven years' rec-

[1]A record by T. M. Cope and A. S. Hawkins, published in *Forest Leaves*, 1934, 24:26, possibly applies to the Black-billed species.

ords of its arrival at Beaver lie between May 6 (1913) and 19 (1910), and yield May 12 as the average date (Todd and Wickham). In Allegheny County, its earliest occurrence at Pittsburgh was on May 17 (1913 and 1914—Burleigh), and the earliest arrival dates for Sewickley are May 15 and 18 (1923, 1924—Christy). On the other hand, it has been reported from Waynesburg as early as May 5 and 7 (1891, 1892—Jacobs), from Washington on May 4 (1892—Gans), and from as far north as Warren on May 5 (1899—Simpson). It has been seen at State College as early as May 6 (1919—Burleigh), and at Renovo on May 11 (in several years), although the average arrival date there is May 17 (Pierce). The rapidity and long duration of the migration flight of this species have been attested by the examination of a bird shot at Beaver on June 2. This bird had in its stomach the remains of a certain ant which is known only in Mexico and the West Indies. Migration is always accomplished during the night.

In the fall the Yellow-billed Cuckoo usually remains until late September, but a few birds occasionally linger into October. The following are late records: Presque Isle, September 21, 1900 (Todd); Crystal Lake, Crawford County, September 24, 1925 (Sutton); Beaver, September 27, 1902 (Todd); Sewickley, October 18, 1901 (Christy); Wilkinsburg, September 29, 1899 (Atkinson); Pittsburgh, October 16, 1912 (Burleigh); Warren, October 3, 1900 (Simpson); State College, September 23, 1915 (Burleigh); Renovo, October 18, 1919, and November 12, 1911 (Pierce). This last occurrence was of course accidental.

Habits—Both the cuckoos of our region are primarily forest birds, but the Yellow-billed has been able to adapt itself to the changed conditions wrought by civilization and often comes to shade trees and orchards to feed and to nest. It is more frequently heard than seen; and its loud, characteristic notes, somewhat resembling the syllables *kow-kow-kow*, repeated in series, slowly at first, then more rapidly, and retarded toward the end, are a sure clue to its presence. This call, sometimes heard in the night and said to be given oftener in cloudy weather than in clear, is supposed by many to presage rain; hence the vulgar name of "Rain Crow." Usually this cuckoo keeps well concealed in the shade of thick foliage; in general it is a shy, secretive, solitary, and unobtrusive bird. When discovered, it is likely to be headed away from the observer and peering back at him with a curious intensity and equanimity. As it passes furtively from tree to tree through the forest openings, it seems to be gliding rather than flying, so silently and swiftly does its long, slender body seem to float through the air; and the whole impression it gives is one of stealth.

The food habits of both our cuckoos have been carefully studied in the field and in the laboratory. An outstanding peculiarity is their fondness for hairy caterpillars, which are distasteful to most birds. The tent caterpillar (*Clisiocampa americana*) and the fall webworm (*Hyphantria cunea*)—two of the worst pests known to orchard, shade, and forest trees—are in particular favor and are eaten in immense numbers. More than one hundred tent caterpillars have been taken from a single cuckoo stomach. Moreover, the birds feed on the larvae of such species as the Io moth, the caterpillars of which are actually spiny and poisonous to human touch. The lining of a cuckoo's stomach often becomes completely felted with caterpillar hairs, without thereby causing any apparent inconvenience to the bird. Other insects, such as beetles, cicadas, and grasshoppers, are also taken, and towards the end of the season a little wild fruit—but not enough to invalidate the claim that the cuckoos not only are truly insectivorous, but also are among the most valuable destroyers of insect pests.

Of all our tree-nesting birds the cuckoos are possibly the most slovenly in constructing their nests. They are perfectly satisfied with a few dry twigs and bits of leaves hastily thrown together and so loosely arranged that often the eggs can be counted from beneath. The nest is so flat that a breeze may even cause the eggs to roll out when the bird is absent, and it is often so small that when she is on her nest, her head and tail project well beyond the edge. If in an orchard tree, the nest is seldom more than twenty feet from the ground, and is lodged, rather than placed, on a horizontal branch. If in wild land, some thick-set tree, such as a haw, crab-apple, or wild plum, is a frequent choice, and sometimes the nest is as low as three feet. Three eggs are the average set, but sometimes only two are laid; four and even five have been found, however. They are pale dull green, but often the color is not uniform. They are oval in shape and average 1.19 by .90 inches, but there is great variation in size, even in the same set. Moreover, there is often, although not always, a considerable interval between their deposition. It is not unusual to find a nest containing newly hatched young, an incubated egg, and one egg nearly fresh. There is also a wide discrepancy in the time of nesting. In our region nests with eggs have been found as early as May 20 (Atkinson) and as late as August 26 (Burleigh); June, however, is the most favored month. This may mean that two broods are sometimes reared, or that the later nestings are delayed ones. The young are ugly, with blackish skin, and are almost naked at first; the growing feathers are stiff and bristlelike until they finally burst their sheaths.

It is a well-known fact that this species occasionally reverts to the parasitic habit of its European cousin and lays its eggs in the nests of other birds. According to all accounts, the Black-billed Cuckoo is a frequent victim of this imposition, but occasionally the situation is reversed. J. W. Jacobs (1934) reports that once an egg of a black-billed cuckoo was found in a nest of a yellow-billed, and that in another instance the latter species had laid in a cardinal's nest.

Coccygus americanus Townsend, *Proc. Acad. Nat. Sci. Philadelphia*, 1883, 65 (Latrobe, Westmoreland Co.).

Coccyzus americanus Todd, *Auk*, 1893, 10:39 (Two Lick, Indiana Co., June)—Jacobs, *Summer Birds Greene Co., Pa.*, 1893, 6 (Greene Co., nesting)—Beal, *Bull. Biol. Surv.* no. 9, 1898, 8 (western Pa., food)—Todd, *Ann. Carnegie Mus.*, 1904, 2:558 (Presque Isle, Erie Co., summer)—Todd, in Bausman, *Hist. Beaver Co., Pa.*, 1904, 2:1199 (Beaver Co., summer)—Forrest, *Oölogist*, 1911, 28:116 (Washington, Washington Co., summer).

"Yellow-billed Cuckoo" Stone, *Cassinia*, 1906, 9:43 (McConnellsburg, Fulton Co., June)—Pitcairn, *Bird-Lore*, 1907, 9:155 (Riverview Park, Allegheny Co., nesting)—Dickey, *Oölogist*, 1914, 31:171 ([Charter Oak], Huntingdon Co., June)—McConnell, *Oölogist*, 1918, 35:150 (McKeesport, Allegheny Co.)—McClelland, *Am. Mid. Nat.*, 1922, 8:36 (Washington, Washington Co., summer)—Street, *Cassinia*, 1923, 24:12 (Greencastle to Ft. Loudon, and region, Franklin Co., June)—Christy, *Cardinal*, 1924, v. 1, no. 4, p. 10 (Big Traverse Valley, Beaver Co., June)—Eastwood, *Bird-Lore*, 1926, 28:274 (Sandy Lake, Mercer Co., May, *fide* Squier)—Boulton, *Bird-Lore*, 1928, 30:337 (Pittsburgh region, summer)—Jacobs, *Oölogist*, 1934, 51:19 (Waynesburg, Greene Co., nesting; parasitic habits)—Miller, *Bird-Lore*, 1934, 36:301 (Springs, Somerset Co., nesting; food).

Coccyzus americanus americanus Harlow, *Auk*, 1912, 29:471 (southern Centre Co., summer)—Christy, *Cardinal*, 1923, v. 1, no. 1, [p. 6] (Sewickley, Allegheny Co., summer)—Burleigh, *Wilson Bull.*, 1923, 35:86 (Allegheny Co., nesting); 1924, 34:71; and 1931, 43:41 (State College, Centre Co., migration, nesting)—Sutton, *Ann. Carnegie Mus.*, 1928, 18:139 (Crawford Co. localities, summer)—Oberholser, *Bird-Lore*, 1931, 33:249 (Beaver, Beaver Co., and Renovo, Clinton Co., migration)—Burleigh, *Cardinal*, 1932, 3:75 (near Uniontown, Fayette Co., summer).

BLACK-BILLED CUCKOO (Plate 13)

COCCYZUS ERYTHROPTHALMUS (Wilson)

Description—Similar in general to the Yellow-billed Cuckoo, but *bill entirely black, wings without any rufous color*, and tail dull grayish below, with *small and inconspicuous white tips*.

Range—The summer range of this cuckoo is more restricted towards the west than is that of the Yellow-billed, since it does not extend beyond the Rocky Mountains; and the species is not common westward. Northward, however, it is commoner than the other and regularly enters the Canadian Life Zone. The differences in the range and abundance of the two species are reflected in their status in western Pennsylvania. In the valley country the Black-billed Cuckoo is only about a fifth as numerous as its Yellow-billed cousin, while in the plateau section the reverse is true. Even at Pymatuning Swamp the Black-billed is the commoner of the two, as it is also in the hill country and mountain ridges of the central counties.

Migration—The winter home of the Black-billed Cuckoo is in South America, and like the other species it is one of the later migrants in the spring. Certain records from our region, it is true, indicate an earlier average date of arrival for the Black-billed, but this indication is not substantiated by a study of the extralimital records available. For example, J. W. Jacobs reported it from Waynesburg on May 1 (1892), which is certainly an early date. My only arrival dates for Beaver are May 6 (1902) and May 8 (1889). For Renovo, May 14 is the average date of arrival, and May 5 (1902), the earliest. Records from sundry other localities are somewhat later: Meadville, May 7, 1909 and 1910 (First); Springs, Somerset County, May 9, 1930

(Miller); Erie, May 11, 1875 (Sennett); Sewickley, May 14, 1899, and May 15, 1919 (Christy); Hollidaysburg, May 15, 1921 (Berg). Fall records of departure are, as usual, fewer, but September 20 is the average date in thirteen years' observations at Renovo, with October 4 (1919), the latest. Other late dates from various places are: Beaver, September 25, 1909; Sewickley, September 29, 1929; Hartstown, September 23, 1925. These records correspond for the most part with those from neighboring states.

Habits—In general habits our two cuckoos are much alike. The Black-billed, however, seems to be more partial to woodland and does not seek the orchards and shade trees so frequently—although I have, to be sure, found its nest in just such places. R. B. Simpson writes that in Warren County, where the Black-billed Cuckoo is common, it seems to be quite at home in the big forests of pine and hemlock about the headwaters of Tionesta Creek. At Pymatuning Swamp, according to G. M. Sutton (1928), it is found "most commonly in the shrubbery about the lakes, and in the upgrown borders of woodlands, often near the roads." It is rather unusual that two species of the same genus, similar in appearance, haunts, and habits, should occur together over such a vast area. Personally I confess that I have never learned to tell them apart by their call notes, which some claim to be distinctive, and I have never ventured to enter either species in my field notes unless I could get a satisfactory view of one of the diagnostic markings.

S. K. Eastwood (1926) thus describes the method of producing the call notes: "During the nesting-season, a pair of Black-billed Cuckoos was discovered perched on the topmost branches of a tree in a densely wooded tract. As they began their call note of *cow-cow*, their tails began to move up and down in pump-handle fashion, as if to punctuate the call. It appeared as if the effort exerted in getting out the note *cow* caused the bird such exertion as to threaten its balance, and that this movement of the tail was to offset this effort. In the case of the female bird, the amount of motion was noticeably greater than that of the male bird. This would tend to support the theory that the tail is used to maintain the balance, as in general, the female of the species is somewhat weaker physically. The call notes of both birds seemed to have equal vigor, indicating the same amount of exertion required by both to produce the note which in the case of the weaker bird required greater balancing tactics to maintain the equilibrium." Mr. Eastwood leaves us in the dark, however, as to his method of distinguishing the sexes.

The nest is usually placed in a low tree or bush, sometimes not over three feet from the ground; like that of the Yellow-billed species, it is rough and crude as a rule, although occasionally a partial lining of catkins or oak blossoms is inserted. Eggs have been found as early as May 20 (Sutton), a fact which indicates that at least some pairs lose little time after their arrival in beginning their nesting; June, however, is the more usual month. E. G. Holt, on the other hand, writes that in 1925 at Rector, Westmoreland County, he found a bird incubating a set of eggs as late as July 30. Mr. Jacobs believes that incubation proceeds more regularly with this species than with the Yellow-billed, but T. D. Burleigh's record of a nest found at State College on June 6, 1916, which held three small young in various stages of growth and one well-incubated egg, offsets this opinion. Oddly enough, although the two species of cuckoos are virtually of the same size, the eggs of the Black-billed are considerably smaller in size (averaging only 1.07 by .81 inches) and are a deeper green in color. It is not at all unusual for the two species to lay their eggs in each other's nests, or even occasionally in the nests of other birds; this is perhaps to be expected in view of their relationship to the European Cuckoo, in which the parasitic habit is highly developed. Mr. Simpson and R. C. Harlow report once finding a black-billed cuckoo sitting on a clutch of seven eggs; this was doubtless the result of two females laying in the same nest, since the normal set does not exceed four.

Coccyzus erythrophthalmus Townsend, *Proc. Acad. Nat. Sci. Philadelphia*, 1883, 65 (Latrobe, Westmoreland Co., breeding)—Dwight, *Auk*, 1892, 9:135 (Cresson, Cambria Co., June)—Jacobs, *Summer Birds Greene Co., Pa.*, 1893, 6 (Greene Co., nesting)—Baily, *Auk*, 1896, 13:293 (Williamsville, Elk Co., June–July)—Todd, *Ann. Carnegie Mus.*, 1904, 2:558 (Erie and Presque Isle, Erie Co., summer)—Todd, in Bausman, *Hist. Beaver Co., Pa.*, 1904, 2:1199 (Beaver Co., summer)—Harlow, *Auk*, 1912, 29:471 (Bald Knob, Bear Meadows, and region, Centre Co., and "Stone Valley," Huntingdon Co., summer)—Christy, *Cardinal*,

1923, v. 1, no. 1, [p. 6] (Sewickley, Allegheny Co., breeding)—CHRISTY and SUTTON, *Cardinal*, 1928, 2:70 (Cook Forest, Clarion Co., summer)—SUTTON, *Ann. Carnegie Mus.*, 1928, 18:140 (Crawford Co. localities, summer)—BURLEIGH, *Wilson Bull.*, 1931, 43:41 (State College, Centre Co., nesting)—OBERHOLSER, *Bird-Lore*, 1931, 33:252 (Beaver, Beaver Co., and Renovo, Clinton Co., migration)—BURLEIGH, *Cardinal*, 1932, 3:75 (near Uniontown, Fayette Co., nesting).

"Black-billed Cuckoo" BRUMBAUGH, *Wilson Bull.*, 1905, 12:100 (Wilkinsburg, Allegheny Co., July)—SIMPSON, *Oölogist*, 1909, 26:169; 1913, 30:53 (Warren, Warren Co., nesting)—BURLEIGH, *Oölogist*, 1911, 28:156 (Harmarville, Allegheny Co., nesting)—MCCLELLAND, *Am. Mid. Nat.*, 1922, 8:36 (Washington, Washington Co., summer)—STREET, *Cassinia*, 1923, 24:12 (Jordan's Knob, Franklin Co., June)—EASTWOOD, *Bird-Lore*, 1926, 28:130 (Pittsburgh, Allegheny Co., habits)—BOULTON, *Bird-Lore*, 1928, 30:337 (Pittsburgh region, summer)—JACOBS, *Oölogist*, 1934, 51:20 (Waynesburg, Greene Co., nesting habits)—MILLER, *Bird-Lore*, 1934, 36:301 (Springs, Somerset Co., nesting; food).

BARN OWLS

FAMILY TYTONIDAE

THE BARN OWLS are found in the temperate and tropical regions of practically the entire world. Anatomically they differ so markedly from other owls that the members of this single genus have been accorded family rank. In general habits, however, they resemble the members of the typical family, the Strigidae.

BARN OWL (Plate 12)

TYTO ALBA PRATINCOLA (Bonaparte)

Description—A medium-sized owl, with a wingspread of about forty-five inches; facial disc very prominent; eyes black; *legs long and slender. Upperparts* (including top of head) *mottled with gray and deep buff* in varying proportions, and showing fine black and white spots; wings and tail similar, with some dusky barring; facial disc white or whitish, with a prominent dark (brownish) border all around, and a dark area on the inside border of each eye; *underparts white or buff*, with small dusky spots, rather evenly distributed. Some individuals (possibly younger birds) are heavily suffused both above and below with rusty buff, while others are grayish and white.

Range—The North American Barn Owl is now considered to be a geographical variant of a species that is virtually cosmopolitan in its distribution. Like the typical Old World race (*alba*), it does not go far north, although it has a wide east-and-west range. When J. A. Allen brought out his celebrated paper on the faunal areas of eastern North America in 1871, he included the Barn Owl in the list of species confined to the Carolinian Fauna in their northward range.[1] There seems to be a distinct impression that since then the Barn Owl has gradually been pushing northward into the Alleghanian Fauna, although as a representative of that fauna it is still far from common. It may be, however, that in the early days it was merely overlooked. At any rate, records from more northerly localities have continued to multiply, until now the species is recognized as occurring regularly in regions where it was once unknown.[2] This would seem to be the case in Ohio[3] and also, by inference, in western Pennsylvania, although so little ornithological work was done in our region in earlier years that there is no proper basis for comparison. There is in fact no certain record before 1878, when one bird was taken at Meadville by H. C. Kirkpatrick. (It is significant that he did not again encounter the species until 1914.) One was reported as taken at Washington in December, 1882, and another at the same place a year later. Warren, who cites these occurrences among others (all of which are perhaps not authentic), also states that he himself saw one barn owl near Somerset in January, 1890. For the thirty or more years thereafter there are likewise only a few odd records, but since 1922 so many have been received from various sources that when plotted on the map they indicate a fairly even distribution from the Ohio boundary eastward as far as Chestnut Ridge. For Allegheny County alone there are no less than twelve records, several of them supported by specimens. The western half of Crawford County is also fairly well spotted. In the northern counties of the plateau region the Barn Owl is apparently unknown, except for a single record from Millport, Potter County, reported by G. M. Sutton on the

[1] *Bulletin Museum Comparative Zoölogy*, 1871, 2:375–450.
[2] Compare T. S. ROBERTS' remarks on this question, in *Birds of Minnesota*, 1932, 1:599.
[3] Compare LYNDS JONES, *Birds of Ohio*, 1903, p. 101.

basis of a dead bird found on March 15, 1928, by a resident of that place. There are a few scattered records also from the ridge and valley section, where the species reappears.

It is true that fall and winter records for this owl greatly predominate and that as yet there are few actual breeding records. The Barn Owl supposedly is resident wherever found, but it may be partially and irregularly migratory near the northern limit of its range. We may not be justified in predicating the breeding of this species at Somerset on the basis of Warren's winter record, although there is partial confirmation in the fact that a barn owl was killed at New Lexington, in the same county, on May 11, 1928—a date when it should have been breeding (Sutton). One bird was noted some two miles west of Erie on June 27, 1928 (Hicks). This is almost certainly a breeding record. Dr. Sutton cites two unquestionable instances of breeding in Crawford County (Conneaut Lake and near Linesville), and S. J. Seiple, two for Mercer County (Osgood and New Hamburg), while H. M. McQuiston says that the species nests near Sharon in the latter county. In Westmoreland County it has been found nesting near Blairsville (Christy) and at New Alexandria (Trimble). There are several nesting records from Allegheny County, vouched for by B. H. Christy and H. H. Elliott. S. S. Dickey reports several more from Greene County. It is probable that the Barn Owl also nests at other points within its recognized local range.

Habits—Owls, because of their nocturnal habits, silent and shadowy flight, peculiar physiognomy, and weird and uncouth cries, have come to be regarded with something akin to superstitious fear, or even as omens of ill to be avoided at all hazards. The Barn Owl receives more than its share of this obloquy, at least in the Old World, where it is often found in the neighborhood of human habitations, haunting such resorts as church belfries and ruined buildings. It is to this species that the poet Gray refers in his lines:

> Save that, from yonder ivy-mantled tower,
> The moping owl does to the moon complain
> Of such, as wand'ring near her secret bower,
> Molest her ancient solitary reign.

On this side of the Atlantic, however, the Barn Owl is wont to use natural cavities in trees as roosting and nesting sites. Most of the nests found in our region were in hollow trees (oaks and sycamores); one was in a church belfry; and one in a barn.

The nest itself is merely a mass of the rubbish that naturally collects in such situations, together with old castings, dropped by the birds. The eggs are said to number from four to seven; like all owls' eggs they are perfectly white; they measure (on an average) 1.67 by 1.28 inches. I am unaware of any sets collected in our region, however, and the laying season is uncertain but is probably about the first week in April. Dr. Dickey writes that a nest found near Kirby, Greene County, had five half-grown young on May 11, 1935, while another found near Jefferson had five eggs on June 4, 1929. This latter nest was used every season (except one) until 1938. Nearly grown young, just learning to fly, were taken from a nest in a hollow tree on August 1, 1925, in Westmoreland County, about two miles west of Blairsville. They were sent alive to the Carnegie Museum, where I had the opportunity of examining them. They were able, according to Mr. Christy (1926), "to move the feathers of their facial discs, and so to alter in most comical manner their expression. They had a way, when approached, of craning forward until head downward their faces were hidden beneath their tails, and when in that

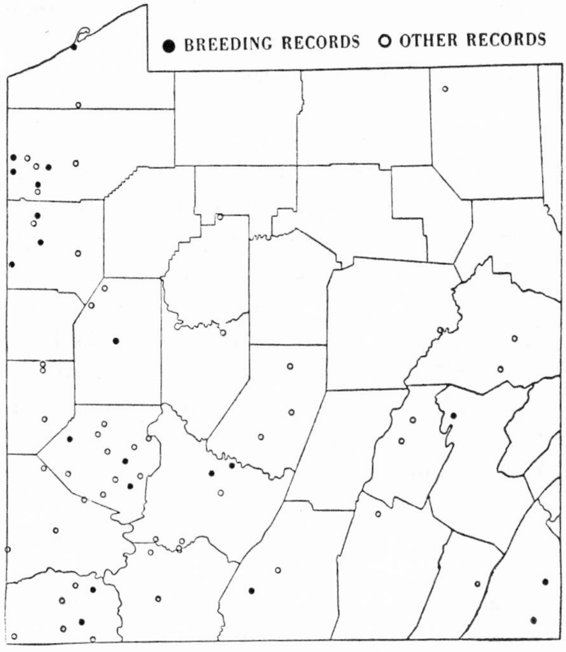

LOCAL RANGE OF THE BARN OWL

strange attitude they would hiss and shake their heads violently. And it was remarkable that while manifestly they could see nothing before them, still any nearer approach, detected by some other sense, invariably caused increase of their agitation."

The Barn Owl is more strictly nocturnal in its activities than are some of the other owls (the Great Horned, for example) and for this reason doubtless escapes casual observation to a large extent. It keeps concealed during the day but sallies forth at dusk in search of food. It preys almost exclusively upon small mammals, particularly the mice that are destructive to growing crops; it seldom takes small birds and never touches poultry or the larger game birds. Rats, old and young, are taken at all times if they can be found. A pair of barn owls about a farmhouse are far more effective in controlling vermin than is a cat, yet most farmers make the mistake of killing the one and coddling the other. It has been estimated that a single pair of barn owls with their brood of young would consume more than 150 rats and mice in a single day. The amount of good that they do in the aggregate is incalculable, and the amount of harm is inconsiderable. They should be protected and encouraged in every way, to the end that their numbers may be increased throughout our territory.

Dr. Sutton has written the following concerning the feeding habits of this species: "The stomach of a barn owl which came in this afternoon (February 4, 1922) was exceedingly full, having the remains of at least five short-tailed shrews (*Blarina*) and one field mouse (*Microtus*). The skull was in every case crushed toward the rear, apparently by the forceful manipulations of the owl's jaws. It seemed that the head had then been pulled off before the remainder of the body was eaten, and that in at least three cases the latter was swallowed at one gulp. One *Blarina* was apparently swallowed whole, and, judging from its undigested condition, it was the last one eaten. A large amount of much longer fur, probably of the common rat, was present, but I could find no bones." W. H. Meyer (1939) reports the results of an examination of an accumulation of pellets or castings found in an old barn near State College, as follows: eastern meadow mouse, seventy-five per cent; house mouse, ten per cent; also unidentified small rodents, a short-tailed shrew, a New York weasel, and one small bird, probably an English sparrow.

Dr. Dickey relates an interesting experience with this owl in Greene County. He says that the nest located near Jefferson on June 4, 1929, was fifty feet from the ground in a cavity fully ten feet deep in the decayed top of a giant oak overlooking the valley of a stream. "This pair of barn owls regularly disappear after the summer is over. In 1937 they left their 'den' about the middle of August.

"While this owl is considered harmless to game, yet I know of instances of destructive propensity. A farmer told me that he once (in January) watched one of these owls swoop out of a barn loft into a brier patch to capture a bob-white, whereupon he shot the owl. At another farm the owls were in the habit of quartering the fields near the house to pick up young rabbits, whose squeak could still be heard as they were borne off to the owls' den in a large sycamore."

A. K. Fisher has written concerning this owl: "Besides its shrieking or screeching note, which is heard more often in spring, it has a nasal one which has been termed a 'snore.' The peculiar and almost ludicrous expression of the physiognomy of this bird, as it sits upright with half-closed eyes, has suggested to the minds of many a fanciful resemblance to a monkey; hence the origin of the name 'Monkey-faced Owl,' which is a common appellation for the bird in many parts of the country."[1]

"Barn Owl" WARRICK, *Ornithologist and Oölogist*, 1883, 8:31 (Washington, Washington Co., December)—PORTMAN, *et al.*, *Bird-Lore*, 1926, 28:31 (Thompsonville and region, Washington Co., December)—WOOD, *Wilson Bull.*, 1932, 44:238 (State College, Centre Co., two records).

Strix pratincola WARREN, *Birds Pa.*, ed. 2, 1890, 144 (distribution by counties)—TODD, *Ann. Carnegie Mus.*, 1904, 2:556 ([Edinboro], Erie Co.).

Aluco pratincola CHRISTY, *Cardinal*, 1926, v. 1, no. 8, p. 17 (Westmoreland Co., near Blairsville [Indiana Co.], and Harmarville, Allegheny Co., breeding); 1932, 3:68 ([near Glenshaw], Allegheny Co., December).

Tyto alba pratincola SUTTON, *Ann. Carnegie Mus.*, 1928, 18:133 (Crawford Co. records and references)—CHRISTY, *Cardinal*, 1932, 3:93 ([near Glenshaw, Allegheny Co.])—HEGNER, *Cardinal*, 1934, 3:172 (Sewickley, Allegheny Co., May)—MEYER, *Auk*, 1939, 56:187 (State College [2 miles north], Centre Co., food).

[1]*Hawks and Owls of the United States*, 1893, p. 138.

OWLS

FAMILY STRIGIDAE

Owls are found in all parts of the world except Polynesia. Several hundred different forms are recognized; nine of these occur in western Pennsylvania, although several are merely accidental visitors. Prominent characteristics exhibited by the members of this family are as follows: large, immovable eyes directed forward and surrounded by a pronounced facial disc; the eyes have lashes, and the upper lid is used in closing the eye; the feet are usually densely feathered, and the toes with their sharp, recurved claws are well fitted for perching, as well as for grasping and tearing prey; the plumage is soft and fluffy; the bill is strongly hooked and provided with a cere. Owls assume an upright position in perching, which, with their facial expression and weird, half-human calls, contributes to their appearance of importance and wisdom.

Because of their raptorial habits and the shape of their bills and feet, the Owls were formerly regarded as related to the Hawks, but anatomically they are widely different, their affinities being rather with the Goatsuckers. As nocturnal birds of prey, Owls feed largely upon mammals. The small animals are swallowed whole, and the larger ones torn into pieces; after the soft parts have been digested, the hair, bones, feathers, and other indigestible portions are ejected from the mouth in the form of pellets. Some Owls build rude nests; others appropriate discarded nests of other large birds; many nest in holes in trees, in deserted buildings, or in natural cavities. Their eggs are white, almost spherical in shape, and vary in number from two to ten. The young are covered with thick, white down when hatched. Almost all Owls, with the possible exception of the Great Horned, are beneficial in their food habits. They perform an invaluable service in controlling the numbers of mice, rats, rabbits, ground squirrels, and other rodents, and thus deserve careful protection.

Warren's record for the Hawk Owl in Allegheny County (*Report on the Birds of Pennsylvania*, ed. 2, 1890, p. 159) is unverifiable and unacceptable.

EASTERN SCREECH OWL

OTUS ASIO NAEVIUS (Gmelin)

Description—A *small owl, with conspicuous "horns" or ear tufts;* height in life about eight inches. *Rufous phase:* general color above, rufous, with narrow black shaft-streaks; wings and tail similar but duller, the former with some buffy-white spots on the quills and coverts; underparts and flanks varied with rufous and black markings, in a streaked pattern; the abdomen (medially) and under tail-coverts, white; the sides of the "face" show a dark stripe; iris yellow. *Gray phase:* similar to the rufous phase, but general color dull gray instead of rufous, the dark streaks above and below usually more prominent, those below often connected with narrow crossbars, giving a herringbone effect. There is also a brownish intermediate phase. These color phases are independent of sex, age, or season; their significance is not yet understood. In *juvenal dress* the general plumage displays grayish bars or rufous bars, as the case may be.

Range—The Screech Owl in one or another of its forms ranges through the United States and southern Canada from coast to coast. It is a plastic species and readily responds to the varying climatic and environmental conditions prevailing throughout its wide range. No less than fifteen races are now recognized. The eastern race, to which birds from western Pennsylvania belong, ranges from eastern Canada to Minnesota, and southward to Virginia and Tennessee. It is the common owl throughout our region, and there are records from nearly every county in the district. Some claim that the gray phase predominates in particular localities, but the correctness of a generalization on such a basis, as applied to our area as a whole, is doubtful. The species is believed to be a permanent resident, except perhaps near the northern limit of its general range; it tends to wander somewhat in the winter in search of food.

Habits—An acquaintance with the Screech Owl may well be gained on an evening in early spring. The sun has set, but the air is still warm with that balmy mildness that is the earnest of the coming summer. A lone robin is quartering back and forth over the lawn in hope of finding some last morsel, but soon he retires to rest. Twilight deepens into dusk, and all is quiet, save the chorus of frog music that is wafted through the still air from a distant pond. We wait and listen, and finally a long-drawn-out, tremulous cry falls on our ears. Faint and far away it seems at first, but as it rises and then falls in volume—*crescendo e diminuendo*—we sense its nearness. It can indeed be heard at a long distance, but it has such a ventriloquistic quality that when close at hand it may be hard to locate in the dark. I have had the experience of looking for its author in the trees, when all the time the bird was perched on my window sill. This call is the owl's mating song and is oftenest heard in early spring, but not infrequently also in the fall and winter months. Its eerie quality has caused it to be regarded by the superstitious as having an ominous significance and has earned for this owl an unenviable reputation.

Although the Screech Owl can see perfectly well in the daytime, it prefers to do all its hunting under cover of darkness. During the day it remains concealed in a hollow tree or in a dense evergreen, hugging the trunk in a studied effort to remain inconspicuous, so that it generally escapes observation. On dark, cloudy days it may sometimes leave its safe retreat and venture into the open shrubbery, but if discovered by the small birds of the vicinity it is sure to be mobbed and perhaps driven to seek shelter. An unusual commotion among the small birds may often be traced to a screech owl. I remember one occasion, in the fall of the year, when I planted a stuffed screech owl in the path of a company of tufted titmice. The moment they discovered it their cries of alarm instantly brought towards the spot all the small birds from within a hundred yards' radius. The excitement lasted for several minutes, and soon the trees were filled with birds of many kinds, of which migrating warblers were the most numerous. The Screech Owl never seems to turn on its tormentors under such circumstances. Probably it could not catch them if it did, as it is slow of flight, and the small birds, knowing this, feel perfectly safe in thus heaping abuse upon their sworn enemy. But at nightfall, after they have ceased their usual activities, the Owl comes out and secures by stealth what it could not gain by open attack. Noiselessly it floats along, a shadow among shadows, with every sense alert to detect the slightest movement, and ready to pounce on any unlucky mouse that may venture forth, or to drag unaware from its perch some sleeping bird, whose waking cry is throttled in a death grip. The Owl hunts not only in the woods, but also in cultivated lands, in orchards and meadows, and even among the shade trees in towns and in the city parks. Numerous screech owls have been seen and taken within the city limits of Pittsburgh.

A. K. Fisher, after investigating the food of this species, reported (1893) that it consisted mainly of mice and insects, with small birds a much less prominent element. Out of 255 stomachs examined, 100 contained remains of insects (including not only night-flying kinds, but also various caterpillars), 102 held mice and other small mammals, and only 38 contained wild birds—several of which were English sparrows. Consequently a fairly strong case was made out in favor of the Screech Owl. Dr. Fisher's findings have since been challenged by A. A. Allen of Ithaca, New York, who made a study of the feeding habits of a pair of these birds and of their brood.[1] Dr. Allen's owls, it is true, were feeding upon insects regularly, also on crayfish, amphibians, mammals, fish, spiders, snails, and reptiles, in the order named, but by far the larger part of their food consisted of small birds. Over one hundred birds were consumed by the young from the time of hatching until the parents ceased feeding them. It is a curious fact, as Dr. Allen points out, that the sum total of the adult bird population of this particular area (a private bird sanctuary) was in nowise diminished by the owls' depredations; in fact, it increased slightly. He accounts for this seeming paradox on the ground that the survivors of mated pairs of most Passerine birds secure new mates soon after losing their first. Thus the owls' destructiveness to bird life was in a measure concealed. Dr. Allen remarks:

"There can be little doubt that the number of insects and small mammals destroyed by this pair of Owls could never compensate for the destruction of one tenth of the insectivorous birds eaten by the young. Though the Owls might spend the rest of the year feeding entirely upon insects and meadow mice, they could not possibly consume the equivalent of what would have been eaten by the 98 birds destroyed during the short space of eight weeks.

"From the data here presented it seems evident that the Screech Owl is a powerful factor in maintaining the balance of nature but, from the standpoint of increasing insectivorous birds, he is an equally powerful menace."

Nevertheless, I do not advocate the indiscriminate destruction of the Screech Owl. In cities and towns it must take a considerable toll of English sparrows and starlings. In country districts it is not common enough to give serious trouble. In sanctuaries it should of course be under control, but in the ordinary economy of nature it has its proper part to play, and man's efforts to restore a balance have many times resulted in maladjustment.

The Screech Owl often takes up its abode in old orchards, where there are natural cavities in the trees, suitable for nesting sites. Sometimes it utilizes the deserted nest of a flicker, and it can even be persuaded to accept a box put up for the purpose. There is no serious effort to construct a nest proper, and the eggs, from three to six in number (usually four or five), are laid on whatever rubbish happens to accumulate at the bottom of the hole. They are pure white and measure about 1.40 by 1.18 inches. Incubation lasts about three weeks, and the male often remains in the nest cavity with the female while she is sitting on the eggs. Both parents are assiduous in the care of the young and will often defend them vigorously, flying at an intruder and snapping their mandibles in threatening fashion. Fresh eggs may be found in Allegheny County, according to D. A. Atkinson, from March 28 until May 10, and usually during April. The young are often on the wing by the first week in June.

The Screech Owl seems to be holding its own fairly well, even in settled districts, in spite of the fact that it is generally regarded with disfavor and on occasion wantonly killed. In addition to man, its worst enemies are the larger owls, which, hunting at night, have no scruples against killing their smaller relatives. At Pymatuning Swamp, where the Barred Owl used to be common, the Screech Owl was correspondingly rare, and Dr. Sutton tells of taking the remains of a screech owl from a barred owl's stomach. The instance is certainly suggestive of the method by which the balance of nature is normally maintained. If man had not interfered by killing off the larger owls, the Screech Owl would always be held in check and could never become a menace to the smaller, insectivorous birds.

Scops asio Townsend, *Proc. Acad. Nat. Sci. Philadelphia*, 1883, 65 (Latrobe, Westmoreland Co., resident).

"Screech Owl" Warrick, *Ornithologist and Oölogist*, 1883, 8:32 (Washington, Washington Co.)—Pitcairn, *Bird-Lore*, 1908, 10:32 (West View, Allegheny Co., December)—Simpson,

[1] *Auk*, 1924, 41:1–16.

Oölogist, 1909, 26:169 (Warren, Warren Co., nesting); 1912, 29:329 (head of Tionesta Creek, Warren Co., summer)—MILLER (M. H.), *In the Open*, Feb., 1915, 5:48 (McKinley Park, Pittsburgh, Allegheny Co.)—BOULTON, *Bird-Lore*, 1918, 20:67 (Beaver, Beaver Co., winter)—MILLER (R. F.), *Oölogist*, 1919, 36:155 (State College, Centre Co., nesting)—McCONNELL, *Bird-Lore*, 1920, 22:31 (Emsworth, Allegheny Co., December)—STAHL, *et al.*, *Bird-Lore*, 1921, 23:18 (Forest Hills to Deer Creek, Allegheny Co., December)—McCLELLAND, *Am. Mid. Nat.*, 1922, 8:35 (Washington, Washington Co., resident)—MILLER |(A. B.), *Bird-Lore*, 1923, 25:25 (Springs, Somerset Co., December)—PARKER, *Cardinal*, 1924, v. 1, no. 4, p. 2 (Allegheny Co., food habits)—PORTMAN, *et al.*, *Bird-Lore*, 1926, 28:31 (Thompsonville and region, Washington Co., December)—SAVAGE, *et al.*, *Bird-Lore*, 1927, 29:28 (McKeesport and region, Allegheny Co., December)—BERKHEIMER, *Bird-Lore*, 1933, 35:27 (near Osterburg, Bedford Co., December).

Megascops asio JACOBS, *Summer Birds Greene Co., Pa.*, 1893, 6 (Greene Co., nesting; Waynesburg, Greene Co., winter)—COPE, *Cassinia*, 1902, 5:14 (Tamarack Swamp, Clinton Co., June)—KEIM, *Cassinia*, 1905, 8:38 (Port Allegany, McKean Co., summer)—FORREST, *Oölogist*, 1911, 28:114 (Washington, Washington Co.).

Otus asio TODD, *Ann. Carnegie Mus.*, 1904, 2:557 (Erie and Presque Isle, Erie Co., resident)—TODD, in Bausman, *Hist. Beaver Co., Pa.*, 1904, 2:1199 (Beaver Co., resident).

Otus asio asio HARLOW, *Auk*, 1912, 29:471 (State College, Centre Co., nesting)—CHRISTY, *Cardinal*, 1923, v. 1, no. 1, [p. 5] (Sewickley, Allegheny Co., resident)—BURLEIGH, *Wilson Bull.*, 1923, 35:86 (Allegheny Co., breeding); 1924, 36:69; and 1931, 43:40 (State College, Centre Co., nesting).

Otus asio naevius CHRISTY and SUTTON, *Cardinal*, 1928, 2:70 (Cooksburg, Clarion Co., resident)—SUTTON, *Ann. Carnegie Mus.*, 1928, 18:137 (Crawford Co. records)—BURLEIGH, *Cardinal*, 1932, 3:75 (near Uniontown, Fayette Co., summer).

"Eastern Screech Owl" WOOD, *Wilson Bull.*, 1932, 44:239 (State College, Centre Co.).

GREAT HORNED OWL

BUBO VIRGINIANUS VIRGINIANUS (Gmelin)

Description—A *large owl, with conspicuous "horns" or ear tufts* and a wingspread of from four to five feet; general coloration dark. Female about twenty inches high in life; male smaller. Upperparts mottled with dusky and whitish markings, the top of the head mottled with black and buff; ear tufts black, as is also a line over the eyes which curves down to border the "face"; throat whitish, crossed by a broad band of black and brownish streaks; wings and tail mottled with buffy brown, with darker bars; general color of underparts whitish, more or less washed with buff and showing dusky spots on the breast, which become bars on the sides and flanks; abdomen (medially) almost immaculate; bill black; eyes bright yellow. *Nestlings* are at first covered with pure white down, but soon assume a buffy-white plumage, with faint dusky barring throughout.

Range—The Great Horned Owl has an extensive range, from South America on the one hand to the limit of trees in North America on the other. Like many other widely distributed species, it breaks up into numerous subspecies, of which ten are recognized within the geographical limits of the American Ornithologists' Union *Check-List*. Western Pennsylvania is included within the range of the typical eastern race. In this region the Great Horned Owl is well known to be resident wherever found; it wanders away from its chosen nesting ground only under stress of threatened starvation, and in due course of time it will return. Forty and fifty years ago it was rather common—insofar as any solitary and sedentary large bird can be said to be common—but it has been so unremittingly persecuted by farmers because of its depredations on poultry, and by sportsmen in general because of its destructiveness to game, that its ranks are rapidly thinning. The cutting of the timber wherein it is wont to find shelter and nesting sites is another factor in its disappearance. But the persistence with which a pair of great horned owls will cling to the remnants of the woodland, even in as thickly a settled county as Allegheny, is surprising. Although most of our records come from the western tier of counties, this species is probably most numerous at the present time in the forest areas of the plateau region and of the mountains in general.

Habits[1]—Toward the evening of a gray day in late winter, the hooting of the Great Horned Owl may be heard coming from the woodland. The notes are deep and have something of the quality of the distant tooting of a locomotive. The call may be phrased thus: *hoo-hoo, hoo; hoo, hoo.* The second note is short, and the one preceding the last is of slightly higher pitch than the others.

[1]Account contributed by BAYARD H. CHRISTY.

The call is usually repeated at intervals of a minute or more. Sometimes two birds may be heard calling antiphonally from opposite sides of a ravine; and then it will be noticed that the call of one is pitched in a higher key. At all seasons owls call after nightfall, particularly when the moon is bright. In the north woods I have known the owls to come about a campfire and utter terrific yells such as are described in the accounts of Wilson and Audubon, but in Pennsylvania I have had no such experience.

It is seldom that the birds are seen. They are large—with a wing-spread about equal to that of the Red-tailed Hawk—and are of a soft ocher-brown color. They fly with deep flappings of their wings; and the quick eye will detect the great, round head, quite unlike that of a hawk. I have seen an owl sail overhead in the moonlight on wide-spread wings.

In March and April particularly, while the trees are still bare, a crow may discover a great horned owl on its day perch. The crow shouts a *ha, ha*, readily distinguishable in quality from its usual call (and seeming to mean *owl*), and immediately every crow within hearing responds. They come with a hundred repetitions of the shout and throng about their victim—perching, flapping, and calling in wild excitement. Now and again a venturesome one hovers above and swoops sharp-beaked upon the owl. It flies, and the crows pursue and swarm about it when it perches again. Thus they harry it through the woods. A man may follow at a distance but will not easily make a close approach. The crows, even in their excitement, do not forget to be alert; and one of them presently, sighting the intruder, sounds a very different *caw*. At once the owl-baiting ceases; the crows take wing; and then the owl leaps from its perch and is gone. The enmity of the crows is well grounded. It is not unusual to find a fragment of a crow's body lying with other prey on the rim of an owl's nest.

In nesting, the Great Horned Owl is the earliest of all our native species. I have found the complement of two eggs as early as February 9; and I have a record of a nest found on February 22 in which one of the eggs was already pipped. After hatching, the young remain for about two months in the nest. J. W. Jacobs, who has found many nests of this owl, remarks that sets of two eggs are twice as frequent as sets of three. The eggs are pure white, rounded oval in shape, and measure about 2.20 by 1.82 inches.

Though I have found evidence that owls have repaired the nests that they were occupying, I have never known them to build for themselves an entirely new structure. Usually they appropriate the past year's nests of red-tailed hawks, built high in forest trees; sometimes they lay their eggs in cavities in standing stubs and even upon the ledges of cliffs. Of the ten nests that I have found along the boundary between Allegheny and Beaver counties, and on both sides of the Ohio River, three were in hollow trees and seven were open nests. These figures, however, do not signify very much; for the open nests are much easier to find.

Red-tailed hawks, if undisturbed, will reoccupy a nest during successive years; and I suspect that often the hawks are dispossessed by owls, for the owls are the earlier nesters by about a month. I have in mind, however, an instance in which a pair of red-tails built a new nest upon an old one which the year before had been occupied by owls.

In addition to the minor repairs that the owls may make, their occupied nests are more or less fully lined with down. Whether the parent bird actually plucks herself, or merely works feathers free from her breast as she moves about upon her bed, I do not know. When the birds find nesting places in cavities, they do not, according to my knowledge, do any building, but lay their eggs on the bare floor of the cavity. A nest described by Mr. Jacobs (1890) was, accordingly, an exceptional one. It was built in the cavity of a hollow oak. "The nest was a new one, composed of a mass of leaves, twigs and bark nicely hollowed out and lined sparingly with feathers."

A typical nest that I examined was evidently a last-year's structure of a red-tailed hawk, built in the top of a red oak in the strip of woods that extends from the base of the cliff at "Patton's Point" on Raccoon Creek, Beaver County, down the slope to the stream. To a person standing at the rim of the cliff and looking down upon the bare forest, the nest lay fully exposed to view, at a drop of about thirty feet and at a distance of not more than seventy feet. The nest, in turn, high in the treetop, commanded a wide outlook southward across the valley. On April 10—a bleak day of heavy skies and sweeping wind—one of the parent birds lay prone in the nest, while the two owlets stood on its rim, facing her. They kept swaying and moving about and squealing faintly. The parent, after a moment's gaze at the intruders, leaped up and made off through the woods and was neither seen nor heard again. The young, when presently they too discovered the cause of the mother's flight, immediately became mute and rigid, like two staring images. In the nest lay a fragment of the body of a rabbit. Beneath the tree, casts were picked up which seemed to consist wholly of the hair and teeth of rabbits. In the face of the cliff was a much-used perch, presumably of the male bird.

On April 27 the nest was still occupied, but three days later it was empty. The owlets were at the time hardly old enough to fly; on the other hand, no evidence of violence was discovered. And I have repeatedly found that when a nest has been disturbed, the young have disappeared. I suspect that they take themselves off, even though they cannot fly, climbing parrot-wise from tree to tree and to new places of concealment.

Before the eggs are hatched, the instinct to protect them is not fully developed; ordinarily an intruder at a nest will not see the parent bird again, after her initial flight, although he may hear her hooting from the woods near by. When, however, the young are hatched, and particularly when they are nearly grown, both the parent birds manifest great concern and may become very fierce and menacing. I have never known them actually to attack, but on one occasion when my companion had climbed to the nest, both parent birds flew near, leaped excitedly from perch to perch, fluffed out their feathers, snapped their beaks, and uttered loud, barking shouts. G. M. Sutton (1928) writes of finding a half-grown owl on the ground in woods near Pymatuning Swamp, and says, "When I picked it up the parent (probably a female, since it was very large) swooped at me menacingly, and snapped her beak between fits of angry grunting and shrieking."

It is common to find food lodged on the rims of owls' nests that contain young—fragments of rabbits, chiefly, and sometimes of a skunk, a squirrel, a crow, or a grouse. When watching young owls that were still in the nest, though nearly grown and almost ready to fly, I have seen them, shortly after sunset, lay aside their familiar, stolid demeanor, and become at once as agile as kittens. They have then engaged in wing-waving, in leaping and flapping from perch to perch on and near the nest, and in falling upon and tearing with their beaks the food that lay at the rim of the nest. And I infer that toward the end of the nesting period the parents do not actually feed their young but merely keep the larder supplied.

It sometimes happens that a pair of owls will establish themselves near a poultry yard and prey upon the fowls; and in such cases, manifestly, the depredators must be destroyed. It does not by any means follow, however, that owls generally and at large should be destroyed. On the contrary, they should be protected. The preying of animal upon animal is universal and is an important matter that is sadly misunderstood. In the economy of nature it is the predator's part to eliminate the weaklings and the diseased. Owls do not lie in wait for grouse; but when a grouse droops, flutters on the ground, or lies dying, the owl should be there to make away with it. It is because birds of prey have been ignorantly destroyed, and sick birds have thus not been eliminated, that diseases among grouse flourish. I believe the recent overabundance of squirrels to be a result of the killing off of the larger hawks and owls, of which they are the natural prey. The smaller birds, whose nests the squirrels purloin, suffer from this increase. Paradoxical though it may seem, the presence of the predators that Nature has provided is just as necessary to the well-being of the game birds (and of other birds as well) as are the conditions of food supply and cover. The woods where owls nest will still be found to be well tenanted by grouse. These observations are abundantly confirmed; it is only prejudice that refuses to recognize their validity. In further support of the case for the owl I would add the comment that the splendid feline fierceness of the Great Horned Owl is a notable feature of our avifauna.

Years ago a friend and I, as boys, captured a fledgling great horned owl in the woods and kept it for a year in captivity. We were ourselves in the Stone Age and had no apprehension of the skill in handling by which a wild creature may be rendered docile. We kept our owl for a time in a piano box, with chicken wire nailed over one open side. Afterwards, we gave it the greater freedom of a barn loft.

When fully grown the bird was large, and—rightly, no doubt—we assumed it to be a female. She was always ready to eat and bolted whatever food we offered her—mice, rats, English sparrows. June bugs she took willingly. For the most part, however, we fed to her scraps of meat from the butcher's. I never saw her tear any article of food; invariably she swallowed whole whatever was given her: on one occasion a red squirrel, on another a sparrow hawk. Indigestible matter was thrown up again in casts.

This bird was always fierce; at best, she tolerated our presence. When left alone by day she sat motionless upon her perch, her feathers compressed, her nictitating eyelids drawn, and her eyes nearly closed. She remained thus, regardless of many sparrows that at times congregated and made great chatterings about her; but let a cat pause before her box, and at once she was all animation. And as the owl grew menacing, the cat was sure to retreat. When people approached, she would awake, crouch on her perch, inflate her plumage, sway, shift her weight from one foot to the other, and make an audible exhalation through her open beak. If further disturbed, she would snap her beak viciously and utter a chuckling, quavering call, resembling that of a screech owl. She submitted unwillingly to handling, and we dared only to approach her gently and scratch the crown of her head.

We attempted to make photographs of her by flashlight, but without success; her reflexes were more rapid than the flash powder then available. By daylight, however, we obtained some fair pictures.

The burden of caring for our owl, the realization of the truth that she was untamable, and our admiration for her wild, fierce nature—all these considerations led us to the decision to set her free. One evening in May we bound her, carried her to the woods, and released her. At first she flew stupidly for a few feet and settled on the ground. We disturbed her, and she then flew rather heavily but much farther than she ever before had had opportunity to fly, and perched in a dead treetop. There for the last time we saw her, against the evening sky. We never knew whether or not she survived our ignorant and cruel disturbance of her life pattern.

Bubo virginianus Townsend, *Proc. Acad. Nat. Sci. Philadelphia*, 1883, 65 (Latrobe, Westmoreland Co., resident)—Jacobs, *Oölogist*, 1890, 7:144 ([Greene Co.], nesting)—Jacobs, *Summer Birds Greene Co., Pa.*, 1893, 6 (Greene Co., nesting)—Baily, *Auk*, 1896, 13:293 (Straight Creek, near Williamsville, Elk Co., June–July)—Keim, *Cassinia*, 1905, 8:38 (Port Allegany, McKean Co., summer)—Simpson, *Oölogist*, 1915, 32:10 (Warren, Warren Co., resident)—Little, *Cardinal*, 1931, 3:17 (Dixmont, Allegheny Co., July)—Jacobs, *Oölogist*, 1932, 49:30 (Greene Co., nesting).

"Great Horned Owl" Warrick, *Ornithologist and Oölogist*, 1883, 8:32 (Washington, Washington Co.)—Simpson, *Oölogist*, 1909, 26:169 (Warren, Warren Co., nesting)—Dickey, *Oölogist*, 1912, 29:219 (Greene Co., nesting); 1914, 31:171 ([Charter Oak], Huntingdon Co., May)—Miller, *Bird-Lore*, 1916, 18:28, etc. (Springs, Somerset Co., December)—Dickey, *Bull. Audubon Soc. W. Pa.*, 1923, 1:21 (Greene Co.[?], etc., nesting)—Street, *Cassinia*, 1923, 24:12 ("Rocky Hollow Ravine," Ft. Loudon, Franklin Co., June)—Christy, *Cardinal*, 1924, v. 1, no. 4, p. 11 (Big Traverse Valley, Beaver Co., May), 21 ("Patton's Point," Raccoon Creek, Beaver Co., nesting)—Eastwood, *Bird-Lore*, 1926, 28:207 (Forest Hills, Allegheny Co., breeding); 1927, 29:272 (Harmarville, Allegheny Co., April, *fide* Reiter and Squier)—Christy and Hegner, *Bird-Lore*, 1929, 31:38 (Frankfort Springs, Beaver Co., December)—Beal and Peterson, *Bird-Lore*, 1934, 36:33 (Presque Isle, Erie Co., December)—Cope and Hawkins, *Forest Leaves*, 1934, 24:26 (E. Tionesta Forest Reserve, Warren and McKean Co., summer)—Arthur, *Country Rambler*, 1934, 85 (upper Raccoon Creek, Beaver Co., nesting; habits).

Asio magellanicus virginianus Todd, *Ann. Carnegie Mus.*, 1904, 2:558 (near Erie, Erie Co., resident)—Todd, in Bausman, *Hist. Beaver Co., Pa.*, 1904, 2:1199 (Beaver Co., resident).

"Horned Owl" Simpson, *Oölogist*, 1909, 26:25, 26; 1911, 28:202 (near Warren, Warren Co., nesting, etc.); 1912, 29:329 (head of Tionesta Creek, Warren Co., summer).

Bubo virginianus virginianus Harlow, *Auk*, 1912, 29:471 (Bald Knob and Bear Meadows, Centre Co.; "Stone Valley" and

Monroe Furnace, Huntingdon Co.); 1918, 35:26 (Waynesburg, Greene Co., and Charter Oak, Huntingdon Co., nesting)—Dickey, *Oölogist*, 1915, 32:49 ([Greene Co.], nesting)—Christy, *Cardinal*, 1923, v. 1, no. 1, [p. 6] (Sewickley, Allegheny Co., resident)—Burleigh, *Wilson Bull.*, 1924, 36:69 (State College, Centre Co., resident)—Christy and Sutton, *Cardinal*, 1928, 2:70 (Cook Forest, Clarion Co., resident)—Sutton, *Ann. Carnegie Mus.*, 1928, 18:138 (Crawford Co. nesting records)—Burleigh, *Wilson Bull.*, 1931, 43:41 (near State College, Centre Co., breeding).

SNOWY OWL

NYCTEA NYCTEA (Linnaeus)

Description—About as large as the Great Horned Owl, but without any ear tufts. General color *white*, sometimes nearly pure, but usually with more or less dark mottling or barring, except on the "face," which is always immaculate; eyes yellow; legs and feet heavily feathered.

Range—The Snowy Owl is a species of the Arctic Life Zone; it breeds north of the tree line in both Eurasia and North America and migrates southward in winter—irregularly, on the American side, to the middle states and the Ohio Valley. Probably every year there is a southward movement of limited extent, affecting only a certain proportion of the individuals; but when, as sometimes happens, the usual food supply in the North fails, there is a forced southward migration involving virtually the entire Snowy Owl population. During these wholesale migrations, the species, which under normal circumstances is merely a rare and casual winter visitor, may become fairly common (as owls go) and generally distributed over a considerable area. Often, but not always, these periodic irruptions coincide with similar movements on the part of the Goshawk. This was true of the last invasion, during the winter of 1926–27, which has been competently dealt with from the local standpoint by G. M. Sutton (1927), and from a general standpoint by A. O. Gross.[1] The greatest concentration on this occasion was in the New England states, and thence westward to Minnesota. In our region, more records came from the western counties than from those in the plateau and mountain sections, while the reverse is true of the records for the Goshawk. This is understandable in view of the fact that the Goshawk is a forest-loving species, while the Snowy Owl is a bird of the open country. Moreover, as Dr. Sutton suggests, the snowy owls that appeared in the northwestern counties may have come directly across Lake Erie, while the goshawks did not venture to do so.

Wilson speaks of seeing at Pittsburgh, in February, 1810, a snowy owl that had been captured some time before, and additional ones down the Ohio River; thus there probably was a special movement that winter. Invasions are known to have occurred during the years 1876–77, 1882–83, 1889–90, 1892–93, 1896–97, 1901–2, 1905–6, 1917–18, and, as already stated, in 1926–27. Some of our local records fall in these seasons, but many others do not. Thus, of seven individuals recorded by R. B. Simpson from the vicinity of Warren, the date for only one comes in the above category. He calls the species a rare visitor during severe winters, and this statement applies as well to our region as a whole, if the extraordinary invasions are disregarded. On these special occasions the severity of the weather plays no part; an invasion is just as likely to happen in a mild winter as in a severe one. Unfortunately, we have but an imperfect picture of the various irruptions previous to the last one, since only a few of the many birds that must have been killed were ever properly recorded. There is reason to believe, however, that some of these invasions must have equaled the last in numbers and extent.

Migration—By the use of a striking graph, Dr. Gross indicates the suddenness with which the snowy owls appeared during the invasion of 1926–27. Only a very few were noted in October, but during the first week of the following month their numbers increased sharply, reaching a peak on November 16; after that there was a pronounced falling off, and then a gradual decrease through December, January, February, and March, until no more were recorded. The records accumulated by Dr. Sutton for our region bear out these general results. The earliest fall record is October 20, from Philipsburg, Centre County; the latest spring date is March 17, from Russell, Warren

[1] *Auk*, 1927, 44:479–493.

County. The largest number of records are for November and early December. Records from earlier years are also mainly for these same months. How many of these northern invaders ever succeed in getting back to their homes in the arctic tundras is left to the imagination.

Habits—My own experience with the Snowy Owl has been confined to the Barren Grounds of Canada, where in the summer it is a conspicuous figure against the dark background of rocky hills. When it comes south in the winter it is likewise conspicuous when the hills are bare, but when the ground is covered with snow this owl blends so well with its surroundings that while at rest it easily escapes notice. It hunts by day as often as at dusk, and as it always inhabits open country, perching by choice on the crest of some hill or exposed knoll, or quartering over the fields, it often attracts the attention of the gunner and falls a victim to his curiosity or prejudice. It is indeed unfortunate for the Snowy Owl that the period of its greatest abundance coincides with the open season for legitimate game. Moreover, many individuals seem to be so starved after their long flight and so weak upon their arrival that they are easy to approach, and they are sometimes taken alive. In the north country, lemmings are the staple food of this species, with an occasional ptarmigan or other bird, and some fish. When the owls come south, a more varied diet is the rule. Dr. Sutton examined 123 stomachs, of which 63 were empty. He writes (1927):

"In the other stomachs were found various food items, usually several items in each. In 15 were remains of poultry (9, chicken; 3, pigeon; 3, duck); in 8 were game-birds (3, Ruffed Grouse; 4, Bob-white; 1, Ring-necked Pheasant); in 30 were game mammals (26, Cottontail Rabbit; 3, Gray Squirrel; 1, Fox Squirrel); in 19 were remains of other small mammals (9, Field Mouse; 1, Skunk; 9, unidentifiable fur remains, doubtless of small rodents); in 9 were small birds (8, sparrows or other small, unidentified species; 1, Blue Jay); in 3 were scales and bones of fish; one stomach held several fruits of the Red-haw, and one held kernels of corn, which may have been swallowed with the gizzard or crop of some granivorous bird."

One may admit the lapses of the Snowy Owl on its visits here without therefor consigning it to the fate of the Great Auk. Every poultry farmer has of course a perfect right to protect his property against the raids of this owl or of any other predatory species. But the wanton killing of a rare and beautiful bird such as the Snowy Owl, out of curiosity, or for ornament, or because of ignorance and prejudice, is utterly indefensible and merits the strongest condemnation. Far better that we should spare some of our game birds and mammals for its subsistence during its infrequent visitations, than that we should endeavor to annihilate this strikingly handsome and interesting visitor, one of the very few that come to our region from the arctic wastes.

Strix nyctea Wilson, *Am. Orn.*, 1811, 4:53 (Pittsburgh, Allegheny Co., February).

Nyctea scandiaca Townsend, *Proc. Acad. Nat. Sci. Philadelphia*, 1883, 65 (Latrobe, Westmoreland Co., very rare).

"Snowy Owl" "A. A. A.," *Forest and Stream*, February 3, 1887, 28:24 (North East, Erie Co.)—Simpson, *Oölogist*, 1909, 26:26; and 1912, 29:370 (Warren, Warren Co., winter)—Jacobs, *Oölogist*, 1922, 39:123 (near Waynesburg, Greene Co., November 24, 1894; [December 9, 1918])—Christy, *Cardinal*, 1927, 2:16 ("Shiery's Hill" and Donegal, Westmoreland Co.; Presque Isle, Erie Co., *fide* Perry; Conneaut Lake, Crawford Co., *fide* Welshons)—Eastwood, *Bird-Lore*, 1927, 29:55 (Scottdale, Westmoreland Co., *fide* Gordon; Everson, Fayette Co., *fide* newspaper)—Wood, *Wilson Bull.*, 1932, 44:238 (State College, Centre Co., winter, *fide* Musgrave).

Nyctea nyctea Rhoads, *Auk*, 1899, 16:311 (Bailey Run, Cameron Co., *fide* Larrabee)—Todd, *Ann. Carnegie Mus.*, 1904, 2:558 (Erie, Erie Co., winter)—Deane, *Auk*, 1906, 23:292 (Erie, Erie Co., November, *fide* Clark)—Sutton, *Cardinal*, 1927, 2:35 (western Pa. records and references; food)—[Christy], *Cardinal*, 1927, 2:41 (Carnegie, Allegheny Co., December)—Sutton, *Ann. Carnegie Mus.*, 1928, 18:138 (Crawford Co. localities, winter)—Sutton, *Cardinal*, 1928, 2:104 (northern Washington Co., October, *fide* McNall)—Seiple, *Cardinal*, 1929, 2:130 (Greenville, Mercer Co., November)—Bergstrom, *Cardinal*, 1930, 2:186 (Conneaut Lake and Shermansville, Crawford Co., February)—Perry, *Cardinal*, 1938, 4:177 (Presque Isle, Erie Co., December).

NORTHERN BARRED OWL (Plate 12)

STRIX VARIA VARIA Barton

Description—A moderately large owl (smaller than the Great Horned), *without ear tufts*, and with *brownish-black eyes*. Barred above with dusky brown and white; "face" with a dark border all around and indistinct concentric dusky bars; *breast barred* with dusky brown and white; *rest of underparts display abrupt dusky streaks* on a whitish background; wings and tail barred with dusky brown and white, like the upperparts in general; bill yellowish.

Range—The typical race of the Barred Owl ranges throughout the region covered by the Upper Austral, Transition, and Canadian life zones, west to the eastern foothills of the Rocky Mountains. In the Lower Austral Zone the species is represented by other races. In the northern part of its range it is said to be more or less migratory, or at least a winter wanderer, but elsewhere it is virtually sedentary. Collation of the records from our region indicates that while this owl is generally distributed throughout, it is commonest in the more heavily timbered areas of the mountainous and plateau sections. It is (or was) common in Pymatuning Swamp but in many places is rated as rather rare. The majority of records are for the fall and winter months, but this signifies merely that during the hunting season there are more fatalities.

Habits—The favorite haunts of the Barred Owl are dense woods—not necessarily of high growth, such as the Great Horned Owl prefers, but with plenty of thick shrubbery and heavy foliage. Tamarack Swamp, Clinton County, where I saw a barred owl on December 4, 1902, must have been an ideal spot; and Pymatuning Swamp, with its tangled undergrowth and leafy canopy, also exactly suits the requirements of this species. In Warren County, where it is the commonest owl, R. B. Simpson says that it has a liking for cool mountain streams in deep, shady woods and is often flushed from the water's edge in such places. In the winter, when the trees are bare of leaves and the ground is covered with snow, it keeps well hidden in dense hemlocks and is then likelier to escape notice than in the summertime. As a rule it is not very shy and may often be approached within shotgun range. With its big, black, staring eyes and its barred and streaked plumage, so fully in keeping with its somber surroundings, it seems in its shady retreats to be a part of Nature's mood. Like the Great Horned Owl, it can see perfectly well in the daylight, but it is most active in the dusk of the evening or morning, and during overcast days. Should it be discovered by crows during its diurnal excursions, it is mobbed and tormented, sometimes for hours at a stretch. It hoots very often during the daytime in cloudy or rainy weather. The regular hoot, as described for me by B. H. Christy, is much higher-pitched than that of the Great Horned Owl, and is repeated about eight times, in two sets of four syllables each, with a slight pause between; the last note is deeper, with a distinct falling cadence. Mr. Simpson remarks that at a distance the hoots sound a great deal like the barking of a dog. This owl is said also to have a great variety of calls and hoots, some of them almost human in quality. It is particularly noisy during the breeding season, and when one bird begins to answer the calls of another, the result is interesting. G. M. Sutton (1928) says that on one occasion in September, "three were heard at once in a weird and discordant chorus."

The Barred Owl shares in the prejudice with which all owls have come to be regarded by the unthinking. A dispassionate study of its food habits shows, however, a balance in its favor from a purely economic standpoint. In any event it certainly has much less against it than has the Great Horned Owl, for it seldom extends its forays into the poultry yard, and it preys to an even greater extent on mice and other injurious rodents. Testimony to this effect is given by A. K. Fisher, after the examination of 109 stomachs secured from all parts of the country; and local observers all agree that the species is more beneficial than otherwise. Mr. Simpson says that it usually preys on squirrels and small rodents and that he has never known a barred owl to rob a henroost. He relates an amusing incident that occurred when he lay down to sleep in the woods, with a string of squirrels beside him. He awoke to find a big barred owl flapping just above him and so close that it seemed to fill the whole view. On another occasion he watched a barred owl snatch a red squirrel from a tree trunk by a sudden upward swoop.

Evidence as to the food of owls is always afforded by the examination of the pellets that they disgorge. W. E. Coon (1917) tells of finding the roost of a barred owl at Conneautville, Crawford County. This bird had been living almost wholly on small rodents (unidentified) of at least three different kinds. "One particularly large pellet had the jaws of five rodents in the mass. Of the remaining pellets, one held the jaws of three rodents; several, two; and the rest, one each. One pellet had a large snail-shell crushed while another one had a small shell, whole. A couple more had the remains of a single crawfish in addition to a rodent each. . . . Of all the pellets that were examined—sixty in number—not one yielded the remains of a bird."

The relations of the Barred Owl to other owls are interesting. More than one writer has noted that the Screech Owl often falls a victim to the larger owls, the Barred Owl included. Dr. Sutton (1928) attributes the scarcity of the Screech Owl at Pymatuning Swamp to the comparative abundance of the Barred Owl there. He adds: "On May 31, 1923, a Barred Owl was seen chasing a Screech Owl, the smaller creature crying out in mortal terror. One killed on May 12, 1922, had the remains of a Screech Owl and a Field Mouse in its stomach." There is also reason to believe that the Barred Owl does not always get along amicably with its larger cousin, the Great Horned. A. B. Miller writes that in the extreme southern part of Somerset County he has seldom found the two species in the same tract of timber, but has several times known them to exchange locations —one moving into the locality previously occupied by the other. Both are found only in the larger tracts of good-sized timber. Mr. Miller has found the Barred Owl using an old hawk or crow nest, and also a hollow tree. All the nests that Mr. Simpson has found in Warren County, however, have been in hollow trees—usually not over thirty or forty feet up, and in rather shallow cavities. He says that sometimes nests are in the tops of broken-off stubs and are thus exposed to the weather. H. C. Kirkpatrick reports a nest found near Meadville by a Mr. Cook, on March 1, 1906, on which date it held one egg. It was an old crow nest in a pine tree. Five eggs were laid at intervals, and incubation lasted three weeks. The number of eggs seems most unusual; for Mr. Simpson has never found more than three eggs to a set, and often only two. He says that March 25 is the proper time to look for fresh eggs. In one instance, however, he found newly hatched young as early as March 29, and in another, he found a female sitting on three addled eggs as late as June 1. R. L. Fricke secured a set of two eggs (about one-fourth incubated) on March 17, 1938, from a nest in a woods near the head of Pymatuning Lake; it was an old hawk or crow nest in a beech, with hemlocks all around, and was about forty feet from the ground.

The eggs of this species are pure white in color, rounded ovate in shape, and measure about 1.95 by 1.68 inches. The young are generally out of the nest by the end of April, but remain with the parents for some time thereafter. On May 23, 1934, a party from the Carnegie Museum came upon two half-grown barred owls in the thick woods on the west side of Pymatuning Swamp. They were perched in hemlock trees, not far apart, and were about fifteen feet from the ground. When teased they showed resentment by sharply clicking their mandibles. This action brought both parents to the scene; they perched on the tops of neighboring stubs, whence they peered down anxiously, occasionally uttering their weird hoots, but not coming very close. A young bird that was shown to me on May 17, 1935, also at Pymatuning Swamp, was much smaller and was unable to stand; it had probably fallen from the nest.

Syrnium nebulosum Teulon, *Jour. Boston Zoöl. Soc.*, 1883, 2:11 (Bradford, McKean Co., spring)—Jacobs, *Summer Birds Greene Co., Pa.*, 1893, 6 (Greene Co., uncommon)—Baily, *Auk*, 1896, 13:293 (Williamsville, Elk Co., July).

Strix nebulosa Townsend, *Proc. Acad. Nat. Sci. Philadelphia*, 1883, 65 (Latrobe, Westmoreland Co., resident).

"Barred Owl" Warrick, *Ornithologist and Oölogist*, 1883, 8:32 (Washington, Washington Co.)—Simpson, *Oölogist*, 1909, 26:25, 169; 1911, 28:52; and 1922, 39:36 (Warren Co., nesting, food, etc.); 1912, 29:329 (head of Tionesta Creek, Warren Co., summer)—Coon, *Bird-Lore*, 1917, 19:266 (Conneautville, Crawford Co., January; food)—Hoffman, *et al.*, *Bird-Lore*, 1923, 25:23 (Grove City, Mercer Co., December) —Sutton, *Bird-Lore*, 1924, 26:122 (Oakmont, Allegheny Co., February, *fide* Liphart)—Eastwood, *Bird-Lore*, 1927, 29:272 (Harmarville, Allegheny Co., May, *fide* Manley)—Miller, *Bird-Lore*, 1932, 34:47 (Springs, Somerset Co., December).

Syrnium varium Todd, *Ann. Carnegie Mus.*, 1904, 2:557 (Erie,

Erie Co., resident)—Keim, *Cassinia*, 1905, 8:38 (Port Allegany, McKean Co., occasional)—Simpson, *Oölogist*, 1915, 32:9 (Warren, Warren Co., resident; habits, etc.).
Strix varia varia Harlow, *Auk*, 1912, 29:478 (southern Centre Co., March); 1918, 35:26 (Warren Co., nesting; range)—Sutton, *Ann. Carnegie Mus.*, 1928, 18:135 (Crawford Co. records and references).
"Northern Barred Owl" Cope and Hawkins, *Forest Leaves*, 1934, 24:26 (E. Tionesta Forest Reserve, Warren and McKean Co., summer).

GREAT GRAY OWL

SCOTIAPTEX NEBULOSA NEBULOSA (Forster)

Description—A large owl, equaling or exceeding the Great Horned in size, but *without ear tufts;* general color *mottled gray and dusky;* eyes yellow, and small for the size of the head.

Range and local status—This owl is a characteristic species of the coniferous-forest belt of Canada, but wanders southward in the winter to the northern United States, where it is an irregular and casual visitor. Even in the north country it is accounted rare. Warren cites a few records for Pennsylvania, all but one of which are for the eastern counties. That one constitutes a report from Sennett to the effect that a great gray owl had been found in the smokestack of a steamboat at Erie. Whether the specimen was preserved is not stated, and under the circumstances the record is not entirely satisfactory. A record from Greene County, however, from J. W. Jacobs, is authentic. He writes that on February 16, 1898, he examined the head of a great gray owl, brought to him for identification by Charles Church. The bird had been shot and wounded by a Mr. Johnson, near Rogersville, about six miles west of Waynesburg. Mr. Johnson had kept it alive in a box for about a week, and had then killed it, cutting off its wings and tail for ornaments. Mr. Church, realizing that it must be of a different species from any he had seen, investigated and, finding the bird dead and mutilated, brought the head back for identification. The occurrence of this owl as far south as Greene County is somewhat surprising; it might be expected instead along our northern border.

Ulula cinerea Warren, *Birds Pa.*, ed. 2, 1890, 151 (Erie, Erie Co., *fide* Sennett)—Warren, *Bull. Pa. Dept. Agric.*, no. 17, 1897, 236 (Erie, Erie Co.).

LONG-EARED OWL (Plate 12)

ASIO WILSONIANUS (Lesson)

Description—An owl of medium size, slender build, and generally dark coloration, and with *conspicuous ear tufts, rather close together*. Upperparts marked with dusky, buffy, and whitish mottling; wings and tail dark-colored, with paler barring; ear tufts black with rufous-buff edges; facial disc blackish around the eyes (inside) and rufous buff on the sides, with a blackish outer margin; forehead marked with dusky and whitish mottling; chin white; underparts display irregular dusky streaks on a buffy ground-color, with much white spotting, these streaks tending to become bars on the belly; tarsi and feet deep buff, unspotted; eyes yellow; bill black.

Range—The Long-eared Owl is the North American representative of the Eurasian *Asio otus*, of which it is considered by some authors to be a subspecies. In temperate North America it ranges across the entire continent and from the southern United States northward well into Canada, where, however, it is apparently only a summer resident. While it seems to be generally distributed throughout western Pennsylvania, it is not common anywhere. Nevertheless, it is probably more numerous in any given locality than most observers suspect, even in the well-settled parts. It has actually been taken within the city limits of Pittsburgh (Schenley Park and Squirrel Hill), and there are no less than fourteen records for Allegheny County alone. I have never found it in Beaver County, but in December, 1911, a friend shot one not far beyond the borough limits of Beaver.

Most of the records available for this species refer to birds seen or taken during the fall or winter months, but whether these were migrants from farther north, or strictly residents, is not clear. Actual breeding records from widely separated localities, however, leave no doubt of its nesting throughout our region in general. Audubon tells of finding a nest along the Juniata River, very possibly within our limits, many years ago. A nest with young was taken along the Allegheny River at Edgecliff, Westmoreland County, early in May, 1903, by G. A. Link, Sr. B. H. Christy found a brood just out of the nest, near Frankfort Springs, in southern Beaver County, late in May, 1923. For Crawford County there are H. C. Kirkpatrick's record of a nest containing young found on May 12, 1924, about four miles up the Cussewago Valley from Meadville; another of two nearly grown young that had been taken from a nest near Hartstown, in May, 1897; and S. S. Dickey's record of a nest near Cambridge Springs. Dr. Dickey also found the species at Tamarack Swamp in Erie County. R. B. Simpson considers it rare at Warren; he reports finding a nest with young on May 31, 1930. R. L. Keesler sent me a picture of a nest with young that he found near Forestville, Butler County, on May 3, 1917. In the Carnegie Museum there is a set of eggs "collected for Richard C. Harlow" which is said to have been taken near Tyrone, Blair County, on April 23, 1919.

Habits—The Long-eared Owl is decidedly more nocturnal in its habits than many of the other owls and may therefore be overlooked by the casual observer. It keeps well concealed in thick covert during the daytime and sallies forth at dusk to begin its hunting. Dense hemlock thickets and thick evergreens are favorite roosting haunts. If surprised in these retreats, the Long-eared Owl often seeks to escape notice by shrinking its already slender body and "freezing" into the resemblance of a dead stub. If forced to take wing, however, it is able to find its way through the maze of branches without trouble, flying noiselessly but somewhat erratically. Although properly a woodland bird (at least in our region), much of its hunting must be done in the open country, if one may judge from the character of its food. This owl, as A. K. Fisher says (1893), "is preëminently a mouser, but it also destroys some insects and probably small batrachians and reptiles." Of 107 stomachs examined by him, 84 contained mice; 5, other mammals; 15, small birds; and 1, a game bird (bob-white). The mice taken were largely meadow mice, pine mice, and house mice—all injurious species. There is absolutely nothing to show that this owl ever raids the poultry yard, and when seen in the farmyard or about houses it is doubtless in search of mice and English sparrows.

The largest prey that the Long-eared Owl has been known to capture is the Ruffed Grouse, and an instance reported from Cameron County by G. M. Sutton (1926) on the authority of C. E. Logue, is exceptional enough to call for special remark: "On December 24, 1925, an Owl was flushed from the shadow of a low hemlock, where a partially eaten Grouse was found. Three days later and not far away, the same kind of Owl (possibly the same individual) was found eating another Grouse. This time the Owl was shot and sent in for identification. In both cases there was evidence that a struggle had taken place, not only in the boughs of the hemlock where feathers clung, and in the grape vines where the Owl had evidently first attacked its prey, but also in the snow where the Grouse had struggled. The Grouse were both torn at the neck, but most of the feeding had been done about the head and in the visceral region.

"These Grouse-killing proclivities are probably due either to a local abundance of Grouse or to a great scarcity of other food, for it seems hardly possible that so slight a creature as the Long-eared Owl should customarily kill creatures so much heavier than itself, although such a habit is not without a parallel among the other birds of prey."

Certainly from an economic standpoint the normal food habits of this owl place it high in the scale of value and justify its fullest protection.

Very seldom does the Long-eared Owl trouble to build its own nest, especially when it can find an old squirrel or crow nest to remodel. Audubon, however, says that the nest he found along the Juniata River was of the owls' building; it "was composed of green twigs with the leaflets adhering, and lined with fresh grass and sheep wool, but without feathers." All the other nests from our region about which we have any particulars were second-hand structures. Three nests found by Dr. Dickey were old crow nests—one was only fifteen feet from the ground. The Tyrone nest described by Mr. Harlow was also an old crow nest, forty feet up in a chestnut tree, and had not been added to or altered. Mr. Simpson's find, another crow nest, was twenty-five feet up in a hemlock, and Mr. Keesler's was in a haw tree, only ten feet up. The best account of the behavior of old birds and young, from a local source, is one given by Mr. Christy (1923):

"On May 26th a brood of Long-eared Owls was found near their nest,—which manifestly they had but recently left, for they still were unable to fly,—in hemlock woods, near Frankfort Springs. The nest was in a hemlock, about twenty-five feet from the ground. It seemed to have been originally a squirrel's nest; the bulk of it was composed of matted oak leaves. The owls had left it a flat and fouled platform, about a foot across. The young though unable to fly climbed about freely parrot-like from tree to tree, and perched at a height of twenty feet or more in hemlock trees. During the hours of feeding, which on the moonlight night when they were found lasted from sunset to sunrise, they kept up a continual calling: a single note, a shrill mew or high thin scream, repeated at intervals of about three seconds. They were found in the early evening, and then when approached they crouched, spread their feathers, clapped their beaks, and hissed. The parent birds were solicitous and flew anxiously about. One flew to the ground and there scrambled over the leaves with spread and drooping wings, as though to divert attention from the young. They made a low hooting, like a little dog heard barking far away,—hoo-hoo, hoo-hoo. A band of crows fell on the disturbed parent owls and harried them. The owls flew with heavy flapping through the woods, and one rose and escaped the crows by circling high in air."

The eggs are probably laid in early April in our region, since a "badly stained" set was found by Dr. Dickey on April 18, and callow young were observed early in the following month. The eggs number from three to six, with five as the average set. Like all owls' eggs, they are pure white and round ovate; they measure (on an average) 1.58 by 1.37 inches.

Strix otus AUDUBON, *Orn. Biog.*, 1838, 4:572 (Juniata River, Pa., nesting).

"Long-eared Owl" WARRICK, *Ornithologist and Oölogist*, 1883, 8:32 (Washington, Washington Co.)—[CHRISTY], *Cardinal*, 1923, v. 1, no. 2, [p. 8] (Frankfort Springs, Beaver Co., nesting)—ELLAIR, *et al.*, *Bird-Lore*, 1927, 29:29 (Thompsonville and region, Washington Co., December)—WOOD, *Wilson Bull.*, 1932, 44:238 (State College, Centre Co.).

Nyctalops wilsonianus TODD, *Ann. Carnegie Mus.*, 1904, 2:556 (Erie, Erie Co., resident).

Asio wilsonianus HARLOW, *Auk*, 1912, 29:477 (southern Centre Co., fall and winter)—CHRISTY, *Cardinal*, 1923, v. 1, no. 1, [p. 5] (Sewickley, Allegheny Co., resident)—SUTTON, *Auk*, 1926, 43:236 (Firstfork, Cameron Co., food).

Asio otus wilsonianus CHRISTY and SUTTON, *Cardinal*, 1928, 2:69, 75 (Cook Forest, Clarion Co., resident)—SUTTON, *Ann. Carnegie Mus.*, 1928, 18:134 (Crawford Co. records and references).

SHORT-EARED OWL (Plate 12)

ASIO FLAMMEUS FLAMMEUS (Pontoppidan)

Description—A medium-sized owl, with very short, inconspicuous ear tufts and general pale coloration. *Upperparts* dark *brown*, heavily *streaked and mottled with buff;* wings and tail barred with brown and buff, but extensively white underneath; facial disc buffy white with a darker border all around, and blackish around the eyes; chin white; *underparts streaked with brown on a buffy-white ground* (most heavily on the breast); the lower belly, under tail coverts, tibiae, tarsi, and feet, are unmarked; eyes yellow.

Range—The Short-eared Owl is one of the most widely distributed birds and occurs in all the continents except Australia. It ranges unmodified across Eurasia and North America, breeding northward and wintering southward. On this continent it is one of the few species of land birds that breed from the arctic tundras southward as far as the middle states without undergoing any racial change. It is far commoner as a breeding bird in the north country than elsewhere, but western Pennsylvania is evidently on the southern edge of its breeding range. It is best known in our region as a transient or a winter resident, commonest (or at least most frequently recorded) in the late fall. While there are scattered records for several of the counties in the mountain and plateau sections, the species is much more regular, as might be expected, in the open, flat country of the northwestern counties, where it finds congenial haunts. It has also been seen and taken at a number of places in the upper Ohio Valley; but at Warren, on the upper Allegheny River, it is rare.

The first intimation that the species might possibly be breeding in our region came from S. E. Bacon, who encountered it near Erie on two different occasions in July under suggestive circumstances. Positive evidence of its breeding in Crawford County has been brought forward by H. C. Kirkpatrick (quoted by G. M. Sutton, 1928), on the authority of Edgar Huidekoper and J. E. Reynolds, who reported finding a nest with eggs on April 20, 1906. The exact locality, according to Mr. Kirkpatrick, was about a mile south of Geneva. In substantiation of this report, L. E. Hicks states that he has several recent summer records of this owl from Pymatuning Swamp, and that he found a nest in the Ohio section on May 31, 1931. Still more recently (May, 1935) a nest was found by Robert Van Sicklin near Linesville, and two of the eggs were sent to the Carnegie Museum. Thus the breeding of the species within our region may be considered fully established. Probably its local breeding range originally included the whole area from Erie to Lawrence counties, wherever suitable swampy land existed. The species appears as "not common" on Van Fleet's manuscript list of the breeding birds of DuBois.

Migration—The Short-eared Owl has been observed at Erie as early as August 12 (1934), September 22 (1875), and September 28 (1896), but such early dates are somewhat questionable as evidence of migration, since they might conceivably refer to summering birds. The latter part of October, when the species arrives in the greatest numbers at Erie, is also, according to Mr. Kirkpatrick, the time of its first appearance at Meadville (October 22, 1905; October 30, 1925) and is probably the more usual time of arrival. November is a month of many records, but in the winter the species is less numerous, doubtless because many birds go farther south. Late spring records are: Erie, April 26, 1875 (Sennett); Conneaut Lake, April 10, 1911 (Welshons); State College, April 15, 1909 (Harlow); Hartstown, May 4, 1922 (Sutton).

Habits—Birds of prey as a class are universally distributed and occupy all types of habitats. One is accustomed to think of owls as inhabitants of the woodland, courting the obscurity of its shadows and seldom venturing forth from their sylvan retreats. But owls, like hawks, are needed everywhere to maintain the balance of nature, and they have been able to accommodate themselves to varied ecological conditions. The deep forests of the Northwest, the deserts of the Southwest, and the prairies of the interior, all have their appropriate species of owl—each perfectly fitted to its own environment. Thus in the East, the Short-eared Owl has forsaken the ways of its ancestors and near relatives and has taken to living in the open country. Grassy meadows overflowed at times by a sluggish stream, and wide expanses of marshy ground where rushes and cattails grow in lush profusion, are its chosen haunts. Here it finds abundant subsistence and no competition except from the Marsh Hawk. Like the latter, it often extends its excursions to dry upland fields, particularly if they support a growth of long grass and harbor plenty of field mice. As a mouser the Short-eared Owl is probably without a peer. We may find it perched on some low prominence, turning its head from side to side, on the alert for its prey, which it captures by a quick, silent dash. Again, we may see it coursing over its hunting grounds in erratic fashion, reminding us somewhat of a gigantic moth in its wavering flight, sometimes skimming low over the tops of the vegetation, and again flying higher, but always ready to make a sudden swoop on some unwary mouse that has ventured away from its burrow. Although often active in the evening and during the night, it hunts in daylight as well, a fact that frequently causes it to be mistaken for a hawk.

Of 101 stomachs of this owl examined by A. K. Fisher, 77 contained mice; 7, other mammals; 11, small birds; 7, insects; and 14 were empty. Its economic value is thus demonstrated beyond question. It has never been known to attack poultry, and it deserves the fullest protection as a species beneficial to agriculture.

The nest referred to above as found near Geneva was built on the ground in the matted marsh grass at the foot of a small bush, and contained six eggs. The nest Mr. Van Sicklin found was on dry ground on Whaley Island, and held five eggs. In size the eggs of this species average 1.54 by 1.23 inches, and in color and shape they are similar to the eggs of other owls. Observers in the Erie-Crawford district should be on the watch for nests.

"Short-eared Owl" Warrick, *Ornithologist and Oölogist*, 1883, 8:32 (Washington, Washington Co., winter)—Harlow, *Cassinia*, 1912, 15:20 (Center Furnace Swamp, Centre Co., winter)—Dickey, *Oölogist*, 1914, 31:171 ([Charter Oak], Huntingdon Co., May)—Sutton, *Bird-Lore*, 1924, 26:418 (Ligonier, Westmoreland Co., October, *fide* Shrawder)—Beal and Peterson, *Bird-Lore*, 1934, 36:33 (Presque Isle, Erie Co., December).

Asio accipitrinus Warren, *Birds Pa.*, ed. 2, 1890, 148 (distribution by counties).

Nyctalops accipitrinus Todd, *Ann. Carnegie Mus.*, 1904, 2:556 (Erie, Erie Co., transient)—Todd, in Bausman, *Hist. Beaver Co., Pa.*, 1904, 2:1199 (Beaver Co., winter).

Asio flammeus Burleigh, *Wilson Bull.*, 1924, 36:77 (State College, Centre Co., November)—Sutton, *Ann. Carnegie Mus.*, 1928, 18:135 ([near Geneva], Crawford Co., nesting, *fide* Kirkpatrick; Crawford Co. records and references)—Luttringer, *Cardinal*, 1930, 2:233 (Fenelton, Butler Co., February)—O'Neil, *Cardinal*, 1931, 3:18 (Wall Rose, Beaver Co., and "Coraopolis Heights," Allegheny Co., November).

RICHARDSON'S OWL

CRYPTOGLAUX FUNEREA RICHARDSONI (Bonaparte)

Description—Size of the Screech Owl, but *without ear tufts*. General color deep brown (not gray), with white spots on the head, upper back, and wings; white predominates on the underparts; the facial disc has a dusky margin.

Range and local status—This owl is the American representative of a species that inhabits the boreal region of the Old World as far north as the limit of trees. It ranges in coniferous forests from Alaska to Nova Scotia, and in winter wanders irregularly and infrequently to the northern part of the United States. It is considered rare.

A single specimen, shot by D. A. Atkinson near Wilkinsburg on March 12, 1896, and now in the Carnegie Museum exhibition collection, constitutes the only record for western Pennsylvania. Dr. Atkinson states that this bird was killed at the edge of a woods in the afternoon.

Nyctala tengmalmi richardsoni Rhoads, *Auk*, 1899, 16:311 (Allegheny Co., *fide* Atkinson).

SAW-WHET OWL

CRYPTOGLAUX ACADICA ACADICA (Gmelin)

Description—Smaller than the Screech Owl, and without ear tufts. *Adult:* upperparts brown, with slight white mottling; the "face" shows narrow white streaks; underparts white, with broad, irregular rufous-brown streaks. *Young: upperparts dark brown;* wings brown, with white spots; the "face" white; *breast deep brown* like the back; rest of *underparts deep buff*.

Range—This diminutive owl ranges from the Atlantic coast to the Pacific but is rather northerly in its distribution, at least in the breeding season. Its breeding range and its migration routes have not been definitely determined, and it is uncertain whether it should be regarded in our region as a resident species wherever found or as an irregular transient and a winter wanderer. Its small size and retiring disposition combine to shield it from frequent observation, so that it may be much commoner than the available records indicate. The prevalence of winter records may signify either that its numbers are increased at that season by an influx from the north, or merely that the bird is easier to observe when the trees are bare.

While no nests with eggs have been found in western Pennsylvania, young in the brown plumage have been taken at several widely separated places. Moreover, May and June records are presumably of breeding individuals. On this basis it may be concluded that the Saw-whet Owl breeds at the following localities: Erie (Sennett); Pymatuning Swamp (Hicks); Meadville (Van Cleve); Warren (Simpson); Heart's Content, Warren County (Hicks); Tiona, Warren County (Dickey); Rasselas, Elk County (Baily); northern Huntingdon County (Harlow); Endeavor, Forest County (Dickey; specimen in the Carnegie Museum); DuBois (Van Fleet); and Pittsburgh (Todd, *et al.*). Nonbreeding records, additional to those cited in the references below, are as follows: Lake Pleasant, Erie County, November 15, 1894 (Bacon; specimen in the Carnegie Museum); New Florence, Westmoreland County, January 5, 1904 (J. M. Medsger; specimen in the Carnegie Museum); "Wilson's Grove," near Washington, March, 1897 (Nease); Dunbar, Fayette County, no date (O. P. Medsger); Racine, Beaver County, no date (W. D. Hunter); McKees Rocks, Allegheny County, March 18, 1892 (Atkinson); Verona, Allegheny County, December 18, 1898 (Atkinson); Renovo, February 20, 1907 (Pierce); and Kane, McKean County, December 10, 1898 (Pierce). All these records are based on the capture of specimens.

Habits—The Saw-whet Owl is a secretive bird that retires by day to the hollow of a tree or to the depths of an evergreen thicket and moves out in search of its prey only at night. It is not necessarily shy, and when disturbed it does not attempt to go far. It preys on mice and insects and very seldom kills small birds. The young are so unlike the adults that for many years they were supposed to be of a different species. They remain together for a time after they leave the nest. A curious instance of a young bird found alive in one of the basement storerooms of the Carnegie Museum in June, 1927, was duplicated in July, 1932. There must have been a nesting pair in the immediate vicinity, although one would scarcely expect this owl within the city limits. L. E. Hicks found a nest with three young on Hemlock Island, Pymatuning Swamp, on May 30, 1931. It was in a hollow stub in a hemlock grove.

Nyctala acadica Warren, *Birds Pa.*, ed. 2, 1890, 152 (Venango and Elk Co.)—Stone, *Birds E. Pa. and N. J.*, 1894, 91 (Rasselas, Elk Co., breeding)—Baily, *Auk*, 1896, 13:291, 292, 293 (Williamsville [Rasselas], Elk Co., June–July)—Rhoads, *Auk*, 1899, 16:311 (South Side Cemetery, Pittsburgh, Allegheny Co., *fide* Link).

Cryptoglaux acadica Todd, *Ann. Carnegie Mus.*, 1904, 2:557 (Erie, Erie Co., resident)—Harlow, *Auk*, 1918, 35:26 (Huntingdon Co., May)—Elliott, *Cardinal*, 1935, 4:18 ([near Jamisonville], Butler Co., November)—Perry, *Cardinal*, 1938, 4:177 (Erie, Erie Co., October).

"Acadian Owl" Simpson, *Oölogist*, 1911, 28:184; and 1922, 39:55 (Warren, Warren Co., June).

"Saw-whet Owl" Simpson, *Oölogist*, 1922, 39:55 (Warren, Warren Co.)—Sutton, *Bird-Lore*, 1924, 26:122 (Coudersport, Potter Co., February, *fide* Van Cleve)—Cope and Hawkins, *Forest Leaves*, 1934, 24:26 (E. Tionesta Forest Reserve, Warren and McKean Co., summer).

Cryptoglaux acadica acadica Christy, *Cardinal*, 1923, v. 1, no. 1, [p. 5] (Sewickley, Allegheny Co., winter)—Todd, *Cardinal*, 1927, 2:44 (Pittsburgh, Allegheny Co., June)—Sutton, *Ann. Carnegie Mus.*, 1928, 18:136 (Crawford Co. localities and records)—Sutton, *Cardinal*, 1929, 2:129 (?Altoona, Blair Co., December)—Hicks, *Wilson Bull.*, 1933, 45:183 ([Hemlock Island], Pymatuning Swamp, Crawford Co., nesting).

GOATSUCKERS

FAMILY CAPRIMULGIDAE

THIS CLEARLY defined family of more than one hundred species is represented in western Pennsylvania by two fairly common and well-known forms: the Nighthawk and the Whip-poor-will, both summer residents. The family is abundantly represented in the tropical regions of both hemispheres. Its members have soft, lax plumage similar to that of owls, in somber shades of brown, buff, and black, blended to harmonize with the birds' surroundings. Their heads are large, and their big eyes and large ear openings assist them in feeding at night. From the short bill an enormous mouth, or gape, extends back as far as the eyes; in some species its efficiency as an insect trap is increased by a fringe of long bristles. The feet are small and weak; the anterior toes are coherent at the base, and the middle toe is elongated, the nail bearing a comb-like fringe. Birds of this family build no nests, but lay their two mottled eggs on the ground. The newly hatched young are down-covered.

EASTERN WHIP-POOR-WILL

ANTROSTOMUS VOCIFERUS VOCIFERUS (Wilson)

Description—A dark-colored, long-winged bird, about as large as the Robin. It is mottled with brown, black, gray, and buff, the latter prevailing on the underparts. The *male* has a white collar and large white spots on the outer pairs of tail-feathers. In the *female* the collar is buffy, and the spots on the tail are much smaller, and buffy in color. The wings (in both sexes) are dark brown, with rusty-buff spots and bars.

Range—The Whip-poor-will winters along the South Atlantic and Gulf coasts to Mexico and Central America. Its breeding range corresponds in general with the accepted limits of the Carolinian and Alleghanian faunas, although it tends to exceed them in both directions. Our entire region is included in the general breeding range of the species. There is reason to believe, however, that it was never very common in the plateau country until lumbering began, and even today it is not common in heavy timber and seems to prefer sections where there are some clearings and openings. On the other hand, several observers (myself included) report a marked decrease in its numbers during recent years. I used to count on seeing it regularly every season in Beaver County, but now it is rather rare there. A. B. Miller writes that it was once a common breeding bird in southern Somerset County but that within the last ten years its numbers have greatly decreased: "In fact, it has almost entirely disappeared from the settled, cultivated sections, and for the past two years I have failed to hear a single individual. It still occurs more or less plentifully, however, in remote clearings and along the wooded mountainsides." R. B. Simpson says that it is rather scarce in Warren County and that it keeps to the hill country and avoids the river valley. Nowhere and at no time have I found it more numerous than at the head of Standing Stone Creek in extreme northeastern Huntingdon County, in June, 1895. It is probably commoner in the ridge and valley section than elsewhere at the present time.

Migration—Major Stephen Long's expedition reported observing the Whip-poor-will along the Ohio River on May 5, 1819—doubtless in Beaver County. This old-time record is a trifle late (seasonally speaking) compared with my own arrival dates from the same region, which range from April 23 (1910) to May 1 (1889). The greater part of the available arrival records made in the other western counties fall within these limiting dates. On occasion the species may appear in our region a little earlier, as is established by the following records: Monroe, Butler County, April 22, 1899 (Todd); Butler, April 22, 1895 (Roth); Jacobs Creek, Westmoreland County, April 19, —— (Medsger); Springs, Somerset County, April 20, 1916 (Miller); "Patton's Point," Beaver County, April 14, 1929 (Arthur). In the northern counties the average date of arrival is apt to be later; thus Mr. Simpson has not recorded the species before April 28 (1902) at Warren, and the earliest date for Presque Isle, also supplied by Mr. Simpson, is April 26 (1902). From Renovo, in the upper Susquehanna Valley, the average date in a series of arrival records covering twenty-seven years is May 3, and the earliest is April 23 (Pierce). At State College the earliest record is April 26 (1915—Burleigh). Thus the Whip-poor-will may be expected at about the time that the warblers begin to arrive in force.

In the spring the Whip-poor-will makes its arrival known by its characteristic cry, but in the fall its departure cannot thus be determined, since at that season it calls very little and very irregularly. I have never observed it in Beaver County later than September 24 (1890), while at Renovo the latest date supplied by A. K. Pierce is September 20 (1914). Since there are numerous October records for other outlying stations equally far north, these dates may be unseasonably early.

Habits—To the casual passer-by the Whip-poor-will is a voice and nothing more. A disembodied voice it seems, crying out in the silence of the night, when respectable creatures have gone to rest and only bats and owls and other such uncanny wanderers are abroad. Little wonder that this weird, lugubrious cry has come to be regarded as an omen of ill by the superstitious and as an object of suspicion even by some people who should be less credulous. Beyond question the Whip-poor-will is a remarkable bird—remarkable not only for the peculiar call notes from which it takes its name, but also for its structure, its habits, its nesting, and its place in nature. An outlying representative of a small, highly specialized group of birds, mainly characteristic of the tropics, it shares with them their protective coloration, nocturnal habits, and outlandish calls.

The Whip-poor-will is in full voice at the time of its vernal appearance, which it heralds by the monotonous iteration of an insistent and querulous demand for the further punishment of a mythical offender. The name itself provides a fairly good rendering of the call, although the sound varies with distance. The last syllable is strongly accented, and it alone is audible when the bird is far off. On a still summer evening the cry can be heard at a surprisingly far distance. Heard thus, it has a soothing quality, but close at hand its effect is far from soporific. Under these circumstances, four syllables instead of three come to the ear, the fourth being a low clucking sound between the calls—*whip-poor-will* (*cluck*)—*whip-poor-will* (*cluck*). Sometimes there are two or three clucks before each regular call. When the bird is excited, the calls are confused and abbreviated and the last syllable is omitted. Sometimes they are deep-toned and croaking and last eight or ten seconds. The song period continues throughout the breeding season until about the middle of July, but seldom later. While the bird is molting, its cries cease entirely, but they are occasionally heard again in September. It is noisiest and most active in the hours just after sunset and before daybreak, but it is usually silent during the middle of the night. On rare occasions the call is heard during the daytime.

During the day the Whip-poor-will lies close in the deep woods, either on the ground, on a fallen log or branch, or on a low limb. It always perches lengthwise, the more effectively to conceal itself. When at rest it blends so perfectly with its surroundings that I have often failed to descry it even when I knew I was looking at the right spot. When flushed it gets up as silently as a shadow, spreads its long wings, flutters off in erratic fashion, as might a giant moth, and drops down again just out of sight. I have never seen it abroad in the daytime, even in dark and cloudy weather. After sunset it seeks some open place, or the edge of the woods, and there begins its wild vociferations and its hunt for insect prey. Favorable spots, such as a deserted clearing in the midst of the forest, may draw a number of whip-poor-wills together. In such a place I have at times encountered a dozen birds, and on these occasions the glade echoed with their cries as each tried to outdo the others. (One realizes then the appropriateness of the name *vociferus*.) Often, too, the birds extend their nocturnal peregrinations to the vicinity of farmhouses and invade orchards and gardens. Sometimes they hunt over the water, attracted by the insect life abundant there. H. M. McQuiston writes that he has observed the species along the Big Bend of the Shenango River in Mercer County, coursing over the stream at dusk and perching on the trees along the bank.

The Whip-poor-will feeds on night-flying moths and is perfectly adapted for capturing them. The enormous gape, fringed all around with long bristles, is a perfect insect trap; and the bird's large eyes and keen vision enable it to detect its prey at a considerable distance. Rudyerd Boulton (1922) thus describes its feeding habits: "At about eight o'clock . . . that evening I saw a Whip-poor-will hunting. It was perched lengthwise on a branch about fifteen feet from the ground, and regularly, about every thirty seconds it would very silently flutter up in the air and down again to the same perch. Undoubtedly, the night moths knew to their sorrow just exactly what it was doing." Beetles and smaller insects, and even mosquitoes, are also eaten by this species, so that from an economic standpoint it is one of our most useful birds. As it flies by night, it doubtless falls a victim at times to the larger owls, while prowling cats and other predatory mammals must also take their toll.

The Whip-poor-will makes no nest, but lays its two eggs on the dry leaves of the forest floor, selecting a secluded spot in the shelter of some low bushes or shrubbery. A pair will become attached to a given locality and if undisturbed will return there year after year to rear their broods. The eggs are hard to find and are discovered oftener by accident than by special search. The incubating bird sits very closely, and when she does leave she goes so noiselessly that unless one is looking directly at her she may escape detection. Sometimes, however, she will attempt to decoy an intruder away from the eggs or young by feigning a broken wing and will flutter and tumble over the ground just beyond reach, uttering a nondescript whining, guttural cry. I once surprised a bird that was brooding newly hatched young. She flew to a fence near by and sat lengthwise on the top rail, letting her wings drop down on either side, trembling violently and crying piteously. The eggs are laid on alternate days, and fresh sets may be looked for about May 20. They are as a rule almost or exactly equal-ended, and average 1.15 by .84 inches, being thus large for the size of the bird. They are white, rather evenly spotted with pale gray or lavender and sometimes with brown. J. W. Jacobs (1898) speaks of finding a set of eggs that were virtually unmarked. The young are at first covered with buffy-yellow down. It is said that the parent will sometimes remove the young or the eggs if she is unduly disturbed, and that she carries the latter in her capacious mouth, but I have no evidence to offer in support of this statement.

Caprimulgus vociferus James, Long's *Exped. Pittsburgh to Rocky Mts.*, 1823, 4 (Ohio River, western Pa., May)—Jacobs, *Curiosity World*, 1887, v. 1, no. 5, [p. 2] (Waynesburg, Greene Co.; nesting).

Antrostomus vociferus Townsend, *Proc. Acad. Nat. Sci. Philadelphia*, 1883, 64 (Latrobe, Westmoreland Co., summer)—Todd, *Auk*, 1893, 10:39 (Two Lick, Indiana Co., June), 44 (Coalport, Clearfield Co., June)—Jacobs, *Summer Birds Greene Co., Pa.*, 1893, 7 (Greene Co., nesting)—Jacobs, *Gleanings from Nature*, 1898, 1:17 (Greene Co., description of eggs)—Cope, *Cassinia*, 1902, 5:14 (Tamarack Swamp, Clinton Co., and Oleona, Potter Co., June)—Todd, *Ann. Carnegie Mus.*, 1904, 2:561 (Erie and Presque Isle, Erie Co., summer)—Todd, in Bausman, *Hist. Beaver Co., Pa.*, 1904, 2:1199 (Beaver Co., summer)—Harlow, *Auk*, 1912, 29:472 (southern Centre Co., summer)—Dickey, *Oölogist*, 1913, 30:74 (Waynesburg, Greene Co., nesting)—Reiter, *Cardinal*, 1931, 3:43 ([near "Patton's Point"], Beaver Co., nesting).

Antrostomus vociferus vociferus Harlow, *Auk*, 1918, 35:27 (Greene Co., nesting)—Burleigh, *Wilson Bull.*, 1924, 36:71; 1931, 43:42 (State College, Centre Co., breeding, migration)—Christy, *Cardinal*, 1923, v. 1, no. 1, [p. 6] (Sewickley, Allegheny Co., nesting)—Oberholser, *Bird-Lore*, 1926, 28:118 (Renovo, Clinton Co., and Beaver, Beaver Co., migration)—Burleigh, *Cardinal*, 1932, 3:75 (Summit, Fayette Co., summer).

"Whip-poor-will" Enty, *Ornithologist and Oölogist*, 1885, 10:79 (Templeton, Armstrong Co., May)—Todd, *Oölogist*, 1887, 4:89 (Beaver, Beaver Co., nesting)—Stone, *Cassinia*, 1906, 9:44 (Scrub Ridge, west of McConnellsburg, Fulton Co., June)—Simpson, *Oölogist*, 1912, 29:329 (head of Tionesta Creek, Warren Co., summer)—Dickey, *Oölogist*, 1918, 35:105 (Waynesburg, Greene Co., nesting)—McConnell, *Oölogist*, 1918, 35:150 (near McKeesport, Allegheny Co., summer)—McClelland, *Am. Mid. Nat.*, 1922, 8:37 (Washington, Washington Co.)—Boulton, *Oölogist*, 1922, 39:72 (near Beaver, Beaver Co., May; habits)—Street, *Cassinia*, 1923, 24:10, 13 (Ft. Loudon, Franklin Co., June)—Christy, *Cardinal*, 1924, v. 1, no. 4, p. 10 (Big Traverse Valley, Beaver Co., June)—Eastwood, *Bird-Lore*, 1925, 27:337 (Bradford Woods, Allegheny Co., July, *fide* Frederick)—Boulton, *Bird-Lore*, 1928, 30:271 (Frick Park, Pittsburgh, Allegheny Co., April, *fide* Knauz)—[Christy, ed.], *Cardinal*, 1933, 3:150 (near New Kensington, Westmoreland Co., breeding, *fide* Auerswald).

Setochalcis vocifera vocifera Christy and Sutton, *Cardinal*, 1928, 2:70 (Cook Forest, Clarion Co., summer)—Sutton, *Ann. Carnegie Mus.*, 1928, 18:148 (Crawford Co. localities, summer).

EASTERN NIGHTHAWK

CHORDEILES MINOR MINOR (Forster)

Description—In size and form about the same as the Whip-poor-will. Upperparts dusky black, mottled with gray and buff; tail black, indistinctly barred with gray; *wings* black, with a *large white spot about the middle;* throat white (male) or buffy (female); breast marked with dusky, buffy, and grayish mottling, and the rest of the underparts barred with the same shades. The color pattern of the wings will always serve to distinguish this species from the Whip-poor-will.

Range—A species of tropical origin and affinities, the Nighthawk has succeeded in pushing far beyond its presumed original limits. Few North American land birds have a more extensive breeding range: from the West Indies to the Mackenzie River, and all the way across the continent. The species splits up into a number of geographical races, only one of which occurs in our region[1]—the eastern and northern bird, typical *minor*, which is more or less common as a summer resident and abundant as a transient, especially in the fall. It has accommodated itself to existing conditions to such an extent that it often nests on the flat roofs of houses in the cities, and one wonders whether it could ever have been as common in prehistoric times, when the whole face of the country was forested, as it is today. It ranges over the mountains and the valley country indiscriminately and of course nests throughout; but oddly enough, not many actual instances of breeding have been recorded for our region outside the cities and towns.

Migration—The Eastern Nighthawk is distinctly migratory; it summers from the middle states northward to Hudson Bay and winters in South America. As it comes from such a distance and proceeds so much farther north, it is necessarily a late migrant in our region. For Beaver, where I have recorded its arrival in fifteen different years, my earliest date is May 2, 1891 (not April 27, 1911, as erroneously given in H. C. Oberholser's list—1914), while the average date is May 9. Corresponding dates from Sewickley, based on fourteen years' records made by B. H. Christy, are May 4 (1888; 1913) for the earliest and May 9 for the average. The species has been noted at Butler on May 2, 1895 (Roth); at Slate Lick, Armstrong County, on May 1, 1894 (Keener); and at Wilkinsburg on April 29, 1891 (Atkinson). The latter is the earliest spring date on record. As the Nighthawk is a strong flier, one would expect little difference between the average time of its arrival in the upper Ohio Valley and that of its arrival in the mountains. A series of records from Renovo, however, covering twenty-four years (Pierce), indicates that the northward movement there is retarded by about a week. These records yield May 17 as the average date and May 8 (1902) as the earliest. The reason for this discrepancy is obscure. To judge by the flocks that are sometimes in evidence, migration continues even during the last weeks in May, when the summer residents are presumably settled for the season.

During the spring migration, flocks are the exception rather than the rule, but in the fall the reverse is true. The fall migration begins early, sometimes (in Beaver County) by August 11 (1910). There are usually two or three days of excessive movement, when large flights occur and scores of birds are in sight at one time, winging their way in the same general direction—not necessarily southward. These large flights generally take place during the last week in August or the first week in September. The latest date that I have ever noted for Beaver County is September 15 (1918)—but this is exceptional, as is also a record for September 17 made at Pittsburgh in 1924 (Sutton). A single bird was seen flying over Presque Isle on September 23, 1900, and the same date in 1899 is the latest recorded at Renovo by A. K. Pierce. At Frick Park, in Pittsburgh, the species was reported on September 23, 1937, by P. P. Malley.

It has been assumed that these loose, straggling companies (it is hardly correct to speak of them as "flocks") are in actual migration. Mr. Christy has published (1928) some interesting observations anent this theory: "The appearance, toward the end of August, of Nighthawks in large numbers, is a phenomenon familiar to all who follow the ways of the birds. They ordinarily are seen in early evening, tumbling about in erratic flight,

[1]According to L. E. Hicks, specimens referable to certain of the western races have been taken in Ohio during fall migration.

just above the tree-tops. In time past I took it for granted that these birds in their antics were actually on migration, feeding as they went. I have even thought that I perceived a drift southward of the scattered and zigzagging companies. Further particular observations, however, indicate that the inference should be corrected. Repeatedly now, and in successive years, I have noted another movement of the Nighthawks, a movement which until recently escaped my attention. On September 4th, 1922, on August 29th and September 1st, 1924, and on September 1st, 1927, in the evening, soon after sunset, I descried Nighthawks high in air, 500 feet up or more, flying, not in the familiar, tumble-about manner, but orderly, in wide-spread but coherent flocks, with measured wing-beats, and on set course. And that course, not southward, but actually northward, or slightly to the west of northward, and down the [Ohio] river valley. In each instance, this lofty and ordered flight occurred when migrating Nighthawks had for several preceding days been about, in noticeably augmented numbers. One further item of evidence remains to be added. On August 26th, 1922 (again, after the annual influx had begun), I saw from the Cemetery hill a flock of Nighthawks milling about in the air, higher than the hilltops, and directly above the river.

"From these observations it would seem fair to conclude that the Nighthawks as at this season we most commonly see them, flitting low overhead, are not actually in course of migration. Their journeying has been intermitted; they are feeding merely. When travel is resumed, their flight is direct, orderly, and at greater altitude, perhaps above the level of food supply. The direction here in Sewickley, though northward, is down-stream, and this circumstance suggests the inference that the streams of rivers may be the clues which the travelling birds follow."

The procedure is analogous, according to Mr. Christy, to the behavior of a flock of warblers when they scatter through an area of woodland to feed during the day but gather at dusk into close formation for the next stage in their migratory flight. It is only fair to state that Mr. Christy's observations were anticipated to some extent by G. M. Sutton's in 1924.

Habits—The Nighthawk is often confused with the Whip-poor-will. The latter is strictly nocturnal; it is never seen abroad in the daytime and is not seen at all unless startled from its shady retreats. The Nighthawk, on the other hand, is more crepuscular than nocturnal, and while it is sometimes active for part or all of the night—especially if there is a moon—it prefers the late afternoon and evening hours for flying and feeding. But it is not at all unusual to find it in the air in the morning hours, even in bright sunshine. As a rule it dozes during the daytime; it rests on the ground in some open place, or on the rail of a fence or the horizontal branch of a tree, and always perches lengthwise, so that it resembles an excrescence on the bark.

The Nighthawk is of course not a hawk at all, but a somewhat aberrant member of the Nightjar family. In flight its long, narrow wings, with a large white spot near their middle—appearing like a hole when seen against the sky from below—will always serve to identify it. Its easy, graceful, but erratic flight, accomplished with long, sweeping strokes of the wings, is characteristic. In the spring it invariably arrives in pairs and, coursing high in the air, attracts attention by the constant repetition of its flight call. This note sounds to me very much like the word "being"—uttered with emphasis; it is harsh, nasal, and penetrating in quality. During warm summer afternoons and evenings the Nighthawk is one of the most conspicuous birds of the air, as it flies back and forth and up and down in quest of insect prey, uttering its odd call. At intervals it may be seen to indulge in a strange performance: starting from a point high in the air, it suddenly takes a nose dive with nearly closed wings until within a few yards of the ground; then it swiftly checks its drop and sweeps upward again on spread pinions. This aerial maneuver is always accompanied by a loud booming sound, which has been aptly likened to that made by blowing vigorously across the bunghole of a barrel. As in the case of the Woodcock, this noise is supposedly produced by the rush of air through the wing feathers.

This performance is the expression of the mating instinct in the male and seems to be put on for the benefit of the female when she is at the nest. It is hardly correct to use the term "nest" in connection with a bird of this type, which lays its eggs on the bare ground, without any protection whatever. Many a time I have watched the birds perform, but could never find the nest. It is always in an open place, however, where the mottled colors of the sitting bird simulate the surroundings so well that she readily escapes detection. V. M. Kemery (1925) tells of a nighthawk that actually laid her eggs between the rails of a railway track that was in daily use. Mr. Christy once found a nest among loose stones and tufts of grass on an exposed bar along the Ohio River. Two nests reported by D. A. Atkinson from Wilkinsburg were in fields planted with corn; the eggs had been laid in a slight depression of the ground. In the country districts the great majority of breeding pairs probably lay their eggs in similar situations.

One would scarcely expect a bird such as the Nighthawk deliberately to seek out cities and towns for the purpose of nesting, yet for many years it has been known to do this very thing. There its eggs are laid on the flat gravel roofs of buildings, where they are probably safer from molestation than they would be in the open fields of the countryside. There are reports of such nestings from several places: Warren (Simpson); Meadville (Kirkpatrick); New Castle (Raney); and Pittsburgh. In 1893 and 1894 two other instances came to the notice of A. D. Johnston from the North Side of Pittsburgh (formerly Allegheny). In more recent years T. D. Burleigh has on six different occasions found eggs in Pittsburgh proper. F. L. Homer found a pair nesting for two successive seasons on the roof of the Schenley High School building in the same city. The species is certainly a more desirable addition to the avifauna of our cities than are the English Sparrow and the Starling.

As do the other birds of this family, the Nighthawk lays only two eggs. As a rule they are nearly equal-ended, or elliptical in outline, and measure on an average 1.18 by .86 inches. The ground-color is white, or sometimes a pale stone gray, "obscurely mottled all over with pale purplish gray or neutral shell-markings, over which is laid a marbling or scratchy fret-work of dark olive-gray. The tone of the markings—rather, the number and intensity of the markings, resulting in the general tone of coloration—is extremely variable, some very pale, scarcely clouded, eggs being met with."[1] Most of the eggs that I have examined remind me, in their markings, of those of the Cowbird. The eggs are usually laid during the last week in May or the first week in June, but occasionally not until the latter part of June—perhaps because nestings are sometimes delayed by accident. Incubation lasts about two weeks, and in eighteen days thereafter, according to Mr. Homer, the young are able to fly. This observer has described (1923) the actions of two broods as follows: "The appearance and habits of the young birds were most amusing. Long before they could fly, they would, if prodded, raise their wings and run rapidly, using their wings as sails. And on their short legs were long feathers which irresistibly suggested little pantalettes. It

was surprising to observe how fast they could run, and most delightful to see their dainty little pantalettes encasing their short, stout legs.

"Still more curious was another habit exhibited by both pairs of young birds. If they did not choose to run when teased, they would spring at their tormentor most aggressively, opening wide their mouths and hissing in a strangely reptilian fashion. They would land from their jump with wings outspread and mouth open . . . There can be no doubt as to the meaning of the action—it is clearly intended to frighten the intruder; and it does make a strangely formidable impression of danger upon the intruder. It is a very effective device; and surely a most interesting example of what is called instinct. . . .

"As soon as the young birds could fly they ceased from their threatening ways and flew about. Their flight was singularly easy, graceful, and noiseless. One day one of the first brood flew through a window into the corridor of the building. As it flew up and down, it strongly suggested a small owl."

[1]Elliott Coues, *Birds of the Northwest*, 1874, p. 265.

S. K. Eastwood (1925) reports seeing a young nighthawk, barely able to fly, as late as August 20, when transients were already on their southward way; it must have been hatched about the first of that month. The great flights that occur in our region about this time are composed of individuals from the north and must not be taken as an indication of the numbers and density of the breeding population. These flights, comprised of thousands of individuals, may last for hours at a time and cover a wide area of country. The birds move leisurely, drifting along in the same general direction, sometimes flying at a height of five hundred feet or more, and again skimming low over the ground. Their powers of flight are truly wonderful and suggest those of members of the falcon tribe. With rapid strokes of their long wings they mount upward into the sky, and again sail gracefully on set pinions for a long distance, with intervals of twisting and turning and doubling back and forth and up and down in pursuit of their agile insect prey. These aerial gyrations are accomplished in absolute silence, and no matter how many birds may be on the wing at one time, they never seem to interfere with each other. The food of this bird consists wholly of insects secured in flight—both large and small kinds, from moths and beetles down to mosquitoes. Instead of being shot at for "sport," as unfortunately sometimes happens, this valuable species should be carefully cherished and protected.

Chordeiles popetue Townsend, *Proc. Acad. Nat. Sci. Philadelphia*, 1883, 64 (Latrobe, Westmoreland Co., summer)—Teulon, *Jour. Boston Zoöl. Soc.*, 1883, 2:10 (Bradford, McKean Co.).

Chordeiles virginianus Dwight, *Auk*, 1892, 9:136 (Cresson, Cambria Co., June)—Todd, *Auk*, 1893, 10:44 (Coalport Clearfield Co., June)—Jacobs, *Summer Birds Greene Co., Pa.*, 1893, 7 (Greene Co., summer)—Cope, *Cassinia*, 1902, 5:14 (Tamarack Swamp, Clinton Co., June)—Todd, *Ann. Carnegie Mus.*, 1904, 2:561 (Presque Isle, Erie Co., summer; migration)—Todd, in Bausman, *Hist. Beaver Co., Pa.*, 1904, 2:1199 (Beaver Co., summer)—Keim, *Cassinia*, 1905, 8:38 (Port Allegany, McKean Co., August)—Forrest, *Oölogist*, 1911, 28:115 (Washington, Washington Co., summer).

"Nighthawk" Stone, *Cassinia*, 1906, 9:43 (McConnellsburg, Fulton Co., June)—Pitcairn, *Bird-Lore*, 1907, 9:155 (Riverview Park, Allegheny Co., nesting)—Simpson, *Oölogist*, 1912, 29:329 (head of Tionesta Creek, Warren Co., summer)—McConnell, *Oölogist*, 1918, 35:150 (McKeesport, Allegheny Co., [summer])—McClelland, *Am. Mid. Nat.*, 1922, 8:37 (Washington, Washington Co.)—Street, *Cassinia*, 1923, 24:13 (Conococheague Creek and Ft. Loudon, Franklin Co., June)—Homer, *Bull. Audubon Soc. W. Pa.*, 1923, 1:36 (Pittsburgh, Allegheny Co., nesting)—Christy, *Cardinal*, 1924, v. 1, no. 4, p. 10 (Big Traverse Valley, Beaver Co., June)—Sutton, *Bird-Lore*, 1924, 26:418 (Pittsburgh and Sewickley, Allegheny Co., migration)—Kemery, *Bird-Lore*, 1925, 27:251 (Johnstown, Cambria Co., nesting)—Eastwood, *Bird-Lore*, 1925, 27:338, 406 (Pittsburgh, Allegheny Co., August)—Christy, *Cardinal*, 1928, 2:105 (Sewickley, Allegheny Co., migration).

Chordeiles virginianus virginianus Harlow, *Auk*, 1912, 29:472 (southern Centre Co., summer)—Oberholser, *Bull. U. S. Nat. Mus.* no. 86, 1914, 35 (Erie, Erie Co., May)—Christy, *Cardinal*, 1923, v. 1, no. 1, [p. 7] (Sewickley, Allegheny Co., nesting)—Burleigh, *Wilson Bull.*, 1923, 35:88 (Pittsburgh, Allegheny Co., nesting); 1924, 36:71; and 1931, 43:43 (State College, Centre Co., summer; migration).

Chordeiles minor minor Oberholser, *Bird-Lore*, 1926, 28:255 (Beaver, Beaver Co., and Renovo, Clinton Co.; migration)—Christy and Sutton, *Cardinal*, 1928, 2:70 (Cooksburg, Clarion Co., summer)—Sutton, *Ann. Carnegie Mus.*, 1928, 18:149 (Crawford Co. localities, transient and summer resident)—Sutton, *Cardinal*, 1929, 2:121 (Hartstown, Crawford Co., September)—Burleigh, *Cardinal*, 1932, 3:75 (Chestnut Ridge, near Uniontown, Fayette Co., summer; migration).

SWIFTS

FAMILY MICROPODIDAE

THE SWIFTS, as their name implies, are birds of extremely rapid flight. Structurally they are very similar to the Hummingbirds, but their bills are small, flat, and triangular, with a wide gape. They are rather small birds with plain plumage, and in flight and feeding habits they resemble the Swallows, from which, however, they are anatomically different.

Most species nest in colonies. Their natural nesting sites are hollow trees and caves. The nests are composed of various materials, fastened together by a glutinous secretion of the salivary glands. The eggs are white, and the young are naked when hatched. Swifts are pre-eminently aerial; they secure their insect food entirely from the air while in flight and almost never alight on the ground or perch in trees.

About one hundred species and subspecies are known; they are found throughout the world except in the cold regions, where insect food is not available. Only one—the Chimney Swift—occurs in our region.

CHIMNEY SWIFT

CHAETURA PELAGICA (Linnaeus)

Description—As seen in flight, this bird resembles a swallow, but the *tail is short and pointed*, and the *wings* are long and slender, *somewhat bowed*. General color sooty brown, paler and grayer below, especially on the throat.

Range—In summer the Chimney Swift is found in North America east of the Rocky Mountains, as far north as southern Canada and Newfoundland and as far south as the Gulf coast. Its winter home is unknown but is surmised to be in South America. It occurs throughout western Pennsylvania as a common summer resident, and it is often exceedingly numerous in the late summer and early fall months in certain localities, as a result no doubt of a concentration from surrounding areas, preparatory to the southward movement.

Migration—The Chimney Swift is wont to make its appearance in our region during the third or fourth week in April, the time depending somewhat on the advance of the season. Thus in 1922 it arrived at Beaver on April 11, during a period of unseasonably warm weather, while in 1910 it was delayed until May 1. The average date of arrival there during twelve years' observations is April 20—a date that corresponds with similar records from across the Ohio boundary. Twenty years' observations of its arrival at Sewickley, made by B. H. Christy, yield April 22 as the average date. At Wilkinsburg, according to D. A. Atkinson, it comes between April 14 (1898) and 26 (1891). Other and confirmatory early records are: Waynesburg, April 17, 1891 (Jacobs); Pittsburgh, April 21, 1912 (Burleigh); Washington, April 13, 1896 (Nease); New Castle, April 18, 1930 (Raney); Warren, April 19, 1901 (Simpson); State College, April 14, 1916 (Burleigh). It is odd that the Renovo records of A. K. Pierce (covering a period of twenty-two years) are so much at variance with the others; the earliest date is April 26 (1904), and the average is May 5. Either the species is retarded on its migration through the mountains, or there has been a constant error in recording its appearance.

Fall migration begins in August, judging from the very noticeable increase in numbers that often takes place at that season as the birds gather at favorite feeding and roosting places on their southward way. They are usually common through most of September, and the last stragglers do not leave until the first week in October or even later. The following late dates are on record: Washington, September 26, 1895 (Gans); Wilkinsburg, October 4, 189_ (Atkinson); Sewickley, October 7, 1903 (Christy); Beaver, October 8, 1889 (Todd); State College, October 2, 1915 (Burleigh); Renovo, October 11, 1897 (Pierce); Erie, October 10, 1874 (Sennett).

Habits—The Chimney Swift is well named, for it is one of the swiftest fliers, and its association with chimneys is more than accidental and connotes a remarkable adaptation to the changed conditions brought about by civilization. The species was probably no less abundant in the early days, when the country was one unbroken wilderness, than it is at the present time. It then had to depend on hollow trees for roosting and nesting sites, as it still does today in the more thinly settled parts of the country. But it has not been slow to take advantage of the made-to-order facilities afforded by chimneys, large and small, which are unused by man during the period of its stay in the North.

As the Chimney Swift migrates by day, feeding as it goes, and rests during the hours of darkness in some hidden retreat, it is best known as a bird of the air. Arriving in our region in April, sometimes before the weather is settled, it announces its advent by its twittering cry, given as it courses overhead. The birds fly swiftly hither and yon in scattered companies of animated cigar-shaped forms, with wings held out stiffly, like bows. If the day is fine they keep above the treetops—sometimes far above—but in rainy or cloudy weather they come lower and in their headlong dashes may barely clear such obstructions as buildings and fences. Small flying insects constitute their only food, and in order to secure enough of these they must cover considerable territory in their daily flights.

The Chimney Swift is a past master in the art of flying; most of its waking hours, indeed, are spent on the wing. Its feeding and mating activities, and even the collecting of nesting material, are all carried on in the air. The rapid beating of its long, narrow wings alternates with gliding, and at times, as when two mating birds are flying together, one will sail with the wings uplifted, in a V-position. In a timely and interesting article in the *Cardinal* (1928), G. M. Sutton has called attention to the fact that in flight the wings of the Chimney Swift are always fully extended and are never partially closed as are the wings of the Passerine birds in general, and of the Swallows in particular. He writes: "It may be stated broadly, therefore, that the Chimney Swift wing, so far as its spreading is concerned, has but two normal positions; one, folded at rest, the other, open for flight, whether that flight be rapid forward flapping, soaring, coasting, or even sudden descent. Herein does the Swift's wing differ widely from the swallow's; the wing of the latter bird may, and usually does, assume several intermediate positions which are plainly noticeable in the field." This peculiarity, he points out, is correlated with a difference in the relative size and proportions of the wing bones in these two respective groups.

Dr. Sutton's observations were made in connection with a flock of these swifts that he watched at close range descending into a chimney for the night. Even when the birds were dropping in rapid succession through this comparatively narrow opening, the wings were kept fully spread. He was "amazed at their precision and speed. As a rule, they slowed up abruptly just before making the final plunge, this being accomplished by a spreading and lowering of the tail, and by rapid, vigorous, downward and forward strokes of the wings, during which the loosely and widely spread primaries seemed to aid in checking the speed. When a proper point above the mouth of the chimney was reached the birds suddenly pressed the spread tail downward as far as possible, and with outstretched wings high above the back, still loosely fluttering through an arc of about forty-five degrees, either dropped directly, turned jerkily from side to side, or twirled gracefully down the chimney." They seemed to find footing inside with the greatest ease; holding against the rough walls with their sharp claws, they used the spiny tail as a prop, woodpecker-fashion.

Sometimes a chimney swift in apparently aimless flight may be seen to approach the dead branch of a tree, pause for a tiny moment, and then go on.

Close watch will show that it has broken off a bit of brittle twig with its feet and is carrying this to use in its nest in some near-by chimney. Should the twig chosen fail to break off readily the bird may return for a second attempt, or else give it up and try some other. The nest itself is a crude affair, built of bits of twigs glued together into a solid mass and firmly attached to the inside wall of the chimney by a liberal supply of the bird's saliva, which hardens rapidly on exposure to the air and serves as a cement. Some nests are large, substantial, and serviceable, while others are so small and flat that it is amazing that they could ever keep the eggs from rolling out. A pair will customarily return to the same chimney year after year if not disturbed, as banding records have definitely proved. The same nest may even be used again if its condition is still good. Four or five eggs are laid; they are pure white and measure about .79 by .52 inches, being thus rather long ovate in shape. D. A. Atkinson has found nests with fresh eggs in Allegheny County (Wilkinsburg) as early as May 10 and as late as June 27, but both these extremes are exceptional; the usual time is about the first of June. No doubt rainy weather has a tendency to delay completion of the nest.

Instances are on record of this bird nesting in barns, sheds, or other unexpected places. E. G. Holt (1927) has described and figured the nest of a pair that built on a plastered wall in the attic of an occupied house, which they had entered through a broken window. R. B. Simpson once found a nest inside an abandoned boiler smokestack, and another inside an old shanty in the woods. Dr. Sutton found several nests at Conrad, Potter County, in May, 1925. He writes (1925) that one was "in an old, open stable, three in adjoining implement sheds, and one in a rather well built garage." He thinks that the birds deliberately chose these places in preference to the chimneys, which were in use on occasion by the occupants of the houses. Even greater interest attaches to instances of nesting in primitive fashion in hollow trees. This practice is so common in many of the wilder parts of our region that I frequently wonder whether all the birds I see can actually be using chimneys. T. H. Jackson refers (1909) to "a colony of Chimney Swifts flying in and out of the top of a huge hollow pine that had been broken off about forty feet from the ground." This was in Warren County. On June 22, 1898, on the wooded hill crest just south of Coudersport, I found a pair nesting in a hollow stub. The nest was attached to the inside wall, about ten feet from the ground, and was evidently nearly or completely finished at this date, yet it seemed incredible that eggs could ever be laid and incubated in such a slight structure. With plenty of chimneys in sight from this very point, these particular birds had chosen to nest in the same way as did their ancestors. To what extent the old habit has been retained is an interesting speculation.

The young are fed by regurgitation. They are usually on the wing sometime in July. In August old and young congregate at certain favorable points, in the neighborhood of some chimney large enough to accommodate them all for the night. During the day they spread out widely to feed, but towards evening they collect near their rendezvous, in bands numbering hundreds of individuals, and mill around overhead. After all have arrived, about dusk, their circling flight narrows, until at length they begin to descend in a living vortex and drop into the chimney to rest for the night. Similar performances have also been observed in the spring of the year, just after the birds' arrival from the South. It is likely that during migration the species always travels in flocks and flies high. Having been successful in adjusting itself to the new conditions it has encountered, and with few enemies to fear, the Chimney Swift bids fair to survive the changes that have wrought havoc with so many other members of the feathered tribe.

Chætura pelasgica Townsend, *Proc. Acad. Nat. Sci. Philadelphia*, 1883, 64 (Latrobe, Westmoreland Co., breeding)—Teulon, *Jour. Boston Zoöl. Soc.*, 1883, 2:10 (Bradford, McKean Co.).

Chætura pelagica Dwight, *Auk*, 1892, 9:136 (Cresson, Cambria Co., June)—Todd, *Auk*, 1893, 10:39 (Two Lick, Indiana Co., June), 44 (Coalport, Clearfield Co., June)—Jacobs, *Summer Birds Greene Co., Pa.*, 1893, 7 (Greene Co., nesting)—Baily, *Auk*, 1896, 13:293 (Williamsville, Elk Co., June–July)—Cope, *Cassinia*, 1902, 5:14 (Clinton and Potter Co., June)—Todd, *Ann. Carnegie Mus.*, 1904, 2:562 (Erie and Presque Isle, Erie Co., summer)—Todd, in Bausman, *Hist. Beaver Co., Pa.*, 1904, 2:1199 (Beaver Co., summer)—Keim, *Cassinia*, 1905, 8:38 (Port Allegany, McKean Co., summer)—Harlow, *Auk*, 1912, 29:472 (State College, Centre Co., breeding)—Christy, *Cardinal*, 1923, v. 1, no. 1, [p. 7] (Sewickley, Allegheny Co., breeding); 1923, v. 1, no. 2, [p. 17] (Clinton Pond, Allegheny Co., April)—Burleigh, *Wilson*

Bull., 1923, 35:88 (Pittsburgh, Allegheny Co., nesting); 1924, 36:71; and 1931, 43:43 (State College, Centre Co., breeding; migration)—SUTTON, *Auk*, 1925, 42:586 (Conrad, Potter Co., nesting)—OBERHOLSER, *Bird-Lore*, 1926, 28:9 (Beaver, Beaver Co., and Renovo, Clinton Co., migration)—SUTTON, *Ann. Carnegie Mus.*, 1928, 18:149 (Crawford Co. localities, summer)—SUTTON, *Cardinal*, 1928, 2:85 (Crystal Lake, Crawford Co., and Slippery Rock, Butler Co., flight)—BURLEIGH, *Cardinal*, 1932, 3:75 (near Uniontown, Fayette Co., breeding).

"Chimney Swift" BRUMBAUGH, *Wilson Bull.*, 1905, 12:100 (Wilkinsburg, Allegheny Co., July)—STONE, *Cassinia*, 1906, 9:43 (McConnellsburg, Fulton Co., June)—PITCAIRN, *Bird-Lore*, 1907, 9:155 (Riverview Park, Allegheny Co., breeding)—JACKSON, *Cassinia*, 1909, 12:10 (Warren, Warren Co., May)—SIMPSON, *Oölogist*, 1912, 29:330 (head of Tionesta Creek, Warren Co., nesting)—ROGERS, *Bird-Lore*, 1914, 16:272 (near Pittsburgh, Allegheny Co., migration)—MCCONNELL, *Oölogist*, 1918, 35:150 (McKeesport, Allegheny Co.)—CHRISTY, *Cardinal*, 1924, v. 1, no. 4, p. 10 (Big Traverse Valley, Beaver Co., June)—HOLT, *Bird-Lore*, 1927, 29:184 (Coo ksburg, Forest Co., nesting)—COPE and HAWKINS, *Forest Leaves*, 1934, 24:26 (E. Tionesta Forest Reserve, Warren and McKean Co., summer)—CHRISTY, *Cardinal*, 1938, 4:166 ([Sewickley, Allegheny Co.], May).

Chætura vauxii (error) FORREST, *Oölogist*, 1911, 28:115 (Washington, Washington Co., breeding).

"Swift" MCCLELLAND, *Am. Mid. Nat.*, 1922, 8:36 (Washington, Washington Co., summer)—STREET, *Cassinia*, 1923, 24:13 (Greencastle to Ft. Loudon, Franklin Co., June).

HUMMINGBIRDS

FAMILY TROCHILIDAE

HUMMINGBIRDS—called by Audubon "glittering fragments of the rainbow"—are easily recognized by their diminutive size, their long bills, the humming sound made by their wings, and their rapid, darting flight. They exhibit a marvelous variety and brilliance of color, which is most highly pronounced in the metallic plaques on the throats of the males. Crimson, emerald, purple, blue—they flash and glow like jewels in changing light. Peculiar to the New World, Hummingbirds range from Alaska to Patagonia, but are most numerous in the tropics. More than six hundred forms have been described; eighteen occur within the United States, but only one—the Ruby-throat—is found in eastern North America.

Long, pointed wings are controlled by powerful breast muscles; the feet are very small and weak, suitable only for perching; the tongue is extensile, tubular, and brush-tipped, appropriately adapted for feeding on the nectar of flowers and on minute insects. A hummingbird nest is a dainty, cup-shaped affair, fashioned of plant down and decorated with spider webs and bits of lichen; so tiny does it appear that it might well be mistaken for an excrescence on the limb to which it is attached. The eggs are white and never more than two in number. The period of incubation of the Ruby-throat is fourteen days. The young are naked when hatched and are fed by regurgitation.

RUBY-THROATED HUMMINGBIRD

ARCHILOCHUS COLUBRIS (Linnaeus)

Description—The diminutive size, long and very slender bill, greenish back, and manner of flight, are characteristic. In the *adult male* the *throat* is glittering *ruby red;* in the *female* it is *whitish,* as are the rest of the underparts; and in the *young male* it is whitish, with indistinct dusky stripes.

Range—This is the only species of hummingbird occurring in eastern North America. In summer it ranges westward to the Great Plains and northward to southern Canada, well into the Canadian Life Zone. It winters from the Gulf coast to Central America. It occurs throughout our region as a more or less common summer resident, but is less numerous in the "big woods" than in opener areas. It is a species that has been able to accommodate itself to the changing conditions of environment and is probably fully as numerous today as it was in primitive times.

Migration—The Ruby-throat is a rather delicate bird and a late migrant; it comes north with the warblers in May, but not as a rule until the second or even third warbler wave in that month. It has been recorded at Meadville, however, as early as April 25 (1896—Kirkpatrick) and at Waynesburg on April 29 (1891—Jacobs). On the other hand, there have been seasons when it has not been observed until May 21 or later, but on such occasions its actual arrival may simply have been overlooked. The average date of arrival for Sewickley is May 14 (earliest May 1, 1888) and for Beaver, May 13. These dates, although each is based on twelve seasons' observations, seem late when compared with a series of records from Oberlin, Ohio, which yields May 8 as the average. The average arrival date in twenty years' records from Renovo is May 16, and the earliest is May 7 (1901). Other early records are: State College, May 13, 1915 (Burleigh); Springs, Somerset County, May 8, 1927 (Miller); Warren, May 9, 1901 (Simpson); Templeton, Armstrong County, May 8, 1883 (Enty); Wilkinsburg, May 7, 1891 (Atkinson); Slate Lick, Armstrong County, May 6, 1894 (Keener); Johnstown, May 6, 1928 (Auerswald); Hollidaysburg, May 10, 1923 (Berg).

Hummingbirds are sometimes very common in August, when they congregate at certain favorite spots for feeding, but the southward movement does not actually get under way before September. Most of them leave by the middle of that month, but a few remain a little longer, and stragglers are occasionally seen in October. Some late fall dates are as follows: Sewickley, September 21, 1903 (Christy); Beaver, September 26, 1890 (Todd); Meadville, September 25, 1894 (Kirkpatrick); State College, October 2, 1915 (Burleigh); Conneaut Lake, October 2, 1928 (Bergstrom); Renovo, October 15, 1904 (Pierce); Warren, September 29, 1900 (Simpson).

Habits—As the sole outlying representative in eastern North America of a large and diversified tropical family, the Ruby-throated Hummingbird excites our interest and compels our admiration for more reasons than one. It is not a conspicuous bird, in the sense that a hawk or a heron is conspicuous, but its very smallness intrigues the curiosity of the casual beholder. The burnished emerald green of its upper plumage, and the rich sheen of its throat gorget, glittering in the sunshine with ruby reflections, make it the living gem of the bird world. Its darting flight, so swift that the eye can scarcely follow; its unique way of procuring food; its close association with and dependence upon flowers, both wild and cultivated; and its dainty and curious nest, combine to secure our attention. Originally a bird of the wild, and to some extent still found in the woodland (where not too thick), it has evidently accepted the new order of things and is now a familiar inhabitant of orchards and parks and a welcome visitor to gardens. There it may be found at home during the flower season, and a given pair will often return year after year to the same spot. It is indeed wonderful that such a tiny creature can find its way across two thousand miles of land and sea, to come unerringly at last to the very same place where it had nested the year before. It is not at all unusual for a pair of hummingbirds to build their nest over the remains of an earlier one.

The flight of the Ruby-throated Hummingbird is swift, direct, and well sustained. Like other small migratory birds, it probably flies at some height when traveling to and from its winter quarters, but otherwise it seldom goes above the level of the treetops. It is so small that it looks like a giant bee, and like a bee it can change its course very suddenly, swerving to avoid an obstruction looming up ahead. S. P. Hayes (1929) estimated the speed of a ruby-throat flying beside his automobile and found that it was making forty-five miles an hour. Some hummingbirds that I have watched for short distances, however, were certainly flying much faster than that. The Ruby-throat can easily outstrip the Chimney Swift, and the latter is a fast flier. Moreover, the Ruby-throat possesses the power, shared by only a few other birds (such as the Belted Kingfisher, the Osprey, and the Sparrow Hawk), of maintaining itself in the air in a fixed position; when it is thus balanced its little wings whir so rapidly—as indeed they do also in direct flight—that they appear only as a surrounding haze or aura. The bird will poise before a cluster of flowers, with slightly swaying body and quivering tail, and will then approach to probe their tubes, one after the other, with its long bill. Sometimes its whole head may be thrust into a very deep flower and hidden there for a time. It is a nervous, excitable little creature, as it passes from flower to flower, exploring each in its turn and darting off suddenly at the least alarm, only to return when all is quiet to resume its interrupted feeding.

A pair of ruby-throated hummingbirds that have settled in a given locality will make daily rounds of all the flowering plants within a certain radius and will drive off all intruders of their own kind from their chosen domain. There are certain flowers of which they are especially fond. On their arrival in the spring the birds are often seen in orchards, then in full bloom, where they revel amidst the sweet-scented blossoms; when satiated they retire to a dead twig to rest and to preen their plumage. Later in the season they visit such flowers as the scarlet salvia, azalea, fuchsia, geranium, larkspur, and caragana. Flowers with deep tubes or cups, such as the trumpet creeper, tiger lily, morning-glory, nasturtium, and gladiolus, seem to offer peculiar attractions, and the birds show great partiality to red flowers of several kinds. Among the native flowers most frequently visited are those of the wild columbine, touch-me-not, bee balm, and honeysuckle. It was once supposed that hummingbirds fed entirely upon the nectar secreted by the flowers, but it is now known that minute insects form perhaps the larger portion of their food. Small flies, beetles, and particularly spiders, are eaten in large numbers. There is reason to believe that hummingbirds first visited flowers for insects and that the taste for sweets has been incidentally acquired. Nectar is a part of their diet, however, and as they are also fond of the sweet sap of certain trees, they follow in the wake of the Yellow-bellied Sapsucker and feed at the holes it has drilled. They may be attracted by small vessels encased in red paper, in imitation of flowers, and filled with sweetened water, on which they feed eagerly.

Hummingbirds are pugnacious among themselves and sometimes quarrelsome with other birds as well. In the mating season they are continually fighting and chasing each other. Relying on their small size and incredible agility, they do not hesitate to attack and drive off other birds to whose presence they may object. Even a crow or a hawk is not immune from their swift and disconcerting dashes and may be compelled to quit the field. The "pendulum flight" of the male hummingbird, which comes under the head of courtship antics, is a unique and interesting performance. The bird swings back and forth in the air through an arc several yards in length, with great rapidity, as if suspended from above by an invisible string; displaying its scintillating throat-shield to the fullest extent, it twitters continuously in evident excitement. This performance, indulged in for the benefit of the female, may be repeated from three or four to many times. The amazing thing about it is the quickness with which the turns are made at the end of each swing. But the Hummingbird seems able to do almost anything in the air, from flying straight upward to suddenly doubling on its course. Sometimes its swinging flight describes a U-shaped curve, one end of which may be higher than the other.

Nest-building is usually under way during the latter part of May, and fresh eggs have been found in Greene County, according to Mr. Jacobs, as early as May 21, but this date is unusual. The first week in June is the accepted time to look for full sets, although I have found fresh eggs in Beaver County as late as June 27 (1889). Finding the nest is by no means an easy matter, because of its small size and inconspicuous position and because of the difficulty of following the female bird with the eye for any great distance. Patient watching and following of the birds, however, usually have their eventual reward.

The nest itself is an exquisite bit of bird architecture, less than two inches in diameter, and very deeply cupped. It is so small and so well camouflaged in color and design that it might easily pass for an excrescence on the branch. The sugar maple is a favorite nesting tree, but other kinds—beech, sycamore, oak—may be utilized, and an apple tree in an orchard is by no means an infrequent choice. D. A. Atkinson writes that he has even found the nest built in vines on the porch of a house. Ordinarily, however, it is saddled on a horizontal or slanting branch of a tree, well out from the main trunk, seldom over twenty-five feet from the ground and usually much lower. The main body of the nest is of cottony or downy material—dandelion and milkweed down, and lint from the leaves of certain plants—sometimes mixed with seed capsules and other fine stuff. Although it is of such soft material, it is rather compact and fairly durable. The outside is completely and neatly covered with a stucco of bluish-gray lichens, and the whole is firmly bound to the supporting branch with spider webs. It is a really beautiful and artistic structure, in design and workmanship fully worthy of the diminutive builder. The two eggs which constitute a set are pure white and are equal-ended. They are very small, measuring only .51 by .33 inches, and of course are exceedingly fragile.

Two broods are frequently, if not usually, reared, and the second set of eggs is laid during the latter part of July. Sometimes material from the first nest is used in building the second. Incubation lasts about two weeks, and the young remain in the nest for a month. The following account of the home life of this hummingbird is condensed from the detailed and careful studies made and published by C. W. Schlag, whose observations were made near Glenshaw, Allegheny County, during several seasons, beginning in 1928. He noticed that the female approached the nest by short stages, resting on some exposed perch at intervals of every few yards as she gradually drew closer. After the last rest she would rise in the air to a point about three feet above and to one side of the nest, and then slowly zigzag down and, perching on the edge of the nest, feed the young by regurgitation. She came in at fairly regular half-hour intervals and gave the young from eight to ten regurgitations at each feeding period. The young grew rapidly and were soon sticking their bills above the edge of the nest. "They were short, chubby little things; their backs were covered with pale green, and the under parts were white; their bills were not noticeably long." In another week their bills had grown longer, the birds were more active, and their bodies were showing above the edge of the nest. This particular brood came to grief in some unknown way—perhaps a red squirrel chanced to run across it. During the unusually dry season of 1930 one of a brood that was being reared actually died of starvation; the mother bird was unable to find sufficient nourishment even for herself, until provided with a supply of syrup in a small vial. By the time the young are ready to leave the nest, the structure is pretty well flattened.

Hummingbirds have few enemies, and the casualties they suffer are usually from accident. They can easily evade cats and birds of prey, but they sometimes become entangled in the burs of the common burdock. Storms and cold weather must also take their toll, as the birds are delicate and suffer under severe weather conditions.

Trochilus colubris TOWNSEND, *Proc. Acad. Nat. Sci. Philadelphia*, 1883, 65 (Beatty, Westmoreland Co., nesting)—TEULON, *Jour. Boston Zoöl. Soc.*, 1883, 2:10 (Bradford, McKean Co.)—JACOBS, *Ornithologists' and Oölogists' Semi-Ann.*, 1889, 1:34 (Waynesburg, Greene Co., nesting)—DWIGHT, *Auk*, 1892, 9:136 (Cresson, Cambria Co., June)—TODD, *Auk*, 1893, 10:39 (Two Lick, Indiana Co., June), 44 (Coalport, Clearfield Co., June)—JACOBS, *Summer Birds Greene Co., Pa.*, 1893, 7 (Greene Co., nesting)—BAILY, *Auk*, 1896, 13:293 (Williamsville, Elk Co., June–July)—COPE, *Cassinia*, 1902, 5:14 (Clinton and Potter Co., June)—TODD, *Ann. Carnegie Mus.*, 1904, 2:562 (Presque Isle, Erie Co., summer)—TODD, in Bausman, *Hist. Beaver Co., Pa.*, 1904, 2:1199 (Beaver Co., summer)—KEIM, *Cassinia*, 1905, 8:38 (Port Allegany, McKean Co., summer)—FORREST, *Oölogist*, 1911, 28:115 (Washington, Washington Co., breeding).

"Hummingbird" ENTY, *Ornithologist and Oölogist*, 1885, 10:79 (Templeton, Armstrong Co., May)—STONE, *Cassinia*, 1906, 9:43 (McConnellsburg, Fulton Co., June)—SCOVILLE, *Cassinia*, 1920, 23:15 ([Charter Oak, Huntingdon Co.], May)—MCCLELLAND, *Am. Mid. Nat.*, 1922, 8:36 (Washington, Washington Co., summer; migration)—STREET, *Cassinia*, 1923, 24:13 (Conococheague Creek, Greencastle, Franklin Co., June)—EASTWOOD, *Bird-Lore*, 1925, 27:338 ([Mt. Chestnut], near Butler, Butler Co., summer; Highland Park, Pittsburgh, spring); 1926, 28:273 (Rector, Westmoreland Co., May)—BOULTON, *Bird-Lore*, 1928, 30:271 (Johnstown, Cambria Co., May, *fide* Auerswald)—COPE and HAWKINS, *Forest Leaves*, 1934, 24:26 (E. Tionesta Forest Reserve, Warren and McKean Co., summer)—SCHLAG, *Cardinal*, 1940, 5:57 ([Glenshaw, Allegheny Co.], habits).

"Ruby-throated Hummingbird" JACOBS, *Hawkeye Ornithologist and Oölogist*, 1888, 1:88 (Waynesburg, Greene Co., May)—JORDAN, *Ornithologist and Oölogist*, 1893, 18:105 (Johnsonburg, Elk Co.)—JACOBS, *Bull. 16 Wilson Orn. Chapt. Agassiz Assoc.*, 1897, 62 (Waynesburg, Greene Co., nesting)—PITCAIRN, *Bird-Lore*, 1907, 9:155 (Riverview Park, Allegheny Co., breeding)—MCCONNELL, *Oölogist*, 1918, 35:150 (McKeesport, Allegheny Co.)—DICKEY, *Oölogist*, 1919, 36:48 ([Waynesburg, Greene Co.?], nesting)—CHRISTY, *Cardinal*, 1924, v. 1, no. 4, p. 10 (Big Traverse Valley, Beaver Co., June)—HAYES, *Auk*, 1929, 46:116 (Erie, Erie Co., August; flight)—[CHRISTY, ed.], *Cardinal*, 1933, 3:150 (North Park, Allegheny Co., nesting, *fide* Auerswald).

"Hummer" SIMPSON, *Oölogist*, 1909, 26:26 (Warren, Warren Co., breeding).

Archilochus colubris HARLOW, *Auk*, 1912, 29:472 (State College, Centre Co., nesting)—CHRISTY, *Cardinal*, 1923, v. 1, no. 1, [p. 7] (Sewickley, Allegheny Co., breeding)—OBERHOLSER, *Bird-Lore*, 1924, 26:108 (Renovo, Clinton Co., migration)—BURLEIGH, *Wilson Bull.*, 1923, 35:88 (Harmarville, Allegheny Co., nesting); 1924, 36:71; and 1931, 43:43 (State College, Centre Co., summer; migration)—CHRISTY and SUTTON, *Cardinal*, 1928, 2:71 (Cook Forest, Clarion Co., summer)—SUTTON, *Ann. Carnegie Mus.*, 1928, 18:150 (Crawford Co. localities, summer)—SCHLAG, *Cardinal*, 1930, 2:195; 1931, 3:10; 1935, 4:13; and 1939, 5:17 (near Glenshaw, Allegheny Co., nesting habits)—BURLEIGH, *Cardinal*, 1932, 3:75 (near Uniontown, Fayette Co., summer)—CHRISTY, *Cardinal*, 1933, 3:148 (nesting material; Sewickley, Allegheny Co., September).

KINGFISHERS

FAMILY ALCEDINIDAE

THE KINGFISHERS are widely distributed in the warmer parts of the world and are most numerous in the Australian region. More than two hundred species and subspecies are known, but only one occurs in northeastern North America. Kingfishers are stocky birds with big heads and large, heron-like bills. Their feet are small, weak, and unfit for walking; the middle and outer toes are joined at the base for half their length. All the American species are fish-eaters and live near the water. They excavate tunnels in clay banks for use as nesting holes, and their eggs are white.

EASTERN BELTED KINGFISHER

MEGACERYLE ALCYON ALCYON (Linnaeus)

Description—About the size of the Northern Flicker; bill strong and heavy, about two inches long. General color of upperparts, bluish slate; wings and tail blackish, with white bars and spots; head conspicuously crested, the feathers with narrow black shaft-stripes; sides of head bluish slate, with a white spot on the under eyelid; underparts white, with a broad collar of bluish slate across the breast (and in the female a second band of rufous chestnut, spreading out over the sides); under wing coverts and wings below, largely white; bill blackish. A white band across the hindneck, joining the white throat below, is often visible. In *young birds* the breast markings are suffused with rufous and brownish tints.

Range—The Belted Kingfisher occurs in North America at large, as far north as the Barren Grounds, but in the northern part of its range it is only a summer resident. In western Pennsylvania it is fairly common in the summer and also occurs occasionally in the winter. It is a hardy species and can stand cold weather without apparent inconvenience, provided that food is available. But when the streams freeze over and interfere with its fishing, it is hard pressed. To find a belted kingfisher in winter in the Ohio Valley is not unusual, although somewhat surprising; and the species has likewise been reported at that season from Erie, Warren, and Mercer counties, as well as from several points east of the Allegheny divide.

The wholesale pollution of our streams has naturally been unfortunate for this species, as it is almost wholly dependent on their animal life for its subsistence. More and more it has been forced to leave the larger rivers and creeks, as their waters have become fouled, and to retire to the smaller streams, where there are plenty of small fish. Yet there are still a few kingfishers along the Ohio River, eking out a precarious existence, and while in most sections the species is admittedly not so common as formerly, it seems in no especial danger of extermination.

Migration—We do not know whether our wintering kingfishers are birds that have bred here or birds that have arrived from farther north. February records certainly, and early March records probably, refer to wintering birds. But after the middle of March, when a few warm days have given promise of spring, we may expect to see the first migrant kingfisher, arriving with such other species as the Northern Flicker, the Mourning Dove, and the Cowbird. Most of the spring arrival dates fall in the last week in March. A few of the earlier dates are: Waynesburg, March 27, 1892 (Jacobs); Deer Creek, Allegheny County, March 21, 1913 (Burleigh); Sewickley, March 24, 1888 (Christy); Beaver, March 15, 1933 (Todd);

Slippery Rock, Butler County, March 20, 1930 (Raney); Warren, March 26, 1904 (Simpson); State College, March 28, 1916 (Burleigh); Renovo, March 15, 1898 (Pierce); Johnstown, March 14, 1928 (Canan); Rowena, Somerset County, March 11, 1934 (Mostoller).

The Belted Kingfisher remains very late in the fall, until November or even December—although records made during the latter month refer largely to wintering, rather than migrating, individuals. I have seen this bird at Raccoon Creek, Beaver County, as late as November 28 (1901), and in Crawford County "it generally remains until Christmas, if the water is sufficiently open" (Sutton, 1928). Failure of the food supply rather than cold weather is primarily responsible for its southward movement.

Habits—No sooner has the ice melted away from the edges of our streams and ponds under the warmth of the returning sun than the Belted Kingfisher puts in its appearance and begins fishing operations. All through the spring and summer months and far into the fall, its raucous, rattling cry may be heard as it passes from pool to pool, or flies across country from one stream to another. The Kingfisher is a land bird which, like the Osprey among the hawks, has adopted an aquatic diet without having acquired aquatic habits or structure. Its heavy, straight, and pointed bill does indeed suggest a piscivorous function, but its short, weak feet and rounded wings belie this indication. Nevertheless, the Kingfisher lives up to its name, for it is expert in capturing members of the finny tribe.

We may encounter a kingfisher perched on some branch overhanging the water and commanding a good view. He chooses an exposed perch and makes no effort to conceal himself. As we watch, he presently flies out over the water, poises for a few moments in the air on rapidly beating pinions, ten to twenty-five feet above the surface, and then dives headlong into the water with a great splash; in an instant he reappears with his wriggling prey firmly grasped in his bill. If it is small he swallows it at once, head first, but if it is larger he carries it to his stand to devour it at leisure. Sometimes he dives directly from his perch, and sometimes he repeats the poising performance several times, shifting his position as the fish below moves, before he makes the final plunge; on the whole his efforts are peculiarly successful.

I have never seen a kingfisher try to swim, but it can rise into the air directly from the water with ease, even when burdened with a good-sized fish. Seeing it on the wing for the first time, one would never suspect that such a comparatively slow and awkward-looking bird could capture anything so agile as a fish. Its ordinary flight appears labored; beginning with a downward drop from its perch, the bird continues low over the water, and rises again at the end of its effort. When flying over the land, however, it often keeps at a height of from one to several hundred feet. It will not usually permit anyone to approach it closely. Unfortunately this bird has come under the ban of the fisherman—without just cause. I maintain that the Kingfisher has just as much moral right to the fish in the streams as has his human competitor—even more, because it was here first! Certainly it has as much right to the fish as, in my opinion, the Goshawk has to the grouse or as the Cuckoo has to the caterpillars. This argument aside, however, scientific investigation has shown that the kinds of fish habitually taken are mostly those of little economic value—small, shallow-water species, such as minnows of various kinds, chubs, and suckers. The harm done to the interests of the fishermen by the Kingfisher is imaginary or infinitesimal. It is only when the birds discover and begin to pay especial attention to ponds or hatcheries where trout and other valuable species of fish are being artifically reared that their visits should be discouraged. Under such circumstances they are unhappily capable of doing considerable damage. In the natural state they feed also on frogs, salamanders, crayfish, aquatic and other insects, and even fruit.

Kingfishers are solitary birds, except, of course, in the breeding season, when they occur in pairs, each pair with its recognized territorial limits, beyond which it does not customarily pass and within which it permits no competition from other birds of the same species. All else being equal, a stream rich in aquatic life will support a greater number of pairs than one which is poor in such life. Kingfishers prefer lowland streams fringed with trees and shrubbery; they avoid small watercourses flowing through dense woodland, and mountain streams in general, but will sometimes ascend these when they happen to furnish an abundant food supply. Another consideration is that of suitable nesting sites.

The nest is a burrow dug by the birds in the face of a vertical bank, where they are fairly safe from most enemies. In regions where the banks of streams are all sloping, the birds have to go elsewhere, sometimes far from water. I have several times found nests in banks where sand was being excavated, and others have been found in road cuts. Some of my earliest written records concern the nesting of this species along Raccoon Creek, where it used to be common, as it found there ideal conditions. I have dug out a number of nests from the numerous clay banks along this stream with an old hatchet brought along for the purpose. I never found the burrows more than three feet below the top of the bank, so that it is quite feasible to dig them back from above. They vary in length, however, from three to fully six feet, and while some are nearly straight, others are more or less crooked, even to being bent at a right angle. The entrances to the burrows are about four inches in diameter and nearly circular, but as the burrows proceed they flatten out somewhat and end in a low chamber, the nesting cavity proper. Here a quantity of fishbones and bits of the horny covering of crayfish are accumulated as a bed for the eggs. The holes have a very disagreeable deadfish odor. The eggs, six or seven in number, are (when freed from nest stains) pure glossy white. They are broad ovate in shape and measure 1.34 by 1.05 inches.

My experience leads me to believe that the first week in May is about the right time to look for full sets of fresh eggs. I have found young several days old as early as May 17, but other observers report fresh eggs up to the end of May. A given pair will return to the same bank and will often use the same burrow, year after year, if undisturbed. The young are blind and naked when hatched but soon become covered with a growth of pinfeathers. At this stage they are ungainly and unprepossessing objects, with disproportionately large heads and bills. They remain in the dark burrow until fully fledged and ready to fly, and are carefully tended by both parents. They always sit facing the mouth of the burrow and if forcibly removed will try to back in again. It is quite impossible to induce them to go in head first; always they must back in, waddling on their short feet in comical fashion. July usually finds them on the wing, but they remain under the care of their parents for some time thereafter—until fully able to fend for themselves—and then the old and young are ready to leave for their winter home. Let us hope that they may return each spring with ranks unbroken, to begin a new kingfisher generation and to carry on the kingfisher tradition, and that they may continue to be for all time a picturesque adjunct of our waterways.

Ceryle alcyon Townsend, *Proc. Acad. Nat. Sci. Philadelphia*, 1883, 65 (Latrobe, Westmoreland Co., breeding; December, one record)—Teulon, *Jour. Boston Zoöl. Soc.*, 1883, 2:10 (near Bradford, McKean Co., July)—Dwight, *Auk*, 1892, 9:135 (Cresson, Cambria Co., June)—Todd, *Auk*, 1893, 10:39 (Yellow Creek, near Two Lick, Indiana Co., June)—Jacobs, *Summer Birds Greene Co., Pa.*, 1893, 6 (Greene Co., nesting)—Baily, *Auk*, 1896, 13:293 (Clarion River and Straight Creek, near Williamsville, Elk Co., June–July)—Cope, *Cassinia*, 1902, 5:14 (Little Kettle Creek, near Oleona, Potter Co., June)—Todd, *Ann. Carnegie Mus.*, 1904, 2:559 (Erie and Presque Isle, Erie Co., breeding; January, one record)—Todd, in Bausman, *Hist. Beaver Co., Pa.*, 1904, 2:1199 (Beaver Co., summer)—Keim, *Cassinia*, 1905, 8:38 (Port Allegany, McKean Co., summer)—Christy, *Cardinal*, 1923, v. 1, no. 1, [p. 6] (Sewickley, Allegheny Co., summer; occasional in winter).

"Kingfisher" Jacobs, *Hoosier Nat.*, 1887, 2:78 (Waynesburg, Greene Co., occasional in winter)—Jacobs, *Hawkeye Ornithologist and Oölogist*, 1888, 1:88 (Waynesburg, Greene Co., April)—Stone, *Cassinia*, 1906, 9:43 (McConnellsburg, Fulton Co., June)—Simpson, *Oölogist*, 1912, 29:329 (head of Tionesta Creek, Warren Co., summer)—Warfield, *Bird-Lore*, 1920, 22:31 (Chambersburg, Franklin Co., December)—Hoffman, *et al.*, *Bird-Lore*, 1923, 25:23 (Grove City, Mercer Co., December)—Street, *Cassinia*, 1923, 24:12 (Little Cove Creek, Foltz, Franklin Co., June)—Sutton, *Bird-Lore*, 1924, 26:122 (Glenfield, Allegheny Co., winter, *fide* Henrici)—[Christy], *Cardinal*, 1925, v. 1, no. 5, p. 20 (Big Traverse Creek, Beaver Co., December)—Boulton, *Bird-Lore*, 1928, 30:195 (Schenley Park, Allegheny Co., March, *fide* Homer).

"Belted Kingfisher" Simpson, *Ornithologist and Oölogist*, 1890, 15:63 (Warren, Warren Co., January)—Burleigh, *Oölogist*,

1911, 28:156 (Harmarville, Allegheny Co., nesting)—McConnell, *Oölogist*, 1918, 35:150 (Long and Jacks Runs, near McKeesport, Allegheny Co.)—Christy, *Cardinal*, 1923, v. 1, no. 2, [p. 16] (Clinton Pond, Allegheny Co., spring); 1924, v. 1, no. 4, p. 10 (Big Traverse Valley, Beaver Co., June)—Eastwood, *Bird-Lore*, 1926, 28:273 (Rector, Westmoreland Co., May)—Jones, *et al.*, *Bird-Lore*, 1926, 28:30 (Deer Creek, Allegheny Co., December)—Elliott, *Cardinal*, 1934, 3:171 (Raccoon Creek, Beaver Co., December).

Ceryle alcyon alcyon Harlow, *Auk*, 1912, 29:471 (southern Centre Co., nesting)—Burleigh, *Wilson Bull.*, 1923, 35:87 (Deer Creek, Allegheny Co., nesting; occasional in winter); 1924, 36:71; and 1931, 43:41 (State College, Centre Co., breeding; migration; one winter record).

Streptoceryle alcyon alcyon Christy and Sutton, *Cardinal*, 1928, 2:70 (Cook Forest, Clarion Co., summer)—Sutton, *Ann. Carnegie Mus.*, 1928, 18:140 (Crawford Co. localities, summer; occasional in winter).

Megaceryle alcyon alcyon Burleigh, *Cardinal*, 1932, 3:75 (Lake Seaton, Fayette Co., breeding).

WOODPECKERS

FAMILY PICIDAE

THE WOODPECKERS are a distinctive family the members of which are found in forested regions all over the world except in Madagascar and Australia. Several hundred different forms are recognized; of the sixty-five that occur in North America, seven are found in western Pennsylvania. All these breed within the limits of our region. The Red-headed Woodpecker, the Flicker, and the Yellow-bellied Sapsucker, are largely migratory; the others are considered to be permanent residents.

Certain structural features characteristic of all typical woodpeckers adapt them admirably for an arboreal existence of creeping and climbing. Among these are short, stout legs and "yoke-toed" feet (two toes directed backward and two forward) with sharp, well-developed claws; stiff, pointed tail feathers (twelve in number, with the outermost pair rudimentary), which serve as support in climbing; a stout, chisel-like bill that is an efficient tool for drilling nesting sites or for digging out grubs; a barbed tongue that may be extended to a great length, because of the bony rods that curl from its base over the head and are inserted in the front of the skull. A woodpecker's skull is extremely thick and hard and thus is able to withstand the constant hammering to which it is subjected.

The food of Woodpeckers consists mainly of wood-boring insects and their larvae; thus the family is of great economic importance in protecting our forests, since the birds' drilling does little harm to living trees. The diet is sometimes varied to include nuts, berries, and fruit. Nests are usually excavated in dead or decaying trees. Both sexes take part in the construction, as well as in incubation. The eggs are spherical and glossy white.

NORTHERN FLICKER

COLAPTES AURATUS LUTEUS Bangs

Description—Somewhat larger than the Robin; bill about one and one-half inches long. Top of head, plain brownish gray, as are the sides of the neck; a bright crimson band on the nape; back pale brown, with regular black bands, the *rump white* in strong contrast (conspicuous in flight); wings when closed show broad bands of black and pale brown like those on the back; *flight feathers* black, *with bright yellow shafts;* under surface of the wings, dull yellow; tail black above, dull yellow below, with black tip; upper and under tail coverts barred with black and white; sides of the head, together with the throat, wood brown; *breast* marked by a *broad black crescent;* rest of underparts dull white, more or less washed with brown and marked with *round black spots* in fairly regular pattern. The *male* has a broad *black "mustache,"* absent in the *female.*

Range—The Flicker occurs in eastern North America, north to the limit of trees, west to the

Great Plains, and through northwestern Canada to Alaska. A northern and a southern race, distinguished mainly by size, are now recognized. The larger, northern form is truly migratory over much of its range and is a common summer resident in the eastern United States and in the adjacent parts of Canada. In the latitude of western Pennsylvania, most birds of this species leave for warmer climes as soon as cold weather comes on, but almost every year there are a few hardy stragglers (or are they migrants from farther north?) that elect to spend the winter months in our region. The Flicker now appears regularly in *Bird-Lore*'s yearly "Christmas Census" from the upper Ohio Valley, but long before the first of these lists was published it had been reported by several observers as an occasional winter visitant in Beaver, Washington, and Greene counties. In Crawford County it is by no means uncommon in winter, and it has even been reported from Erie County. For Warren, where the winters are severer as a rule, R. B. Simpson has one record, and there is a February date for the highlands of Somerset County (Mostoller). East of the Allegheny divide, the species has been noted during the winter at State College (Burleigh), Hollidaysburg (Berg), and Barree, Huntingdon County (Sutton).

Migration—The Belted Kingfisher and the Northern Flicker migrate at about the same time. Both winter occasionally and thus give rise to some unseasonably early records, but the real migratory movement does not begin till sometime in March and, in exceptionally backward seasons, may be delayed even until April. My own records of arrival for Beaver County, covering twenty-two different years, range between March 13 (1921) and April 10 (1891), with March 26 as the average. Precisely the same average arrival date is cited from State College, on the eastern edge of our region, by T. D. Burleigh. Sixteen years' records from Renovo, however, yield the average date of April 8 (Pierce). At Springs, Somerset County, in the plateau region, close to the Maryland boundary, the Flicker arrives between March 22 and April 7, the average date being March 30 (Miller), but it has been recorded as early as March 14 (1928) at Johnstown (Canan). At Warren, on the other hand, it has not been known to appear before March 26 (1904—Simpson). The earliest recorded date for Erie County is March 12 (1898). The species was exceedingly abundant on Presque Isle in the fall of 1900, when the migratory movement began about September 15 and continued for about two weeks. Similar flights have been observed at other localities. Not until the latter half of October is there any marked diminution in numbers, but after that there is a decided falling off, although some birds linger into November. Such a wide discrepancy obtains among the various records supposed to refer to final departure that they are scarcely worth citing in detail. Many of these later dates unquestionably pertain to potential winter residents.

Habits—The Flicker is the commonest and certainly the best-known woodpecker in our region. Not content to remain in the forest (indeed, it rather avoids the "big woods"), it comes boldly into orchards and parks and gardens, and commands our attention. It is an individualist among birds, even if a degenerate among woodpeckers. Without having altogether abandoned the trees to which its relatives keep so closely, it has extended its sphere of operations to include open ground, where it finds a plentiful supply of the food of which it is inordinately fond—ants of various species, large and small. When the Flicker comes to lawns in country or city, it renders good service in devouring these minute insects. On the ground it can only progress by awkward hops, but it seems to get along well enough. It is interesting to watch a flicker at its work, as it repeatedly sticks its bill in an anthill, feels about with its long extensile tongue, and picks up its insect prey on the sticky surface. I have examined birds that had eaten hundreds of ants, and in each case the true stomach (proventriculus) was greatly distended by the mass. In the late summer and fall, without wholly giving up its insect diet, the Flicker turns in addition to various wild fruits, which it consumes in large quantities. Wild cherries, wild grapes, elderberries, pokeberries, and many similar fruits, including poison-ivy berries, are eaten at this season. A flicker in the top of an elderberry bush, making clumsy and awkward efforts to reach the clusters of ripe berries, appears at a decided disadvantage. On the wing, too, the bird is far from graceful; it progresses by a series of undulatory leaps, closing its wings after each stroke.

The arrival of the Flicker in the spring is signalized by its loud but not unpleasing call notes, of which there are several. Indeed, in this respect the Flicker is perhaps the most voluble and versatile of all our woodpeckers. While its vocal performances are not comparable to the melodious song effects of many of the finished artists of the bird world, its efforts are nevertheless among the most welcome of the voices of the spring. Its ordinary alarm-note is a loud and penetrating call of one syllable, rather high-pitched in tone. What corresponds to the song of other birds is a somewhat similar but shorter note, repeated from a half-dozen to many times, with a rising and then a falling inflection; this also can be heard at a long distance. When two birds meet they often utter a series of notes that have been aptly likened to the sound produced by whetting a scythe. There are a great variety of other notes, conversational and otherwise, and in addition to all these, the Flicker, in common with other woodpeckers, has the habit of drumming on some resonant sounding board. F. L. Burns has written (1900): "This form of instrumental music is a by no means insignificant addition to the Flicker's repertoire. It is a musical long roll of vibrant, far-reaching effect, sometimes evidently demanding an answer as the bird will assume a listening attitude, and at other times preceding or succeeding a vocal call or song. In the springtime it is a very popular means of attracting the attention of a mate or sounding an assembly. It is seldom heard after the nesting season has well progressed and ends before the young have hatched." Usually the bird selects a dead but sound end of a stub on which to exercise its drumming propensities, but when its choice happens to be the gable end of a tin roof, no alarm clock is ever necessary.

The Flicker's elaborate courting antics begin shortly after the arrival of the females (which come somewhat later than the males, generally speaking) and continue for two or three weeks. From the standpoint of the dispassionate observer they constitute an amusing, almost grotesque, performance, while the attitude of the female seems critical or indifferent. The male goes through all sorts of posturings, "bowing, hopping, prancing, dancing, strutting, flirting his wings, [as he] pleads and urges his suit with flickering, wacuping and hick-cupping notes; finally he sidles up to her, she coyly sidles away, and perhaps takes wing, followed by the one or more suitors to another tree, where the whole performance is repeated" (Burns, 1900). These preliminaries over, the mated pairs settle down to housekeeping duties. The site chosen is generally the main trunk of a dead tree, seldom a branch, and is always on the under side. Orchard trees are often selected, but almost any kind of forest tree may be used; the birds do not seem to have any special preference, nor do they take pains to pick an inaccessible site. They are just as likely to start a hole low down, within easy reach of the ground, as in the top of a high dead stub. No rule can be stated, either, for the size of the cavity, since it varies greatly in different instances. Sometimes the hole goes down only ten inches, but it is often much deeper, and a similar variation obtains in its diameter at the bottom. Both birds usually work at the task of excavating, relieving each other at frequent intervals; the work is carried on as unobtrusively as possible.

Many odd nesting sites have been reported. Pairs have been known to drill a hole in the gable of a house, and they are often willing to take advantage of a natural cavity, if suitable, or to enlarge the hole originally dug by some smaller woodpecker. Nor is it hard to persuade them to utilize an artificial box set up for the purpose, especially if it is provided with some sawdust for a bottom-covering. There is never any lining other than the fine chips at the base of the cavity where the eggs are deposited. The eggs vary from six to ten (rarely more or fewer) in number; like all woodpeckers' eggs they are pure glossy white in color and approximately ovate in shape, although in this respect they vary somewhat. Average measurements are 1.10 by .85 inches. May is the usual and normal nesting time, but fresh eggs have been found in Allegheny County from April 29 to June 24 (Atkinson), while young birds have been noted as early as May 18 (Christy). A pair of flickers will return year after year to the same hole, use it for several seasons in succession perhaps, and then dig another near by. The birds' attachment to their nesting places is marked, as the following incident will show. In May, 1887, I found a flicker's nest in a private yard in Vanport, Beaver County, dug in an apple tree and about ten feet from the ground. In order to reach the bottom of the cavity with my hand, I cut the entrance down some six or eight inches, but I was disappointed to find that no eggs had yet been laid. Naturally I supposed that this mutilation of their new home would cause the birds to desert, and I was surprised several days later to find that they were still using it. Upon investigation I found three eggs, of which I took two. On May 21 I secured six eggs, so that I had a nice set of eight, all fresh. On June 4, nine more eggs were taken, all but two of which were in various stages of incubation. Despite all this interference, more eggs were laid, and the parents succeeded in raising a brood of young that season. The next year they returned to the same nest and again raised a brood. In 1889, however, what I believe to have been the same pair of birds enlarged the old nest of a hairy woodpecker in a neighboring tree and used it for their own. Other observers have reported similar incidents.

The young are blind and naked when hatched and are the opposite of handsome. After they have gained some feathering they clamber up the walls of the cavity to the entrance and keep up a continual hissing or buzzing sound that is very characteristic. They are fed by regurgitation, during which process the parents seem to be pumping food down their throats. They grow rapidly and after leaving the nest are still fed for some time by the parents. The family groups remain together until joined by others in preparation for the fall migration. Flickers are sometimes inordinately abundant in September, when they seem to be very partial to wild cherry trees. The Flicker is prolific, versatile, and adaptable; it has shown its ability to cope with the changes induced by civilization and bids fair to continue in goodly numbers unless, indeed, it gives way to the European Starling in competing for nesting sites.

"Flicker" Warrick, *Oölogist*, 1878, 4:27 (Washington, Washington Co., nesting)—Van Ostrand, *Osprey*, 1896, 1:38 (Morganza, Washington Co., fall; food)—Forrest, *Oölogist*, 1901, 18:136 (Washington, Washington Co., nesting)—Stone, *Cassinia*, 1906, 9:43 (McConnellsburg, Fulton Co., June)—Pitcairn, *Bird-Lore*, 1907, 9:155 (Riverview Park, Allegheny Co., breeding)—Leete, *Wilson Bull.*, 1909, 16:48 (North East, Erie Co., December)—Simpson, *Oölogist*, 1911, 28:72 (Warren, Warren Co., nesting); 1912, 29:370 (winter), 329 (head of Tionesta Creek, Warren Co., summer)—Boulton, *Bird-Lore*, 1918, 20:67 (Beaver, Beaver Co., nesting)—McConnell, *Oölogist*, 1918, 35:150 (McKeesport, Allegheny Co., seasonal occurrence)—Stahl, *et al.*, *Bird-Lore*, 1921, 23:18 (Forest Hills to Deer Creek, Allegheny Co., December)—Nicholson, *Bird-Lore*, 1921, 23:18 (Grove City, Mercer Co., December)—McConnell and Savage, *Bird-Lore*, 1921, 23:18 (Emsworth, Allegheny Co., December)—Street, *Cassinia*, 1923, 24:13 (Greencastle to Ft. Loudon, Franklin Co., June)—[Christy], *Cardinal*, 1924, v. 1, no. 3, p. 19 (Raccoon Creek, Beaver Co., December); 1924, v. 1, no. 4, p. 10 (Big Traverse Valley, Beaver Co., June)—Eastwood, *Bird-Lore*, 1926, 28:207 (Pittsburgh region, Allegheny Co., March); 1927, 29:197 (Springs, Somerset Co., March, *fide* Miller)—Christy and Hegner, *Bird-Lore*, 1927, 29:29 (Sewickley and region, Allegheny Co., December)—Boulton, *Bird-Lore*, 1928, 30:195 (Sandy Lake, Mercer Co., February, *fide* Homer; Logan's Ferry, Allegheny Co., February, *fide* Eastwood, *et al.*)—Elliott and Squier, *Bird-Lore*, 1929, 31:37 (Deer Creek Valley, Allegheny Co., December)—Berkheimer, *Bird-Lore*, 1933, 35:27 (near Osterburg, Bedford Co., December).

Colaptes auratus Townsend, *Proc. Acad. Nat. Sci. Philadelphia*, 1883, 65 (Latrobe, Westmoreland Co., summer)—Teulon, *Jour. Boston Zoöl. Soc.*, 1883, 2:11 (Bradford, McKean Co.)—Jamison, *Ornithologist and Oölogist*, 1888, 13:134; and Dwight, *Auk*, 1892, 9:135 (Cresson, Cambria Co., June)—Todd, *Auk*, 1893, 10:44 (Coalport, Clearfield Co., June)—Jacobs, *Summer Birds Greene Co., Pa.*, 1893, 7 (Greene Co., nesting)—Baily, *Auk*, 1896, 13:293 (Williamsville, Elk Co., June–July)—Burns, *Wilson Bull.*, 1900, no. 31, p. 15, 17, 33 (Waynesburg, Greene Co., nesting; migration).

"Yellow-shafted Flicker" Jacobs, *Hoosier Nat.*, 1887, 2:78 (Waynesburg, Greene Co., common in winter)—Wickham, *Oölogist*, 1888, 5:92 (Beaver, Beaver Co., February).

Colaptes auratus luteus Cope, *Cassinia*, 1902, 5:14 (Clinton and Potter Co., June)—Todd, *Ann. Carnegie Mus.*, 1904, 2:560 (Erie and Presque Isle, Erie Co., summer)—Todd, in Bausman, *Hist. Beaver Co., Pa.*, 1904, 2:1199 (Beaver Co., summer)—Keim, *Cassinia*, 1905, 8:38 (Port Allegany, McKean Co., summer)—Harlow, *Auk*, 1912, 29:472 (southern Centre Co., nesting)—Christy, *Cardinal*, 1923, v. 1, no. 1, [p. 6] (Sewickley, Allegheny Co., breeding)—Burleigh, *Wilson Bull.*, 1923, 35:88 (Allegheny Co., nesting; occasional in winter); 1924, 36:71; and 1931, 43:42 (State College, Centre Co., nesting; migration)—Oberholser, *Bird-Lore*, 1927, 29:110 (Renovo, Clinton Co., migration)—Christy and Sutton, *Cardinal*, 1928, 2:70 (Cook Forest, Clarion Co., summer)—Sutton, *Ann. Carnegie Mus.*, 1928, 18:147 (Crawford Co., summer; winter, *fide* Kirkpatrick)—Bergstrom, *Cardinal*, 1930, 2:186 (Hartstown, Crawford Co., winter)—Burleigh, *Cardinal*, 1932, 3:75 (near Uniontown, Fayette Co., summer).

"Northern Flicker" Beal and Peterson, *Bird-Lore*, 1934, 36:33 (Presque Isle, Erie Co., winter)—Elliott, *Cardinal*, 1934, 3:171 (Raccoon Creek, Beaver Co., December)—Cope and Hawkins, *Forest Leaves*, 1934, 24:26 (E. Tionesta Forest Reserve, Warren and McKean Co., summer).

NORTHERN PILEATED WOODPECKER

CEOPHLOEUS PILEATUS ABIETICOLA Bangs

Description—Our largest woodpecker; wingspread twenty-eight inches or more; general color *black; head striped with black and white* and displaying a conspicuous *crimson crest;* the *wings* have *white edges* and a large *white spot,* and are *white underneath.* Whole top of head scarlet (male) or scarlet with fore part brown (female), margined below by a thin white line; a dark stripe through the eye, and below this a broad white line from the nostrils down the sides of the neck and breast; chin and throat white, bordered on either side by a broad crimson (male) or dusky (female) stripe; bill mostly dark; eyes yellow.

Range—The general range of this woodpecker is extensive, both in latitude and in longitude. It is a species that is equally at home in the cypress swamps of the southern states and in the spruce forests of eastern Canada, and it ranges thence westward to the Pacific coast. Some geographical variation is in evidence, and several races are currently recognized. Over much of its range it is now rare and local, having been largely extirpated with the felling of the forest and the advance of civilization into its primitive haunts. Maximilian, Prince of Wied, who crossed the Allegheny Mountains in 1832, commented on its abundance around Ebensburg, Cambria County. Originally it must have ranged over our entire region indiscriminately, but it soon began to retire before the ax and gun of the settlers. Long regarded as legitimate game, and still killed for "sport" by too many unprincipled gunners, it has held its own surprisingly well. In 1890 Warren gave a résumé of its local status, which, although based on reports from correspondents of varying degrees of reliability, was on the whole a faithful picture. The species, so far as I know, does not occur in the upper Ohio Valley, although there are a few hearsay records for Beaver County. One bird was taken near Natrona, Allegheny County, however, by D. A. Atkinson on November 12, 1896, and, more surprising still, one was identified by Harwood Werkheiser at Logan's Ferry, in the same county, as recently as April, 1933.

J. W. Jacobs was the first scientific observer to find and record the nest of this woodpecker within the limits of our region. He discovered nests at four places in Greene County (one close to Waynesburg) in the spring of 1887, but only one of the pairs continued to breed there. S. S. Dickey has also found the species breeding in Greene County, close to the West Virginia boundary, but it is uncertain whether any nestings take place there at the present time. Once fairly common, this bird seems to have succumbed to the inroads of civilization. But it is still fairly numerous in the mountainous and wooded parts of the state, if we may judge from the references cited below and from unpublished reports from various counties. G. M. Sutton's map and outline of the present status and abundance of the species in Pennsylvania (1930) is correct in the main. More nests seem to have been found in the wilderness of northern Huntingdon County than elsewhere in the state, but this does not necessarily signify that the Pileated Woodpecker is commonest there. Indeed, all the evidence tends to show that it is fully as common in the region south of the Juniata River as it is north of that stream, other conditions being equal, and it is certainly found throughout the plateau section wherever timber remains, especially through the northern counties, from Warren to Potter inclusive. R. B. Simpson's observations in Warren County, covering many years, lead him to believe that it is one of the first birds to disappear after lumbering has cleared the land.

It is difficult, therefore, to account for the fact that in the region just to the westward, in Erie and Crawford counties, much of which was cleared years ago and where the remaining tracts of timber are few and small by comparison, this woodpecker seems not only to have held its own, but also actually to have increased in numbers in recent years. In Pymatuning Swamp, in the adjoining timbered uplands, and in the scattered tracts of woodland in various parts of these two counties, and of Mercer County as well, the Pileated Woodpecker is by no means rare. Forty years ago I was surprised to find one of these birds at Waterford, Erie County, close by the railroad track, but my subsequent experience and that of others show that there are breeding pairs dispersed all over this region, often in unexpected places. The Pileated Woodpecker is primarily a lover of the "big woods," but in northwestern Pennsylvania and northeastern Ohio[1] it has learned to adapt itself to conditions the reverse of ideal, so that one is no longer surprised to find it in scattered trees in clearings and in plain sight of roads and dwellings—in good flicker territory. S. J. Seiple writes that he found a nest with young in a tract of woods about a mile and a half north of Osgood, Mercer County, in late May, 1929. Although the forest conditions farther south, in the rougher country approaching the Ohio River, seem even more favorable for this woodpecker than they are in the Erie-Crawford district, the bird is unknown there. The element of protection is not a consideration here, and why the species seems to have survived and be doing well in one section while it has been extirpated in the other, is not apparent.

This woodpecker is a resident in our region and is able to withstand the severest winters without apparent inconvenience, but it wanders more or less at that season and is likely to appear in places at some distance from its regular nesting haunts. Fall and winter records (of which there are many) cannot therefore be accepted as indicative of breeding. A case in point is reported by Professor Seiple, who examined a living bird that had been caught in Greenville in November, 1933. The Carnegie Museum collection contains a number of specimens killed "by mistake" in various parts of the state by hunters during the open season. The elimination of this practice would contribute more towards conserving this woodpecker in our state than all the reforestation programs thus far proposed.

Habits—In the early days "Penn's Woods" must have abounded with woodpeckers of this species, and their large size, striking coloration, spectacular appearance, and noisy habits, brought them to the notice of the inhabitants, with eventual unfortunate results for the birds. "Pileated Woodpecker" is a "book name," used only by ornithologists; the species is popularly known as "Log-cock," "Woodcock," "Cock-of-the-woods," or "Indian Hen"—the last in allusion to its cry. For many years, even down to the present century, it was regarded as a game bird and was offered for sale in the markets under the supposition that it was the "Woodcock" of the game list. Even today there are uninformed persons who know no better, and there are also some gunners who never miss a chance to kill this woodpecker, because to them any large bird is a mark. Like the Ivory-billed Woodpecker of the South, now nearly extinct, the Pileated Woodpecker has claimed the attention of naturalists from an early date, and its nests and eggs have long been the objects of special search. Thus it figures rather prominently in past and current ornithological literature. It may be looked for in the heavy forest, where high trees keep the ground well shaded and where dead and dying trunks are scattered among the living. It is not, however, a high-climbing woodpecker; indeed, it prefers to remain rather low, and it may often be found at work on a fallen tree trunk. In flying at ease through the forest it keeps well under cover of the treetops, and when feeding it sometimes moves only from one tree to the next. When unduly alarmed, or when passing from one tract of woods to another, it may fly higher in the plunging, direct fashion common to all woodpeckers.

Some authors say that the Pileated Woodpecker is among the wildest and wariest of birds and can be approached only by accident or by stealth; others on the contrary aver that on occasion it is as unheeding as the Red-headed species. My own experience lends weight to both statements. In northern Ontario and in Minnesota, where it is seldom persecuted, it has little fear of man, and the same observation holds true (more or less) for the Erie-Crawford region of Pennsylvania. Although I often traversed the mountains and other forested parts of the western section, I never saw this bird (or at least never recognized it) until June, 1898, when I encountered one in the high woods south of Coudersport. Attracted by my

[1]Compare L. E. Hicks, *Wilson Bulletin*, 1934, 45:183.

"squeaking," it came up within gunshot and was soon secured—a magnificent male bird. It was not dead when picked up, and its yellow eyes glared with an expression of untamable wildness that I have yet to see equaled. Another bird seen the same month on the summit of Chestnut Ridge, near Kingston, Westmoreland County, however, could not be approached, and the same was true of those observed in November on Jacks Mountain, south of Mount Union, Huntingdon County. According to other observers, the behavior of different pairs on their nesting grounds also varies.

I now think that for some years I must have confused the call notes of the Pileated Woodpecker with those of the Flicker. The call of the former, however, is pitched higher in the scale, is more penetrating, and can be heard at a greater distance. I am referring now, of course, to the long-drawn-out call that corresponds to the song of Passerine birds. The alarm-note is a loud, discordant shriek. Besides these, the bird has a variety of rough cackling and low whining notes, the latter suggesting those of the Yellow-bellied Sapsucker. The cackling notes are often given when the bird is in flight, but are then interrupted. In the spring the Pileated drums in the manner of other woodpeckers, as a part of its courtship activities; it is a noisy bird at that season. Its sight and hearing are very keen, so that it can easily detect an intruder in its domain, and when followed it usually starts on a long flight and leaves its pursuer behind. Like the Raven, however, it has a streak of curiosity in its make-up, and it will often respond to an imitation of its cackling cry or even to the noise made by pounding rapidly on a tree with a stick, and will come up boldly to ascertain the cause of the disturbance. Its sudden appearance under such circumstances is sometimes most disconcerting. Flying through the woods, it appears almost as big as a crow; the white underneath its wings flashes with every stroke, and its brilliant red crest looms up as it approaches and swings into position against a tree trunk.

In traversing the woods, one may sometimes detect the presence of woodpeckers by their drillings in dead wood and by the fallen chips beneath the trees. The smaller, weaker species naturally dig small holes and do not leave much litter, but the workings of the Pileated are unmistakable. A big, powerful bird, it is easily able to split off large slabs of bark and to dig deep holes into the wood, leaving a great pile of chips on the ground below. Mr. Simpson (1910) says that in Warren County, in the larger stands of timber, the Pileated is not hard to discover. Its presence may be at once inferred wherever huge old hemlock stubs have been stripped of their bark from top to bottom. "Large holes are cut into logs and fallen timber in quest of ants and grubs. I have seen where they have dug holes from one to two feet long and three inches wide into the very heart of large and ant-infested timber, and when such trees happen to be oak or chestnut, the work must take some time." Dr. Sutton (1930) writes to the same effect:

"The industry and strength of the Pileated Woodpecker are remarkable. It has a powerful beak, and the chips which it digs out are sometimes surprisingly large. So determined is it upon securing larvæ or ants, that it sometimes tears whole tree trunks asunder, digging deep holes in one side, and continuing its search for food, until the top of the dead tree may give way during even a light wind. Chips and drillings found in our woodlands indicate that the birds customarily prefer to search for food in fallen tree trunks, and drillings are often made near the ground on trunks still standing.

"In some sections the species appears to prefer the hard-woods, where drillings are to be found, chiefly in red maple and ash. In other sections it is fond of the yellow birch. Occasionally it frequents hemlock woods, where it often searches for food in living trees. As a rule, it seems not to like pines, though in Huntingdon and Centre Counties it is sometimes seen on the high barrens. In these open situations the bird appears to be restless and ill at ease."

The food of this woodpecker, as determined by F. E. L. Beal,[1] consists of 72.88 per cent animal matter and 27.12 per cent vegetable matter. Ants (carpenter ants in particular) and the larvae of wood-boring beetles make up most of the former, and wild fruits of several different kinds compose the bulk of the latter. From one stomach as many as 2,600 ants were taken. Dr. Sutton confirms these results after examining the stomachs of birds killed in Pennsylvania. There is no doubt that the Pileated Woodpecker is a valuable con-

[1]U. S. Department of Agriculture, Biological Survey, *Bulletin*, no. 37, 1911, p. 33.

servator of the forest, and as such it deserves rigid protection and all possible incentives to increase its depleted numbers. It was once thought to be unable to stand the encroachments of civilization and to be necessarily confined to wild and uninhabited regions. But word has now come from more than one part of its range that it is learning to accommodate itself to changing conditions and that it would come back if only given a fair chance. Aside from certain ignorant and lawless gunners, it has few enemies. Dr. Sutton tells of once seeing a duck hawk pick a pileated woodpecker off in flight, and Mr. Simpson writes (see page 135) of a woodpecker that was attacked by a sharp-shinned hawk, but escaped through his interference. In another instance he found the remains of one that had fallen victim to a wildcat.

E. W. Arthur (1934) thus describes an account of the courtship performance of this species, as observed by him in Mercer County in April. A female (presumably) was seen to alight "upon a grassy knoll in a pasture to the left of the road, where it walked about for a brief interval, until a second came to the knoll and approached within three or four feet of the first. Then began a curious movement, much resembling the dance of Flickers, wherein with bowing and scraping one bird, stepping sideways, made a circle about the other, who slowly turned, facing the performer. When the dance ceased there was a sudden jerky movement on the part of each, and thereupon they flew away." Part of the interest of this account lies in the fact that the birds came to open country and alighted on the ground.

There was a time when the taking of the eggs of this species was regarded as something of an exploit, but there are now several accounts of its nesting within our limits. The first nest that Mr. Jacobs found in Greene County was in the top of a huge sycamore close by a tract of woodland and was virtually inaccessible by ordinary means. Nests found later in Greene County by Mr. Jacobs and Dr. Dickey were excavated in oak, sugar maple, and sour-gum trees, and were much lower down and not hard to reach. The experiences of these observers in search of the nests are most interesting but are too long to reproduce here. No sets of eggs were ever actually collected, as it happened, and since then, squirrel hunters have practically exterminated the bird in that region. In Warren County Mr. Simpson has found it nesting in sycamore, oak, poplar, and beech trees, and has collected some eggs. Numerous nests have been found in the wilds of northern Huntingdon County by R. C. Harlow, T. D. Burleigh, R. F. Miller, and Dr. Dickey. A trip to this region for pileated woodpecker eggs with the first two of these ornithologists is entertainingly chronicled by Samuel Scoville, Jr. (1920). On this occasion—May 11, 1919—three nests were located and examined. He writes:

"Finally we reached the valley ["Stone Valley," near Charter Oak] ringed around on every side by mountains and followed a fire line through the dripping spring woods. As we neared a live chestnut-oak tree with a dead heart where the ground was covered with large chips for a space of some thirty feet, out from a hole about thirty-five feet from the ground flapped a bird which seemed about the size of a crow with black, white-lined wings. Ordinarily a female Pileated Woodpecker will not leave her nest when she has eggs until the tree is tapped. Before she has eggs she will leave the nest when one is fifty yards away no matter how carefully the tree is approached. This nest went down nineteen inches, twenty inches being the average depth. All around in the neighboring trees were the square feeding-holes and numberless little testing holes made by the birds in live trees and dead ones alike, where they had explored to find if there was any trace of the larva of the long-horned white-pine borer on which they feed extensively. The nesting-hole was round and seemed about twice the size of that of a Flicker, being about three and one-half inches in diameter. Harlow told me that the bird often makes a number of trial nests before it finally carves out one to suit. May 10 is the standard date although the nest is frequently begun as early as March."

Other nests were found in a dead pitch pine, about twenty-five feet up, and in a pignut hickory, fifty-five feet up. The females always displayed much anxiety, and one of them once actually returned to the nest in full view of the observers. The ground below an occupied nest is littered with big chips. A large stub is preferred, but apparently the kind of tree does not matter. The Pileated is not so prolific as most woodpeckers, and four eggs constitute the normal set. They are china white, very glossy, and measure about

1.50 by 1.06 inches (Simpson). The young resemble the parents and acquire the red crown with the juvenal plumage; they are fed by the parents for some time after leaving the nest. Only one brood is raised in a season. Young and unsophisticated birds are often encountered during the fall months. It is to be hoped that in time the species will regain its place as one of the characteristic birds of our wooded areas.

Picus pileatus WIED, *Reise in Innere Nord-America*, 1839, 1:130 (Ebensburg, Cambria Co., September).

Hylotomus pileatus TOWNSEND, *Proc. Acad. Nat. Sci. Philadelphia*, 1883, 65 (Latrobe, Westmoreland Co.)—TEULON, *Jour. Boston Zoöl. Soc.*, 1883, 2:11 (Bradford and region, McKean Co., April)—GIBSON, *Ornithologist and Oölogist*, 1883, 8:94 (Renovo, Clinton Co., October)—JACOBS, *Bay State Oölogist*, 1888, 1:31 (Waynesburg, Greene Co., nesting).

Ceophlœus pileatus WARREN, *Birds Pa.*, ed. 2, 1890, 170 (distribution by counties)—[DWIGHT], *Abstr. No. 4 Proc. Linnæan Soc. New York*, 1892, 2 (near Erie, Erie Co., *ex* Sennett *fide* Bacon)—JACOBS, *Summer Birds Greene Co., Pa.*, 1893, 6 (Greene Co., nesting)—RHOADS, *Auk*, 1899, 16:311 (Laughlintown, Westmoreland Co.; Round Island, Clinton Co.).

"Pileated Woodpecker" SIMPSON, *Oölogist*, 1911, 28:54, 72, 165; and 1920, 37:25, 92, 134 (near Warren, Warren Co., nesting, etc.); 1912, 29:329 (head of Tionesta Creek, Warren Co., summer)—MILLER (A. B.), *Bird-Lore*, 1914, 16:38; etc. (Springs, Somerset Co., December)—DICKEY, *Oölogist*, 1914, 31:65 ([Greene Co.], summer), 170 ([Charter Oak], Huntingdon Co., nesting)—SCOVILLE, *Cassinia*, 1920, 23:14 ([Charter Oak, Huntingdon Co.], nesting)—KEESLER, *Oölogist*, 1921, 38:171 (Harrisville, Butler Co., fall)—EASTWOOD, *Bird-Lore*, 1927, 29:272 (Schellsburg, Bedford Co., May, *fide* Manley)—[CHRISTY, ed.], *Cardinal*, 1930, 2:233 (Laurel Hill, east of Ligonier, Westmoreland Co., June, *fide* Reiter); 1933, 3:150 (Cook Forest, Clarion Co.; and Slippery Rock, Butler Co., *fide* Hesse)—COPE and HAWKINS, *Forest Leaves*, 1934, 24:26 (E. Tionesta Forest Reserve, Warren and McKean Co., summer).

"Northern Pileated Woodpecker" SIMPSON, *Oölogist*, 1909, 26:169 (near Warren, Warren Co., nesting)—DICKEY, *Oölogist*, 1913, 30:280 ([Charter Oak], Huntingdon Co., nesting)—HARLOW, *Oölogist*, 1914, 31:82 ([Charter Oak, Huntingdon Co.], nesting)—MILLER (R. F.), *Oölogist*, 1919, 36:155 (Harry's Valley, Huntingdon Co., nesting).

Ceophloeus pileatus abieticola SIMPSON, *Oölogist*, 1910, 27:147 (near Warren, Warren Co., nesting)—BURLEIGH, *Cardinal*, 1932, 3:75 (near Summit, Fayette Co., breeding)—ARTHUR, *Cardinal*, 1934, 3:173 (Barmore Run, near Grove City, Mercer Co.; habits)—CHRISTY, in Bent, *Bull. U. S. Nat. Mus.* no. 174, 1939, 171 ([near Fort Loudon], Fulton Co.; nesting habits).

Phlœotomus pileatus abieticola HARLOW, *Auk*, 1912, 29:471 ("Stone Valley," Huntingdon Co., and Bear Meadows, Centre Co., nesting); 1918, 35:27 (Shingletown, Centre Co.; Monroe Furnace, Mooresville, and Charter Oak, Huntingdon Co., nesting)—RIDGWAY, *Bull. U. S. Nat. Mus.* no. 50, 6, 1914, 156 (measurements), 160 ("Erie" and Lake Pleasant, Erie Co.; Clinton Co.)—BURLEIGH, *Wilson Bull.*, 1924, 36:69 ("State College," Centre Co., resident)—DICKEY, *Oölogist*, 1916, 33:64 (Greene Co., nesting; habits; range)—MILLER (R. F.), *Auk*, 1918, 35:480 (Huntingdon Co., nesting)—CHRISTY and SUTTON, *Cardinal*, 1928, 2:70 and 75 (Cook Forest, Clarion Co., rare resident)—SUTTON, *Ann. Carnegie Mus.*, 1928, 18:145 (Pymatuning Swamp, Crawford Co., resident)—BOULTON, *Cardinal*, 1928, 2:105 (Sandy Lake, Mercer Co., nesting)—BURLEIGH, *Oölogists' Record*, 1929, 9:22 (Charter Oak, Huntingdon Co.)—EASTWOOD, *Wilson Bull.*, 1930, 42:54 ("McGinnis Run" [near Laughlintown], Westmoreland Co., June)—SUTTON, *Cardinal*, 1930, 2:207 (western Pa. localities; habits, etc.)—BURLEIGH, *Wilson Bull.*, 1931, 43:42 ("State College" [Musser's Gap], Centre Co., October; Charter Oak [and Monroe Furnace], Huntingdon Co., nesting).

Phloeotomus pileatus pileatus (error) JACOBS, *Oölogist*, 1933, 50:2 (Greene Co., nesting).

RED-BELLIED WOODPECKER (Plate 13)

CENTURUS CAROLINUS (Linnaeus)

Description—A medium-sized woodpecker, a little smaller than the Flicker; bill about one and one-quarter inches long. *Upperparts* (including wings externally) *barred with black and white*, the rump noticeably whiter; tail black, with a white middle streak; whole crown and nape crimson (male), or crown gray and only the nape crimson (female); *underparts* plain *soiled grayish* (smoke gray), the lower belly more or less washed with crimson, and the flanks and under tail coverts paler (whitish), with some dark markings; bill black.

Range—The generic group to which the Red-bellied Woodpecker belongs is clearly of tropical origin, and only this one species has succeeded in penetrating any distance into the Temperate Zone. It is common in the southern United States as far west as Texas, but becomes less so northward. There its limit coincides in general with that of the Carolinian Fauna, although it seems to be slowly extending its range, as are some other species properly belonging to that Fauna. In western Pennsylvania its center of abundance is in the Ohio Valley and the region just to the south, in Beaver, Allegheny, Washington, and Greene counties. Thence it ranges eastward at least to Chestnut Ridge; and it even enters the Ligonier Valley—at Idlewild, Westmoreland County (Preble). North of the Ohio Valley (away from the river itself) there are no records from nearer than northern Butler County (Jamisonville) and western Mercer County, but whether the species is actually or only apparently absent from the intervening country has not yet been determined. At any rate, it reappears in the vicinity of Sharon and Greenville; and in Crawford County, in the deciduous woodland around Pymatuning Swamp, it is a "rare, and somewhat irregular permanent resident" (Sutton, 1928).

There is reason to believe, judging by analogy, that the Red-bellied Woodpecker was not originally an inhabitant of this section and that its invasion of the area has occurred within comparatively recent times. Although not known to be migratory, in the sense that the Yellow-bellied Sapsucker and the Flicker are migratory, it is accustomed to wander about considerably during the winter months and is just as likely to stray northward as in any other direction. Thus it happens that it has been found during the winter at such unlikely places as Warren; Emporium, Cameron County; and Springs, Somerset County—localities in the plateau region that are beyond its breeding range.[1] It is not known to breed in Erie County, although it has been taken there from October to February. In western New York also, according to E. H. Eaton, it seems to be more numerous in the wintertime. My own experience in Beaver County leads me to believe that it is seen oftener at that season because it wanders more widely and is more conspicuous, while when breeding it is more local and is also quieter. I used to see it there almost every winter but found no evidence of its breeding until May 12, 1902, when, at "Pine Grove," near Industry, I found a pair under circumstances that convinced me that they had a nest near by. Previously, however, on August 28, 1889, I had shot a young bird with downy feathers still showing on its head.

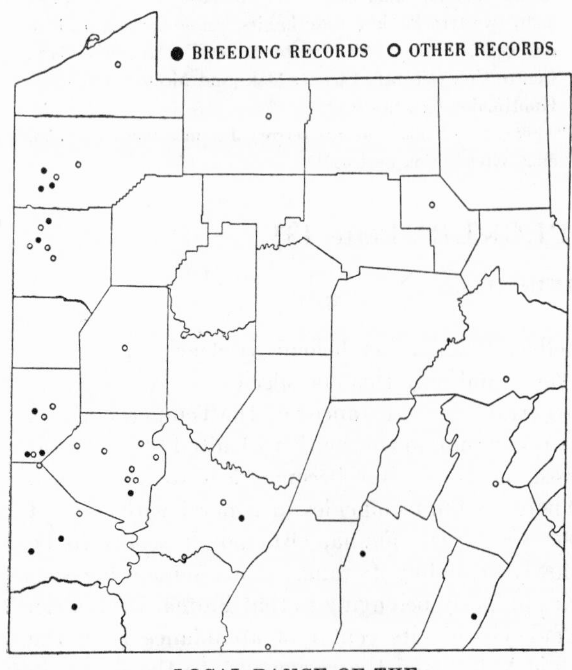

LOCAL RANGE OF THE
RED-BELLIED WOODPECKER

Almost certainly, therefore, the breeding range of this species is being extended by birds that wander northward during the winter months and, with the onset of the breeding season, settle down wherever they may happen to be. The range depends on winter, rather than on summer, conditions—a circumstance that must be true of all our permanent residents. Thus may be explained the fact that the first records from outlying localities for this and certain other species are usually made in the winter season. Our winters are admittedly growing milder—a tendency that may account for the wider dispersal of these birds.

In southeastern Pennsylvania (around Philadelphia) the Red-bellied Woodpecker is likewise a fairly common resident. It is not so well known in the mountain valleys, but, in common with certain other Carolinian species, it apparently ranges across the hill country of Franklin, Fulton, Bedford, Huntingdon, and Centre counties, all the way to the eastern base of the main Allegheny divide (New Paris, Bedford County—Preble). There are but two records (nonbreeding) for State College.

Habits[2]—My field experience with the Red-bellied Woodpecker in southwestern Pennsylvania dates from 1897 and shows that this bird is somewhat local in its distribution and that pairs occur in various sections in areas of deciduous woodland. Although I have seen it a few times (always in win-

[1]Wharton Huber writes me that in the collection of the Academy of Natural Sciences of Philadelphia there is a specimen labeled "Elk County, October 20, 1858, E. D. Cope."
[2]Account contributed by SAMUEL S. DICKEY.

ter) within the corporate limits of Waynesburg (twice in my own back yard), it rarely enters our towns and villages, but is more at home where solitude reigns. It seems to prefer oak woodland for the purpose of nesting and will choose a site in a deep gully or on a steep hillside or cliff above running water. I have found it nesting, however, in an apple orchard, and even in an odd tree standing alone in a pasture. From the crossbarred pattern of its back, it is locally known as "Zebra Woodpecker," and I have heard woodchoppers in Greene County call it "Indian Hen"—a name often given to the Pileated Woodpecker. On entering its haunts one becomes aware of its presence by hearing its peculiar clucking call notes—*tchurr-tchurr-tchurr*—uttered in a characteristic tin-panny voice. Or one may observe it leaving the higher branches of some mighty white oak to pass in undulating course across a valley into a distant tract of woodland. At times during the fall and winter months I have encountered a single red-bellied woodpecker that had joined one of the roving bands of smaller birds common at those seasons and was accompanying them through the woods. Usually the woodpecker would be the first to become aware of my presence and would retire deeper into the forest before my approach.

This woodpecker seeks its insect food both in living and in dead trees and is especially fond of several kinds of black beetles (and their larvae) that infest the trunks and branches. Ants and grasshoppers are also favorite items, and even small tree frogs are sometimes eaten. More than two-thirds of its food, however, is of a vegetable character and is thus similar to that of the Red-headed Woodpecker. Wild fruits and mast constitute the bulk of the vegetable food. In the fall it is not unusual to find red-bellied woodpeckers haunting the tangled masses of grapevines suspended from trees in the forest, or feeding on the fresh and dried fruit. The bird is not known to attack cultivated fruits in this part of the country, as it does in the South.

I first became acquainted with this woodpecker some years ago while I was plodding across the uplands of Greene County in search of nesting red-tailed hawks and other birds of prey. This was in March and early April when the woodpeckers were mating and noisy and were chasing each other through the woods, occasionally pausing to drum upon some resonant stub. Now and then two males would be seen fighting, and sometimes while I was climbing to a hawks' nest a mated pair would show considerable anxiety and move from one tree to another, to a more favorable vantage point nearer the climber. Finding my first nest of this species was just good fortune. One day early in April I had gone to a narrow stretch of mixed timber about two miles north of Waynesburg to examine the nest of a red-tailed hawk, and I was lounging on a bed of dry leaves in a gully, when a pair of red-bellied woodpeckers began to be alarmed at my presence. I noticed that they kept flying towards a large white ash near by, and at once I lost interest in the hawks and began a search for the woodpeckers' abode. A half-hour of close watching from behind a brush heap brought the secret to light. Eventually one of the birds flew to the ash, slid around its main trunk at a point about thirty-five feet from the ground, and disappeared from view on the under side of a large, sloping branch. As soon as I ran to the base of the tree, out popped the red-naped owner from her newly made nest. It was a neat, circular aperture, drilled in resistant live wood, but in such a position that a climber could not very well reach it.

Several seasons intervened before I again found a nest of this species. A day in early April, 1907, found me in an open grove of red and chestnut oaks some three miles southeast of town. All at once I noticed a red-bellied woodpecker quietly, almost stealthily, perform a descending flight from high in a red oak to some chestnut-oak boles. A slight move brought me to within sight of the spot from which the bird had just flown, and there, fifty feet from the ground, was a newly made hole. It seemed folly to disturb the nest so early in the season, and not until May 7 did I investigate. All was silent, with no woodpecker in sight, as I ascended the tree. I discovered that the excavation had been dug in a living branch. Some tools brought along for the purpose served to open the cavity to view. The incubating female was faithful to her charge till I reached the nest, when she turned about and lunged from the entrance. Both birds of the pair then remained near by, behaving in an excited and anxious manner. There were four eggs in this nest, resting on a bed of fine chips at the bottom of the hole; they were slightly incubated.

Other nests have since come to my notice, built in white ash, red oak, black oak, sugar maple, yellow locust, and apple trees. As a rule the site chosen was rather high—in one instance it was sixty-five feet from the ground—but one nest (in an apple tree) was only nine feet up. Almost all the nests were excavated in living branches. One nest was found in a locust standing alone in an open field within sight of a much-traveled highway; but this was an exceptional choice. Another time the birds had made use of a hole originally excavated by a pair of hairy woodpeckers. On June 5, 1920, the parents were very active in feeding their young at this nest, while the latter were uttering a peculiar squeaking and buzzing sound in their demands to be fed.

The eggs of this species are glossy white, as are those of all our woodpeckers, and are usually four in number, but sometimes three or five. They average .99 by .73 inches, and they are laid about the first week in May.

Centurus carolinus TOWNSEND, *Proc. Acad. Nat. Sci. Philadelphia*, 1883, 65 (Latrobe, Westmoreland Co.)—TODD, *Ann. Carnegie Mus.*, 1904, 2:560 (near Erie [Greene Tp.], Erie Co., winter)—TODD, in Bausman, *Hist. Beaver Co., Pa.*, 1904, 2:1199 (Beaver Co., resident)—DICKEY, *Oölogist*, 1913, 30:146 ([Greene Co.], nesting; habits)—HARLOW, *Auk*, 1918, 35:27 (Washington and Greene Co., breeding)—CHRISTY, *Cardinal*, 1923, v. 1, no. 1, [p. 6] (near Sewickley, Allegheny Co.; Frankfort Springs, Beaver Co., resident)—BURLEIGH, *Wilson Bull.*, 1924, 36:132 (State College, Centre Co., March)—SUTTON, *Ann. Carnegie Mus.*, 1928, 18:147 (Crawford Co. localities, resident)—CHRISTY, *Cardinal*, 1929, 2:130 (Sewickley, Allegheny Co., winter); 1931, 3:44 ("Patton's Point," Beaver Co., nesting).

Melanerpes carolinus WARREN, *Birds Pa.*, ed. 2, 1890, 173 (Washington, Washington Co., nesting, *fide* Warrick; distribution by counties)—JACOBS, *Summer Birds Greene Co., Pa.*, 1893, 7 (Greene Co., nesting)—STONE, *Birds E. Pa. and N. J.*, 1894, 96 (Bedford Co., November, *fide* Dillin)—RHOADS, *Auk*, 1899, 16:311 (Allegheny Co., *fide* Link; Emporium, Cameron Co., *fide* Larrabee).

"Red-bellied Woodpecker" [Secretary], *Abstr. Proc. Delaware Valley Orn. Club*, 1900, 3:14 (Waynesburg, Greene Co., winter, *fide* Jacobs)—STONE, *Cassinia*, 1906, 9:42, 44 (Big Cove Tannery, Fulton Co., June)—SIMPSON, *Oölogist*, 1911, 28:72 (Warren, Warren Co., December)—MCCLELLAND, *Am. Mid. Nat.*, 1922, 8:35 (Washington, Washington Co., resident)—JONES, *et al.*, *Bird-Lore*, 1923, 25:25 (Deer Creek, Allegheny Co., December)—SUTTON, *Bird-Lore*, 1923, 25:132, 194; and 1924, 26:56 (Greenville[?], Mercer Co., *fide* Homer)—CHRISTY, *Cardinal*, 1924, v. 1, no. 4, p. 10 (Big Traverse Valley, Beaver Co., June)—CHRISTY and HEGNER, *Bird-Lore*, 1924, 26:30, etc. (Raccoon Creek Valley, Beaver Co., December)—WOOD, *Wilson Bull.*, 1932, 44:239 (State College, Centre Co., January, *fide* Large)—CHRISTY and HEGNER, *Bird-Lore*, 1933, 35:28 (Big Traverse Valley, Beaver Co., December)—ELLIOTT, *Cardinal*, 1934, 3:171 (Raccoon Creek, Beaver Co., December).

RED-HEADED WOODPECKER

MELANERPES ERYTHROCEPHALUS (Linnaeus)

Description—A woodpecker of medium size, with a bill one inch long. *Adult:* whole *head, throat, and upper breast, crimson;* rest of underparts white; back black, the rump and upper tail coverts pure white in abrupt contrast, as well as the overlying part of the wing (secondaries); wings otherwise black; tail black, the outer feathers tipped with white; bill dark. *Immature birds* very different: crown and sides of the head, dark brownish gray, with or without a wash of crimson; the black feathers of the back and wing coverts have pale edgings to the feathers, producing a scaled appearance; broad black bars or spots on the white area of the wings; underparts soiled whitish, with *dusky streaks on the throat, breast, and sides.*

Range—The general range of this woodpecker is considerably more extensive than that of the Red-bellied. In particular, the bird is not so distinctively southern in its predilections and is thus common in the Transition Life Zone, which the other species barely reaches. In many parts of the country, however, its seasonal status and relative abundance have varied so widely from year to year that it has gained a reputation as one of the most erratic of North American birds. The reason for these fluctuations is not fully understood. In the Adirondacks of northern New York the migratory habit of the Red-headed Woodpecker is correlated with a particular food supply, but this relationship is not apparent in our own region. In general, the species is to be classed as a summer resident in western Pennsylvania, but there are a score of localities, from Lake Erie to the northern boundary of Maryland, where it has been irregularly observed during the winter months. Most of these records are of sporadic occurrences that seem to be unrelated to each other, or to any known circumstance. Once common and generally distributed throughout our region, this woodpecker is becoming increasingly rare and local. But even forty or more years ago it was subject to unexplainable aberrations. For instance, during the season of 1890 I saw barely half a dozen individuals, all told, in Beaver County, although the species was common enough the year before and the year following. The slump in its numbers observable in recent years, however, may well be laid to its conflict with civilized conditions.

Migration—Although a hardy bird, the Red-headed Woodpecker is a comparatively late migrant in the spring and does not move north until the warblers make their appearance in late April or early May. Supposed earlier dates of arrival almost certainly pertain to wintering individuals. The dates in thirteen years' records from Beaver vary between April 26 and May 8, the average being May 3. An equally long series of observations made at Sewickley by B. H. Christy yields the same average, although his earliest date is April 22 (1889). In Crawford County the arrival of the species has been noted between May 2 and May 10 (Sutton), and at Erie, on April 30 (1900—Todd). It was "plentiful" at State College on April 28 (1916—Burleigh). Renovo arrival records made by A. K. Pierce are with one exception all in May.

The southward movement takes place in September, but available records are neither many nor entirely dependable. Latest recorded dates are: Erie, October 8, 1900 (Todd); Renovo, October 1, 1916 (Pierce); Beaver, September 28, 1889 (Todd); Hollidaysburg, September 26, 1923 (Berg); Pittsburgh, September 22, 1913 (Burleigh); Sewickley, September 19, 1903 (Christy); Shermansville, Crawford County, October 4, 1925 (Bergstrom); Wilkinsburg, October 3, 1899 (Atkinson). Migration observations at both seasons are necessarily complicated, because of the risk of introducing records of potential wintering birds.

Habits—In almost every large group of birds there are certain forms that are more or less aberrant in haunts and habits—forms that have adopted a different mode of life from that of their relatives and that are therefore conspicuous and peculiarly interesting. Such are the Woodcock among the shore birds, for example, the Osprey among the birds of prey, and the Flicker among the woodpeckers. The Red-headed Woodpecker may rightfully be listed in the same category; for the peculiarities of its feeding habits are no less outstanding.

This woodpecker may be discovered in some exposed position, in the dead top of a tree in a woodland grove, in an isolated tree growing in a field or along the roadside, or on a telegraph pole. In the days when rail fences were much commoner than they are now, they too were utilized as perches. By nature neither shy nor secretive, this bird selects a perch in full view and, heedless of the ensuing publicity, advertises its presence by its gaudy tricolored plumage and its loud call note. If we watch it for a time, we discover that it is not as interested as other woodpeckers are in digging out insects that infest the dead or living wood; instead it uses its perch as a watchtower from which to sally forth, flycatcher-like, and snap up passing insects. At this game it is almost as expert as the Kingbird itself. Often, too, it descends to the ground for grasshoppers, beetles, and other insects of terrestrial habit, and either devours them on the spot or carries them back to its perch. The larger kinds are preferred.

Were this the whole truth about this woodpecker's food, the verdict would naturally be in its favor, but there are other factors that enter into the case. It has been accused of eating the eggs of other birds and even of killing their young, and these charges have been substantiated. It is doubtful, however, that such habits are general. None of the local observers whose notes are before me mentions the practice. As shown by F. E. L. Beal's investigations,[1] most woodpeckers consume more animal food than vegetable, but this species eats twice as much of the latter as it does of the former. Mast—mostly acorns and beechnuts—constitutes a large share of the vegetable food, particularly in the fall and winter months. Like the California

[1]U. S. Department of Agriculture, Biological Survey, *Bulletin*, no. 37, 1911.

Woodpecker of the West, the Red-headed Woodpecker has a habit of storing nuts for future use, driving them into crannies of the wood, either singly or in quantity, and returning for them whenever the need arises. Fruits of numerous varieties, both wild and cultivated, are eaten in large quantities. It is at this point that the Red-head's tastes conflict with the interests of the farmer and of the horticulturist. One of my earliest ornithological observations pertains to the damage the red-headed woodpeckers were inflicting on the crop of early apples on my grandfather's estate near Leasuresville, Butler County. So persistent and active was their work that the fruit of these particular trees (of the variety known as "Early Harvest") was largely rendered unfit for use. Earlier in the season, cherries receive a good deal of attention, and some other cultivated fruits as well. Planting mulberry trees near by would probably prove a counterattraction to these thieving birds. Surely the sins of the Red-headed Woodpecker are not flagrant enough to doom its kind to an untimely end. The woods and orchards that have resounded with the loud, resonant calls of this woodpecker would seem strangely silent in its absence, and no plenitude of fruit could ever quite make up for the passing of this striking bird.

E. H. Forbush has written concerning this species (1927): "It is a rather noisy bird during the breeding season, and often the sexes pursue one another with loud cries and excited flutterings. At times they are active and playful and amuse themselves with drumming on various objects; at other times they are quiet and sedentary." Nesting begins directly after the birds arrive. In Greene County, J. W. Jacobs has found nests in orchard trees and in sycamores along streams. My own observations in Beaver County lead me to think that locusts and oaks are the favorite trees. As it happens, I have never succeeded in locating a nest that was easy of access. In Crawford County, according to G. M. Sutton (1928), this bird nests in high, dead stubs, mostly oaks. He thinks that it selects harder wood than that chosen by any other species of woodpecker: "It spurns the soft wood of the dead hemlocks and black birches, and selects the toughest oak, which is extremely hard to cut with a knife or hatchet." Telegraph poles along the roads are not infrequently chosen. It has even been known to nest in the dead top of a red oak in a vacant lot in the heart of the North Side of Pittsburgh (Johnston). May 25 is an average date for full sets of eggs in Greene County, but fresh sets have been found in Centre County as late as July 10 (Harlow). Four to six eggs are laid, five being the usual number. They are pure glossy white and average .99 by .76 inches. During August and September, and until the time when southward migration begins, family groups composed of adults and young birds in the mottled plumage are much in evidence, especially in beech woodland, where they feed actively and noisily on the beech mast.

The flight of this woodpecker is undulating and jerky, and the birds fly so low that they are often killed by automobiles on the highways. From the naturalists' point of view, the diminution in numbers due to this cause and to unwonted persecution is deplorable.

Melanerpes erythrocephalus Townsend, *Proc. Acad. Nat. Sci. Philadelphia*, 1883, 65 (Latrobe, Westmoreland Co.)—Teulon, *Jour. Boston Zoöl. Soc.*, 1883, 2:10 (Bradford, McKean Co., resident)—Dwight, *Auk*, 1892, 9:135 (Cresson, Cambria Co., June)—Todd, *Auk*, 1893, 10:39 (between Two Lick and Homer City, Indiana Co., June), 44 (Coalport, Clearfield Co., June)—Jacobs, *Summer Birds Greene Co., Pa.*, 1893, 7 (Greene Co., nesting)—Baily, *Auk*, 1896, 13:293 (Clarion River, near Williamsville, Elk Co., June–July)—Todd, *Ann. Carnegie Mus.*, 1904, 2:560 (Erie, Erie Co., summer; occasional in winter)—Todd, in Bausman, *Hist. Beaver Co., Pa.*, 1904, 2:1199 (Beaver Co., summer; rare in winter)—Keim, *Cassinia*, 1905, 8:38 (Port Allegany, McKean Co., summer)—Pitcairn, *Auk*, 1908, 25:476 (Allegheny, Allegheny Co.)—Harlow, *Auk*, 1912, 29:472 (State College, Centre Co., nesting); 1918, 35:27 (Centre and Warren Co.)—Stone, *Cassinia*, 1915, 18:55 (State College, Centre Co., winter, *fide* Mason); 1920, 23:34 (Altoona, Blair Co., winter, *fide* McGraw)—Christy, *Cardinal*, 1923, v. 1, no. 1, [p. 6] (Sewickley, Allegheny Co., breeding; accidental in winter)—Burleigh, *Wilson Bull.*, 1923, 35:87 (Allegheny Co., nesting); 1924, 36:69; and 1931, 43:42 (State College, Centre Co., nesting)—Burleigh, *Cardinal*, 1932, 3:76 (Uniontown and Chalk Hill, Fayette Co., nesting).

"Red-headed Woodpecker" Jacobs, *Hoosier Nat.*, 1887, 2:78 (Waynesburg, Greene Co., occasional in winter)—Van Ostrand, *Osprey*, 1896, 1:38 (Morganza, Washington Co., fall; food)—Stone, *Cassinia*, 1906, 9:43 (McConnellsburg, Fulton Co., June)—Pitcairn, *Bird-Lore*, 1907, 9:155 (Riverview Park, Allegheny Co., nesting)—Simpson, *Oölogist*, 1912, 29:329 (head of Tionesta Creek, Warren Co., summer)—McConnell, *Oölogist*, 1918, 35:150 (McKeesport, Allegheny Co.)—McClelland, *Am. Mid. Nat.*, 1922, 8:36 (Washington, Washington Co., summer)—Street, *Cassinia*, 1923, 24:13 (Greencastle to Ft. Loudon, Franklin Co., June)—

Sutton, *Bird-Lore*, 1924, 26:122 (Wildwood, Allegheny Co., winter), 190 (Brown Station, Allegheny Co., March, *fide* Blair)—Eastwood, *Bird-Lore*, 1925, 27:337 (Wildwood, Allegheny Co., and Canonsburg, etc., Washington Co., July), 406 (Edgebrook, Allegheny Co., September); 1926, 28:136 (Harmarville, Allegheny Co., January, *fide* Squier), 137 (Deer Creek, Allegheny Co., February, *fide* Squier), 273 (Ridgway, Elk Co., May, *fide* Alsop).

Melanerpes erythrocephalus erythrocephalus Oberholser, *Bird-Lore*, 1926, 29:411 (Beaver, Beaver Co., migration)—Sutton, *Ann. Carnegie Mus.*, 1928, 18:146 (Crawford Co. localities, summer).

YELLOW-BELLIED SAPSUCKER (Plate 13)

SPHYRAPICUS VARIUS VARIUS (Linnaeus)

Description—A woodpecker of medium size, a little smaller than the Red-headed; bill less than one inch long. *Adult male:* upperparts black, the back and wings spotted with white, the wings having a large white patch on the coverts; crown and throat crimson, superciliary line whitish, bordered above and below by a black stripe; a broad whitish line from the base of the bill down either side of the neck to the sides of the breast, and below this a *black stripe*, spreading out on the *breast* into a *broad black patch; underparts* white, more or less *tinged with yellow*, the sides and flanks mottled with black; tail mostly black, with a white stripe down the middle. *Adult female* similar to the male, but throat white, and crown usually black (but sometimes crimson). The *immature bird* lacks the distinctive pattern of the head and underparts; these are brown, with dusky mottling; the belly is merely yellow-tinged. Older birds exhibit plumage that is variously intermediate between that of the immature bird and that of the adult.

Range—The typical or eastern race of the Yellow-bellied Sapsucker breeds in the Canadian Life Zone and in the upper part of the Transition Life Zone from Alberta to Cape Breton Island and southward along the Appalachian highlands. In Massachusetts its breeding range is chiefly confined to the Berkshires (Forbush); in New York it is confined to the Adirondacks and the Catskills, although a few birds breed also in the elevated areas near the Pennsylvania boundary (Eaton). In our region its known breeding range occupies the highlands west of the main Allegheny divide, as well as an outlying (but perhaps not disconnected) area in the northwestern counties. According to my observations, it is (or at least was) common in June in Potter County, especially along the highway between Sweden Valley and Cherry Spring. It was common also at Tamarack Swamp, Clinton County, and I once found a nest near the summit of the mountain south of Renovo. R. B. Simpson says that in Warren County it is found only as a transient in the river valley and that it retires to the hill country to breed—it is numerous, for example, at the headwaters of Tionesta Creek. While the available records are not many (a scarcity that seems to suggest a distribution somewhat local in character), they suffice to carry the breeding range southward into Cambria and Somerset counties, all the way to the Maryland line. At Springs, on the southern edge of Somerset County, the Sapsucker was formerly a regular and rather common breeding bird, but in recent years, according to A. B. Miller, it has virtually disappeared. E. A. Preble found it along the west slope of Negro Mountain in June, 1893. It is not

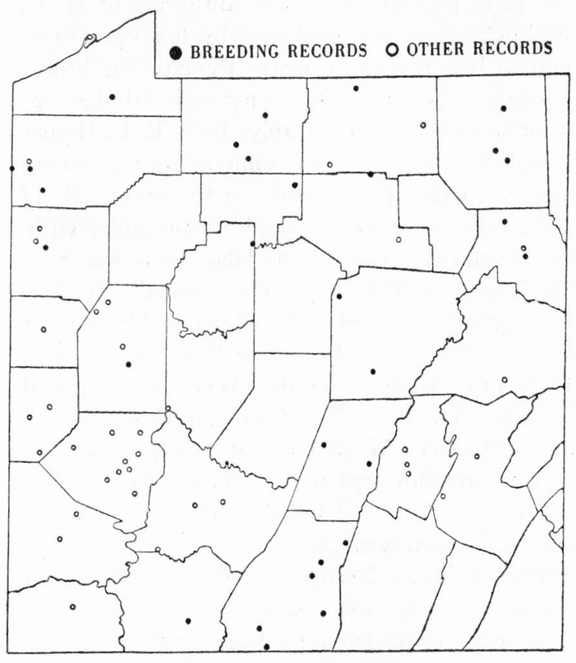

LOCAL RANGE OF THE YELLOW-BELLIED SAPSUCKER

known to breed on Chestnut Ridge, although it was recorded by T. D. Burleigh from Chalk Hill, in high country east of the ridge proper.

It is odd that this species has not been found breeding in the mountains east of the main Allegheny divide, where several other birds of nearly similar distribution and faunal affinities are common enough. Were it to summer anywhere in that region, surely it would be in the wilds of northern Huntingdon County; yet the several observers who have worked this area have never encountered it there. C. W. G. Eifrig noted it at Johnsburg, Somerset County, on June 4, 1900, on a spur of the Alleghenies. A sight record that I received from Fulton County (Phelps) I consider very doubtful. There are, however, a few records from these southeastern counties made during the season of migration.

Years ago (on June 28, 1899) I was not surprised to discover a pair of yellow-bellied sapsuckers in Pymatuning Swamp, near Hartstown, and I naturally assumed that the breeding range of the species in that region was confined to this boreal island. Since then nests have actually been found there by G. M. Sutton and more recently by L. E. Hicks (at Hemlock Island). (A supposed breeding record from Meadville referred to by the former observer, on the authority of H. C. Kirkpatrick, is not confirmed by his manuscript notes.) It now seems that the Pymatuning breeding area of this sapsucker is not so isolated as has been supposed. Early in July, 1895, F. L. Homer found the species "rather common" in the swamp near the edge of the woods on the north side of Lake Le Bœuf, and a young bird was collected in the bottomland east of the lake. Thus was Sennett's surmise that it bred occasionally in Erie County duly confirmed. In addition, Mr. Homer later took a young bird near his home at New Hamburg, Mercer County. When the wooded swamps of eastern Crawford and Erie counties and of western Warren County shall have been more thoroughly explored, the Yellow-bellied Sapsucker may be found breeding there also—a circumstance that would be in accord with the range of the species as already worked out in this latter county. The records just cited necessarily conform with those from adjacent parts of Ohio.[1] There is one other and very surprising breeding record, so isolated that I regard it as referring to a sporadic instance. It pertains to a nest found by P. W. Roth near Butler on May 27, 1895, and reported to me at the time.

Except as aforesaid, this woodpecker occurs mainly as a transient in the western third of our region. In some years it is very common, especially in the fall, and even in those places where it has been recorded as breeding it is far more numerous during the migrations. As a winter resident in our region it is rare and irregular, but has been found as such at several localities, mostly in the Ohio Valley. It has been detected in winter, too, as far north as Hartstown and as far south and at as high an altitude as Springs, so that apparently it winters almost anywhere on occasion.

Migration—The northward movement of this species begins in the South in March but does not reach Pennsylvania as a rule until the end of that month or early in April. My earliest date for the first migrant at Beaver is March 31 (1907), and my latest is April 18 (1890). The height of the migration occurs sometime during the second or third week in April, and for a few days the birds may be exceedingly common. Most of them leave by the end of the month, but during some seasons a few may linger a little later (May 8, 1889). Collation of the records from other places gives these statements a more general significance. Earliest arrival dates supplied by other observers are: Pittsburgh, March 22, 1913 (Burleigh); Morganza, Washington County, March 29, 1897 (Van Ostrand); State College, March 30, 1916 and 1919 (Burleigh); Springs, Somerset County, March 15, 1937 (Miller); Sewickley, March 26, 1922 (Christy); Renovo, April 5, 1903 and 1907 (Pierce); Lakemont, Blair County, March 31, 1918 (McGraw); Erie, March 31, 1893 (Bacon); Warren, April 11, 1889 and 1890 (Simpson).

The fall movement begins in September and lasts for two or three weeks. Thus, in the fall of 1900 the Yellow-bellied Sapsucker was first noted at Presque Isle on September 18, was abundant on September 26, and was last seen on October 12. At Pymatuning Swamp the first influx of migrants was noted on September 17 in 1925, and the last bird was seen on October 15 (Sutton). Within the city limits of Pittsburgh the species has been noted between September 22 and October 11 (1913—

[1]Compare L. E. Hicks, *Wilson Bulletin*, 1933, 45:184.

Burleigh). Several of A. K. Pierce's "last-seen" dates for Renovo are in late October, but there is the possibility that these records may have been based on potential winter residents. Mr. Burleigh has seen this bird at State College as late as October 14 (1915), and also in November.

Habits—The Yellow-bellied Sapsucker is by no means the least interesting member of its family. Although given a bad name by reason of its peculiar feeding habits and although undoubtedly deserving the epithet of "Sapsucker," it must nevertheless play a useful part in the economy of nature, in spite of the seemingly destructive character of its activities. While the woodpeckers as a class are truly conservators of the forests in which they live, feeding on the tree-boring insects that infest the bark and wood, the Sapsucker, on the other hand, feeds primarily on the sap, the very life-blood of the tree, and on the inner bark, the cambium layer, which is essential to the tree's well-being. The net result of the Sapsucker's operations is thus to kill trees rather than to conserve them.

Rambling through an orchard in the spring, one may find that a tree that was healthy enough the previous fall has many dead branches and only a few sickly leaves on the others. On closer examination one finds rings of punctures, commencing on the main trunk and extending for some distance up the larger branches. Each ring is about six inches distant from the one below it, and the punctures are close together and extend through the bark, so that the effect is the same as it would be had the tree been girdled with an ax. These rings are the earmarks of the Sapsucker's work, performed during the interludes in its northward migration, at the season when the sap is flowing freely. Orchard and shade trees persistently treated thus by the Sapsucker are eventually total losses, but fortunately they are not frequently attacked. Few if any of the forest trees are exempt, but the soft-barked kinds are the ones that suffer oftenest—poplar, birch, maple, tulip tree, wild cherry, and white pine. Instead of rings, the Sapsucker sometimes drills a series of squarish holes in a regular up-and-down pattern, or it may even loosen the bark over a considerable area.

Through the winter months the Sapsucker is so quiet and inconspicuous and adopts such solitary habits that it may easily be overlooked. In migration it is a familiar but rather unobtrusive figure in our woodlands and often invades orchards and the shade trees of parks and streets. Although a tract of woods may harbor many sapsuckers, each bird seems to work independently. If several come together, it is not because of any flocking instinct, but because of a common attraction. W. C. Grimm (1925), referring to the partiality of the species for the hop hornbeam near Pittsburgh in the spring of 1925, says that often two and sometimes three individuals visited the same tree trunk at once. The sap was flowing freely from the drilled holes, where the birds were feeding in silence. When thus engaged they are not easily frightened away and are sometimes heedless, if not actually stupid. Two birds that I once watched came down a hickory tree to within four feet of me. It is not difficult to approach a sapsucker, but the bird usually sidles around to the opposite side of the tree and thereafter takes pains to keep the trunk between itself and the observer. In passing from one tree to another it flies with a peculiar "floating" motion, suggesting the aerial maneuvers of a flying squirrel.

Evidently this woodpecker migrates at night; for during the height of its season in spring and fall it suddenly appears in numbers in places where the day before no birds were to be seen. The males precede the females. Upon reaching its breeding grounds it abandons its quiet ways and at once begins mating and nesting. It is a loud and persistent drummer at this time and has been known to make use of other than natural sounding boards. Mr. Simpson says: "Once in June, while we were camping on Wildcat Run, near the head of Tionesta Creek, a male sapsucker used to come every morning about daylight and beat a loud tattoo on our shanty roof; he was an excellent alarm clock." This woodpecker also has a variety of odd notes that have been variously described as squealing, whining, and mewing. The first time I ever heard these cries I mistook them for those of the Sharp-shinned Hawk. Referring to the birds' behavior during the breeding season, Dr. Sutton (1928) says: "In late May and June the mewing cry was familiar and they occasionally indulged in strange courtship antics, flashing through the tops of the trees, calling excitedly in tones resembling those of a Flicker, and dancing about with wings and tail spread in a manner utterly foreign to the usually stolid bearing of migrant individuals."

More than forty years ago, in the month of June, I encountered the Sapsucker in the virgin forest that then covered parts of western Cambria County. In the northern counties, however, it is found during the summer in scattered pairs—not so frequently in the "big woods" as in the slashings and cut-over or burned areas, where many tall dead stubs have been left standing. Its nest-holes are drilled in these stubs, but often at such a height that they are virtually impossible to reach, as the stubs are rotten and treacherous. The only two nests that I ever found were in such situations, not over twenty feet from the ground. The nests can readily be located by watching the birds. They become very uneasy and soon alight on the nest-tree to see if all is well. The eggs are laid sometime in May, but I am unable to cite exact dates from local sources. Other writers, however, say that the sets number from five to seven and that the eggs are pure white, measuring (on an average) .88 by .67 inches. Young birds in the nest make a peculiar reiterated buzzing sound that is very apt to attract the attention of the passer-by.

Wherever a pair of sapsuckers settle for the summer they at once begin to tap certain trees in the vicinity for sap, and thereafter they visit them at regular intervals. These "orchards," as they have been called, are used year after year, as long as the mutilated trees survive. After the young leave the nest they are led to the source of supplies and initiated into the art of drilling for sap. Certain kinds of insects—ants in particular—attracted by the flow of sap, are eaten in great numbers. Like the Red-headed Woodpecker, the Sapsucker sometimes captures insects in flight. But by reason of the peculiar formation of its tongue, the bird is not fitted, as are our other woodpeckers, for capturing wood-boring insects, and these do not figure in its diet. Wild fruits of various kinds constitute a large percentage of its food in the late summer and fall months. I decidedly do not favor putting this species on the proscribed list because of the damage it does to forest trees, and feel that only when it attacks orchard or shade trees should protective measures be taken.

Picus varius Wied, *Reise in Innere Nord-America*, 1839, 1:130 (Ebensburg, Cambria Co., September).

Sphyropicus varius Townsend, *Proc. Acad. Nat. Sci. Philadelphia*, 1883, 65 (Latrobe, Westmoreland Co.)—Teulon, *Jour. Boston Zoöl. Soc.*, 1883, 10 (Bradford, McKean Co., summer).

Sphyrapicus varius Warren, *Birds Pa.*, ed. 2, 1890, 168 (distribution by counties)—Baily, *Auk*, 1896, 13:292, 293 (Williamsville, Elk Co., June–July)—Todd, *Ann. Carnegie Mus.*, 1904, 2:559 (Erie and Presque Isle, Erie Co., transient)—Todd, in Bausman, *Hist. Beaver Co., Pa.*, 1904, 2:1199 (Beaver Co., transient).

"Yellow-bellied Woodpecker" Simpson, *Oölogist*, 1909, 26:169; 1911, 28:72 (Warren, Warren Co., nesting); 1912, 29:329 (head of Tionesta Creek, Warren Co., summer).

"Yellow-bellied Sapsucker" McConnell, *Oölogist*, 1918, 35:150 (McKeesport, Allegheny Co.)—Sutton, *Bird-Lore*, 1924, 26:190 (Wilkinsburg, Allegheny Co., *fide* Turner; Wildwood, Allegheny Co., *fide* Tracht, spring)—Grimm, *Bird-Lore*, 1925, 27:329 (Pittsburgh, Allegheny Co., spring; feeding habits)—Eastwood, *Bird-Lore*, 1925, 27:406 (Dixmont, Allegheny Co., September, *fide* Reiter); 1926, 28:207; and 1927, 29:196 (Pittsburgh region, Allegheny Co., migration), 197 (Springs, Somerset Co., April, *fide* Miller)—Boulton, *Bird-Lore*, 1928, 30:196 (McKinley Park, Allegheny Co., April, *fide* Held), 271 (Industry, Beaver Co., May, *fide* Reiter and Squier)—Elliott, *Cardinal*, 1934, 3:171 (Raccoon Creek, Beaver Co., December)—Cope and Hawkins, *Forest Leaves*, 1934, 24:26 (E. Tionesta Forest Reserve, Warren and McKean Co., summer).

Sphyrapicus varius varius Christy, *Cardinal*, 1923, v. 1, no. 1, [p. 6] (Sewickley, Allegheny Co., transient)—Burleigh, *Wilson Bull.*, 1923, 35:87 (Allegheny Co., transient); 1924, 36:77 (State College, Centre Co., transient)—Christy and Sutton, *Cardinal*, 1928, 2:70 (Cook Forest, Clarion Co., June)—Sutton, *Ann. Carnegie Mus.*, 1928, 18:143 (Crawford Co. localities, summer; occasional in winter)—Oberholser, *Bird-Lore*, 1928, 30:253 (Renovo, Clinton Co., and Beaver, Beaver Co., migration)—Burleigh, *Cardinal*, 1932, 3:76 (Chalk Hill, Fayette Co., breeding).

"Sapsucker" Clarke, *Bird-Lore*, 1930, 32:423 (State College, Centre Co., winter).

EASTERN HAIRY WOODPECKER (Plate 13)

DRYOBATES VILLOSUS VILLOSUS (Linnaeus)

Description—A medium-sized *black and white* woodpecker, with a *bill* one and one-quarter inches long (*as long as the head*). Upperparts black, with a broad white stripe down the back and white spots on the wings; head black, with a white stripe over the eye and another from the gape to the sides of the neck; below this a black band, which broadens behind on the sides of the neck; the nape has a crimson band (male) or is plain black like the top of the head (female); *tail* black above (except for white edges), white below (*unbarred*); underparts white. *Immature birds* resemble the adults, but the top of the head is more or less crimson in both sexes.

Range—The Hairy Woodpecker inhabits the wooded regions of North America at large and ranges north to Alaska in the West and to Labrador in the East. The typical race, to which the birds from Pennsylvania belong, is distributed throughout the eastern United States and southern Canada, west to the Great Plains and south to the Gulf states. It occurs as a fairly common resident wherever there is any forest left. It is not entirely sedentary, however, and indulges in considerable wandering during the winter; for many observers have remarked that it is more numerous, or at least more noticeable, at that season, when it frequents the orchards and the shade trees around houses. It is one of the species that figure prominently in *Bird-Lore*'s "Christmas Census" reports. At Pymatuning Swamp, however, it is said to be less common, and sometimes even rare, in winter.

Habits—The accepted name for this species is a misnomer, since it is no more "hairy" than its smaller cousin is "downy." By uninformed persons it is often called "Sapsucker"—a name properly applied to a species that indulges in very different activities, in which the Hairy Woodpecker does not share. Indeed, from an economic standpoint this is one of the most useful birds of the entire family. As shown by stomach examinations, more than three-fourths of its food consists of insects, namely, the larvae of wood-boring beetles, as well as ants, caterpillars, and weevils—nearly all destructive kinds. Wild fruits and seeds, including mast, make up the bulk of its vegetable food. The score is thus overwhelmingly in its favor, and it deserves the fullest protection at all times.

Compared with its smaller relative, the Downy Woodpecker, this species is on the whole a more active and restless bird, rather timid and not always easy to approach. As a rule it is found in pairs. It is essentially a bird of the deep woods (the higher and more extensive the better), but in the wintertime it often appears in orchards and may even come to feeding-stations for a dole. It prefers to work rather high in the trees and seldom descends to the ground as the Downy Woodpecker sometimes does. The two species have many traits in common, however, and are sometimes hard to tell apart, although the difference in size is noticeable when they are together. In addition, the Hairy has a longer bill (as long as the head), and its tail lacks any dark barring below. The call notes of the two are very similar, but that of the Hairy is considerably louder and more penetrating. The latter is in general noisier and altogether more conspicuous. Besides its regular call of one syllable—somewhat similar to that of the Robin—it has a prolonged, insistent, rattling cry of alarm, which sometimes rises almost to a shriek as the bird excitedly swings from tree to tree through the woods. Its flight is rather rapid but undulating, with a jerky, labored flapping that is audible at some distance; it is seldom protracted. C. E. Bendire writes: "Like all Woodpeckers, it is an expert climber, and moves rapidly up and around trees in short hops; it is equally easy for it to go backward or sidewise, and it is astonishing how readily it can move in any direction. The strong feet and sharp claws enable it to hold firmly to the bark, and the stiff, spiney [*sic*] tail feathers also come in play while it is at work, acting as a support for the body which is well thrown back when a blow is delivered with its powerful chisel-like bill."[1]

The Hairy Woodpecker is a strong, hardy species, able to withstand severe winter conditions and breeding unusually early in the season. March finds the males engaged in drumming. Selecting a resonant dead limb in the top of a tall tree, they use it for a sounding board on which to hammer out a loud tattoo; the successive blows, rapidly delivered, give the same impression as that made by a rattle. B. H. Christy has written me the following account of the courtship activities: "The courtship antics, which resemble those of other woodpeckers, begin very early, even in the winter. I have in mind such a performance, witnessed on the third day of February. My attention was caught first by the loud, reiterated calls, *ca-ca-ca-ca-ca*, which caused me to think of hawks—the Sparrow Hawk, perhaps, or the Sharp-shinned. These cries came from some tall trees near the edge of a heavy stand of hardwood. Following them up I soon saw the birds fly, and then stopped and watched, with field glasses ready. The birds, presently relieved

[1]*Life Histories of North American Birds*, 1895, 2:47.

of alarm, alighted on neighboring perches on upright branches in a treetop. Then, with heads straightened and bills turned up, they began a veritable dance, hitching and jerking, tipping this way and that, in unison, and with a slight flicking of wings and tail. This display was accompanied by the occasional loud, rapidly repeated cry that had at first attracted me."

Both sexes work at digging the nest-hole, which usually takes about a week to complete. Any kind of tree will answer, and sometimes a living branch is chosen, but in such instances the heart will prove to be decayed and soft. I once found a nest in an apple tree in an orchard, and other observers have found them in similar situations, on one occasion as low as six feet from the ground. Usually, however, they are placed much higher, even up to eighty feet. At Pymatuning Swamp, where the species finds conditions especially to its liking and is correspondingly abundant, G. M. Sutton located no less than twenty-six nests during the season of 1922. They were drilled near the tops of dead trees, which nearly always stood in water and which were often too weak to be climbed. The average height of the nests was over thirty feet. Of his extensive experience there, he writes (1928): "It may safely be stated that mated pairs begin drilling their nests with the first warm days of spring, probably in latter March. By April 15 probably all the first sets of eggs have been laid, so that during the ensuing three weeks young birds may be looked for. If one would find the eggs of this species in this latitude he must, therefore, search early. Probably second broods are occasionally reared, although this may depend upon the success of the first brood." S. S. Dickey has taken fresh eggs in Greene County as early as April 11, and R. C. Harlow once found a nest with young in Huntingdon County (Charter Oak) on May 2.

The nest itself is a neatly hollowed-out cavity, with a perfectly round entrance just large enough to allow the bird to pass in and out. Often it is drilled beneath an overhanging limb and always on the under side of an inclined trunk or branch, as a protection from rain. It generally runs straight in for about three inches and then downward for a foot or more, gradually enlarging toward the base. The eggs are laid on the chips left at the bottom; they vary from three to five in number and, like all woodpeckers' eggs, are pure glossy white in color. The average size is .93 by .71 inches. The incubating bird sits very closely and sometimes has to be lifted bodily from the nest when one desires to examine it. The male usually excavates another hole near by in which to roost, and presumably these holes are used for roosting at other seasons as well. The young in the nest utter a continuous low purring sound, very characteristic but hard to describe. After they leave the nest they accompany their parents for several weeks, until fully able to care for themselves. In October, after the molt, the Hairy Woodpecker is clean and trim in fresh plumage, but its feathers soon become soiled and worn by contact with the forest trees, and during the breeding season the birds often present a more or less dilapidated appearance.

Picus villosus Wied, *Reise in Innere Nord-America*, 1839, 1:130 (Ebensburg, Cambria Co., September)—Townsend, *Proc. Acad. Nat. Sci. Philadelphia*, 1883, 65 (Latrobe, Westmoreland Co., resident)—Teulon, *Jour. Boston Zoöl. Soc.*, 1883, 2:10 (Bradford, McKean Co., April and November).

Dryobates villosus Todd, *Auk*, 1893, 10:44 (Coalport, Clearfield Co., June)—Jacobs, *Summer Birds Greene Co., Pa.*, 1893, 6 (Greene Co., nesting)—Baily, *Auk*, 1896, 13:293 (Williamsville, Elk Co., June–July)—Cope, *Cassinia*, 1902, 5:14 (Clinton and Potter Co., June)—Todd, *Ann. Carnegie Mus.*, 1904, 2:559 (Erie and Presque Isle, Erie Co., resident) —Todd, in Bausman, *Hist. Beaver Co., Pa.*, 1904, 2:1199 (Beaver Co., resident)—Keim, *Cassinia*, 1905, 8:38 (Port Allegany, McKean Co., summer)—Forrest, *Oölogist*, 1911, 28:114 (Washington, Washington Co., resident).

"Hairy Woodpecker" Stone, *Cassinia*, 1906, 9:44 (Scrub Ridge, west of McConnellsburg, Fulton Co., June)—Simpson, *Oölogist*, 1909, 26:26; etc. (Warren, Warren Co., nesting, etc.)—Miller (A. B.), *Bird-Lore*, 1910, 12:29; etc. (Springs, Somerset Co., December)—Dickey, *Oölogist*, 1911, 28:74 (near Waynesburg, Greene Co., nesting)—Gerberding, *Bird-Lore*, 1912, 14:29 (Greenville, Mercer Co., December)—Simpson, *Oölogist*, 1912, 29:329 (head of Tionesta Creek, Warren Co., summer)—McConnell, *Oölogist*, 1918, 35:150 (McKeesport, Allegheny Co.)—Miller (R. F.), *Oölogist*, 1919, 36:155 (Charter Oak, Huntingdon Co., nesting) —McConnell, *Bird-Lore*, 1920, 22:31; etc. (Emsworth, Allegheny Co., December)—Stahl, *et al.*, *Bird-Lore*, 1921, 23:18 (Forest Hills to Deer Creek, Allegheny Co., December) —Nicholson, *Bird-Lore*, 1921, 23:18; etc. (Grove City, Mercer Co., December)—Street, *Cassinia*, 1923, 24:12 (Greencastle to Ft. Loudon, Franklin Co., June)—Christy, *Cardinal*, 1924, v. 1, no. 4, p. 10 (Big Traverse Valley, Beaver Co., June)—Berkheimer, *Bird-Lore*, 1933, 35:27; etc. (near Osterburg, Bedford Co., December)—Clarke, *Bird-Lore*, 1930, 32:422 (State College, Centre Co., habits).

Dryobates villosus villosus Oberholser, *Proc. U. S. Nat. Mus.*, 1911, 40:598 (western Pa. localities)—Harlow, *Auk*, 1912, 29:471 (Pine Grove Mills, Nittany Mountain, McBride Gap,

Waddle, Centre Co.; "Stone Valley," Huntingdon Co.)—Ridgway, *Bull. U. S. Nat. Mus.* no. 50, part 6, 1914, 201 (mountains of Pa.; measurements)—Christy, *Cardinal*, 1923, v. 1, no. 1, [p. 6] (Sewickley, Allegheny Co., resident)—Burleigh, *Wilson Bull.*, 1923, 35:87 (Allegheny Co., resident; nesting); 1931, 43:41 (State College [and Scotia], Centre Co., resident; nesting)—Christy and Sutton, *Cardinal*, 1928, 2:70, 75 (Cook Forest, Clarion Co., resident; nesting)—Sutton, *Ann. Carnegie Mus.*, 1928, 18:141 (Pymatuning Swamp and region, Crawford Co., nesting; habits)—Burleigh, *Cardinal*, 1932, 3:76 (Chestnut Ridge, near Uniontown, Fayette Co., breeding).

NORTHERN DOWNY WOODPECKER (Plate 13)

DRYOBATES PUBESCENS MEDIANUS (Swainson)

Description—Our *smallest woodpecker;* coloration *black and white,* similar to that of the Hairy Woodpecker except that the outer *tail feathers* are *barred with black;* much *smaller* than that species, and *bill* still *smaller* in proportion, obviously *shorter than the head.*

Range—The Downy Woodpecker in one form or another ranges over the whole of temperate North America (except of course in desert and treeless regions), northward to and including the Canadian Life Zone. The race *medianus* is a common permanent resident throughout western Pennsylvania. So far as our region is concerned the species is perhaps more sedentary than others of its family; there is no obvious migration.

Habits—With the exception of the Flicker, none of our woodpeckers is so common and familiar as the little Downy, often called "Sapsucker," although it has nothing in common with the Yellow-bellied species properly so named. Some differences of opinion exist as to its sap-drinking propensities. Certain observers have reported it feeding on sap flowing from holes in trees, but whether the holes were drilled by this species or by the Yellow-bellied is questionable. I can offer only one small bit of evidence. Years ago (in 1887), early in April, I discovered a downy woodpecker feeding on the sap that was flowing freely from many small holes bored in the bark of a Norway spruce. I naturally assumed that these holes were the work of this bird, since they were in an irregular cluster and not arranged in rings around the trunk, as are those made by the Yellow-bellied Sapsucker. But since the latter species must have been passing through the region at this very time, it is quite possible that the downy was merely taking toll from holes originally drilled by the other. Stomach examinations prove that the Downy Woodpecker is one of the most valuable of our small birds. More than three-fourths of its food consists of animal matter, mostly insects. The larvae of wood-boring beetles, as well as weevils, ants, caterpillars, and scale-insects, comprise the bulk of this type of food. It is one of the few birds known to eat the pupa and larva of the destructive codling moth. Its vegetable food consists of wild fruits, waste grain (a very little), and mast. The berries of the poison ivy are one of its staple foods in winter, and it no doubt spreads the seeds of this noxious plant to some extent.

Unlike its larger cousin, the Hairy Woodpecker, which is more or less shy and suspicious and keeps to the woods, the little Downy is fearless and confiding, and even comes to dooryard trees in its quest for food. There is seldom an orchard of any size that is not regularly visited by one or more of these birds, and often a pair may elect to take up housekeeping duties in such territory. Leaving the heavy timber to the larger woodpeckers, the Downy prefers the edges of woods, open groves, shrubbery along streams, and second-growth woodland. It likes to hunt its food in the branches of the trees and climbs up and around them with ease and dexterity. It may often be seen on tall dead weeds, digging for gall insects, and sometimes it even feeds from the ground. Industrious in habit and rather stolid in disposition, it does not seem to mind being watched while at work, and may often be closely approached. Except in the breeding season it is a rather solitary bird so far as its own kind is concerned, but is wont to associate with black-capped chickadees, tufted titmice, white-breasted nuthatches, and other such kindred spirits as they rove in straggling companies through the woods and orchards in search of food. With them, too, it may readily be induced to come to feeding-stations in the wintertime, and it appreciates a chunk of suet fastened to a tree, or a bone with some meat adhering. Winter has no terrors for the Downy Woodpecker. In the fall it digs a hole in some dead branch, where it remains during the hours of darkness, sheltered from the cold and safe from the attack of any wandering owl. In dark and stormy weather, too, it keeps to its snug retreat, but daytime usually finds it abroad on its tireless quest, and its waking hours are filled with activity.

The ordinary call of this species is a sharp alarm-note, resembling that of its relative, the Hairy Woodpecker, but not so loud. As spring comes on, the males begin to drum. They select for this purpose the stub of a dry, seasoned limb, to which they resort day after day. Probably each individual has its favorite stand, although it may drum indiscriminately whenever it comes across a suitable limb in the course of its wanderings. Even after its advertisement for a mate has been satisfactorily answered, its drumming continues for a time. April and May constitute the nesting period. In their choice of tree the birds show no particular preference—one kind is as good as another—but sometimes the site chosen proves unworkable because of a knot or some other obstruction, and then they may start another hole in the same branch. A living branch may even be taken, if the core is rotten. Nor is the nest necessarily high up or hard to reach. A dead limb in an old orchard tree is often chosen. A nest that I examined on May 2, 1889, was in an old apple tree; it was not more than eight feet from the ground and was close by a much-used roadway. The fresh chips on the ground beneath convinced me that it was a new and occupied excavation. The entrance was eight inches from the chips whereon the eggs were deposited, and the hole was three and a half inches across at its widest part. The entrance was as round as if struck with a compass, and barely large enough to permit the bird to squeeze through. This nest contained six fresh eggs. Five is a more usual number; sometimes four, and rarely only three, are laid. They are pure glossy white and measure about .78 by .61 inches. Fresh eggs have been found as early as April 26 (Atkinson), but the first half of May is the normal time. June nestings have been recorded, but these may have been delayed. Young are usually on the wing before the end of that month.

A noticeable feature of woodpeckers' nests in general is the location of the entrance, which, when in a slanting branch, is always on the under side, doubtless to keep rain from dripping in. Weight is given to this explanation by the exception to the rule—when the hole is under a projecting limb or fungous growth, which serves the same purpose, the entrance may be on the upper side.

Picus pubescens Wied, *Reise in Innere Nord-America*, 1839, 1:130 (Ebensburg, Cambria Co., September)—Townsend, *Proc. Acad. Nat. Sci. Philadelphia*, 1883, 65 (Latrobe, Westmoreland Co., resident)—Teulon, *Jour. Boston Zoöl. Soc.*, 1883, 2:10 (Bradford, McKean Co., resident).

Dryobates pubescens Dwight, *Auk*, 1892, 9:135 (Cresson, Cambria Co., June)—Todd, *Auk*, 1893, 10:39 (Two Lick, Indiana Co., June), 44 (Coalport, Clearfield Co., June)—Jacobs, *Summer Birds Greene Co., Pa.*, 1893, 6 (Greene Co., nesting) —Baily, *Auk*, 1896, 13:293 (Williamsville, Elk Co., June–July).

Dryobates pubescens medianus Cope, *Cassinia*, 1902, 5:14 (Clinton and Potter Co., June)—Todd, *Ann. Carnegie Mus.*, 1904, 2:559 (Erie and Presque Isle, Erie Co., resident)—Todd, in Bausman, *Hist. Beaver Co., Pa.*, 1904, 2:1199 (Beaver Co., resident)—Keim, *Cassinia*, 1905, 8:38 (Port Allegany, McKean Co., August)—Forrest, *Oölogist*, 1911, 28:114 (Washington, Washington Co., resident)—Harlow, *Auk*, 1912, 29:471 ([State College], Centre Co., nesting)—Burleigh, *Wilson Bull.*, 1923, 35:87 (Allegheny Co., resident; nesting); 1931, 43:41 (State College, Centre Co., resident; nesting)—Christy and Sutton, *Cardinal*, 1928, 2:70 and 75 (Cook Forest, Clarion Co., resident)—Sutton, *Ann. Carnegie Mus.*, 1928, 18:143 (Pymatuning Swamp, Crawford Co., resident; nesting)—Burleigh, *Cardinal*, 1932, 3:76 (Chestnut Ridge, near Uniontown, Fayette Co., breeding).

"Downy Woodpecker" Stone, *Cassinia*, 1906, 9:44 (Scrub Ridge, west of McConnellsburg, Fulton Co., June)—Valentine, *Bird-Lore*, 1908, 10:32 (Bellefonte, Centre Co., December)—Miller (A. B.), *Bird-Lore*, 1910, 12:29; etc. (Springs, Somerset Co., December)—Simpson, *Oölogist*, 1911, 28:72 (Warren, Warren Co., breeding)—Burleigh, *Oölogist*, 1911, 28:156 (Harmarville, Allegheny Co., nesting)—Gerberding, *Bird-Lore*, 1912, 14:29 (Greenville, Mercer Co., December) —Simpson, *Oölogist*, 1912, 29:329 (head of Tionesta Creek, Warren Co., summer)—McConnell, *Oölogist*, 1918, 35:150 (McKeesport, Allegheny Co.)—Miller (R. F.), *Oölogist*, 1919, 36:155 (Charter Oak, Huntingdon Co., nesting)—McGraw, *et al.*, *Bird-Lore*, 1919, 21:37; etc. (Altoona, Blair Co., December)—Warfield, *Bird-Lore*, 1920, 22:31; etc. (Chambersburg, Franklin Co., December)—Stahl, *et al.*, *Bird-Lore*, 1921, 23:18 (Forest Hills to Deer Creek, Allegheny Co., December)—Nicholson, *Bird-Lore*, 1921, 23:18 (Grove City, Mercer Co., December)—Street, *Cassinia*, 1923, 24:12 (Greencastle to Ft. Loudon, Franklin Co., June) —Christy, *Cardinal*, 1924, v. 1, no. 4, p. 10 (Big Traverse Valley, Beaver Co., June)—Matuszak, *Bird-Lore*, 1926, 28:29 (Hyde Park, Westmoreland Co., December)—Eastwood, *Bird-Lore*, 1926, 28:137 (Ridgway, Elk Co., winter, *fide* Alsop), 273 (Rector, Westmoreland Co., May, *fide* Knauz); 1927, 29:56 (Thompsonville, Washington Co., November)—Clarke, *Bird-Lore*, 1930, 32:422 (State College, Centre Co., habits)—Christy, *Cardinal*, 1931, 3:43 (McDonald Reservoir, Washington Co., May)—Berkheimer, *Bird-Lore*, 1933, 35:27; etc. (near Osterburg, Bedford Co., December)—Christy, *Cardinal*, 1936, 4:97 ([Sewickley, Allegheny Co.], habits).

Dryobates pubescens pubescens (error) Christy, *Cardinal*, 1923, v. 1, no. 1, [p. 6] (Sewickley, Allegheny Co., resident).

TYRANT FLYCATCHERS

FAMILY TYRANNIDAE

THE TYRANNIDAE are a large and varied family, peculiar to America and most highly developed in the tropics. More than seven hundred forms are known, but of these only about forty inhabit the United States. Nine species occur in western Pennsylvania as summer residents, and all except the Phoebe migrate south of the United States for the winter.

Because of the structure of the voice organ, or syrinx, the Flycatchers are called "songless" perching birds. Their calls are simple, it is true, but they are distinctive and are important clues in identifying certain species that are very similar in appearance. Flycatchers have ten fully developed primary wing feathers. Their feet are small and fitted only for perching; the tarsus is covered all around with scales, or scutella, and lacks the sharp posterior ridge that is common to the other *Passeres*. Their bills are well adapted for the capturing of flying insects. In the typical species they are flat, hooked at the tip, and wide at the base, and the gape is provided with long bristles. Flycatchers feed in a characteristic manner; from a lookout perch they dart into the air after passing insects and then return again to the same perch.

The Arkansas Kingbird (*Tyrannus verticalis*) is a western species for which there are numerous sporadic records in the East, and which might be expected in western Pennsylvania.

EASTERN KINGBIRD (Plate 14)

TYRANNUS TYRANNUS (Linnaeus)

Description—One of our largest flycatchers; about the size of the Catbird. *Upperparts very dark slaty gray,* the head (top and sides) darker (blackish); wings dusky black with slight whitish edgings; *tail black,* with a *narrow white tip; underparts white,* the breast with a slight grayish wash; bill and feet black. The crown has a concealed inner spot of brilliant red and orange, not ordinarily visible in life. *Young birds* are similar but generally duller and browner, and lack the bright-colored crown-spot.

Range—The Kingbird winters in Central and South America, whence it moves northward during the breeding season to occupy the greater part of the United States (except in the West) and southern Canada. It is a common summer resident throughout western Pennsylvania and, in spite of unwarranted persecution in some quarters, has probably gained in numbers since the settlement of the country. A few observers, however, think that it is not so common at the present time as it was some years ago.

Migration—Because of the great distance it must travel, the Kingbird seldom reaches our latitude before the last week in April, and in backward seasons it may not appear until after the first week in May. It may be looked for at the same time as the warblers, which are likewise insect-eaters and are thus also largely governed in their movements at this season by local weather conditions. Some early arrival dates are: Beaver, April 20, 1891 (Wickham); Sewickley, April 22,

1900 (Christy); State College, April 22, 1917 (Burleigh); Washington, April 22, 1896 (Nease); Springs, Somerset County, April 24, 1915 (Miller); Wilkinsburg, April 25, 1898 (Atkinson); Templeton, Armstrong County, April 26, 1881 (Enty); Renovo, April 26, 1903 (Pierce); Conneaut Lake, April 27, 1925 (Langdon); Altoona, May 1, 1915 (McGraw); Warren, May 3, 1899 (Simpson); Erie, May 3, 1900 (Todd). Average dates of arrival (where available) are naturally later: Beaver, May 6; Sewickley, May 3; Renovo, May 2; Warren, May 8. Much later arrival dates have been reported in some years. G. M. Sutton writes (1928): "During 1925 we witnessed the arrival of the first migrants [at Pymatuning Swamp] on May 17. The lateness of this date was due to the severe weather which had just preceded; we came upon at least twenty birds in a compact flock, all of them perched on or near the ground, and plainly worn out. Possibly these birds were temporarily retreating."

The fall migration begins very early, long before there is any apparent necessity for the birds to leave. The Kingbird is common enough in July, but during August its numbers decrease markedly, and by the end of that month only a few birds are left. Stragglers may occasionally be observed in September; thus, individuals have been noted at Erie on September 1, 1900 (Todd); at Franklin, Venango County, on September 4, 1928 (Sutton); at Pymatuning Swamp on September 7, 1925 (Sutton); at Beaver on September 8, 1909 (Todd); and at Renovo on September 15, 1901 (Pierce).

Habits—The Kingbird is well named; it is a typical "tyrant" flycatcher—independent, arrogant, and domineering. Neither shrinking nor furtive in character, it does not skulk in the shrubbery and underbrush as do some of its smaller relatives. Rather does it court the limelight, perching by choice on the topmost spray of a favorite tree, whence it proclaims its presence to all and sundry. Nervous, irritable, and truculent in disposition, always intolerant when it fancies that its proprietary rights have been invaded, and brooking no interference with its domestic arrangements, this tyrant compels the respect of its feathered neighbors. Few birds are able to withstand its attack, and most prefer to beat a hasty retreat when it becomes obstreperous. I once watched a contest between a pair of kingbirds and a crested flycatcher, however, in which the latter came off victorious. The diminutive Ruby-throated Hummingbird, because of its small size and lightning-like speed, can easily elude the Kingbird's pursuit, and the English Sparrow has been known to defeat it by sheer force of numbers, but for the most part its right and title go unchallenged. Crows and hawks are its pet aversion; they are an anathema to its race. It does not hesitate to do battle with such foes and will fly out to meet them with loud and petulant outcries and with a speed and persistency quite unlike its usual fluttering, desultory efforts. Once having gained the upper level, it swoops down on the hapless bird, sometimes even alighting on its back, and deals savage blows with its bill until the enemy retires from the field. To the observer below, such a contest seems unequal; but the larger bird has difficulty in warding off the furious attack of its tormentor, and as long as the Kingbird can maintain the upper position the odds are in its favor. The tables are turned only on rare occasions.

The Kingbird's favorite resorts are orchards, scattered trees along roadsides and watercourses, and the margins of woods. It avoids the dense woods but frequents open groves and is partial to the vicinity of farmhouses. Although usually seen perched in a conspicuous and commanding position in a tree, it sometimes descends to a post or tall weed, and on occasion even to the ground. Like other birds of its family, it dashes out into the air in pursuit of its insect prey, sometimes performing strange aerial contortions before finally capturing the luckless insect with a snap of the bill, and then returns to the same perch or to some other point of vantage to wait for another victim. Because of a supposed preference for honeybees the Kingbird has received the name of "Bee Martin" and has been much persecuted by beekeepers generally. The evidence on this point is contradictory, and the charge is not fully sustained. In a report on the food habits of this species as revealed by the examination of 665 stomachs, F. E. L. Beal states that although Hymenoptera amounted to over 32 per cent of the total food that was consumed, honeybees were found in only 22 stomachs. "The total number in these 22 stomachs was 61, of which 51 were drones, 8 were workers, and 2 indeterminate. When we consider that in the stomachs examined there must have been at least 10,000 insects, and probably three times that number would be nearer the mark, it will at once be seen that the proportion of honeybees in the kingbird's diet is small."[1] This author further points out that the robber flies (Asilidae), which are known to kill honeybees at times in large numbers, and which were found in 19 stomachs, were certainly abundant payment for the few worker bees that had been eaten.

It has yet to be shown that in feeding upon bees the Kingbird discriminates between workers and drones and prefers the latter. Nevertheless, the damage it inflicts upon the apiarist seems to have been considerably exaggerated. Probably the habits of individual birds vary somewhat in this regard. The Kingbird is not exclusively insectivorous, however. I have seen it carrying cherries to its young, and it is well known that it eats a variety of wild fruits. On the whole, its good services far outweigh the harm it does, and it deserves all the protection that the law affords.

Orchard and shade trees are the favorite nesting sites of this bird, and it often chooses the branch of a sycamore overhanging a stream. In such a location, the nest may be as high as sixty feet, but when in an orchard it is seldom placed at a greater elevation than twenty-five or thirty feet, and often much lower. At Pymatuning Swamp, Dr. Sutton found several nests in alder bushes and one in a low hawthorn bush less than four feet from the ground. A given pair of birds become attached to their chosen nesting ground and will return year after year with unfailing regularity. There are probably few orchards of any size in our region that do not harbor a pair of kingbirds. The nest as a rule is easy to find, as it is more or less conspicuous and as the birds themselves seldom stray far away. It is a rather compact, well-built structure, composed of weed and grass fibers, strips of bark, and sometimes a few coarser, woody twigs and lined with finer and softer material—plant down, horsehair, and perhaps rootlets. It is usually placed on a horizontal or slightly sloping branch and is well-cupped, being at least an inch and a half deep. Some nests are bulkier than others, but the general type is much the same. J. W. Jacobs tells of a pair of birds that repaired and utilized an old robin nest.

Kingbirds will defend their nests with great pertinacity and will resent the approach of a climber by flying at him with angry protests. Other birds are seldom welcome, but I have observed that the Baltimore and Orchard orioles are often permitted to nest in the same tree. Perhaps the orioles force their company on the kingbirds in an effort to obtain the benefit of their protection; on the other hand, the two species may form an amicable partnership. In the Southwest a like arrangement is said to hold between the Scissor-tailed Flycatcher and the Orchard Oriole. Nest-building begins not long after the birds' arrival, usually about the second week of May in a normal season, and full sets of eggs have been found as early as May 16 in Allegheny County (Atkinson). From May 25 to June 10, however, is the normal time. Certain observers have found nests with eggs in July and have therefore inferred that a second brood is raised. I prefer to believe that these were instances of delayed nestings.

Three, four, or (rarely) five eggs are laid. They are white, with a slight creamy tint, and spotted with purplish-brown and duller shell-markings. The size and density of the spots vary considerably, from small and sparse to large and dense, but are nearly uniform in the same set. In the usual type of egg the markings take the form of irregular but bold and well-defined spots that show a tendency to cluster about the larger end. A. K. Pierce once took a set of unspotted eggs (near Huntley, Cameron County, on June 20, 1895). Average measurements are .95 by .72 inches.

The young are on the wing in July. Dr. Sutton writes (1928): "The local families congregate somewhat, preparatory to going south in late August. Such a flock, composed mostly of immature birds, was seen August 31, 1925, at Crystal Lake." With the passing of the breeding season the Kingbird loses much of its despotic, quarrelsome disposition and seems to become quieter, milder, and less

[1]U. S. Department of Agriculture, Biological Survey, *Bulletin*, no. 44, 1912, p. 11–19.

aggressive. Before it finally leaves for the South it is much less conspicuous than at other seasons.

Tyrannus carolinensis Townsend, *Proc. Acad. Nat. Sci. Philadelphia*, 1883, 64 (Latrobe, Westmoreland Co., summer)—Teulon, *Jour. Boston Zoöl. Soc.*, 1883, 2:9 (Bradford, McKean Co.).

"Kingbird" Enty, *Ornithologist and Oölogist*, 1885, 10:78 (Templeton, Armstrong Co., April)—Jacobs, *Hawkeye Ornithologist and Oölogist*, 1888, 1:88 (Waynesburg, Greene Co., April)—Stone, *Cassinia*, 1906, 9:43 (McConnellsburg, Fulton Co., June)—Cooke, *Bird-Lore*, 1908, 10:166 (Renovo, Clinton Co., migration)—Simpson, *Oölogist*, 1912, 29:329 (head of Tionesta Creek, Warren Co., summer)—McConnell, *Oölogist*, 1918, 35:150 (McKeesport, Allegheny Co.)—Blair, *In the Open*, July, 1920, 10:22 ([Plains Church], Butler Co., June)—McClelland, *Am. Mid. Nat.*, 1922, 8:36 (Washington, Washington Co., summer)—Christy, *Cardinal*, 1923, v. 1, no. 2, [p. 17] (Clinton Pond, Allegheny Co., April)—Street, *Cassinia*, 1923, 24:13 (Mercersburg, Metal, and near Greencastle, Franklin Co., June)—Eastwood, *Bird-Lore*, 1925, 27:263 (Pittsburgh region, Allegheny Co., April); 1926, 28:273 (Rector, Westmoreland Co., May, *fide* Knauz), 402 ([?]Clinton, Allegheny Co., October, *fide* Squier [probably an error]).

Tyrannus tyrannus Jamison, *Ornithologist and Oölogist*, 1888, 8:134; and Dwight, *Auk*, 1892, 9:136 (Cresson, Cambria Co., June)—Todd, *Auk*, 1893, 10:39 (Two Lick, Indiana Co., June), 44 (Coalport, Clearfield Co., nesting)—Jacobs, *Summer Birds Greene Co., Pa.*, 1893, 8 (Greene Co., nesting)—Baily, *Auk*, 1896, 13:291, 293 (Williamsville, Elk Co., June–July)—Cope, *Cassinia*, 1902, 5:10 (Tamarack Swamp, Clinton Co.), 14 (between New Bergen and Germania, Potter Co., June)—Todd, *Ann. Carnegie Mus.*, 1904, 2:562 (Erie and Presque Isle, Erie Co., summer)—Todd, in Bausman, *Hist. Beaver Co., Pa.*, 1904, 2:1199 (Beaver Co., summer)—Keim, *Cassinia*, 1905, 8:38 (Port Allegany, McKean Co., summer)—Harlow, *Auk*, 1912, 29:472 (southern Centre Co., nesting)—Christy, *Cardinal*, 1923, v. 1, no. 1, [p. 7] (Sewickley, Allegheny Co., summer)—Burleigh, *Wilson Bull.*, 1923, 35:88 (Allegheny Co., summer?); 1924, 36:71 (State College, Centre Co., migration)—Burleigh, *Cardinal*, 1929, 2:117 (Aspinwall, Allegheny Co., August)—Burleigh, *Wilson Bull.*, 1931, 43:43 (State College, Centre Co., nesting)—Burleigh, *Cardinal*, 1932, 3:76 (Chalk Hill, Fayette Co., nesting)—Christy, *Cardinal*, 1935, 4:18 (Hartstown, Crawford Co., migration).

Tyrannus tyrannus tyrannus Christy and Sutton, *Cardinal*, 1928, 2:71 (Cook Forest, Clarion Co., summer; Cooksburg, Forest Co., nesting)—Sutton, *Ann. Carnegie Mus.*, 1928, 18:151 (Crawford Co. localities, summer).

NORTHERN CRESTED FLYCATCHER (Plate 14)

MYIARCHUS CRINITUS BOREUS (Bangs)

Description—About the size of the Kingbird, but tail longer in proportion. The crown has lengthened feathers but is not conspicuously crested. Upperparts dull olive greenish; wings dusky brownish, crossed by two pale bars; the edgings of the inner secondaries also pale; the outer primaries have narrow rufescent edgings; *tail* dull brownish above, *rufescent* below; *sides of head*, as well as *throat and upper breast, dull grayish, passing into the pure sulphur yellow* of the rest of the underparts; bill brownish; feet black.

Range—The Crested Flycatcher is the sole outlying representative in the eastern United States of a compact generic group of birds that is well developed in the American tropics. It passes the winter months with its congeners in these regions and presses northward in the spring as far as southern Canada, but does not regularly invade the Canadian Life Zone. It is a common summer resident throughout the Carolinian and Alleghanian faunas in western Pennsylvania, but is less numerous in the highlands, where it becomes progressively rare or absent toward the north. I have never encountered it in Potter, McKean, Cameron, or Elk counties, nor have others (with one exception) been more fortunate. In Warren County, according to R. B. Simpson, it is regular during migration but rare as a summer resident. It is not uncommon in the bottomlands of the Susquehanna River in Clinton County, however, and may have advanced farther up the valley in the last forty years, as have other species of similar faunal affinities. Nowhere have I found it commoner than along the wooded slopes of the mountain ridges east of the main Allegheny divide, where it seems to find ideal conditions.

Migration—This species is at most only a few days behind the Kingbird in making its vernal appearance. Its arrival has been recorded at Sewickley as early as April 23 (1886) and as late as May 12 (1924), the average date being May 4 (Christy). Corresponding dates for Beaver are respectively April 27 (1891) and May 12 (1908), with May 5 as the average (Todd; Wickham). Early dates for some other localities are: Waynesburg, April 28 (two records by Jacobs); Washington, April 28 (McClelland); Pittsburgh, April 26 (Burleigh); Springs, Somerset County, April 24 (Miller); Meadville, April 28 (First); Erie, May 3 (Todd); and Warren, May 6 (Simpson). In the east the dates correspond: Renovo, April 27 (Pierce); State College, May 2 (Burleigh).

Like the Kingbird, the Crested Flycatcher begins to retire southward in August, but some individuals do not leave until the following month. Thus, the species has been seen at Pittsburgh as late as September 10 (Burleigh); at Hartstown on September 9 (Sutton); at Presque Isle on September 10 (Todd); at Renovo on September 14 (Pierce); and at State College on September 17 (Burleigh). I once saw a single straggler at Beaver as late as September 27 (1902).

Habits—The Crested Flycatcher takes the place of the Kingbird in the forest. Sometimes it comes into orchards and to shade trees in the vicinity of dwellings, but generally speaking it is a bird of the woodland—although not always or necessarily of the deeper parts. When it meets the Kingbird, as occasionally happens, it is well able to hold its own, for it is quite as arrogant and courageous as that species, if not ordinarily so ready to attack larger birds. It is a species of solitary habit, unsocial, and intolerant of others of its kind; a pair defends its chosen territory against all comers with great audacity. Although rather shy, it is one of the noisiest birds in the woods and makes its presence known by a variety of characteristic sounds, audible for a long distance. Its ordinary call note is "an unmusical and unearthly *wheep*," but when excited, angry, or in pursuit of some other bird, it utters a series of shrill shrieking and screaming notes, varied with harsh, rough outcries. By choice it keeps fairly high in the trees, under the canopy of their branches, selecting an exposed position but not necessarily a dead branch. Each bird has several favorite perches within a certain radius and uses them in turn. From these lookouts it sallies forth after insect prey, which it captures in open pursuit with a snap of the bill. The insect food of the Crested Flycatcher comprises moths, beetles (a great variety), dragonflies, cicadas (and other Hemiptera), grasshoppers, crickets, bees and wasps, and some flies. Because of its size and strength this flycatcher is able to capture large insects of several kinds. It is thus a useful bird from an economic standpoint, and when it takes up its abode in an orchard or about houses or gardens it should receive every encouragement. It is known to feed to a small extent on wild fruits, as do most birds of this pre-eminently insectivorous family.

The nesting habits of this bird are unique among our flycatchers, although common to all the species of the genus *Myiarchus*. Of the other flycatchers, the Phoebe alone builds under a shelter. The others build open nests. But the Crested Flycatcher, oddly enough, always places its nest in a cavity in a tree—a natural cavity, an old woodpecker-hole, or even an artificial nest box. One might suppose that its long tail would embarrass its movements in such confined quarters, but this seems not to be the case. If the cavity selected is too deep, it is filled up with trash to the right level before the nest proper is begun. This is a loose mass of small twigs, dry grass and weed stalks, leaves, and the like, lined with some finer and softer material—fine grasses, animal hair, or feathers. Almost invariably there is a castoff snake skin (sometimes several) in the composition of the nest itself or hanging about the outside. Just why this peculiar addition is made is not entirely clear. It has been conjectured that the skin may serve to frighten away would-be intruders, or that its rustle may give warning of an enemy's approach, but neither of these explanations seems quite satisfactory. Intensive studies on this point would be interesting.

Nest-building may begin very shortly after the birds' arrival (it has been observed as early as May 5 in Crawford County), but ordinarily there is a short interval. In Greene County, fresh eggs may be found from May 15 to June 15 (Jacobs), but in our region most pairs probably lay about the first of June. From three to six eggs are laid, four or five being the usual number. In color pattern they are peculiar and characteristic, and differ from those of any other of our birds. The ground-color is a pale cream, and the markings, which in general are of a purplish-brown color, and fine or coarse, as the case may be, tend to run in irregular, broken streaks lengthwise of the egg, creating an unusual appearance. Average measurements are .89 by .69 inches.

Myiarchus crinitus Townsend, *Proc. Acad. Nat. Sci. Philadelphia*, 1883, 64 (Latrobe, Westmoreland Co.)—Dwight, *Auk*, 1892, 9:136 (Wopsononock Mountain, Blair Co., June)

—TODD, *Auk*, 1893, 10:39 (Two Lick, Indiana Co., June), 44 (Coalport, Clearfield Co., nesting)—JACOBS, *Summer Birds Greene Co., Pa.*, 1893, 8 (Greene Co., nesting)—COPE, *Cassinia*, 1902, 5:15 (Clinton and Potter Co., June)—TODD, *Ann. Carnegie Mus.*, 1904, 2:562 (Erie and Presque Isle, Erie Co., summer)—TODD, in Bausman, *Hist. Beaver Co., Pa.*, 1904, 2:1199 (Beaver Co., summer)—HARLOW, *Auk*, 1912, 29:472 (southern Centre Co., nesting)—CHRISTY, *Cardinal*, 1923, v. 1, no. 1, [p. 7] (Sewickley, Allegheny Co., nesting)—BURLEIGH, *Wilson Bull.*, 1923, 35:89 (Allegheny Co., summer); 1924, 36:71; 1931, 43:43 (State College, Centre Co., migration; nesting)—BURLEIGH, *Cardinal*, 1929, 2:117 (Frick Park, Allegheny Co., September).

"Great-crested Flycatcher" JACOBS, *Hawkeye Ornithologist and Oölogist*, 1888, 1:88 (Waynesburg, Greene Co., April)—McCLELLAND, *Am. Mid. Nat.*, 1922, 8:36 (Washington, Washington Co., summer; migration).

"Crested Flycatcher" STONE, *Cassinia*, 1906, 9:43 (McConnellsburg, Fulton Co., June)—PITCAIRN, *Bird-Lore*, 1907, 9:155 (Riverview Park, Allegheny Co., nesting)—COOKE, *Bird-Lore*, 1909, 11:12 (Waynesburg, Greene Co., and Beaver, Beaver Co., migration)—MILLER, *In the Open*, December, 1912, 3:41 (McKinley Park, Allegheny Co., summer)—McCONNELL, *Oölogist*, 1918, 35:150 (Olympia Park, McKeesport, Allegheny Co.)—STREET, *Cassinia*, 1923, 24:13 (Greencastle to Ft. Loudon, Franklin Co., June)—CHRISTY, *Cardinal*, 1924, v. 1, no. 4, p. 10 (Big Traverse Valley, Beaver Co., June)—EASTWOOD, *Bird-Lore*, 1925, 27:262 (Raccoon Creek, Beaver Co., May, *fide* Jones, *et al.*), 263 (Pittsburgh region, Allegheny Co., May); 1926, 28:273 (Rector, Westmoreland Co., May, *fide* Knauz).

Myiarchus crinitus boreus CHRISTY and SUTTON, *Cardinal*, 1928, 2:71 (Cook Forest, Clarion Co., summer)—SUTTON, *Ann. Carnegie Mus.*, 1928, 18:152 (Crawford Co. localities, summer)—BURLEIGH, *Cardinal*, 1932, 3:76 (Chestnut Ridge, near Uniontown, Fayette Co., summer).

EASTERN PHOEBE (Plate 14)

SAYORNIS PHOEBE (Latham)

Description—A flycatcher of medium size; smaller than the Kingbird. Upperparts dull grayish olive, the crown and sides of the head darker and sootier; wings and tail dusky, with paler edgings; underparts soiled whitish, with a darker wash on the sides of the breast; bill and feet blackish.

Range—This well-known species has an extensive range in eastern North America, reaching from the Maritime Provinces of Canada to Manitoba and extending southward in winter to the Gulf of Mexico. As it winters so far north (by comparison with the other flycatchers), it might perhaps be expected to go farther north in summer as well, but this is not the case. Throughout our region it is evenly and commonly distributed as a summer resident. It is a species that has to a considerable extent adapted itself to the changed conditions brought about by human agency and consequently has suffered less than some others.

Migration—The Phoebe is the hardiest of the flycatchers. It is the first to arrive in the spring and the last to leave in the fall, and it has even been observed in the wintertime. We look for it in March, but its arrival is governed to a large extent by the weather, and a backward spring may retard its appearance until the first of the following month. Thus, the extremes in a series of arrival dates for Beaver covering thirteen years are March 15 and April 1, while the average is March 26. Fifteen years' records from Sewickley yield March 24 as the average date and March 13 (1921) as the earliest. A series of records made over a period of twenty-seven years at Renovo reveals the following: earliest, March 15; latest, April 7; average, March 26. There is thus a general agreement in spring records from various parts of our region. Early dates from some other localities may also be cited: March 8, 1926—Greenville (Seiple); March 12, 1928—Pittsburgh (Boulton); March 14, 1924—Springs, Somerset County (Miller); March 15, 1930—Slippery Rock, Butler County (Raney); March 18, 1898—Meadville (Kirkpatrick); March 18, 1927—State College (Sutton); March 19, 1910—Altoona (McGraw); March 19, 1894—Warren (Simpson); March 25, 1932—Presque Isle (Christy, and others).

The ranks of this species begin to thin out in September as the early migrants go south, but the last phoebes do not leave until the latter half of October. My records (covering five years) of "last-seen" dates at Beaver lie between October 16 (1891 and 1921) and 21 (1889). The species has been noted at State College until October 21 (1916—Burleigh) and at Pittsburgh on October 26 (1913—Burleigh). At Renovo it was detected on one occasion as late as October 29 (1917), according to A. K. Pierce, and has often been seen after October 20. It is said to have been seen at Harts-town on November 26 (1921) by E. E. Hunter (Sutton). The most remarkable record, however, concerns a phoebe seen along Deer Creek, near Harmarville, Allegheny County, on December 27, 1925, and again on January 1, 1926, by two different groups of people. It "did not appear hungry and seemed to be getting food from the ground. It looked fat and healthy." It would be interesting to know what happened to this particular bird later in the winter, when the weather turned severe. It seems incredible that such a bird could survive under true winter conditions. There are a number of winter records, however, from adjoining states.

Habits[1]—As demure in dress as the pussy willows with which it makes its appearance, the Phoebe comes each year in the early spring even before all the ice is gone from the streams. No sprightly song and no flash of gaudy plumage betray its presence; but its quiet industry and confident assurance in the goodness of man make it a welcome visitor. The males arrive a week or so in advance of the females, and over and over again from some lookout perch they deliver their querulous chant, *phoe-be, pe-wit, phoe-be*. It seems a petulant reproach of a laggard mate, or perhaps a plaint to the absent one that insect food is still very scarce. Soon the females arrive, and the mated pairs begin the search for suitable summer homes. What a variety of accommodations is offered near country dwellings! The Phoebe hunts the waterside, because there insects are found in greatest abundance, and there, too, will be found the moss and mud necessary for the construction of a nest.

The flycatchers are a versatile family in the matter of nest-building. Some build woven nests; some choose cavities in which to lay their eggs; but the Phoebe exhibits an individuality all its own. It seeks a sheltered ledge on which to plaster its nest of moss and mud, and from the barnyard near by brings hair and feathers for a soft, warm lining. A favorite site is a crossbeam beneath a bridge. This location is so frequently chosen that the Phoebe is sometimes called the "Bridge-bird." Sheds, barns, deserted houses, and boxcars, are common selections. Verandas of summer homes are attractive to house-hunting phoebes in early April, but they must seem fraught with danger when the rightful tenants arrive. I watched with interest a nest that had been built on a safely sheltered ledge above the door of a summer cottage. On July 8—a late date—the nest held four newly hatched young; and the house held a dozen vacationists, including several exuberant children. Slamming of the screen door and shrieks of laughter gave the phoebes great concern. Their wagging tails jerked even more nervously than ever as the birds approached the nest from perch to perch to feed the young; but they were game enough, and the appetites of the lusty nestlings caused both parents to conquer the fear they must have felt. The male seemed more excitable than the female and would often hover on fluttering wings in mid-air near the nest, then fly away, leaving his charges unfed until another time. When the birds were just a day old the male parent delivered his offering of insects to the brooding female, which then fed the young. The phoebes grew rapidly and presented a comical appearance as their down-covered heads wobbled above the edge of the nest and their wide mouths gaped for the insect fare that was busily supplied by both parents. Moths, beetles, grasshoppers, and mosquitoes, were on the menu, and possibly many other kinds as well.

Phoebes nest early and frequently raise two and sometimes three broods in a season. The eggs number from four to six, five being the usual clutch; they are normally pure white in color, although some sets show a slight spotting of cinnamon brown. Average measurements are .78 by .59 inches. Full complements of fresh eggs have been taken as early as April 14 (Atkinson) and as late as July 1 (Granquist). May 10 is about the average time for first layings; eggs taken in June (and later) doubtless represent second sets. Both parents are said to take part in the incubation.

Year after year phoebes revisit a favored spot, and sometimes they will repair an old nest or add another story to a former home. R. C. Harlow tells of finding a nest that had six distinct stories. Another unusual nest, so far as location is concerned, was that found by H. C. Kirkpatrick under a railroad bridge over which freight trains passed frequently, apparently without causing undue annoyance to the incubating bird. Another strange situation was the cement wall of a springhouse, where a nest had been plastered securely beneath the eaves with no supporting ledge at all. A considerable quantity of mud formed the base of this nest, and it must have been built with great difficulty. So carefully was it made, however, that it

[1]Account contributed by Ruth Trimble.

was still in good condition the following season; but I am not sure that it was used again.

Although the Phoebe is commonest about country houses, it is not infrequently found in the forest, far from human habitation. There it resorts to its natural and original nesting places in the recesses of rocky ledges, against the walls of cliffs, under overhanging banks, or occasionally in the roots of an upturned tree, and always in close proximity to water. One nest that I saw was on a rock ledge behind a tiny waterfall, through which the bird flew on her visits to and from the nest. The ledge was not commodious; quarters were so cramped, indeed, that the structure was no more than half the usual depth, and as the bird sat on the nest, her head almost touched the ledge above.

The Phoebe is very restless, and as it perches on a lookout post, awaiting some passing insect, its crest is often raised and lowered and its tail is forever twitching up and down and sometimes from side to side. Its bright black eyes quickly detect its flying prey, and in a flash it darts out, makes its capture in mid-air, and then returns to its perch. It would be difficult, indeed, to find among our native birds many that do more good and less harm than the Phoebe.

Sayiornis fusca Townsend, *Proc. Acad. Nat. Sci. Philadelphia*, 1883, 64 (Latrobe, Westmoreland Co., nesting).

Sayornis fuscus Teulon, *Jour. Boston Zoöl. Soc.*, 1883, 2:9 (Bradford, McKean Co.).

"House Pewee" Enty, *Ornithologist and Oölogist*, 1885, 10:78 (Templeton, Armstrong Co., March).

Sayornis phœbe Dwight, *Auk*, 1892, 9:136 (Cresson, Cambria Co., June)—Todd, *Auk*, 1893, 10:39 (Two Lick, Indiana Co., June), 44 (Coalport, Clearfield Co., June)—Jacobs, *Summer Birds Greene Co., Pa.*, 1893, 8 (Greene Co., nesting)—Baily, *Auk*, 1896, 13:293 (Williamsville, Elk Co., June-July)—Jacobs, *Gleanings from Nature*, 1898, 1:17, 23 (Greene Co., nesting)—Cope, *Cassinia*, 1902, 5:15 (Clinton and Potter Co., June)—Todd, *Ann. Carnegie Mus.*, 1904, 2:562 (Erie and Presque Isle, Erie Co., summer)—Todd, in Bausman, *Hist. Beaver Co., Pa.*, 1904, 2:1199 (Beaver Co., summer)—Keim, *Cassinia*, 1905, 8:38 (Port Allegany, McKean Co., summer)—Harlow, *Auk*, 1912, 29:472 (Pine Grove Mills, Centre Co., nesting)—Christy, *Cardinal*, 1923, v. 1, no. 1, [p. 7] (Sewickley, Allegheny Co., nesting)—Burleigh, *Wilson Bull.*, 1923, 35:89 (Allegheny Co., nesting); 1924, 36:71; and 1931, 43:43 (State College, Centre Co., nesting, etc.)—Christy and Sutton, *Cardinal*, 1928, 2:71 (Cook Forest, Clarion Co., summer)—Sutton, *Ann. Carnegie Mus.*, 1928, 18:152 (Crawford Co. localities, summer)—Burleigh, *Cardinal*, 1932, 3:76 (Chestnut Ridge, near Uniontown, Fayette Co., nesting).

"Phœbe" Forrest, *Oölogist*, 1901, 18:136, 137 (near Arden, Washington Co., nesting)—Stone, *Cassinia*, 1906, 9:43 (McConnellsburg, Fulton Co., June)—Cooke, *Bird-Lore*, 1908, 10:210 (Beaver, Beaver Co., and Renovo, Clinton Co., migration)—Burleigh, *Oölogist*, 1911, 28:156 (Harmarville, Allegheny Co., nesting)—Simpson, *Oölogist*, 1912, 29:329 (head of Tionesta Creek, Warren Co., nesting)—Rogers, *Bird-Lore*, 1914, 16:184 (Pittsburgh, Allegheny Co., migration)—McConnell, *Oölogist*, 1918, 35:150 (McKeesport and region, Allegheny Co.)—Dickey, *Oölogist*, 1919, 36:67 (Waynesburg, Greene Co., nesting)—Miller (R. F.), *Oölogist*, 1919, 36:155 (Charter Oak, Huntingdon Co., nesting)—Miller (M. H.), *In the Open*, June, 1920, 10:24 (Thornhill, Allegheny Co., nesting)—McClelland, *Am. Mid. Nat.*, 1922, 8:36 (Washington, Washington Co., summer)—Christy, *Cardinal*, 1923, v. 1, no. 2, [p. 17] (Clinton Pond, Allegheny Co., March)—Street, *Cassinia*, 1923, 24:13 (Greencastle and Mercersburg, Franklin Co., nesting)—Christy, *Cardinal*, 1924, v. 1, no. 4, p. 10 (Big Traverse Valley, Beaver Co., June)—Jones, *et al.*, *Bird-Lore*, 1926, 28:30 (Deer Creek [Harmarville], Allegheny Co., December)—Eastwood, *Bird-Lore*, 1926, 28:136 (Harmarville, Allegheny Co., winter, *fide* Squier), 273 (Rector, Westmoreland Co., May, *fide* Knauz), 403 (Clinton and region, Allegheny Co., October, *fide* Squier); 1927, 29:196, 197 (Pittsburgh and region, March, *fide* Grimm and Husted; Springs, Somerset Co., March, *fide* A. B. Miller)—Boulton, *Bird-Lore*, 1928, 30:195 (Pittsburgh, Allegheny Co., March), 401 (Millvale, Allegheny Co., October, *fide* Auerswald)—Christy, *Cardinal*, 1931, 3:43 (McDonald Reservoir, Washington Co., May)—Jacobs, *Oölogist*, 1933, 50:154 (Greene Co., eggs and nesting).

"Eastern Phoebe" Cope and Hawkins, *Forest Leaves*, 1934, 24:26 (E. Tionesta Forest Reserve, Warren and McKean Co., summer).

YELLOW-BELLIED FLYCATCHER (Plate 14)

EMPIDONAX FLAVIVENTRIS (Baird and Baird)

Description—One of the smallest flycatchers; much smaller than the Wood Pewee. It is distinguishable from the other species of the same genus by the more decidedly *olive-greenish* color of the *upperparts* and the sides of the head (with a conspicuous pale eye-ring), and in particular by its *uniformly yellowish* (rather than whitish) *underparts*, with some darker (olive-greenish) shading on the breast and sides. The *wing-bars* and wing-edgings are also *yellowish*, rather than buffy, and the under mandible is lighter-colored.

Range—Only a few of our local observers have

dared to record this flycatcher in their lists, and even those who have done so seem sometimes to have confused it with related species. Yet according to my observations in Beaver County, it is by no means uncommon in migration. True, one has to learn where to look for it and how to distinguish it from its near allies. At two other localities in our region where intensive studies of the bird life have been made—Presque Isle and Pymatuning Swamp—it has proved to be a rather common transient in the fall, but rare in the spring. There are only a few odd records for the other counties, but since the species is one that inexperienced observers might readily overlook, it may fairly be assumed to be as common in most areas as in the localities named. Thus it is probably equally common as a transient in the ridge and valley section and in the region west of Laurel Hill and the Allegheny Valley. In the plateau region of the northern counties, however, its status is that of a summer resident, sparingly distributed.

In the breeding season this flycatcher is a characteristic species in the Canadian Life Zone and is thus well known as a summer resident in the Adirondack and Catskill Mountains in New York state. While no nests have actually been found in our region, the species has been observed at several localities during June, a fact that justifies the inference that it was breeding at the time. Warren found it during the summer at Kane, McKean County; and on June 19, 1895, I secured a single specimen at Katrine Swamp in the same county. R. B. Simpson considers it rare in Warren County, both in migration and as a possible summer resident, but he has a few June records of its occurrence there, as well as along Blue Jay Creek in Forest County. Van Fleet includes it in his manuscript list of the breeding birds of DuBois. While I never succeeded in finding it at Tamarack Swamp in Clinton County, it probably summers there also, as well as in the highlands of Potter County. Its local breeding range as thus inferentially worked out seems to coincide very well with that of the Olive-backed Thrush. Like that species, too, it may even range farther south along the Alleghenies, and it should be searched for in summer in the higher parts of Somerset County.

Migration—A late migrant in the spring, this flycatcher follows most of the warblers in May. Leaving its winter home in Central America late in the season, it flies north rather quickly. My records for Beaver all lie between May 14 (1908 and 1909) and June 1 (1910). May 11 (1895) is a very early spring date reported for Swissvale, Allegheny County, by G. E. Hodge (Atkinson). The species has been noted at Altoona on May 13; at Sewickley on May 23; at Crystal Lake, Crawford County, on May 18; at Warren on May 20; at State College on May 19; and at Presque Isle as late as May 31. In the fall it is a correspondingly early migrant and is among the first of the Passerine transients to appear. I took it at Beaver once on the remarkably early date of August 14 (1908), and its arrival has been recorded at Presque Isle and at Pymatuning Swamp on August 25, and at Altoona on August 22. At this season its stay in our region is more protracted, and it is often common through September, while a few birds may even linger into the first week of the following month (Presque Isle, October 3, 1900) or very rarely still later (State College, October 16, 1915).

Habits—This little bird was unknown to Wilson, Audubon, and the other early ornithologists, who must have confused it with related species. It was first discriminated by the brothers Baird from specimens taken by them at Carlisle, Cumberland County, some miles east of the geographical limits of our region. To this day it remains an elusive bird of mystery to many otherwise experienced students. Haunting the shadiest nooks of the forest, where the shrubbery grows thickest; perching near the ground, beneath the shelter of the overhanging branches; and flitting silently ahead of the would-be observer as he tries to penetrate its retreat, it seldom affords one more than a momentary, tantalizing glimpse. In spite of the fact that it is shy, furtive, and secretive, however, one need never be in doubt of its identity so long as one's ears can detect its characteristic cry: a soft, plaintive note of two syllables—*chir-wee*—amazingly like that of the Semipalmated Plover. It has some other low chirps and alarm-notes, but they are not so characteristic.

In the summertime, as in the season of migration, the Yellow-bellied Flycatcher is an inhabitant of low, swampy woodland, thickets along streams, and similar resorts. It obtains its food in typical flycatcher fashion, except that it habitually perches much lower than do its relatives and avoids the exposed positions chosen by them. It is the only one of our flycatchers known to nest on the ground. Several nests found on Pocono Mountain in Monroe County, in northeastern Pennsylvania, are described as hidden in the sides of little mounds of sphagnum moss; they contained eggs during the last week in June.[1] The eggs of this species are creamy white and are spotted.

"Yellow-bellied Flycatcher" WARREN, *Forest and Stream*, 1891, 37:83 (Kane, McKean Co., summer)—SIMPSON, *Oölogist*, 1907, 24:134, 183 (near Warren, Warren Co., May–June)—HARLOW, *Cassinia*, 1912, 15:20 (Center Furnace Swamp, Centre Co., spring)—MALLEY and SHOEMAKER, *Redstart*, 1937, 4:70 ([Frick Park], Pittsburgh, Allegheny Co., migration).

Empidonax flaviventris RHOADS, *Auk*, 1899, 16:311 (Beaver, Beaver Co., May)—TODD, *Ann. Carnegie Mus.*, 1904, 2:563 (Presque Isle, Erie Co., transient)—TODD, in Bausman, *Hist. Beaver Co., Pa.*, 1904, 2:1199 (Beaver Co., transient)—(Secretary), *Cassinia*, 1908, 11:82 ([Blue Jay Creek], Forest Co., summer, *fide* Simpson)—HARLOW, *Auk*, 1918, 35:28 (Warren Co., summer)—STONE, *Cassinia*, 1919, 22:32; and 1920, 23:34 (near Altoona, Blair Co., May, *fide* McGraw)—BURLEIGH, *Wilson Bull.*, 1924, 36:77 (State College, Centre Co., migration)—CHRISTY, *Cardinal*, 1926, v. 1, no. 8, p. 17 (Sewickley, Allegheny Co., May)—SUTTON, *Ann. Carnegie Mus.*, 1928, 18:154 (Crawford Co. localities, transient).

[1]Compare W. L. BAILY, *Auk*, 1916, 33:200.

ACADIAN FLYCATCHER (Plate 14)

EMPIDONAX VIRESCENS (Vieillot)

Description—The largest of the eastern *Empidonaces*, but smaller than the Wood Pewee. Upperparts and sides of head, olive green (duller than in the Yellow-bellied Flycatcher), with distinct, pale yellowish eye-ring; wings dusky, with pale buffy-whitish bars and edgings; underparts white, the breast and sides shaded with dusky green. In fresh fall plumage the wing-bars and wing-edgings are a deeper buff and the underparts are more heavily suffused with yellowish green, although never so uniformly or so richly as in the Yellow-bellied Flycatcher. The Acadian Flycatcher may be distinguished from the Alder Flycatcher, which is about the same size, by its greenish, rather than brownish, upperparts; its more conspicuous eye-ring; and its lighter-colored (thus more conspicuous) wing-bars.

Range—The Acadian Flycatcher winters in northwestern South America and moves north to occupy a large part of the eastern United States in the summer. At this season it is as distinctly austral in its predilections as the Yellow-bellied Flycatcher is boreal. In general, it does not breed north of the Carolinian Fauna, but, like certain other species of that Fauna, it seems to be gradually extending its range. In New England it is rare or casual except in southern Connecticut, and in New York it is largely confined to the Hudson Valley, although it is also found sparingly in the region south of Lake Ontario. In Ohio it ranges across the state, from the Ohio Valley to the shores of Lake Erie. Its breeding range in western Pennsylvania is discontinuous, as it is cut in two by the Appalachian highlands, which act as a faunal barrier. This bird is common in the woodlands of the counties of the western tier as far east as the base of Laurel Hill, which here bounds the plateau region. Nowhere have I seen it more numerous than along the gap of Chestnut Ridge through which Loyalhanna Creek flows.

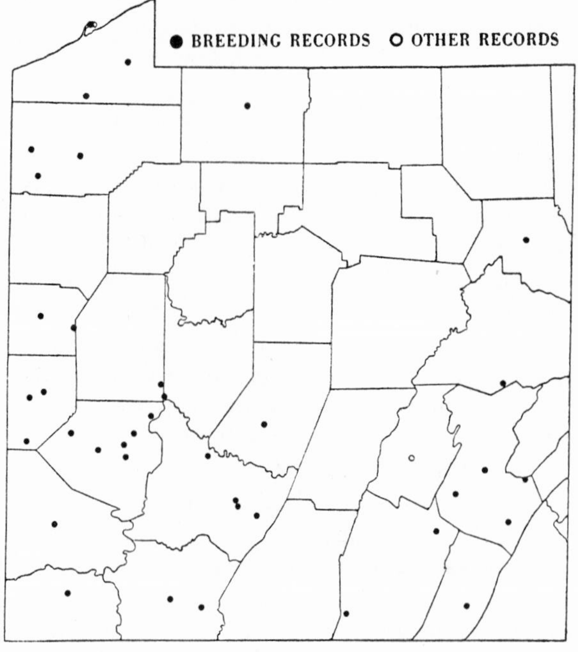

LOCAL RANGE OF THE ACADIAN FLYCATCHER

Farther north, also, I have found it along Two Lick and Yellow creeks in Indiana County, but not beyond the mouth of Buffalo Creek in the Allegheny Valley. Reasoning by analogy, however, I infer that it must regularly range along the Allegheny River as far north at least as Venango County, since it is common enough in parts of Crawford and Erie counties only a little farther west. Indeed, R. B. Simpson found it nesting in the river valley a few miles below Warren in June, 1912—his only record for that locality. Van Fleet's record of its breeding at DuBois is certainly questionable and, since there has been no confirmation of it, should not be accepted.

East of the Allegheny divide the species reappears, but does not seem to be so common there as in the Ohio Valley. There are specimens from a number of places, however, and the bird is probably found throughout this region at the lower levels. Farther north, along the West Branch of the Susquehanna River, it has often been found nesting at Renovo (Pierce), and it may ascend the river still farther. It is confined there to the lowland woods along the river valley and follows the smaller streams a little way up the hillsides.

Migration—Some observers maintain that they have seen this flycatcher during the latter part of April, but, in the light of the following records from adjacent sections, there is good reason to doubt such unseasonably early occurrences. My arrival records for Beaver County lie between May 5 (1909) and 17 (1910 and 1913), with May 11 the average date. D. A. Atkinson has noted the species' arrival at Wilkinsburg between May 3 (1894) and 11 (1895). At Sewickley, B. H. Christy has recorded its vernal appearance between May 4 (1913 and 1930) and 17 (1931). The corresponding dates for Washington are May 10 and 21 (McClelland). In 1922 it reached Hartstown on May 7, and in 1933 it reached Erie on the same date (Guynes). Fall dates must be received with caution, as this bird is difficult to identify at that season unless specimens are actually taken. We know, however, that as a rule it remains in the region through most of September. The following late dates are apparently authentic: September 26, 1891—Beaver (Todd); September 28, 1898—Wilkinsburg (Atkinson); October 3, 1913—Pittsburgh (Burleigh).

Habits—The Acadian Flycatcher is falsely named, for it is the one species of its group that is certainly not found in Acadia (Nova Scotia). It is necessary to discard or at least to question the accounts of the earlier authors, who more or less confused this with other species. Many amateurs find it difficult to discriminate the species of these small flycatchers. As a matter of fact, once one has become familiar with their haunts and habits and in particular with their call notes, it is probably easier to distinguish them in life than as preserved specimens. The Acadian Flycatcher is a lover of deep, shady woods. It likes the cool, damp forest of the bottomlands, where there is little undergrowth, and often follows the ravines of streams to higher ground, but it avoids second growth, orchards, and shade trees, which are favored by some of its congeners. Like other flycatchers, it is a solitary bird; each pair, after having settled for the season, has its own definite territorial limits beyond which it does not pass unchallenged. The birds customarily perch at a moderate elevation in an exposed position, but well below the crown of the tree. Their peculiar and characteristic call notes invariably betray their presence, although the birds themselves, being rather shy and suspicious of an intruder, contrive to keep out of sight. This note is a two-syllabled explosive chirp, defying transliteration or adequate description, but easily identified when once learned.

The nidification of the Acadian Flycatcher is even more characteristic than are its call notes and is alone a sufficient clue to the identity of the bird. When a breeding pair has been located, the nest is easy to find. It is a rather untidy structure of the vireo type, but much shallower (saucer-shaped), and so thin and frail that the eggs can often be counted from below. At a little distance it might readily pass for a bunch of rubbish caught on a limb. It is always suspended from the fork of a horizontal branch, usually far out near the end. A branch that overhangs a small stream winding its way through the woods is preferred. The beech is a favorite, but almost any tree will answer, and I have found nests in hemlocks and even in small bushes. The usual elevation is between eight and fifteen feet; a height of twenty feet is rare; and I once found one only four feet from the ground. The main building materials are dry weed stalks and other vegetable fibers, which are loosely arranged and bound to the supporting twigs by cobwebs and probably saliva. Sometimes there is a partial lining of finer material—rootlets, tendrils, or even horsehair—but while some nests may be less bulky than others, they are all invariably shabby examples of bird architecture. I have examined nests that had pieces of component material trailing a foot below them. The outside of the nest is frequently ornamented with catkins from certain forest trees.

The eggs are usually three in number, but sets of four are not rare. They are a delicate creamy-white hue, with a few (as a rule small) scattered spots of deep chestnut brown, mostly distributed about the larger end, frequently in the form of a wreath. They average .72 by .53 inches. Sometimes two broods are reared in a season. J. W. Jacobs, who has had much experience with this flycatcher in Greene County, states that fresh eggs of the first laying may be looked for from May 25 to June 15, and my own dates for nests in Beaver County fall within the same limits. In Crawford County, too, eggs have been found as early as June 3.

Empidonax acadicus Jacobs, *Oölogist*, 1888, 5:13 (Waynesburg, Greene Co., nesting; habits)—Todd, *Auk*, 1891, 8:399 (Buffalo Creek region, Butler Co., summer); 1893, 10:38, 39 (Two Lick, Indiana Co., June)—Jacobs, *Summer Birds Greene Co., Pa.*, 1893, 8 (Greene Co., nesting)—Rhoads, *Auk*, 1899, 16:311 (Laughlintown, Westmoreland Co., June).

"Acadian Flycatcher" Jacobs, *Hawkeye Ornithologist and Oölogist*, 1888, 1:88 (Waynesburg, Greene Co., migration)—Simpson, *Oölogist*, 1914, 31:91 (near Warren, Warren Co., nesting)—McClelland, *Am. Mid. Nat.*, 1922, 8:36 (Washington, Washington Co., summer; migration)—Christy, *Cardinal*, 1924, v. 1, no. 4, p. 10 (Big Traverse Valley, Beaver Co., June).

Empidonax virescens Jacobs, *Gleanings from Nature*, 1898, 1:17 (Greene Co., nesting)—Todd, *Ann. Carnegie Mus.*, 1904, 2:563 (Erie and Presque Isle, Erie Co., summer)—Todd, in Bausman, *Hist. Beaver Co., Pa.*, 1904, 2:1200 (Beaver Co., summer)—Harlow, *Auk*, 1912, 29:466, 473 (Huntingdon Co., nesting; First and Second Mountains, Centre Co.); 1918, 35:29 (Centre Co., nesting)—Christy, *Cardinal*, 1923, v. 1, no. 1, [p. 7] (Sewickley, Allegheny Co., nesting)—Burleigh, *Wilson Bull.*, 1923, 35:89 (Allegheny Co., nesting)—Sutton, *Ann. Carnegie Mus.*, 1928, 18:154 (Crawford Co. localities, summer).

"Green-crested Flycatcher" Cooke, *Bird-Lore*, 1908, 10:114 (Beaver, Beaver Co., and "Waynesboro" [Waynesburg], Greene Co., migration).

ALDER FLYCATCHER (Plate 14)

EMPIDONAX TRAILLI TRAILLI (Audubon)

Description—About the size of the Acadian Flycatcher, but grayish brown, rather than olivaceous, above; and resembling the Least Flycatcher in general coloration, but slightly larger. It is not certainly distinguishable in life from these two species except by its call notes and mode of nesting.

Range—The Alder Flycatcher is in general a species characteristic of the Hudsonian and Canadian life zones. Its breeding range stretches from New England and the Maritime Provinces of Canada to Athabasca and Alberta. During recent years, however, it has been found nesting in western New York, and it has long been known as a locally common summer resident in Ohio, in regions by no means Canadian in faunal character. In western Pennsylvania its local breeding range, as yet imperfectly worked out, is most peculiar. By analogy we should expect to find it summering throughout the plateau region in general, in common with the Junco, Hermit Thrush, Blue-headed Vireo, and certain members of the warbler tribe. Yet in all my excursions through this section I have failed to discover it, and others in the northern counties have been no more fortunate. Neither R. B. Simpson of Warren nor A. K. Pierce of Renovo has ever encountered it, even in migration. But Van Fleet, in his manuscript list of the breeding birds of DuBois, mentions it as a rare summer resident and adds that it was always noted in thickly wooded ravines along small trout streams. A. B. Miller also considers it a rare summer resident in extreme southern Somerset County. He writes that it frequents the alder thickets near the headwaters of Glade Run, west of Negro

Mountain. He finds it there every season through June and July and, although he has never happened on a nest, is positive that it breeds. This locality, it will be noted, is not far from Mountain Lake Park, Maryland, where E. A. Preble found the species in July, 1899.[1]

It is thus entirely probable that this flycatcher breeds in other parts of the highlands but has been overlooked because of its extremely local habitat; for it is virtually confined to the alder thickets. This association doubtless accounts for the fact that at Pymatuning Swamp, where the hoary alder (*Alnus incanus*) is an abundant and in places a dominant growth, the Alder Flycatcher is a common breeding bird. Since the swamp is a Boreal Zone island, so to speak, the species is not out of place there; its occurrence is strictly in accord with the relatively northern character of the fauna and flora of the locality. It has been seen in summer at other points in Crawford County where similar conditions prevail: Conneaut Marsh and the head of Conneaut Lake. In Erie County, S. S. Dickey has found it in Tamarack Swamp in June,[2] and he has also taken its nest and eggs in the swamp of the same name in Warren County. It has been reported from two localities in Mercer County (Sandy Lake and Mercer), and more recently has been traced south to Gardner Swamp, three miles southeast of New Castle, Lawrence County, where it was seen in June, 1933, by several observers, including myself. In the region west of the Allegheny River and north of the terminal moraine, wherever its favorite ecological conditions obtain, the Alder Flycatcher is thus a locally common summer resident. Future work will no doubt increase the number of its known breeding stations within this area. There is one outlying and exceptional breeding record from Allegheny County, based on a nest with eggs found by D. A. Atkinson near Verona on May 31, 1894. The female parent was shot and was sent for identification to William Brewster, who pronounced it an abnormally colored specimen of this species.

Migration—The Alder Flycatcher is one of the very last spring migrants and follows in the rear of the warbler hosts. It comes all the way from Central and South America. At Beaver, where I consider it a rare transient (as I have only four spring records), my earliest spring date is May 17 (1890) and my latest, May 27 (1910). B. H. Christy has seen the species several times near the mouth of Big Traverse Creek, Beaver County—as late as May 30 in two different seasons. It has been noted at Pymatuning Swamp on May 23 (1922—Sutton) and on Presque Isle on May 21 (1894—Bacon) and May 26 (1900—Todd). At Charter Oak, Huntingdon County, T. D. Burleigh has recorded it on May 12 and 13 (1917) and on May 17 (1919). One might suppose from the date of the Allegheny County nesting above cited that records of occurrence during the last week in May would pertain to breeding individuals. This is not necessarily true, however, because in at least one such instance a bird seen one day failed to appear the next and was therefore presumably migrating.

Fall migration records are few indeed, and some of them are perhaps not entirely dependable, but they indicate that the southward movement takes place in September. I have noted the species at Beaver as early as September 1 (1908) and as late as September 23 (1890). In 1925 it was also seen at Pymatuning Swamp on September 23.

Habits—During migration this flycatcher favors willows and other low growths along streams, but sometimes it ascends the hillsides to higher levels, where it frequents the bushes and shrubbery along the edges of the woods—haunts similar to those preferred by the Least Flycatcher. In general appearance and behavior these two flycatchers are much alike, but the Alder seems the more excitable, and is certainly the shier, of the two. They can invariably be identified in the spring and summer months by their call notes. The ordinary call of the Alder consists of three rapidly given syllables, which Dr. Sutton transliterates as *becky-weér*. This is sometimes abbreviated or run together in such a way that only two syllables are sounded, but in any case it is very different from the staccato *che-béc* of the Least Flycatcher. An alarm-note of one syllable somewhat resembles the sound *wheep* or *thleep*. In the fall migration the species is silent or nearly so, and the only way it can be certainly distinguished from the Least is by having it in hand.

The Alder Flycatcher is well named; for during the breeding season it is one of the birds char-

[1] *Maryland Geological Survey* [*of*] *Allegany County*, 1900, p. 300.
[2] On May 30, 1935, I noted a pair on Presque Isle that behaved as though they had a nest close by.

acteristic of the alder growths. At Pymatuning Swamp, where it is numerous (as flycatchers go) in summer, Dr. Sutton says that the first arrivals customarily perch in exposed positions and call constantly. On June 16, 1923, he found his first nest, which was collected two days later, with its complement of three eggs. It was beautifully constructed and had been placed on an upright alder branch three and a half feet above the water, at the edge of a great clump of black alders. Two other nests were found—on May 30, 1924, and August 21, 1925. The second contained four fairly well-developed young. The late date suggests a delayed nesting or a second brood. The nest found on May 30 was in a wild-rose bush—also a favorite haunt of the species. The nest located near Verona by Dr. Atkinson was in an ash sapling growing in a thicket, and was ten feet from the ground. This flycatcher builds a rather compact, cup-shaped structure, neatly fashioned of dry grasses and lint from certain plants; like that of the Least Flycatcher, it is placed in an upright fork. The eggs, three (or sometimes four) in number, are indistinguishable from those of the Acadian Flycatcher; they are creamy white, with a few reddish-brown spots about the larger end. They average .73 by .53 inches.

Empidonax traillii alnorum TODD, *Ann. Carnegie Mus.*, 1904, 2:564 (Presque Isle, Erie Co., spring transient)—TODD, in Bausman, *Hist. Beaver Co., Pa.*, 1904, 2:1200 (Beaver Co., transient)—BURLEIGH, *Wilson Bull.*, 1924, 36:77 ("State College, Centre Co." [Charter Oak, Huntingdon Co.], May).

"Alder Flycatcher" SUTTON, *Bird-Lore*, 1924, 26:267 (Hartstown, Crawford Co., spring, *fide* Blair), 336 (Pymatuning Swamp, Crawford Co., and Sandy Lake, Mercer Co., nesting)—CHRISTY, *Cardinal*, 1924, v. 1, no. 4, p. 11 (Big Traverse Valley, Beaver Co., May)—EASTWOOD, *Bird-Lore*, 1926, 28:273 (Hartstown, Crawford Co., May, *fide* Blair)—COPE and HAWKINS, *Forest Leaves*, 1934, 24:26 (E. Tionesta Forest Reserve, Warren and McKean Co., summer).

Empidonax traillii traillii SUTTON, *Ann. Carnegie Mus.*, 1928, 18:155 (Crawford and Mercer Co. localities, nesting, etc.)—SUTTON, *Cardinal*, 1929, 2:121 (Lower Lake, Crawford Co., September).

LEAST FLYCATCHER (Plate 14)

EMPIDONAX MINIMUS (Baird and Baird)

Description—Smallest of the *Empidonaces*. General coloration about the same as that of the Alder Flycatcher, but size slightly smaller. In fresh fall plumage the wing-bands and wing-edgings are more buffy than in spring and summer, and the underparts are more distinctly tinged with dull yellow.

Range—This species spends the winter farther north than do any of the eastern members of its genus and is found at that season in Yucatan and northern Mexico. Its summer range is mainly in the Canadian and Transition life zones of eastern and central North America. While it is thus in general a more northerly bird (faunally speaking) than the Acadian Flycatcher, the respective ranges of the two overlap to some extent. This is well illustrated in western Pennsylvania, where the Least is widely distributed as a summer resident and indeed is common over much of the area occupied by the Acadian. In the western tier of counties the two are found associated from Lake Erie to the Ohio Valley, south of which, however, in Washington and Greene counties, the Least is known only as a transient. In Beaver County I have found both species nesting within a few yards of each other. In the ridge and valley section they also occur together, but the Least seems to be less common there, and probably does not reach the valley country of Franklin County, from where, at any rate, it has not been reported.

Migration—Wintering farther north than the other members of this genus, the Least Flycatcher is able to get under way a little earlier in the spring. It is thus the first to arrive and is the only one of the *Empidonaces* known to appear in April. My records of its first appearance for seventeen years (not consecutive) at Beaver lie between April 19 (1909) and May 11 (1908). The average date is May 3 (not April 20, as stated by Cooke, 1908). It so happens that B. H. Christy has not seen the species earlier than this same date at Sewickley, nor has T. D. Burleigh recorded it before May 2 (1914) in the vicinity of Pittsburgh. Other early dates from more northerly points are: May 7, 1933—New Castle (Raney); May 4, 1927—Greenville (Seiple); May 1, 1926—Conneaut Lake (Langdon); May 5, 1900—Erie (Todd); April 30, 1890—Warren (Simpson). The greater number of the arrival dates for Renovo, in the notes of A. K. Pierce, occur in the last week in April and the first week in May, but some that he gives are obviously erroneous. At State College the corresponding dates lie between April 30 and May 7 (Burleigh).

Observers generally have shown a commendable reluctance to record this and the other small flycatchers in the fall, because of the difficulty of identifying them at that season. As a matter of fact, confidence in my own observations remains only in instances where I have secured specimens. One specimen from Presque Isle, bearing the date of September 27, 1900, suggests that the southward movement is not complete in our region until the end of September, although the majority of birds leave two or three weeks earlier.

Habits—The Least Flycatcher is the commonest and best known of the four eastern species of this particular group. It is also the only one of the four that has shown any disposition to adapt itself to the changing conditions brought about by the disappearance of the forest. Moreover, it has adapted itself so well that it is perhaps even commoner now than formerly. It avoids the deep woods and prefers low second growth and shrubbery, and open groves. It also comes into orchards and makes itself at home in the parks and the shade trees of our towns and villages. Like all the flycatchers of this group, it is active and energetic and perches by choice in an exposed position, from which it is ever on the alert to dash out after some luckless insect. Hymenoptera form the largest item of insect food, according to F. E. L. Beal,[1] while Coleoptera, Diptera, Hemiptera, and Lepidoptera, vary its diet, in the order of preference named. This is one of the birds known to eat the striped squash beetle, the twelve-spotted cucumber beetle, and the plum curculio. Although it sometimes takes useful insects (such as ladybird beetles) as well, its diet in general is strongly in its favor. It is not nearly so conspicuous a bird as the larger flycatchers, or even as the Wood Pewee, but calls attention to itself by a very characteristic note of two syllables, which may be transliterated as *che-béc* or *se-wick*, uttered very quickly in staccato time. This note is given through the spring and summer months until the time of the annual molt, after which the birds are usually silent.

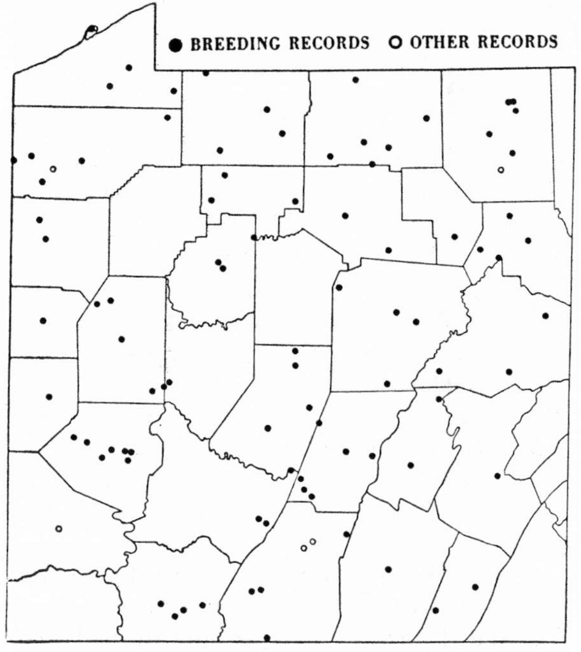

LOCAL RANGE OF THE LEAST FLYCATCHER

My first nest of this species was found (in 1890) by locating a pair of birds and then making a painstaking search of the orchard trees that they seemed to favor—a method of procedure that is usually effective, as the birds do not stray far in the nesting season. The nest was in an apple tree and was eighteen feet from the ground. A second nest that I discovered was in a Norway maple in the middle of the town of Beaver and was placed at the same distance above ground. Any kind of tree may be used, however, from a willow sapling to a mature oak or elm. R. B. Simpson writes that in Warren County he has found nests from ten to forty feet above ground. He has also seen them as low as four feet in alder bushes, and once he found one on the top of a horizontal limb of a hemlock—a very unusual location. The nest is usually placed either in the fork of an upright or sloping branch, or between several twigs growing up from a horizontal branch, so that it is held firmly in place. It is a neat, compact, cup-shaped structure, composed of strips of grapevine bark, weed stalks, lint from various plants, and sometimes bits of string or cloth, and is lined with finer plant fibers, horsehair, feathers, and similar materials. The inside is about an inch

[1]U. S. Department of Agriculture, Biological Survey, *Bulletin*, no. 44, 1912, p. 64.

and a half deep and a little larger in diameter. Four eggs are the usual set, but sometimes there are only three. They are an immaculate white with just the faintest possible shading of buff or cream color. They are laid as a rule during the first week in June, but sets have been taken up to the last of that month. The nest is usually smaller and more neatly built than that of the Alder Flycatcher, but in any case there need be no confusion between the two, since the latter always lays spotted eggs.

Empidonax minimus Teulon, *Jour. Boston Zoöl. Soc.*, 1883, 2:10 (Bradford, McKean Co., nesting)—Warren, *Birds Pa.*, ed. 2, 1890, 197 (Crawford, Erie, McKean, and Cambria Co., summer)—Todd, *Auk*, 1893, 10:37, 39 (Two Lick, Indiana Co., June), 43, 44 (Coalport, Clearfield Co., June)—Baily, *Auk*, 1896, 13:292, 293 (Williamsville, Elk Co., nesting)—Cope, *Cassinia*, 1902, 5:15 (Clinton and Potter Co., June)—Todd, *Ann. Carnegie Mus.*, 1904, 2:564 (Presque Isle, Erie Co., summer)—Todd, in Bausman, *Hist. Beaver Co., Pa.*, 1904, 2:1200 (Beaver Co., summer)—Harlow, *Auk*, 1912, 29:473; and 1918, 35:29 (southern Centre Co., etc., summer)—Christy, *Cardinal*, 1923, v. 1, no. 1, [p. 7] (Sewickley, Allegheny Co., nesting)—Burleigh, *Wilson Bull.*, 1923, 35:90 (Allegheny Co., summer); 1924, 36:71; and 1931, 43:44 (State College, Centre Co., breeding)—Christy and Sutton, *Cardinal*, 1928, 2:71 (Cooksburg, Forest Co., nesting)—Sutton, *Ann. Carnegie Mus.*, 1928, 18:157 (Crawford Co. localities, breeding)—Burleigh, *Cardinal*, 1932, 3:76 ([Wharton Furnace and Chalk Hill] near Uniontown, Fayette Co., nesting).

"Least Flycatcher" Stone, *Cassinia*, 1906, 9:44 (Scrub Ridge, west of McConnellsburg, Fulton Co., June)—Simpson, *Oölogist*, 1907, 24:134 (near Warren, Warren Co., May)—Cooke, *Bird-Lore*, 1908, 10:116 (Beaver, Beaver Co., migration)—Dickey, *Oölogist*, 1914, 31:207 (Cresson, Cambria Co., June)—Boulton, *Bird-Lore*, 1928, 30:271 (Millvale, Allegheny Co., May, *fide* Auerswald)—Cope and Hawkins, *Forest Leaves*, 1934, 24:26 (E. Tionesta Forest Reserve, Warren and McKean Co., summer).

EASTERN WOOD PEWEE (Plate 14)

MYIOCHANES VIRENS (Linnaeus)

Description—Smaller than the Phoebe, and about the size of the Acadian Flycatcher. General coloration dull grayish olive, the crown a little darker; wings dusky, with wing-bars and inner edgings paler (whitish); tail dusky; underparts dull whitish with a slight yellowish cast, the breast and sides washed with grayish olive; bill dark above, yellowish flesh color below. *Young birds* in the fall are similar, but the wing-bars and wing-edgings are buffy.

Range—The Wood Pewee ranges throughout the eastern United States and into southern Canada in summer; it winters in Central and northern South America. It is a common summer resident throughout western Pennsylvania, and it has no special peculiarities of distribution.

Migration—This species may be expected in May, about a week later than the Kingbird, or during the height of the warbler migration. My records for Beaver, covering eleven years, show a variation of nine days in the arrival date—May 6 to 15—the average being May 11. In general, these inclusive dates correspond with those from other parts of our region. H. A. McGraw, however, has noted the species at Altoona as early as May 1 (1917), and J. W. Jacobs has seen it at Waynesburg on May 2 (1892). Other early dates of record are: Washington, May 8 (McClelland, Nease); Wilkinsburg, May 4 (Atkinson); Springs, Somerset County, May 7 (Miller); Johnstown, May 4 (Canan); Slippery Rock, Butler County, May 7 (Raney); Greenville, May 3 (Seiple); Crystal Lake, Crawford County, May 7 (Sutton); State College, May 8 (Burleigh); Templeton, Armstrong County, May 5 (Enty); Frick Park, Allegheny County, May 6 (Knauz). A series of records from Renovo, made over a period of twenty-five years (Pierce), yields arrival dates between May 3 and 18, with May 11 as the average—precisely the same as that for Beaver. The return migration begins in August and continues through most of September; stragglers are occasionally seen in October. Observations covering five seasons at Beaver and seventeen at Renovo establish September 22 as the average departure date. The Wood Pewee has been noted at State College as late as October 3 (Burleigh) and at Wilkinsburg until October 6 (Atkinson).

Habits—Early in my ornithological career my interest was attracted by a small, plainly colored bird that I used to see in the orchards and about the shade trees of the town of Beaver, which was then only thinly settled. Subdued and inconspicuous in color, trim of form, and alert and nervous in disposition, it was wont to perch in some exposed place, with body erect, wings drooping, and head turning from one side to another. There it would await passing insects, dash out in pursuit and capture them by a quick twist of the head and a snap of the bill, and then return to its chosen stand. At intervals it sounded a plaintive note of two syllables—*pee-weé-e-e*—the last prolonged into a characteristic drawl. At length, more by accident than by design, I came across its nest, and afterwards identified it as that of the Wood Pewee; and from time to time in later years I found other nests. The species remains one of my favorites.

One would infer from its common name that the Wood Pewee is a forest bird, and indeed it still is to a considerable extent. R. B. Simpson writes of seeing it in the "big woods" of Warren County, miles from any clearing, and my own experience in other forested parts of the state has been similar. But in many sections the Wood Pewee has become almost as domestic in its preferences as the Phoebe itself, and it is certainly more numerous and more generally distributed than that species. Orchards have become favorite haunts, as have open groves and the scattered trees along roadsides and streams. Year after year a given pair of birds will return to the same spot, and I have found the nest built in precisely the same situation for a number of successive seasons. I have seen nests within a few yards of a dwelling, over a street in the town, and adjacent to a railroad. A horizontal branch, preferably a dead one, is always chosen; the elevation varies from six to twenty feet—if in a forest tree it may be somewhat higher.

The typical nest is a veritable model of bird architecture in general appearance and workmanship; it is a neat, compact, elegant structure, saddled on its supporting branch, often where two smaller branches unite, in such a way that it resembles a natural excrescence on the bark. This resemblance is heightened by the covering of lichens with which its outer walls are stuccoed. The body of the nest is composed of dry grass stems and weed fibers, fine strips of grapevine bark, and sometimes a little moss, bits of paper, or other material, circularly disposed and reinforced by spider webs. The lining is usually of fine, wiry grass stems, but sometimes horsehair is employed. The bottom is as a rule rather thin, so that when the nest is detached from the branch it presents a sievelike appearance. I have observed that second nests give every indication of hasty construction and are very likely to be inelegant.

Three eggs are usually laid, but sometimes only two. Sets of four are very rare. They are of a delicate cream-colored tint. In one type they are boldly blotched and spotted around the larger end with dark rufescent brown and have lilac shell-markings. Often the markings take the form of a wreath. In other examples the spots are much smaller and are not confluent. Between these two types there is every possible degree of variation. The average size of the eggs is .72 by .54 inches. According to my observations, they are usually laid during the first or second week in June, but delayed nestings are not uncommon, and instances are on record of young in the nest as late as September. The parent birds are courageous in defense of their home and will fly at an intruder and show jealousy toward other small birds in the vicinity, much as the Kingbird does. In September, after the young are on the wing, there are sometimes marked movements of this species in connection with the warbler migration, when many individuals, usually in company with other forest-loving birds, may be seen continually on the move in the treetops. Although the Wood Pewee is one of the few birds that sing continuously throughout the summer, it becomes practically silent in the fall and is then easily confused with some of the *Empidonaces*.

Contopus virens Townsend, *Proc. Acad. Nat. Sci. Philadelphia*, 1883, 64 (Latrobe, Westmoreland Co.)—Teulon, *Jour. Boston Zoöl. Soc.*, 1883, 2:9 (Bradford, McKean Co.)—Dwight, *Auk*, 1892, 9:136 (Cresson, Cambria Co., June)—Todd, *Auk*, 1893, 10:39 (Two Lick, Indiana Co., June), 44 (Coalport, Clearfield Co., June)—Jacobs, *Summer Birds Greene Co., Pa.*, 1893, 8 (Greene Co., nesting)—Baily, *Auk*, 1896, 13:293 (Williamsville, Elk Co., June–July)—Jacobs, *Gleanings from Nature*, 1898, 1:17, 29 (Waynesburg, Greene Co., nesting)—Cope, *Cassinia*, 1902, 5:15 (Clinton and Potter Co., June)—Keim, *Cassinia*, 1905, 8:38 (Port Allegany, McKean Co., summer).

"Wood Pewee" Enty, *Ornithologist and Oölogist*, 1885, 10:79 (Templeton, Armstrong Co., May)—Todd, *Oölogist*, 1887, 4:89 (Beaver, Beaver Co., nesting)—Jacobs, *Hawkeye Ornithologist and Oölogist*, 1888, 1:88 (Waynesburg, Greene Co., May)—Stone, *Cassinia*, 1906, 9:41, 43 (McConnellsburg,

Fulton Co., June)—PITCAIRN, *Bird-Lore*, 1907, 9:155 (Riverview Park, Allegheny Co., nesting)—COOKE, *Bird-Lore*, 1908, 10:168 (Waynesburg, Greene Co., Beaver, Beaver Co., and Renovo, Clinton Co., migration)—SIMPSON, *Oölogist*, 1909, 26:170 (Warren, Warren Co., nesting); 1912, 29:329 (head of Tionesta Creek, Warren Co., summer)—DICKEY, *Oölogist*, 1914, 31:171 ([Charter Oak], Huntingdon Co., June)—MCCONNELL, *Oölogist*, 1918, 35:150 (McKeesport, Allegheny Co.)—MCCLELLAND, *Am. Mid. Nat.*, 1922, 8:36 (Washington, Washington Co., summer; migration)—STREET, *Cassinia*, 1923, 24:13 (Greencastle to Ft. Loudon, Franklin Co., June)—CHRISTY, *Cardinal*, 1924, v. 1, no. 4, p. 10 (Big Traverse Valley, Beaver Co., June)—BOULTON, *Bird-Lore*, 1928, 30:271 (Frick Park, Allegheny Co., May, *fide* Knauz)—CHRISTY, *Cardinal*, 1931, 3:44 (["Patton's Point"], Beaver Co., May).

Horizopus virens TODD, *Ann. Carnegie Mus.*, 1904, 2:563 (Presque Isle, Erie Co., nesting)—TODD, in Bausman, *Hist. Beaver Co., Pa.*, 1904, 2:1199 (Beaver Co., summer).

Myiochanes virens HARLOW, *Auk*, 1912, 29:472 (southern Centre Co., nesting)—CHRISTY, *Cardinal*, 1923, v. 1, no. 1, [p. 7] (Sewickley, Allegheny Co., nesting)—BURLEIGH, *Wilson Bull.*, 1923, 35:89 (Allegheny Co., nesting); 1924, 36:71 (State College, Centre Co., summer; migration)—CHRISTY and SUTTON, *Cardinal*, 1928, 2:71 (Cook Forest, Clarion Co., summer)—SUTTON, *Ann. Carnegie Mus.*, 1928, 18:153 (Crawford Co. localities, summer; nesting)—BURLEIGH, *Wilson Bull.*, 1931, 43:43 (State College, Centre Co., nesting)—BURLEIGH, *Cardinal*, 1932, 3:77 (Chestnut Ridge, near Uniontown, Fayette Co., nesting).

"Eastern Wood Pewee" COPE and HAWKINS, *Forest Leaves*, 1934, 24:26 (E. Tionesta Forest Reserve, Warren and McKean Co., summer).

OLIVE-SIDED FLYCATCHER (Plate 14)

NUTTALLORNIS MESOLEUCUS[1] (Lichtenstein)

Description—Slightly larger than the Phoebe and of much stouter build, with a broader, heavier bill. General coloration much the same: plain dark olive above; wings and tail blackish, with slight paler edgings; throat and underparts in general, white, the *sides* and the *breast* (except in the middle), more or less heavily *shaded with dull olive, in a somewhat streaky pattern;* flanks with a large white patch (mostly concealed in life).

Range—From its winter home in northwestern South America the Olive-sided Flycatcher passes north by the land route to occupy a transcontinental summer range in Canada and the northern United States. It is a characteristic bird of the Canadian Life Zone, but its range extends well into the Transition, and it follows these zones southward along the mountain ranges. In the eastern part of the country it breeds regularly but locally on the Atlantic coast, south to eastern Massachusetts and, in the mountains, to western North Carolina. In New York state it is a fairly common summer resident in the Adirondack and Catskill Mountains, at altitudes as low as 1,500 feet. Oddly enough, however, it appears to have no recognized breeding area in western New York; but across the state line, in Warren County, Pennsylvania, it is now a well-known breeding bird. R. B. Simpson has found it nesting at several points in that section. He also reports it from near the head of Blue Jay Creek in eastern Forest County and has likewise noted it (late in May) near Tyler, Clearfield County. Van Fleet lists it as a rare breeding bird at DuBois. On my early travels through the other northern counties I always watched for it, but without success. I could not even find it at Tamarack Swamp, Clinton County, during my several visits to that interesting place, but in June of 1900, F. R. Cope, Jr., and Stewardson Brown saw a bird there that must have belonged to this species. It is fair to assume that throughout this entire group of counties it is a summer resident, although it is rare and local.

To the westward, this flycatcher ranges to Pymatuning Swamp, where it has often been seen late in May by several observers (including myself) and in June by I. B. Boggs and L. E. Hicks. Miss Ruth Trimble reports it from Canadohta Lake in July (1934)—a record that serves to connect the Pymatuning breeding area with the westernmost breeding station in Warren County (Tamarack Swamp, where a party from the Carnegie Museum found a pair in June, 1934). To the southward (within the limits of our region) the species has not been traced beyond Clearfield County (DuBois), but its local range almost certainly includes (or formerly included) the highlands of Cambria and Somerset counties as far as the Maryland border. The elevation of this

[1]The proper name of this species is *Nuttallornis borealis* (Swainson), as shown by A. J. VAN ROSSEM, *Transactions San Diego Society of Natural History*, 1934, 7:352.

area would surely argue against a discontinuous range, other conditions being equal.

Elsewhere in western Pennsylvania the species is a transient, rare and little known. I have recorded it at Beaver on only four occasions, and B. H. Christy has noted it at Frankfort Springs, Beaver County. A few other records are included in the data on migration.

Migration—The few existing migration records for this flycatcher indicate that in the spring it is a very late migrant—even later than the Yellow-bellied. A. K. Pierce identified it only once at Renovo—on May 11, 1900. On the same date in 1919 one bird was observed at Charter Oak, Huntingdon County, by T. D. Burleigh. The species was noted at Hollidaysburg on May 14, 1921 (Berg), and at Beaver on May 14, 1916, and May 12, 1922 (Todd). P. P. Malley observed it at Frick Park, in Pittsburgh, on May 23, 1937, and on May 18, 1938. The migration movement continues up to the last of May or even a little later, as shown by the following dates of arrival at Warren, recorded by Mr. Simpson: June 3, 1901; May 30, 1904; May 26, 1906; May 25, 1910; May 29, 1913; May 24, 1925. Individuals seen during the last week in May, therefore, are not necessarily established for the summer. A bird that I collected near Shermansville, Crawford County, on May 20, 1933, gave me the impression that it was settled for the season, but G. M. Sutton thinks that four birds seen by him near Hartstown on May 31, 1924, were migrants, as undoubtedly was the one found by Mr. Christy at Frankfort Springs, Beaver County, on May 31, 1926.

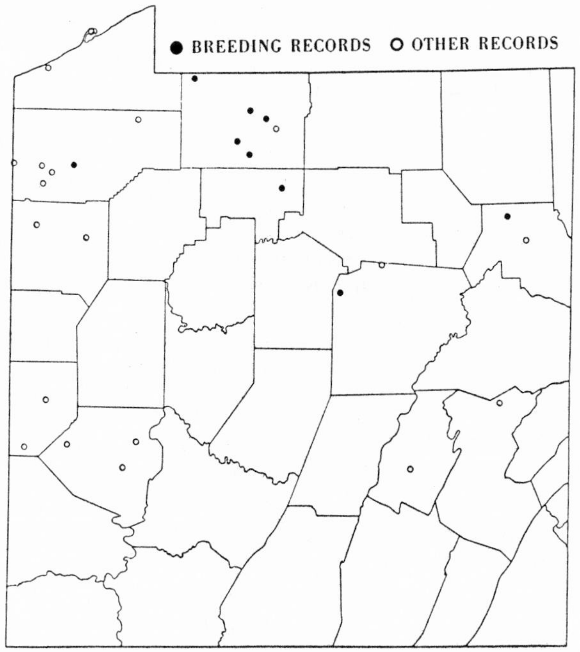

LOCAL RANGE OF THE OLIVE-SIDED FLYCATCHER

The fall movement begins about the first of September and continues for about a month. Beaver dates are: August 27 (1916—Boulton) and September 3 and 16 (1905—Todd). For Presque Isle there are two records at this season: September 18 (1900—Simpson) and September 11 (1931—Hicks). A late date for Conneaut Lake is October 1 (1925—Langdon).

Habits—The Olive-sided is the aristocrat of the flycatcher tribe. No lowly or halfway perch will satisfy it; nothing less than the very tiptop of the tallest tree. From this height it overlooks the scene below with a calm, semidetached air, as if conscious of its superiority. A tall dead stub, or a dead branch rising above the crown of a living tree, is always preferred. On such a perch it may be found from daylight to dark, or it will sometimes use two or more different stations in turn. From its lookout it sallies forth at intervals after high-flying insects, which it captures with a snap of the bill that is distinctly audible from below. Stomach examinations disclose that over 82 per cent of the usual food of this flycatcher consists of Hymenoptera (including some honeybees).[1] The Olive-sided is the most exclusively insectivorous species of the family in North America.

During the migration season this bird may be found in the top of some tall dead tree along the edge of the forest, but seldom in the deep woods. On its breeding grounds, too, it rather avoids the dense tree growth and prefers wild land that has been lumbered over, where many large stubs and some green trees have been left standing, with here and there a small grove. Except for overcoming the difficulties arising from the nature of the ground, locating the bird in its haunts is simple enough, once one has learned to recognize the characteristic call note. This note is a clear whistle of three syllables, the first rather low, the others so loud that on a calm day they can be heard half a mile away. "Yes, I'm here," it seems to say, although a better rendering would probably be

[1]Compare F. E. L. Beal, U. S. Department of Agriculture, Biological Survey, *Bulletin*, no. 44, 1912, p. 41.

pit, per-wheer, as written by Dr. Sutton, with the last syllable accented and prolonged.

The following account of the nesting of this species is adapted from that of Mr. Simpson, who has found no less than six nests in Warren County (from 1904 to 1915). He first became aware of its status as a breeding bird in June, 1900, and with his co-operation I was able to secure a pair for the Carnegie Museum collection. In June, 1904, he located another pair, this time near the head of Ott's Run. It was in the usual kind of place—a slashing with a number of trees and stubs left standing, close to the edge of a heavy woods, mostly hemlock. On June 5 the female of this pair was busy building. She was very restless and kept repeating rapidly, from three to eight times, a call similar to the first low note of the male and not unlike that of the Red Crossbill, but louder and rather harsher. The nest was in a hemlock, fifty feet from the ground and five feet from the trunk, near the end of a horizontal branch. On June 14 Mr. Simpson climbed to this nest, only to find that in the meantime it had been disturbed and robbed, perhaps by some prowling squirrel or jay. Two days later the birds started another nest in the same tree, about fifteen feet lower than the first one, and farther out from the trunk. In building the second nest the female used fully half the material of the first. She habitually perched on an old stub for a time, occasionally catching an insect; then, getting restless, she would begin calling and would make three or four trips to the nest, adding to it each time, after which she would again become quiet and resume her perch. On June 24 this nest held a set of three eggs.

A pair of these birds will return season after season to the same spot. It is easy to locate the nest, as the male, although he takes no part in the building, keeps close to the scene of operations. Generally unsuspicious, the birds pay no attention to a person on the ground. At times they will perch close together and twitter to one another in friendly fashion. When a climber ascends the nest-tree, however, both birds will show their courage by repeatedly darting within a few feet of his head. All the nests found by Mr. Simpson were on horizontal limbs of second-growth hemlocks, from three to twelve feet from the trunk. With one exception, they were well hidden from view. The lowest nest was twenty feet from the ground, and the highest was fifty. They required from five to seven days to build. The material comprised small dead hemlock twigs, on many of which bits of lichen remained; a very few pieces of dry grass were used for lining. The nests were all rather flat, coarse, and flimsy, resembling the Scarlet Tanager's in style. In every instance there were three eggs. These resemble those of the Wood Pewee in color and markings but are of course much larger (.85 by .63 inches). The ground-color is much the same, but the spotting and wreathing about the larger end is heavier. Nestings occur between June 14 and 25.

Professor Hicks writes that he observed the Olive-sided Flycatcher on Hemlock Island, Pymatuning Swamp, at the extreme western edge of our region, on June 16, 1932—the same day that he found a nest across the state line in Ohio.[1] Its breeding at this locality is thus also indicated.

Contopus borealis Warren, *Birds Pa.*, ed. 2, 1890, 194 (Erie, Erie Co., *fide* Sennett; Crawford Co., *fide* Kirkpatrick; Clinton Co., *fide* Van Fleet, transient)—Cope, *Cassinia*, 1902, 5:10, 15 (Tamarack Swamp, Clinton Co., June).

Nuttallornis borealis Todd, *Ann. Carnegie Mus.*, 1901, 1:4 (near head of Hickory Creek and near Thompson Station, Warren Co., June)—Todd, *Ann. Carnegie Mus.*, 1904, 2:562 (Presque Isle, Erie Co., transient)—Stone, *Cassinia*, 1919, 22:32 (Hollidaysburg, Blair Co., May, *fide* McGraw)—Christy, *Cardinal*, 1923, v. 1, no. 1, [p. 7] (Sewickley, Allegheny Co., spring transient)—Burleigh, *Wilson Bull.*, 1924, 36:77 ("State College, Centre Co." [Charter Oak, Huntingdon Co.], May).

"Olive-sided Flycatcher" Simpson, *Oölogist*, 1906, 23:135; 1907, 24:183; 1909, 26:26, 170; 1910, 27:100; and 1911, 28:201 (near Warren, Warren Co., nesting, etc.)—Simpson, *Oölogist*, 1909, 26:193 (Clearfield Co., May; near Warren, Warren Co., nesting)—Jackson, *Cassinia*, 1909, 12:10 (near Warren, Warren Co., nesting)—Simpson, *Oölogist*, 1912, 29:329 (head of Tionesta Creek, Warren Co., summer)—Sutton, *Bird-Lore*, 1924, 26:267 (Hartstown, Crawford Co., May, *fide* Blair)—Eastwood, *Bird-Lore*, 1926, 28:274 (Sandy Lake, Mercer Co., May, *fide* Squier)—Cope and Hawkins, *Forest Leaves*, 1934, 24:26 (E. Tionesta Forest Reserve, Warren and McKean Co., summer)—Boggs, *Redstart*, 1936 3:92 (Linesville, Crawford Co., June)—Malley and Shoemaker, *Redstart*, 1937, 4:70 (Frick Park, Pittsburgh, Allegheny Co., May).

Nuttallornis borealis borealis Sutton, *Ann. Carnegie Mus.*, 1928, 18:153 (Crawford Co. localities, transient).

[1] *Wilson Bulletin*, 1933, 45:185.

LARKS

FAMILY ALAUDIDAE

The larks are almost exclusively an Old World family. There are numerous representatives, arranged in about twenty-five genera. Only one genus occurs regularly in America, and this is represented by a single species that has several congeners in Asia and northern Africa. Two races of the Horned Lark are found in western Pennsylvania—one as a winter wanderer, and the other as a permanent resident.

The structure of the feet of the Alaudidae is highly characteristic and is unique among the so-called "song" birds of the Passerine group; the tarsal covering is scutellate (scaled) but rounded and blunt behind instead of sharply ridged. The hind toe and claw are long and straight in adaptation to terrestrial life. Larks are birds of the open country; they nest on the ground and rarely perch much above the ground level. They are gifted singers, and the North American bird rivals its famous relative, the European Skylark. The song is usually delivered when the bird is in flight. Except in the breeding season, larks are found in small, roving flocks. They feed chiefly on weed seeds, although insects are the principal diet of the young birds.

NORTHERN HORNED LARK

OTOCORIS ALPESTRIS ALPESTRIS (Linnaeus)

Description—About the size of the Wood Thrush. *Adult male:* upperparts grayish brown with a more or less vinaceous cast, especially on the crown and upper back, tail coverts, and wing coverts, and with obscure darker streaks; the wings have slight white spots and edgings; middle tail feathers similar to the back, the others dusky black, the outermost pair with white outer edges; a broad black band on the crown, between the eyes, narrowing on either side into a line which ends behind in a slight projecting "horn"; *forehead and a broad stripe through the eyes, dull yellow*, and below this a black stripe, widening out behind, partially separating this yellow area from the similar *yellow* of the *throat;* below the yellow throat, a broad, black, crescent-shaped band; rest of underparts dull whitish, the breast with some darker shading. In fresh fall plumage the black of the crown is scarcely evident, and the breast below the black band may have a spotted appearance. *Female* similar to the male, but smaller. The black markings of the head and throat are much reduced, often merely indicated. The "horns" are not always conspicuous.

Range—The Horned Lark has an unusually wide distribution in both Eurasia and North America. It is remarkably plastic and breaks up into races in different parts of its extensive range. The main summer home of the typical race is the region of the Labrador Peninsula and the territory to the north. In winter it comes south into the northeastern United States, invading to some extent the regular range of its smaller relative. It is said to be the common form at that season in New Jersey and eastern Pennsylvania, but west of the mountains it can only be considered rare and irregular. One would expect the flocks of horned larks that are wont to appear in the western part of our state during spells of severe weather to be birds of this race; but in almost every instance, collected specimens have proved to be *praticola*. The exceptions were three birds shot from a flock at Duquesne, Allegheny County, on January 15, 1924, by G. M. Sutton, and two taken at Wilkinsburg on February 12, 1899 (in sub-zero weather), by D. A. Atkinson. The northern race would be expected to occur regularly at Erie, if anywhere in our region, but although taken there by Sennett in 1875, there are no recent acceptable records. Dr. Sutton, however, writes of seeing a flock near Hartstown on February 20, 1925, and since members of the other race were present at the same time for comparison, his sight identification is credited.

T. D. Burleigh's record from State College in late winter was based on the capture of specimens (so he writes me) that were identified at the time by Mr. Burleigh and by R. C. Harlow. Other specimens are known to have been taken there as long ago as 1898, according to J. K. Musgrave. Thus it seems that only east of the main Allegheny divide is the northern race of Horned Lark a more or less common and regular winter visitor.[1]

Migration—The local records for this lark are still too few to permit adequate treatment of its migration. The bird is an irregular winter wanderer, and its movements are more or less erratic and dependent on particular conditions of food supply and of weather. In 1916 it remained at State College until April 9.

Habits—The winter habits of this race are virtually the same as those of the Prairie Horned Lark. Flocks of the two respective races tend to remain apart. Further information concerning the occurrence of the northern race in our region is much to be desired, but verification of all identifications by securing specimens is highly important.

Otocoris alpestris Dwight, *Auk*, 1890, 7:141 (Erie, Erie Co.)—Todd, *Ann. Carnegie Mus.*, 1904, 2:564 (Erie, Erie Co., winter).

Otocoris alpestris alpestris Burleigh, *Wilson Bull.*, 1924, 36:77 (State College, Centre Co., February–April)—(?)[Potter, secretary], *Cassinia*, 1926, 25:30 (Greencastle, Franklin Co., winter, *fide* Ziegler)—Sutton, *Ann. Carnegie Mus.*, 1928, 18:158 (Hartstown, Crawford Co., February).

"Prairie Horned Lark" (error) Sutton, *Bird-Lore*, 1924, 26:122, part (Duquesne, Allegheny Co.).

[1]There is a possibility that the record from Franklin County cited in the references may really pertain to *praticola*.

PRAIRIE HORNED LARK

OTOCORIS ALPESTRIS PRATICOLA Henshaw

Description—Similar to the Northern Horned Lark, but slightly smaller. The general coloration is grayer, the *forehead and the line over the eye are whitish* (instead of decidedly yellowish), and the *throat is a paler yellow* (sometimes nearly white). *Young birds in juvenal dress* are mottled with brown and black on the upperparts, which are *dotted with small white spots;* the underparts are dull whitish, and the breast is buffy, with dusky streaks; the black-and-white head pattern is not in evidence.

Range—The original home of this race of the Horned Lark was doubtless in the prairie region of the upper Mississippi Valley, whence it gradually worked its way eastward as the country was cleared and new breeding areas became available. Exception has been taken to this view by some writers, but the summary and argument advanced by a recent authority[1] are sufficiently convincing. The early authors knew the Horned Lark in the eastern United States only as a winter resident, and when a few reports of its breeding began to come in from that area this new status was heralded as a discovery. At length there arose a suspicion that these breeding birds and the winter birds were not the same, and this theory was confirmed in 1884 by H. W. Henshaw, who discriminated the former under the subspecific name *praticola.* The type on which he based his description came from southern Illinois. At once additional breeding records of the newly described race began to appear in print—and this increase in records gave the impression that the bird must have been overlooked before. It is my opinion, however, that the Prairie Horned Lark had only then begun to move eastward in conspicuous numbers, as suitable territory was provided. Its appearance in new areas was merely coincidental with the discrimination of the breeding Horned Lark as a distinct subspecies. Its progressive eastward advance can even be roughly traced, although the picture is still far from complete. Professor Pickwell thinks that it must have reached western New York by way of

[1]G. B. Pickwell, *Transactions Academy of Science, of St. Louis,* 1931, 27:15.

southern Ontario and then turned southward into western Pennsylvania. I believe, however, that it may have reached our region by an eastward advance along the lake shore plain in northern Ohio, where local conditions were (and still are) favorable.

It is notable that as late as 1882 J. M. Wheaton had no knowledge of any Horned Lark breeding in Ohio. The first report of its breeding in Pennsylvania was in 1888, when the species was found at Erie by Sennett and Warren. In 1889 I found it in Butler County (between Leasuresville and Sarver) and in 1891, in Beaver County (near Beaver). J. W. Jacobs, writing in 1893, omits it from his list of the summer birds of Greene County, where it is now common. He writes, however, that he used to observe it regularly, though not commonly, during his trips in quest of the eggs of the Red-tailed Hawk (beginning in the late eighties), but that for some time he supposed it to be only a migrant. In 1898 a nest was found at Schenley Park within the city limits of Pittsburgh—a locality now recognized as a breeding station. W. L. Baily had meanwhile found the species very common in northern Elk County in 1894, and the next year A. K. Pierce took his first nest at Kane, McKean County. By 1900 this lark had been reported from Potter County. Its advent there—the last large area of our region to suffer deforestation—probably marked the completion of its distribution within our borders. At any rate, it has crossed the crest of the Alleghenies and established itself in the ridge and valley section, and towards the south has invaded western Maryland and also West Virginia. Over this entire area it is now more or less common as a breeding bird, although it is perhaps a little more numerous in the northwestern counties of Pennsylvania than elsewhere.

Migration—The large flocks of prairie horned larks that are sometimes seen in the winter almost certainly come from farther north. More than once, in Beaver County, I have encountered mated pairs in their regular haunts, while in fields adjoining there was a flock of birds which, judging from their behavior, were presumably of alien origin. These mated pairs, sometimes accompanied by their progeny, may be seen on or near their nesting grounds throughout the winter; the smaller flocks and family groups break up into pairs very early in the season, usually in February. In the fall the incoming flocks from other regions appear on Presque Isle as early as October, and sometimes do not all leave until March. Banding may eventually enable us to trace the movements of this species more satisfactorily. We do know, however, that by far the greater part of the Horned Lark population in our region in the winter belongs to this race.

Habits—Winter is the season when the Prairie Horned Lark is commonest and most conspicuous. Our other winter birds seek the shelter of the woodland, orchard, or briery thicket—and even the Bob-white, erstwhile bird of the open, takes to the bush—but the Horned Lark is an exception. It is pre-eminently a bird of the great open spaces, where its needs are met not by vegetation but by lack of it. It may be found in the exposed, windswept fields of the uplands, in flocks of its own kind, or perhaps associating with the Snow Bunting—if the weather is severe enough to bring this truly arctic wanderer so far south. The two species have much in common and are often found together in the winter. Both travel in flocks, both affect open country, and both subsist on much the same fare—weed seeds of various kinds. Sometimes these birds appear in immense numbers. Once, in February, I came upon a mixed flock that I estimated contained at least ten thousand birds, scattered over an area of perhaps fifty acres. It was a cold, windy day, and they were very shy and restless, constantly rising here and there to fly off to other parts of the field. Occasionally a great number would rise en masse and swing off in erratic fashion, to drop down again gradually at a little distance. This was the only time I have ever seen so many together, and the sight was certainly impressive. Ordinary flocks seldom number more than two or three hundred and are often much smaller. In flight or against the snow, they attract attention, but against the bare ground the birds are so well camouflaged that more than once I have unwittingly walked right up to them without realizing their presence until they flushed.

The account of this species contained in the following paragraphs is in large measure condensed from G. M. Sutton's readable article published in 1927, which was based in the main on his experience in western Pennsylvania. Concerning the daily activities of a flock that he studied, he remarks: "When first noted all the birds were together wandering about over the ground, searching busily for food. So protectively were they colored that it was almost impossible to keep more than one bird under observation at a time, since to move one's eyes from a bird meant to lose it altogether. Their plumage was fluffed out to retain the body heat and some of them stood much of the time on one foot. When first disturbed the whole flock rose simultaneously, their fluttering wings producing a peculiar explosive sound. With a fine-toned note from each bird upward went the whole mass, higher and higher, in wide circles above the field, seemingly intent on leaving altogether." This flock broke up into smaller flocks, however, which came down in separate parts of the field.

"The actions of this large flock were typical. Once the large mass was disturbed the birds were not found together again, and by the end of the day only small flocks were flushed. On the following day the same flock movements were noted. When undisturbed the flock remained together from morning until night, for during winter Prairie Horned Larks are very sociable."

After describing the awakening of a flock and suggesting that a large number of birds would effectively remove the weed seeds from a given area during the course of a winter, Dr. Sutton continues:

"Occasionally an undisturbed flock circles about the field several times merely for exercise, and settles near the place where it started. It is remarkable how suddenly and yet how simultaneously the whole flock moves; and how accurate every wing stroke is. Yet individuals sometimes lag, and the excitement or fear of the individual left behind is sometimes amusing. . . .

"The ease of flight of these birds is a matter of common knowledge; but when they move off but a little frightened, and glide along the ground in long, sweeping curves, their grace rivals that of deliberate swallows.

"In mid-morning if the sun becomes warm activity slackens somewhat, and they may be seen standing on one foot on a stone, or hunched up on the turf with eyes partly closed. The incessant low twittering subsides as from some remote part of the field drifts a snatch of the spring song, uttered from the ground. Usually at this season the 'horns' on the head are not very prominent, because the plumage is unworn, and is so fluffed out that such protruding tufts are not visible.

"The winter call-notes are usually of one or two syllables, and are low and gentle, suggesting at times that the bird is timid or exhausted. The notes are clearest and loudest during flight, just before the flock alights, in this respect resembling the din made by the huge clouds of Longspurs of the mid-west, as they settle in the grass. Individual birds, apart from the flock, usually utter louder and clearer notes also."

Much praise, in song and story, has been given the vocal performance of the Skylark of Europe. It is truly a beautiful song as I have heard it in France and England, but in my opinion it is not

vastly superior to the efforts of our own Prairie Horned Lark. Sometimes our bird, like the Skylark, sings from the ground or from a fence post. But usually it mounts into the air, flying in high, sweeping circles and pouring forth a song of singular delicacy and sweetness as it soars aloft for several minutes at a time.

Dr. Sutton writes: "Song phrases uttered on the ground seem to have exactly the same number of syllables and the same rhythm as those given in the air. But the flight song is more ecstatic in its feeling because of the increased enthusiasm of the singer and the rapid repetition of the phrases, which transforms the whole performance into an almost continuous outburst of melody. . . . Sometimes these flights are made in wide circles which cross and recross many times; sometimes they are made slowly in one direction for the length of the field and back again; and then again, in windy weather, the bird may remain in the same position above the field although he is ever flying forward. Closely as I have watched and listened to these songs I am not certain that the rapid, ascending close of the song-phrase occurs simultaneously with the fluttering, climbing movement of the flight, since I have always believed that the sound reached my ears more slowly than the impression of the bird's movements reached my eyes. Certainly, however, the impression is given that the wing beats correspond to the *tempo* of the music. The song-stanza has two or three distinct parts, the first two being repetitions of a double note often given on the ground, and the last being the ascending warble referred to above. The song may be described as *tinkling;* and although it is sweet and delicate, it can hardly be called glorious. The flight song, however, possesses an undeniable sublimity as the bird swings back and forth in wide circles, so far above the listener that it is sometimes almost out of view!" This flight song of course presages the breeding season, although I have occasionally heard it also in the fall of the year.

The Prairie Horned Lark is the first of our Passerine birds to nest in the spring. It always begins operations in March, often before all the snow is gone, and so early that its first efforts may be vitiated by the action of the elements. A heavy snowfall may even cover the nest and compel its abandonment. Reports have been received of nests found during the first week in March; and although these records have not been verified, a few days of mild weather at this time would make such occurrences possible. S. S. Dickey has found eggs far advanced in incubation in Greene County as early as March 21, and R. C. Harlow and T. D. Burleigh report a nest with young at State College on March 26. At Warren, R. B. Simpson has taken eggs on March 24, and S. J. Seiple once found a full set in northern Mercer County on March 26; but most of the first nestings reported by others are for the last week in March and early in April. Eggs have been found, however, during all the months from March to July, a fact which proves that the Prairie Horned Lark must raise two and possibly even three broods in a season.

For a nesting site an open spot is always selected, preferably on a high knob or ridge. Bare ground is not a prime requisite, but high grass will not serve at all. In recent years there has been an increasing tendency among these birds to utilize golf courses, with their extensive areas of level expanse and smooth sward, and several such nestings have been recorded in our region. For a number of seasons larks have nested within the oval of the race track at Schenley Park, as attested by several observers independently. Several nests found by A. K. Pierce at Kane were all on the common on the outskirts of the town. Wherever located, the nest is always sunk in a depression in the ground, its edge flush with the surface. It is frequently placed beside a projecting clod or tuft of grass, which serves as a partial protection. Often, too, a "pavement" of flat pebbles or some other thin substance is laid down as an approach to the nest. The nest itself is composed of dry grasses and weed stems, with perhaps some leaves and coarser material, and is lined with finer stuff. While some nests are much bulkier than others, all are loose, simple structures. Three, four, or more rarely five, eggs are laid; they average .85 by .62 inches. The ground-color is occasionally dull white but is usually a peculiar greenish buff; it is almost wholly concealed by small, irregular spots and flecks of cinnamon brown, rather uniformly distributed.

Finding a nest is no easy matter. For a full account of this subject the reader is referred to Dr. Sutton's article (1927). During the period of egg-laying, the actions of the female denote leisure, patience, and unconcern—she remains quietly in one place and keeps preening herself. While the searcher is yet a long way off, an incubating bird will usually abandon her nest and fly low over the ground, where she is soon joined by the male. Both birds affect a casual unconcern which they doubtless do not feel. The female is extremely reluctant to return to the nest so long as the watcher is in sight. This clever ruse is actually very effective in concealing the exact position of the nest.

The young are odd-looking creatures, conspicuously spotted above, and harmonizing in color with their surroundings. At first they are fed extensively on insects. During the summer months the adults also feed largely on insects, and many harmful kinds are on their bill of fare. The economic value of the Prairie Horned Lark to agriculture, however, lies mainly in its destruction of the seeds of noxious weeds.

Otocoris alpestris praticola WARREN, *Birds Pa.*, 1888, 240 (Erie, Erie Co., breeding)—DWIGHT, *Auk*, 1889, 6:198; and 1890, 7:144 (Erie, Erie Co., breeding, *fide* Sennett)—WARREN, *Birds Pa.*, ed. 2, 1890, 198 (Erie Co., summer)—TODD, *Auk*, 1891, 8:236 ([west of Leasuresville], Butler Co., June), 395 (Beaver, Beaver Co., June)—BAILY, *Auk*, 1896, 13:294 (Williamsville, Elk Co., breeding)—RHOADS, *Auk*, 1899, 16:311 (Schenley Park and "Riley's Ford," Allegheny Co., breeding; Beaver and Butler Co.)—[HOLLAND], *Ann. Carnegie Mus.*, 1901, 1:3 (Schenley Park, Allegheny Co., nesting)—COPE, *Cassinia*, 1902, 5:15 (near New Bergen and Germania, Potter Co., June)—OBERHOLSER, *Proc. U. S. Nat. Mus.*, 1902, 24:825 (Erie, Erie Co.; Tidioute, Warren Co., breeding)—TODD, *Ann. Carnegie Mus.*, 1904, 2:564 (Erie and

Presque Isle, Erie Co., resident)—TODD, in Bausman, *Hist. Beaver Co., Pa.*, 1904, 2:1200 (Beaver Co., resident)—BROOKS, *Auk*, 1908, 25:235 (Schenley Park, Allegheny Co., breeding)—HARLOW, *Cassinia*, 1911, 14:15 (near State College, Centre Co., February)—HARLOW, *Auk*, 1912, 29:473 (southern Centre Co., resident); 1918, 35:136 ([Charter Oak], Huntingdon Co.; [State College], Centre Co.; and [Waynesburg], Greene Co., nesting)—DICKEY, *Oölogist*, 1913, 30:48 (Waynesburg, Greene Co., nesting)—CHRISTY, *Cardinal*, 1923, v. 1, no. 1, [p. 7] (Sewickley, Allegheny Co., resident)—BURLEIGH, *Wilson Bull.*, 1923, 35:90 (Schenley Park, Allegheny Co., nesting); 1924, 36:69; 1931, 43:44 (State College, Centre Co., nesting)—CHRISTY, *Cardinal*, 1926, v. 1, no. 8, p. 18 (near Clinton, Allegheny Co., nesting; Schenley Park, Allegheny Co., nesting, *fide* Sutton)—SUTTON, *Wilson Bull.*, 1927, 39:132 (western Pa., etc., habits; nesting)—CHRISTY and SUTTON, *Cardinal*, 1928, 2:71 (Cook Forest, Clarion Co., June)—SUTTON, *Ann. Carnegie Mus.*, 1928, 18:158 (Crawford Co. localities, resident)—CHRISTY, *Cardinal*, 1931, 3:45 (Butler, Butler Co., May)—HEGNER, *Cardinal*, 1932, 3:93 (Sewickley and Oakmont, Allegheny Co., nesting)—CHRISTY, *Cardinal*, 1932, 3:93 (southern Beaver Co., May).

"Prairie Horned Lark" STONE, *Cassinia*, 1906, 9:43 (McConnellsburg, Fulton Co., June)—JACKSON, *Cassinia*, 1909, 12:12 (Warren, Warren Co., May)—DICKEY, *Oölogist*, 1910, 27:48 (near Waynesburg, Greene Co., nesting)—DEBES, *Bird-Lore*, 1912, 14:111 (Wilkinsburg[?], Allegheny Co., February)—MILLER (R. F.), *Oölogist*, 1919, 36:155 (Masseyburg, Huntingdon Co., nesting)—SCOVILLE, *Cassinia*, 1920, 23:19 ([Charter Oak, Huntingdon Co.], May, song)—STAHL, *et al.*, *Bird-Lore*, 1921, 23:18 (Edgewood, Allegheny Co., December)—SAVAGE, *Bird-Lore*, 1923, 25:24; etc. (McKeesport, Allegheny Co., December)—MILLER (A. B.), *Bird-Lore*, 1923, 25:25; etc. (Springs, Somerset Co., December)—SUTTON, *Bird-Lore*, 1923, 25:132, 194; and 1924, 26:122, part (Duquesne, Allegheny Co., winter and nesting, *fide* Galloway and Chandler)—CHRISTY and HEGNER, *Bird-Lore*, 1924, 26:30; etc. (Raccoon Creek and region, Beaver Co., December)—EASTWOOD, *Bird-Lore*, 1926, 28:137 (Deer Creek, Allegheny Co., February, *fide* Squier), 273 (New Kensington, Westmoreland Co., February–April, *fide* Manley)—MATUSZAK, *Bird-Lore*, 1926, 28:29 (Hyde Park, Westmoreland Co., December)—BOULTON, *Bird-Lore*, 1928, 30:127 (Wilkinsburg, Allegheny Co., February, *fide* Jones), 196 ("Patton's Point," Beaver Co., March, nesting, *fide* Christy), 337 (Pittsburgh region)—ELLIOTT, *Cardinal*, 1934, 3:171 (Raccoon Creek, Beaver Co., December).

"Horned Lark" (error) SIMPSON, *Oölogist*, 1912, 29:370 (Warren, Warren Co., winter)—EASTWOOD, *Bird-Lore*, 1925, 27:337 (near Pittsburgh, Allegheny Co., July, *fide* Blair)—(?)BERKHEIMER, *Bird-Lore*, 1934, 36:33 (near Osterburg, Bedford Co., December).

Otocoris alpestris alpestris (error) STONE, *Cassinia*, 1919, 22:32; and 1920, 23:34 (Altoona, Blair Co., March–April, *fide* McGraw).

"Northern Horned Lark" (error?) UPSON, *et al.*, *Bird-Lore*, 1935, 37:47 (Presque Isle, Erie Co., December).

Additional breeding records: Washington, seen April 26, 1896, by W. T. Warrick (Nease)—Jacobs Creek, Westmoreland Co., in song, 1903 (Medsger)—Morganza, Washington Co., noted April 17, 1897 (Van Ostrand)—Mount Pleasant, Westmoreland Co., June 29–July 3, 1893, a flock seen; Jenner Crossroads, Somerset Co., June 23, 1893, seen on east slope of Laurel Hill (Preble)—Tamarack Swamp, Erie Co., July 17–18, 1895; New Hamburg, Mercer Co., March–April (Homer)—Springs, Somerset Co., local in summer (Miller)—New Castle, Lawrence Co., breeding (Raney)—near Wing, Crawford Co., May 7, 1933 (Todd)—near Espyville, Crawford Co., nest, April 11, 1933 (Dilley)—Cambridge Springs, Crawford Co., not uncommon, breeding; Canadohta Lake, Crawford Co., May (Dickey)—Sharon, Mercer Co., nesting (McQuiston)—Johnstown (Airport), Cambria Co., summer (Freer and Mostoller)—near Jamisonville, Butler Co., breeds regularly (Elliott)—Leech's Corners, Mercer Co., nest, March 26, 1934 (Seiple).

SWALLOWS

FAMILY HIRUNDINIDAE

SWALLOWS are found all over the world, and some genera, notably *Hirundo* and *Petrochelidon*, are cosmopolitan in range. Living exclusively on insects, the family is best represented in warm countries; in cold and temperate regions its members are migratory, as are the six species that occur in western Pennsylvania.

The Swallows are distinguished from other Passerine birds by a combination of well-defined characters: long, strong wings with nine primary feathers; a more or less forked tail; short tarsi and weak feet, fitted only for perching; and a short, flat, triangular bill with a wide gape that provides a capacious mouth for capturing insects. In their general appearance, rapid, graceful flight, and habit of feeding on the wing, they resemble the Swifts; but the resemblance is only superficial, for structurally they differ greatly.

"The habits of swallows best illustrate the modifying influences of civilization on indigenous birds. Formerly they all bred on cliffs, in banks, in hollows of trees, and similar places, and many do so still. But most of our species have forsaken these primitive haunts to avail themselves of the convenient artificial nesting-places that man, intentionally or otherwise, provides."[1] They nest in pairs or in colonies, and in migration gather in enormous flocks.

[1]Elliott Coues, *Key to North American Birds*, ed. 4, 1894, p. 321.

TREE SWALLOW

IRIDOPROCNE BICOLOR (Vieillot)

Description—Easily recognized among our swallows by the steel-blue color of the head, upperparts, and sides of the breast, and by the *pure white underparts*. *Females* are duller above (nearer steel green), and *young birds* in the fall are still duller, with some white edgings showing on the inner wing feathers. The tail is but slightly emarginate.

Range—The Tree Swallow is a species characteristic of North America, where it has a general transcontinental range. On the whole it is a relatively northern swallow; some others of this family go as far north in summer, it is true, but these are also found much farther south at the same season. In New England and the adjacent parts of Canada the Tree Swallow is a common breeding bird, but in southern New York and in Ohio it is local and not nearly so numerous. In western Pennsylvania it is an irregular transient and a locally common summer resident. Pymatuning Swamp is the only place in our region where it is at all common and regular in summer. Nests or nesting pairs have been found also at Conneaut Lake and at Meadville, and H. H. Elliott writes that it breeds regularly in small numbers at Sandy Lake, Mercer County. It has been found breeding within the city limits of Erie, but not on Presque Isle, although it appears there in considerable numbers during migration. In June, 1898, I found a nesting pair at Bear Lake, Warren County; and late in April, 1900, I discovered several pairs lingering about some dead willow stubs at Waterford, Erie County. The species has been seen in summer at Cook Forest, Clarion County (Sutton), and at Forestville, Butler County (Keesler). R. B. Simpson doubts its breeding at Warren, although he has seen a few stragglers there in June and July. It appears, however, on Van Fleet's manuscript list of the breeding birds of DuBois, and it was noted on June 20, 1935, along Blacklick Creek in Indiana County, by J. K. Terres and D. M. Baird (Trimble). Warren in 1891 said that it was "a regular and rather plentiful summer resident" at Renovo, although A. K. Pierce never once encountered it during many years' active work there. In Centre County it has been recorded as breeding only at Scotia.

Many years ago J. W. Jacobs found a nest of this species in Greene County. He now recognizes this nesting as a unique and highly exceptional circumstance, because of the general scarcity of the bird in the Ohio Valley and southward—a region where it has never before or since been found breeding. Unpublished records (nonbreeding) for this latter region may be cited as follows: Beaver, noted in April (Rhoads; Wickham); Edgeworth, Allegheny County, May 1, 1909 (Todd); Sandy Creek, Allegheny County, one shot May 2, 1896 (Atkinson); Washington, April (Gans); Jacobs Creek, Westmoreland County (Medsger). Transients have also been noted at Springs, Somerset County (Miller); at Lakemont and Hollidaysburg (McGraw and Berg); and at Chambersburg (Sutton).

Migration—The hardy character of this swallow is reflected by the early date of its appearance in the spring and by its late stay in the fall. Wintering on the South Atlantic and Gulf coasts, farther north than our other swallows, it makes an early start and has been known to reach our latitude on the last day of March. It was noted on March 31, 1934, west of Espyville, Crawford County, "flying low over ice and water" (Dilley; Seiple). Otherwise the few records from our region place its usual arrival during the second week in April. Thus, it has first appeared at Pymatuning Swamp on April 5 (1933) to 14 (1930—Dilley; Seiple); at Erie on April 9 (1900—Todd); at Warren on April 9 (1914) to 15 (1901—Simpson); at Meadville on April 9 (1897—Kirkpatrick); at State College on April 9 (1919—Burleigh); and at Waynesburg on April 14 (1891—Jacobs). On the other hand, stragglers are apt to pass through the region sometime in May; they have been noted at Hollidaysburg until May 15 (Berg), and at Springs, Somerset County, until May 21 (Miller). Fall migration records are scanty, but those reported indicate a movement in September, which extends into the following month. Dates of "last-seen" birds are October 22, 1916—State College (Burleigh); October 13, 1906—Warren (Simpson); September 21, 1900—Erie (Todd); September 19, 1925—Crystal Lake, Crawford County (Sutton).

Habits—The Tree Swallow (so-called because of its partiality for trees as nesting and roosting sites) is seldom found far from water. It prefers lakes and ponds to running water, and the larger the expanse the better. On the single occasion that I saw it along the Ohio River, the birds were flying at a point where the stream had overflowed its banks and had spread out over the lowlands in a miniature lake. Similarly, Mr. Simpson writes that he never sees many tree swallows at Warren except during periods of high water in May, and that then they are fairly common about the overflowed meadows. When feeding, this bird, like other swallows, often skims low over the surface of the water, circling about and returning again and again; when satisfied, it retires to rest on the stubs of dead trees and branches at the edge of the pool. As it appears before the weather is settled, it is sometimes hard pressed to find food and may succumb to cold and hunger, especially when a snowstorm supervenes. It almost always arrives in flocks, small or large, which later in the season are usually joined by other species of swallows, all apparently on amicable terms with each other. It is May before these flocks move northward or break up and the local pairs begin to choose their nesting sites. Pymatuning Swamp offers ideal conditions, of which the species seems to have taken full advantage in the past. Whether the transforming of much of its former breeding area into a lake will work against the bird's interests remains to be seen.

Natural cavities in dead stubs, and abandoned woodpecker-holes, are favorite nesting sites. If the stub stands in or near the water, so much the better. The distance of the hole from the ground is immaterial and may vary from six to thirty-five feet. These stubs are often so rotten that the nests are virtually inaccessible. Feathers—often picked up in the farmyard—are used for lining the nest proper, which is otherwise composed of dry grasses, straws, or other similar light material, piled in to fill up the cavity. The eggs are pure white and average .74 by .55 inches. Four to six compose the usual set; in one instance when seven were laid there was reason to suspect that two females were involved. The last of May or the first of June is about the right time to look for fresh sets.

In some parts of the country the Tree Swallow has adopted artificial bird boxes as nesting sites, as has its cousin, the Purple Martin. I know of only one such nesting in our region, however. This took place in Erie within the city limits. R. L. Keesler, of Forestville, Butler County, wrote that he had tried unsuccessfully to induce this species to use the nest boxes he had provided, although every season some birds came to inspect them. The advent of the European Starling is bound to affect the Tree Swallow unfavorably in this respect.

This is the only one of our swallows that consumes a sizable amount of vegetable food. The berries of the wax myrtle (*Myrica carolinensis*) are eaten by it in large quantities in other parts of its habitat, but thus far there are no reports to this effect from Presque Isle, where alone in our region the plant is known to occur.

Tachycineta bicolor Teulon, *Jour. Boston Zoöl. Soc.*, 1882, 1:51 (Bradford, McKean Co.)—Jacobs, *Summer Birds Greene Co., Pa.*, 1893, 12 (Greene Co., nesting).

"Tree Swallow" Warren, *Forest and Stream*, 1891, 37:182 (Renovo, Clinton Co., summer[?])—Christy, *Cardinal*, 1923, v. 1, no. 2, [p. 17] (Clinton Pond, Allegheny Co., spring).

Iridoprocne bicolor Todd, *Ann. Carnegie Mus.*, 1904, 2:577 (Erie, Erie Co., nesting)—Todd, in Bausman, *Hist. Beaver Co., Pa.*, 1904, 2:1200 (Beaver Co., transient)—Harlow, *Auk*, 1912, 29:478 (southern Centre Co., *fide* Musgrave); 1918, 35:140 (Scotia, Centre Co.)—Burleigh, *Wilson Bull.*, 1924, 36:72 (State College, Centre Co., migration); 1931, 43:49 (Scotia, Centre Co., nesting)—Christy and Sutton, *Cardinal*, 1928, 2:73 (Cook Forest, Clarion Co., June)—Sutton, *Ann. Carnegie Mus.*, 1928, 18:196 (Crawford Co. nesting and migration records).

BANK SWALLOW (Plate 15)

RIPARIA RIPARIA RIPARIA (Linnaeus)

Description—Our smallest swallow, easily recognized by its small size, uniformly brownish upperparts (with the wings a little darker), and *white underparts*, with a *broad dusky bar across the breast*, continued down the middle of the abdomen as irregular spots. Tail slightly forked.

Range—The Bank Swallow is the only species of Passerine bird known to range unmodified through Eurasia as well as North America. On this side of the Atlantic it is found in summer from Labrador to Alaska and as far south as Virginia and Alabama; in winter it retires to South America. As western Pennsylvania is thus well within its breeding range, it might be expected to occur commonly throughout the region. This may at one time have been the case, but it is certainly not true today. All observers agree that there has been a remarkable decrease in the numbers of this swallow in the past forty or fifty years and that it is now rare or absent in many places where once it was common and well known. It is probably more local in its present distribution than the Tree Swallow, and whether there are any really large colonies left is questionable. One is tempted to believe that the encroachments of civilization have forced this species to abandon many of its old haunts, but perhaps this is not the whole story. Whatever the cause, a shifting of the Bank Swallow population in recent years has removed this bird from large areas of our region. To many of our local observers it is virtually unknown, even in migration. It is perhaps more numerous along the lake shore plain in Erie County, where there are high banks along the streams, than in any other locality. April 26, 1924, is the date of my last migration record of this swallow along the Ohio River, although the species was once rather common there, and a few birds used to breed.

Migration—There is some doubt concerning the reliability of the available records of this swallow, since it is easily confused with the Rough-winged species, which comes north at about the same time. The few absolutely trustworthy arrival records for the western counties were nearly all made about April 25. The species has been noted at Waynesburg, however, between April 14 and 20 (1888, 1892—Jacobs); at New Castle on April

13 (1933—Raney); and at State College on April 19 (1916—Burleigh). At Lakemont, Blair County, the available dates are a little later: April 21 and 23 (1918, 1916—McGraw). Twenty seasons' records from Renovo by A. K. Pierce yield an average date of April 29, with April 13 (1897) as the earliest. R. B. Simpson has never seen the species at Warren earlier than May 12 (1901). Transients have been recorded at Clinton Pond, Allegheny County, until May 17 (1923—Christy). Fall migration apparently begins very early, since nearly all the birds leave by the end of August, and often sooner. A few late dates may be cited: August 30, 1903—Renovo; August 28, 1925—Pymatuning Swamp; August 21, 1889—Beaver; September 3, 1934—Presque Isle.

Habits—The nervous, jerky, and somewhat erratic character of its flight distinguishes this swallow from its relatives. Yet it is not less graceful on the wing than they. Daintily picturesque is a flock of these plainly colored little swallows feeding over a body of water, skimming back and forth over its surface and along its shores with the greatest ease and swiftness, and darting hither and yon to snap up small insects. Like the Rough-winged Swallow, this species prefers the vicinity of water, and it digs its burrows in the banks of streams. It has yielded to new conditions only in occasionally utilizing road cuts and artificial sandbanks for nesting sites. A sociable bird at all times, it likes to live in communities, although odd pairs sometimes nest by themselves. A nesting colony that I visited some years ago was located in the sandy banks of a ravine leading down to the shore of Lake Erie, a few miles west of the city of Erie. There about five hundred pairs had congregated, and the birds coming and going and hovering in the air were a pretty sight. Their burrows were mostly near the top of the bank, where there was a sheer drop, so that they were not readily accessible from below. In certain places the face of the bluff was thickly punctured, appearing as if honeycombed. In my 1904 report I wrote that apparently "no eggs were laid at this time [May 28], although no nests were actually examined. Some of the birds were seen carrying in nesting material, however. As a rule the birds entered their holes in pairs, but in more than one case three individuals were seen to enter the same opening in rapid succession."

The burrows are not necessarily straight and are usually not over two or three feet long, although sometimes they may be as long as six feet. It is astonishing that this bird, with its short and feeble bill, can dig out a burrow of such size in the dry earth. The nest itself is merely an accumulation of dry grasses and any other rubbish at hand, with plenty of feathers for lining, and is placed at the slightly enlarged extremity of the burrow. There are usually four or five eggs (five to seven, *fide* J. W. Jacobs); they are pure white in color and very fragile. They tend to be rather long ovate, averaging .72 by .47 inches. According to Mr. Jacobs, the season for full complements of fresh eggs in Greene County is from May 15 to June 15; and I have seen eggs (but not full sets) that were taken on May 17 along Raccoon Creek in Beaver County. D. A. Atkinson, however, has collected fresh sets near Duquesne, Allegheny County, as late as July 13.

After the young are on the wing, usually in August (sometimes earlier), bank swallows collect in flocks, preparatory to their departure for the South, and roost in great numbers along the telegraph wires in certain localities.

"Bank Swallow" Enty, *Ornithologist and Oölogist*, 1885, 10:78 (Templeton, Armstrong Co., April)—Jacobs, *Hawkeye Ornithologist and Oölogist*, 1888, 1:88 (Waynesburg, Greene Co., April)—Stone, *Cassinia*, 1906, 9:44 (McConnellsburg, Fulton Co., June)—McConnell, *Oölogist*, 1918, 35:151 (Long Run, near McKeesport, Allegheny Co.)—Christy, *Cardinal*, 1923, v. 1, no. 2, [p. 17] (Clinton Pond, Allegheny Co., May).

Clivicola riparia Jacobs, *Summer Birds Greene Co., Pa.*, 1893, 12 (Greene Co., nesting).

Riparia riparia Todd, *Ann. Carnegie Mus.*, 1904, 2:577 (Erie, Erie Co., nesting)—Todd, in Bausman, *Hist. Beaver Co., Pa.*, 1904, 2:1200 (Beaver Co., summer)—Christy, *Cardinal*, 1923, v. 1, no. 1, [p. 11] (Sewickley, Allegheny Co., nesting)—Burleigh, *Wilson Bull.*, 1924, 36:129 (State College, Centre Co., spring transient).

Riparia riparia riparia Oberholser, *Bird-Lore*, 1917, 19:326 (Renovo, Clinton Co., migration)—Sutton, *Ann. Carnegie Mus.*, 1928, 18:197 (Crawford Co. localities, summer).

ROUGH-WINGED SWALLOW (Plate 15)

STELGIDOPTERYX RUFICOLLIS SERRIPENNIS (Audubon)

Description—A small swallow with an even, dull brown tail and dull brownish (mouse-colored) upperparts and wings; *throat and breast shaded with brown*, which gradually fades into white on the rest of the underparts. There is *no distinct dark band across the breast*, as in the Bank Swallow. *Young birds* are similar, but have cinnamon-colored wing-edgings.

Range—Our Rough-winged Swallow is the northern representative of a group that is otherwise confined to tropical America. Although the species ranges across the continent, it does not go very far north, and it winters in Mexico and Central America. For many years supposed to be limited by the Carolinian Fauna in its northern distribution, it is now known to range through much of the Alleghanian Fauna as well. Some think that this extension of range is a development of recent years and that the species was not merely overlooked by the earlier writers. But it seems likelier that this bird was confused at first with the Bank Swallow. At one time I, too, shared the impression that in western Pennsylvania the Rough-winged Swallow is a true Carolinian species, but after collating and mapping the available records, I have changed my opinion.

Although not actually common anywhere within our limits, this swallow seems on the whole to be more numerous, or at least more generally distributed, in the region of the Ohio Valley and in the ridge and valley section, than elsewhere. It is reported as local in Crawford County and as a rare breeding bird at DuBois, on the western edge of the plateau section (Van Fleet). With the exception of a single bird (possibly a transient) seen by G. M. Sutton at St. Marys, Elk County, on May 2, 1928, there are no records for the plateau region. The species enters the eastern edge of the highlands in Clinton County, however, as far west as Renovo (Pierce) and Round Island (Rhoads), and may ascend the valley of the West Branch of the Susquehanna River still farther, into Clearfield County. R. B. Simpson's notes from Warren are interesting and suggestive. He writes that the Rough-wing seems to be growing more numerous each year, while the Bank Swallow is growing scarcer. The former has doubtless reached this locality by way of the Allegheny River Valley.

Migration—This swallow reaches our region at about the same time in the spring as the Bank Swallow, although it has far less distance to travel. I used to see it regularly at Beaver from April 14 (1891) to 22 (1889), but I have no recent records. It has been observed along Pine Creek, Allegheny County, as early as April 16 (1899—Atkinson); at Clinton Pond, in the same county, on April 23 (1923—Christy); at Erie on April 26 (1902—Simpson); at Warren on April 24 (1899—Simpson); and near Pittsburgh on April 18 (1914—Burleigh). In the eastern part of our region the available arrival records correspond closely: State College, April 17 (1915—Burleigh); Hollidaysburg, April 20 (1923—Berg). This swallow must begin its return migration very early; for it generally disappears from its usual resorts after the young are on the wing, and thereafter data on its movements are fragmentary. It has been reported from Sewickley(?) on August 27 (1922—Christy); from Presque Isle (a flock of two hundred) on September 1 (1928—Hicks); and from Wilkinsburg on September 3 (1894—Atkinson).

Habits—Swallows are sociable birds, and during the season of migration several species are often found together in a mixed flock, coursing over the fields and waters. The Rough-winged Swallow may be a member of one of these scattered companies, and as such its plain coloration and dull-colored throat and breast suffice to identify it. But in the breeding season the pairs scatter more or less, just as those of the Tree Swallow are compelled to do, in order to find suitable nesting sites. Whereas the bank swallows dig their own burrows and live by choice in communities, the rough-wings, because they cannot dig, must make use of natural cavities or the deserted burrows of other birds—and these are not likely to be close together. Hence more than a pair or two are seldom found at any one spot. Invariably the site is near water (usually running water), and each pair hunts over considerable territory. My personal knowledge of this swallow is largely based on observations made at Raccoon Creek, Beaver County, where it is as common as it is anywhere. It is usually seen flying along the creek, over the water, and it sometimes perches at a considerable elevation in tall trees. It is not a conspicuous bird and is easily overlooked.

Above a highway bridge over Raccoon Creek, where a pinnacle of rock overhangs the water, the Rough-winged Swallow has nested for many successive seasons. The limestone has weathered, leaving a network of crevices, fully sheltered from above by the jutting overhang of the rock, and there the birds nest. On May 25, 1899, when I first examined this rock with the aid of a long ladder, three pairs were established there. The nests were merely shapeless heaps of rubbish carried in by the birds—straw and weed stems sufficient to fill up the crevice—with a depression in the center to hold the eggs. Earlier in the same month, in the hope of finding eggs of this species, I had dug out several shallow burrows in clay banks, only to discover that they were old and unoccupied. Old burrows of the Belted Kingfisher frequently serve as nesting sites, and I have also seen birds entering crevices in the masonry of bridges and of old stone chimneys, where they probably had nests. Both Dr. Sutton (1928) and S. S. Dickey (1919) refer to nests found in tile drain pipes, a location suggesting that the species is able to adapt itself to modern conditions to some extent.

Unlike the Bank Swallow, the Rough-winged does not use feathers for nest-lining, but sometimes there may be green leaves and petals from various trees and shrubs. The eggs are usually five or six in number (rarely four or seven), pure white in color, and rather long ovate in outline, measuring about .75 by .52 inches—a little larger than the Bank Swallow's. They are laid during the last week of May.

Stelgidopteryx serripennis Townsend, *Proc. Acad. Nat. Sci. Philadelphia*, 1883, 62 (Youngstown, Westmoreland Co.)—Jacobs, *Summer Birds Greene Co., Pa.*, 1893, 12 (Greene Co., nesting)—Todd, *Ann. Carnegie Mus.*, 1904, 2:578 (Presque Isle, Erie Co., April, *fide* Simpson)—Todd, in Bausman, *Hist. Beaver Co., Pa.*, 1904, 2:1200 (Beaver Co., summer)—Harlow, *Auk*, 1912, 29:475 ([State College], Centre Co., nesting); 1918, 35:140 ([State College], Centre Co., and Warren, Warren Co., nesting)—Dickey, *Oölogist*, 1914, 31:154 (Waynesburg, Greene Co., nesting)—Christy, *Cardinal*, 1923, v. 1, no. 1, [p. 11] (Sewickley, Allegheny Co., nesting)—Burleigh, *Wilson Bull.*, 1923, 35:97 (Allegheny River and Deer Creek [Harmarville], Allegheny Co., nesting); 1924, 36:72; and 1931, 43:50 (State College, Centre Co., migration; nesting).

"Rough-winged Swallow" Simpson, *Oölogist*, 1907, 24:133 (Warren, Warren Co., nesting)—McConnell, *Oölogist*, 1918, 35: 151 (Long Run, near McKeesport, Allegheny Co., summer?) —Dickey, *Oölogist*, 1919, 36:18 (Waynesburg, Greene Co., nesting)—Miller, *Oölogist*, 1919, 36:156 (Lemont, Centre Co., nesting)—Street, *Cassinia*, 1923, 24:16 (Conococheague Creek, Greencastle, Franklin Co., June)—Christy, *Cardinal*, 1923, v. 1, no. 2, [p. 17] (Clinton Pond, Allegheny Co., April); 1924, v. 1, no. 4, p. 10 (Big Traverse Valley, Beaver Co., June)—Christy, *Cardinal*, 1931, 3:43 (McDonald Reservoir, Washington Co., May).

"Bank Swallow" (error) Burleigh, *Oölogist*, 1911, 28:156 (Harmarville, Allegheny Co., nesting).

Stelgidopteryx serripennis serripennis Oberholser, *Bird-Lore*, 1917, 19:328 (Beaver, Beaver Co., migration)—Christy and Sutton, *Cardinal*, 1928, 2:73 (Cooksburg, Forest Co., June) —Sutton, *Ann. Carnegie Mus.*, 1928, 18:198 (Crawford Co. localities, summer; nesting).

Stelgidopteryx ruficollis serripennis Burleigh, *Cardinal*, 1932, 3:77 (Lake Seaton, Fayette Co., summer)—Christy, *Cardinal*, 1939, 5:46 (Sewickley, Allegheny Co., nesting).

BARN SWALLOW

HIRUNDO ERYTHROGASTER Boddaert

Description—A swallow distinguishable from our other swallows by its *deeply forked tail.* Upperparts (except forehead) glossy steel blue; wings and tail duller, less glossy, the latter with a V-shaped white band across the middle; *forehead and throat, rufous chestnut*, separated from the rusty buff of the rest of the underparts by a half-collar of steel blue, broken in the middle. *Females* are usually duller, and their posterior underparts are paler (whitish). *Young birds* in the fall are still duller, and their tails are much less deeply forked. Albinism is not infrequent in this species.

Range—Our Barn Swallow is considered by some (I think rightly) to be only a geographical race of the Eurasian *Hirundo rustica.* It inhabits North America at large as far north as the tree line and winters mainly in South America. Within the boundaries of our region it is evenly distributed as a summer resident, but it seems to be less common than formerly. Most observers agree that many breeding stations have been abandoned in the past twenty-five or thirty years. It is possible that this circumstance may be partly a result of the general decrease in the use of horses.

Migration—The Barn Swallow used to appear during the second week in April, but in recent years its northward movement has often been retarded by unseasonable weather and its arrival postponed until the third or even the fourth week of that month. Thus, from 1887 to 1891 I recorded its arrival at Beaver between April 11 and 15, while from 1899 to 1924 the corresponding dates are all between April 18 and 27. But even when the season is forward, the early migrants are few in number, and the majority of birds do not appear until a week or ten days later. At Sewickley, B. H. Christy has noted the species' vernal appearance from April 13 (1888) to 26 (1903). Some early arrival dates from other localities are: April 15, 1891—Waynesburg (Jacobs); April 19, 1914—Pittsburgh (Burleigh); April 12, 1927—Transfer, Mercer County (Seiple); April 14, 1897—Morganza, Washington County (Van Ostrand); April 9, 1897—Meadville (Kirkpatrick); April 19, 1901—Warren (Simpson); April 13, 1895—Butler (Roth); April 15, 1894—Slate Lick, Armstrong County (Keener); April 7, 1921—near Huntingdon (Sutton); April 6, 1916—Oak Hall, Centre County (Burleigh); April 12, 1892—Wilkinsburg (Atkinson); April 13, 1912 and 1933—Springs, Somerset County (Miller); April 9, 1919—Altoona (McGraw).

The autumnal movement begins in August, when old and young collect in flocks, sometimes of large size. They go southward by degrees, their numbers lessening after every storm, until by the end of the month very few are left. It is the exception to find any stragglers after the second week in September. They have been reported, however, up to September 19 (1896) at Wilkinsburg (Atkinson), and even until September 29 (1908) at Renovo (Pierce).[1]

Habits—Truly, "one swallow does not make a summer," but when the barn swallows arrive in force they give the season's final touch to any rural scene. Companionable and adaptable to an unusual degree among birds, they have elected to attach themselves to man and to share in his fortunes. Not as parasites nor as dependents on his bounty, but of their own free will, do they seek his dwelling places. Why they should favor certain buildings and avoid others is hard to say, but having once taken up their abode in a given spot, they tend to return year after year. Barns are chosen most frequently; and these they enter through a break in the boarding, or through a hole left for that very purpose. They are attractive as well as useful birds, and their presence is generally welcome. Before the country was settled they nested in caves and under rocky cliffs, as they still do in some remote parts of the West. But after the coming of the white man they soon learned to take advantage of his structures.

Barn swallows are elegant, active creatures, swift and graceful in flight, neighborly with other birds, and sociable among themselves. Most of their waking hours are necessarily passed on the wing. In the spring they congregate in loose flocks, mixed with other swallows, and course back and forth over and near streams and still water. Although at all times partial to the vicinity of water, in the summer they extend their excursions to fields and meadows. Nearly all their food—consisting of insects in general, and flies (Diptera) of various kinds in particular, as well as beetles, bugs, and ants—is secured during flight. Many kinds of insects injurious to agriculture have been identified in the contents of their stomachs. It sometimes happens that, lured northward too soon by unseasonably mild weather, they are hard pressed for food when the inevitable relapse occurs. Under such circumstances their best chance of finding anything is over water. H. C. Kirkpatrick writes that on April 9, 1897, during a severe snowstorm at Meadville, many barn swallows were seen hov-

[1]In New Hampshire I have seen young still in the nest as late as the end of August.

ering and flying over a small pond, where they kept close to its surface.

By the second week in May, if the season is a normal one, nest-building is under way. Usually the nest is stuck against the side of a rafter of a barn or other outbuilding, but sometimes, where mud is scarce or hard to get, it is placed on the top of a rafter; on rare occasions it is even built against the outside of a building, under the eaves, as are the nests of the Cliff Swallow. Nests have also been found under bridges. The nests do not vary much in composition; they are built up of pellets of mud, intermixed with straw, all firmly plastered against the side of the support and profusely lined with feathers and sometimes horsehair. The eggs, according to most observers, number from four to six, but R. B. Simpson writes that he has never found a nest at Warren that contained more than three. In shape the eggs vary from ovate to rather long ovate (with a tendency towards the latter); in color they are white, with irregular small spots and flecks of dull grayish or reddish brown, fairly well distributed but never obscuring the ground-color. The markings are rarely blotched. Average measurements are .75 by .55 inches.

The last week in May is the time to look for full sets of fresh eggs, although they may be found both a little earlier and a little later. When, in about two weeks, the eggs hatch, busy times begin for the parents. A nestful of young swallows requires a great deal of attention and a constant supply of food, and there is much twittering and calling back and forth as the old birds pursue their duties. Once the young are on the wing, the swallows usually desert the neighborhood of their nursery (except perhaps for roosting); joining others of their kind, they roam over the country in flocks wherever food is easiest to get. Telegraph and telephone lines along the roadsides become perches and roosts for countless numbers of birds. Some years ago, before the Ohio River had been "improved" and contaminated, I used to see immense mixed flocks of swallows (mostly of this species) on the beach, where I was accustomed to hunt shore birds in August. The birds must have been attracted to this spot by the hordes of insects that they found there. As they skimmed through the air in every direction, twittering constantly, they reminded me of a swarm of bees, and when they alighted in a body, the stones seemed fairly black with their assembled forms. I have seen similar flocks in Canada and elsewhere. As with most other species of this family, barn swallows migrate by day, feeding as they go, and roost at night in some suitable resort.

Hirundo horreorum Teulon, *Jour. Boston Zoöl. Soc.*, 1882, 1:51 (Bradford, McKean Co., April).

Hirundo erythrogastra horreorum Townsend, *Proc. Acad. Nat. Sci. Philadelphia*, 1883, 62 (Latrobe, Westmoreland Co.).

"Barn Swallow" Jacobs, *Hawkeye Ornithologist and Oölogist*, 1888, 1:88 (Waynesburg, Greene Co., April)—Stone, *Cassinia*, 1906, 9:44 (McConnellsburg, Fulton Co., June)—McConnell, *Oölogist*, 1918, 35:151 (McKeesport, Allegheny Co.)—McClelland, *Am. Mid. Nat.*, 1922, 8:36 (Washington, Washington Co., summer; migration)—Christy, *Cardinal*, 1923, v. 1, no. 2, [p. 17] (Clinton Pond, Allegheny Co., May)—Street, *Cassinia*, 1923, 24:16 (Greencastle, Ft. Loudon, and Metal, Franklin Co., June)—Eastwood, *Bird-Lore*, 1925, 27:262 (Pittsburgh region, Allegheny Co., April); 1927, 29:273 (Springs, Somerset Co., April, *fide* Miller).

Chelidon erythrogaster Todd, *Auk*, 1893, 10:40 (Two Lick, Indiana Co., June), 45 (Coalport, Clearfield Co., June)—Jacobs, *Summer Birds Greene Co., Pa.*, 1893, 11 (Greene Co., nesting).

Chelidon erythrogastra Baily, *Auk*, 1896, 13:295 (Williamsville, Elk Co., nesting).

Hirundo erythrogastra Cope, *Cassinia*, 1902, 5:17 (Tamarack Swamp, Clinton Co., breeding)—Keim, *Cassinia*, 1905, 8:40 (Port Allegany, McKean Co., summer)—Harlow, *Auk*, 1912, 29:475 (southern Centre Co., nesting)—Burleigh, *Wilson Bull.*, 1923, 35:97 (Harmarville, Allegheny Co., nesting); 1924, 36:72; and 1931, 43:49 (State College, Centre Co., migration; nesting).

Hirundo erythrogaster Todd, *Ann. Carnegie Mus.*, 1904, 2:576 (Erie, Erie Co., summer)—Todd, in Bausman, *Hist. Beaver Co., Pa.*, 1904, 2:1200 (Beaver Co., summer)—Christy, *Cardinal*, 1923, v. 1, no. 1, [p. 11] (Sewickley, Allegheny Co., breeding)—Burleigh, *Cardinal*, 1932, 3:77 (Lake Seaton and Chalk Hill, Fayette Co., nesting)—Wood, *Wilson Bull.*, 1937, 49:96 (Cherry Spring, Potter Co., nesting).

Hirundo erythrogastris Oberholser, *Bird-Lore*, 1918, 20:150 (Renovo, Clinton Co., migration).

Hirundo rustica erythrogastris Sutton, *Ann. Carnegie Mus.*, 1928, 18:195 (Crawford Co. localities, summer).

Hirundo rustica erythrogaster Christy and Sutton, *Cardinal*, 1928, 2:73 (Cooksburg, Forest Co., nesting).

NORTHERN CLIFF SWALLOW (Plate 15)

PETROCHELIDON ALBIFRONS ALBIFRONS[1] (Rafinesque)

Description—A bird the size of the Barn Swallow. Easily distinguished from our other swallows by its *even tail* and by the *rusty-buff* color of its *rump*, which contrasts with the dark-colored upperparts. Forehead (broadly) buffy white; crown glossy black; sides of head deep chestnut, this color also invading the throat, which has an irregular black area in the middle; upperparts bluish black, more or less glossy, the wings and tail duskier; *rump rusty buff;* underparts whitish, the breast and under tail coverts washed with buffy gray. *Young* in juvenal dress are much duller, with the head pattern merely indicated; the rusty-buff shade of the rump, however, is conspicuous.

Range—The Cliff Swallow winters in South America and summers in North America, where its breeding range is almost as extensive as that of the Barn Swallow. Once a common summer resident throughout western Pennsylvania, equaling the Barn Swallow in abundance, in recent years it has decreased in numbers to an even greater extent than has that species. It is now of only local occurrence as a breeding bird and is rare in most sections even during the seasons of migration. At the present time there are probably more colonies in Crawford County, particularly in the vicinity of Pymatuning Swamp, than in any other area of equal size in our region. Numerous observers have remarked upon the progressive disappearance of this swallow both within and without our limits, but offer no satisfactory reason therefor. E. H. Forbush suggests that in New England the swallows may have been driven off when the English sparrows began to appropriate their nests and when painted barns (on which the nests would not stick) superseded the rough, unpainted buildings of the older type.

The history of the advance of this swallow has been admirably outlined by Elliott Coues,[2] Forbush,[3] and other authors, but the story of its recession is yet to be told. The bird was unknown to Wilson and the early writers and did not come to Audubon's attention until 1815. To have escaped the notice of this keen observer it must have been extremely local, if it was present at all in the eastern United States at that period. Coues thinks, however, that the records of its appearance in various parts of the country merely mark the dates when, forsaking its primitive nesting places in cliffs, it began to build under eaves, and so established colonies where none existed before. The fact that A. E. Verrill discovered a colony nesting on the cliffs of Anticosti Island in 1861 lends significance to the latter view. The available records and evidence, however, are not conclusive.

Migration—The migration route of this species has been worked out by W. W. Cooke,[4] who shows that it skirts the Gulf of Mexico and thence extends northeastward to New England. According to his theory, the first migrants should reach the western counties of Pennsylvania before they strike the mountain section. Generally speaking, our records of arrival bear out this view. April 20 is the average date in eight seasons' records of "first-seen" birds at Beaver, and April 11 (1891) is the earliest. Odd records from the other western counties correspond. A series of records from Renovo covering twelve years shows that the average date there is later by nine days—April 29—and that April 22 (1899) is the earliest. At State College the average date is still later—May 1. April 21 (1918) is the earliest date for Blair County (McGraw). It is significant that at Warren the species does not arrive as a rule until the first week in May, while April 23 (1894) is the earliest date.

Data for the fall migration are meager but indicate an early southward movement. Before the end of August nearly all the cliff swallows have gone. I saw a few at Beaver on September 3, 1891; a few at Presque Isle on the same date in 1934; and some at Springdale, Allegheny County, on September 2, 1918. Ten seasons' notes from Renovo by A. K. Pierce yield August 26 as the average "last-seen" date and September 18 (1908) as the latest. The species has not been observed at Pymatuning Swamp (Hartstown) after August 27 (1925).

Habits[5]—The Cliff Swallow has adapted itself completely to the ways of man. It is truly a "barn" swallow, but, in addition to dissimilarities in form

[1]The earliest and proper specific name for this swallow is unquestionably *pyrrhonota* of Vieillot.
[2]*Birds of the Colorado Valley*, 1878, p. 428 *et seq.*
[3]*Birds of Massachusetts*, 1929, 3:144–145.
[4]U. S. Department of Agriculture, *Bulletin*, no. 185, 1915, p. 19, 20,26.
[5]Account contributed in part by Bayard H. Christy.

and color, it differs from the bird to which the name Barn Swallow has been given in two particulars: first, its habit of communal nesting is more highly developed; and second, its nests are placed outside, instead of inside, a building, under the protection of the eaves or overhang. Single nests are occasionally found, but communities are the rule. One of the most graceful sights in the world of birds is that afforded by a company of cliff swallows wheeling about in some sunny barnyard and darting to and fro about their nests under the eaves.

For some years there has been a nesting colony on the Voegtly farm near Harmony, in southern Butler County. The barn is old and roomy, and the stable yard fronts toward a meadow that falls away to Connoquenessing Creek. The main floor of the barn projects over the doors of the cow stable, and under this overhang, between the beams that support it, the cliff swallows' nests are built. In 1931 I wrote:

"Forty-one nests, all told, make up the colony. They are scattered somewhat. One, isolated, spans with its extended walls a space of a foot or more; but the tendency and manifest preference is to build nest against nest. In one space there were as many as seventeen nests so clustered.

"The type is retort-shaped, globular, with a neck springing from above and turned to open downward: a beautiful, symmetrical structure. The shape however is modified to suit the space—truncated or extended, as need requires; and where the nests are close-set, the chamber within, though pouch-like, is not truly symmetrical. A more secure foundation manifestly is desired than the vertical face of board or timber affords; for without exception the nests were fixed either in the angle formed by a nailed-on strip or to the rough rotundity of an adjacent nest. These clustered jugs of clay suggested the cells of the mud-wasps high under the eaves, in the gable-end of the barn.

"The nests are built of pellets of mud laid wet and retaining in the finished structure, each its smooth-rounded individuality. The walls speak of cunning and labor and of security, as does a wall of human masonry.

"It was a lovely sight, the swallows flitting in the sunny barnyard and darting into the shadow of their nursery. It was interesting to look up from below and see the birds within the portals of their dwellings, peering down from above: their little heads broad and flat, with wide-set black eyes, and black dots of bills between; their plumage showing patches of red, white, and blue."

In coloration the eggs of this swallow are practically indistinguishable from those of the Barn Swallow. They are white, spotted with wood brown; the markings vary greatly, however, in size and density, ranging from small flecks to heavy blotches. Average measurements are .81 by .55 inches. Three to six eggs are laid. The earliest sets are completed during the last week in May, but many birds do not lay their eggs until sometime in June. The mud nests are warmly lined with soft materials—usually dry grasses, leaves, or feathers. By July, or August at the latest, the young are on the wing.

Petrochelidon lunifrons Teulon, *Jour. Boston Zoöl. Soc.*, 1882, 1:51 (Bradford, McKean Co., nesting)—Townsend, *Proc. Acad. Nat. Sci. Philadelphia*, 1883, 62 (Latrobe, Westmoreland Co., breeding)—Barrows, *Bull. Econ. Orn. and Mammal.*, no. 1, 1889, 89 (New Lexington, Somerset Co., relation to English Sparrow, *fide* Moore)—Warren, *Birds Pa.*, ed. 2, 1890, 254 (New Lexington, Somerset Co., nesting, *fide* Moore)—Dwight, *Auk*, 1892, 9:138 (Cresson, Cambria Co., nesting)—Todd, *Auk*, 1893, 10:40 (Two Lick, Indiana Co., June)—Jacobs, *Summer Birds Greene Co., Pa.*, 1893, 11 (Greene Co., nesting)—Baily, *Auk*, 1896, 13:295 (Williamsville, Elk Co., August)—Cope, *Cassinia*, 1902, 5:17 (Clinton and Potter Co., June)—Todd, *Ann. Carnegie Mus.*, 1904, 2:576 (Erie, Erie Co., summer)—Todd, in Bausman, *Hist. Beaver Co., Pa.*, 1904, 2:1200 (Beaver Co., summer)—Keim, *Cassinia*, 1905, 8:40 (Port Allegany, McKean Co., summer).

"Cliff Swallow" Stone, *Cassinia*, 1906, 9:44 (McConnellsburg, Fulton Co., June)—Sutton, *Bird-Lore*, 1923, 25:260 (western Pa., spring)—McClintock, *Cardinal*, 1933, 3:129 (Ligonier, Westmoreland Co., July).

Petrochelidon lunifrons lunifrons Harlow, *Auk*, 1912, 29:474 (southern Centre Co., summer)—Oberholser, *Bird-Lore*, 1917, 19:320 (Beaver, Beaver Co., and Renovo, Clinton Co., migration)—Christy, *Cardinal*, 1923, v. 1, no. 1, [p. 11] (Sewickley, Allegheny Co., breeding; Raccoon Creek, Beaver Co., May)—Burleigh, *Wilson Bull.*, 1923, 35:97 ([near Pittsburgh], Allegheny Co., May); 1924, 36:72 (State College, Centre Co., migration); 1931, 43:49 (Oak Hall, Centre Co., and Charter Oak, Huntingdon Co., nesting).

"Eave Swallow" Simpson, *Oölogist*, 1914, 31:40 (Warren, Warren Co., nesting).

Petrochelidon albifrons albifrons Christy and Sutton, *Cardinal*, 1928, 2:72 (near Brookville, Jefferson Co., July)—Sutton, *Ann. Carnegie Mus.*, 1928, 18:194 (Crawford Co. localities, summer; nesting)—Burleigh, *Cardinal*, 1932, 3:77 (Lake Seaton and Chalk Hill, Fayette Co., nesting).

Petrochelidon albifrons Christy, *Cardinal*, 1931, 3:20; and 1936, 4:97 (near Harmony, Butler Co., nesting habits).

"Northern Cliff Swallow" Wood, *Wilson Bull.*, 1932, 44:239 (Pennsylvania Furnace, Huntingdon Co., nesting).

PURPLE MARTIN

PROGNE SUBIS SUBIS (Linnaeus)

Description—Our largest swallow, with a wingspread of about sixteen inches. Tail slightly forked. *Adult male: uniform glossy deep bluish black*, the wings and tail duller. *Adult female:* upperparts bluish black, less glossy than the male, with the forehead and nape dark gray; underparts whitish, the throat, breast, and sides clouded with dull gray in somewhat mottled pattern; wings and tail dark-colored, but not glossy. *Immature male:* similar to the adult female, but usually with some bluish-black feathers on the throat. The bird breeds in this plumage.

Range—The Purple Martin ranges through North America in summer, north to British Columbia, Manitoba, and New Brunswick, and south to Florida and Mexico; it winters in South America. It is generally distributed throughout western Pennsylvania as a summer resident but, like our other swallows, has become much less common in recent years. There was a time when almost every town of importance, and many smaller ones as well, could boast of one or more colonies of purple martins, but most of these colonies are no longer in existence. Fifteen years ago C. W. Parker was able to list only nine colonies in Allegheny County. There used to be two large colonies in the town of Beaver, where now there are none. A large colony at Waynesburg made famous by J. W. Jacobs is also a thing of the past. The diminution in numbers seems to have been progressive, but I am unable to say whether or not it is still going on.

There are some signs that the Martin has been one of the beneficiaries of the newly awakened popular interest in bird life and conservation. Yet many well-meaning bird-lovers confess defeat in their efforts to establish new colonies. There are apparently several reasons for the general defection. Failure to keep the nest boxes in repair is one obvious cause. Many a colony has been lost merely because its regular accommodations fell into decay. (I have known colonies, however, to refuse new boxes that had been provided during their absence in the South.) By taking possession of the boxes in advance of the martins' arrival, the English Sparrow and lately the European Starling have come to be a real menace. Unseasonably cold spring weather has also been a factor in reducing the Martin population, and whole communities have occasionally been extirpated by cold and starvation.

In a letter written in 1934, Mr. Jacobs comments on the extinction of his once flourishing colony, which comprised eighty-four nesting pairs in 1903. Without any apparent reason, except the cutting away of the forest and the draining of the old "Book Dam" along Ten-mile Creek, the atmospheric conditions seemed to change. "Cold, frosty mornings in spring greeted the martins, and cold, raw winds met them in the evenings. Such has been the usual condition ever since. My colony was at a standstill in 1910, but it soon began to dwindle, although I could see a steady increase at the houses I had put up for others on the hill, where the climatic conditions were less disagreeable in April and May—the frost less biting and the morning sun warmer. Then a new element entered into the situation: screech owls seemed to abound in this part of town, although I never could catch them in the act of taking any birds. Samuel M. Smith, who at one time had as many as fifty nesting pairs, with all conditions favorable, lost his colony, too, although at the time he never thought of blaming it on the screech owls that were present. The colony melted away gradually. There are far fewer martins in Waynesburg now than there were twenty-five years ago."

On the other hand, some of the present colonies are known to have been in existence for fifty and sixty years. It is to be hoped that any further localizing of this species can be avoided.

Migration—Most of the birds that winter in South America are late migrants in the spring. The Purple Martin is an exception to this rule. It pushes northward so early in the season that it not infrequently arrives in our region before its insect food is on the wing. Under these circumstances it either perishes or is forced to retire southward temporarily. It has been known to anticipate the Tree Swallow, which has far less distance to travel. Thus, it has been observed at

Greencastle, Franklin County, as early as March 8 (1921), at Waynesburg on March 15 (1914), and at Washington on March 22 (1897). Weather conditions influence its movements to a marked degree, as shown by W. W. Cooke,[1] and this circumstance accounts for unusually early dates as well as for unusually late ones. In "normal" seasons (scarcely any in recent years can be considered normal) the Purple Martin should appear in our region during the first week in April. Five seasons' records of its arrival at Beaver yield an average date of April 5. At Ambridge, only a few miles distant, it is said to come about April 3 (Graham). The average date of arrival at Waynesburg, however, is March 27; and at Greencastle, Franklin County, east of the mountains, it is still earlier—March 24. But in some seasons, when its movements are retarded by cold, wet weather, the Martin may not come until the second or third week in April, or even later. At Warren, where it is uncommon, R. B. Simpson writes that he has never seen it earlier than April 21 (1901).

This species, like others of its tribe, leaves its summer haunts early. The larger number of our summer-resident martins depart toward the end of August—long before there is any shortage in the food supply—but migrants from farther north may often be seen passing through in September. In 1913 I noted such transients at Beaver on September 8 and 11 and even as late as September 24. T. D. Burleigh reports one bird at State College on September 30, 1915.

Habits—The Purple Martin is now almost wholly dependent upon nesting accommodations provided by man, but this situation has not always prevailed. Under primitive conditions the species utilized hollow trees, old woodpecker-holes, and similar cavities. But even in the Indian days it is said to have made use of hollow gourds, suspended from a pole set up in the camp. In the southern states this is still a favorite and usual site. In the North the martins' use of man-made community bird boxes is so general that we seldom hear of any other nesting location. A pair of martins once built a nest in a corner under the cornice of my home, where a rainspout gave support; and Mr. Simpson says that he has found nests under the shades of arc lamps and in crevices in buildings. The bird-box habit is now so firmly established that it has become a controlling factor in the local distribution of the species. The Martin not only takes advantage of the changes brought about through man's agency, as do our other swallows, but also welcomes his assistance in its behalf. With a little help and encouragement, it is ever ready to take up its abode on his premises. There is a certain reciprocity, too, for the Martin more than repays the hospitality it enjoys by its destruction of noxious insects. An established colony of martins is a valuable economic asset.

"What can add more in life, color and action to a country place than a handsome martin box with a great colony of Purple Martins? Their loud and cheerful voices, their rapid, aërial evolutions, and their swift massing for attack on an enemy of the flock, always attract attention. When domiciled in the yard of a farm home, they protect the chickens by attacking hawks and crows *en masse* the moment these marauders appear in the vicinity."[2] I am inclined to agree with Mr. Parker, however, who wrote (1924) that "the Martins are essentially birds of the village and the suburb, and are apparently semi-domesticated in their desire to associate with man." Several satisfactory accounts of certain colonies in our region have appeared in print. The best-known colony (because of the publicity it received) was that on the outskirts of Waynesburg on the property of Mr. Jacobs, who has entertainingly described its history (1903). This colony was started in 1896 by the erection of a suitable bird box, and in a few years had increased to occupy three similar boxes, while the overflow found quarters in boxes distributed throughout the

[1]U. S. Department of Agriculture, Division of Economic Ornithology, *Bulletin*, no. 2, 1888, p. 223.
[2]E. H. Forbush, *Birds of Massachusetts*, 1929, 3:140.

town. Provided that their boxes are kept in repair, martins tend to return to the same spot year after year, even if the surroundings alter in the meantime. A colony in Greencastle, Franklin County, lives in the very heart of the town, undisturbed by the surrounding noise and bustle, because it has been carefully cherished and protected by the inhabitants. There are other colonies of long standing in the towns of Ligonier and Mount Pleasant, Westmoreland County.

The first martins to arrive in the spring are lone representatives—scouts that come to spy out the land. They are always adult males that stay only a few hours, disappearing as quickly as they come, only to return some days later at the head of a larger band. Mr. Jacobs writes (1903): "Sometimes we have disagreeable weather in April after the birds become comparatively common, but unless freezing temperature is experienced, they do not appear to be affected, and not a few times have I seen an old male bird thrust his head out of his door, surrounded by little heaps of snow on the porch, and twitter in seeming contentment." Birds of the preceding year (in imperfect breeding plumage) arrive a week or ten days later than the adults. Mr. Jacobs continues:

"Nest building covers a period of several days, the male assisting, though he often gets in the wrong room. They collect twigs, straws, bits of wood and grass from the garden and street, and along the creek, not going far from the premises. In nearly every instance a small wall of mud is built around the front of the nest, just inside the entrance. Generally by May 5th some nests are ready for the reception of the eggs, though the bulk are not ready for some days later; especially those of the young of the previous year, who are a few days behind their parents in this respect as in their return from the South.

"The nest varies in depth, some being deep cup-shaped structures, while others are very shallow; and, in a few instances, only a scanty supply of twigs and grass were spread upon the floor for the eggs. In one room the eggs had been deposited on the bare floor without a single piece of nest material to prevent them from rolling about."

Four, five, or even six eggs are laid, and very rarely seven. They are pure white and vary in shape from ovate through elliptical ovate to elongate ovate, averaging .99 by .68 inches. They usually hatch in June. The young are at first naked, repulsive creatures, but they grow very rapidly after the fifth day and are clamorous for food. "At the end of eighteen days," according to Mr. Jacobs, "the young are pretty well feathered, and somewhat resemble the mother birds. They gather at the door of their room and crane their necks, scanning the surroundings or watching for the return of the parent birds with food. Sometimes five or six young birds will have their heads thrust out of the door to their room at the same time, but more often only the tips of their beaks protrude.

"From twenty-four to twenty-eight days elapse from the time the young break the shells until they are strong enough to leave the nest and safely soar away with their parents during the day." Young that leave the nest prematurely may be killed by the fall, or die of starvation or neglect, as the old birds do not seem to feed them under these conditions and will approach them only in an effort to make them fly. A period of continued cold and rainy weather has been known to spell disaster to the unfledged young, and some of the old birds may even succumb from inability to secure sufficient food. Should such a misfortune befall at hatching time, the chances are that the surviving parents will again lay eggs and bring out late broods, but should it happen when the young are well grown, no further attempt will be made that season.

For a week or ten days after the young are on the wing they are brought back to the box to spend the night. After that (about July 25 in a normal season), old and young flock together to roost outside, on buildings, dead trees, or telegraph wires. These flocks are augmented daily by new accessions, as late broods come in; and, as August progresses, their restlessness increases. Some morning we wake up to find that they have gone in the night, and that is the end of them until the following spring.

A few suggestions for attracting martins are quoted from Mr. Parker: "To have Martins, a suitable martin house and a proper location are essential. The house should contain many rooms, not less than twenty, and the more the better; it should be of fancy design or architecture, painted white or other bright color, erected on a stout pole, 15 or 20 feet high, in a prominent place, where the sun shines brightest, away from trees, and if possible where traffic passes. The Martin is an aristocrat, and wants a mansion of many rooms on the best avenue."

The English Sparrow must at all costs be kept away, not only by a liberal use of the shotgun, but also by blocking entrance to the box until the martins arrive. The latter are well able to hold their own in a contest with the sparrows, but sparrows once in possession of a box are hard to dislodge, and the martins are apt to give up and go elsewhere. There is always a chance that new boxes may be taken even up to the end of May; for birds of the previous year, late-comers that they are, often find themselves crowded out of the boxes where they were hatched, and are forced to seek new quarters.[1]

Progne subis TEULON, *Jour. Boston Zoöl. Soc.*, 1882, 1:52 (Bradford, McKean Co., nesting)—TOWNSEND, *Proc. Acad. Nat. Sci. Philadelphia*, 1883, 62 (Latrobe, Westmoreland Co., breeding)—MERRIAM, *Auk*, 1885, 2:57 (New Lexington, Somerset Co., migration [*fide* Moore])—DWIGHT, *Auk*, 1892, 9:138 (Altoona, Blair Co., nesting)—JACOBS, *Summer Birds Greene Co., Pa.*, 1893, 11; *Gleanings from Nature*, 1903, 2:1; *Bull. Michigan Orn. Club*, 1903, 4:87ff. (Waynesburg, Greene Co., nesting)—TODD, *Ann. Carnegie Mus.*, 1904, 2:576 (Erie, Erie Co., summer)—TODD, in Bausman, *Hist. Beaver Co., Pa.*, 1904, 2:1200 (Beaver Co., summer)—FORREST, *Oölogist*, 1911, 28:115 (Washington, Washington Co., breeding)—GRAHAM, *Cardinal*, 1924, v. 1, no. 4, p. 4 (Ambridge, Beaver Co., nesting).

"Purple Martin" JACOBS, *Hawkeye Ornithologist and Oölogist*, 1888, 1:88 (Waynesburg, Greene Co., April)—JACOBS, *Bird-Lore*, 1903, 5:165 (Waynesburg, Greene Co., nesting; habits)—STONE, *Cassinia*, 1906, 9:44 (McConnellsburg, Fulton Co., June)—JACOBS, *Nature and Culture*, 1911, v. 2, no. 3, p. 18 (Waynesburg, Greene Co., nesting colonies)—MCCONNELL, *Bird-Lore*, 1914, 16:116 (McKeesport, Allegheny Co., nesting); 1918, 20:130 (Kittanning, Armstrong Co.; Pittsburgh and McKeesport, Allegheny Co.; and Waynesburg, Greene Co.); 1921, 23:75 (McKeesport, Allegheny Co., and Kittanning, Armstrong Co., nesting)—MCDOWELL, *Bird-Lore*, 1917, 19:146 (Uniontown, Fayette Co., nesting)—MCCONNELL, *Oölogist*, 1918, 35:151 (McKeesport, Allegheny Co., breeding)—MCCLELLAND. *Am. Mid. Nat.*, 1922, 8:36 (Washington, Washington Co., summer; migration)—ZIEGLER, *Auk*, 1923, 40:431 (Greencastle, Franklin Co., summer; habits; migration)—CHRISTY, *Cardinal*, 1923, v. 1, no. 2, [p. 17] (Clinton Pond, Allegheny Co., April)—STREET, *Cassinia*, 1923, 24:10, 16 (Greencastle and Ft. Loudon, Franklin Co., June)—PARKER, *Cardinal*, 1924, v. 1, no. 4, p. 1 (Allegheny Co., nesting colonies)—CHRISTY, *Cardinal*, 1924, v. 1, no. 4, p. 10 (Big Traverse Valley, Beaver Co., June); 1925, v. 1, no. 5, p. 20 (Sewickley, Allegheny Co., nesting)—EASTWOOD, *Bird-Lore*, 1925, 27:262 (Pittsburgh region, Allegheny Co., April); 1927, 29:197 (Schellsburg, Bedford Co., April, *fide* Manley).

Progne subis subis HARLOW, *Auk*, 1912, 29:474 (State College, Centre Co., breeding)—JACOBS, *Bull. Audubon Soc. W. Pa.*, 1923, 1:34 (Waynesburg, Greene Co., nesting)—CHRISTY, *Cardinal*, 1923, v. 1, no. 1, [p. 11] (Sewickley, "Coraopolis Heights," Clinton, Allegheny Co.; Frankfort and Ambridge, Beaver Co., nesting)—BURLEIGH, *Wilson Bull.*, 1923, 35:97 (Allegheny Co., transient); 1924, 36:132 (State College, Centre Co., September and May)—CHRISTY and SUTTON, *Cardinal*, 1928, 2:72 (Clarion, Clarion Co., and Brookville, Jefferson Co., nesting)—SUTTON, *Ann. Carnegie Mus.*, 1928, 18:193 (Crawford Co. localities, summer)—SUTTON, *Cardinal*, 1929, 2:121 (Hartstown, Crawford Co., September)—BURLEIGH, *Cardinal*, 1932, 3:77 (Uniontown, Fayette Co., nesting)—SUTTON, *Introd. Birds Pa.*, 1928, 121 (Coudersport, Potter Co., breeding).

[1]Persons intending to erect martin boxes are advised to communicate with J. Warren Jacobs, Waynesburg, Pennsylvania.

CROWS, JAYS

FAMILY CORVIDAE

THE CORVIDAE are a large family, found all over the world except in New Zealand. In western Pennsylvania the Crow and the Blue Jay are common and widely distributed representatives; the Raven is limited to remote, unsettled regions; and the Canada Jay is an accidental straggler.

The Crows and Ravens (Subfamily Corvinae) are large birds—among them are the largest of the Passerine series—and all are black or dull-colored. They have well-developed feet, strong bills with stiff bristles about the base, and nostrils that are covered with dense tufts of feathers. The Jays (Subfamily Garrulinae) are smaller and usually brightly colored. The Crows and Ravens walk over the ground; the Jays hop. As carrion-eaters and destroyers of insects, all these birds may be credited with beneficial food habits; but as destroyers of fruit and grain, as well as of the eggs and young of other birds, they are held in disrepute.

The Fish Crow (*Corvus ossifragus*) has been attributed to the eastern part of our region, but the records are unacceptable.

CANADA JAY

PERISOREUS CANADENSIS CANADENSIS (Linnaeus)

Description—A bird the size of the Blue Jay, but without a crest; tail rounded, with slight whitish tip. Slaty gray above (including wings and tail); top of head, and throat, white, darkening on the breast to dull gray; a black hood covers the nape and hindneck and extends forward on either side to include the eyes; bill and feet black.

Range—The Canada Jay (with its several races) is a common and characteristic species of the Canadian and Hudsonian life zones of boreal America. It is mainly a sedentary bird, but, like others of its class, it has been known at rare intervals to wander southward in the winter. The Adirondack Mountains in New York are its nearest regular breeding grounds, and probably the single example reported from Clarington, Forest County, by A. R. Hillard,[1] in February, 1923, was a straggler from that region. This observer wrote that it resembled the Blue Jay in all but color—that is, in size, general habits and behavior, and call notes—but that it was much tamer and would come to the back door of his dwelling and to the chicken coop, and would even enter the barn.

[1] In a letter to O. E. Jennings, February 18, 1923.

NORTHERN BLUE JAY

CYANOCITTA CRISTATA CRISTATA (Linnaeus)

Description—A larger bird than the Robin; head with a *full crest.* General color *blue,* varying in shade; the wings have a conspicuous white bar and broad white tips to the inner feathers, which are also barred with black; the tail is barred with black and has a broad white tip; throat and sides of head, white, surrounded by a black band, which is continued upward into the crest and forward to the eyes; lores and forehead (narrowly) black; rest of underparts soiled whitish, the breast and sides washed with brownish gray.

Range—The Blue Jay as a species ranges throughout eastern North America from Canada to the Gulf of Mexico, and west to the Great Plains. It is subject to geographic variation from north to south, and three races are currently recognized. The northern race, to which our Pennsylvania birds belong, is the largest and most richly colored. It is generally distributed throughout our section, but is now rare over a considerable area where it was once common. As a boy I used to find it nesting in my back yard in Beaver, but now I seldom see a single bird in the adjacent countryside during the course of a year. It seems largely to have disappeared from all the country south of the Ohio River and north for an indefinite distance, and wherever it is still found it is rare and local. The reason for this disappearance, which became noticeable about the beginning of the present century, is not understood. Whatever the cause may have been, its operation must have been restricted to this particular section, as the bird is still common in the mountains and in the northern part of our region in general, west to Mercer and Crawford counties. Its presence is not easily overlooked.

Migration—Although the Blue Jay is regularly found at all seasons, several years' observations have convinced me that it is actually migratory. An influx of northern-bred individuals seems to take place in September, and during this and the following month its numbers increase noticeably; after that there is a decrease. Comparatively few birds remain through the winter, and these only in certain favorite localities. With the advent of spring a similar fluctuation takes place just before the breeding season, although it is by no means so marked as in the fall. Other observers have also noted seasonal changes in abundance that tend to confirm the above explanation.

Habits[1]—Under the hunting law of the late nineties, "squirrel season" came in during September, after the heat of summer had somewhat abated and when fogs shrouded the valleys and wooded hillsides. Then, when the voices of most birds were silent, the youthful squirrel hunters upon the hills of western Pennsylvania could hear the shrill, irritating cry of *ja-a-ay, ja-a-ay!* across the valleys suddenly swell into riotous racket by other shouters near at hand. Whether because of intuitive resentment at the jeering of "the blue jay, that noisy coxcomb, in his light blue coat and white underclothes" (as he appears in "The Legend of Sleepy Hollow"), or because they thought that this clamorous fellow and his companions would alarm the squirrels, even then all too few among the river hills, the youth of the land in general and the hunters among them in particular were none too kindly disposed toward the blue jays.

There is something furtive in the approach of these handsome birds, which seem to prefer evergreens or close growths of foliage for cover. I recall a hill slope covered with wild grapevines where one could always arouse them. If, like the wood warblers, titmice, and nuthatches, the blue jays were industrious and reasonably silent, the impression they create might be improved; but there is an air of easy and mischievous idleness about them, whether seen singly or in groups, that evokes a certain distrust. Indeed, W. L. Dawson goes far in denunciation: "Beautiful he undoubtedly is in his panoply of blue and white, and we are moved to an admiration which is never quite dispelled; but the heart of him is deceitful and cruel beyond belief.... Cunning, mischievous, thieving, cruel, noisy, boastful, quarrelsome, treacherous, wanton—one is tempted to empty the vials of opprobrious epithets upon his devoted head—but the vision of his saucy beauty and the memory of his ringing *delary, delary* stays, as it always will, the hand of justice.

"The trouble with Blue Jay is that we all fall in love with him in the winter when he is being good, but lose sight of him in the spring and summer when he is practicing his villainies."[2]

This author's remarks are prompted by the well-known fondness of the Blue Jay for the eggs and young of the smaller birds at nesting time. Its depredations along this line have been greatly advertised—perhaps unduly so. As a matter of fact, about three-fourths of its food consists of fruit, grain, and nuts (especially acorns), with insects and small animals accounting almost entirely for the remaining one-fourth. From a purely economic point of view, therefore,

[1]Account contributed by Edmund W. Arthur.
[2]*Birds of Ohio*, 1903, p. 8.

the Blue Jay must be rated a beneficial species—in spite of its admitted lapses—and under the circumstances, it is certainly entitled to all benefit of doubt.

Of this bird, B. H. Christy writes as follows: "The Blue Jay is a conspicuous, and therefore a well-known, bird, although it can no longer be called abundant. In Allegheny County, at least, it is of strangely local occurrence. Weeks may pass without my hearing or seeing a single bird, and yet I have in mind particular places, two or three hundred acres in extent, where I can count on finding jays by a little searching. There are times, on bright, golden afternoons in September, when the woodlands fairly ring with their loud calls, but throughout the rest of the year they are less in evidence. The Blue Jay's vocal powers are notable. The family to which it belongs is peculiar in having an apparent vocabulary that, in variety, notes, and stress, expresses a considerable range of meaning. Besides its loud and strident shout, which is susceptible of great variety of utterance, it has soft, and even bell-like, notes—expressive perhaps of a sense of well-being or of satisfaction in companionship, and at the appropriate season certainly amative. An unusual although characteristic call is so nearly identical with the scream of the Red-tailed Hawk that it often deceives the human ear."

The Blue Jay builds a rather large and deeply cupped nest and chooses a tree with dense foliage. Conifers are much in favor, as they effectively screen the nest. Usually it is placed in a crotch no more than ten or twelve feet from the ground. The materials vary with the site and are chosen from available local supplies. In the forest, dry twigs or rootlets are used, while a nest in the orchard may include in its make-up, paper, rags, cord or yarn, and similar substances. If a site near human habitation is chosen, it is generally in some sheltering Norway spruce or hemlock. The nesting season in western Pennsylvania is from mid-April to mid-May, depending to some extent on the latitude. Four to six eggs are laid, sets of the latter number being by no means uncommon. They vary in ground-color from rich buff to olive or pea green; the markings are irregular spots, and sometimes blotches, of different shades of brown, usually heaviest around the larger end. Average measurements are 1.10 by .81 inches.

One summer we were sojourning on a spur of Negro Mountain just across the Pennsylvania border in Maryland. Our cottage was in the midst of an open wood of oak trees, white, red, and black. Blue jays abounded. They confined themselves largely to a noisy circuit of the treetops, but when food became available on or near the ground, it did not long remain unmolested. We were feeding white-breasted nuthatches, black-capped chickadees, tufted titmice, and brown creepers. Our efforts were thwarted by fox squirrels and blue jays. The former had been semidomesticated among the cottagers. The latter grew bolder as the season advanced. We therefore built a feeding shelf and suspended it between pillar and pilaster of a veranda. No location could be found high enough to keep the squirrels from leaping up from the porch rail or down from the roof beams, but the blue jays stood off and did not venture to approach the shelf.

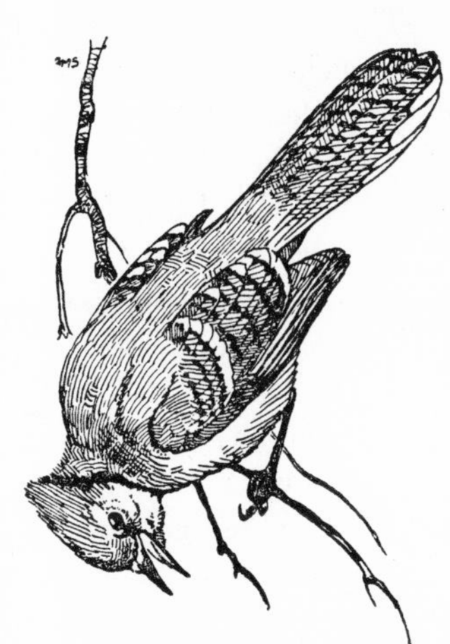

They molted in August and became sorry-looking spectacles with long, scrawny, bare necks and generally disheveled plumage. They resembled the summer cottagers that one sees now and again who esteem personal untidiness a *sine qua non* of their vacation. We say "esteem" after deliberation, for there is in their attitude a certain pride. So with the blue jays. During the days when well-behaved birds, bedraggled in the molt, seek seclusion, the jays, as conspicuous in their tatters as in their beauty, not only circulate publicly in their grotesquely forlorn and often meager attire, but also manifest a sort of brazen pride in so doing.

Yet it is easy to fall into the error of interpreting the behavior of lesser creatures according to human patterns. We are too prone, perhaps, to charge birds, animals, or reptiles with moral delinquency when in following the law of their being they despoil, torment, or kill. We say they are "guilty" of this or that breach of our code and forget that they are by nature under obligations very different from ours; of these, self-preservation has been termed the first.

Again, one's impression of the Blue Jay may be the result of resentment engendered by an introduction to it through Audubon's portrayal of the species: a picture of stirring invaders, ruthless and cold-blooded, that have pillaged the nest of some wretched lesser bird and have been caught by the brush of the artist in the very act of breaking and devouring the eggs. That displeasing picture may linger long in one's subconscious mind, and even newer and more pleasant contacts and experiences may fail to efface the scene.

But whatever grade or status the Blue Jay may be assigned, it can hardly be gainsaid that it possesses an individuality and a personality as conspicuous and assertive as its color is attractive. Even its flamboyance, its intrusiveness, and its crude, unpleasant manner and conduct, express a distinctive character that is brought to mind whenever its cry is heard, or its plumage seen, or its name mentioned.

Cyanurus cristatus Teulon, *Jour. Boston Zoöl. Soc.*, 1883, 2:9 (Bradford, McKean Co., resident).

Cyanocitta cristata Townsend, *Proc. Acad. Nat. Sci. Philadelphia*, 1883, 64 (Latrobe, Westmoreland Co., resident)—Jamison, *Ornithologist and Oölogist*, 1888, 13:134; and Dwight, *Auk*, 1892, 9:136 (Cresson, Cambria Co., June)—Todd, *Auk*, 1893, 10:39 (Two Lick, Indiana Co., June), 44 (Coalport, Clearfield Co., June)—Jacobs, *Summer Birds Greene Co., Pa.*, 1893, 8 (Greene Co., nesting)—Baily, *Auk*, 1896, 13:294 (Williamsville, Elk Co., June–July)—Cope, *Cassinia*, 1902, 5:15 (Clinton and Potter Co., June)—Todd, *Ann. Carnegie Mus.*, 1904, 2:565 (Presque Isle, Erie Co., resident)—Todd, in Bausman, *Hist. Beaver Co., Pa.*, 1904, 2:1200 (Beaver Co., resident)—Keim, *Cassinia*, 1905, 8:38 (Port Allegany, McKean Co., summer).

"Blue Jay" Stone, *Cassinia*, 1906, 9:44 (Scrub Ridge, west of McConnellsburg, Fulton Co., June)—Simpson, *Oölogist*, 1909, 26:170 (Warren, Warren Co., nesting)—Miller (A.B.), *Bird-Lore*, 1910, 12:29; etc. (Springs, Somerset Co., December)—Gerberding, *Bird-Lore*, 1912, 14:29 (Greenville, Mercer Co., December)—Morris, *Bird-Lore*, 1913, 15:29 (Eagle Rock, Venango Co., December)—McConnell, *Oölogist*, 1916, 33:114; and 1918, 35:150 (McKeesport, Allegheny Co.)—Miller (R.F.), *Oölogist*, 1919, 36:155 (Charter Oak, Huntingdon Co., nesting)—McGraw, *et al.*, Bird-Lore, 1919, 21:37; etc. (near Altoona, Blair Co., December)—McConnell, *Bird-Lore*, 1920, 22:31; etc. (Emsworth, Allegheny Co., December)—Nicholson, *Bird-Lore*, 1921, 22:18 (Grove City, Mercer Co., December)—McClelland, *Am. Mid. Nat.*, 1922, 8:35 (Washington, Washington Co., resident)—Street, *Cassinia*, 1923, 24:14 (Greencastle to Ft. Loudon, Franklin Co., June)—Christy, *Cardinal*, 1924, v. 1, no. 4, p. 10 (Big Traverse Valley, Beaver Co., June)—Eastwood, *Bird-Lore*, 1926, 28:137 (Ridgway, Elk Co., winter, *fide* Alsop), 274 (Sandy Lake, Mercer Co., May, *fide* Squier)—Boulton, *Bird-Lore*, 1928, 30:14 (Pittsburgh region), 127 (Raccoon Creek, Beaver Co., December, *fide* Christy and Hegner)—Elliott, *Cardinal*, 1934, 3:171 (Raccoon Creek, Beaver Co., December)—Cope and Hawkins, *Forest Leaves*, 1934, 24:26 (E. Tionesta Forest Reserve, Warren and McKean Co., summer).

Cyanocitta cristata cristata Harlow, *Auk*, 1912, 29:473 ([Pine Grove Mills], Centre Co., nesting)—Christy, *Cardinal*, 1923, v. 1, no. 1, [p. 7] (Sewickley, Allegheny Co., resident)—Burleigh, *Wilson Bull.*, 1923, 35:90 (Harmarville, Allegheny Co.); 1924, 36:69 (State College, Centre Co., resident); 1931, 43:44 (State College, Centre Co.; Charter Oak, Huntingdon Co., nesting).

Cyanocitta cristata bromia Oberholser, *Auk*, 1921, 38:86 (Leasuresville, Butler Co., and Redbank, Clarion Co., June)—Christy and Sutton, *Cardinal*, 1908, 2:71 and 75 (Cooksburg, Forest Co., resident)—Sutton, *Ann. Carnegie Mus.*, 1928, 18:159 (Crawford Co. localities, resident; nesting).

"Northern Blue Jay" Wood, *Wilson Bull.*, 1932, 44:239 (Shingletown, Centre Co., September).

NORTHERN RAVEN

CORVUS CORAX PRINCIPALIS Ridgway

Description—An entirely *black bird, much larger* than the Crow; head and bill proportionately larger, and *tail longer and wedge-shaped.*

Range—In one form or another the Raven ranges through both Eurasia and North America. The ravens from eastern and northern North America belong to the race *principalis*, although one authority[1] has segregated the birds of the Appalachian highlands under another name. In the unsettled parts of Canada, the Raven is still common, as it once must also have been in the mountains of Pennsylvania, where now it is growing scarcer year by year. Indeed, it probably ranged originally throughout western Pennsylvania. Over one hundred years ago Wilson spoke of it "as entirely supplanting the Crow on the southern shores of Lake Erie" in Ohio, where it is now extinct. Its later local range, as nearly as it can be reconstructed, seems to have occupied all

[1]H. C. Oberholser, *Ohio Journal of Science*, 1918, 18:215.

the plateau region—from the Allegheny River in Warren County to Potter County (and farther east) and the territory to the south in Clearfield, Cambria, and Somerset counties and beyond our southern boundary. But its range to the eastward is by no means limited by the Allegheny divide, as are those of so many other species of boreal origin and affinities. Instead, the Raven spreads over the ridge and valley section, finding congenial haunts and suitable nesting grounds in the maze of minor ridges crossing that part. But the present outlook for this species there is not encouraging. A nesting was recorded by B. H. Christy in 1935, and the indications are that a few pairs still breed in the mountains of Clinton, Centre, and Huntingdon counties, in spite of hunters, automobile roads, and CCC camps.

The wild jumble of ridges and knobs known as the Seven Mountains, along the boundary between Centre and Huntingdon counties, used to harbor more nesting pairs of ravens, perhaps, than any other area of equal size in the state. Most of the sets of eggs collected by R. C. Harlow in the years from 1909 to 1920 came from this region. There are two sets in the Carnegie Museum from near Mill Creek in Huntingdon County (Sutton), and one from the mountains six miles south of Renovo, near the mouth of Benjamin Run in Clinton County (Pierce). The latter, collected on April 6, 1894, is the first authentic set of eggs of the Raven taken in Pennsylvania.

In June, 1893, I encountered a family group of ravens near Ebensburg, Cambria County, and E. A. Preble saw some during the same month on the crest of the Alleghenies farther south, near Crumb, Somerset County. Five years later I noted the species at Dunlo, Cambria County. But so completely has this entire region been lumbered over since then, that I doubt whether even a single raven remains. It is not a bird that can adjust itself to changing conditions, and as the wilderness has retreated, it has steadily retired before the encroachments of civilization. Inasmuch as the species has survived in Europe in the face of the same changes, its status here is hard to understand. Certainly it is now rare and local in our region, and whether anything further can be done to conserve the few remaining individuals is questionable.

Migration—Even in the far North the Raven remains through the bitter cold of the long arctic night. With us it is likewise mainly a sedentary bird, but, like others in that category, it may wander somewhat in the winter, when pressed for food. It has been reported as a straggler at that season in Erie County (Warren, 1890).

Habits—My introduction to this bird of reputed ill omen took place in June of 1893, while I was making my way on foot through the wilds of western Cambria County. Scarcely had I left the environs of Ebensburg and plunged into the woods, when my ears were assailed by a series of unearthly screeches coming from a distance. I had no idea what these sounds might be until from a tree near by came a hoarse croak, answered at once by other croaks and screeches. Then I knew that I was listening to a group of ravens, and I hastened toward the sounds. Following a woodland road leading down over the bed of a small stream, I soon sighted the place, but before I was fully aware of their nearness the birds discovered me and took to the surrounding trees, where they kept up a screeching and moaning and croaking and grumbling such as I had never heard before; it was pandemonium let loose. There were eight or ten birds in all. But I could not get within shotgun range, as they kept well ahead of my advance, never ceasing their uncouth mutterings and nondescript cries. In flying through the denser growth they seemed constantly to be striking their wings against obstructing branches. At the spot where they had been congregated I found that they had been feeding upon the remains of a couple of dead horses. Concealing myself behind a tree, I waited awhile in the hope that they might return, but when one of them flew over and discovered me they all moved farther down the ravine and I saw no more of them.

On a few subsequent occasions I have encountered ravens in various sections of the state, but I have never been able to approach within gunshot. The Raven is in all respects a sublimated Crow, with the characteristics of the Crow developed to a higher degree. Wary though the Crow may be, the Raven is still more alert, watchful, and circumspect. It is even more cautious than most hawks, so far as direct approach is concerned, and for this reason probably seldom falls victim to the unprincipled gunner. Yet it has a streak of curiosity in its make-up and will sometimes return to the scene of its first alarm, swinging over to take another look at the intruder, only to be off again shortly with a hoarse croak of disapproval. The significance of a gun is as well understood by the Raven as by the Crow. In life the two species may be distinguished by the great disparity in their sizes and by the differences in their ways of flying. The Crow flies with a steady flapping of the wings, but the Raven intersperses its flapping with periods of soaring, suggestive of a hawk. Moreover, the voice of the Raven is in general deeper and hoarser than that of the Crow, and its vocabulary, so to speak, is more varied. According to Mr. Harlow (1922), "The Raven shows great individuality in its notes while the voice of the male is much deeper and stronger than that of the female. . . . During the period of courtship and incubation there are two distinct notes that I have not heard at any other time. One is a soft 'crawk,' which the male gives to the female when he is sitting near her while she is on the nest ledge or incubating. The other is a series of 'crawks' given while on the wing and with rarely a note best expressed by the syllables 'ge-lick-ge-lee' given either between the 'crawks' or still more rarely as a single note.

"This note which I have never seen described has a metallic gurgle which does not carry very far. Then there is of course the usual 'crruck' given either singly or repeated any number of times but very frequently repeated three times when the bird is alarmed. There is also a 'crroak' given by the male and often repeated four times as a form of song when undisturbed and near the nest, though it may be given singly. These last two notes are given either upon the wing or while perched. The usual wing note is the rolling guttural 'crruck.' As I have said before, nearly every Raven I have met has some note that is distinctive but the above are the usual types. . . . The note of the young is easily distinguished up to the age of at least six months as I have raised the young from the nest up until this time. It is a harsh 'cawr' when in the nest, more like the note of a Crow than a Raven. The young are very noisy and from sad experience in my home I can testify that their desire for food is insatiable and backed up by strong lungs from dawn till dark."

The same author remarks that "during the winter and early spring the Raven is largely omnivorous. I have known them to eat the buds of various trees when hard pressed for food. At this season, however, they feed largely upon refuse picked up about the various deer camps which are so numerous throughout this territory. [This observation is confirmed from other sources.] Bits of fat, flesh adhering to old bones and skin and legs of deer, all of which are commonly left in the vicinity of these camps are greedily sought out. Corn fields on the edge of their mountain fastnesses are visited and any corn that may have been left, devoured. Any dead animal is a feast and I have observed five Ravens feeding on the carcass of a dead dog in the snow.

"A fact that I do not believe is generally known is that these birds disgorge pellets after the custom of our Owls. I have repeatedly picked up these pellets on their nesting and roosting ledges and found them during the spring to contain the indigestible portions of various species of insects (chiefly Coleoptera) with bones and fur of smaller rodents in several instances. In several nests I have climbed to when they held young birds, I have found remains of frogs and small garter snakes. In no instance have I noted the Raven destroying birds' nests or eggs in the manner of the Crow and the Grackle. . . .

"In the case of the male bird especially the species is one of striking individuality. One male of a pair which I have studied for four years is very fearless, very noisy and possesses a deep voice which may easily be distinguished from that of any other Raven. Another male of a pair I have visited four times is invariably silent, soaring once and then leaving the cliff entirely, never varying this procedure year to year. Still another whose home I have visited three times always utters a note (in addition to the usual vocabulary) that is strikingly like a hoarse laugh 'haw-haw-haw-haw.' Then there is the striking individuality in nesting of certain pairs. One pair builds always in trees, several times nesting within a hundred yards of one of the finest and most typical cliffs I know. Another pair always uses a cliff surrounded by a splendid forest containing numerous tree sites. One thing is sure, in so far as my experience goes, a pair which one discovers nesting in a tree will always be found thereafter in trees and a pair which once chooses a cliff always remains true to their first choice. Other characteristics are evident also to prove the same birds present at the same nests year after year. One male always comes to meet me when I am yet a quarter of a mile away, taking the same course each year, another always warns the female with a low note and sneaks away over the back of the ridge. Females, likewise, possess the same striking individuality of voice and action as the males. Then in addition to the choice of nest sites as evidenced above, different females lay very distinct types of eggs which, as a rule run very true. One nest always contains very dark uniform eggs while another holds very lightly marked specimens with a pale bluish-green background. The first nest of the two just mentioned runs to very small eggs, scarcely larger than [a] Crow's, while the second nest always holds large sized eggs. The number in the set does not hold as true, though certain pairs never lay over four eggs and commonly three while others run to four and five. However, this is a problem which seems to be largely controlled by the vitality of the female at the time of reproduction, i. e.—dependent upon her age and the abundance of food during the winter months."

Mr. Harlow is "firmly convinced" that ravens remain mated for life, and his reasons for this belief are unusually interesting and suggestive. A given pair will return year after year to the same spot; and even after they have become so old that they are no longer able to produce eggs, their instinct leads them to repair or construct a nest and stand by in the breeding season. In one instance where a pair had occupied a certain cliff for sixty years, no eggs were laid during seven successive seasons. Then "the female was shot by a hunter, and the following spring the male returned with a new mate, the old nest was rebuilt and three eggs were laid." Pairs have been known to shift their nesting site from one spot to another when disturbed and to return later to the original site.

Of the courtship of the Raven, the same writer says: "Mating takes place during the first ten days of February. A bird occasionally roosts upon one of the old nesting ledges during the winter as is evident by excrement found there but this is by no means usual. The pair return to the cliff together usually the first week in February, at first only for a short visit each day, and later for several visits. A heavy storm at this time usually delays these visits for several days. At this time I have seen them go to the nesting ledge, the female usually alighting on the ledge and the male on a dead stub nearby and spend ten or fifteen minutes there. At this time they often soar together high up in the air with wing tips touching, the male always slightly above the female. At times he will give a wonderful display of his prowess on the wing, either dropping like a meteor for several hundred feet and fairly hissing through the air in the manner of the male Duck Hawk, or tumbling like a Pigeon over and over. During this period also, I have found them perched close together high up in an old dead tree caressing each other with bills touching."

Our Pennsylvania ravens have two distinct types of nesting sites: cliffs and trees. The former outnumber the latter about eight to one. When the nest is on a cliff, the ledge chosen is almost invariably near the top of the mountain, so that the birds have a clear outlook of the country for miles around. The ledge is not necessarily near the top of the cliff but is usually the one most difficult of access; moreover, it must be sheltered from above either by a projecting shelf or by overhanging hemlocks. When trees are chosen, none but the highest available will answer, and there must be good cover in its top. A nest found in Clinton County by A. K. Pierce was in a giant hemlock, 103 feet from the ground. "The tree nests," Mr. Harlow remarks, "are giant structures over four feet across and yet the birds conceal them so well in the very top of the tree that they are frequently very hard to see from the ground. Usually the wildest mountain swamp is chosen where there still remain some large white pines and hemlocks. I have never known of a tree nest of the Raven to be used two years in succession even though absolutely undisturbed and when young were reared in safety. The birds usually return to the same swamp but the nest site may be shifted from a hundred yards to a mile or more."

Nest-building, requiring from fourteen to eighteen days, usually begins in February, and is carried on almost entirely by the female. The nest itself is a huge but neat structure that always conforms in contour with the ledge or crotch on which it is placed. It may be five feet across but is usually smaller than that, with a cavity averaging a foot wide and six inches deep; it is thus a fairly symmetrical structure. Its body is composed of broken sticks, while the lining is made up of softer and finer stuff, such as shreds of bark and deer hair.

Several days elapse between the completion of the nest and the laying of the first egg. The first or second week in March is about the right time to look for full sets. One egg is laid each day until the set is complete. Four or five compose the usual set, although sometimes there are only three, or rarely six. Once seven were found (Harlow). Except for their larger size (1.90 by 1.28 inches), they resemble the eggs of the Crow, and they exhibit precisely the same variations of color and markings. Mr. Harlow writes: "The ground color is a pale bluish green or light olive green, spotted, dashed, blotched, streaked or smeared with greenish brown, dark brown and sometimes fewer markings of purplish and black. Some types are so heavily marked that the ground color is almost obscured and the color is uniform owing to the density of the markings." The incubation period is twenty days. The male stands by, ready to warn the female of an intruder, but relieves her only when she has to leave the nest for food in bad weather. Both parents feed the young, however, and defend their home from enemies when necessary, driving off crows on occasion, as well as hawks. But they seem to get along after a fashion with the Duck Hawk, which sometimes nests on the same cliffs. The Duck Hawk is in fact about the only bird with which this species comes in contact during the breeding season. Otherwise, as Mr. Harlow says, the Raven is "essentially a solitary bird, and the nests of different pairs are usually a considerable distance apart. The only pairs I know of which nest at all near to one another are six miles apart."

Corvus corax Townsend, *Proc. Acad. Nat. Sci. Philadelphia*, 1883, 64 (Westmoreland Co.).

Corvus corax principalis Warren, *Birds Pa.*, ed. 2, 1890, 201 (distribution by counties)—Warren, *Forest and Stream*, 1891, 37:182 (Centre Co., critical)—Stone, *Birds E. Pa. and N. J.*, 1894, 103, note (Fulton and Centre Co.)—Warren, *Bull. Pa. Dept. Agric.*, no. 17, 1897, (260), 276 (near Glen Union, Clinton Co.)—Smith, *Abstr. Proc. Delaware Valley Orn. Club*, 1898, 2:2 (Clearfield Co.)—Keim, *Cassinia*, 1904, 8:39 (Port Allegany, McKean Co., summer)—Ridgway, *Bull. U. S. Nat. Mus.* no. 50, part 3, 1904, 259 (western Pa., measurements)—Harlow, *Auk*, 1911, 28:266 (mountains of southern Centre Co., nesting; Huntingdon Co., May); 1912, 29:473 (southern Centre Co., resident); 1918, 35:136 (Mifflin, Centre, Blair, Clinton, Juniata, and Huntingdon Co.)—Dickey, *Oölogist*, 1915, 32:106 (near State College, Centre Co., nesting)—Stone, *Cassinia*, 1920, 23:34 (Centre Co., nesting, *fide* Harlow)—[Editor], *Cassinia*, 1926, 25:39 (Tyrone, Blair Co., nesting, *fide* Scoville)—Burleigh, *Wilson Bull.*, 1931, 43:44 (Charter Oak, Huntingdon Co., and mountains near State College, Centre Co., nesting).

Corvus corax sinuatus (error) Stone, *Auk*, 1891, 8:245 ("Delaware Co." [Fulton Co.], December)—Rhoads, *Auk*, 1899, 16:311 ([Round Island], Clinton Co.).

"Raven" Simpson, *Oölogist*, 1910, 27:100 (Warren, Warren Co., spring); 1912, 29:329 (head of Tionesta Creek, Warren Co.)—Sutton, *Bird-Lore*, 1923, 25:195 ("Huntingdon" [near Mill Creek], Huntingdon Co., nesting)—Christy, *Cardinal*, 1935, 4:43 ([near Mill Creek, Huntingdon Co.], nesting; habits).

"Northern Raven" Harlow, *Cassinia*, 1911, 14:11 (near State College, Centre Co., nesting; western Pa. localities and records)—Dickey, *Oölogist*, 1914, 31:171 ([Charter Oak], Huntingdon Co., nesting), 207 (Cresson, Cambria Co., June)—Miller, *Oölogist*, 1919, 36:155 ([near] State College, Centre Co., nesting)—Scoville, *Atlantic Monthly*, 1920, 126:32 (Seven Mts., Centre Co., nesting, March)—Harlow, *Auk*, 1922, 39:399 (distribution in Pa.; breeding habits).

EASTERN CROW

CORVUS BRACHYRHYNCHOS BRACHYRHYNCHOS Brehm

Description—Entirely black; excepting the Raven, our largest Passerine bird; wingspread about thirty-five inches.

Range—The American Crow inhabits North America at large from near the Mexican boundary north to the coniferous forests of Canada. Several races are currently recognized, but in my opinion these are of doubtful validity. This question aside, the species is a common and evenly distributed one throughout western Pennsylvania. Its seasonal status, however, varies unaccountably in different parts of its local range. In the northern tier of counties it seems to be in the main a summer resident and rare or casual during the winter months; and this is likewise its status for an undetermined distance over the higher country to the south. At Springs, Somerset County, close to the Maryland boundary, A. B. Miller writes that during very severe winter weather the Crow disappears for a time, to reappear as soon as the weather moderates. In the valley country of the ridge and valley section, from Centre County southward, the species is common all the year around.

As the Crow is regularly migratory in the northern part of its range, the conditions described above are normal. But in the western counties, a curious state of affairs exists in the Ohio Valley. Although this is the very region where one would naturally expect to see the Crow in winter, the species deserts this section during the coldest part of the year and is as regularly migratory as the Robin. It is a mystery to me that some observers contrive to include the Crow in their "Christmas Census" lists from Beaver County, for in the course of a long experience there I have detected it but once along the Ohio River in December, and only once in January. Since it is common there at other seasons, its absence in winter is all the more noticeable. I have seen it, however, on a few occasions during this season in Allegheny County, along the Ohio, and also once at the mouth of Big Traverse Creek in Beaver County. According to present information, the area from which the Crow is generally absent in winter covers most of Beaver and Washington counties and the adjacent part of Allegheny County. The reason for its avoidance of this area is not apparent.

On the other hand, winter crow roosts have been reported from several points within our region. The largest, estimated to contain two hundred thousand birds, was located near Bellefonte, Centre County, and must have attracted crows over a radius of many miles. Another and much smaller one was at Boston, Allegheny County. "Several thousand" stay every winter at a roost near Mercer Junction, Mercer County (Keesler). The present status of these various roosts is unknown. Doubtless there are others that have not come to the notice of any of our observers.

Migration—Even where the Crow as a species is a year-round resident, a migratory movement takes place, as evidenced by seasonal fluctuations in abundance. Such movements occur in February and March, and again in October and November. Whether our breeding crows are sedentary, or whether they all retire southward for the winter and are replaced by migrants from farther north, has not been determined. Banding may eventually solve this question. Where the Crow is a summer resident only, its arrival is soon made known to ear and eye. In Beaver County, according to my experience, it is invariably the earliest herald of spring and returns on the first mild day—about the middle of February. The dates of its arrival over a period of twenty-nine years lie between February 8 and March 4, with February 18 as the average. Its arrival date at Sewickley, Allegheny County, corresponds closely. After this first appearance, migrant birds are usually seen winging their way northward in large, straggling flocks until the first week in March, after which the species attains its normal numbers for the season. Farther north, in Warren County, it also arrives from the South late in February or early in March (from February 14 to March 1), while the higher hills are still more or less snow-covered.

The return movement is performed in October, and, as in spring, the species migrates in large, straggling flocks. By the last of the month nearly all the crows have gone. On November 25, 1888, I saw a belated flock on its way southward in Beaver County. Single birds or flocks noted here during December and January may be regarded as wintering.

Habits—Excepting the Robin (and not counting the ubiquitous English Sparrow), the Crow is probably better known to the casual passer-by than any other native bird. It is a good example of a fairly large and necessarily conspicuous bird that has, by its sagacity, resourcefulness, and persistence, contrived to maintain its own under the devastating changes brought about by the advance of civilization and even in the face of unrelenting persecution and attempted extermination. So long as there are any bits of woodland left, there will be crows to make their homes there. Even on the plains of Saskatchewan, where the few trees grow only along the watercourses or near houses, the number of crows is surprising. The Crow is assuredly a hardy and eminently successful species. One could wish that it were also ornamental and useful.

Unlike the Raven, the Crow is a clannish bird, and even in the breeding season it is not uncommon to find a number of nests in the same tract of woods. In its semiannual migratory movements it sometimes appears in large companies. B. H. Christy relates that he "observed what seemed an endless stream of crows flying high in the air, in an easterly direction across the river valley; the stream was not continuous; one band followed another and stragglers filled the intervals; in a few minutes I counted several hundred individuals." This gregarious propensity reaches its height during the winter season in the communal roosting. An observer stationed at the roosting site will see, towards evening, flocks of crows converging from all directions. The incoming birds find their places amid terrible din and confusion. Each seems bent on making as much noise as possible, until the place becomes a veritable bedlam. "Acres of trees blackened by masses of noisy crows is the usual impression one gets of the winter night rendezvous" (McConnell, 1917). As darkness falls, there presently comes a lull in the babel of cries, and at last all is quiet as the birds finally settle down for the night. In the morning the din is renewed as they disperse to their several feeding grounds.

T. D. Burleigh contributes the following account of the Centre County roost, which he visited in January, 1917:

"A crow roost that I found today was located on a hillside covered with second-growth hemlock and white pine, a mile and a half east of Bellefonte, along the main road. Fully two hundred thousand crows congregate there every night, coming from a radius of probably fifty miles. They begin to arrive a little after 4 P.M. and from then until 5:30 stream into the roost in ever increasing numbers, clouds of them appearing from all directions. For the last half-hour, they drop in at the rate of a hundred a second or six thousand a minute. They do not at once enter the roost proper but gather in the surrounding fields until the ground is black with their forms; many alight in a small wood lot near by and gather there until the limbs of the trees bend beneath their weight. As dusk comes on, they gradually drift into the roost, and the uproar that begins then continues until it is dark."

The Crow has learned by sad experience that every man's hand is raised against it, but it has also learned how best to take care of itself. Shy and suspicious, it avoids potentially dangerous ground by some uncanny intuition; to steal up on it is well-nigh impossible. Inherently cautious by nature, and endowed with keen sight and hearing, it is ever watchful and alert, ready to decamp at the first alarm. A flock of crows seldom descends to the ground to feed without leaving one or more birds perched aloft as sentinels. One warning call from the lookout, and the whole flock is off. The Crow is usually credited with more intelligence than most birds, and while there are those who decry this theory, one acquires, after matching wits with this species, a certain respect for it. The Crow certainly understands the meaning of a gun and will give the gunner a wide berth—greatly to its own advantage. Unlooked-for immunity from this source, however, may make it reckless. Some years ago in the spring, when I passed daily over a road leading out of town to my regular collecting grounds, a pair of crows would fly out to meet me every morning from the other side of the valley. They would perch in the trees overhead, abusing me in crow language as long as I was in sight. In time they became very bold and would come within shotgun range, and I could easily have killed them had I so desired. Evidently the gun that I carried singled me out in their eyes from other walkers along this road, to whom they paid no especial attention.

Other than man, the Crow has few enemies. True, it is hated and feared by the smaller birds, because of its nest-robbing tendencies, but only the Kingbird seems able to give it battle successfully. The larger owls—the Great Horned and the Barred—must prey on it by night, however, for when it happens to discover them in the daytime there ensues a "mob scene" as dramatic as any that occurs in the bird world. A series of wild outcries soon brings all the crows within hearing to the spot, and the poor owl is ringed in by an excited and angry mob, which may keep pestering it for hours. Sometimes the owl turns on its tormentors and, singling one crow out of the throng, contrives to capture it by a sudden sally. This sortie may put a temporary quietus upon the enthusiasm of the crows; but more frequently the owl, caught at a disadvantage, attempts to retire into thicker covert or to a hole in a hollow tree, and is followed in its retreat by the whole throng of taunting birds. When their attention is thus distracted, it is sometimes possible for an observer to approach the scene of the disturbance without detection. Hawks and eagles also come in for their share of mobbing, but these birds easily shake off the crows by resorting to flight. R. B. Simpson once found some crows stampeding a red fox that had probably earned their displeasure.

In some parts of the country the Crow does not

seem to be very particular about its choice of a nest-tree and often picks one that is easy to climb. From my own experience I would conclude that it deliberately chooses a site high above ground and hard to reach by ordinary means, and that its nest is likely to be relatively as inaccessible as that of the Red-tailed Hawk. Of all the nests I have found I have been able to examine only a very few, although an expert climber with the proper equipment could doubtless have reached most or all of the others. Two nests that I found at Pymatuning Lake in the spring of 1935 were built in young pines, only about fifteen feet up. These sites were exceptional, however, and the average nest would be nearer sixty or seventy feet from the ground. The kind of tree does not matter—an oak, a pine, a maple, a tulip tree, even a hemlock or a willow, will serve. Usually the nest is built next the trunk of the tree, where it is less conspicuous, but even then it is easy to find before the trees are in leaf.

The body of the nest is built of dry sticks and twigs, while the lining is of finer and softer material of various kinds—grapevine bark, coarse, dry grasses, weed stalks, leaves, bits of corn stalks, old potato vines, straw, moss, or hair from cattle. A typical nest is about two feet across, with a cavity about a foot wide and four to six inches deep. There is no uniformity in the time of nest-building. Some pairs begin in March, if the weather permits, and have their sets of eggs complete by the end of that month, while others dally along and are not ready to incubate until May. The eggs number from three to six, four or five being the usual set. Mr. Christy writes: "Crows' eggs vary much in size, in form, and in color; some eggs are greatly tapered at the smaller end, while others are more like a hen's egg in shape. There are two types of coloring; in one case the ground-color is pale greenish blue and the markings are well defined; in the other case the ground-color is olive green and the markings are heavy and obscure. Eggs of the latter type present a much darker appearance than those of the former. Eggs of both types may be found in a single set." J. W. Jacobs has in his collection a remarkable set in which the ground-color is a creamy clay instead of greenish. The average measurements, estimated from a large series of eggs of this species, are 1.63 by 1.15 inches.

Crows are rather quiet and unobtrusive about their nests and avoid noisy demonstrations that might betray the location. The incubating bird sits very closely and sometimes will not leave until a climber is almost at the nest, when she slips off silently. The eggs hatch in about two weeks, and the callow young—blind, almost naked, and entirely unprepossessing—are fed at first on soft foods—spiders, caterpillars, and birds' eggs—but later they get beetles, crustaceans, small mammals, and grain.

There arises for consideration at this point the whole matter of the economic status of the Crow. Much has been written on this question, both pro and con, but fortunately there are available the results of an impartial investigation, reported by E. R. Kalmbach in his article, *The Crow and Its Relation to Man*,[1] which will ensure a just verdict. One of the major counts against the Crow is that it pulls sprouting corn. Farmers generally complain of this habit, and in some parts and some seasons the damage is extensive. Replanting of seed becomes necessary to repair the loss. Later in the season, after the corn is in the milk, the Crow tears open the growing ears to get at the tender grain. Ripe corn left in the field in shocks is also subject to attack. All these charges against the Crow are sustained by stomach examinations, which prove that corn is the principal food of the adult birds. Some of it must be waste grain, picked up after the harvest, but the damage to a crop is often considerable. Tarring the seed before planting has been found by experiment to act as a deterrent against its being pulled up. It is a more effective method than the scarecrows on which some farmers still rely. The bodies of a few crows hung up in plain sight are also a salutary warning that usually brings results.

The Crow is known to eat other grain to some extent and also cultivated fruit on occasion. Wild fruits constitute a considerable proportion of its food, especially in the fall months. It is charged with spreading the seeds of the poison ivy and poison oak, but since many other agencies work toward the same end, the damage it does in this respect need not be taken too seriously.

The second major count against the Crow is its habit of destroying wild birds and their eggs—a practice that is all too often directed against do-

[1]U. S. Department of Agriculture, *Bulletin*, no. 621, 1918, p. 92, pl. 1.

mestic birds as well. It is surprising how large a bird the Crow will venture to attack. Mr. Simpson has seen it swoop at ducks and grebes on the water, and S. E. Bacon tells of a crow that was shot in the act of carrying off a flicker. Mr. Burleigh once saw one trying to secure a tree sparrow from a flock. Young poultry sometimes suffers severely. Under such circumstances the owner's only recourse is the shotgun, and individual crows that fall into bad habits should be summarily dealt with. The ornithologist is naturally more concerned with the toll of bird life taken by the Crow through the robbing of nests. Just how much damage a given marauder inflicts on the smaller birds during the course of a season cannot be estimated, but in the aggregate it is probably heavy. I believe that the Crow goes about its search for nests systematically. Once in April, a few years ago, I was surprised to see a crow flying into the town of Beaver from across the Ohio River—an unusual circumstance, even in the early morning. As I watched, it flew directly and without hesitation to a robin's nest in a shade tree on the street; this nest it proceeded to despoil, over the angry protests of the parent birds. I received the impression that the crow must have located this particular nest at an earlier date, and was returning to get the eggs after they were laid.

In some parts of the West where the Crow abounds, it is a great menace to ducks and other ground-nesting birds. In the East, too, it plays havoc at times with numbers of our useful insectivorous kinds. There is only one palliative feature about this nest-robbing habit: it is mostly carried on while the young crows are small, and largely for their benefit. Thus a second laying by the victims may readily escape spoliation. But there is no doubt that the Crow, in thus unduly reducing the number of our useful birds, is indirectly rendering a disservice to mankind. As F. M. Chapman puts it, "The Crow, therefore, in addition to the direct damage it may do to our crops, robs us of the services of birds far more desirable than itself."[1]

But the Crow is not quite so black as it is here painted. At the very time that it is pulling corn for itself it may be feeding its young on white grubs, so destructive to vegetation. Speaking of its insect food, Mr. Kalmbach states: "Nearly a fifth of the adult crows' yearly sustenance comes from such sources, and a great part of the insect material is eaten early in the spring, a time when the life cycles of many of the most destructive pests are at their lowest ebb. A little later, nestling crows appear on the scene, outnumbering their parents two to one, and assist in the work of destruction. Not only do the young birds eat a much larger proportion of insect food than do their parents at the same time of year, but the quantity of food required to develop their rapidly growing bodies is considerably greater." Beetles (especially May beetles, and their larvae), grasshoppers, and caterpillars, are eaten in large quantities by both adult and young crows.

Because of its comparatively large size and general abundance, the Crow is a potential force for good or for ill. Mr. Kalmbach thus sums up the case for and against it: "When feeding on injurious insects, crustaceans, rodents, and carrion, and when dispersing seeds of beneficial plants, the crow is working largely for the best interests of man; when destroying small reptiles, amphibians, wild birds, poultry, corn, and some other crops, when molesting livestock and distributing their diseases, and when spreading seeds of noxious plants, the bird is one of the farmer's enemies; when destroying spiders and mollusks, however, its work appears in the main to have a neutral effect. The misdeeds of which the crow has been convicted greatly outnumber its virtues, but these are not necessarily equal in importance. Much of its damage to crops and poultry can be prevented, while the bird's services in the control of insect pests can ill be spared. At the same time no policy can be recommended which would allow the crow to become so numerous that its shortcomings would be greatly accentuated. As the capabilities of the crow for both good and harm are great, it is believed that an extermination of the species would have ultimate consequences no less serious than an overabundance."

The Crow population of western Pennsylvania is not so excessive that wholesale measures for further reduction seem necessary or advisable, the Pennsylvania Game Commission to the contrary notwithstanding. It is right and proper that the Crow should be without the protection of the law, but at the same time no special incentives for its destruction should be offered. Bounties are absolutely wrong in principle, and costly in practice.

[1] *Economic Value of Birds to the State*, p. 39 (State of New York Forest, Fish and Game Commission, 1903).

The matter can safely be left in the hands of the farmers—the class most affected. As Mr. Kalmbach says: "The attitude of the individual farmer toward the crow should be one of toleration when no serious losses are suffered, rather than one of uncompromising antagonism resulting in the unwarranted destruction of these birds which at times are most valuable aids to man."

If crows are considered too numerous, it may be well to point out that their superabundance has been brought about by the indiscriminate killing of the larger birds of prey—hawks and owls—which formerly kept this species under control.

Corvus americanus AUDUBON, *Orn. Biog.*, 1834, 2:322 (Pittsburgh, Allegheny Co.)—TEULON, *Jour. Boston Zoöl. Soc.*, 1883, 2:9 (Bradford, McKean Co.)—JAMISON, *Ornithologist and Oölogist*, 1888, 13:134; and DWIGHT, *Auk*, 1892, 9:136 (Cresson, Cambria Co., June)—BARROWS and SCHWARZ, *Bull. Div. Orn. and Mammal.*, no. 6, 1895, (7), 39, 70 (East Brook, Lawrence Co., food, *fide* Fisher)—BURNS, Bull. 5, *Wilson Orn. Chapt. Agassiz Assoc.*, 1895, (3), 15 (Erie, Erie Co., breeding), 33 (Waynesburg, Greene Co., nesting)—TODD, *Auk*, 1893, 10:39 (Two Lick, Indiana Co., June), 44 (Coalport, Clearfield Co., June)—JACOBS, *Summer Birds Greene Co., Pa.*, 1893, 8 (Greene Co., nesting)—BAILY, *Auk*, 1896, 13:294 (Williamsville, Elk Co., June–July)—JACOBS, *Gleanings from Nature*, 1898, 1:18, 23 (Waynesburg, Greene Co., description eggs)—COPE, *Cassinia*, 1902, 5:15 (Clinton and Potter Co., June).

Corvus frugivorus TOWNSEND, *Proc. Acad. Nat. Sci. Philadelphia*, 1883, 64 (Latrobe, Westmoreland Co., breeding).

"Crow" ENTY, *Ornithologist and Oölogist*, 1885, 10:78 (Templeton, Armstrong Co., migration)—HOMER, *Ornithologist and Oölogist*, 1893, 18:61 (Elmer, Potter Co., June)—SIMPSON, *Oölogist*, 1894, 11:256; and 1911, 28:202 (Warren, Warren Co., habits, etc.)—SIMPSON, *Nidiologist*, 1895, 3:19 (description albino from Warren, Warren Co.)—WARREN, *Bull. Pa. Dept. Agric.*, no. 17, 1897, 118 (western Pa., economic relations)—MORRISON, *Bird-Lore*, 1902, 4:31 (northwestern Pa.; habits)—STONE, *Cassinia*, 1906, 9:43 (McConnellsburg, Fulton Co., June)—PITCAIRN, *Bird-Lore*, 1908, 10:32 (West View, Allegheny Co., December)—MILLER, *Bird-Lore*, 1908, 10:32; etc. (Springs, Somerset Co., December)—GERBERDING, *Bird-Lore*, 1912, 14:29 (Greenville, Mercer Co., December)—BURLEIGH, *Bird-Lore*, 1913, 15:29 (Aspinwall, Allegheny Co., December)—MCCONNELL, *Bird-Lore*, 1914, 16:37; etc. (McKeesport, Allegheny Co., December)—MCCONNELL, *Auk*, 1917, 34:478 (Boston, Allegheny Co., winter roost)—MCGRAW, *et al.*, *Bird-Lore*, 1919, 21:37; etc. (Altoona, Blair Co., December)—WARFIELD, *Bird-Lore*, 1919, 21:37; etc. (Chambersburg, Franklin Co., December)—MCCONNELL, *Bird-Lore*, 1920, 22:31 (Emsworth, Allegheny Co., December)—SCOVILLE, *Cassinia*, 1920, 23:21 ([Charter Oak, Huntingdon Co.], May; habits)—MCCLELLAND, *Am. Mid. Nat.*, 1922, 8:35 (Washington, Washington Co., resident)—HOFFMAN, *et al.*, Bird-Lore, 1923, 25:23 (Grove City, Mercer Co., December)—JONES, *et al.*, *Bird-Lore*, 1923, 25:25 (Deer Creek, Allegheny Co., December)—STREET, *Cassinia*, 1923, 24:14 (Greencastle to Ft. Loudon, Franklin Co., June)—CHRISTY, *Cardinal*, 1924, v. 1, no. 4, p. 10 (Big Traverse Valley, Beaver Co., June)—[CHRISTY], *Cardinal*, 1925, v. 1, no. 5, p. 15 (Pittsburgh, Allegheny Co., Lambdin's record)—MATUSZAK, *Bird-Lore*, 1926, 28:29 (Hyde Park, Westmoreland Co., December)—EASTWOOD, *Bird-Lore*, 1926, 28:59 (Jefferson, Greene Co., October; East Pittsburgh, Allegheny Co., October, *fide* Elliott; Hartstown, Crawford Co., November, *fide* Squier); 1927, 29:55 (Wildwood, Allegheny Co., winter roost, *fide* Allison and Reiter; Little Pucketa Creek, [near New Kensington], Westmoreland Co., December, *fide* Manley and Taylor)—ELLAIR, *et al.*, *Bird-Lore*, 1927, 29:29 (Thompsonville and region, Washington Co., December)—BOULTON, *Bird-Lore*, 1928, 30:13 (Little Pucketa Creek, [near New Kensington], Westmoreland Co., October, *fide* Manley and Taylor)—JACOBS (M.K.), *Oölogist*, 1931, 48:7 (Waynesburg, Greene Co., habits in captivity)—SAVAGE, *Bird-Lore*, 1932, 34:44 (Presque Isle, Erie Co., December)—BERKHEIMER, *Bird-Lore*, 1933, 35:27; etc. (near Osterburg, Bedford Co., December)—ELLIOTT, *Cardinal*, 1934, 3:171 (Raccoon Creek, Beaver Co., December)—CHRISTY, *Cardinal*, 1939, 5:45 (Raccoon Creek, Washington Co., and Sewickley and Bradford Woods, Allegheny Co., winter).

Corvus brachyrhynchos TODD, *Ann. Carnegie Mus.*, 1904, 2:565 (Erie and Presque Isle, Erie Co., nesting)—TODD, in Bausman, *Hist. Beaver Co., Pa.*, 1904, 2:1200 (Beaver Co., summer)—KEIM, *Cassinia*, 1905, 8:39 (Port Allegany, McKean Co., summer).

Corvus brachyrhynchos brachyrhynchos HARLOW, *Auk*, 1912, 29:473 (southern Centre Co., breeding)—CHRISTY, *Cardinal*, 1923, v. 1, no. 1, [p. 8] (Sewickley, Allegheny Co., nesting; occasional in winter)—BURLEIGH, *Wilson Bull.*, 1923, 35:90 (Allegheny Co., resident; nesting); 1924, 36:69; 1931, 43:45 (State College, Centre Co., nesting)—CHRISTY and SUTTON, *Cardinal*, 1928, 2:71, 75 (Cook Forest, Clarion Co., resident)—SUTTON, *Ann. Carnegie Mus.*, 1928, 18:160 (Crawford Co. localities, resident)—BURLEIGH, *Cardinal*, 1932, 3:77 (Chestnut Ridge, near Uniontown, Fayette Co., breeding).

TITMICE

FAMILY PARIDAE

THE PARIDAE are a family of boreal affinities, with many representatives in the Old World and relatively few in North America, where they are found as far south as Mexico. The three species that occur in western Pennsylvania are permanent residents.

The Titmice are small woodland birds, associates of the Nuthatches and Creepers. Their short, unnotched bills, with nostrils concealed by tufts of stiff feathers, distinguish them from these closely allied families. Structurally they are similar to the Jays, but are much smaller. They are sociable birds and are usually found in small groups except during the breeding season. Those that occur in our region build their nests in holes in trees and lay large clutches of eggs.

BLACK-CAPPED CHICKADEE[1] (Plate 15)

PENTHESTES ATRICAPILLUS ATRICAPILLUS (Linnaeus)

Description—A small, stocky bird with a rather long tail. *Top of head, nape, and throat, black,* in strong contrast with the sides of the head (below the eyes), which are grayish white; upperparts gray with a slight brownish wash; *wings and tail* dusky gray, *with hoary feather-edgings;* underparts (below the black throat) whitish, the sides and flanks more or less washed with buff; bill and feet black.

Range—The eastern race of the Black-capped Chickadee (as currently recognized) ranges from Newfoundland west to northern Ontario[2] and south to Illinois and northern New Jersey, and in the Appalachian highlands to North Carolina.[3] Farther south the Black-capped species is replaced by the Carolina Chickadee. The respective ranges of the two species are not entirely complementary, however, and there is a strip of territory, of undetermined width, where they overlap. The Black-capped species occupies by far the greater part of western Pennsylvania. It is the prevailing form throughout the highlands and from there to and across the western tier of counties south to the Ohio Valley, where it is found together with the Carolina Chickadee. There are both breeding and winter specimens available to support this statement, but we do not yet know whether the Black-capped Chickadee impinges upon the Carolina Chickadee in the region south of the Ohio and east of the Monongahela rivers, where the latter is presumed to be the prevailing form. True, there are numerous records for this region, but since all are based on sight identifications alone they cannot be completely trusted. It is unfortunate that the identity of so many sets of eggs taken in Beaver County is uncertain. Five breeding specimens from the ridge and valley section are all referable to the Black-capped species, but additional material from this area is desirable, and amateur observers are cautioned against the off-hand identification of chickadees from this and other disputed territory.

The Black-capped Chickadee is a permanent resident, although all observers agree that there is considerable seasonal fluctuation in its abundance.

[1]The accounts of this and the next species have already appeared (in modified form and with omissions of the published references) in the *Cardinal*, 1936, 4:90–95.

[2]The Chickadee of northern Ontario has recently been separated as *Penthestes atricapillus anamesus* Todd, *Auk*, 1938, 55:116.

[3]The Chickadee of the Appalachian highlands has recently been separated as *Penthestes atricapillus practicus* Oberholser, *Proceedings Biological Society Washington*, 1937, 50:220. The range of this new form is given as including "southwestern Pennsylvania," where, however (so far as I know), only *P. carolinensis* occurs.

Apparently it is more numerous in fall and winter than in spring and summer. If it could be shown that it occurs in Washington and Greene counties as a winter visitor only and that it leaves this section entirely to the other species in the summer, the postulation of a distinct north and south migration might be justified. Careful studies made by W. K. Butts at Ithaca, New York,[1] tend, however, to discredit such an assumption. Dr. Butts says: "In considering these evidences of a migratory movement, it should be remembered that even if birds appear to be more numerous during the winter, it is not proved that there really are more individuals present. Many birds are so much more conspicuous in winter than in summer that they may seem to be more abundant. The distributional records show that there is a movement of Chickadees, but it is not proved that there is a distinct north and south migration." The records adduced by Dr. Butts show that individual birds seldom wander far from their regular territory, which as a rule is rather circumscribed.

These records doubtless indicate the true status in a normal season, but I can well remember some winters when chickadees invaded the town of Beaver in large numbers. Since they had never been known to breed there, they must have come from a distance. T. L. McConnell wrote from McKeesport in 1915: "Last year, we are all aware, was one of the greatest for chickadees. Thousands of them invaded the hillside near our home and made themselves conspicuous in many ways. . . . This year we note a general scarcity of black-capped titmice and have yet to find a single chickadee on our nearby hillside." It would seem then that this species, although normally sedentary, does on occasion become a winter wanderer into new and untried territory.

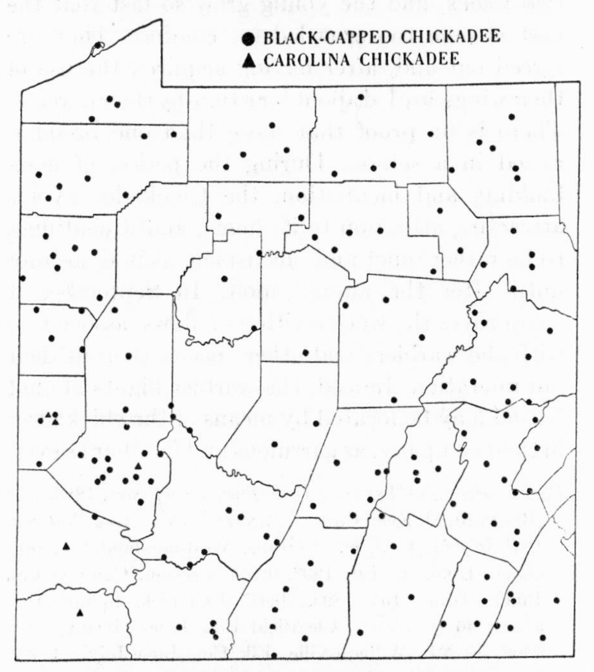

LOCAL RANGES OF THE BLACK-CAPPED CHICKADEE AND OF THE CAROLINA CHICKADEE

Habits[2]—In the wintertime, when bird life in general is at its lowest ebb, the Black-capped Chickadee reaches its high tide in numbers and prominence. When "the melancholy days have come" and most of our feathered visitors have hied themselves to warmer climes, the Chickadee remains to enliven by its cheery presence and song the otherwise dreary winter months. Cold weather has no terrors for it; come sun or storm, it is always the same familiar, restless, odd little bird, full of life and action, industry and good cheer. Of a sociable nature, it is rarely found alone and usually travels in straggling flocks or groups of a dozen or more, which carry on among themselves an animated conversation in their own peculiar style as they flit from tree to tree in their eager, restless quest of food. Very often they admit to their fellowship numbers of tufted titmice, white-breasted nuthatches, and golden-crowned kinglets, and perhaps a brown creeper or two. A downy woodpecker usually brings up the rear. Among the members of this motley company the best of feeling seems to prevail as they rove in irregular fashion through the woods, each group searching for food in its own characteristic way. The Slate-colored Junco, although a seed-eater, may also join such a wandering flock. Sometimes, too, the Chickadee betakes itself to the haunts of the Tree Sparrow, where its efforts are devoted to some extent toward picking up small seeds.

But one need not go to the woods to make the Chickadee's acquaintance; it may not even be necessary to leave one's own dooryard. For this bird and its friends will pass and repass through the orchard, overlooking no corner until the leafless branches have been completely culled of insect eggs and pupae. The amount of good done

[1] *Bird-Banding*, 1931, 2:1–26.
[2] Adapted from an essay written by the author in 1890.

in this way is incalculable. Seldom is the Chickadee still for a moment at a time. It is always peering into the crevices of the bark, exploring every little nook and cranny, twisting and turning and posing in fantastic attitudes—the very personification of action. Far from being shy or retiring, it seems rather to court the presence of man, and it evinces a boldness and a curiosity that are sometimes most amusing. One cannot very well invade its haunts without sooner or later encountering it; it seems, in its familiarity and confidence, quite heedless of any possible danger. Oftentimes, pausing to rest during the course of a winter tramp, I have been surrounded with a gay and noisy company of chickadees; some of the bolder and more curious spirits have approached within a yard of me, pretending to ignore my presence but in reality peeping at me all the time with their little beady eyes and talking to each other, so to speak, in a low, querulous strain. Fancy being discussed by a group of birds, none of them larger than one's thumb! They soon learn to come to feeding-stations and may even be taught, with a little patience, to take food from the hand.

The Chickadee has a great variety of notes, the best known of which is the one from which it derives its name. Another consists of the syllables *as yet*, solemnly uttered in a deep, guttural tone. But its most beautiful note by far is the *phe-bee* call, oftenest heard on mild days in late winter, when, under the warming touch of a February sun, the bird hails the coming spring. It is a clear, plaintive call of two syllables, given in an exquisitely pure tone, fairylike in its delicacy. The sadly sweet notes often seem to come from far off, when in reality the tiny singer is close at hand. In March this call is heard more frequently, for then the winter flocks break up into pairs and the breeding season is approaching. After selecting a suitable place for housekeeping, which is usually in a decayed stump soft enough to be easily worked, the pairs dig holes for themselves, in almost the same way that woodpeckers do; the cavity is roomy, although with a small entrance. The interior is not nearly so smooth as in the holes of the woodpeckers, nor is the entrance so exactly round; for the chickadees, being smaller and weaker, are less skilled as carpenters. Often they save themselves labor by occupying some natural cavity—an old woodpecker-hole, a hollow post, or other convenient retreat. The nesting site may be chosen long before actual construction begins. The nest proper is a rather loose and bulky structure, with moss prominent in its composition; it is snugly lined with soft substances, such as matted rabbit fur, feathers, and plant down.

Full sets of eggs have been taken in Allegheny County as early as April 17 (Atkinson), while a set from Stoneboro, Mercer County, in the Carnegie Museum, is dated June 14 (Sutton). This set was found in a nest located twenty feet from the ground, whereas the nests are usually built much lower down. Most of the available records for fresh eggs were made during the first and second weeks in May. Six to eight eggs comprise the normal set, although I once found nine; and sometimes only five are laid. They are white, with a rosy blush when fresh, and are speckled with reddish brown. The exact shade varies from vinaceous cinnamon to pecan brown. Usually all the eggs of a set are much the same, but different sets vary considerably; in some the eggs are lightly and almost uniformly speckled, while in others the markings are heavier and clustered or wreathed about the larger end. Average measurements are .60 by .47 inches, and the shape approaches rounded ovate. The eggs hatch in about two weeks, and the young grow so fast that the nest is soon too crowded for comfort. They are forced out and, after having acquired the use of their wings, are led about for a time by their parents. There is no proof that more than one brood is raised in a season. During the period of nest-building and incubation, the Chickadee avoids attracting attention to its home, and it continues to be rather quiet and inconspicuous in demeanor until after the annual molt. In September it again roves the woods with its fellows, associating with the warblers and other species then in their fall migration. Indeed, the warbler flights at that season may be located by means of the chickadees in their company, as garrulous and familiar as ever.

Parus atricapillus Teulon, *Jour. Boston Zoöl. Soc.*, 1882, 1:50 (Bradford, McKean Co.)—Townsend, *Proc. Acad. Nat. Sci. Philadelphia*, 1883, 60 (Latrobe, Westmoreland Co., resident)—Dwight, *Auk*, 1892, 9:140 (Cresson, Cambria Co., June)—Todd, *Auk*, 1893, 10:41 (Two Lick, Indiana Co., June), 46 (Coalport, Clearfield Co., June)—Baily, *Auk*, 1896, 13:297 (Williamsville, Elk Co., June–July)—Cope, *Cassinia*, 1902, 5:20 (Clinton and Potter Co., June)—Todd, *Ann. Carnegie Mus.*, 1904, 2:591 (Presque Isle, Erie Co., resident)—TODD, in Bausman, *Hist. Beaver Co., Pa.*, 1904, 2:1202, part (Beaver Co., resident)—KEIM, *Cassinia*, 1905, 8:41 (Port Allegany, McKean Co., summer).

"Black-capped Chickadee" (?)TODD, *Oölogist*, 1887, 4:89 (Beaver, Beaver Co., nesting)—(?)WICKHAM, *Oölogist*, 1887, 4:102 (Beaver, Beaver Co., nesting; habits)—STONE, *Cassinia*, 1906, 9:44 (Scrub Ridge, west of McConnellsburg, Fulton Co., June)—WRIGHT, *Bird-Lore*, 1911, 13:31, (part?) (Pittsburgh, Allegheny Co., December)—GERBERDING, *Bird-Lore*, 1912, 14:29 (Greenville, Mercer Co., December)—MCCONNELL, *Oölogist*, 1918, 35:152, (part?) (McKeesport, Allegheny Co.)—STAHL, *et al.*, *Bird-Lore*, 1921, 23:18, (part?) (Forest Hills to Deer Creek, Allegheny Co., December)—NICHOLSON, *Bird-Lore*, 1921, 23:18 (Grove City, Mercer Co., December)—STREET, *Cassinia*, 1923, 24:19 (Greencastle and Jordan's Knob, Franklin Co., June)—EASTWOOD, *Bird-Lore*, 1927, 29:56, (part?) (Logan's Ferry, Allegheny Co., October; and Thompsonville, Washington Co., November, *fide* Ellair)—BERKHEIMER, *Bird-Lore*, 1933, 35:27; etc. (Osterburg, Bedford Co., December).

"Chickadee" MILLER, *Bird-Lore*, 1908, 10:32; etc. (Springs, Somerset Co., December)—VALENTINE, *Bird-Lore*, 1908, 10:32 (Bellefonte, Centre Co., December)—SIMPSON, *Oölogist*, 1912, 29:248; etc. (Warren, Warren Co., fall and winter)—MORRIS, *Bird-Lore*, 1913, 15:29 (Eagle Rock, Venango Co., December)—HARLOW, *Oölogist*, 1915, 32:29 ([near Pine Grove Mills], Centre Co., nesting)—MCCONNELL, *Oölogist*, 1915, 32:35, (part?) (McKeesport, Allegheny Co.)—BURLEIGH, *Oölogist*, 1915, 32:119 (State College, Centre Co., April)—MCGRAW, *et al.*, *Bird-Lore*, 1919, 21:37; etc. (Altoona, Blair Co., December)—WARFIELD, *Bird-Lore*, 1919, 21:37; etc. (Chambersburg, Franklin Co., December)—MATUSZAK, *Bird-Lore*, 1926, 28:29 (Hyde Park, Westmoreland Co., December)—ALSOP, *Bird-Lore*, 1927, 29:29 (Ridgway, Elk Co., December)—ELLIOTT, *Cardinal*, 1934, 3:171, (part?) (Raccoon Creek, Beaver Co., December).

Penthestes atricapillus atricapillus HARLOW, *Auk*, 1912, 29:477 ("Stone Valley," Centre Co., nesting); 1918, 35:146 (Fayette and Huntingdon Co. to Warren Co.)—CHRISTY, *Cardinal*, 1923, v. 1, no. 1, [p. 14], part (Sewickley, Allegheny Co., resident)—BURLEIGH, *Wilson Bull.*, 1923, 35:144 (?Harmarville, Allegheny Co., nesting); 1931, 43:54 (State College, Centre Co., resident; Charter Oak, Huntingdon Co., nesting)—CHRISTY and SUTTON, *Cardinal*, 1928, 2:74 and 75 (Cook Forest, Clarion Co., resident)—SUTTON, *Ann. Carnegie Mus.*, 1928, 18:233 (Pymatuning Swamp and region, Crawford Co., resident; nesting habits)—BURLEIGH, *Cardinal*, 1932, 3:77 (Chestnut Ridge, near Uniontown, Fayette Co., summer)—TODD, *Auk*, 1938, 55:116 (western Pa.; critical).

CAROLINA CHICKADEE[1] (Plate 15)

PENTHESTES CAROLINENSIS CAROLINENSIS (Audubon)

Description—Similar to the Black-capped Chickadee, but slightly smaller and with a relatively *shorter tail;* the *edgings* of the wings and tail are *grayish* rather than white and are therefore less conspicuous.

Range—This species is more southerly than the Black-capped Chickadee and does not breed north of the Carolinian Fauna, in which it replaces the other. As long ago as 1890, C. H. Merriam suggested in a letter to me that the Carolina Chickadee, rather than the Black-capped, might be the bird that occurs in Beaver County. A careful study, undertaken a few years ago, of the series of chickadees in the collection of the Carnegie Museum serves partly to confirm Dr. Merriam's suspicion. Somewhat to my surprise, I discovered that both species occur along the Ohio River in Beaver County, not only in the breeding season, but also in the fall and winter. There is now no way of telling to which form my earlier records of nesting pertain, but I am provisionally referring them to the Black-capped species. Winter records appear under both headings, since the two birds occur together at that time and have not been discriminated by most observers (including myself). Long ago, however, I discovered that in the

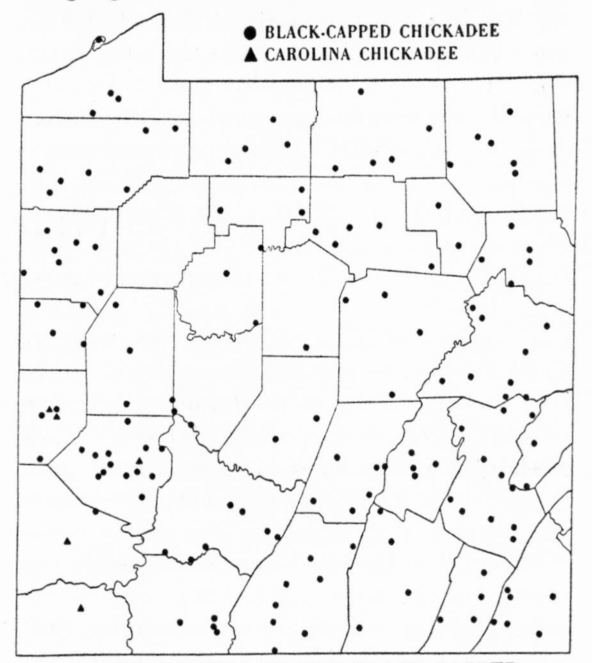

LOCAL RANGES OF THE BLACK-CAPPED CHICKADEE AND OF THE CAROLINA CHICKADEE

[1]Compare footnote 1 under preceding species.

museum collection a single specimen from Washington was a Carolina chickadee. This led me to suspect that the latter was the prevailing form in Washington and Greene counties—a suspicion later fully confirmed by S. S. Dickey, after he had examined a number of nesting birds. As yet there are no records to prove that the Black-capped species also occurs in these counties, but it probably appears there during the winter at least. In the museum collection a single skin from Squaw Run, Allegheny County, bearing the date of December 25, 1899, however, is a Carolina chickadee, and very likely this is the form that breeds east to Fayette County, as suggested by Dr. Dickey. It may also reach the southeastern border of our district in Franklin County, but this remains to be proved.

Habits—The Carolina Chickadee so nearly resembles the Black-capped in habits and general appearance that the two species are difficult to distinguish in life. Having myself failed to discriminate them, I can only present the information offered by other observers. The Carolina not only is smaller in size, with a shorter tail and less hoary coloration (which in worn plumage is not obvious), but is also said to have a call note of softer quality. Its *phe-bee* song is elaborated somewhat—each of the two sustained notes is preceded by a grace note. The nesting habits of the two species are entirely similar, and the eggs are not certainly distinguishable, although those of the Carolina average slightly smaller. A set of seven eggs of this chickadee (with the parent birds) is in the collection of the Carnegie Museum; it was taken on May 17, 1909, on the south side of the Ohio River, opposite Beaver. The nest was in an old woodpecker-hole in a dead stub and was ten feet from the ground; it was composed of plant down and a little rabbit fur, mixed with fine vegetable fibers.

Parus carolinensis (?)Warren, *Birds Pa.*, ed. 2, 1890, 319 (Clinton Co., *fide* Van Fleet).

Parus atricapillus (error) Jacobs, *Summer Birds Greene Co., Pa.*, 1893, 14 (Greene Co., nesting)—Todd, in Bausman, *Hist. Beaver Co., Pa.*, 1904, 2:1202, part (Beaver Co., resident)—(?)Forrest, *Oölogist*, 1911, 28:114 (Washington, Washington Co., winter).

"Black-capped Chickadee" (error) Jacobs, *Hoosier Nat.*, 1887, 2:78 (Waynesburg, Greene Co., resident; nesting).

Penthestes carolinensis carolinensis Dickey, *Auk*, 1915, 32:499 (Waynesburg, Greene Co., and Washington, Washington Co., local range)—Cooke, *Bird-Lore*, 1916, 18:14 (southwestern Pa., in range)—Harlow, *Auk*, 1918, 35:146 (Greene Co.)—Baker, *Wilson Bull.*, 1933, 45:35 (Beaver Co., May)—Jacobs, *Oölogist*, 1938, 55:7 (Waynesburg, Greene Co., habits).

"Chickadee" Jacobs, *Oölogist*, 1920, 37:36 (Waynesburg, Greene Co., nesting)—McClelland, *Am. Mid. Nat.*, 1922, 8:35 (Washington, Washington Co., resident)—(?)Boulton, *Oölogist*, 1922, 39:72 (opposite Beaver, Beaver Co.)—(?)Christy, *Cardinal*, 1924, v. 1, no. 4, p. 10 (Big Traverse Valley, Beaver Co., June)—Elliott, *Cardinal*, 1934, 3:171, (part?) (Raccoon Creek, Beaver Co., December).

"Carolina Chickadee" (?) Christy and Hegner, *Bird-Lore*, 1932, 34:47; etc. (Big Traverse Creek, Beaver Co., December).

Penthestes atricapillus atricapillus (error) Christy, *Cardinal*, 1923, v. 1, no. 1, [p. 14], part (Sewickley, Allegheny Co., resident).

Penthestes carolinensis extimus Todd and Sutton, *Proc. Biol. Soc. Washington*, 1936, 49:70 (western Pa., in range).

TUFTED TITMOUSE

BAEOLOPHUS BICOLOR (Linnaeus)

Description—Larger than the Black-capped Chickadee; about the size of the Junco; *head conspicuously crested.* General color above, *slaty gray*, the back with a slight brownish wash; forehead blackish; lores and underparts soiled grayish white, the flanks rufescent; bill and feet blackish.

Range—The Tufted Titmouse ranges in the eastern United States, west to the edge of the Great Plains and north (regularly) to Iowa, Ohio, and New Jersey and (casually) to Ontario and Maine. The Titmouse is one of those Carolinian species that seem to be extending their ranges northward as conditions change. In our region it is common and characteristic wherever true Carolinian conditions prevail, as they do from the Ohio Valley southward, and east to Chestnut Ridge. It is also common north of the Ohio River in Lawrence, Mercer, and Crawford counties, and thence east to the Allegheny River (Foxburg, Clarion County—Harlow). There is reason to believe that its advent in Crawford County has been comparatively recent. At Meadville, for example, it was not noted until 1890, and thereafter not until 1908. As late as 1922 it was considered rare in the vicinity of Pymatuning Swamp, but a noticeable increase in numbers has taken place since 1924, and it is now comparatively common there. Farther north, in Erie County, however, Sennett secured several specimens as early as 1874, although the species was unknown to S. E. Bacon, and only in recent years has it been encountered on Presque Isle during the breeding season. One bird was recorded from North East, in the same county, in 1908.

The Tufted Titmouse is properly rated a permanent resident, but, like the Black-capped Chickadee, it seems to be more numerous, or at least more conspicuous, in the winter. Towards the northern part of its range it is not strictly sedentary, however, as individuals show a decided tendency to wander during the cold season. These winter wanderers are just as likely to stray beyond their regular limits in one direction as in another. It is a noteworthy fact that first records of the Titmouse in new localities are always in the winter. Sooner or later some of these strays, finding conditions to their liking, remain to breed. Thus new territory is added to the breeding range. It follows that the winter conditions, rather than the mean temperature of the breeding season, must determine the presence of the Titmouse at

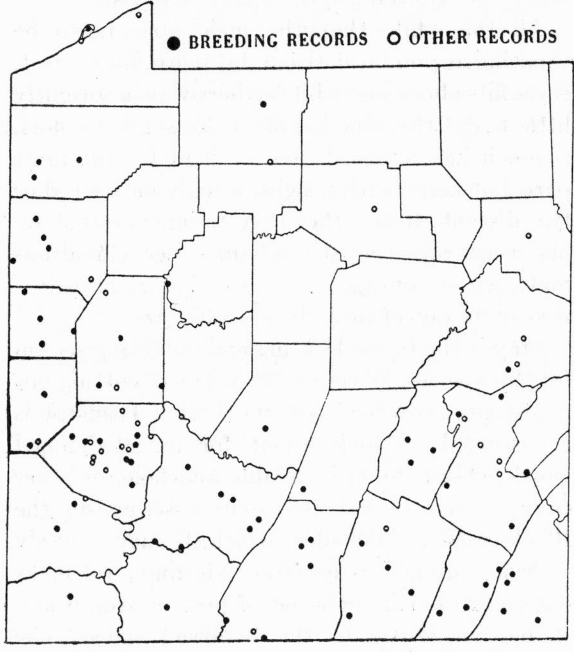

LOCAL RANGE OF THE TUFTED TITMOUSE

a given locality, as well as its general distribution. The increasing mildness of our winters is doubtless one of the factors in the gradual extension of its range. The process seems to be going on all along the northern edge of this range, as is pointed out by other authors. In western Pennsylvania the species has thus spread from the Ohio Valley eastward, and northward all the way to the shores of Lake Erie. It is rather common also in Franklin, Fulton, and Bedford counties, in the valley country, but less so in Blair, Huntingdon, and Centre counties. Until lately it was quite unknown in the plateau region, but at the present time an invasion from both sides is indicated. Already it has occupied the Ligonier Valley, and it has been reported from Chestnut Ridge, southeast of Uniontown. At Springs, Somerset County, according to A. B. Miller, it is rather common and generally distributed, and he has seen it on the top of Negro Mountain (the highest point in the state) in winter. It has been noted near Wilbur Mine and Stoyestown, in the same county, and near Johnstown on a few occasions in May, June, and July (Mostoller).

These Somerset and Cambria county records are clearly incompatible with the assumption that the Tufted Titmouse is a species peculiar to the Carolinian Fauna in Pennsylvania. As already suggested, such an allocation may originally have been perfectly proper, but it is certainly not correct now. Farther north a similar invasion of the highlands is apparently in progress. In this connection, the records from Warren County are significant. The Tufted Titmouse was first noted there in the spring of 1903, when a specimen was taken at Warren by F. L. Homer. Other birds were recorded at rare intervals (in March, April, and early May) up to 1920, but not until the season of 1928 was a nest found (Granquist) and the species finally established as a breeding bird. R. B. Simpson, however, had observed it in July, 1901, in big timber along Fool Creek, near the Forest County line. And G. M. Sutton writes that on September 29, 1928, he observed a family group at St. Marys, Elk County, which suggested its breeding in that locality. A. K. Pierce did not detect it at Renovo until April 14, 1905; his notes mention it as a breeding bird, but it is evidently a newcomer in that part of the country also.

Future developments in its attempted advance across the highlands will be awaited with interest.

Habits[1]—As one grows older, one grows wary of general statements and instinctively seeks to avoid them and those who are given to making them. Otherwise, considering our admiration and love for the sprightly Tufted Titmouse, we should probably ascribe to him without hesitation the first place in our hearts. He presents many claims to the rank of first nobleman of the forest realm. His presence is genial and pleasing, his plumage attractive, his alertness conspicuous; and his

habits are good. Although not a songster, he has a clear, melodious voice and a distinctive, spirited call that is readily recognized in any of its several phrases and tempos. Throughout twelve months of the year, patrolling the oaks and elms of our lawns, accompanying us within sight or earshot every time we step a few rods into the wooded valley or ravine, calling or scolding as the case may be, the Tufted Tit is most companionable. Although somewhat unresponsive to a challenge during midwinter when he knows and we should know that he is not in voice, he may even then resent an unseasonable *peto, peto, peto* whistle by settling down on some near-by branch and scolding, with an accompaniment of agitated twisting and shaking of body and limb.

But when midwinter begins to break, yes, as early as Washington's Birthday, the sunshine awakens and revitalizes his spirit of romance to such an extent that, hearing him eagerly practicing beside the dog-path, you may be tempted to loiter and prejudice your reputation for punctuality by missing the morning train. These first unnatural tones suggest a youth whose voice is changing—high, low, hoarse, clear for an instant, then lost. In a week or two, however, the Titmouse attains full voice, and then in hurried tones from the dogwood tree he hurls his familiar *peto, peto, peto*. Later in the season he will occasionally change to a drawled *purr-rr-dy, purr-rr-dy*, but early in spring his animation accelerates the tempo to a rapidity difficult to imitate. The tone is high, the first note about a half-tone interval above the second. The call is rather easy of imitation with a little practice, and as snows melt and "the voice of the turtle is heard in the land," mating season approaches and there is a new meaning in the homely phrases of the call, which your imitation may also express.

Each pair of tufted titmice has a domain of its own during mating season. Over this the birds exercise a jealous sway, at least insofar as errant titmice are concerned. Enter upon this domain and without too much fuss begin to whistle the titmouse challenge. Directly you will excite vigorous replies from the lord of the manor. If you persist—and you probably will—he will approach to within a few feet of you. If you carry in your hand a hat or a sizable piece of dark cloth or a box, his lordship seems to think you have another bird in captivity. He will shake himself as if with rage, or in defiance, and drop, scolding, almost within arm's length, where as long as you continue to answer him, he will remain to scold and protest. This course of conduct he will pursue, not once, but as often as you repeat your visit.

All the while that the male appears to be shouting at you his derision, his scorn, his protest, there flits about just a bit farther away, a sprightly little mate who, but for her more somber colors, is much like her lord. She is silent for the most part, but keeps within sight, usually only a rod or two distant. It is rather easy to imagine that by her very presence she inflames her chivalrous mate, whose courage is expressed in an aggressiveness quite out of proportion to his size.

May is the house-hunting and outfitting season for this species. Without the means of cutting out a nesting cavity for itself, the Tufted Titmouse is accustomed to look about for an abandoned woodpecker-hole, an available knothole, or other cavity in tree or post. Not so its lesser cousin, the Black-capped Chickadee, which, though scarcely so well equipped as its larger kinsman, yet picks out the rotted inner wood of post or stump and shapes an abode in the hollowed space. The

[1]Account contributed by Edmund W. Arthur.

Tufted Titmouse, lacking constructive talent, might be called a tenant or a squatter. Having chosen the nesting site, however, the pair fit it up neatly with soft down, vegetal silk, and feathers, thus making a very snug and cozy abode. Six eggs are the usual number, but they vary from five to eight. They are white, rather evenly speckled with reddish brown, and, except for their larger size (averaging .71 by .55 inches), are scarcely different from those of the Black-capped Chickadee. They are laid about the first of May.

The Tufted Titmouse is largely a meat-eater. About two-thirds of its food consists of insects—chiefly caterpillars and wasps—and of spiders. Insects seem to be welcome diet, whether as eggs and larvae, or fully developed. These birds are industrious, tireless foragers; with the chickadees, the nuthatches, the brown creepers, and the downy woodpeckers, they patrol the trunks and exposed roots of our forest trees throughout the long winter. Economically valuable for their services in thus reducing the noxious-insect population of the woodland, the Tufted Titmice are equally welcome for their attractive personality.

How many times have you strolled into a sheltered woodland on a winter day and fallen in with a passing company of foragers? First the solo downy woodpecker announces you to his battalion and it to you with his rousing watchman's-rattle call. Next come the tufted titmice, a corporal's guard, cocked hats on cocked heads as they mark time restlessly with inquiring poses. Then the chickadees and juncos, and perhaps a band of gray-clad goldfinches or a hairy woodpecker, drop in or deploy about right or left flank. For a few moments the branches and tree trunks, the understory and carpet of the woodland, all seem alive. Suddenly, with a thin fugue of wheezy tones, the company passes, the trees are deserted—deserted, yes, except for a pair of tufted titmice, which linger furtively but with undisguised interest until you, resuming the trail, pass out of their bailiwick.

Lophophanes bicolor Townsend, *Proc. Acad. Nat. Sci. Philadelphia*, 1883, 60 (Latrobe, Westmoreland Co., resident)—Jacobs, *Bay State Oölogist*, 1888, 1:15 (Waynesburg, Greene Co., nesting)—Jacobs, *Oölogist*, 1889, 6:72 (Waynesburg, Greene Co., nesting; habits).

"Tufted Titmouse" Todd, *Oölogist*, 1887, 4:89 (Beaver, Beaver Co., nesting)—Stone, *Cassinia*, 1906, 9:44 (McConnellsburg, Fulton Co., June)—Valentine, *Bird-Lore*, 1908, 10:32 (Bellefonte, Centre Co., December)—Leete, *Wilson Bull.*, 1909, 21:48 (North East, Erie Co., December)—Miller, *Bird-Lore*, 1910, 12:29; etc. (Springs, Somerset Co., December)—Wright, *Bird-Lore*, 1911, 13:31 (Pittsburgh, Allegheny Co., December)—Dickey, *Oölogist*, 1913, 30:149 (near Waynesburg, Greene Co., nesting); 1914, 31:170 ([Charter Oak], Huntingdon Co., May)—McConnell, *Oölogist*, 1918, 35:152 (McKeesport, Allegheny Co.)—Stahl, *et al.*, *Bird-Lore*, 1921, 23:18 (Forest Hills to Deer Creek, Allegheny Co., December)—McClelland, *Am. Mid. Nat.*, 1922, 8:35 (Washington, Washington Co., resident)—Hoffman, *et al.*, *Bird-Lore*, 1923, 25:23 (Grove City, Mercer Co., December)—Blair, *Bull. Audubon Soc. W. Pa.*, 1923, 41 (West View, Allegheny Co.)—Street, *Cassinia*, 1923, 24:19 (Greencastle to Ft. Loudon, Jordan's Knob, and Horse Valley, Franklin Co., June)—Christy and Hegner, *Bird-Lore*, 1924, 26:30; etc. (Raccoon Creek Valley and region, Beaver Co., December)—Christy, *Cardinal*, 1924, v. 1, no. 4, p. 10 (Big Traverse Valley, Beaver Co., June)—Matuszak, *Bird-Lore*, 1926, 28:29 (Hyde Park, Westmoreland Co., December)—Portman, *et al.*, *Bird-Lore*, 1926, 28:31 (Thompsonville, Washington Co., December)—Eastwood, *Bird-Lore*, 1926, 28:273 (Rector, Westmoreland Co., May, *fide* Knauz)—Berkheimer, *Bird-Lore*, 1933, 35:27; etc. (Osterburg, Bedford Co., December)—Beal and Peterson, *Bird-Lore*, 1934, 36:33; and Upson, *et al.*, *Bird-Lore*, 1935, 37:47 (Presque Isle, Erie Co., December)—Elliott, *Cardinal*, 1934, 3:171 (Raccoon Creek, Beaver Co., December).

Parus bicolor Todd, *Auk*, 1893, 10:38, 41 (Two Lick, Indiana Co., June)—Jacobs, *Summer Birds Greene Co., Pa.*, 1893, 14 (Greene Co., nesting).

Bæolophus bicolor Todd, *Ann. Carnegie Mus.*, 1904, 2:591 (Erie, Erie Co., December)—Todd, in Bausman, *Hist. Beaver Co., Pa.*, 1904, 2:1201 (Beaver Co., resident)—Allen, *Bull. Am. Mus. Nat. Hist.*, 1907, 23:473 (Beaver Co.), 478 (Erie, Erie Co.; Crafton, Allegheny Co.; Beaver, Fulton, and Bedford Co.)—Harlow, *Auk*, 1912, 29:466, 477 (southern Centre Co., summer); 1918, 35:146 (southwestern Pa.; Centre Co., summer)—Christy, *Cardinal*, 1923, v. 1, no. 1, [p. 14] (Sewickley, Allegheny Co., resident)—Burleigh, *Wilson Bull.*, 1923, 35:144 ([Harmarville], Allegheny Co., nesting); 1931, 43:53 (State College, Centre Co., resident)—Sutton, *Ann. Carnegie Mus.*, 1928, 18:232 (Meadville and Pymatuning Swamp, Crawford Co., resident)—Burleigh, *Cardinal*, 1932, 3:77 (Chestnut Ridge, near Uniontown, Fayette Co., summer)—Jacobs, *Oölogist*, 1938, 55:6 (Waynesburg, Greene Co.; habits).

NUTHATCHES

FAMILY SITTIDAE

THE SITTIDAE constitute a small family, restricted mainly to the Northern Hemisphere. The four North American species (with their several geographical races) are all members of the genus *Sitta*, which is common also in the Old World. Two species occur in western Pennsylvania: the White-breasted Nuthatch, a permanent resident throughout the region; and the Red-breasted Nuthatch, a transient except in the northern counties and high mountains.

The Nuthatches are small birds, resembling to some extent both the Titmice and the Creepers. Their bills, however, are slender, straight, and tapering; their wings are relatively long and pointed; and their tails are soft and short. Nuthatches are rather active and scramble about the limbs and trunks of trees, often head downward, in their search for insects and larvae. Their common name is derived from the habit of sticking nuts and seeds in the cracks in bark, and hammering until they break the shell.

WHITE-BREASTED NUTHATCH

SITTA CAROLINENSIS CAROLINENSIS Latham

Description—Smaller than the Downy Woodpecker; about the size of the Tufted Titmouse. Head above, nape, and upper back, black; rest of upperparts bluish gray; wings bluish gray externally, with some black; tail medially bluish gray like the back, the lateral feathers black with a white spot near the end; sides of head and neck and entire underparts, soiled white, the flanks and under tail coverts splashed with rufous chestnut. The crown and the nape in the *female* are washed with bluish gray.

Range—The White-breasted Nuthatch, with its several races, ranges over most of Mexico, through the United States (in wooded regions), and northward into Canada, but not far into the Canadian Life Zone at any point. In western Pennsylvania, as in adjacent states, it is a common permanent resident wherever there is woodland. Like the Chickadee, the Nuthatch seems to be commoner in the fall and winter months, but this condition is probably more apparent than real. Careful studies of its status at Ithaca, New York, made by W. K. Butts,[1] indicate that it is more decidedly sedentary than even the Black-capped Chickadee. Admittedly, however, it must be more prone to wander in fall and winter than at other times; for then it is wont to enter orchards and parks in towns and villages, where ordinarily it does not nest.

Habits—To most observers the White-breasted Nuthatch is best known as a component of the roving flocks of small birds that in the wintertime wander through the woods in loose formation, with black-capped chickadees usually leading the van. The association, although presumably not fortuitous, is of course only a temporary one, brought about by the circumstance that all these birds are in search of the same kinds of food. But nuthatches are not gregarious as are chickadees, and more than a pair or two are seldom in evidence at any one time. Their dissimilar feeding habits

[1]*Bird-Banding*, 1931, 2:59–76.

keep them from coming in conflict with their associates. Whereas the chickadees tend to stay out on the terminal branches of the trees, the nuthatches confine their efforts to the trunks and larger branches, over which they scramble with the greatest ease and agility, prying into the crevices of the bark, scrutinizing each hidden recess, and even venturing into natural cavities in quest of their insect prey. With their strong feet and sharp claws, they are as well able to cling to the surface as are woodpeckers themselves, but unlike woodpeckers they do not use the tail for climbing. In descending a tree, a woodpecker has to back down in rather awkward fashion, but a nuthatch can run down the trunk or branch headfirst as easily as it can go up or around. An inverted pose is a perfectly natural and characteristic one.

Active and restless, the Nuthatch is seldom still for an instant, and its spirits seem unaffected even in the coldest weather. The usual note is a nasal *qu'aank*, several times repeated—a distinctive sound, easily recognized in the woods. There is also a variety of low twittering or conversational notes that do not carry far. At times I have seen a nuthatch strike a conspicuous pose and utter a clear, rolling call that could be heard for a considerable distance; I believe this is the mating "song." With the coming of spring, the pairs begin to search for suitable nesting sites. A natural cavity in a tree is the site most frequently chosen; occasionally, however, an old woodpecker-hole or the old nest of a squirrel may be utilized. A knothole in a living tree is the favorite location in Centre County, according to several observers. I once found a nest in a dead tree, only about eight feet from the ground, but this elevation was exceptional; the usual height is much greater—from thirty to forty-five feet—while nests have been found as high as sixty feet. The nests themselves follow the style of those of the Black-capped Chickadee but are always larger. They are "substantial matted beds of soft shreds of inner bark and rabbits' fur, with rarely a little wool, cow hair, and chicken feathers" (Burleigh, 1931). Invariably they are placed at the far end of the cavity, if this is in a horizontal branch, and as a rule the eggs are not visible from the entrance. The eggs vary from five to nine, and sets of the latter number are not infrequent. They resemble those of the Black-capped Chickadee in general coloration, but are of course larger, averaging .75 by .57 inches. They are white, sprinkled with specks, and sometimes splashes, of vinaceous cinnamon, and show lilac shell-markings.

As I have found newly hatched young on the last of April at Beaver, I infer that nidification must sometimes begin as early as the first of that month. In Allegheny County full sets of eggs have been found on April 18 (Atkinson). In Centre County the last week in April is about the right time to look for fresh sets. Almost the only way to find the nest is to watch the female while she is building, or later to trail the male as he carries food to his incubating mate. The watching required is often a long-drawn-out process. The Red Squirrel seems to be a persistent enemy of this bird, as might be expected. A considerable proportion of the nests found by R. F. Miller in Centre County in the spring of 1918 were broken up by this animal. Dr. Butts's studies at Ithaca indicate that few individual nuthatches survive for more than three or four years, so that they must have other active enemies as well. Yet the rate of increase seems ample to maintain the species in fair numbers in spite of such handicaps.

The Nuthatch is a true conservator of the forest, for it feeds largely on destructive insects, in both their adult and young stages. One half of its food consists of insects and spiders, the other half of seeds, large and small. It has the usual nuthatch habit of storing seeds in crevices of bark for future use. Where regular winter feeding-stations are maintained, white-breasted nuthatches become daily visitors, although they never seem to grow dependent on this source of food alone. They deserve all encouragement and protection, for both aesthetic and economic reasons.

Sitta carolinensis Teulon, *Jour. Boston Zoöl. Soc.*, 1882, 1:50 (Bradford, McKean Co., resident)—Townsend, *Proc. Acad. Nat. Sci. Philadelphia*, 1883, 60 (Latrobe, Westmoreland Co., resident)—Jacobs, *Bay State Oöl.*, 1888, 1:3 (Waynesburg, Greene Co.; nesting)—Jacobs, *Hawkeye Ornithologist and Oölogist*, 1888, 1:120 (Waynesburg, Greene Co., nesting)—Dwight, *Auk*, 1892, 9:140 (Cresson, Cambria Co., June)—Todd, *Auk*, 1893, 10:37, 41 (Two Lick, Indiana Co., June), 46 (Coalport, Clearfield Co., June)—Jacobs, *Summer Birds Greene Co., Pa.*, 1893, 14 (Greene Co., nesting)—Baily, *Auk*, 1896, 13:297 (Williamsville, Elk Co., June–July)—Cope, *Cassinia*, 1902, 5:20 (Clinton and Potter Co., June)—Todd, *Ann. Carnegie Mus.*, 1904, 2:590 (Erie and

Presque Isle, Erie Co., resident)—Todd, in Bausman, *Hist. Beaver Co., Pa.*, 1904, 2:1201 (Beaver Co., resident)—Christy, *Cardinal*, 1923, v. 1, no. 1, [p. 14] (Sewickley, Allegheny Co., nesting).

"White-breasted Nuthatch" Stone, *Cassinia*, 1906, 9:44 (McConnellsburg, Fulton Co., June)—Valentine, *Bird-Lore*, 1908, 10:32 (Bellefonte, Centre Co., December)—Miller (A. B.), *Bird-Lore*, 1908, 10:32; etc. (Springs, Somerset Co., December)—Gerberding, *Bird-Lore*, 1912, 14:29 (Greenville, Mercer Co., December)—Morris, *Bird-Lore*, 1913, 15:29 (Eagle Rock, Venango Co., December)—Harlow, *Oölogist*, 1917, 34:64 (State College, Centre Co., nesting)—McConnell, *Oölogist*, 1918, 35:152 (McKeesport, Allegheny Co.)—Miller (R. F.), *Oölogist*, 1919, 36:157; and 1922, 39:28 (State College, Centre Co., nesting)—McGraw, *et al.*, *Bird-Lore*, 1919, 21:37; etc. (Altoona, Blair Co., December)—Warfield, *Bird-Lore*, 1919, 21:37; etc. (Chambersburg, Franklin Co., December)—Stahl, *et al.*, *Bird-Lore*, 1921, 23:18 (Forest Hills to Deer Creek, Allegheny Co., December)—Nicholson, *Bird-Lore*, 1921, 23:18 (Grove City, Mercer Co., December)—McClelland, *Am. Mid. Nat.*, 1922, 8:35 (Washington, Washington Co., resident)—Christy, *Cardinal*, 1924, v. 1, no. 4, p. 10 (Big Traverse Valley, Beaver Co., June)—Christy and Hegner, *Bird-Lore*, 1924, 26:30; etc. (Raccoon Creek Valley and region, Beaver Co., December)—Matuszak, *Bird-Lore*, 1926, 28:29 (Hyde Park, Westmoreland Co., December)—Portman, *et al.*, *Bird-Lore*, 1926, 28:31 (Thompsonville and region, Washington Co., December)—Miller (R. F.), *Oölogist*, 1928, 45:134 (Nittany Valley, Centre Co., nesting)—Berkheimer, *Bird-Lore*, 1933, 35:27; etc. (Osterburg, Bedford Co., December)—Elliott, *Cardinal*, 1934, 3:171 (Raccoon Creek, Beaver Co., December).

Sitta carolinensis carolinensis Harlow, *Auk*, 1912, 29:476; 1918, 35:146 (Centre Co., nesting)—Dickey, *Oölogist*, 1914, 31:66 (State College, Centre Co., nesting)—Burleigh, *Wilson Bull.*, 1923, 35:144 (Harmarville, Allegheny Co., nesting); 1931, 43:53 (State College, Centre Co., resident)—Burleigh, *Cardinal*, 1932, 3:77 (Chestnut Ridge, near Uniontown, Fayette Co., breeding).

Sitta carolinensis cookei Oberholser, *Auk*, 1917, 24:186 (Erie, Erie Co.; Newton Hamilton, Mifflin Co.; Beaver, Beaver Co.; and Leasuresville, Butler Co.)—Christy and Sutton, *Cardinal*, 1928, 2:74, 75 (Cook Forest, Clarion Co., resident)—Sutton, *Ann. Carnegie Mus.*, 1928, 18:231 (Pymatuning region, Crawford Co., resident).

RED-BREASTED NUTHATCH (Plate 15)

SITTA CANADENSIS Linnaeus

Description—Much smaller than the White-breasted Nuthatch. General color of upperparts, slaty bluish, the wings duller, the tail medially slaty blue like the back, the lateral feathers black, with a white spot near the tip; head and nape black, bordered by a *broad white line over the eye;* below this a broad band of black through the eye and spreading out on the sides of the neck; *underparts* soiled whitish, more or less heavily washed with *rufescent buff*, the sides of the head (below the black band), whitish. In the *females* the top of the head is washed with slaty blue. *Young birds* resemble the adult female but are duller in coloration.

Range—*Sitta canadensis* is so closely related to certain Palaearctic nuthatches that by some authors it is considered conspecific therewith. It is a Nearctic species of general transcontinental range but with certain anomalies in its seasonal and local distribution. In the breeding season it is properly a species characteristic of the Canadian Life Zone, and as such occurs in New England (south to Massachusetts), in the Adirondack and Catskill Mountains in New York, and southward in the Appalachian highlands to North Carolina. In the latter state it was found in summer by William Brewster in 1885, breeding at an elevation of from four to six thousand feet. It was thus fair to infer that it occurred also in the mountains of Pennsylvania, and at a lower altitude. At that time, however, the Pennsylvania mountains were a virtual terra incognita, insofar as their bird life was concerned. Warren, indeed, writing in 1888 and again in 1890, quotes certain of his correspondents on the presence of the species in this region, but his lack of precision and his failure to realize the significance of his statements leave a vague impression. The following year, in a note in a sportsmen's journal, he included the Red-breasted Nuthatch among the breeding birds of Kane (where later it was found by A. K. Pierce). Until 1897 these were the only published records bearing on the breeding of this species in our region; in that year Witmer Stone published one for Round Island, Clinton County, on the authority of S. N. Rhoads.

As early as 1894, however, I had discovered that the Red-breasted Nuthatch was a common breeding bird in Tamarack Swamp, Clinton County. The following year I traced it northward into the then heavily timbered region of Potter County, and in 1899 over to the westward, into Elk and

Forest counties, where similar conditions obtained. In the same year, I secured a breeding specimen on the summit of the mountain ridge south of Renovo. In Warren County, R. B. Simpson has reported it from the head of Tionesta Creek, where, indeed, it was noted in 1931, at Heart's Content, by L. E. Hicks. S. S. Dickey found it during the last week in May, 1923, in a virgin hemlock forest five miles east of Clarendon, Warren County, where it was apparently breeding. It is present also in Cook Forest, Clarion County, and is included by Van Fleet in his manuscript list of the breeding birds of DuBois.

As thus far outlined, the local breeding range of this nuthatch coincides with that of the Olive-backed Thrush. Both species occupy the plateau region from the New York state boundary line to northern Clearfield County. From the Susquehanna River (West Branch) in the latter county, southward through Cambria and Somerset counties, however, there is not a single summer record for the Red-breasted Nuthatch, and, indeed, we find none until we enter western Maryland, where the species reappears.[1] But I am by no means convinced that there is any real gap in its range, especially since its distribution farther to the southward is virtually continuous. Certainly the elevation of the main Allegheny divide would suffice to carry its range across, other conditions being equal. It is far likelier that the reduction of the original coniferous forest in these regions has reacted unfavorably against this bird. But even in 1893, before this reduction had gone so far, E. A. Preble failed to observe the species in his traverse across the high country of Somerset County; nor was I any more fortunate in Cambria County. At the present time A. B. Miller finds it at Springs, close to the Maryland boundary, as a transient only.

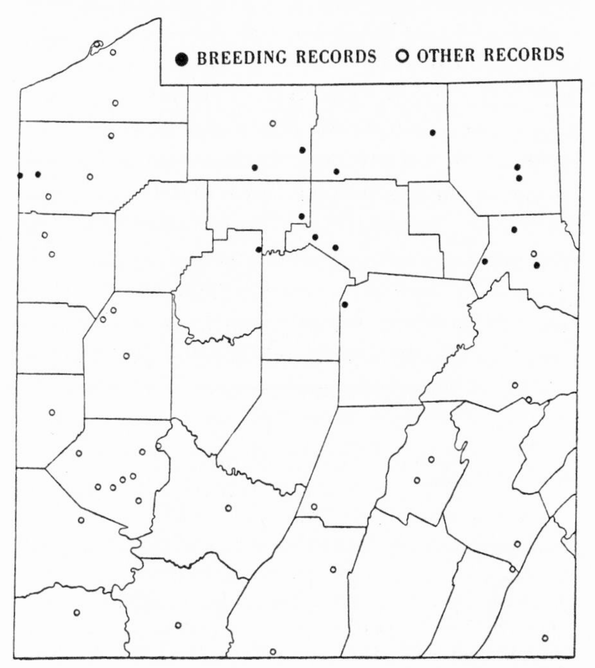

LOCAL RANGE OF THE RED-BREASTED NUTHATCH

Sennett's vague statement, quoted at second hand by Warren, concerning the supposed breeding of this species in Crawford County, has lately received unexpected corroboration. G. M. Sutton records seeing "a nesting pair about a mile south of Linesville in a rather dense hemlock woods," and Professor Hicks writes that he saw others on Hemlock Island and found a nest on the Ohio side. The status of the species as a breeding bird of Pymatuning Swamp is thus fully confirmed, and the swamp's character as an outlying island of the Canadian Life Zone is more completely established.

Migration—The winter range of this species will be considered under this head also. W. W. Cooke wrote in 1915: "The Red-breasted Nuthatch is the only member of the genus that is decidedly migratory, but its movements are so irregular that little can be said with certainty concerning its migrations. . . . The irregularity of the wintering is the most serious drawback to an exact statement of the average time of migration in both spring and fall. While most of the birds of the eastern United States winter south of latitude 41°, some remain at this season north to Nova Scotia, central Ontario and northern Wisconsin, nearly to the normal northern limit of the breeding range." Thus, in our region we find the species wintering (at least irregularly) throughout its entire known breeding range in the northern counties of the state, as shown by the available records. Migration dates from this part consequently have but little value. The species was reported as common at Greencastle, Franklin County, in the extreme southeastern corner of our region, during the winter of 1921–22 (Ziegler, 1926). There are three winter records for Allegheny County (McKees-

[1]E. A. Preble, in *Maryland Geological Survey* [*of*] *Allegany County*, 1900, p. 306.

port, Sewickley, and Deer Creek) and one each for Beaver County (near Aliquippa, *fide* Ristich) and Greene County (Waynesburg, *fide* Dickey). Elsewhere this nuthatch has been found only as a transient visitant during migration, but it is not nearly so common nor so well known as the white-breasted species and has doubtless been overlooked by many observers.

March and early April dates should probably be considered as wintering records. Individuals have been seen near Erie on April 4, 1925 (Dickey), and near Wilkinsburg on April 4, 1898 (Atkinson). At Beaver, where the Red-breasted Nuthatch has never been detected in winter, the first migrants usually appear during the last week in April or the first week in May. April 23 (1908) is my earliest date. In 1909 and 1913 the last bird was noted on May 19. Earliest and latest spring dates for Erie in 1900 were April 19 and May 19, respectively. For State College, April 14 (1915) is the earliest spring date (Burleigh). At Hollidaysburg the species was seen as late as May 26 in 1915 (Berg); and at Springs, Somerset County, a pair observed on May 27, 1919, suggested possible breeding (Miller). Sundry spring records from various other localities fall within the limits above indicated.

Fall migration begins early in the season. The species has been seen at Summit, Fayette County, on August 30 (Burleigh) and has appeared at Beaver as early as September 6 (1903), although most of my scattered records are for the second and third weeks in September and for the months of October and November, up to December 1 (1888). Its relative numbers at this season fluctuate. In the vicinity of Warren, according to Mr. Simpson, it is as a rule rather rare and irregular, but at intervals of five or six years it becomes plentiful, and a large flight passes through. Such phenomena are common with this species; it is as if the nuthatch population of large areas is condensed into a narrow stream during migration. The latest fall date for State College is November 14 (1914—Burleigh).

Habits—In general, the habits of this nuthatch resemble those of the White-breasted species, but there are certain points of difference. Not often are the two birds found together. The rasping call notes of the Red-breasted, much higher-pitched than those of the other species, are perfectly distinctive, and when once learned cannot be mistaken. Were it not for these whining, nasal notes, the bird might readily be overlooked, as it is otherwise inconspicuous, although not particularly shy. During migration it frequents the terminal branches of the forest trees, consorting with the warblers, which are passing through at the same time, and it may easily be mistaken for one of their number. Sometimes it joins the warblers in their invasion of orchard and shade trees; I remember on one occasion finding a group of a half-dozen birds in an apple tree, busily engaged in feeding among the smaller branches and nearly silent while they worked.

Occasionally this nuthatch comes near the ground, but its preference for treetops is marked, especially in the breeding season. At Tamarack Swamp in Clinton County, where I found it common on my several visits during the month of June, it haunted the spruce area and associated with the Black-capped Chickadee and several kinds of warblers. As a rule the nuthatches remained rather high in the matted tops of the trees, and at that distance they were sometimes difficult to distinguish from the chickadees, although their habit of creeping along the branches and trunks of the trees ordinarily serves to differentiate them. Always partial to conifers, they are at home in hemlock timber, and, although active and restless and moving frequently from tree to tree, they keep well hidden in the thick tops of the highest ones. During the latter part of June small family groups of old and young are encountered; I judge from this circumstance that the eggs are laid about the middle of May, but no locally collected eggs are yet available for description. From other sources we know that they resemble those of the White-breasted Nuthatch but are of course smaller. The nesting habits are also similar to those of the commoner species.

Sitta canadensis Townsend, *Proc. Acad. Nat. Sci. Philadelphia*, 1883, 60 (Latrobe, Westmoreland Co., spring transient)—Warren, *Birds Pa.*, 1888, 248 (Crawford Co., breeding, *fide* Sennett); ed. 2, 1890, 316 (Erie Co., fall; Crawford Co., breeding, *fide* Sennett)—Stone, *Auk*, 1897, 14:324 (Round Island, Clinton Co., May–June, *fide* Rhoads)—Todd, *Ann. Carnegie Mus.*, 1904, 2:590 (Erie and Presque Isle, Erie Co., transient)—Todd, in Bausman, *Hist. Beaver Co., Pa.*, 1904, 2:1201 (Beaver Co., transient)—Keim, *Cassinia*, 1905, 8:41 (Port Allegany, McKean Co., summer)—Harlow, *Auk*,

1918, 35:146 (Warren Co., summer)—STONE, *Cassinia*, 1920, 23:39 ([near] Altoona, Blair Co., May, *fide* McGraw)—CHRISTY, *Cardinal*, 1923, v. 1, no. 1, [p. 14] (Sewickley, Allegheny Co., transient)—BURLEIGH, *Wilson Bull.*, 1923, 35:144 (Allegheny Co., migration); 1924, 36:131 (State College, Centre Co., migration)—[Editor], *Cassinia*, 1926, 25:35 (Greencastle, Franklin Co., winter, *fide* Ziegler)—CHRISTY and SUTTON, *Cardinal*, 1928, 2:74 and 75 (Cook Forest, Clarion Co., resident)—SUTTON, *Ann. Carnegie Mus.*, 1928, 18:232 (Pymatuning Swamp and region, Crawford Co., transient; rare resident)—BURLEIGH, *Cardinal*, 1932, 3:78 (near Summit, Fayette Co., August).

"Red-bellied Nuthatch" WARREN, *Forest and Stream*, 1891, 37:83 (Kane, McKean Co., summer)—SIMPSON, *Oölogist*, 1912, 29:330 (head of Tionesta Creek, Warren Co., summer); 1920, 37:25 (Warren, Warren Co., fall).

"Canada Nuthatch" SIMPSON, *Oölogist*, 1907, 24:87 (Warren, Warren Co., winter).

"Red-breasted Nuthatch" COOKE, *Bird-Lore*, 1915, 17:443 (Beaver, Beaver Co., migration)—SAVAGE and MCCONNELL, *Bird-Lore*, 1918, 20:37 (McKeesport, Allegheny Co., December)—MCCONNELL, *Oölogist*, 1918, 35:152 (McKeesport, Allegheny Co., transient)—EASTWOOD, *Bird-Lore*, 1925, 27: 407 ("Slack Hollow," Allegheny Co., September, *fide* Grimm); 1927, 29:127 (Deer Creek, Allegheny Co., February, *fide* Squier and Reiter)—BOULTON, *Bird-Lore*, 1928, 30:13 (Burnt Cabins, Fulton Co., October)—COPE and HAWKINS, *Forest Leaves*, 1934, 24:26 (E. Tionesta Forest Reserve, Warren and McKean Co., summer)—CHRISTY, *et al.*, *Bird-Lore*, 1937, 39:44 (Pymatuning region, Crawford Co., December).

Sitta canadensis canadensis STONE, *Cassinia*, 1923, 24:33 (Greencastle, Franklin Co., March, *fide* Ziegler).

CREEPERS

FAMILY CERTHIIDAE

THE CERTHIIDAE are apparently of Old World origin and are represented there by three subfamilies and many species. The species to which the North American Creepers belong is circumpolar in distribution; a number of geographical races, however, are recognized from different parts of its wide range.

Creepers are small, inconspicuously colored birds that seek their insect food on the trunks of trees. Their slender, curved bills; long, sharp claws; and stiff, pointed tail feathers, are perfectly adapted to their mode of life. Quiet, sedate, and industrious, they often escape detection. Except in a few northern counties and in the mountains of western Pennsylvania, the Brown Creeper is merely a winter visitor.

BROWN CREEPER

CERTHIA FAMILIARIS AMERICANA Bonaparte

Description—A small, slender bird with a rather long, weak bill, slightly curved downward, and a long, stiff tail with pointed feathers. Upperparts dull brown, mottled with buffy gray, the rump more rufescent; underparts plain dirty white. *Young* similar, with more buffy mottling above and a shorter bill.

Range—The species to which our Brown Creeper belongs occurs in Eurasia as well as in North America. In both continents it is relatively northern in its distribution and breeds in the coniferous forests of the Boreal region and southward along the mountains. The present race is primarily a characteristic breeding bird of the Canadian Fauna, but it occurs in the Alleghanian as well, although by no means so commonly. Thus, it is known to breed over most of New England (Connecticut and Rhode Island excepted), in the Adirondack and Catskill Mountains of New York, and thence southward along the Appalachian highlands to North Carolina.

The breeding range in western Pennsylvania can now be fairly well defined from available data, and it corresponds in general with that of other supposedly Canadian species. Pertinent records from across the border in New York are wanting, but in Pennsylvania the regular breeding area extends from the Allegheny River in Warren County to Potter County (and beyond), and thence southward, gradually diminishing in width but embracing all the elevated country as far as the Maryland boundary. There are no reports, however, for the minor mountain ridges east of the main divide, excepting H. J. Roddy's Centre County record, which, he assures me, refers to a point near the top of Tussey Mountain, a little west of Bear Meadows—an occurrence that is, by analogy, perfectly understandable. Faunally speaking, Pymatuning Swamp in Crawford County, like Bear Meadows, is an island of the Canadian Life Zone, and there too the Brown Creeper used to find temperature and other conditions suited to its needs, and summered in considerable numbers. H. M. McQuiston discovered a pair building a nest in the swamp south of Shermansville in May, 1936. According to Sennett (as quoted by Warren), the species also breeds in the "elevated parts of Erie County," and there is a possibility therefore that certain tamarack swamps in that section may have supported a few nesting pairs. Significance is lent to this statement by a report from S. S. Dickey to the effect that early in June,

1925, he discovered a bird of this species in a swampy woods some two miles east of Cambridge Springs, Crawford County. He was unable, however, to locate its nest.

Outside the area here defined, the Brown Creeper is a common migrant and a fairly common and regular winter resident. In fact, it occurs in winter throughout its entire breeding range, where its status is therefore that of a permanent resident. It appears on many of the "Christmas Census" lists from our region—a sufficient proof of its regularity at that season.

Migration—During migration this species is much more abundant than at any other time, summer or winter. Evidently most of our brown creepers summer farther north and winter farther south. In general, the Brown Creeper comes and goes with the Winter Wren. Like that species, it is hardy and is not a particularly early migrant in the fall; it seldom appears south of its breeding range before the middle of September, and the majority of birds do not arrive until about the first of October. A few early fall dates are: September 13, 1914—State College (Burleigh); September 14, 1900—Presque Isle (Todd); September 17, 1913—Pittsburgh (Burleigh); September 19, 1928—Glenshaw, Allegheny County (Schlag); September 20, 1890—Beaver (Todd). During

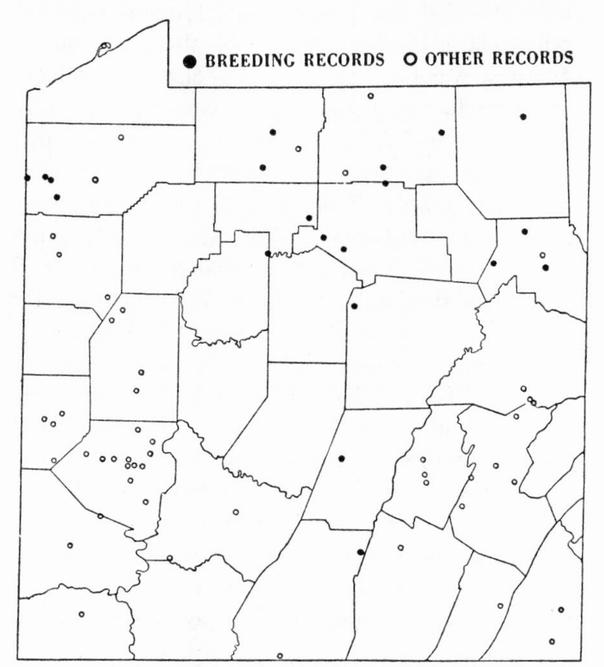

LOCAL RANGE OF THE BROWN CREEPER

October and part of November the migration is in full swing; after that the species assumes its normal numbers for the winter.

In the spring the first transients arrive from the South late in March and materially swell the Creeper population. During the first weeks in April the birds are fairly abundant at intervals, but after that time their numbers dwindle until few if any remain by the end of the month. Laggards are occasionally seen in May, although by then the birds farther north are already nesting. I have never seen the Creeper at Beaver later than April 30 (1889), and I therefore consider the Industry, Beaver County, record for May 13, supplied by O. C. Reiter and P. F. Squier (1928), as exceptional indeed. T. D. Burleigh, however, has seen the species at State College as late as May 14 (1917), but has not seen it at Pittsburgh after May 2 (1914). In 1900 the last bird was seen on Presque Isle on May 7. S. J. Seiple reports the Creeper from Greenville during the first week in May, but it is just possible that he may have been observing breeding individuals. We do not yet know whether our summer birds are stationary on their breeding grounds or whether they go south and give way to northern-bred birds for the winter. Banding may some day solve this problem.

Habits—The Brown Creeper is best known as a component of the wandering bands of birds ranging the woods during the colder months. These bands include the Black-capped Chickadee, the Tufted Titmouse, the White-breasted Nuthatch, the Downy and Hairy woodpeckers, and sometimes others. By reason of their numbers and loquacity these birds thrust themselves upon our attention when we invade their haunts. But the Creeper usually travels singly in such company; it is inconspicuously colored, quiet by comparison, and easily escapes observation. The color of this little brown bird blends into the tree trunks up which it climbs, and it effaces itself so completely that when at rest it is hard to detect. The Creeper combines the climbing habits of the woodpeckers with the activity and nervous action of the nuthatches. While searching for food, it confines itself to the main trunks and larger ascending branches of the trees and normally works upward, although it can sidle around the trunk very quickly indeed in order to elude observation. Beginning near the ground, the bird climbs the trunk in a more or less spiral, or zigzag, fashion, covering a great deal of surface in a short space of time. It pauses only to pick out its minute insect food, and it works "in a preoccupied, near-sighted manner."[1] After reaching the top, it dives down to the base of an adjoining tree—to begin all over again. Its tail is used as a prop in climbing, exactly as is that of the Woodpecker.

The Creeper's usual note is a weak, lisping chirp, in timbre not unlike that of the Golden-crowned Kinglet, but easy to distinguish therefrom. During the season of migration one may sometimes observe large flights of these birds; the woods seem full of them, and their faint chirps coming from all sides produce a very pleasing effect. Towards the end of the spring movement, the mating song may occasionally be heard, but ordinarily it is reserved until the birds reach their breeding grounds. The first time I ever heard this song was during June, 1893, in the "big woods" of western Cambria County. Until I discovered the real author I thought that I was listening to some warbler new in my experience. The song is not loud, but sweet and warbler-like in timbre and delivery; according to G. M. Sutton (1928), it is "usually given while the bird [is] perched on the tree trunk, its head held high and out from the body. One song I syllabized as 'dee-dwee, did-i-ly, dee-dwee.' " In the breeding season the Creeper is more at home in heavy timber; it avoids smaller growth and finds its subsistence on the larger trees. In Tamarack Swamp, Clinton County, I used to find it in the spruces, and I have also encountered it among the red pines on the summit of the mountain south of Renovo, in the same county. In Potter, McKean, and Elk counties I have met with it in the extensive tracts of original forest of hemlock and hardwoods that were once a feature of these regions. In Warren County it prefers "well timbered swamp," according to R. B. Simpson, who was the first to find the eggs of this bird in western Pennsylvania. His timely article (1921) on its nesting habits as observed in that county is condensed herewith:

The Creeper seems to be rather tame and unsuspicious and pays little attention to the presence of human beings. The only way I could ever discover its nest was by watching the birds and detecting them in the act of building. The proper time to look for nests is from about April 20 to 25. I have found that the male sings more or less regularly, and a pair may be located by hearing the song where otherwise they might easily be overlooked. Once the female has started to build, she works steadily, and the male often accompanies her on her trips to the nest.

With one exception, the nests that I have found have been in old hemlock stubs. A large tree, from which the bark hangs loosely or has partly fallen, is chosen. For nesting, the birds select a spot where they can get under the bark through a break or crevice, or beneath a place where a piece has fallen off and the bark remaining has loosened from the trunk, leaving a space about two inches across. Three or four inches back from the opening the birds fill up the space with a loosely constructed nest, built of fine pieces of dead wood, with an occasional small twig, and lined with cobwebs and fine plant fibers. On one occasion when a large birch instead of a hemlock was chosen, the nest was built in one of the curled-up rolls of loose bark. Nests have been placed from six to thirty-five feet from the ground. May 8 to 10 is about the right time to expect full sets of eggs. The eggs number from five to six and are very small, averaging about .59 by .47 inches; they are white, evenly but thinly speckled with reddish brown, and closely resemble the more lightly spotted type of the Black-capped Chickadee.

A nest containing young was found early in June, 1893, near Crumb, Somerset County, by E. A. Preble. It was built, as were those described by Mr. Simpson, behind a large flake of loose bark on a big dead hemlock, about ten feet from the ground. The entrance was so narrow that it barely accommodated the parent bird. In the northern counties I have encountered young going about in family groups under the charge of their

[1] F. M. Chapman, *Handbook of Birds of Eastern North America*, revised edition, 1932, p. 400.

parents as early as the middle of June. The plumage of the adult birds soon becomes worn and ragged. Neither old nor young are particularly shy, and they seem to rely on their diminutive size and general inconspicuousness for protection. In the summer they are often found among the chickadees and other birds with which they so frequently associate in winter.

Certhia familiaris Teulon, *Jour. Boston Zoöl. Soc.*, 1882, 1:50 (Bradford, McKean Co., spring)—Townsend, *Proc. Acad. Nat. Sci. Philadelphia*, 1883, 60 (Latrobe, Westmoreland Co.).

Certhia familiaris americana Warren, *Birds Pa.*, ed. 2, 1890, 313 (Erie Co., breeding, *fide* Sennett; Centre Co., summer, *fide* Roddy)—Baily, *Auk*, 1896, 13:292, 296 (Williamsville, Elk Co., June–July)—Cope, *Cassinia*, 1902, 5:10, 20 (Tamarack Swamp, Clinton Co., June)—Todd, *Ann. Carnegie Mus.*, 1904, 2:590 (Erie and Presque Isle, Erie Co., transient)—Todd, in Bausman, *Hist. Beaver Co., Pa.*, 1904, 2:1201 (Beaver Co., winter)—Keim, *Cassinia*, 1905, 8:41 (Port Allegany, McKean Co., summer)—Forrest, *Oölogist*, 1911, 28:115 (Washington, Washington Co., April)—Harlow, *Auk*, 1918, 35:146 (Warren Co., summer)—Stone, *Cassinia*, 1919, 22:37; and 1920, 23:39 (Altoona, Blair Co., migration, *fide* McGraw)—Christy, *Cardinal*, 1923, v. 1, no. 1, [p. 14] (Sewickley, Allegheny Co., transient; winter)—Burleigh, *Wilson Bull.*, 1923, 35:144 (Allegheny Co., winter resident); 1924, 36:131 (State College, Centre Co., migration)—Christy and Sutton, *Cardinal*, 1928, 2:74 (Cook Forest, Clarion Co., summer)—Sutton, *Ann. Carnegie Mus.*, 1928, 18:230 (Pymatuning Swamp, Crawford Co., resident).

"Brown Creeper" Simpson, *Oölogist*, 1920, 37:143 (head of Tionesta Creek, Warren Co., nesting); 1921, 38:153 (Warren, Warren Co., nesting, etc.)—Pitcairn, *Bird-Lore*, 1908, 10:32 (West View, Allegheny Co., December)—Miller, *Bird-Lore*, 1913, 15:30; etc. (Springs, Somerset Co., December)—McConnell, *Oölogist*, 1918, 35:152 (McKeesport, Allegheny Co., transient)—Christy and Hegner, *Bird-Lore*, 1924, 26:30; etc. (Raccoon Creek Valley and region, Beaver Co., December)—McGraw and Hays, *Bird-Lore*, 1920, 22:31 (Altoona, Blair Co., December)—Warfield, *Bird-Lore*, 1920, 22:31 (Chambersburg, Franklin Co., December)—McConnell and Savage, *Bird-Lore*, 1921, 23:18 (Emsworth, Allegheny Co., December)—Stahl, *et al.*, *Bird-Lore*, 1921, 23:18 (Forest Hills to Deer Creek, Allegheny Co., December)—McClelland, *Am. Mid. Nat.*, 1922, 8:35 (Washington, Washington Co., winter)—Hoffman, *et al.*, *Bird-Lore*, 1923, 25:23 (Grove City, Mercer Co., December)—Eastwood, *Bird-Lore*, 1925, 27:406 (Dixmont, Allegheny Co., *fide* Reiter); 1927, 29:56 (Logan's Ferry, Allegheny Co., November, *fide* Manley)—Boulton, *Bird-Lore*, 1928, 30:13 (Milltown, Allegheny Co., October, *fide* Auerswald *et al.*), 271 (Industry, Beaver Co., May, *fide* Reiter and Squier)—Boulton, *Bird-Lore*, 1928, 30:401 (Glenshaw, Allegheny Co., September, *fide* Schlag)—Berkheimer, *Bird-Lore*, 1933, 35:27 (near Osterburg, Bedford Co., December)—Beal and Peterson, *Bird-Lore*, 1934, 36:33; and Upson, *et al.*, *Bird-Lore*, 1935, 37:47 (Presque Isle, Erie Co., December)—Elliott, *Cardinal*, 1934, 3:171 (Raccoon Creek, Beaver Co., December)—Cope and Hawkins, *Forest Leaves*, 1934, 24:26 (E. Tionesta Forest Reserve, Warren and McKean Co., summer).

Certhia familiaris fusca [Editor], *Cassinia*, 1926, 25:35 (Greencastle, Franklin Co., April, *fide* Ziegler).

WRENS

FAMILY TROGLODYTIDAE

THE WRENS are a rather large family, sparingly represented in the Old World but abundant in the American tropics. A half-dozen species occur in our region. The Carolina Wren is sedentary; the Winter Wren is a transient that breeds in the highlands; and the others are summer residents that migrate south in the winter.

As a group the Wrens are fairly distinctive. They are small to medium-sized birds having short, rounded wings with ten primary feathers; slender, down-curved bills; scutellate (scaled) tarsi; and toes that are more or less united at the base. Members of this family are plainly colored; brown in its various tones is the prevailing shade. The sexes are alike.

"Wrens, as a rule, are haunters of the undergrowth in well-thicketed places, but some species are marsh-inhabiting and others live among rocks. They are active, nervous little creatures, whose usually up-cocked tail is an index to their excitable dispositions. Their notes of alarm or displeasure are loud, harsh and insistent, but the songs of most species are marked by rare sweetness and brilliancy of execution. Their irrepressible energy finds expression in nests of great size or complex structure as well as in exceptionally large sets of eggs."[1]

[1]F. M. CHAPMAN, *Handbook of Birds of Eastern North America*, revised edition, 1932, p. 401.

EASTERN HOUSE WREN

TROGLODYTES AEDON AEDON Vieillot

Description—One of the smaller wrens; bill about half an inch long. General color above, dull brown, faintly barred with black on the wings and tail, and with a pale line over the eye; underparts dull whitish, with some brownish or buffy wash, and the flanks and crissum barred with brown. The *young* are similar, but the underparts are barred or spotted with dusky brown, except the flanks and crissum, which are plain rufescent brown.

Range—Our House Wren is an outlying North Temperate Zone representative of a generic group that is widely distributed in the American tropics. In the breeding season it ranges from the northern United States into the southern provinces of Canada, and across the entire continent. A western race, *parkmani*, has long been recognized. H. C. Oberholser (1934) has undertaken to discriminate the trans-Appalachian House Wrens from those of the Atlantic slope region, which latter he regards as the typical race. Lack of comparable material for examination prevents me from verifying his conclusions; hence for the purposes of this work I shall continue to adhere to the arrangement of the American Ornithologists' Union *Check-List*. I cannot find any differences of moment between breeding examples from the western tier of counties and those from the ridge and valley section, and it is worth noting that Dr. Oberholser himself records both alleged races from the latter region, thus indicating that it must be debatable ground.

The eastern race (or races) breeds mainly in the Carolinian and Alleghanian faunas and regularly, although less commonly, in the lower part of the Canadian. It winters south to the Gulf coast. Its breeding range "falls largely within the *Acer-Fagus* (maple-beech) Association"—an "interesting and significant correlation."[1] Beyond question, however, there has been a tremendous increase in the numbers of this species in the past hundred years—particularly notable since the beginning of the present century—and its original range may have been much more restricted. Audubon, indeed, who speaks of it as "extremely abundant" in the states along the Atlantic seaboard from Pennsylvania to Virginia, elsewhere significantly states that "very few are seen to the west of the Alleghanies, and none in Kentucky or Louisiana." Even in his day this wren had become so domesticated in its haunts and habits that on one occasion when he found several birds in a deep woods in Maine, he was led to consider them a different species altogether. In primitive times, before the coming of the white man, this bird must have been wholly a "Wood" Wren, although it was probably confined to the vicinity of rivers and streams. Since it dislikes the deep woods as a nesting ground, its advent in our region has doubtless been comparatively recent. Even as late as 1893, in my traverse of the then heavily forested area of western Cambria County, I did not see a single house wren until I emerged into the cleared and cultivated country along the border of Indiana County. It is fair to presume that with forested conditions obtaining over our entire area, the species must have found the environment unfavorable. Probably it appeared first in the Ohio and Susquehanna valleys and has advanced into the highlands from both directions. At the present time it occupies our entire region indiscriminately. Its relations with Bewick's Wren will be discussed under the head of that species.

Migration—For the spring migration there is no dearth of records for this species. April 24 is the average date of its arrival at Beaver, and April 17 (1922 and 1938), the earliest, as deduced from twenty-five years' observations. The essential accuracy of these dates is shown by their close accord with those from near-by localities. Thus, the corresponding dates for Sewickley, based on records covering thirteen years, are April 24 and April 16 (1921), respectively (Christy). Nine years' records from the immediate environs of Pittsburgh (made by several different observers) yield April 23 as the average date. The species has appeared at Meadville as early as April 18 (First) and at Springs, Somerset County, on April 16, although the average date at the latter locality is about May 1 (Miller). R. B. Simpson writes that he does not expect it at Warren until about the first of May, and it probably reaches the plateau region a little later. From Renovo there is also a satisfactory series of arrival records covering twenty-five years, ranging between April 18 and May 1 and yielding April 26 as the average date (Pierce). At State College the earliest spring record is April 19 (1917), and the average date is April 26 (Burleigh). Odd records from neighboring localities correspond closely with those here cited. The species has been reported from the southwestern part of the state as early as the first week of April, but the suspicion persists that these records actually pertain to Bewick's Wren.

In the fall the retiring habits of the House Wren often cause it to be overlooked, so that departure records are neither so numerous nor so trustworthy as those for the spring movement. Such as they are, however, they indicate that the species regularly remains with us at least until the end of September or early in October. The dates in five seasons' records from Beaver lie between September 22 (1890) and October 3 (1908), and the average is September 27. D. A. Atkinson, indeed, has noted this wren in Allegheny County as late as October 12 (1898), and T. D. Burleigh has listed it still later—October 16 (1912). The last-named observer has also seen it in Centre County as late as October 11 (1914). The only long series of fall departure dates available are those made at Renovo by A. K. Pierce; these cover twenty-two seasons (not consecutive). The earliest date is September 17; the latest, October 7; and the average, September 27. The species was noted at Shermansville, Crawford County, until October 4 in 1926 (Bergstrom), and at Erie until October 7 in 1904 (Simpson).

Habits—The House Wren was, I believe, the first bird to attract my attention, or at least the first of which I have any distinct recollection. It was in the early eighties, when the town of Beaver was largely given over to gardens and orchards and when my activities as a small boy were necessarily curtailed, that I became intrigued by a little brown bird that season after season used to return

[1]S. C. Kendeigh, *Ecological Monographs*, 1934, 4:305.

to build in a cherry tree in our spacious back yard. It had its nest in a cavity in a dead branch, with the entrance on the under side—a hole that I now know must have been originally dug out by a woodpecker. I spent many hours in watching the antics of this (to me) curious little bird, in listening to its sprightly song, and in trying to peep into its nest. Not until several years later, after I had begun to study birds in earnest, did I learn its proper name. In those days no one ever thought of putting up nest boxes for any birds except purple martins, so that the house wrens were obliged to content themselves with natural cavities. Old woodpecker-holes were utilized, as well as hollow fence posts and crevices about buildings. Many curious nesting sites have been recorded. Sennett (1889) relates that he once found a nest in a hole in a sandbank that had formerly been tenanted by a belted kingfisher, and Dr. Atkinson writes of having seen nests in old pumps, mailboxes, and rainspouts. Cavities in trees and stumps are still favorite sites in the wooded and more thinly settled sections of our state, where the House Wren is numerous in the burnt-over tracts and in areas of second growth, in which it finds congenial surroundings. In my notebooks I find that I have repeatedly remarked its abundance in various parts of our region remote from houses but where suitable nesting sites were in evidence on every hand.

Nowadays the erection of bird boxes especially for the House Wren has become a fad, and the concerted effort to attract this bird to the vicinity of houses has been eminently successful, since it is an adaptable species and one that has deliberately sought out human society. Its sociable traits were noted by the early writers and led to its being christened *Sylvia domestica* by Wilson in 1808. Since the practice of erecting boxes has been in vogue, there has been a great increase in the number of pairs of house wrens inhabiting villages, towns, and outlying urban districts. To my personal knowledge there are now ten times as many house wrens within the borough limits of Beaver as there were forty or more years ago, despite the virtually complete elimination since then of natural nesting sites. Everyone agrees that "the Wren is a nice bird to have around the house." Admittedly it is much better than the English Sparrow —that foreign interloper that has pre-empted the place of our native birds to such a large extent. Moreover, unlike the Sparrow, the Wren is not only pleasing in appearance and song, but is also valuable from an economic standpoint. In the garden and orchard it performs estimable service as an insect destroyer. "Wrens are industrious foragers, searching every tree, shrub, or vine for caterpillars, examining every post and rail of the fence, and every cranny in the wall for insects or spiders. They do not, as a rule, fly far afield, but work industriously in the immediate vicinity of their nests."[1] Since the Wren feeds on virtually nothing but insects, the number of these consumed by a growing family must be enormous in the aggregate.

But there is, unfortunately, another side to the picture—one not nearly so well known. The Wren is naturally pugnacious and aggressive in disposition, and soon comes in conflict with other native birds. In particular it resents the presence in its chosen territory of species with similar nesting preferences, such as the Purple Martin, the Tree Swallow, the Bluebird, and the Chickadee, and it usually succeeds in driving them off and in appropriating their nesting sites. Not only on these does it wage war, but on other species as well—never openly, but surreptitiously—by the simple method of puncturing eggs and heaving them out of the nest. The evidence for this villainous habit is abundant and conclusive and has been aptly summarized by Miss A. R. Sherman in her timely article, "Down with the House Wren Boxes," to which the doubtful reader is respectfully referred.[2] The Wren has its defenders, but the weight of evidence is against it. Miss Sherman points out that "the destructive habit has increased disproportionately with the increase of the species," and she rightly attributes this increase in numbers to "the campaign for erecting boxes for wrens; boxes with small openings that protected the wrens from their natural enemies and enabled them to breed in undue numbers. That the species needs no such protection, but survives in plentiful numbers in the remote portions of its breeding range is another fact proved by the regional lists printed in the bird magazines." Miss Sherman also shows that the marked decrease in the numbers of certain other birds that formerly frequented our orchards and gardens can be directly connected with the un-

[1] F. E. L. Beal, U. S. Department of Agriculture, *Farmers' Bulletin*, no. 54, 1897, p. 36.
[2] *Wilson Bulletin*, 1925, 37:5–13.

wonted increase in the ranks of the House Wren.

This is merely another instance of the disastrous results produced by man's interference with the balance of nature. I fully indorse the remedy suggested, which is not the extermination of the species, but the removal of the nest boxes, which would place the bird on its own resources, as of old. Either we must do this, or else we must be prepared to justify, to future generations and to ourselves, the dearth of such birds as the Yellow Warbler, the Chipping Sparrow, the Baltimore Oriole, the Warbling Vireo, the Bluebird, and others equally beautiful and desirable. I wish to put myself on record as being absolutely opposed to any further partiality towards the House Wren and to making it the chief beneficiary of the new interest in bird life that has come into vogue. Its excessive increase in numbers is as deplorable as the decrease in the numbers of our waterfowl and birds of prey.

Another unusual and interesting (even if not reprehensible) habit of the House Wren is one that was first publicized by S. P. Baldwin of Cleveland, Ohio, in connection with the looseness of its "marriage relations." Not only are the males polygamous at times, but it is the exception for the same pair to mate again for the raising of a second brood; there is generally a new deal made at that time, with all the cards reshuffled.

The arrival of the House Wren on its breeding grounds is signalized by the sputtering but not unmusical song of the male, delivered in extra-fast time as the bird sits erectly on its favorite perch. Beginning early in the morning, it keeps up the performance more or less all day, pausing only at intervals to feed, until the constant reiteration becomes trite indeed. It may sing as often as three or four times a minute. Nest-building begins at once after the birds are settled. With infinite labor and enthusiasm they collect and drag into the chosen cavity a plentiful supply of small coarse twigs and miscellaneous rubbish—enough to fill it well if it happens to be too roomy. The hollow left in this mass is usually lined with feathers or other soft material. A castoff snake skin occasionally adorns the outside. The eggs vary from five to nine in number, but six or seven form the usual set. They are laid during the latter half of May or early in June, and there is a second laying in July or even as late as August. The eggs average about .65 by .50 inches and are distinctive in appearance, although they vary somewhat in coloration. The ground-color runs from white to vinaceous buff and is rather heavily dotted with russet or fawn-colored specks, which sometimes coalesce to form a clearly defined band around the larger end. Incubation requires about fourteen days.

By the first of September the House Wren has apparently forsaken its summer haunts; at any rate, all the birds seen after that date seem to be migrants. These differ greatly from the summer birds in their haunts and habits. They are always found in the woodland, accompanying the warblers and other species and frequenting the thickest shrubbery and the densest underbrush. In their retiring ways they remind one of Winter Wrens. They sometimes sing at this season, too, but while the succession of notes is the same, the song itself is strangely faint, soft, and low. I have noted individuals in the woods in the spring behaving in a similar manner, except that they were entirely silent, and I have assumed that they were birds on their way northward.

Troglodytes œdon Teulon, *Jour. Boston Zoöl. Soc.*, 1882, 1:50 (Bradford, McKean Co., nesting).

Troglodytes domesticus Townsend, *Proc. Acad. Nat. Sci. Philadelphia*, 1883, 61 (Latrobe, Westmoreland Co., nesting).

"House Wren" Todd, *Oölogist*, 1887, 4:89 (Beaver, Beaver Co., nesting)—Stone, *Cassinia*, 1906, 9:44 (McConnellsburg, Fulton Co., June)—Pitcairn, *Bird-Lore*, 1907, 9:155 (Riverview Park, Allegheny Co., nesting)—McClintock, *Bird-Lore*, 1909, 11:198 (Pittsburgh, Allegheny Co., nesting; habits)—Simpson, *Oölogist*, 1912, 29:330 (head of Tionesta Creek, Warren Co., nesting)—Rogers, *Bird-Lore*, 1914, 16:273 (near Pittsburgh, Allegheny Co., migration)—Dickey, *Oölogist*, 1914, 31:171 ([Charter Oak], Huntingdon Co., June)—Miller, *In the Open*, Aug., 1915, 5:45 (McKinley Park, Pittsburgh, Allegheny Co., nesting)—McConnell, *Oölogist*, 1918, 35:152 (McKeesport, Allegheny Co., nesting)—McClelland, *Am. Mid. Nat.*, 1922, 8:36 (Washington, Washington Co., summer; migration)—Street, *Cassinia*, 1923, 24:18 (Greencastle to Ft. Loudon, and Horse Valley, Franklin Co., June)—Shacklett, *Bird-Lore*, 1924, 26:177 (Erie, Erie Co., nesting)—Christy, *Cardinal*, 1924, v. 1, no. 3, p. 13 (Beaver, Allegheny, Washington, and Greene Co., local range)—Lehman, *Bird-Lore*, 1925, 27:245 ([Chambersburg, Franklin Co.], nesting)—Eastwood, *Bird-Lore*, 1925, 27:263 (Pittsburgh region, Allegheny Co., April); 1927, 29:273 (Springs, Somerset Co., April, *fide* Miller)—Wallace, *Bird-Lore*, 1933, 35:268 (McKean, Erie Co., nesting)—Thompson, *Bird-Lore*, 1933, 35:320 (Erie, Erie Co., nesting).

Troglodytes aëdon Sennett, *Auk*, 1889, 6:76 (Erie, Erie Co., nesting)—Warren, *Birds Pa.*, ed. 2, 1890, 310 (Washington Co., summer)—Dwight, *Auk*, 1892, 9:140 (Cresson and

Gallitzin, Cambria Co., June)—Todd, *Auk*, 1893, 10:46 (Coalport, Clearfield Co., June)—Jacobs, *Summer Birds Greene Co., Pa.*, 1893, 14 (Greene Co., nesting)—Baily, *Auk*, 1896, 13:296 (Williamsville, Elk Co., June–July)—Cope, *Cassinia*, 1902, 5:20 (Clinton and Potter Co., June)—Todd, *Ann. Carnegie Mus.*, 1904, 2:589 (Erie and Presque Isle, Erie Co., nesting)—Todd, in Bausman, *Hist. Beaver Co., Pa.*, 1904, 2:1201 (Beaver Co., summer)—Keim, *Cassinia*, 1905, 8:40 (Port Allegany, McKean Co., summer)—Harlow, *Auk*, 1912, 29:476 (southern Centre Co., summer)—Burleigh, *Wilson Bull.*, 1923, 35:143 (Pittsburgh, Allegheny Co., nesting); 1924, 36:74 (State College, Centre Co., migration)—Christy, *Cardinal*, 1923, v. 1, no. 1, [p. 14] (Sewickley, Allegheny Co., nesting)—Sutton, *Ann. Carnegie Mus.*, 1928, 18:226 (Pymatuning Swamp and vicinity, Crawford Co., summer)—Christy, *Cardinal*, 1930, 2:234 (Cook Forest, Clarion Co., nesting).

Troglodytes aëdon aëdon Christy and Sutton, Cardinal, 1928, 2:74 (Cook Forest, Clarion Co., summer)—Burleigh, *Wilson Bull.*, 1931, 43:53 (State College, Centre Co., nesting)—Burleigh, *Cardinal*, 1932, 3:78 (Chestnut Ridge, near Uniontown, Fayette Co., nesting).

Troglodytes domesticus domesticus Oberholser, *Ohio Jour. Sci.*, 1934, 34:87 (Gallitzin, Cambria Co., Altoona, Blair Co., Saltillo, Huntingdon Co., and Mercersburg, Franklin Co., June–July; critical).

Troglodytes domesticus baldwini Oberholser, *Ohio Jour. Sci.*, 1934, 34:90 (Calvin, Huntingdon Co.; Linesville, Crawford Co.; Tionesta, Forest Co.; and Erie, Erie Co., June–August; critical).

EASTERN WINTER WREN (Plate 15)

NANNUS HIEMALIS HIEMALIS (Vieillot)

Description—A bird resembling the House Wren, but a little smaller, and with a *much shorter tail*. General color above, brown, the wings and tail showing obscure dusky bars; a pale stripe over the eye; underparts similar but paler, the abdomen, flanks, and under tail coverts showing dusky and whitish markings, giving a spotted or barred effect.

Range—Although the generic group to which our so-called Winter Wren belongs may not be of Palaearctic origin, it is widely distributed in that region and is unusually plastic, appearing in different forms in the several divisions of its range. Indeed, the Common Wren of Europe is so similar to the American bird in coloration that it is regarded by some authors as conspecific therewith. The eastern race of the Winter Wren breeds commonly in the coniferous forests of the Canadian Life Zone and winters southward to the Gulf states. Its breeding range in New York comprises the Adirondack and Catskill Mountains and certain isolated areas in the western part of the state (Eaton). Many years ago Audubon found it breeding in the "Great Pine Swamp" near Mauch Chunk, Pennsylvania (east of our limits), and since then its breeding range has been traced southward along the Appalachian highlands to northern Georgia.

Breeding records from western Pennsylvania have gradually accumulated, until the summer distribution of the species can now be plotted with considerable precision. Generally speaking, it breeds (or used to breed) throughout the plateau section; elsewhere it is a common transient and rather rare winter resident. Thus it has about the same local status and distribution as have the Red-breasted Nuthatch and the Brown Creeper. The breeding records from western New York mapped by E. H. Eaton are merely outliers of the extensive area in western Pennsylvania occupied by this species in summer. This area comprises all of Potter and McKean counties and most of Warren County, to and beyond the Allegheny River, and the territory thence southward over the highlands to the Maryland boundary. Its extension westward to Crawford County is conceivable, at least under primeval conditions when a heavy coniferous growth covered this part of the country also. Indeed, Sennett is quoted by Warren as saying that the species "breeds occasionally" in that county, and S. S. Dickey writes that on May 26, 1926, he discovered a male winter wren singing and apparently settled for the season "in a vast pine and hemlock swamp" a few miles east of Cambridge Springs, where the Northern Water-Thrush was found nesting. But I am inclined to believe that if the Winter Wren breeds at present in Crawford County, its range, like that of the Water-Thrush, is local and insular, and discontinuous with the main area inhabited. The only suggestion that the species may breed in the Pymatuning area comes from G. M. Sutton, who noted a supposedly mated pair (possibly only migrants) west of Linesville on May 4, 1922.

I have found the Winter Wren in June on the

mountainside above Renovo, in the Susquehanna Valley, and have traced it across Cameron, Elk, and Forest counties during the same month. Cook Forest, in the northwestern corner of Clarion County, seems to be about its western limit in this direction in the breeding season. Thence its range swings off to the southeast to include Clearfield and Cambria counties and gradually contracts to the southward; its eastern boundary follows the crest of the Alleghenies. The only breeding records for this wren in Somerset County come from just west of the Allegheny divide (at Crumb and Keystone Junction—Preble), but it is very likely that under the right conditions the species would breed all the way across the county to Laurel Hill, as do the Junco, the Blue-headed Vireo, and other birds of similar faunal affinities. There is no indication that it breeds anywhere in the ridge and valley section, although we might reason by analogy that it formerly bred at Bear Meadows, Centre County.

While it has been detected in the dead of winter at Warren and Renovo, this wren is rare during that season at both places. Other than in its recognized breeding range it is found regularly in the winter as far north even as Erie County, but it is still far from being as common then as it is during migration. There was a time when I believed that it was only a transient in Beaver County, but after encountering it on a few occasions from December to February inclusive, I had to revise this opinion somewhat. Nevertheless, my experience leads me to believe that one cannot be certain of seeing this species during the winter. According to T. D. Burleigh, it occurs regularly in Allegheny County, but one wonders whether some of the observers making the "Christmas Census" lists have not confused it with the Carolina Wren, which is far more conspicuous and prominent.

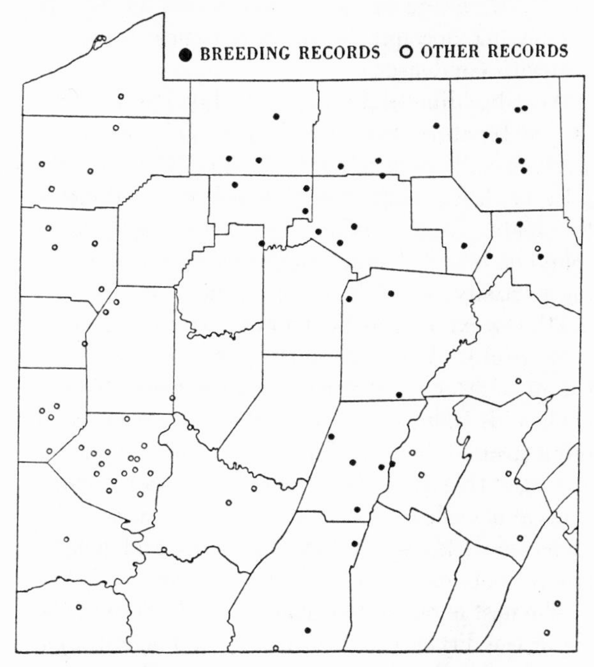

LOCAL RANGE OF THE EASTERN WINTER WREN

Migration—As already intimated, the great bulk of the Winter Wren population breeds north of Pennsylvania and winters to the south; hence the species is far more numerous in our region during the season of migration than at any other time. In Allegheny and Beaver counties the first fall migrants appear during the third or fourth week in September (September 17, 1922—Sewickley; September 20, 1913—Pittsburgh; September 23, 1899 and 1909—Beaver). Later fall arrival records from other points farther north are probably subject to correction. Mr. Burleigh's earliest fall record for State College is September 19, 1914, and Dr. Dickey saw one bird on Presque Isle on September 14, 1927. In October there are usually two or three days of special movement, when great numbers of winter wrens may be found in the woods everywhere. The regular autumnal migration covers a period of about five weeks, after which the species resumes its normal numbers for the winter. Migrants arriving from the South during the last week in March noticeably swell the total, and the height of the northward migration is reached sometime during the first week or ten days of April. As in the fall, there are days of great movement, when the woods swarm with winter wrens. The last do not pass through until toward the end of April, and I have seen stragglers at Beaver as late as May 4 (1889) and at Erie (Presque Isle) until May 10 (1900). The latest spring date from State College, a locality where the species is not known to breed, is May 14 (1917—Burleigh). Thus both spring and fall movements at any one place cover about five weeks.

Habits—As is evident from the foregoing remarks, the common name of "Winter Wren," under which this species has long been known, is singularly inappropriate, at least in a large part of its range. "Wood Wren," describing the bird's chosen haunts rather than the season of its occurrence, would be a much better name. In the winter and during migration, this wren is confined exclusively to woodland, where it creeps around, mouselike, in brush piles and grapevine tangles and about fallen treetops, prostrate trunks, and old stumps. In such places it easily contrives to keep out of sight, but if due care and patience are used, one may in time catch a glimpse of this little brown bird as it flies in buzzing fashion, furtively and near the ground, from one bit of covert to another. It is remarkable that a bird of such apparently weak flying powers and pronounced ground habits can essay a migration covering hundreds of miles.

Although the Winter Wren is shielded from easy detection by its small size and inconspicuous coloration, which resembles that of the dead leaves of the forest floor and the decaying trunks of the fallen trees, it nevertheless gives itself away by its characteristic call note. This note somewhat resembles that of the Song Sparrow but is lower in tone and sharper in delivery. Like all wrens, this species is nervous, active, and irascible. It has a scolding note also, a prolonged *chir-r-r-r*, usually delivered when the bird comes into some open situation; then it cocks its tail at an impertinent upward angle and moves its body up and down in a series of convulsive jerks—a typical wren performance.

During the spring migration, when this bird is sometimes very common, an enterprising male may occasionally indulge in a snatch of the song usually reserved only for the breeding grounds. Always it comes as a surprise that such a tiny mite possesses a song so rich, sustained, and melodious. In these respects its song is comparable with that of the Ruby-crowned Kinglet. The Kinglet, however, sings constantly on its northward journey, while the Wren conserves its efforts for the most part until it is settled for the season. Even in the summer the Winter Wren is the same shy recluse, haunting the deepest, shadiest, and coolest recesses of the hemlock woods, where there are fallen trees and plenty of brush for cover. Along the gullies and mountain streams, where the rhododendron growth is dense and where moss-covered logs lie scattered about, with here and there the upturned stump of some fallen forest giant, this wren is fully at home, and often several males can be heard singing at once, so closely is their territory occupied. The male sings constantly through the months of May and June. Choosing a dead stub for its perch, or the top of a low hemlock, it pours out its feelings in a rippling, voluble melody that seems to partake of the very spirit of the wilderness. Whether heard ringing out full and clear close at hand, or more faintly from a distance, it is delightful to the ear. Enchanted music it seems to be, from a source hidden and unseen, as the shy little performer, elusive as Ariel, moves about from spot to spot in an attempt to elude pursuit. In this game of hide-and-seek, all the advantage is on his side.

Even where the original forest has been cut away, the Winter Wren may persist; for it is capable of surviving where other boreal species are not. When I visited Katrine Swamp in McKean County, in June, 1895, the place had been largely cut over, but this wren still found good shelter among the brush and fallen logs. Indeed, I can recall no other spot where I have ever seen it so numerous in summer. In June, 1899, I also found it common in the lumber slashings in northern Clearfield County. Second-growth hemlock, if sufficiently dense, will not necessarily be shunned. Several nests have been found in Warren County by R. B. Simpson, who has written (1914) an interesting account of his experience, which is herewith condensed:

Nest-building begins early in May. Close search of the territory frequented by a pair of winter wrens usually results in the finding of four or five false or decoy nests, but the real nest is difficult to locate. In this region the nests are usually found on the lower side of a decayed, moss-covered log partially raised from the ground, or else beneath the exposed roots of a fallen tree (preferably a hemlock). When the nest is underneath a log, the crevice or cavity must be excavated by the bird, as is indicated by the fresh pieces of wood lying around below. When it is under a partly uprooted tree, it is placed among the roots, which conceal it well. I have also found nests in crevices underneath large overhanging rocks and among mossy roots on steep banks along streams.

The nest is rather bulky and is built close to the log or the dirt of the upturned root. The entrance is a small hole about one and a quarter inches wide. The nest is composed mainly of moss, intermixed with a few dry sprigs of hemlock, and the entrance is always rimmed about with such sprigs. The cavity is thickly lined with feathers. Decoy nests are smaller and less bulky than the real nest and are never lined.

The eggs are usually all laid by May 15 or 20. Five is the normal clutch, but often no more than four are laid, and on one occasion six were found. A close sitter, the female is slow to leave when disturbed. Once when I actually pulled a nest out for examination and then replaced it, the female did not desert but laid a full set of eggs.

Two nests that were taken by A. K. Pierce at Kane are now in the Carnegie Museum; they are substantially similar to those described by Mr. Simpson. The first, collected on May 9, 1895, contained three eggs—probably an incomplete set. The second, collected on May 30, 1901, held a full set of six eggs, about three days incubated. The eggs are white, sparsely dotted with pale reddish brown; some are nearly immaculate. They measure about .69 by .49 inches.

Anorthura troglodytes hiemalis Townsend, *Proc. Acad. Nat. Sci. Philadelphia*, 1883, 61 (Latrobe, Westmoreland Co., [winter] resident).

Troglodytes hyemalis Van Fleet, *Ornithologist and Oölogist*, 1884, 9:108 (DuBois, Clearfield Co., July).

Troglodytes hiemalis Warren, *Birds Pa.*, 1888, 248 (Crawford Co., breeding, *fide* Sennett)—Todd, *Auk*, 1893, 10:46 (Coalport, Clearfield Co., June)—Baily, *Auk*, 1896, 13:296 (Straight Creek, near Williamsville, Elk Co., June–July).

"Winter Wren" Warren, *Forest and Stream*, 1891, 37:83 (Kane, McKean Co., summer)—Pitcairn, *Bird-Lore*, 1908, 10:32 (West View, Allegheny Co., December)—Jackson, *Cassinia*, 1909, 12:12 (Warren, Warren Co., May)—Simpson, *Oölogist*, 1910, 27:98; and 1914, 31:91, 186 (Warren, Warren Co., nesting, etc.)—Wright, *Bird-Lore*, 1911, 13:31 (Pittsburgh, Allegheny Co., December)—Miller (M. H.), *In the Open*, Dec., 1912, 3:41 (McKinley Park, Allegheny Co., transient)—Simpson, *Oölogist*, 1912, 29:330 (head of Tionesta Creek, Warren Co., nesting)—Miller (A. B.), *Bird-Lore*, 1913, 15:30; etc. (Springs, Somerset Co., December)—Burleigh and Anderson, *Bird-Lore*, 1914, 16:38; etc. (Harmarville, Allegheny Co., December)—McConnell, *Oölogist*, 1918, 35:152 (McKeesport, Allegheny Co., winter)—McGrew, *Oölogist*, 1918, 35:162 (Endeavor, Forest Co., nesting)—Warfield, *Bird-Lore*, 1920, 22:31; etc. (Chambersburg, Franklin Co., December)—McConnell and Savage, *Bird-Lore*, 1921, 23:18; etc. (Emsworth, Allegheny Co., December)—McClelland, *Am. Mid. Nat.*, 1922, 8:35 (Washington, Washington Co., winter)—Hoffman, *et al.*, *Bird-Lore*, 1923, 25:23 (Grove City, Mercer Co., December)—Christy and Hegner, *Bird-Lore*, 1925, 27:41; etc. (Raccoon Creek Valley and region, Beaver Co., December)—Sutton, *Bird-Lore*, 1923, 25:194 (Schenley Park, Pittsburgh, Allegheny Co., April, *fide* Blair); 1924, 26:190 (Castle Shannon, Allegheny Co., April, *fide* Smith)—Squier and Elliott, *Bird-Lore*, 1925, 27:40; etc. (Deer Creek region, Allegheny Co., December)—Eastwood, *Bird-Lore*, 1925, 27:407 ("Slack Hollow," Allegheny Co., September, *fide* Grimm); 1926, 28:207 (Deer Creek, Emsworth, and "Slack Hollow," Allegheny Co., April)—Matuszak, *Bird-Lore*, 1926, 28:29 (Hyde Park, Westmoreland Co., December)—Eastwood, *Bird-Lore*, 1927, 29:56 (Thornburg, Allegheny Co., November, *fide* McCracken)—Boulton, *Bird-Lore*, 1928, 30:271 (Sandy Lake, Mercer Co., May, *fide* Freni and Stanton)—Elliott, *Cardinal*, 1934, 3:171 (Raccoon Creek, Beaver Co., December)—Beal and Peterson, *Bird-Lore*, 1934, 36:33 (Presque Isle, Erie Co., December).

Anorthura hiemalis Cope, *Cassinia*, 1902, 5:10, 11, 20 (Tamarack Swamp, Clinton Co., and Kettle Creek Valley, Potter Co., June).

Olbiorchilus hiemalis Todd, *Ann. Carnegie Mus.*, 1904, 2:589 (Erie and Presque Isle, Erie Co., transient; rare in winter)—Todd, in Bausman, *Hist. Beaver Co., Pa.*, 1904, 2:1201 (Beaver Co., transient)—Keim, *Cassinia*, 1905, 8:41 (Port Allegany, McKean Co., summer).

Nannus hiemalis hiemalis Harlow, *Auk*, 1918, 35:145 (Warren and Clinton Co., summer)—Stone, *Cassinia*, 1919, 22:37 (Altoona, Blair Co., winter, *fide* McGraw)—Christy, *Cardinal*, 1923, v. 1, no. 1, [p. 14] (Sewickley, Allegheny Co., winter)—Burleigh, *Wilson Bull.*, 1923, 35:143 (Allegheny Co., winter); 1924, 36:130 (State College, Centre Co., migration)—[Editor], *Cassinia*, 1926, 25:34 (Greencastle, Franklin Co., December, *fide* Ziegler).

Nannus troglodytes hiemalis Christy and Sutton, *Cardinal*, 1928, 2:74 (Cook Forest, Clarion Co., summer)—Sutton, *Ann. Carnegie Mus.*, 1928, 18:227 (Meadville and Pymatuning Swamp, Crawford Co., transient; occasional in winter).

"Eastern Winter Wren" Cope and Hawkins, *Forest Leaves*, 1934, 24:26 (E. Tionesta Forest Reserve, Warren and McKean Co., summer).

BEWICK'S WREN (Plate 15)

THRYOMANES BEWICKI BEWICKI (Audubon)

Description—Similar in general to the House Wren, but slightly larger; *tail much longer and more distinctly barred, extensively blackish, with white tips* to the outer feathers. Upperparts rufescent brown, nearly uniform; the head has a conspicuous white stripe over the eyes; underparts soiled white. Smaller than the Carolina Wren.

Range—Bewick's Wren as a species inhabits

the Austral Life Zone and a part of the Transition, across the entire continent. West of the Mississippi River it splits up into numerous races; the eastern form has a much more extensive range than have the western ones. It is virtually unknown in New England and New York, however, and is scarcely more than a straggler in the District of Columbia, where it is not known to breed. Not until we enter the Appalachian foothills in Maryland and Virginia do we encounter it as a regular summer resident. Thence it ranges into the south-central counties of Pennsylvania, where it is fairly common and characteristic. Through Franklin, Fulton, and Bedford counties, northward across Huntingdon County, and into southern Centre County, its range is virtually continuous. It has been noted in early September at Johnsburg, Somerset County (Eifrig); the fact that it has not been authoritatively recorded from Blair County is without significance. It is therefore safe to include the entire ridge and valley section within its breeding range. In this region it ranges over the mountains and the valleys indiscriminately, environmental conditions being equal.

West of the Allegheny divide, Bewick's Wren reappears in the southwestern counties; it ranges eastward as far as Chestnut Ridge and irregularly northward at least to Mercer County. It is perhaps most numerous in Greene County, as certified by several observers. To the northward it decreases in numbers and in Beaver County is rather rare. Almost every season I find a few there, however, about farmhouses in the country districts, and in 1939 a pair built a nest under a back porch in the town of Beaver, and hatched six young. Another recent record concerns a nest with six eggs found at Slippery Rock, Butler County, on May 13, 1939 (Ristich). Near Jamisonville, in the same county, the species is listed as an irregular summer resident (Elliott), and it was noted in June, 1935, near Sharon, Mercer County (McQuiston).

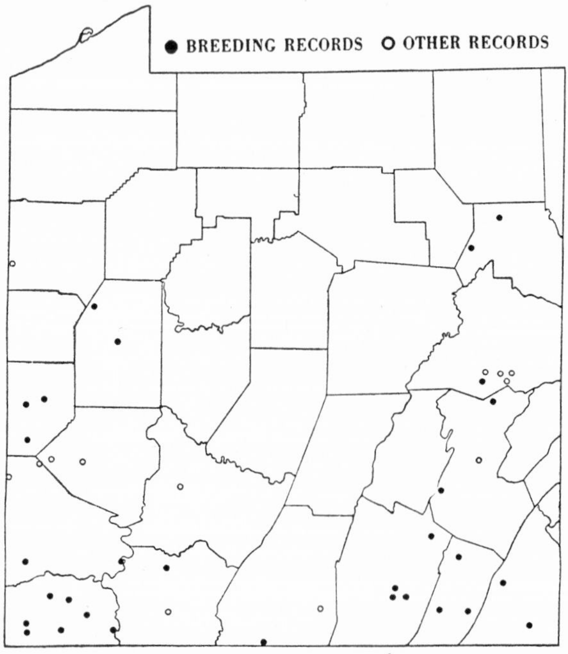

LOCAL RANGE OF BEWICK'S WREN

B. H. Christy has written an interesting account of the local range and status of Bewick's Wren in the Ohio Valley. In his opinion, the northern limit of its range not only falls at about this latitude but also fluctuates from year to year and in 1923, at least, was recessive. He points out that the recession corresponded to an advance by the House Wren, and quotes Robert Ridgway's remarks on the incompatibility of the two species.[1] Undoubtedly there are some grounds for this belief, but the evidence is contradictory. I am more inclined to think that Bewick's Wren, in common with certain other species of austral affinities, has been gradually pushing northward in spite of the House Wren. Writing more than forty years ago, J. W. Jacobs stated that in Greene County the former species was "met with commonly," while the latter was "sparingly distributed." The status of each was thus about the same as it is today. Farther north, in the Ohio Valley, where the House Wren has always been common, Bewick's Wren was not actually observed until 1898, and it now seems to be slowly increasing in numbers. True, it may have been overlooked there during earlier years, but I have received the impression that it is a recent immigrant.

The authorities on the bird life of Ohio, Indiana, and Michigan also agree that Bewick's Wren is advancing its range from south to north. Lynds Jones remarks: "It appears that this wren, which was unknown as an Ohio bird in 1882, has extended its range northeastward almost if not quite to our northern border as far east as Oberlin, where it has twice been recorded within the last five years. It is gradually but surely replacing the House Wren in the southern counties, pos-

[1] *Bird-Lore*, 1915, 17:196.

sibly because it is the resident form while the House Wren migrates. It is common now as far east as Scioto county, and nearly as far north as Columbus."[1]

Since L. E. Hicks gives two recent records from Ashtabula County, Ohio, just across our northwestern border,[2] the species should be looked for in all the counties of the western tier. It seems to be extending its range also in the eastern part of our region, and in a highly irregular and anomalous manner. Its occurrence at Springs, Somerset County, in high country close to the Maryland boundary, is vouched for by A. B. Miller, and the situation there resembles that described by Mr. Ridgway in southern Illinois. Mr. Miller writes: "Fifteen years or more ago, the House Wren was almost unknown here, and Bewick's Wren was the common species, although it was never so common as the House Wren is now. Since then the House Wren has become very numerous and Bewick's Wren as a breeding species has almost disappeared, although it is generally noted during migration." (The two species live side by side in Bedford and Fulton counties, however, although there are no data on their relative abundance in the past.) The extraordinary thing is not the decrease in numbers at Springs, but the fact that the species occurs there at all. Bewick's Wren, a bird of supposedly Carolinian predilections, on the top of the Allegheny Mountains! Its case is paralleled, however, by those of the Cardinal and the Tufted Titmouse in this same area. No less surprising is its presence in Clinton County, where it has been detected in the valley of the Susquehanna River (West Branch) at Round Island, and at Tamarack Swamp—a locality where a flora and fauna characteristic of the Canadian Life Zone obtain. It has not been seen in the swamp itself, of course, but on its outskirts. It is difficult to believe that Bewick's Wren was ever an original inhabitant of the Canadian Fauna. It must have followed in the wake of the clearing and settlement of the country.

Migration—There is not much local information on the migration of this species. It is resident in small numbers as far north as southern Ohio and, according to S. S. Dickey, winters occasionally in Greene County. A hardier bird than the House Wren, it precedes it in late March or early April. It has been recorded at Springs as early as March 25 (Miller); at State College on April 1 (1917—Burleigh); and near Huntingdon on April 7 (1921—Sutton). Near Jamisonville, Butler County, it arrives about March 30 (Elliott). In the fall the species has been taken at Beaver on October 2 (1909—Todd) and noted at "Bushy Run Battlefield," Westmoreland County, as late as October 7 (1934—Trimble).

Habits[3]—If any member of the avian tribe may be said to epitomize the essence of a fair April day, it is Bewick's Wren. Its gentle manner and exquisite song quickly endear it to the amateur field naturalist. Ordinarily it is a bird of the gardens, where it flits along fence rows and forages for insects among brush piles. Sometimes it favors high ground and seeks out the tops of ridges and mountain ranges. Furtive in its actions, it is customarily observed scuttling about old rail fences, under sheds and barns, or among the clusters of wind-blown dry leaves in fence corners. When feeding and at ease, it utters a series of conversational sounds that may be expressed as *plit-plit;* and when disturbed it responds with a variety of low buzzing notes in true wren-fashion. Its song is eerie ecstasy and is delivered from some high point of vantage. With head thrown back and long, graceful tail jerking nervously, this quaint little brown bird pours forth a vibrant, potent melody that may be heard half a mile away. The song is scarcely wrenlike, but bears a strange resemblance to the songs of the Field Sparrow and the Song Sparrow.

Odd and wonderful are the sites that Bewick's Wren habitually chooses for its summer home. Away from the haunts of man, it selects locations suggesting its primitive habits—knotholes in fallen trees in the woods or open fields, natural cavities and woodpecker-holes in trees, or now and then the center of a dense brush heap. But civilization has provided this bird with an unusual variety of homes. Any opening of ready access invites its attention; among those used are holes in fence posts, tin cans, empty barrels, discarded clothing hung in buildings, baskets, bird boxes, deserted automobiles, oil wells, and crevices in stone, brick, or tile walls.

I made the acquaintance of Bewick's Wren

[1]*Birds of Ohio*, 1903, p. 198.
[2]*Wilson Bulletin*, 1933, 45:187.
[3]Account contributed by Samuel S. Dickey.

many years ago, yet the finding of the first occupied nest is still a vivid memory. It was during one of those early May days when, following the drab, rainy weather of April, the sun bursts forth, and the hills, basking in its warm rays, call the saunterer out for a pleasant walk on the round earth. May 9 found me among the sheep ranges a mile south of my home on the edge of Waynesburg. I had stopped in a farmyard to slake my thirst at a windlass well when the sight of an old woodshed suggested at once the possibility that a wren might be nesting there. Through the closed door I pushed my way, and there, on a narrow shelf above the inner lintel of the door was a bulky nest of dark twigs, coarse weed stalks, hay, and spider cocoons. A mere gesture with my hand caused the owner to leave her treasures and dart out the open door. Immediately she began scolding noisily, and was soon joined by her mate. In the cozy cup, warmly lined with chicken feathers, were seven fresh eggs—virtual gems that were wreathed and speckled with umber, lavender, and brown. (Average measurements are about .66 by .50 inches.)

Since that first experience more than fifty nests have come to my attention, and I have taken delight in observing the habits of this, my favorite bird. It raises two broods annually. Nests for the first brood are completed late in April or in May; and the second layings occur in late June or in July. Clutches of the first laying average seven eggs, but eight or even nine eggs are not unusual. In the second layings, four, five, or six are customary. Bewick's Wren will return year after year to a favored nesting site. A pair of birds, thought to be the same individuals, nested in an ancient building for many successive seasons. The clutches in later years consisted of but four or five eggs, only two or three of which proved fertile.

Thryothorus bewickii WARREN, *Birds Pa.*, ed. 2, 1890, 309 (southwestern Pa., summer)—JACOBS, *Summer Birds Greene Co., Pa.*, 1893, 14 (Greene Co., nesting)—RHOADS, *Auk*, 1899, 16:313 (Tuscarora Mountain, Fulton Co., breeding; Beaver, Beaver Co., and Round Island, Clinton Co.).

"Bewick's Wren" WARREN, *Forest and Stream*, 1891, 37:182 (southwestern Pa., summer)—STONE, *Cassinia*, 1906, 9:42, 44 (Big Cove Tannery, Fulton Co., June; Springville, Bedford Co., *ex* Oberholser)—HARLOW, *Auk*, 1911, 28:489 (near State College, Centre Co., April)—DICKEY, *Oölogist*, 1912, 29:299 (Greene Co., summer; habits)—CARTER, *Oölogist*, 1914, 31:231 (Waynesburg, Greene Co., nesting)—STREET, *Cassinia*, 1923, 24:11, 18 (Horse Valley, Franklin Co., June)—CHRISTY, *Cardinal*, 1924, v. 1, no. 3, p. 12 (near Harshaville, Beaver Co., nesting; range in southwestern Pa.)—EASTWOOD, *Bird-Lore*, 1927, 29:273 (Springs, Somerset Co., April, *fide* Miller).

Thryomanes bewickii bewickii OBERHOLSER, *Proc. U. S. Nat. Mus.*, 1898, 21:423 (Clearville, Springville, and Charlesville, Bedford Co., and Needmore, Fulton Co., breeding)—HARLOW, *Auk*, 1912, 29:478 (Shingletown, Centre Co., April); 1918, 35:145 (Greene, Centre, and Huntingdon Co., nesting)—CHRISTY, *Cardinal*, 1923, v. 1, no. 1, [p. 14] (Clinton and vicinity, Allegheny Co.; Raccoon Creek and region, Beaver Co., breeding)—STONE, *Cassinia*, 1923, 24:49 (Greencastle, Franklin Co., nesting, *fide* Ziegler)—BURLEIGH, *Wilson Bull.*, 1924, 36:74 (State College, Centre Co., migration); 1931, 43:53 (State College and region, Centre Co., and Charter Oak, Huntingdon Co., nesting)—[Editor], *Cassinia*, 1926, 25:34 (Greencastle, Franklin Co., April, *fide* Ziegler)—SUTTON, *Wilson Bull.*, 1930, 42:15 (Huntingdon Co., nesting habits)—BURLEIGH, *Cardinal*, 1932, 3:78 (Chestnut Ridge, near Uniontown, Fayette Co., summer).

Thryomanes bewickii TODD, in Bausman, *Hist. Beaver Co., Pa.*, 1904, 2:1201 (Beaver Co., summer)—STONE, *Cassinia*, 1906, 9:65 (western Pa. records)—DICKEY, *Oölogist*, 1913, 30:119 (near Waynesburg, Greene Co., nesting).

CAROLINA WREN (Plate 15)

THRYOTHORUS LUDOVICIANUS LUDOVICIANUS (Latham)

Description—Our largest wren. Upperparts rufous chestnut, nearly uniform, the wings and tail with obscure darker barring; a conspicuous whitish stripe over the eyes; chin and upper throat, whitish, deepening into the rufescent buffy tone of the rest of the underparts; under tail coverts marked with dark bars.

Range—The Carolina Wren, as its name implies, is a species of southern predilections. It ranges from the Atlantic coast westward to Texas and Nebraska, and from the Gulf coast northward to southern New England and to a corresponding latitude in the interior. Once considered to be a species limited by the Carolinian Fauna, it is now known to occur considerably farther north, and there is reason to believe that it is gradually expanding its distribution in that direction. Beyond its regular breeding range is a zone of indeterminate width where the species occurs as a more or less casual or accidental visitant—a circumstance that indicates a tendency to wander unduly. In the course of time some of these adventuring individuals remain to breed, and thus new vantage ground is gained. E. H. Eaton recounts such an advance into western New York, while Lynds Jones, writing in 1903, postulates a similar movement in Ohio. There are signs that an extension of range is also in progress in western Pennsylvania. Both Wilson and Audubon mention having seen this wren near Pittsburgh, where it is still a fairly common resident and has been found breeding within the city limits. It is likewise common in Beaver, Washington, and Greene counties, and thence east to Chestnut Ridge. New Castle (Raney) is apparently its regular northern limit on the west, and the Buffalo Creek region of Armstrong County (Todd), its limit on the east.

Beyond these limits, the Carolina Wren has been noted in December and March at Johnstown (Canan), and in August at Somerfield, Somerset County (Sutton). It was also detected at Springs, Somerset County, on July 27, 1917—a post-breeding occurrence no doubt—and in 1931 a male (in full song) remained from April to June, although no mate appeared. In June, 1935, however, two young birds recently out of the nest were found just across the Pennsylvania boundary in Maryland (Miller). To the northward the species has been observed at New Hamburg and Greenville, Mercer County (Homer; Seiple). The fact that it was noted at the latter place on April 27 suggests possible breeding. It was seen near Erie in April, 1898 (Bacon), but so far as I am aware, this is the only record of its occurrence there. G. M. Sutton has not found it at Pymatuning Swamp, so that this locality is presumably beyond its present breeding range.

In my intensive study of the Buffalo Creek region of Armstrong and Butler counties, made in 1889, I failed to find this species, and am all but convinced that it did not occur there at that time. But in May, 1934, on a brief visit to that section, one of the first birds that I encountered was the Carolina Wren. R. B. Simpson's experience with the species at Warren affords additional presumptive evidence for the extension of its range in recent years. One would hardly expect to find this relatively southern bird in a region characterized by so many breeding species of Canadian affinities, and until 1933 Mr. Simpson considered it little more than a straggler. He had seen and taken a few birds in late July, August, and September, and had known of one being taken in the spring. In late February, 1933, however, he found a pair, and kept track of them until April, when their nest was located and photographed. Whether or not the species ever becomes a regular breeding bird in that locality, this outlying record is certainly noteworthy. Scarcely less so is the discovery by Lloyd Scherer, Jr., of one bird "singing loudly" at Port Allegany, McKean County, on March 24 in 1937.

In my travels through the country east of the Allegheny divide I never found the Carolina Wren, and I consider it far less common in that section than Bewick's Wren. It is only a straggler at State College, but H. A. McGraw writes that it breeds in Huntingdon County, near Barree and Marklesburg; and S. S. Dickey saw one bird on May 2, 1919, at Spruce Creek. Miss A. E. Berg includes it in her list of the birds of Hollidaysburg. R. V. Mostoller saw three on July 19, 1934, along the Raystown Branch of the Juniata River, between Mann's Choice and Wolfsburg, Bedford County. The species has also been noted at Greencastle, Franklin County, in the southeastern corner of our region.

My impression is that this wren is far less com-

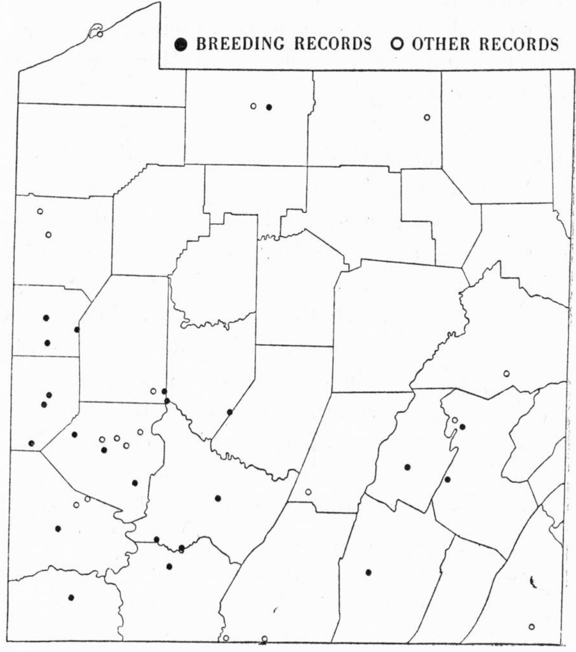

LOCAL RANGE OF THE CAROLINA WREN

mon, at least in Beaver County, than it was some forty years ago. Although a permanent resident, it seems to be more numerous in fall and winter, but this is perhaps because it tends to wander more widely at those seasons and is thus more in evidence. No reason for any permanent decrease in its numbers can be adduced.

Habits[1]—The Carolina Wren is the largest and most distinctly red-brown of the six wrens found in western Pennsylvania. It lives in valley woodlands, where it hunts its food about fallen trees, along the dank borders of weed clumps, and in piles of rotting brush. It is usually thought to be nonmigratory, for in most parts of its range it is a characteristic winter bird. The distinct buffy-white line above the eye is a dependable field mark.

All wrens are given to bustling about with tails lifted; all are by nature energetic, secretive, and curious; all scold noisily if their suspicions are aroused. But to the best of my knowledge the Carolina is the only wren that entertains us with a duet vocal performance. Not that rival males sit side by side shouting out their *tea-kettle, tea-kettle, tea-kettle* in unison; not that female birds sing with the males; but one bird scolds while another sings. My study of these duets is in its early stages. I do not know whether the scolding is done by a rival male or by some neighborhood termagant. In either case—or even if what I have called scolding be the praise of a loving mate—the effect is amusing: the ringing, rhythmic syllables of the songster are accompanied by the harsh, even gruff, and almost equally loud *djeer* of the other bird. I have heard this droll duet hundreds of times.

The Carolina Wren's song is more emphatic, more bubbling, more ebullient than that of the Cardinal or the Tufted Titmouse; but the songs of these species may easily be confused, because the rhythm is much the same in all three. The Wren's song has been variously syllabized. I recall writing it down in one of my early notebooks as *pea-deedle, pea-deedle, pea-deedle*. Also as *which jailer? which jailer? which jailer?* During the course of a day's singing, the same wren may change the meter and pitch of its song considerably from time to time. Songs frequently are terminated by a loud, rippling *djeer*, almost the same scolding cry as that given in the "duet" described above.

Whether or not the species is gifted as a mimic I cannot from personal experience tell. Although I have heard innumerable variations of the familiar *tea-kettle* song and many strange call notes that could not properly be called songs, I have yet to hear definite imitations of the songs of other birds. This ability to mimic is mentioned by many ornithological writers, however.

It is my belief that these wrens frequently mate for life. To be sure, I have not trapped banded individuals known to be mated. But I have observed, season after season, pairs of birds that appeared to me to be the same—the same in habits, in voice, and in mannerisms. Whether or not they mate for life, the birds customarily go about in

twos throughout the winter, and their gay songs may be heard at all seasons.

The nesting habits of this wren have changed with the encroachments of man on their breeding sites. Originally always built about fallen logs, in brush piles, or in hollow trees, nowadays its nests are much likelier to be found about sawmills, woodsheds, blacksmith shops, and village dwellings, or in almost any sort of crevice in a secluded, shadowy place. In building their nests the birds work feverishly, hauling in long, cumbersome, dead weed stalks; bulky mouthfuls of dry leaves; pieces of castoff snake skin; and feathers, roots, and grasses. So far as I know, the male does not fill its spare hours with dummy nest-building as do certain other wrens.

Not far from my home in Bethany, West Virginia (a few miles west of the Pennsylvania boundary), a pair of Carolina wrens used to make their way into an upstairs bedroom of a large, rambling, tree-sheltered house at the edge of town. Since certain windows were open nearly all the time, the birds came and went at will. All at once they began building a nest on the top of a chiffonier,

[1]Account contributed by George M. Sutton.

in the midst of pincushions, photographs in silver frames, hairbrushes, and combs. The birds' human friends were so amused at this high-handed invasion that they permitted the uncouth nest to remain, and the brood of four young was successfully reared. Other nests observed in this region were built on rafters in woodsheds or outhouses, about barns, and in the shelter of vine-covered porches. Nests are neatly domed, deeply cupped, and bulky. The foundation material in one old nest that I found more than filled a peck basket.

The eggs are usually laid in the middle or latter part of April in this latitude. They are white or pinkish white, considerably spotted and flecked with brown, lilac, and gray, and measure about .75 by .58 inches. They number five or six as a rule, although sets of two (Sutton) and of eight (Forbush) have been recorded. Normally but one brood is reared during the season. Spiders form a large part of the food of young birds in the nest.

The Carolina Wren is a friendly bird. Especially in winter it learns to come regularly to the feeding counter. During the winter of 1914–15 I slept out-of-doors on an unscreened porch. Almost every morning a pair of red-brown, bright-faced wrens wakened me, perching on the mounds of counterpane at the foot of the bed, scolding noisily, bobbing in curiosity, suspicious of my opened eyes.

Many writers have called attention to the fact that the numbers of this wren fluctuate considerably from year to year. To some extent this fluctuation may be due to the egg-puncturing proclivities of the House Wren, to severe winters, or to the clearing away of brush piles and woodlands that furnish the bird a suitable home. On the other hand, it may be due principally to the species' strong tendency to wander at the close of the nesting season.

Troglodytes ludovicianus Wilson, *Am. Orn.*, 1811, 3:83 (Pittsburgh, Allegheny Co., range)—Audubon, *Orn. Biog.*, 1831, 1:399 (Ohio River, near Pittsburgh, Allegheny Co.).

Thryothorus ludovicianus Jacobs, *Hawkeye Ornithologist and Oölogist*, 1888, 1:37 (Waynesburg, Greene Co., nesting)—Jacobs, *Summer Birds Greene Co., Pa.*, 1893, 13 (Greene Co., nesting)—Homer, *Auk*, 1894, 11:330 (New Hamburg Mercer Co., January)—Todd, *Ann. Carnegie Mus.*, 1904, 2:588 (Erie, Erie Co., April, *fide* Bacon)—Todd, in Bausman, *Hist. Beaver Co., Pa.*, 1904, 2:1201 (Beaver Co., resident)—Forrest, *Oölogist*, 1911, 28:115 (Washington, Washington Co., breeding)—Dickey, *Oölogist*, 1914, 31:158 ([Greene Co.], nesting).

"Bewick Wren" (error) Homer, *Ornithologist and Oölogist*, 1891, 16:46 (New Hamburg, Mercer Co., January).

"Carolina Wren" Pitcairn, *Bird-Lore*, 1908, 10:32 (West View, Allegheny Co., December)—Miller, *Bird-Lore*, 1908, 10:32 (McKinley Park, Pittsburgh, Allegheny Co., December)—Simpson, *Oölogist*, 1909, 26:26 (Warren, Warren Co., September)—Wright, *Bird-Lore*, 1911, 13:31 (Pittsburgh, Allegheny Co., December)—Burleigh, *Bird-Lore*, 1913, 15:29 (Aspinwall, Allegheny Co., December); 1915, 17:34 (Harmarville and vicinity, Allegheny Co., December)—McConnell, *Oölogist*, 1918, 35:152 (McKeesport, Allegheny Co., resident)—Dickey, *Oölogist*, 1919, 36:67 (Waynesburg, Greene Co., nesting)—Christy and Hegner, *Bird-Lore*, 1924, 26:30; etc. (Raccoon Creek Valley and region, Beaver Co., December)—Sutton, *Bird-Lore*, 1924, 26:56 (Glenshaw, Allegheny Co., December)—Christy, *Cardinal*, 1924, v. 1, no. 3, p. 15 (local range in western Pa.); 1924, v. 1, no. 4, p. 10 (Big Traverse Valley, Beaver Co., June)—Portman, *et al.*, *Bird-Lore*, 1926, 28:31 (Thompsonville and vicinity, Washington Co., December)—Boulton, *Bird-Lore*, 1928, 30:14 (Pittsburgh region, Allegheny Co., status)—Elliott, *Cardinal*, 1934, 3:171 (Raccoon Creek, Beaver Co., December)—Christy, *Cardinal*, 1936, 4:97 (local range and abundance).

Thryothorus ludovicianus ludovicianus Christy, *Cardinal*, 1923, v. 1, no. 1, [p. 14] (Sewickley, Allegheny Co., resident)—Burleigh, *Wilson Bull.*, 1923, 35:143 (Allegheny Co., nesting); 1924, 36:132 (State College, Centre Co., winter)—[Editor], *Cassinia*, 1926, 25:34 (Greencastle, Franklin Co., March–April, *fide* Ziegler)—Burleigh, *Cardinal*, 1929, 2:120 (Allegheny Co., September).

Thryothorus ludovicianus carolinianus Lowery, *Auk*, 1940, 57: 101 (Beaver and Bellowsville, Beaver Co.; critical).

LONG-BILLED MARSH WREN

TELMATODYTES PALUSTRIS PALUSTRIS (Wilson)

Description—Upperparts brown; the sides of the head blackish; the middle of the back also black, with a few white streaks; a buffy-white streak over the eye; wings and tail brown, with blackish crossbars; underparts dull white, with some buffy-brown wash on the sides and flanks.

Range—The Long-billed Marsh Wren is not only commoner than its short-billed relative but has a much more extensive range. It breeds from the Gulf of Mexico to southern Canada, and from the Atlantic coast to the Pacific. It divides into a number of geographic races, the exact inter-relationships of which are not yet fully understood. Marsh Wrens from western Pennsylvania are in my opinion referable to the interior race. While our region at large comes within the general breeding range of the species, the Long-billed Marsh Wren is extremely local; for its habitat requirements restrict it to the few localities in our area where suitable conditions exist. For nesting it must have open swamps of marsh grasses, rushes, and cattails, and furthermore these must be of considerable extent; small and isolated tracts apparently do not suffice. These requirements are met at Pymatuning Swamp, Conneaut Lake, Edinboro Lake, and on Presque Isle, where this Marsh Wren is common and well known as a summer resident. S. S. Dickey reports a nest at Tamarack Swamp, Erie County, in May, 1925. The species has been found in June in a swamp north of Mercer (Raney), and probably occurs also in some of the smaller swamps of Mercer County, as yet unworked, and thence southward to the terminal moraine; at any rate, I have traced it to Gardner Swamp in Lawrence County, and in July, 1935, I found it in a swamp near New Galilee, Beaver County. Miss A. E. Berg writes that she has found the nest of this wren in Blair County (presumably near Hollidaysburg). This is the only other local breeding station on record.

Elsewhere in western Pennsylvania the Long-billed Marsh Wren, because of lack of suitable covert, is merely a transient, rare and local. I took it once at Beaver in the fall, in a dense weedy growth along the Ohio River. D. A. Atkinson cites two records for Allegheny County—one from Pitcairn (May 3, 1898) and one from Harmarville (September 8, 1898)—and I have examined a bird that was found dead (in the woods) at Swissvale on September 15, 1908. Dr. Dickey observed one bird near Waynesburg on May 5, 1916. This is the only record from Greene County. C. H. Townsend includes the species in his Westmoreland County list, but gives no particulars. R. B. Simpson considers it a rare visitor at Warren in the spring. A. K. Pierce took at least two specimens at Renovo, in the spring and fall respectively. In the fall of 1916, T. D. Burleigh found the species fairly numerous at Center Furnace Swamp, Centre County, but observed it only once in the spring. It is a bird that is likely to occur almost anywhere as a casual migrant.

Migration—This wren arrives from the South in the latter part of April or early in May. It has been observed at Presque Isle on April 30 (1900), at Center Furnace Swamp on April 26 (1916), and once at Warren as early as April 23 (1893). Mr. Simpson has also noted it at the last-named locality as late as May 27 (1904)—an occurrence proving that its migration at this season may cover a month or more. The fall movement begins in September; one of the Pierce specimens from Renovo is dated September 20 (1901), and there are several records for that month from various other localities. The last birds have been recorded from Shermansville, Crawford County, on October 2 (1925—Bergstrom); from Presque Isle on October 8 (1904—Simpson); and from Center Furnace Swamp on October 25 (1916—Burleigh)—the last an unusually late date.

Habits—On entering a marsh inhabited by this wren, one seldom remains long in ignorance of its presence. Sooner or later its queer, rasping, explosive song greets the intruder, and presently one of the little birds, curious over the unseemly invasion of its sacred precincts, hops into sight and is followed shortly by another a little farther away, and perhaps by a third or fourth. For a brief minute they appear—long enough to satisfy their curiosity and to deliver a scolding chatter—and then drop down again into the rank growth. Most of the Marsh Wren's activities are carried on under cover of the matted aquatic vegetation and are thus concealed from the casual beholder. As a rule, however, the bird will respond to persistent "squeaking." Industrious and active in seeking its insect food, it is forever on the move, although it occasionally pauses to utter its odd song, which is delivered with the tail cocked up over the back and the head thrown well up, in comical pose. Occasionally some exuberant male sings on the wing, bobolink-like, as it flies in buzzing fashion from one spot to another over the marsh. The birds are naturally expert in clambering among the rushes and cattails and often assume grotesque positions in the course of their wanderings.

The Marsh Wren's nest is a globular structure of coarse, dry grasses, lined with finer material of the same sort and supported on the growing stems of marsh plants, the leaves and stalks of which are built into its walls. If the nest is in a cattail marsh, down from that plant is often used as lining. The distance of the nest above the surface of the water varies from one to four feet. The entrance is on one side and is well concealed; in fact, the whole structure is so well camouflaged by the surrounding vegetation that at a little distance it is inconspicuous. This wren, like some others, has the curious habit of building a number of nests and using only one for its eggs. H. C. Kirkpatrick writes that on July 1, 1897, he found no fewer than fifteen newly built nests in the marsh on the west side of Conneaut Lake; of these, only one was in use, and it contained but a single egg. All these nests were found within a twenty-foot circle, and they were apparently the work of one pair of birds that flew about scolding and sputtering at the intrusion. On May 31, 1900, I examined a number of dummy nests in the marsh at Niagara Pond, Presque Isle, before finally locating the real nest, which held six eggs. G. M. Sutton describes a similar experience at Pymatuning Swamp. Why these extra nests are built is not exactly understood. One supposition is that they are intended to draw attention away from the occupied nest, while another is that they are built by the males for shelters and roosting places. The dummy nests are unlined. There are other wrens that have the same habit, but none indulges in it to the extent that this species does.

The eggs of the Long-billed Marsh Wren are a rich chocolate-brown color, but vary considerably in uniformity and intensity of coloration, even in the same set. They number from five to eight and measure about .65 by .49 inches.

Telmatodytes palustris Townsend, *Proc. Acad. Nat. Sci. Philadelphia*, 1883, 61 (Latrobe, Westmoreland Co.)—Todd, *Ann. Carnegie Mus.*, 1904, 2:589 (Presque Isle, Erie Co., nesting).
Cistothorus palustris Todd, in Bausman, *Hist. Beaver Co., Pa.*, 1904, 2:1201 (Beaver Co., fall).
"Long-billed Marsh Wren" Simpson, *Oölogist*, 1912, 29:249 (Presque Isle, Erie Co., nesting)—Sutton, *Bird-Lore*, 1924, 26:267 (Pymatuning Swamp, Crawford Co., nesting).
Telmatodytes palustris palustris Burleigh, *Wilson Bull.*, 1924, 36:131 ("State College" [Center Furnace Swamp], Centre Co., migration)—Sutton, *Ann. Carnegie Mus.*, 1928, 18:229 (Hartstown, Conneaut Lake, etc., Crawford Co., summer).
[*Telmatodytes palustris*] *iliacus* Todd, *Proc. Biol. Soc. Washington*, 1937, 50:23 (Presque Isle, Erie Co., and Linesville, Crawford Co.; range; critical).

SHORT-BILLED MARSH WREN

CISTOTHORUS STELLARIS (Naumann)

Description—A wren resembling in general the Long-billed Marsh Wren, but much more buffy in color, and slightly smaller in size; bill very much shorter than the head; crown and back narrowly but conspicuously streaked with buffy white.

Range—The general breeding range of this diminutive wren is included in the Alleghanian and Carolinian faunas of eastern North America, but the species is notably local in its distribution, and over large areas within its range it is virtually unknown. Indisputable evidence of its nesting within our limits is forthcoming from only a few localities: Presque Isle, Conneaut Lake, and Pymatuning Swamp—all in the Erie-Crawford region. Warren records it from Crawford County on the authority of H. C. Kirkpatrick, who writes that he has "met with it in June and July in marshy ground at Conneaut Lake, where it no doubt breeds. In the latter part of May, 1880, a single specimen was taken in a swamp a short distance south of Meadville." The Conneaut Lake record has been fully confirmed by the researches of G. M. Sutton, who also discovered the species at several points in the Pymatuning Swamp area. Between 1930 and 1937, R. L. Fricke and I located some additional nesting colonies in this general region and collected a few sets of eggs. We think that the species is increasing in numbers.

From Presque Isle comes a similar report. The capture of a specimen there on May 17, 1900, and of another on May 19, 1905 (this by R. B. Simpson), naturally suggested that the species might be breeding. In June, 1932, Mr. Simpson discovered about fifteen nests in high marsh grass at the head of Niagara Pond, but despite vigorous efforts he failed to put up any of the birds. The nests, however, were unquestionably those of the Short-billed species. Since then local observers at Erie have found a spot near the western end of Presque Isle where the species now nests regularly. This development has apparently come about since 1900.

From what has been learned of the habits of this wren, its potential breeding at certain points outside the Erie-Crawford region may be inferred. There is good reason for believing that occurrences after the middle of May pertain to birds already settled for the season. Records of this kind come from McDonald Reservoir, Washington County, and from Center Furnace Swamp, Centre County. Almost certainly, a male present throughout the month of June, 1934, in a boggy meadow near Springs, Somerset County, was breeding, according to the report of A. B. Miller. The same remark applies to birds noted in the swamp north of Mercer in June, 1933, by E. C. Raney. This species seems to have come to the attention of but few observers.

Migration—The Short-billed Marsh Wren passes the winter in the southern states. It moves northward in the spring in time to reach our region in late April or early May. In 1933 it was noted at Erie on April 30 (Guynes). Specimens have been taken at Pitcairn, Allegheny County, on May 4, 1894 (Atkinson), and near Rector, Westmoreland County, on May 5, 1928 (Fricke). In the fall, dates of "last-seen" birds are September 25, 1927—Hartstown, Crawford County (Seiple); and September 25, 1930—Presque Isle (Hicks).

Habits—The Short-billed Marsh Wren is much rarer than the Long-billed and is also more retiring in its habits. It is harder to flush from its weedy retreats and is thus more elusive. At least, this is true of the bird in winter and during migration. In the breeding season, however, there is a period when the male leaves the cover of the dense swamp grasses where most of its time is spent and seeks a higher perch from which to deliver its ridiculous little song. So intently does it perform that it pays no particular attention to the presence of an intruder only a few feet away. Hopping up on a dead weed stalk that rises above the general level, the bird cocks its tail, throws up its head, and utters its feeble, insect-like trill. This consists of three separate notes, which are followed by others in more rapid succession. In tempo and structure the song somewhat resembles that of the Nashville Warbler, but the timbre is cricket-like and not at all musical.

The Short-billed Marsh Wren is content with a much smaller area of suitable covert than is the Long-billed, which requires a fairly good-sized tract for nesting purposes. In fact, beyond their general appearance, these two wrens have little in common. The Short-billed avoids the cattails and other strictly aquatic growths, preferring instead the drier parts of the marsh, the high grass, and the rushy areas along the edge. The two species thus never come in conflict, although they may be within sight and hearing of each other. Moreover, the Short-billed is fond of its own kind and usually settles in a little colony of a half-dozen pairs or so, which all nest in a restricted area, even though the total amount of suitable territory is considerably larger.

Dr. Sutton has published (1928) an interesting account of his experience with this species in the Pymatuning area. After remarking on the elusive character of the bird, he says:

"Although it doubtless nested in the Swamp during 1922, it was not until May 31, 1923, that we found it in a portion of the open, grassy marsh west of Shermansville. Here a pair were observed for some time. They were both remarkably tame and allowed us to approach to within four or five feet. In the center of their grassy habitat were two slender dead stubs upon which they were often seen, and where the male customarily sang his ridiculously *clacketty* songs. One song frequently heard might be written 'Chip, chip, chi-i-i-i-i-i.' When closely approached, they seemed hesitant to leave their perches, and often leaned far over toward the ground before dropping to it or buzzing away to trail into the grass, whence it was often very difficult to frighten them.

"On June 16, upon returning to the spot where the birds had first been seen, we immediately found them. When we watched quietly they were nowhere to be seen; but once flushed, they went to the upright stubs and started singing and scolding. On this date a dummy nest was found built into the top of a tussock of grass and only about six inches from the ground. It was globular with a very small, almost completely hidden, entrance at the side. Two other dummy nests were subsequently found, but the nest with eggs was not located. Later in the day another pair of birds were found across the corduroy-road only a few hundred yards away. Songs given by both male birds on June 18 reminded me strongly of the insect-like performance of the Dickcissel, particularly the latter portion of the song. This song might be written 'Dick, putt, jik, plick, chick-chick-chick.'

"On May 16, 1925, after walking through the grass, where the birds had formerly nested, there was no sign of them. In re-traversing the section, however, I literally kicked them from the grass, and once they were discovered, they were everywhere in evidence, this year four pairs of them. No nests were found, however.

"It was noticeable that the Short-billed and Long-billed Marsh Wrens were nowhere found together during summer. At Conneaut Lake the Short-billed Marsh Wrens lived only in a grassy meadow several hundred yards northwest of the cat-tail stretches, which the Long-billed Marsh Wrens frequented. The Short-billed Marsh Wrens seemed to be more constant in their occurrence. Long-billed Marsh Wrens were known to be entirely absent at Pymatuning during the spring of 1922, for they were constantly searched for and not found."

The Short-billed Marsh Wren's nest is easily distinguished from that of the Long-billed. It is smaller, less bulky, and composed of finer materials. All those that I have examined were built in the midst of thick tufts of high marsh grass, the blades of which were pulled in above to form a sort of peaked or conical cover. The nest is thereby well concealed and can only be discovered by a painstaking search of the area frequented by the birds. It is snugly lined with feathers and plant down. Six or seven eggs form the usual complement; they are pure white and measure .62 by .47 inches. Sets are complete by the end of May.

Cistothorus stellaris Warren, *Birds Pa.*, ed. 2, 1890, 311 (Crawford Co., summer, *fide* Kirkpatrick)—Rhoads, *Auk*, 1899, 16:313 ([Pitcairn], Allegheny Co., *fide* Atkinson)—Todd, *Ann. Carnegie Mus.*, 1904, 2:589 (Presque Isle, Erie Co., May)—Harlow, *Auk*, 1912, 29:478; 1918, 35:145 (Center Furnace, Centre Co., May)—Sutton, *Ann. Carnegie Mus.*, 1928, 18:227 (Pymatuning Swamp and Conneaut Lake, Crawford Co., summer)—Fricke, *Cardinal*, 1929, 2:131 (Rector, Westmoreland Co., May)—Fricke, *Auk*, 1930, 47:572 (Pymatuning Swamp, Crawford Co., May; Linesville, Crawford Co., nesting)—Christy, *Cardinal*, 1931, 3:46 (McDonald Reservoir, Washington Co., May).

"Short-billed Marsh Wren" Harlow, *Cassinia*, 1912, 15:21 (Center Furnace Swamp, Centre Co., spring)—Simpson, *Oölogist*, 1912, 29:247 (Presque Isle, Erie Co., May).

MOCKING THRUSHES

FAMILY MIMIDAE

THE MIMIDAE are peculiar to America. Most of the sixty-odd species are restricted to the tropics. In western Pennsylvania there are three: the Brown Thrasher and the Catbird are common summer residents; the Mockingbird is local as a resident, but is apparently extending its range.

The members of this family resemble both the thrushes and the wrens to some extent. From the thrushes they differ in having relatively longer tails, more fully developed outermost primaries, noticeably curved bills, and scutellate instead of booted tarsi. From the wrens they differ in being larger and in having prominent rictal bristles. They inhabit the open woods, thickets, or brushland, and spend much of their time on the ground. Their songs, however, for which they are famous, are generally delivered from lofty perches. Several members of the family, including the immortal Mockingbird, are gifted mimics. They are plainly clad, chiefly in browns and grays. Their nests are crude and bulky and are built in bushes, usually near the ground.

EASTERN MOCKINGBIRD

MIMUS POLYGLOTTOS POLYGLOTTOS (Linnaeus)

Description—A bird resembling the Brown Thrasher in form and proportions, but not quite so large. Upperparts gray; wings dusky, with a large white spot at the base of the primaries; tail dusky black, the outer feathers mostly white; underparts soiled whitish.

Range—The Mockingbird is decidedly southern in its predilections. In the East the Carolinian Fauna marks its normal northward limit, but it sometimes appears considerably beyond that limit and is one of the species of this fauna that are gradually working farther north. Especially is this true in New England; west of the mountains the tendency is less pronounced. In Ohio the species occurs regularly only in the southern half of the state, and its breeding range in western Pennsylvania is obviously an eastward extension of this Ohio area. In our region it is virtually confined to the section south of the Ohio River and west of the Monongahela, where it is apparently becoming commoner, or at least more regular, year by year. There are also a few records from outlying localities. A. B. Miller reports the species as a rare straggler at Springs, Somerset County, where he has seen male birds in full song on two occasions —May 18, 1907, and April 19, 1920—and a supposed female between April 13 and 16, 1937. Again, one bird appeared at his feeding-station on November 6, 1938, and was still present on November 26, when his report was made. The occurrence of this bird so high in the mountains is certainly unusual and most surprising. On February 22, 1940, S. J. Seiple reported that a mockingbird had been observed on the college campus at Grove City, Mercer County, through the winter. L. E. Hicks saw a single mockingbird in Crawford County, a mile south of Pymatuning Dam, on August 21, 1932. He has also found the species nesting just across the Pennsylvania boundary in Ohio. J. E. Perry and A. J. Woodward saw one bird on Presque Isle on April 26, 1936; and one was identified at Port Allegany, McKean County, in the spring of 1937, by a Mrs. Swort, as reported to me by Lloyd Scherer, Jr.

In an article written in 1914, J. W. Jacobs aptly summarizes the evidence for an extension of the range of this species in Greene County. He writes:

"As long ago as 1892 and 1894, I observed singing males in bushy tracts of pasture lands in Greene county, not far from Waynesburg. In more recent years, in the vicinity of the original observations, on rare occasions, I have encountered the birds. One of these bushy tracts has existed for years on the farm of the late Thomas Hook, a mile south of Waynesburg; another on the farm of the late William Reese, a mile west; and the third, on the border of a wooded hillside, near the MacNay school house, northwest of this town.

"In each instance only one male mocker was seen, and as my presence in the vicinity was for bird study, diligent search failed to reveal the hiding place of a nest or any trace of a female bird. These Mockingbirds were recorded in my journals as 'stragglers,' a term applied to birds which wander out of their established habitat or range.

"The Mockingbirds most likely to migrate farthest north are non-breeding males, and once they find a community with conditions very similar to their southern haunts, they are very likely to return there again the next year, and probably induce others—possibly a mate,—to proceed to the new haunts."

Mr. Jacobs calls attention to the changes that took place in Greene County from 1884 to 1914. The once extensive tracts of virgin forest gave way to cultivated fields and pasture lands, and these in turn grew up to briers and bushes, thus affording precisely the kind of cover that the Mockingbird likes. The species was found nesting at a certain farm a few miles north of Waynesburg during four successive years, beginning in 1911, and may have been present before that year. This was near the place where Mr. Jacobs had observed a single male bird some twenty years before. "The offspring reared by these Mockingbirds will extend the range of the species to other fields, and as the present known breeding-ground is within six miles of Washington county, the Mockers will soon be heard in this neighboring county, and in time their progeny will extend the range as far north as Allegheny county, which latitude represents the northern limits of its possibilities."

Mr. Jacobs' prediction has since been amply verified, as attested by the records from Washington and Allegheny counties cited below. There are places in Beaver County, too, that seem suitable for the Mockingbird, and no doubt in due course it will appear there also. Although it seems to be increasing in numbers throughout its present territory and gradually extending its range, its local status remains unstable. In certain recent articles Mr. Jacobs remarks on the circumstance that the mockingbirds in Greene County frequently nest in a different locality each year. He suggests that some of the local birds succumb to unduly severe weather in winter and that the pairs found nesting the next season have come in from other regions. This thesis, of course, remains to be proved, but the fluctuation is an ascertained fact. In the spring of 1934 Mr. Jacobs took me to a half-dozen farms in the vicinity of Waynesburg where mockingbirds had nested the previous year, but we were unable to locate a single bird.

Migration—There are no records concerning the migration of the Mockingbird in this section. It might be expected to retire southward in winter, and doubtless some individuals do so, but others elect to remain throughout the whole season. The species has been observed through the winter months as far north as Bellevue, Allegheny County (Arthur, 1935), and Grove City, Mercer County (Seiple). There is also a winter record for State College (Wood, 1932).

Habits—Among the songbirds of the New World the Mockingbird is the acknowledged peer. To its own varied repertoire it adds imitations of the songs of other birds, including even the cock's crow or any mechanical squeak or noise that may attract it. E. H. Forbush writes:

"The Mocker is more or less a buffoon, but those who look upon him only as an imitator or clown have much to learn of his wonderful originality. His own song is heard at its best at the height of the love season, when the singer flutters into the air from some tall tree-top and improvises his music, pouring out all the power and energy of his being in such an ecstasy of song that, exhausting his strength in the supreme effort, he slowly floats on quivering, beating pinions down through the bloom-covered branches until, his fervor spent, he sinks to the ground below. His expanded wings and tail flashing with white in the sunlight and the buoyancy of his action appeal to the eye as his music captivates the ear. On moonlit nights at this season the inspired singer launches himself far into the air, filling the silvery spaces of the night with the exquisite swells and trills, liquid and sweet, of his unparalleled melody. The song rises and falls as the powers of the singer wax and wane, and so he serenades his mate throughout the live-long night."[1] This vocal performance may be heard during almost every month in the year. In August, in the molting period, the song is stilled, and in the winter months it is more or less spasmodic, but in late January and early February, it begins again in earnest.

This gifted songster is a recent comer to western Pennsylvania, and a most welcome one; for the Mockingbird seeks out the dwellings of man and makes himself at home in the dooryard. Mr. Jacobs has found nests in rosebushes, lawn shrubbery, grape arbors, and fruit trees. B. H. Christy (1926) records two Washington County nestings, at Houston and Finleyville, respectively: "On the first of June five young flew from the nest near Houston, leaving behind the frail remains of a sixth, which for some reason had proved unequal to the struggle for existence. And by the middle of June the parent birds were reported to be nest-building for another brood. The Finleyville nest on the 8th of June contained four half-grown fledglings." Thomas John (1936) describes a nest found in Hickory, Washington County, on July 6 (not on April 6, as published) as "built of weed-stems, rootlets, lined with horsehair, fine grass, a few bits of wool and a piece of string. The nest contained four bluish-green eggs, which were spotted and blotched with shades of brown. . . . On July 11, upon return to the nest for purposes of photography, I found an adult again brooding four eggs."

The Mockingbird is an aggressive species and at winter feeding-stations is not slow to drive other birds away (Arthur, 1935). In defending the nest it is fearless and will attack any birds or marauding cats that attempt to molest the young.

The song of the Mockingbird is not its only virtue; for its food habits are economically beneficial. "In spring and early summer, the Mockingbird feeds largely upon insects such as ants, flies, wasps, harvestmen, bugs, caterpillars, beetles (including curculios) and grasshoppers . . . it takes many spiders. In late summer and autumn it feeds chiefly on wild fruit, swallowing the fruit and ejecting later the indigestible seeds."[2]

Mimus polyglottus Jacobs, *Nat. Companion*, 1886, 2:58 (Waynesburg, Greene Co., occasional).

"Mockingbird" Jacobs, *In the Open*, Aug., 1914, 4:41 (Waynesburg, Greene Co., summer resident; nesting, *fide* Piatt)—McClelland, *Am. Mid. Nat.*, 1922, 8:37 (Washington, Washington Co., one record)—Eastwood, *Bird-Lore*, 1926, 28:273 (Finleyville, Washington Co., May, nesting, *fide* Steffler), 274 (Houston [5 miles northwest], Washington Co., nesting, *fide* Pates; [Experiment], Allegheny Co., *fide* Allison)—Boulton, *Bird-Lore*, 1928, 30:271 (Finleyville, Washington Co., nesting)—[Christy, ed.], *Cardinal*, 1933, 3:150 (South Park, Allegheny Co., July, *fide* Knox; Wilkinsburg, Allegheny Co.)—Arthur, *Cardinal*, 1935, 4:16 (Bellevue, Allegheny Co., winter).

Mimus polyglottos polyglottos Harlow, *Auk*, 1918, 35:144 (Waynesburg, Greene Co.)—[Christy], *Cardinal*, 1925, v. 1, no. 5, p. 24 ([near "Blackburn"], Allegheny Co., February)—Christy, *Cardinal*, 1926, v. 1, no. 8, p. 19 (Washington and Greene Co., nesting)—Arthur, *Cardinal*, 1934, 3:198 (Bellevue, Allegheny Co., resident?)—Jacobs, *Auk*, 1934, 51:382 (Greene Co., seasonal status)—Jacobs, *Oölogist*, 1934, 51:147, 149 (Greene Co., nesting, etc.)—John, *Redstart*, 1936, 3:91 (near Hickory, Washington Co., nesting).

Mimus polyglottos [Christy], *Cardinal*, 1928, 2:107 (Finleyville, Washington Co., nesting).

"Eastern Mockingbird" Wood, *Wilson Bull.*, 1932, 44:238 (State College, Centre Co., winter).

[1]In *Birds of America* (Nature Lovers Library), 1917, 3:176.
[2]E. H. Forbush, *Birds of Massachusetts*, 1929, 3:321.

CATBIRD

DUMETELLA CAROLINENSIS (Linnaeus)

Description—Smaller than the Robin. General color plain gray, a little lighter below; tail blackish, and top of the head black; under tail coverts deep chestnut; bill black. Sexes alike, and *young birds* similar.

Range—The Catbird is a distinctively North American species that goes north in the summer as far as southern Canada and retires in the winter to the southern United States, Cuba, Mexico, and Central America. Occasional birds may winter much farther north, however, even in our latitude. With us the species is a common and universally distributed summer resident, exceedingly numerous in such places as Pymatuning Swamp, where the local environment is peculiarly suited to its needs. Especial interest attaches to the few reports of the Catbird's wintering in our region. These all come from a comparatively restricted area about the head of the Ohio River, including Industry in Beaver County, and McKeesport, McKinley Park, Harmarville, and Deer Creek, in Allegheny County. Possibly the comparative mildness of our recent winters has induced a few hardy individuals to remain, but thus far the occurrences are merely sporadic.

Migration—The Catbird reaches our region in late April or early May and becomes common almost at once. Its arrival usually coincides closely or exactly with that of the Baltimore Oriole; for the two species apparently migrate at about the same time and rate of speed. J. W. Jacobs claims to have noted the Catbird at Waynesburg as early as April 15 in two different seasons, and certain other observers have reported still earlier dates of arrival. If not errors in observation, these occurrences are certainly highly exceptional. According to my own records, which cover eighteen seasons, the species arrives at Beaver between April 23 and May 5, the average date being April 29. Were the dates for later years excluded, the average would be a few days earlier—perhaps about April 26, which is the average date in B. H. Christy's series of records from Sewickley. Unseasonable spring weather often delays the arrival of this and other species. Farther north, in the Erie-Crawford district, the Catbird usually appears a few days later. There seems to be a definite retardation of the northward movement in the mountains, as suggested by a collation of the A. K. Pierce records for Renovo, which cover twenty-seven seasons. Only six of these lie in April; the earliest date is April 27, while the average is May 3. For State College the average arrival date is said to be May 2 (Burleigh). At Warren, R. B. Simpson does not look for this bird before the first week in May.

During September the species is unusually numerous and conspicuous in its regular haunts, and its departure does not take place until the following month. Eight years' records of "last-seen" dates from Beaver range from October 2 (1909) to 15 (1921) and yield October 8 as the average departure date. Similar records from Renovo, made by Mr. Pierce and covering twenty-three seasons, lie between September 23 (1909) and November 2 (1913), but such extremes are exceptional, and the average is again October 8. At State College the average date of departure is October 7 (Burleigh). Miscellaneous late records from other sources correspond with those just cited: Wilkinsburg, October 12, 1896 (Atkinson); Sewickley, October 7, 1928 (Christy); Presque Isle, October 8, 1900 (Todd).

Habits—The arrival of the Catbird in our region is signalized by its unmistakable song—a continuous, intricate, seemingly strained effort, but pleasing in spite of its lack of pattern or theme and in spite of the harsh and unmusical notes with which it is interspersed. It lacks the volume and, in large part, the mimetic quality of the Brown Thrasher's song, to which it is decidedly inferior. Only occasionally does the Catbird assume the role of mimic. Once, however, I heard it imitate the notes of the Whip-poor-will with startling accuracy, and snatches from the songs of other birds may at times be recognized in its repertoire. The climax of the song period comes in May during the time of the construction of the nest and the laying of the eggs. At this season the male sings almost continuously during the morning and evening hours, and often far into the night as well. The Catbird's singing lasts through June and July, or until the annual molt begins. The ordinary note of the species, from which its name is derived, is the well-known mewing call that greets the invader of its haunts.

The Catbird is a familiar summer denizen of our orchards and gardens, as well as of bushy thickets, woody undergrowth, shrubbery along streams, and the edges of forests. Very seldom is it found in deep woods. Nest-building begins almost at once after its arrival, and full sets of eggs have been found in Allegheny County as early as May 9 (Atkinson) and thence until the latter part of June. Nests are usually built in low bushes in thickets, or among dense underbrush, and are generally three or four feet from the ground. They are sometimes placed at a greater elevation, however. I once found one in an apple tree at a height of twenty-five feet, and other observers have had similar experiences. D. A. Atkinson found one built on the top rail of a fence (a site often chosen by robins). The nest itself is a rather coarse structure, composed of small dead twigs, dry weed stalks, dry leaves, and grapevine bark, loosely and irregularly arranged toward the rim, but compact toward the center. It is fairly well cupped and is neatly lined with finer material, of which rootlets compose the larger part. The regular set comprises four eggs, but three are by no means infrequent. Of one hundred and ninety nests examined by G. M. Sutton in the region of Pymatuning Swamp, only five had five eggs; this number, therefore, is unusual. The eggs are plain bluish green, deeper in tone than those of the Robin and the Wood Thrush, and measure about .94 by .67 inches.

According to Dr. Atkinson, the Catbird will often throw the eggs of the Cowbird from its nest; at any rate, it is seldom imposed upon by that species. It is bold and courageous in defense of its home, but is of course powerless against an invader such as the black snake. It needs only a little encouragement to take up its abode near houses, and I have known it to build its nest in vines on the porch of a dwelling.

The diet of the Catbird consists chiefly of fruit, except in the spring months, when insects are eaten to a considerable extent. Some farmers and orchardists resent the fact that it steals cultivated fruit, and their charges are sustained by the results of stomach examinations. According to S. D. Judd, at least a third of the fruit diet is taken from cultivated crops.[1] The problem is to conserve both the birds and the fruit. Dr. Judd writes: "Experiments . . . show that catbirds prefer mulberries to strawberries and cherries, hence it may be inferred that these two latter crops may be protected by planting the prolific Russian mulberry, which, if planted in hen yards or pig runs, will afford excellent food for the hens and pigs, besides attracting the birds away from more valuable fruit. Wild cherry, buckthorn, dogwood, wild grape, and elder should be encouraged by the farmer who wishes to escape the depredations of the birds and still receive their benefits."

Mimus carolinensis Teulon, *Jour. Boston Zoöl. Soc.*, 1882, 1:49 (Bradford, McKean Co., nesting)—Townsend, *Proc. Acad. Nat. Sci. Philadelphia*, 1883, 60 (Latrobe, Westmoreland Co., summer).

"Catbird" Enty, *Ornithologist and Oölogist*, 1885, 10:78 (Templeton, Armstrong Co., April)—Jacobs, *Hawkeye Ornithologist and Oölogist*, 1888, 1:88 (Waynesburg, Greene Co., April)—Stone, *Cassinia*, 1906, 9:44 (McConnellsburg, Fulton Co., June)—Simpson, *Oölogist*, 1907, 24:182 (Warren, Warren Co., nesting)—Pitcairn, *Bird-Lore*, 1907, 9:155 (Riverview Park, Allegheny Co., nesting)—Burleigh, *Oölogist*, 1911, 28:156 (Harmarville, Allegheny Co., nesting); 1913, 30:279 (Harmarville and McKinley Park, Allegheny Co., winter)—Miller, *Bird-Lore*, 1913, 15:311 (Springs, Somerset Co., song)—McConnell, *Oölogist*, 1918, 35:152 ("Christy Park," Allegheny Co., breeding)—McConnell and Savage, *Bird-Lore*, 1919, 21:37 (McKeesport, Allegheny Co., December)—Sutton, *Bird-Lore*, 1923, 25:132 (Deer Creek, Allegheny Co., January, *fide* Jones)—Street, *Cassinia*, 1923, 24:18 (Greencastle to Ft. Loudon, Franklin Co., June)—Christy, *Cardinal*, 1924, v. 1, no. 4, p. 10 (Big Traverse Valley, Beaver Co., June)—Reiter and Squier, *Bird-Lore*, 1927, 29:28 (Industry, Beaver Co., December).

Galeoscoptes carolinensis Jamison, *Ornithologist and Oölogist*, 1888, 13:134; and Dwight, *Auk*, 1892, 9:140 (Cresson, Cambria Co., June)—Todd, *Auk*, 1893, 10:37, 41 (Two Lick, Indiana Co., June), 43, 46 (Coalport, Clearfield Co., June)—Jacobs, *Summer Birds Greene Co., Pa.*, 1893, 13 (Greene Co., nesting)—Homer, *Ornithologist and Oölogist*, 1893, 18:61 (Elmer, Potter Co., June)—Baily, *Auk*, 1896, 13:291, 296 (Williamsville, Elk Co., nesting)—Cope, *Cassinia*, 1902, 5:10, 20 (Clinton and Potter Co., June)—Todd, *Ann. Carnegie Mus.*, 1904, 2:588 (Erie and Presque Isle, Erie Co., summer)—Todd, in Bausman, *Hist. Beaver Co., Pa.*, 1904, 2:1201 (Beaver Co., summer)—Keim, *Cassinia*, 1905, 8:40 (Port Allegany, McKean Co., summer)—Forrest, *Oölogist*, 1911, 28:115 (Washington, Washington Co., nesting).

Dumetella carolinensis Harlow, *Auk*, 1912, 29:476 (southern Centre Co., nesting); 1918, 35:145 (western Pa.)—Christy, *Cardinal*, 1923, v. 1, no. 1, [p. 14] (Sewickley, Allegheny Co., nesting)—Burleigh, *Wilson Bull.*, 1923, 35:142 (Allegheny Co., nesting; winter); 1924, 36:74; and 1931, 43:52 (State College, Centre Co., migration; nesting)—Christy and Sutton, *Cardinal*, 1928, 2:74 (Cook Forest, Clarion Co., summer)—Sutton, *Ann. Carnegie Mus.*, 1928, 18:225 (Meadville and Pymatuning Swamp, Crawford Co., nesting)—Burleigh, *Cardinal*, 1932, 3:78 (Chestnut Ridge, near Uniontown, Fayette Co., summer).

[1] U. S. Department of Agriculture, *Yearbook for 1895*, 1896, p. 406–411.

BROWN THRASHER

TOXOSTOMA RUFUM (Linnaeus)

Description—A bird a little larger than the Robin and with a slenderer form; tail longer in proportion, and strongly rounded. General color *above, rufous brown,* duller on the head; *wings crossed by two pale bars; underparts* buffy white, *heavily streaked with brown* except on the middle of the throat and abdomen and on the under tail coverts; iris yellow.

Range—The Thrashers as a group reach their highest development in the southwestern United States and adjacent parts of Mexico. The Brown Thrasher alone has attained a more extensive distribution, and ranges northward and eastward to southern Canada and the Atlantic coast. In its northward range it is normally limited by the Alleghanian Fauna, but it is one of those species that seem to have pushed their way into the Canadian as a consequence of deforestation. A reflection of this condition appears in its local range. Although now found throughout western Pennsylvania as a summer resident, it is decidedly less common in the more northern and elevated parts. It is perhaps significant that during my traverse of western Cambria County in June, 1893, I did not find this species anywhere in the "big woods," nor indeed until I emerged into the opener and more cultivated country west of the county line. F. L. Homer remarked its apparent absence in northern Potter County in 1891,[1] and it was considered rare there in 1900 by F. R. Cope, Jr. I have never seen it in that county myself, although I found it rather numerous along the course of Drury Run in Clinton County, in June, 1894. The data are insufficient to justify generalization; but my impression is that the species is a comparatively recent immigrant in the plateau region of western Pennsylvania. I doubt whether it inhabited this section at all when the country was heavily timbered with original forest. It has taken advantage of changing conditions to establish itself almost everywhere. According to my observation and experience, however, it is now much less common, although more generally distributed, than it was forty years ago.

Migration—The Brown Thrasher winters in the southern states and casually farther north.[2] It starts its migration in March and has been known to reach our latitude by the last of that month. A. B. Miller has recorded its arrival at Springs, Somerset County, as early even as March 28 (1921). In 1907 I encountered a singing male at Beaver on March 30. These remarkably early dates may be attributed to the unseasonably warm weather that was prevalent. My dates for other years lie between April 10 (1910) and 23 (1901), with the average April 17; and these correspond in general with those from adjacent counties. Early dates from other localities are: Sewickley, April 9, 1922 (Christy); Schenley Park, Pittsburgh, April 9, 1921 (Boulton); McKinley Park, Pittsburgh, April 10, 1917 (Burleigh); Hollidaysburg, April 12, 1921 (Berg). The species usually arrives later in the Erie-Crawford district; while the earliest spring date at Renovo, according to A. K. Pierce, is April 18 (1920), and during several years he did not observe it there until May. Like the Catbird and some other species, the Brown Thrasher seems to have a retarded spring migration in the mountains.

Only a few observers have supplied departure records for this species. My own from Beaver range from September 24 (1890) to October 13 (1901). T. D. Burleigh finds that in Allegheny County, October 6 is the average date for the last birds of the season, although he once saw a belated straggler as late as November 26 (1915). The species was noted at Presque Isle until October 6 in 1900 (Todd), and at Hartstown on October 10 in 1923 (Hunter). October 4 (1894) is the latest fall record for Renovo (Pierce), and October 17 (1915), the latest for State College

[1] *Ornithologist and Oölogist,* 1893, 18:61.

[2] A winter record for Allegheny County (S. K. Eastwood, *Bird-Lore,* 1926, 28:136) lacks confirmation. R. M. Edeburn, however, found a dead thrasher on February 16, 1936, in a ravine near Aliquippa, Beaver County.

(Burleigh). In general, the southward migration of the Brown Thrasher and that of the Catbird coincide.

Habits—Cut-over lands and wastelands grown up to hawthorn shrubbery, briery thickets, and underbrush, are the favorite haunts of the Brown Thrasher. For so large a bird, it conceals itself with surprising ease, dodging in and out of the bushes as if playing hide-and-seek with the too curious onlooker. If the quest be pursued insistently, the observer may catch sight of the bird as it passes from one clump of cover to the next, flying across the open space in jerky, irregular fashion, low over the ground. The Brown Thrasher is more primitive in its tastes than its relative the Catbird, and is less likely to invade orchards and gardens. In the spring, announcing its arrival by its song, it often visits the neighborhood of houses and of parks and shade trees in cities and towns. As a songster and mimic, the Brown Thrasher is second only to the Mockingbird of the South; indeed, by some it is considered superior. Disdaining its customary lowly habit, it mounts to some lofty and prominent perch in full view of all beholders, to deliver its matutinal concert. Its song is a rather loud and pleasing medley of musical phrases, mostly original, but interspersed with recognizable fragments from the songs of other birds; and the performance may be continued indefinitely, at the pleasure and caprice of the performer. Although seemingly an involved and complicated effort for the singer, it is spontaneous and agreeable, since it lacks almost entirely the harsh notes that mar the song of the Catbird. Mr. Miller (1913) comments on the duration of the song period:

"The birds arrive with us [in Somerset County] from April 4 to April 20, and are in nearly full song at the time of arrival, although the song does not attain its perfection until the latter part of the month. This continues without interruption until about May 20, at which time the female is usually sitting.

"Thenceforth there is gradual diminution in both the volume and the frequency of singing, so that by the first week in June songs are rare and of brief duration, and later than the fifteenth the bird is practically silent, so far as song is concerned."

Courtship and mating activities must be brief, for nest-building begins promptly after the birds' arrival. It is by no means unusual to find complete sets of eggs during the first week in May, and Mr. Burleigh once found one as early as April 24. A hawthorn bush is a favorite site, as are thick clumps of blackberry briers, brush piles, or hedgerows. Ground nests are by no means infrequent; I have found two, and other observers have discovered additional ones. As a rule, however, the nests are from one to five feet from the ground, although D. A. Atkinson once found one at a height of twenty feet in a pear tree in an orchard. Wherever built, the nest is a loose structure, even less compact than the Catbird's; it is composed in the main of small dead twigs, dry weed stalks and leaves, and strips of bark, and is lined with finer weed stalks and rootlets. Dry leaves enter extensively into the make-up of the ground nests. Four or five eggs are usually laid, but occasionally there are only three. They have a distinctive, although variable, color pattern. The ground-color ranges from pale buff to pale greenish white and is very finely but thickly speckled or sprinkled with dull rufous brown, sometimes quite uniformly, but oftener with the dots tending to cluster about the larger end. Average measurements are 1.06 by .78 inches.

Inasmuch as sets of fresh eggs can be found in July, it seems probable that two broods are often reared. Eggs have even been found as late as August 14 (Atkinson). Near the nest the parents are bold and courageous, driving off other species and protesting fearlessly to a human invader with a ceaseless reiteration of their loud, clicking alarm-notes.

The food habits of the Brown Thrasher place it definitely in the category of the economically useful species. Wild fruits, such as elderberry, pokeberry, dogwood, and wild cherry, greatly outweigh cultivated kinds in its diet. True, it eats some cultivated fruit, but to a much less extent than does the Catbird, and these depredations are more than offset by its insect-destroying propensities. S. D. Judd thus sums up its economic status:

"Two thirds of the bird's food is animal; the vegetable food is mostly fruit, but the quantity taken from cultivated crops is offset by three times that volume of insect pests. In destroying insects, the thrasher is helping to keep in check organisms the undue increase of which disturbs the balance of nature and threatens our welfare."[1]

Harporhynchus rufus Teulon, *Jour. Boston Zoöl. Soc.*, 1882, 1:49 (Bradford, McKean Co., May)—Townsend, *Proc. Acad. Nat. Sci. Philadelphia*, 1883, 60 (Latrobe, Westmoreland Co., breeding)—Jamison, *Ornithologist and Oölogist*, 1888, 13:134; and Dwight, *Auk*, 1892, 9:140 (Cresson, Cambria Co., June)—Todd, *Auk*, 1893, 10:37, 41 (Two Lick, Indiana Co., June), 43, 46 (Coalport, Clearfield Co., June)—Jacobs, *Summer Birds Greene Co., Pa.*, 1893, 13 (Greene Co., nesting)—Cope, *Cassinia*, 1902, 5:20 (Germania, Potter Co., June).

"Brown Thrasher" Enty, *Ornithologist and Oölogist*, 1885, 10:78 (Templeton, Armstrong Co., April)—Van Ostrand, *Osprey*, 1896, 1:38 (Morganza, Washington Co., fall; food)—Todd, *Ann. Carnegie Mus.*, 1904, 2:588 (Erie and Presque Isle, Erie Co., summer)—Todd, in Bausman, *Hist. Beaver Co., Pa.*, 1904, 2:1201 (Beaver Co., summer)—Keim, *Cassinia*, 1905, 8:40 (Port Allegany, McKean Co., summer)—Stone, *Cassinia*, 1906, 9:44 (McConnellsburg, Fulton Co., June)—Pitcairn, *Bird-Lore*, 1907, 9:155 (Riverview Park, Allegheny Co., nesting)—Nuss, *Oölogist*, 1910, 27:129 (southwestern Pa., nesting)—Miller, *Bird-Lore*, 1913, 15:311 (Springs, Somerset Co., summer; song)—Burleigh, *Oölogist*, 1913, 30:55 (Pittsburgh, Allegheny Co., nesting)—McConnell, *Oölogist*, 1918, 35:152 ("Christy Park," Allegheny Co., breeding)—McClelland, *Am. Mid. Nat.*, 1922, 8:36 (Washington, Washington Co., summer)—Street, *Cassinia*, 1923, 24:18 (Greencastle, Little Cove Creek, and Ft. Loudon, Franklin Co., June)—Eastwood, *Bird-Lore*, 1925, 27:338 (Edgewood, Allegheny Co., nesting, *fide* Aiken), 407 (Sandy Creek, Allegheny Co., September, *fide* Woodin); 1926, 28:207; and 1927, 29:197 (Pittsburgh region, Allegheny Co., April), 273 (Springs, Somerset Co., April, *fide* Miller)—Boulton, *Bird-Lore*, 1928, 30:196 (McKinley Park, Allegheny Co., April, *fide* Held)—Cope and Hawkins, *Forest Leaves*, 1934, 24:26 (E. Tionesta Forest Reserve, Warren and McKean Co., summer).

Toxostoma rufum rufum Harlow, *Auk*, 1912, 29:476 (southern Centre Co., summer).

Toxostoma rufum Christy, *Cardinal*, 1923, v. 1, no. 1, [p. 14] (Sewickley, Allegheny Co., breeding)—Burleigh, *Wilson Bull.*, 1923, 35:142 (McKinley Park, Allegheny Co., nesting); 1924, 36:74; and 1931, 43:52 (State College, Centre Co., migration; nesting)—Burleigh, *Cardinal*, 1932, 3:78 (Chestnut Ridge, near Uniontown, Fayette Co., nesting).

Toxostoma rufa rufa Christy and Sutton, *Cardinal*, 1928, 2:74 (Cook Forest, Clarion Co., summer)—Sutton, *Ann. Carnegie Mus.*, 1928, 18:225 (Meadville, Conneaut Lake, and Pymatuning Swamp, Crawford Co., summer).

---

[1]U. S. Department of Agriculture, *Yearbook for 1895*, 1896, p. 413.

THRUSHES

FAMILY TURDIDAE

THE THRUSHES are a large family comprising over seven hundred species and subspecies and are common and widely distributed throughout the world. The North American forms number about thirty-five, only seven of which occur in western Pennsylvania. The Robin, the Bluebird, and the Wood Thrush are common summer residents throughout the region; the Olive-backed Thrush and the Hermit Thrush are limited in the breeding season to the plateau region; the Veery breeds at somewhat lower altitudes; and the Gray-cheeked Thrush is a transient that nests farther north.

Thrushes show great variation in general appearance and habits, but as a group they exhibit a combination of well-marked characters: spotted plumage in the young; a booted, or undivided, tarsus; and ten primary wing feathers, the outermost being a small spurious one. Many members of this family are noted for the beauty of their songs. Most are woodland dwellers, and all seek their food chiefly upon the ground. Their diet consists mainly of insects, earthworms, and centipedes, as well as of berries and soft fruits. All the species found in our region are migratory in this latitude, but most of them winter within the United States.

EASTERN ROBIN

TURDUS MIGRATORIUS MIGRATORIUS Linnaeus

SOUTHERN ROBIN

TURDUS MIGRATORIUS ACHRUSTERUS (Batchelder)

Description—Our largest thrush. *Male in spring:* head black, with a short white streak over the eye and a white spot below it; upperparts and wings externally, brownish gray; tail black, with a small white spot on the tips of the outermost feathers; chin white, and throat white, with black stripes; lower abdomen and under tail coverts white; rest of underparts rufous chestnut; bill yellowish, with darker tip. *Female* similar, but general coloration duller. *Fall and winter birds:* upperparts duller (brownish), the head not distinctly darker, and the throat more extensively white; underparts lighter in color and varied with white; bill dark. *Juvenal plumage:* upperparts brownish olive, with dark spots and buffy shaft-streaks on the feathers of the back and wing coverts; underparts rufous buff, heavily spotted with black.

Range—This well-known North American bird has an extensive distribution; it ranges from coast to coast, north to the limit of trees, and south to Mexico. It varies to some extent geographically, and several races are now recognized. In the northern part of its range it is strictly migratory, and all the individuals retire southward for the winter. It is abundant and widespread and is probably more numerous now than at any earlier period. One authority believes that its numbers today are greater in the aggregate than those of the Passenger Pigeon ever were, and this may not be an overstatement. At any rate, the Robin has been an eminently successful species and is one of the few that have profited through association with man. There has even been a perceptible increase in its numbers in the past thirty years, due, in my opinion, to the growing interest in bird life and its protection.

The proper status of the Robin in western Pennsylvania, as elsewhere in the northern and eastern United States, is that of a summer resident, abundant and generally distributed. Interest naturally centers on the winter occurrences in our region, many of which are on record. The Robin is hardy and in winter does not need to go very far south in order to find suitable conditions. Banding returns are lacking as yet, but it is probable, judging by analogy, that most of our summer-resident robins winter in Kentucky, Tennessee, and Alabama and do not cross the mountains.[1] Forty years ago robins were rarely seen here in winter, but in recent years winter occurrences, once sporadic, have become usual and normal. The season of 1911–12 was the first during which wintering flocks were actually noticed. Today they are no longer a novelty, and their fairly regular occurrence has been remarked by various observers. This increasing tendency toward winter residence can perhaps be correlated with the mildness of our recent winters, as compared with conditions in the eighties and nineties. A food supply is of course a prime requisite; with it assured during certain seasons, the Robin can easily withstand the lowered temperature.

Are these wintering robins birds that have elected to remain through the winter in the place in which they have summered, or are they migrants from farther north—from Canada and the Hudson Bay country? It has been shown that with certain species, northern-bred birds are the ones that go farthest south in winter—a rule that, if applied to the Robin, would argue against the second alternative just suggested. Study of an ample series of winter specimens would solve this problem, since we now know that northern-bred robins average a little larger than our local breeding birds. The only winter specimen that I have examined is apparently one of these larger birds.

Migration—Plotting the migration of the Robin is complicated by the problem just stated. Since the species is among the earliest to arrive in the spring and one of the latest to leave in the fall, winter records and migration records are apt to overlap. Experienced observers, however, learn to discriminate between the two intuitively. A robin seen in February has not necessarily just arrived; but if several appear suddenly during a spell of mild weather in places where they had not been seen up to that time, it is relatively certain that they are newcomers. The Robin pushes north at the first breath of spring, usually in February; seldom is its arrival delayed until the following month, and then only by reason of unseasonably cold and stormy weather. My records of its vernal appearance at Beaver date from 1887, with certain omissions. February 7 (1923) is my earliest date, and March 11 (1901), my latest, while the average is February 23. The rule is to expect the Robin on the first mild day after the middle of February. Two or three weeks pass, however, before it is really common and before the great tide of migration sweeps northward. In the Erie-Crawford district, it arrives about five days later, while at Warren and Renovo it seldom appears until after the first of March. At Springs, in southern Somerset County, however, February 25 is the average date; the higher general elevation at this point apparently retards migration by a few days. The effect of elevation is even more marked farther north, at Renovo.

The majority of our robins leave for warmer climes during October, and by the end of that month only a few remain. But to specify a date for the departure of the last stragglers is difficult, since it is hard to distinguish these from actual or potential winter residents. In general, however, the last migrants have all gone by November 10 or 15 at the latest; any birds seen after that date are likely to remain all winter.

Habits—The main facts in the life history of the Robin are so familiar that they scarcely require an extended account. The name "Robin" is an unfortunate misnomer, traceable to the early colonists, who fancied a resemblance in coloration and habits between this species and the "Robin Redbreast" of Europe. Actually, our bird is much closer genetically to the European Blackbird, *Turdus merula*, and a more accurate name for it would have been "Migratory Thrush." The songs of these two species are not unlike; that of the Blackbird, however, excels in melody, depth of tone, and variety of notes. The Robin is a pleasing though somewhat

[1]After this account had gone to press, A. D. Kirk wrote me that a young robin that he had banded at Forest Hills, Allegheny County, on July 10, 1938, was recovered at Webster, Florida, on February 15, 1939. Another robin, banded on September 25, 1937, was found dead at Perry, Florida, on March 3, 1939.

monotonous songster and is always welcome as a harbinger of spring. It might well be called the "Morning Bird," so consistently does it announce the peep of dawn. A dozen birds within hearing at one time are a full chorus. The concert continues well into the morning hours and toward nightfall is resumed again, with some desultory singing between. The song period is a long one, lasting from the birds' arrival in February until sometime in August, when the onset of the annual molt dampens their spirits. It is not at all unusual, however, for some enterprising individuals to sing snatches of their usual melody during the fall months.

The essentially gregarious nature of the Robin is not generally recognized. In bygone winters I used to find only a few birds in sheltered spots around a springhead and near a supply of dogwood berries. The increase in the number of wintering birds in recent years, however, has revealed the flocking tendency. This habit is normal in the regular winter quarters in the South; when the birds leave for the North in the spring, a whole company may travel together. I have repeatedly observed compact flocks of many hundreds flying northward high overhead late in the evening, and again when they had obviously stopped to rest on the way. Transient flocks have been noted from the day of first arrival until as late as the first week in April, when the local birds are already beginning to build their nests. In the fall, too, the Robin is often exceedingly abundant in September and October, thronging the woods and flying in great droves. This same flocking instinct operates in the breeding season and leads to the establishment of roosts, to which the robins of all the surrounding region resort at night. For several years a group of shade trees in the town of Beaver, not far from my home, was used as a roost. I used to watch the robins gathering there every evening during the spring and summer months. The number of birds may be judged from the circumstance that after the great cyclonic storm that swept the town on June 30, 1924, two bushel basketfuls of dead robins were picked up under these trees.

Compared with the Purple Martin, for example, the Robin is by no means dependent upon man. It can and does inhabit forest lands to some extent. In June, 1893, I found it in the deep woods of western Cambria County, far from human habitation, and I have also found it in the wilds of Potter County. In the fall and winter months, when wild fruits are its main fare, it virtually deserts open country for the woods and travels in straggling flocks, large or small. In other seasons it is our most familiar dooryard bird, living by preference near dwellings, securing its food from lawns and gardens, and nesting in shade or orchard trees as well as in and about buildings. Its eminently successful adaptation to the new conditions brought about by civilization has been promoted in a large measure by the clearance and cultivation of vast stretches of land. The Robin is preeminently a lover of open ground; its advent in the spring follows the melting of the winter snows and the laying bare of the earth, from which its food at this season is largely obtained. Cold, rainy weather never gives it any particular concern. On the other hand, a fresh fall of snow is nothing short of a catastrophe and may even force a temporary southward retirement. In such an event the frightened birds may be seen huddled in the gutters and beside the streams and ponds, looking desperately for sustenance.

Until early fruits become available, earthworms are the Robin's main food during the spring months. A robin pulling earthworms from a lawn or from freshly plowed ground is a common and familiar sight. Its ability to locate them near the surface seems uncanny, and it is certainly expert at digging them out. Its consumption of earthworms does not seem perceptibly to lessen their abundance—a fortunate fact, since they are known to be beneficial to the soil. The Robin may be credited with the destruction of beetles, caterpillars, and some other insects. To its discredit is its great fondness for cultivated fruits, which brings upon it the anathemas of the farmer and householder. More than half the Robin's food, by and large for a year, consists of fruit. Four-fifths of this is of wild species, it is true, but when the Robin population of a given district concentrates on the cultivated kinds, much damage is bound to result. Early cherries suffer the most, but strawberries, raspberries, blackberries, and occasionally larger fruits, are not spared. I have known entire cherry crops to be practically ruined by the depredations of these birds. This situation occurs in the total absence of wild fruit, as in the neighborhood of towns. The planting of mulberry or other ornamental fruit trees as counterattractions is a suggested remedy.

Unquestionably the Robin is now far too numerous in most places. Finding comparative safety and protection about the abodes of man, it has multiplied to a point where it has become a nuisance and a potential menace to his interests. Interference with the balance of nature is just as deplorable when exercised in favor of a given species as when directed against it, as already pointed out in the discussion of the House Wren. In the present quasi-domestic status of the Robin, the house cat has become its chief enemy. Many of the young just out of the nests, as they go flopping about the lawns, are killed by cats. Could the cats only be taught to discriminate and to confine their destructive tendencies to the Robin alone, little harm would be done!

The nesting habits of the Robin are too well known to require much description here. The nest may be placed almost anywhere—in an orchard or shade tree, on the projecting cornice of a building, on a fence or stump, under a bridge, or even (although very rarely) on the ground. Many curious sites have been described by various observers. The nest itself is stoutly built of dry grasses and weed stalks, intermixed with bits of rag or paper, or anything else at hand, and is plastered inside with a good coat of mud and lined with finer grasses and vegetable fibers. The eggs are usually four in number, occasionally only three, and very rarely five. At Forestville, Butler County, R. L. Keesler once found a female sitting on seven eggs; but it is possible that they were laid by two birds. The eggs are plain greenish blue (robin's-egg blue) and measure about 1.15 by .78 inches. The first laying usually takes place during the latter part of April, and the second, early in July, but there is considerable irregularity in the times. On occasion as many as three broods may be raised. As a rule, a new nest is built for each laying, but sometimes the birds use the first nest again. A pair that had a nest under the cornice of my house used it for several seasons and repaired it in the spring of each year. H. H. Elliott (1933) tells of a pair that used the same nest for three successive broods.

T. D. Burleigh (1929) has recorded an August nesting, but the most extraordinary circumstance is H. C. Kirkpatrick's finding of a nest with two eggs on December 9, 1889, at Buchanan, near Meadville. This nest was discovered on one of the under-timbers of a railroad bridge, with the female in occupancy. A visit a few days later showed that it had been robbed. The reason and significance of this late nesting date are not clear.

"Robin" Sage, *Ornithologist and Oölogist*, 1881, 6:38 (Sewickley, Allegheny Co., albino, *fide N. Y. Daily Times*)—Elliott, *Young Oölogist*, 1884, 1:113 (Mercer, Mercer Co., nesting)—"T. L. A.," *Young Oölogist*, 1884, 1:119 (Meadville, Crawford Co., nesting)—Enty, *Ornithologist and Oölogist*, 1885, 10:78 (Templeton, Armstrong Co., migration)—Todd, *Oölogist*, 1887, 4:89 (Beaver, Beaver Co., February)—[Bacon], *Oölogist*, 1888, 5:60 (Erie, Erie Co., winter, food)—Wickham, *Oölogist*, 1888, 5:92 (Beaver, Beaver Co., February)—Barrows, *Bull. Div. Econ. Orn. and Mammal.*, no. 1, 1889, 90 (Mansfield [Carnegie], Allegheny Co., relation to Sparrow, *fide* Walker)—Kirkpatrick, *Forest and Stream*, 1889, 33: 22 (Meadville, Crawford Co., December nesting)—Homer, *Ornithologist and Oölogist*, 1893, 18:61 (Elmer, Potter Co., June)—Van Ostrand, *Osprey*, 1896, 1:38 (Morganza, Washington Co., fall; food)—Stone, *Cassinia*, 1906, 9:44 (McConnellsburg, Fulton Co., June)—Cooke, *Bird-Lore*, 1907, 9:76 (Waynesburg, Greene Co.; Beaver, Beaver Co.; and Renovo, Clinton Co., migration)—[Simpson], *Oölogist*, 1907, 24:182 (Warren, Warren Co., nesting)—Harlow, *Oölogist*, 1911, 28:167 ([State College, Centre Co.], nesting)—Debes, *Bird-Lore*, 1912, 14:111 (Wilkinsburg, Allegheny Co., and Washington Co., January)—Simpson, *Oölogist*, 1912, 29:370, 402 (Warren, Warren Co., winter; food)—Rogers, *Bird-Lore*, 1914, 16:182 (near Pittsburgh, Allegheny Co., migration)—Miller, *Bird-Lore*, 1915, 17:34; etc.; 1918, 20:302; and 1930, 32:202 (Springs, Somerset Co., December; nesting)—Burleigh, *Oölogist*, 1915, 32:119 (State College, Centre Co., albino)—Burleigh and McGrew, *Bird-Lore*, 1916, 18:28 (Harmarville, Allegheny Co., December)—McConnell and Savage, *Bird-Lore*, 1917, 19:23; etc. (McKeesport, Allegheny Co., December)—McConnell, *Oölogist*, 1918, 35:152 (McKeesport, Allegheny Co., nesting)—Dickey, *Oölogist*, 1919, 36:67 (Waynesburg, Greene Co., nesting)—McGraw and Hays, *Bird-Lore*, 1920, 22:31 (Lakemont and vicinity, Blair Co., December)—Nicholson, *Bird-Lore*, 1921, 23:18 (Grove City, Mercer Co., December)—Stahl, *et al.*, *Bird-Lore*, 1921, 23:18 (Pittsburgh, Allegheny Co., December)—McIntosh, *Bird-Lore*, 1922, 24:152 (Franklin, Venango Co., food)—McClelland, *Am. Mid. Nat.*, 1922, 8:36 (Washington, Washington Co., summer; occasional in winter)—Hoffman, *et al.*, *Bird-Lore*, 1923, 25:23 (Grove City, Mercer Co., December)—Street, *Cassinia*, 1923, 24:19 (Greencastle to Ft. Loudon, Franklin Co., June)—Sutton, *Bird-Lore*, 1923, 25:132, 194; and 1924, 26:122 (Pittsburgh region, Allegheny Co., winter)—Christy, *Cardinal*, 1924, v. 1, no. 4, p. 10 (Big Traverse Valley, Beaver Co., June)—Lehman, *Bird-Lore*, 1925, 27:245 ([Chambersburg, Franklin Co.], nesting)—Eastwood, *Bird-Lore*, 1926, 28:137 (Frick Park and Deer Creek, Allegheny Co., January–February, *fide* Barnes and Squier; Ridgway and Johnsonburg, Elk Co., January; and New

Castle, Lawrence Co., January, *fide* Alsop); 1927, 29:127 (Oakdale, Allegheny Co., January, *fide* Portman)—CHRISTY, *Cardinal*, 1926, v. 1, no. 8, p. 20 (Sewickley, Allegheny Co., January)—HOLT, *Bird-Lore*, 1927, 29:184 (Cooksburg, Forest Co., nesting)—BOULTON, *Bird-Lore*, 1928, 30:14 (Schenley Park, Pittsburgh, Allegheny Co., December), 127 (Buffalo Creek, Armstrong Co., and Allegheny Co., winter records)—HITCHCOCK, *Bird-Lore*, 1930, 32:134 (Erie, Erie Co., nesting)—MALLEY, *Bird-Lore*, 1932, 34:46 (near Pittsburgh, Allegheny Co., December)—UPSON, *et al.*, *Bird-Lore*, 1933, 35:27 (Presque Isle, Erie Co., December)—BERKHEIMER, *Bird-Lore*, 1933, 35:27 (near Osterburg, Bedford Co., December)—NELLIS, *Bird-Lore*, 1933, 35:97 (Schenley Park, Pittsburgh, Allegheny Co., nesting habits)—SHONTZ, *Bird-Lore*, 1933, 35:155 (Sharon, Mercer Co., January)—ELLIOTT, *Cardinal*, 1933, 3:130 ([Wilkinsburg, Allegheny Co.], nesting habits), 171 (Raccoon Creek, Beaver Co., December)—ARTHUR, *Country Rambler*, 1934, 43 (Pymatuning Swamp, Crawford Co., and Guyasuta Run, Allegheny Co., winter)—BURLEIGH, *Cardinal*, 1934, 3:199 (western Pa. winter records)—CHRISTY, *Cardinal*, 1937, 4:121 (nesting habits); 1939, 5:45 (Allegheny Co., migration).

Turdus migratorius TEULON, *Jour. Boston Zoöl. Soc.*, 1882, 1:48 (Bradford, McKean Co., nesting)—TOWNSEND, *Proc. Acad. Nat. Sci. Philadelphia*, 1883, 60 (Latrobe, Westmoreland Co., breeding; occasional in winter)—MCCLINTOCK, *Cardinal*, 1933, 3:125 (Ligonier, Westmoreland Co.; habits, etc.)—CHRISTY, *Cardinal*, 1934, 3:174 (western Pa. winter records)—MANLEY, *Cardinal*, 1934, 3:175 (Brackenridge, Allegheny Co., nesting)—RANEY, *Auk*, 1939, 56:337 (New Castle, Lawrence Co., nesting with mourning dove).

Merula migratoria JACOBS, *Nat. Companion*, 1886, 2:58 (Waynesburg, Greene Co., summer; occasional in winter)—JAMISON, *Ornithologist and Oölogist*, 1888, 13:134; and DWIGHT, *Auk*, 1892, 9:141 (Cresson, Cambria Co., June)—HOMER, *Ornithologist and Oölogist*, 1889, 14:88 (New Hamburg, Mercer Co., nesting)—TODD, *Auk*, 1893, 10:41 (Two Lick, Indiana Co., June), 46 (Coalport, Clearfield Co., June)—JACOBS, *Summer Birds Greene Co., Pa.*, 1893, 14 (Greene Co., nesting)—BAILY, *Auk*, 1896, 13:297 (Williamsville, Elk Co., June–July)—JACOBS, *Gleanings from Nature*, 1898, 1:20 (Waynesburg, Greene Co., nesting)—FORREST, *Oölogist*, 1901, 18:137 (Washington Co., nesting)—COPE, *Cassinia*, 1902, 5:10, 21 (Clinton and Potter Co., June)—TODD, *Ann. Carnegie Mus.*, 1904, 2:593 (Erie and Presque Isle, Erie Co., summer; occasional in winter)—TODD, in Bausman, *Hist. Beaver Co., Pa.*, 1904, 2:1202 (Beaver Co., summer)—KEIM, *Cassinia*, 1905, 8:41 (Port Allegany, McKean Co., summer)—FORREST, *Oölogist*, 1911, 28:115 (Washington, Washington Co., breeding).

Planesticus migratorius PITCAIRN, *Oölogist*, 1910, 27:23 (Rowan, Butler Co., nesting)—HARLOW, *Auk*, 1912, 29:477 (southern Centre Co., breeding); 1918, 35:147 (State College, Centre Co., breeding)—CHRISTY, *Cardinal*, 1923, v. 1, no. 1, [p. 15] (Sewickley, Allegheny Co., nesting; occasional in winter)—BURLEIGH, *Wilson Bull.*, 1923, 35:146 (Allegheny Co., summer, nesting; occasional in winter).

Turdus migratorius migratorius CHRISTY and SUTTON, *Cardinal*, 1928, 2:75 (Cook Forest, Clarion Co., summer)—SUTTON, *Ann. Carnegie Mus.*, 1928, 18:238 (Meadville and Pymatuning Swamp, Crawford Co., summer; occasional in winter)—BURLEIGH, *Cardinal*, 1932, 3:78 (Chestnut Ridge, near Uniontown, Fayette Co., summer resident).

Planesticus migratorius migratorius BURLEIGH, *Cardinal*, 1929, 2:120 (Harmarville, Allegheny Co., August nesting)—BURLEIGH, *Wilson Bull.*, 1924, 36:74; and 1931, 43:54 (State College, Centre Co., migration; nesting).

Turdus migratorius achrusterus TODD, *Auk*, 1939, 56:190 (western Pa., critical).

WOOD THRUSH (Plate 16)

HYLOCICHLA MUSTELINA (Gmelin)

Description—The largest of the *Hylocichlae*, but smaller than the Robin. *Upperparts russet*, deepest on the crown and *passing into olive on the rump, tail, and wings externally; underparts* white, with *distinct, rounded spots of black*, except on the middle of the throat and on the under tail coverts; the sides of the head show dusky and white markings; eye-ring also white; mouth yellow; feet pale. The comparatively large size, the uniformly and heavily spotted underparts, and the color pattern of the upperparts serve to distinguish this species from its allies.

Range—This thrush is the most southern of its generic group, insofar as its breeding range is concerned; it is also distinctively eastern and does not reach the Rocky Mountains. From a zonal standpoint it is a bird of the Carolinian and Alleghanian faunas, and it invades the Canadian Fauna only to a limited extent. It passes the winter in Central America, or rarely on the Gulf coast of Florida. It is the only species of *Hylocichla* having a breeding range that extends entirely across western Pennsylvania. In the Carolinian valleys of the southwestern and southeastern counties it is common and, indeed, is the only thrush of the *Hylocichla* group in summer. In the northern and more elevated parts of our region it is somewhat less common and is often found associated with the other kinds, haunting the same woods.

Migration—The Wood Thrush is not a very early migrant, and when it is reported earlier than the third week in April we may be fairly sure that the Hermit Thrush was the bird actually seen. April 15 (1921) is the earliest authentic spring record; it applies to Pittsburgh (Schenley Park?) and is supplied by G. M. Sutton. I have noted the species' arrival at Beaver between April 22 and May 2, and the average date there is April 25. These limiting and average dates are corroborated by observers from adjoining counties. At Warren the Wood Thrush does not arrive as a rule until

after the first of May, and in the mountains generally, it appears to be uniformly later than in the western counties of the same latitude. In twenty-six seasons' records from Renovo, made by A. K. Pierce, arrival dates range from April 25 to May 7, and May 2 is the average. The species arrives in western Pennsylvania before it reaches New Jersey, and this circumstance suggests that its route swings off to the northeastward, as do those of certain other species that advance by the land route through Mexico.

The departure of the Wood Thrush takes place in October, just when the Hermit Thrush is beginning to appear from the North. October 1 is the average date for Beaver, while the extremes are September 25 (1888) and October 8 (1890); these dates are again corroborated by observations in adjacent counties. In the Pierce records from Renovo, the average date is so very much later that I strongly suspect some confusion in the identifications on which the records were based.

Habits—The Wood Thrush, the best known of our small thrushes, is appropriately named, for it is primarily a bird of the woods. In recent years, however, it has shown a tendency to invade parks, orchards, and the vicinity of houses, especially where the surrounding grounds are planted with ornamental shrubbery. In the residential sections of Pittsburgh adjacent to Schenley Park and other favorable spots, this thrush is now a regular and welcome visitor, as it is also in many of our smaller towns and country villages. Nevertheless, it is in the woods that the great majority live, as their ancestors must likewise have done long before the white man cleared away the primeval forest. Deep woods with plenty of undergrowth remain this bird's most congenial resort. Here it spends much of its time on the ground, where its russet and olive livery matches the dry leaves of the forest floor. It flies up into the shrubbery on occasion, but it seldom rises above the lower branches of the trees. It is shy but curious, and is likely to steal cautiously up to an intruder for a good look before withdrawing again into its sylvan retreat.

As a songster the Wood Thrush ranks high. There are those who consider its song superior even to that of the Hermit Thrush, although to this dictum I can scarcely assent. Its clear, flute-like notes, falling on the ear in the early morning hours or in the cool of the evening, carry with them a suggestion of the forest solitudes and deep, shady nooks from which they come. Rich yet mellow music, they are singularly appropriate to the time and place. Several birds singing in concert, vying with each other in their vocal efforts, are at their best. Unlike the Brown Thrasher and some others, the singing Wood Thrush often perches at a low or moderate elevation. The song period lasts from the birds' arrival until late July, when the annual molt begins. The ordinary call note has a sharp, clucking quality that is characteristic.

Nest-building begins shortly after the birds arrive, and I have found full sets of eggs as early as May 10. The nest is usually placed in a sapling, or on the lower branches of a tree; as it is seldom over twenty feet from the ground, and generally much lower, it is often easy to examine without climbing. The vicinity of a small stream or of a highway passing through the woods is often chosen, and there is no particular effort at concealment. The nest is firmly wedged into a crotch, saddled on a horizontal limb, or placed against the main trunk of the tree. Its general make-up suggests the nest of the Robin, in that it has an outer foundation of weed stalks, dry grasses, dead leaves, and bits of paper picked up at random; an intermediate layer of mud; and an inner lining of fine black rootlets. It is a compact structure, about two inches deep inside, and so well built that it often holds its shape and character long after the young have flown. Four eggs comprise the standard set, but sometimes only three are laid, and very rarely five. They measure about 1.02 by .72 inches and are plain greenish blue in color, a trifle deeper in tone, on an average, than those of the Robin. As nests with eggs have been found early in July, the belief that some pairs may rear two broods in a season is perhaps warranted, but it is possible that these late records pertain to delayed nestings. There is one record of a nest found on August 22, with young just ready to leave (Sutton, 1928).

Concerning the nesting habits of this species, Cornelius Weygandt writes: "The Wood Thrush, like all his kind with which I am familiar, like Bluebird and Robin, like Hermit Thrush and Veery, is a good husband and father. He takes his place on the eggs to relieve his mate and he helps in the feeding of the young. He is valiant in resisting attacks on his brood and capable of creating as great a hubbub over the presence of marauders as Redbreast himself. Head feathers raised into almost a crest, wings beating and drooped, and tail uptilting, all of him aquiver and jerked about by his excitement, he will scold from some low limb at skulking cat or persistently threatening squirrel until he has driven off the enemy or the nest is rifled. Before the latter happens, however, the thief must run a gauntlet of dauntless swoops and dashes from both male and female bird. These sometimes carry the excited bird so close that its beating wings may force the thief to jump from the limb he is following toward the nest. I am afraid that Chickaree [the red squirrel] when once he has found a nest will watch his chance and return when it is unguarded, but a cat so discomfited will not often return."[1]

Studies of the food of this thrush made by F. E. L. Beal[2] show that it consists of three parts of animal matter to two parts of vegetable matter. The former includes beetles, caterpillars, ants, and other insects, some of which are economically harmful. The vegetable food is mostly wild fruit. The species deserves protection and encouragement, and it is unfortunate that its numbers now seem to be diminishing.

Turdus mustelinus Teulon, *Jour. Boston Zoöl. Soc.*, 1882, 1:49 (Bradford, McKean Co., nesting)—Townsend, *Proc. Acad. Nat. Sci. Philadelphia*, 1883, 60 (Latrobe, Westmoreland Co.)—Jamison, *Ornithologist and Oölogist*, 1888, 13:134; and Dwight, *Auk*, 1892, 9:140 (Cresson, Cambria Co., June)—Todd, *Auk*, 1893, 10:37, 41 (Two Lick, Indiana Co., June), 43, 46 (Coalport, Clearfield Co., June)—Jacobs, *Summer Birds Greene Co., Pa.*, 1893, 14 (Greene Co., nesting)—Baily, *Auk*, 1896, 13:297 (Straight Creek, near Williamsville, Elk Co., June–July).

"Wood Robin" Enty, *Ornithologist and Oölogist*, 1885, 10:78 (Templeton, Armstrong Co., April).

Hylocichla mustelina Cope, *Cassinia*, 1902, 5:12, 20 (Tamarack Swamp, Clinton Co., June; Kettle Creek Valley, Potter Co., nesting)—Todd, *Ann. Carnegie Mus.*, 1904, 2:592 (Erie, Erie Co., summer)—Todd, in Bausman, *Hist. Beaver Co., Pa.*, 1904, 2:1202 (Beaver Co., summer)—Keim, *Cassinia*, 1905, 8:41 (Port Allegany, McKean Co., summer)—Harlow, *Auk*, 1912, 29:477 (southern Centre Co.)—Christy, *Cardinal*, 1923, v. 1, no. 1, [p. 15] (Sewickley, Allegheny Co., summer)—Burleigh, *Wilson Bull.*, 1923, 35:146 (Allegheny Co., nesting); 1924, 36:74; and 1931, 43:54 (near State College, Centre Co., migration; nesting)—Christy and Sutton, *Cardinal*, 1928, 2:74 (Cook Forest, Clarion Co., breeding)—Sutton, *Ann. Carnegie Mus.*, 1928, 18:236 (Meadville and Pymatuning Swamp, Crawford Co., summer)—Burleigh, *Cardinal*, 1932, 3:78 (Chestnut Ridge, near Uniontown, Fayette Co., summer).

"Wood Thrush" Stone, *Cassinia*, 1906, 9:44 (Scrub Ridge, west of McConnellsburg, Fulton Co., June)—Cooke, *Bird-Lore*, 1907, 9:32 (Beaver, Beaver Co., migration)—Pitcairn, *Bird-Lore*, 1907, 9:155 (Riverview Park, Allegheny Co., nesting)—Burleigh, *Oölogist*, 1911, 28:156 (Harmarville, Allegheny Co., nesting)—Simpson, *Oölogist*, 1912, 29:276 (Warren, Warren Co., nesting), 330 (head of Tionesta Creek, Warren Co., summer)—Miller, *Oölogist*, 1919, 36:157 (Charter Oak, Huntingdon Co., nesting)—McClelland, *Am. Mid. Nat.*, 1922, 8:36 (Washington, Washington Co., summer)—Street, *Cassinia*, 1923, 24:19 (Greencastle, Ft. Loudon, Jordan's Knob, and Horse Valley, Franklin Co., June)—Christy, *Cardinal*, 1924, v. 1, no. 4, p. 10 (Big Traverse Valley, Beaver Co., June)—Eastwood, *Bird-Lore*, 1925, 27: 263 (Pittsburgh region, Allegheny Co., April); 1926, 28:273 (Rector, Westmoreland Co., May, *fide* Knauz)—Boulton, *Bird-Lore*, 1928, 30:271 (Millvale, Allegheny Co., April, *fide* Auerswald).

[1]*Cassinia*, 1911, 14:23.

[2]U. S. Department of Agriculture, *Bulletin*, no. 280, 1915, p. 5–8.

EASTERN HERMIT THRUSH (Plate 16)

HYLOCICHLA GUTTATA FAXONI Bangs and Penard

Description—A slightly smaller bird than the Wood Thrush. Upperparts brown, the *tail russet, in decided contrast with the back;* underparts white or whitish, the breast with dusky spots, and the sides with a slight brownish-olive wash. In fresh fall plumage the throat and breast are more or less suffused with buff.

Range—Several races of the Hermit Thrush occur in the mountains of the West. The eastern race ranges in summer from Newfoundland to Yukon Territory, in northwestern Canada, and thence into the northern United States and southward in the Appalachian highlands at least to Virginia. Although primarily a species of the Canadian Fauna, it regularly invades the Alleghanian Fauna at various places, as for example in Massachusetts, over the greater part of which it is known as a summer resident. In New York its breeding range includes not only the Adirondack and Catskill Mountains, but also an area in the highlands of the western section, adjoining the northern boundary of Pennsylvania.[1] This circumstance implies a wide contiguous distribution south of this line. Its summer range as worked out for our region includes the entire plateau section. It breeds commonly throughout Potter and McKean counties and in the greater part of Warren County, and also in the counties immediately to the southward, wherever suitable conditions obtain. In 1934 I traced the species to Tamarack Swamp, near Pine Valley, in the northwestern corner of Warren County. Clarion and Mayport, where it occurs at an elevation of only about 1,100 feet, are doubtless close to the western edge of its range in Clarion County. Thence the line limiting its range swings off sharply to the eastward to include Punxsutawney, Jefferson County, and then runs southward along the western border of Cambria County and presumably along that of Somerset County.

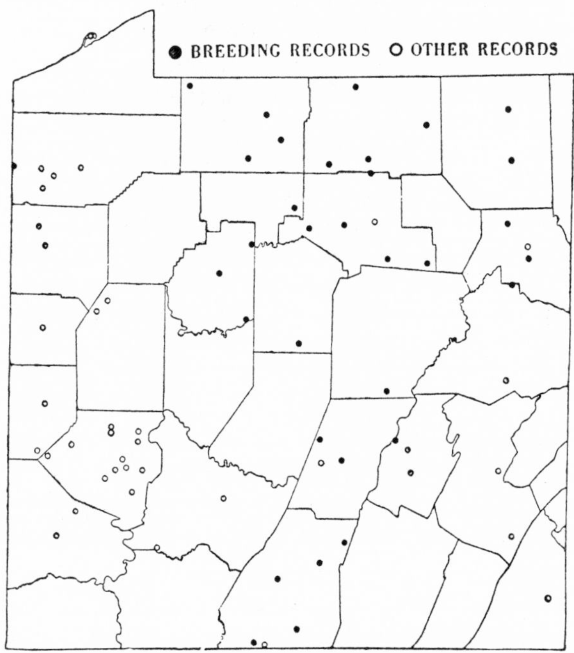

LOCAL RANGE OF THE EASTERN HERMIT THRUSH

I have searched for the Hermit Thrush on the summit of Laurel Hill, but have thus far failed to find it, although E. A. Preble has taken it near Somerset. The Junco and the Hermit Thrush have virtually the same range elsewhere in our region, and since the former species occurs on Laurel Hill, it is logical to infer that the latter does also—or at least that it once did. In Clinton County I have encountered it in summer at Tamarack Swamp and at two different points on the summit of Beech Creek Mountain, south of the West Branch of the Susquehanna River. (I doubt, however, whether it nests in the lowland valley of that stream.) Thence southward its breeding range is sharply delimited on the east by the crest of the Allegheny Mountains, all the way to our southern boundary. Throughout the ridge and valley section the species is only a transient, and the same status holds for all that part of the country west of its breeding range as marked out above. Pymatuning Swamp, as an island of the Canadian Life Zone, might be expected to harbor a certain quota of breeding individuals, but local conditions there are not favorable for a bird that prefers dry uplands. L. E. Hicks, however, reports that he noted hermit thrushes on Hemlock Island on July 9, 1928, and on May 30, 1930, and that on June 15, 1932, he found a nest in the Ohio section of the

[1]E. H. Eaton, *Birds of New York*, 1910, 1:30.

swamp. It is possible that under primeval conditions this outlying breeding station was connected with the main range to the eastward.

In New Jersey and southeastern Pennsylvania this thrush is occasional in winter, and its occurrence at that season in our region is therefore not surprising. Several winter records come from various parts of the country: near Raccoon Creek, Beaver County (Todd, Elliott, *et al.*); Big Traverse Valley, Beaver County (Christy); Aliquippa, Beaver County (Ristich, Edeburn); three miles southeast of Bakerstown, Allegheny County (Fricke); near Sewickley (Christy); Johnstown (Auerswald); Meadville (Kirkpatrick); Barree, Huntingdon County (McGraw). All these records were made between 1917 and 1936.

Migration—The Hermit Thrush is the hardiest of its group; it comes from the South earlier in the spring and stays later in the fall than any of the others and occasionally, as has just been shown, remains throughout the winter. In the vernal migration it passes through our region in April and on days of special movement is sometimes very numerous. P. P. Malley reports it from Frick Park, Pittsburgh, on March 25, 1938; A. B. Miller has noted it at Springs, Somerset County, as early in the season as March 28 (1921); and G. M. Sutton saw one bird at Mill Creek, Huntingdon County, on March 29, 1923; but all these dates are rather exceptional. My earliest date for Beaver County is April 4 (1889), which corresponds with the early records of other observers: April 5, 1913—Sewickley (Christy); April 6, 1913—Pittsburgh (Burleigh); April 3, 1917—State College (Harlow); April 4, 1893—Wilkinsburg (Atkinson); April 5–8—Greenville (Seiple); April 2–7—Erie (Guynes). R. B. Simpson, however, does not look for it at Warren before the middle of April; his earliest date is April 11 (1892). Spring arrival dates in a series covering twenty-two years from Renovo range from April 2 to 24, with April 16 as the average (Pierce).

The height of migration is usually reached during the third week in April, and by the end of that month most of the birds have passed through, except at places where the species remains to breed. Almost every season, however, a few linger until the first week in May and sometimes even a little later. Five seasons' records of "last-seen" dates at Beaver lie between May 1 (1889) and 9 (1925). In 1921 B. H. Christy saw the Hermit Thrush at Sewickley as late as May 8, while a single laggard was noted at Raccoon Creek, Beaver County, on May 13, 1928, by Rudyerd Boulton; and another, at Meadville on May 20, 1899, by H. C. Kirkpatrick. In 1917 the species was seen at State College on May 12 (Burleigh). But these are all exceptional records; they prove the rule that the northward movement of the Hermit Thrush through our region is performed in April and that most of the migrants of this species pass through before the other thrushes arrive. The Wood Thrush is the next to reach us, and although its migration period overlaps that of the other to some extent, there is no excuse for confusing the two species.

The Hermit Thrush is the last of all its tribe to reappear in the fall (at places where it does not breed) and as a rule does not arrive until the other thrushes have gone. I once observed it at Beaver as early as September 28 (1910), but my other fall arrival dates lie between October 3 (1899) and 11 (1890). It has been noted at Wilkinsburg on September 29 (1893—Atkinson) and at Pittsburgh (Frick Park) on September 26 (1937—Malley). October 3 was the date of its fall arrival at Presque Isle in 1900. In general, October is the month of greatest movement in the fall, just as April is, in the spring. Similarly also, the movement is largely over by the end of the month, although stragglers may be seen in November. On November 7, 1926, I saw two hermit thrushes near Vanport, Beaver County. November 8 (1914) is the latest fall record for State College (Burleigh). One bird was seen at Guys Run, Allegheny County, on November 6, 1927, by O. C. Reiter and others, while of the records of "last-seen" dates at Renovo nearly one-third lie in the first week in November (Pierce).

Habits—October finds our woodlands a splash of colors. Under the touch of the Frost King, all the varied hues of autumn come into being for a time—a picture to delight the eye. Mild days and cool nights give a foretaste of winter chill. As the season wanes a strange quiet comes to brood over the scene. Only the leaves, drifting down one by one or falling in a rustling shower before a vagrant breeze, break the eerie stillness. Otherwise the woods seem silent and deserted. The feathered choristers of the summer have nearly all set out for a warmer clime, leaving only a few hardy ones to brave the rigors of the cold season. Others have come down from the North to linger with us a little while before resuming their way. Among these is the Hermit Thrush, in modest garb and with quiet, unobtrusive ways. Shy, almost furtive in its movements as it works over the ground or wings its way from branch to branch, keeping rather low and uttering a subdued "chuck" as its only note, it is the very personification of the spirit and mood of the woods in autumn. Solitary in habit and retiring in disposition, the Hermit Thrush bears a singularly appropriate name. Like most thrushes, however, it has a streak of curiosity in its make-up, and it will often investigate an intruder stealthily and in a roundabout way.

In the spring its behavior is much the same. Arriving in April, before the trees are in leaf, it is easily observed, although as a rule it is silent. The other thrushes of this group are all more or less musical from the moment of their first arrival, but on only a very few occasions have I heard the Hermit Thrush sing during the spring migration, and never was the full song given. This it apparently reserves until it reaches its nesting grounds, when it makes up for its previous silence. Early morning and late evening are the hours devoted to vocal effort. On many a June morning in years gone by, while exploring for birds in the Pennsylvania highlands, have I paused to listen entranced to the Hermit's incomparable music, ringing out full and clear from the depths of the forest, like a voice from another world. In its flutelike quality, mode of delivery, and general scope and variety of notes, the Hermit's song suggests that of its cousin, the Wood Thrush. It is not so rich, perhaps, but there is about it an exquisite purity of tone and a liquid sweetness of modulation that the latter bird does not attain. And there is about the song, too, a quality that can only be suggested, but not described, by the word "spiritual"—a quality that is missing from the song of the other bird, of a high order though it be. As one writer declares, "The Hermit Thrush, if you like, catches an echo in its song from harps struck in some land that is happier than any man knows." Listening to its aspiring strains, one seems to be carried on the wings of the morning to a higher plane of being, where the inmost longings and deepest desires of one's nature may find full fruition. Thus closely does the Hermit Thrush's song come to expressing the inexpressible.

No feeble word picture that I can devise does justice to the music of this peerless leader of the sylvan choir. Where the species is common, one may often hear a half-dozen or more birds singing at once, perhaps together with some of the other thrushes. The song has a strangely elusive quality that makes it difficult to locate. I have searched some time for a singing bird, only to find it at last directly overhead. Unlike the Wood Thrush, the male Hermit Thrush usually selects the topmost spray of a tree as his singing perch and remains there during the whole session. I have, however, occasionally encountered single birds wandering through the deep, cool recesses of the forest, singing at intervals along the way. In the fall migration, too, it is not unusual to hear a few birds singing very softly and in subdued key, but the sounds carry only a short distance. I once collected a singing bird, which proved to be an immature male. I have heard the female utter a note that bears a striking similarity to a vireo's harsh call. Another note resembles the mewing call of the Catbird, except that it is less prolonged.

The Hermit Thrush is naturally partial to the deep woods, but it is by no means averse to making its summer home in second-growth timber, about old clearings, and on the outskirts of the forest. Burned-over tracts grown up to ferns and bushes are not shunned. Thus it will doubtless continue to live in areas that many other forest birds have been forced to leave. Although this species reaches its breeding grounds far ahead of the other thrushes, its time of nesting does not seem to be any earlier. Considerable variation, however, is indicated, since sets of eggs have been taken by A. K. Pierce at Kane from May 14 until as late as June 30. Mr. Simpson and H. L. Granquist have found nests near Warren during June, and W. L. Baily found several at Williamsville, Elk County, during the same month. The normal nesting site is on the ground, and Mr. Baily found several nests "on mossy banks at the side of the road," while Mr. Simpson has found them built on big boulders on a rocky hillside, among the growing ferns.

A typical nest found by Mr. Pierce is described as an artistic structure composed of dry whitish strips of wood, bark fiber, hemlock twigs, and dark-colored rootlets, ornamented outside with dry green moss, and lined with fine rootlets. Inside dimensions are given as two and one-half inches wide by one and three-quarters inches deep. The nest was placed in a depression on the ground, concealed beneath some young beech sprouts and surrounded by dead beech leaves. Like the Wood Thrush, however, this bird frequently constructs its nest in a sapling or low tree. Mr. Simpson has found several so built—one six feet from the ground, in a cherry sapling, and others in hemlocks four feet up. One of the nests collected by Mr. Pierce was in the top of a young hemlock (one of a clump) and was five feet from the ground.

Three or four eggs compose the set. They are not certainly distinguishable in either color or size from those of the Veery, but their bluish-green color is perhaps on the average a little paler. Average measurements are .88 by .69 inches.

Turdus pallasi Teulon, *Jour. Boston Zoöl. Soc.*, 1882, 1:49 (Bradford, McKean Co., spring).

Turdus unalascæ nanus Townsend, *Proc. Acad. Nat. Sci. Philadelphia*, 1883, 60 (Latrobe, Westmoreland Co.).

Turdus aonalaschkæ pallasii Dwight, *Auk*, 1892, 9:133, 134, 141 (Wopsononock Mountain, Blair Co., June; song)—Todd, *Auk*, 1893, 10:42, 43, 46 (Coalport, Clearfield Co., June)—Baily, *Auk*, 1896, 13:291, 292, 297 (Williamsville, Elk Co., nesting).

Hylocichla guttata pallasii Todd, *Ann. Carnegie Mus.*, 1904, 2: 593 (Presque Isle, Erie Co., transient)—Todd, in Bausman, *Hist. Beaver Co., Pa.*, 1904, 2:1202 (Beaver Co., transient)—Christy, *Cardinal*, 1923, v. 1, no. 1, [p. 15] (Sewickley, Allegheny Co., transient)—Burleigh, *Wilson Bull.*, 1923, 35:146 (Allegheny Co., transient; migration); 1924, 36:131 (State College, Centre Co., transient; migration).

"Hermit Thrush" Cooke, *Bird-Lore*, 1907, 9:123 (Beaver, Beaver Co., and Renovo, Clinton Co., migration)—Simpson, *Oölogist*, 1911, 28:162 (Warren, Warren Co., nesting); 1912, 29:330; and 1920, 37:143 (head of Tionesta Creek, Warren Co., nesting)—McConnell, *Oölogist*, 1918, 35:152 (McKeesport, Allegheny Co., transient)—McClelland, *Am. Mid. Nat.*, 1922, 8:36 (Washington, Washington Co., transient)—Sutton, *Bird-Lore*, 1924, 26:55 (Harmarville, Allegheny Co.), 190 (Pittsburgh region, Allegheny Co., spring)—Eastwood, *Bird-Lore*, 1926, 28:207; and 1927, 29:196, 197 (Pittsburgh region, Allegheny Co., April)—Boulton, *Bird-Lore*, 1928, 30:14 (Guys Run, Allegheny Co., November, *fide* Reiter, *et al.*), 195 (Johnstown, Cambria Co., February, *fide* Auerswald), 271 (Raccoon Creek, Beaver Co., May)—Christy and Hegner, *Bird-Lore*, 1933, 35:28 (Big Traverse Creek, Beaver Co., December)—Elliott, *Cardinal*, 1934, 3:171 (Raccoon Creek, Beaver Co., December).

Hylocichla guttata faxoni Christy and Sutton, *Cardinal*, 1928, 2:74 (Cook Forest, Clarion Co., nesting)—Sutton, *Ann. Carnegie Mus.*, 1928, 18:238 (Crawford Co. localities, transient; occasional in winter).

"Eastern Hermit Thrush" Cope and Hawkins, *Forest Leaves*, 1934, 24:26 (E. Tionesta Forest Reserve, Warren and McKean Co., summer).

OLIVE-BACKED THRUSH (Plate 16)

HYLOCICHLA USTULATA SWAINSONI (Tschudi)

Description—Upperparts plain olive, the *tail uniform with the back;* underparts white, with obscure dusky spotting on the upper abdomen, breast, and throat (except in the middle); the breast, throat, and *sides of the head are more or less washed with buff*, and the sides of the body are shaded with dusky olive.

Range—Like the Hermit Thrush, the Olive-backed Thrush (together with its western race, the Russet-backed) has a transcontinental distribution. It is, however, a more northerly bird on the whole than the eastern race of Hermit Thrush; their respective ranges coincide in large degree, but the latter does not go beyond the Canadian Fauna in the summer. The Olive-backed, on the other hand, ranges well into the Hudsonian Fauna, but not to any extent into the Alleghanian. Moreover, while the Hermit Thrush winters mainly in the Gulf states, the Olive-backed goes to Central and South America. The differences in the respective faunal affinities of the two species are reflected in their local distribution within our area. Where the Olive-backed occurs in summer, the Hermit may be expected also, but the converse of this proposition is not necessarily true. In fact, the Olive-backed was not even suspected of breeding in Pennsylvania until 1890. In 1891 Warren reported it summering at Kane—a report that I was able to confirm three years later by securing a specimen in June. Several sets of eggs have since been collected there by A. K. Pierce. Subsequently I took the species at Katrine Swamp and Port Allegany, in the same county (McKean), and found it particularly common in Potter County, and in Tamarack Swamp, Clinton County.

To the westward, the range of this thrush has been worked out to include at least the eastern half of Warren County, eastern Forest County

(Parrish), western Elk County (Croyland, Hallton), and northern Clearfield County (Anderson Creek). So far as I know, this last locality is at present the southernmost breeding station in Pennsylvania. The species apparently does not follow the Hermit Thrush south into Cambria and Somerset counties. At Springs, in the latter county, close to the Maryland boundary, A. B. Miller has indeed observed it in early June, but he thinks that the birds he saw were merely late migrants. One would expect, however, that the altitude there, which in some places exceeds three thousand feet, would suffice to attract this thrush if the environmental conditions were otherwise suitable. However this may be, it reappears farther south along the mountains, in the spruce belt of West Virginia. The chances are that under primitive conditions its range was actually continuous, but that the species has not been able to withstand nearly so well as has the Hermit Thrush the changes brought about in its natural environment by deforestation.

Beyond the limits above described, this thrush is merely a transient visitant in spring and fall, rather common, but often confused by the amateur with the Hermit and Gray-cheeked species. There are records for nearly all the counties in the western tier, and for Blair and Centre counties in the eastern section.

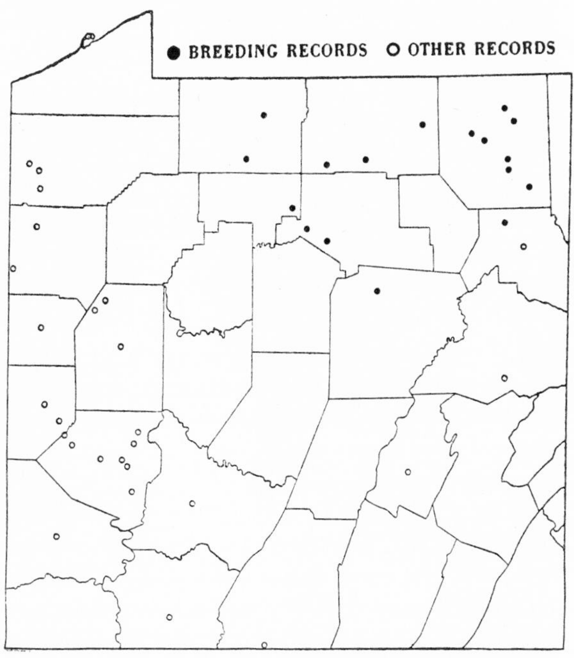

LOCAL RANGE OF THE OLIVE-BACKED THRUSH

Migration—Very seldom does the Olive-backed Thrush reach our region before the first of May; in fact, I have only one such early record for Beaver—April 30, 1902. My first dates for other seasons run from May 3 to 14. The species has been observed near Aliquippa, Beaver County, however, on April 28 (1933—Sollberger) and at Greensburg on the same date (1935—Trimble), while T. D. Burleigh reports one bird at Pittsburgh as early as April 24 (1914). These early dates are exceptional; ordinarily we do not look for the Olive-backed Thrush until the warblers appear in force, and sight records made in April are more or less questionable because of possible confusion with the Hermit Thrush, although as a rule the latter has gone by the time the former arrives. The migration continues into the last week in May, and odd birds have been known to linger into June. Every spring there are usually one or more days during which a considerable flight occurs, and then the species becomes exceedingly common. In the autumnal movement the Olive-backed Thrush usually reaches the Ohio Valley shortly after the first of September, although the earliest recorded date for Pittsburgh is August 29 (1927—Burleigh). It attains its fullest numbers in the next two or three weeks, and does not disappear until the first week in October—at about the time the Hermit Thrush reappears. Some late dates are: October 6, 1890—Beaver (Todd); October 10, 1912—Pittsburgh (Burleigh); October 12, 1897—Wilkinsburg (Atkinson); October 14, 1903—Renovo (Pierce). Large flights are frequent in fall as well as in spring.

Habits—As a transient visitant in spring and fall, the Olive-backed Thrush comes and goes with the warblers, which it often accompanies through the forest. Unlike the Hermit Thrush, which remains on or near the ground in low bushes and shrubbery, the Olive-backed stays more in the treetops, where it flits about in true warbler fashion, evidently feeding on insects. Stomach examinations show that not quite two-thirds of its food consists of animal matter. In the fall it feeds extensively on wild fruits of various kinds, for which it descends to lower levels than usual. I have several times noticed it feeding on pokeberries at the edges of woods, and in specimens collected, the viscera have been deeply stained. Often the Olive-backed Thrush is shy and hard to approach closely enough to identify, while at other times it will, apparently out of curiosity, stalk an intruder cautiously and by easy stages. On days when a large flight is under way, the species is in evidence not only in the woods (its ordinary habitat), but also in opener places, such as orchards, groves, shrubbery along fences and streams, and almost any place where there is some cover.

The ordinary call note is a low "chuck," resembling that of the Hermit Thrush; this is the only note heard during the fall migration. Some individuals sing at intervals during their northward progress in the spring. But to hear the full range and power of the song of the Olive-backed Thrush, one must make the acquaintance of the bird after it is settled on its breeding territory. In the coniferous forest that used to cover our northern counties, I have often listened to its music. The species was particularly numerous at Tamarack Swamp, Clinton County, on the several occasions when I visited that interesting locality. There it haunted the spruce belt and, although shy and elusive, was so common that a half-dozen birds could often be heard singing at once on the edge and in the depths of the swamp. Beginning before the break of day, they sang almost continuously during the morning hours. The song may at once be recognized as that of a *Hylocichla* by its characteristic flutelike timbre. It is rather louder than that of the Hermit Thrush, and deeper in tone, but, as Jonathan Dwight remarks, is delivered with more swing and emphasis. Although the Olive-backed is no mean performer, it is inferior as a vocalist both to the Hermit Thrush and to the Wood Thrush.

A nest that I found at Tamarack Swamp on June 14, 1895, was placed on a low tamarack, only about a yard from the ground. Another found at Coudersport on June 22, 1898, was in a low sapling in deep woodland. In Warren County, R. B. Simpson has often found nests built in small hemlocks or in laurel bushes. One nest was saddled on a piece of fallen bark that had become firmly lodged in the fork of a beech sapling, and another was placed among the branches of a dead hemlock that had blown down. The elevation, he notes, ranges from three to fifteen feet from the ground. Several nests with eggs, taken by Mr. Pierce at Kane, are in the Carnegie Museum collection. Of all our thrushes this species builds by far the neatest and prettiest nest. Much green moss is used in its construction, and this gives a pleasing exterior effect. Weed fibers and stalks also enter into its composition, while the lining is of fine rootlets. Three or four eggs are the usual set; they are dull bluish green, spotted sparingly, or fairly heavily, with dull reddish brown. This is the only one of our thrushes that lays a spotted egg. In size the eggs are about the same as those of the Hermit Thrush, or a little larger—.90 by .65 inches. June is the regular month of nesting, but eggs have been found during the latter part of May and again as late as July.

"Olive-backed Thrush" Warren, *Forest and Stream*, 1891, 37:83 (Kane, McKean Co., summer)—Simpson, *Oölogist*, 1906, 23:135; 1907, 24:134; 1909, 26:170; and 1912, 29:277 (Warren, Warren Co., nesting)—Cooke, *Bird-Lore*, 1907, 9:122 (Beaver, Beaver Co., migration)—Simpson, *Oölogist*, 1912, 29:330 (head of Tionesta Creek, Warren Co., summer); 1913, 30:150 (Presque Isle, Erie Co., October)—McConnell, *Oölogist*, 1918, 35:152 (McKeesport, Allegheny Co., transient)—McClelland, *Am. Mid. Nat.*, 1922, 8:36 (Washington, Washington Co., transient)—Boulton, *Bird-Lore*, 1928, 30:401 (Pittsburgh region, fall)—Cope and Hawkins, *Forest Leaves*, 1934, 24:26 (E. Tionesta Forest Reserve, Warren and McKean Co., summer).

Hylocichla ustulata swainsonii Cope, *Cassinia*, 1902, 5:10, 20 (Tamarack Swamp, Clinton Co., and Oleona, Potter Co., June)—Ridgway, *Bull. U. S. Nat. Mus.* no. 50, part 4, 1907, 55 (western Pa., June)—Todd, *Ann. Carnegie Mus.*, 1904, 2:592 (Presque Isle, Erie Co., transient)—Todd, in Bausman, *Hist. Beaver Co., Pa.*, 1904, 2:1202 (Beaver Co., transient)—Christy, *Cardinal*, 1923, v. 1, no. 1, [p. 15] (Sewickley, Allegheny Co., transient)—Burleigh, *Wilson Bull.*, 1923, 35:146 (Allegheny Co., migration); 1924, 36:131 (State College, Centre Co., migration).

Hylocichla ustulata swainsoni Sutton, *Ann. Carnegie Mus.*, 1928, 18:237 (Crawford Co. localities, transient)—Burleigh, *Cardinal*, 1929, 2:120 (Allegheny Co., fall migration).

GRAY-CHEEKED THRUSH (Plate 16)

HYLOCICHLA MINIMA ALICIAE (Baird)

Description—A thrush closely resembling the Olive-backed, but slightly larger; the *sides of the head* and the eye-ring are *grayish*, without the buffy tinge evident in the other species.

Range—This thrush winters in Central and South America and breeds in the upper coniferous forest region of Canada and Alaska in the Hudsonian Life Zone. It migrates through our area in spring and fall and doubtless occurs uniformly throughout, although the records come mainly from the western tier of counties. It was fairly numerous on Presque Isle in the fall of 1900, despite the fact that I had seen no birds in the spring of that year. At Pymatuning Swamp, however, and in adjacent parts of Crawford County, G. M. Sutton has found it at both seasons, and H. C. Kirkpatrick writes that it is fairly common near Meadville in the spring. Oddly enough, R. B. Simpson does not include it in his Warren County list. In Beaver County I have seen it both in spring and in fall, although more frequently at the latter season; but it is at no time as common as the Olive-backed Thrush. D. A. Atkinson records it from Wilkinsburg in May and from East Pittsburgh in September, and on one occasion it was seen within the city limits of Pittsburgh, as described by Norman McClintock (1926). In the mountain section it has been noted at State College (Burleigh), Renovo (Pierce), and Hollidaysburg (Berg). It is by no means rare and by perfunctory observers is probably often confused with the Olive-backed Thrush.

Migration—One of the later spring migrants, the Gray-cheeked Thrush need not be looked for until the second week of May at the earliest (May 7, 1933—Erie; May 8, 1902—Beaver), while most of the arrival dates fall in the third week of that month.[1] It lingers until the end of the month, and even into June (June 1, 1915—State College). In the fall movement it again follows the Olive-backed Thrush very closely. Some early fall arrival dates are: Presque Isle, September 18, 1900; Pymatuning Swamp, September 8, 1925; Beaver, September 13, 1902 and 1909.[2] At this season there are often one or two days of special movement, when the species appears in greater numbers than usual. The last birds pass through during the first week in October (Presque Isle, October 6, 1900; Beaver, October 3, 1905; October 1, 1908; October 6, 1909).

Habits—In the main this bird prefers the deep, shady woodland during its stay in our region. It is usually seen not far from the ground, to which it often descends in search of food. In the fall, its diet probably consists largely of wild fruits; the viscera of specimens shot in September have often been stained with the juice of pokeberries. The species is if possible even more furtive in its habits than its frequent companion, the Olive-backed Thrush, but it readily responds to "squeaking" and usually can be decoyed within range by this means. It always approaches by slow stages and at length comes into plain sight.

Although it passes through the region at the same time as the Olive-backed Thrush and closely resembles that species in coloration, haunts, and habits, the Gray-cheeked may be recognized by its prolonged call note, which is different from the short, low "chuck" of the Olive-backed. Once this characteristic note has been learned, it is easily recognized, even when heard overhead in the night during migration flights. Ordinarily this is the only note given during the fall movement, but sometimes, as the bird rests undisturbed in its shady retreats, one may hear a variety of other notes, which are snatches from its spring song. Its full song, which I have heard on a few occasions, might pass for an imitation of that of the Veery, but lacks the volume and regularity of the latter.

Mr. McClintock, who once studied a singing male in his own dooryard, wrote (1926): "The bird, apparently, was just outside my bedroom window. But the first repetition of the song, as I listened to it by the open window, plainly told me that it was either a freak song of an Olive-backed Thrush or was not an Olive-backed Thrush at all. While the songs of many individual birds of most species may vary greatly, yet almost invariably there is a basic quality or type that is distinctive and which serves as a sure identification of the species to one familiar with it. The song of this Thrush was far from the basic type of the Olive-backed, with which I am familiar. The song, in my estimation, was not of nearly as high a quality as that of the Olive-backed. It lacked in the quality of the theme, and reminded me more of a good musician tuning up than one performing at his best. The song also differed materially from the basic type of the Veery's song, though part of it reminded me of the latter. I knew it could not possibly be the song of any Hermit Thrush, whose song differs in its entirety from that to which I was listening."

After giving his reasons for deciding that the singer was a Gray-cheeked Thrush, the author says: "There were two distinct parts or phrases to the song, and it was sung with an appreciable

[1]The April date for this thrush cited by S. K. Eastwood, in *Bird-Lore*, 1925, 27:262, is obviously an error.

[2]The date "September 7, 1903," cited by W. W. Cooke (1907) for Beaver, is a clerical error; the record properly refers to the Olive-backed Thrush.

interval between the two: ē-a ba wē′; ē-a bē-a a-oo. Occasionally one or the other of these two phrases was repeated, without alternating the phrases."

Hylocichla aliciæ TODD, *Ann. Carnegie Mus.*, 1904, 2:592 (Presque Isle, Erie Co., transient)—TODD, in Bausman, *Hist. Beaver Co., Pa.*, 1904, 2:1202 (Beaver Co., transient).
"Gray-cheeked Thrush" COOKE, *Bird-Lore*, 1907, 9:121, part (Beaver, Beaver Co., migration)—SIMPSON, *Oölogist*, 1911, 28:144 (Presque Isle, Erie Co., September)—MCCONNELL, *Oölogist*, 1918, 35:152 (McKeesport, Allegheny Co., transient)—BOULTON, *Oölogist*, 1922, 39:73 (Raccoon Creek, Beaver Co., May)—SUTTON, *Bird-Lore*, 1924, 26:418 (Mercer and Allegheny Co., fall migration, *fide* Homer)—MCCLINTOCK, *Cardinal*, 1926, v. 1, no. 7, p. 20 (Pittsburgh, Allegheny Co., song; migration)—BOULTON, *Bird-Lore*, 1928, 30:401 (Pittsburgh region, Allegheny Co., fall).
Hylocichla aliciæ aliciæ BURLEIGH, *Wilson Bull.*, 1924, 36:131 (State College, Centre Co., spring transient).
Hylocichla minima aliciæ SUTTON, *Ann. Carnegie Mus.*, 1928, 18:237 (Crawford Co. localities, transient; Greenville, Mercer Co., May, *fide* Seiple).

VEERY (Plate 16)

HYLOCICHLA FUSCESCENS FUSCESCENS (Stephens)

Description—Upperparts (including wings and tail), *nearly uniform russet brown;* underparts white, the breast and the sides of the throat more or less shaded with buff, and spotted with buffy brown. The spots are *lighter in tone* and not so distinct as in the other species of this generic group.

Range—This thrush, like the Olive-backed and the Hermit, has a transcontinental distribution and also varies geographically from east to west. It is less decidedly northern in its faunal affinities than either of the others, since it enters the Canadian Life Zone only to a limited extent and is far more characteristic of the Transition Zone. This general trend is reflected in its distribution in western Pennsylvania. As it affects low, moist woodland, it finds conditions entirely to its liking in such a place as Pymatuning Swamp, where it is, or was, exceedingly numerous, far outnumbering the Wood Thrush. In all the other wooded swamps of northwestern Pennsylvania that have been investigated, as far south as northeastern Lawrence County, it is common and characteristic, and it occurs as well in all suitable woodland outside the swamp areas proper. It is reported as a regular but not common summer resident at New Castle, Lawrence County (Raney). Farther south, in most of Beaver County and in Washington and Greene counties, where Carolinian conditions obtain, and thence eastward at least to Chestnut Ridge, it is a transient only. The southern limit of its range here can be closely defined. At no point is it known to reach the Ohio River, although at the Big Knob, in eastern Beaver County, it comes within a few miles. Thence it crosses northern Allegheny County, including the North Park area, and swings off across the Allegheny River at Freeport. From this point on, however, no records whatever are available until we come to eastern Indiana County (Pine Flats), where I encountered the species in June, 1893. Much to my surprise, I did not find it in 1892 in the valleys of Two Lick and Yellow creeks in this same county, where they cut through Chestnut Ridge, and the exact range in this particular section has yet to be worked out. Although common on the crest and western slope of Laurel Hill, for some obscure reason the Veery has been recorded from Chestnut Ridge at only one point—Summit, Fayette County. It may be assumed that its range here coincides in general with those of such species as the Black-throated

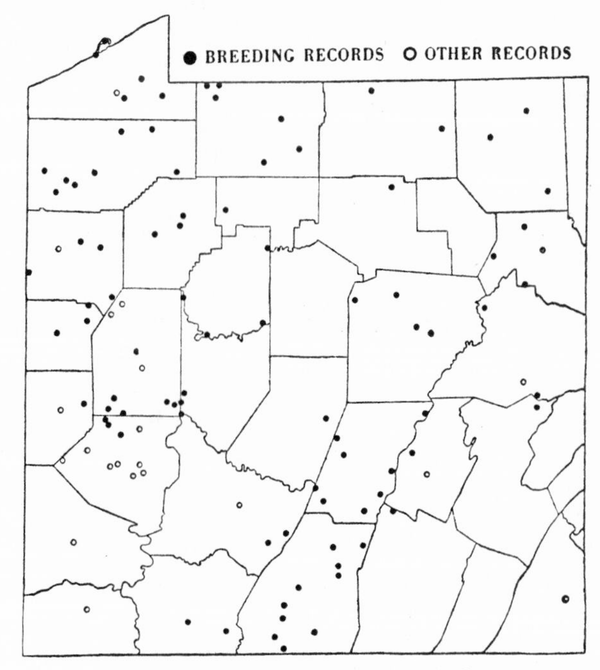

LOCAL RANGE OF THE VEERY

Green Warbler and the Chestnut-sided Warbler. The species is of course common in Somerset and Cambria counties, and ranges thence northward across the plateau region to the New York boundary. Through the northern counties, however, it is neither so numerous nor so generally distributed as the Hermit Thrush.

East of the Allegheny divide I have never found this thrush as a summer resident save in the region of Blue Knob, Bedford County, and at Bear Meadows, Centre County. R. C. Harlow reports it from "Stone Valley," Huntingdon County, just south of Bear Meadows; Jonathan Dwight found it in June in the valley near Altoona; and H. A. McGraw writes that he has observed it on the eastern slope of the Alleghenies west of that place. My own researches in the ridge and valley section, while far from exhaustive, have been sufficiently extensive to warrant the assumption that the absence of the Veery in that region is perhaps as real as it is apparent. The range as plotted on the map is decidedly "spotty"; the species seems to be absent from many localities where one might expect it. During a traverse by automobile of the region along the Armstrong-Indiana line in June, 1927, in company with J. B. Semple and B. H. Christy, I never once saw this bird. There may have been a recent shifting in the population; for in 1889 I found the species very common in the Buffalo Creek region of Armstrong and Butler counties, where recently I have failed to detect it. However secretive it may be in migration, it is not apt to be overlooked on its nesting grounds by anyone familiar with its song.

Migration—There are a few April dates for the Veery from dependable observers, but early records in general are open to suspicion and probably actually pertain to the Hermit Thrush. Mr. Christy reports seeing several veeries at Sewickley on April 22, 1902. G. M. Sutton positively identified two at Pittsburgh on April 22, 1921, and T. D. Burleigh saw one there on April 25, 1914. The species was noted once at Johnstown as early as April 28 (1934—Canan). One bird was taken by G. M. Langdon at Conneaut Lake, Crawford County, on April 29, 1925; Dr. Sutton rightly considers this an exceptionally early date. Most of the acceptable spring arrival dates fall in the first week or ten days of May. Those in five years' records from Beaver range from May 1 to 8. This thrush has been noted by R. B. Simpson at Warren as early as May 1 (1903), and J. S. Nease shot one bird at Washington on the same date in 1883. Other May 1 records come from Butler (1895—Roth) and from Altoona (1917—McGraw). In 1933 the species was first seen at Erie on May 7 (Guynes), and in 1900, was detected there on May 10 (Todd). The arrival dates in the A. K. Pierce records from Renovo range from May 7 (1900) to 16 (1920). May 17 (1911) is my latest spring date for Beaver; and D. A. Atkinson reports the species at Wilkinsburg as late as May 26 (1894)—a date that suggests breeding. As a fall transient, the Veery is rare. I have never observed it at that season myself, and very few occurrences are on record. Dr. Atkinson gives four fall records in all from Wilkinsburg, running from September 8 (1899) to 26 (1894). According to Dr. Sutton (1928), the bird was noted at Pymatuning Swamp until September 22 in 1925. I doubt the validity of the October record cited by him for the same locality.[1]

Habits[2]—So quickly and quietly does the Veery pass through our southwestern counties in the spring that for several years it entirely escaped my observation. As shy and retiring in disposition as its cousin the Hermit Thrush, it may easily be overlooked when not in song, and, like that species, it does not sing with any regularity, nor with all its wonted vim and enthusiasm, before reaching its nesting grounds. Not until the spring of 1889, when I visited the Buffalo Creek region of Armstrong and Butler counties, did I become acquainted with the Veery. It was the very first bird to attract my attention after I left the lonely way station of Monroe on the morning of May 15. I was impressed with its song, which I then heard for the first time, and in its flutelike quality I instantly recognized an affinity with the notes of the Wood Thrush. I decided that the singer must be a Veery, sight unseen. During my stay in this region, while wandering amid the shadowy gloom of the hemlock woods or forcing my way through the swampy thickets, I kept hearing the same song, which may be suggested by the syllables *hee-aweé-aweér-aweér-aweér-aweér-awý*, and which begins loud and clear, but gradually dies away toward the end. It is a far-away, weird song, truly expres-

[1]Compare W. W. Cooke, *Bird-Lore*, 1907, 9:34.
[2]Account adapted in part from the writer's article published in 1891.

sive of the spirit of the remote depths of the primeval forest. The acoustic quality of the notes was such that they seemed always to come from a distance. Despite my suspicion that this was not really the case, the birds always eluded observation while singing, and it was not until June 11 that I was at last rewarded by seeing a singing bird and was able to verify my identification.

Previously, however, on May 27, I had found the nest. On that day, which was rainy and disagreeable, I was accompanied by a local hunter and woodsman, who proposed that we should visit a nest he had found a few days before. After a walk of about a mile, we came to a high woods with a thick undergrowth of laurel and huckleberry, where the bird was presently flushed from the ground. I gave one glance at the nest and another at the bird, exclaimed, "Wilson's Thrush!" and in another moment fired and brought her down, to verify my identification. Returning to the nest, I found that it held three eggs, of exactly the same shade of bluish green as those of the Wood Thrush. They were, of course, smaller, and upon blowing them I found them to be slightly incubated. The nest was not sunk in the ground, but placed on a mound of leaves to protect it from the damp; it was surrounded and canopied over with huckleberry bushes. Leaves, strips of bark, and weed stalks entered into its composition, with broken leaves as lining. Outside it was five inches in diameter by four and one-half inches in depth; the cavity was two and three-quarters inches wide and the same in depth.

Other nests I have examined have been similar. They were all raised above the ground level, either in the same way as the one described, or by being placed on the top of a prostrate tree trunk or in the midst of a clump of woody shoots. The eggs are three or four in number and measure about .88 by .67 inches. Sets have been found from the latter part of May until late in June. Normally, however, only one brood is reared. The female sits very closely and when flushed dives off into the brush. Indeed, this thrush is characteristically partial to low bushes and shrubbery, especially in dank situations. It is found in all the alder swamps of the northwestern counties, and in the rhododendron thickets of the mountains. In such dense covert several males may often be heard trying to outsing each other, all the while keeping well concealed. "Squeaking" usually brings them to the edge for a hurried look at the intruder. The Veery is silent after July.

Turdus fuscescens Teulon, *Jour. Boston Zoöl. Soc.*, 1882, 1:49 (Bradford, McKean Co.)—Townsend, *Proc. Acad. Nat. Sci. Philadelphia*, 1883, 60 (Latrobe, Westmoreland Co.)—Warren, *Birds Pa.*, ed. 2, 1890, 325 (Erie and Crawford Co., breeding, *fide* Sennett)—Koch, *Ornithologist and Oölogist*, 1890, 15:74 (Lloydville, Cambria Co., nesting)—Dwight, *Auk*, 1892, 9:140 (Cresson, Cambria Co., and Altoona, Blair Co., June)—Baily, *Auk*, 1896, 13:292, 297 (Straight Creek, near Williamsville, Elk Co., June–July).

Hylocichla fuscescens Todd, *Ornithologist and Oölogist*, 1891, 16:50 (Buffalo Creek region, Armstrong and Butler Co., nesting)—Cope, *Cassinia*, 1902, 5:12, 20 (Tamarack Swamp, Clinton Co., and Oleona, Potter Co., June)—Todd, *Ann. Carnegie Mus.*, 1904, 2:592 (Presque Isle, Erie Co., nesting)—Todd, in Bausman, *Hist. Beaver Co., Pa.*, 1904, 2:1202 (Beaver Co., transient, rare in summer)—Simpson, *Cassinia*, 1908, 11:82 (Warren, Warren Co., summer)—Pitcairn, *Auk*, 1910, 27:213 ("Allegheny, Allegheny Co." [Rowan, Butler Co.], breeding)—Hegner and Christy, *Cardinal*, 1931, 3:22 (North Park, Allegheny Co., nesting).

"Wilson Thrush" Simpson, *Oölogist*, 1906, 23:135 (Warren, Warren Co., breeding).

Hylocichla fuscescens fuscescens Harlow, *Auk*, 1912, 29:477 ("Stone Valley," Huntingdon Co., breeding); 1918, 35:147 (Bedford, Fayette, Clarion, Blair, Venango, Warren, and Erie Co., summer)—Christy, *Cardinal*, 1923, v. 1, no. 1, [p. 15] (Sewickley, Allegheny Co., spring transient; Valencia, Butler Co., nesting)—Burleigh, *Wilson Bull.*, 1923, 35:146 (Allegheny Co., spring transient); 1924, 36:131 (State College, Centre Co., May)—Christy and Sutton, *Cardinal*, 1928, 2:74 (Thom's Run, Cook Forest, Clarion Co., June)—Sutton, *Ann. Carnegie Mus.*, 1928, 18:236 (Meadville and Pymatuning Swamp, Crawford Co., summer)—Burleigh, *Cardinal*, 1932, 3:79 (Summit, Fayette Co., summer).

"Veery" Dickey, *Oölogist*, 1914, 31:207 (Cresson, Cambria Co., nesting)—McClelland, *Am. Mid. Nat.*, 1922, 8:36 (Washington, Washington Co., transient)—Eastwood, *Bird-Lore*, 1925, 27:337 (Bradford Woods, Allegheny Co., July, *fide* Frederick); 1926, 28:273 (Rector, Westmoreland Co., May, *fide* Knauz)—Cope and Hawkins, *Forest Leaves*, 1934, 24:26 (E. Tionesta Forest Reserve, Warren and McKean Co., summer)—Arthur, *Country Rambler*, 1934, 131 (Wildwood, Deer Creek region, and Bradford Woods, Allegheny Co.; song).

EASTERN BLUEBIRD (Plate 16)

SIALIA SIALIS SIALIS (Linnaeus)

Description—Adult male in spring: upperparts bright blue; underparts rufous brown, the middle of the abdomen and the under tail coverts, whitish. *Female:* similar, but all the colors duller. In fall and winter the blue is "veiled" with rufescent-buffy edgings to the feathers. *Juvenal plumage:* upperparts dusky brown, the back with white spots, the wings and tail with a blue wash; underparts white; the throat, breast, and flanks showing dusky streaks.

Range—In one form or another the Bluebird is found throughout the greater part of North America east of the Rocky Mountains, from the highlands of Guatemala north to southern Canada. In the northern part of its range, which comprises the Alleghanian Fauna and the lower portion of the Canadian, it is migratory, and the breeding birds retire southward for the winter. In western Pennsylvania it is fairly evenly and commonly distributed as a summer resident and is casual and irregular in winter as well. It has been reported during the latter season from stations in the western tier of counties as far north as Meadville, while in the region of the Ohio Valley and southward, winter records are by no means infrequent. R. B. Simpson, however, omits it from his list of winter birds at Warren, and indeed there is nothing to show that it ever winters in the highlands north of Springs, Somerset County, in the extreme south, where it has been noted during mild January weather on four occasions by A. B. Miller. East of the Allegheny divide it has been observed in winter at State College (Harlow; Burleigh), at Altoona (McGraw), and at Chambersburg (Sutton).

The Bluebird is not nearly so common now as it was in the early nineties. The winter of 1894–95 is memorable for the havoc wrought upon the Bluebird population by the long-continued cold. That spring scarcely one bluebird returned out of every hundred that had gone south the fall before. The survivors, of course, were the hardiest of their race, and the species recovered its lost ground with surprising quickness. Five or six seasons brought it almost up to its former numbers. Seemingly the increase was unchecked until it reached a certain point, beyond which it was unable to go. In recent years there has been another notable falling off in numbers, attributable, I believe, to the inroads of the European Starling, which actively competes with the Bluebird for nesting sites and which bids fair, if unchecked, to reduce the numbers of that species to a tithe of what they once were.

Migration—The Bluebird comes and goes with the Robin. It appears as a rule during the latter part of February and seldom later than the first week or ten days of March. Actual dates for Beaver range from February 15 (1915) to March 11 (1923). One must be careful not to confuse wintering individuals with new spring arrivals; the latter, however, usually appear suddenly and simultaneously over a considerable area. The species has not been seen at Warren earlier in the season than February 27 (1892), nor at Renovo before February 19 (1909), and both these dates are exceptional. February 10 (1925; 1938) is the earliest arrival date for Springs (Miller); February 15 (1927), for Johnstown (Canan); February 21 (1915), for Altoona (McGraw); and February 20 (1909), for State College (Harlow). In some years the species is common from the time of its arrival, while in other years, when the season is backward, it may not become really common for two or three weeks. The males arrive some days ahead of the females. The fall movement is accomplished mostly in October, but the last stragglers do not get away until sometime in November, and it is of course difficult to distinguish these from wintering individuals.

Habits—Of all our birds, this soft-voiced harbinger of spring is one of the most eagerly awaited. When winter begins to yield at last to the warming touch of the returning sun; when several days of clearing skies and southerly breezes have loosened the ice-fettered streams, drawn the frost from the ground, and given a balmy tang to the air; and when all nature seems in an expectant mood, vibrant with a new hope and a new promise—the Bluebird returns. Carrying the hue of the sky on its back and of the fresh earth on its breast (as John Burroughs aptly says), it seems the very incarnation of the spirit of the spring, the forerunner of a brighter day. Its soft, pleasing warble, like the gentle murmur of a flowing brook in soothing cadence, awakens a sense of well-being and content in each responsive listener. The Bluebird is a welcome visitor to orchards, farms, and groves, and comes as well into villages and to the edges of towns. Although by no means so familiar and domestic as the Robin, it can sometimes be persuaded to take up its abode near dwellings and even to make use of a nest box, if the English Sparrow and the Starling can be prevented from usurping it.

After the arrival of the females, little time is lost in mating and in beginning the nest, which is built in any suitable hole, such as a hollow fence post, an old woodpecker-hole, or a natural cavity in a tree or dead stub. Old orchards are favorite places, as are also the margins of woods. Seldom is the nesting site more than fifteen feet from the ground, and usually not over five or six, although D. A. Atkinson reports having once found a nest thirty feet up in an oak. The nest proper is composed of grasses and weed stalks, and sometimes feathers, horsehair, and other soft materials; it varies considerably in bulk and is not nearly so compact as that of the Robin. Four to six (usually five) pale blue, unspotted eggs are laid; they measure about .82 by .64 inches. J. W. Jacobs took a set of six pure white eggs on May 21, 1893—the second laying of a pair whose first set of eggs were unusually pale blue. Some, though apparently not all, pairs rear two broods in a season. The eggs for the first brood are laid as a rule from about the middle of April, or sometimes even earlier, to the first week in May; those for the second, from June 10 to the first part of July. At State College in 1920, T. D. Burleigh found a nest with three incubated eggs as late as August 1. The same hole is often used during successive years, presumably by the same pair, but is always relined for each brood. Mr. Jacobs reports an experiment in testing the prolific ability of a pair of bluebirds; they produced five sets of eggs in thirty-five days. He also relates (1893) an interesting anecdote concerning a bluebird appropriating the finished nest of a (Carolina) Chickadee: "The nest was in two parts; one constructed by the Chickadee, and the other, which was the top story, was made by the Bluebird. The first story contained two [eggs] of the Chickadee, and in the next were five eggs of each species."

In 1916 Rudyerd Boulton published a detailed account of the nesting of a pair of bluebirds studied by him at Beaver in the spring of 1914. He had put up two bird boxes made of hollow logs in a tree on the river bank in sight of his house. His report follows:

"February 17. Nest-logs put up.
February 25. First Bluebird seen.
February 28. Three pairs looked at both logs, fought for them, and *my pair* rented it.
March 21. Nest completed.
March 26. First egg laid.
March 27. Second egg laid.
March 28. Third egg laid.
March 29. Fourth egg laid.
March 30. Fifth egg laid.
April 13. Young hatched.
April 29. Young left the nest.

"Prior to March 29, the river bank had been burned over twice for the purpose of improving the grass roots, but the Bluebirds never seemed to mind it, although the nest was enveloped in clouds of thick smoke both times. The last two days of March, and the first two of April were cold, below freezing, with a driving snowstorm followed by sleet; but the Bluebirds' activities never ceased. At this time the male passed the night in the nest with the female, 'twinkling' into the log at sunset. The male was very pugnacious, and seemed not to know fear. He would dash with equal courage at a Flicker or a Song Sparrow, when they approached his tree. Once I saw him actually knock a Flicker off a branch. Perhaps he would not have succeeded had the Flicker been aware of his approach, but the Bluebird came up behind and hit him below the belt. When I would go near the nest, the male would utter 'chuckling' notes, as if to scold and frighten me away. On several occasions he came so close that I could almost touch him.

"When the young were about four days old, I set up my camera, three feet away from the nest, to obtain some pictures. The first time the shutter snapped, the female hopped down on to the branch on which the camera was placed, put her head to one side, and seemed to say, 'What is this that clicks in my face,' and then she hopped all over it, pecking it.

"Both parents were often seen cleaning the nest. They began to feed the young at about eight o'clock every morning, and continued it steadily at an average of every six or seven minutes until about six at night, using as food almost exclusively a certain kind of bug that was very hairy, brownish with black markings, and, except for the hair, might have been mistaken for castor beans, being about the same size. They seemed a huge mouthful for a young Bluebird. Several times a day I would climb up to the nest and whistle softly like a Bluebird before the aperture. The young would crane their necks and stretch their mouths for the supposed food, although none was forthcoming.

"When the young flew from the nest, I felt as though I had lost a family. My grief was not such that I could not capture them, however, and after counting noses, I found that one was missing. I climbed up and there I found 'runtie' at the bottom of the nest, pitifully squeaking at being left alone. I took out the bottom and extracted him. Finally, after half an hour or more of posing, I got several good pictures of the babies on a dead branch. When I opened the nest-log to clean it, I found a little block of grasses about three inches in diameter and one inch high. It fairly glistened with shed feather-sheaths. In the bottom were six or seven bugs, of the species mentioned before, that had evidently escaped the birds. Exactly two months after the first egg was laid, the second nest of the same pair was nearing completion in another of my boxes. Here are the dates:

"May 29. First egg laid.
May 30. Second egg laid.
May 31. Third egg laid.
June 1. Fourth egg laid.
June 16. Young hatched.
June 23. Young have not flown yet.

"While the female was incubating, the male still fed the young of the first brood, although not so often as when they left the nest."

Hence it seems that in a season sufficiently advanced, laying may begin as early as the last of March. S. S. Dickey speaks of finding fresh eggs at Waynesburg on April 2. R. L. Keesler tells of a pair of bluebirds that nested in a bird box on his premises in Forestville, Butler County, for three successive years and that raised twenty-four young from twenty-seven eggs in that period. He writes that the male worked as hard as the female in feeding and caring for the young and relieved his mate of their care after they left the nest and while she was preparing for a second brood. In the fall the parents and their young returned for a last look at their home, so Mr. Keesler believes, before leaving for the South.

Except in the nesting season proper, the Bluebird is fully as gregarious as the Robin. As early as August, flocks composed of old and young may be encountered; the latter, while the postjuvenal molt is still incomplete, may easily be distinguished by their parti-colored plumage. The birds desert their old haunts, avoid the neighborhood of houses, and invade the woodland. September and October find them still roaming about over the country in scattered companies and sometimes larger flocks, often perching together in the top of some tall dead tree. At this season their food consists largely of wild fruits and seeds of various kinds, such as pokeberry, elderberry, dogwood, and sumac. They seldom touch cultivated fruit of any kind. In the winter I have seen a flock in the top of a tulip tree, feeding on the seeds. "The fruit-eating period of the bluebird," as F. E. L. Beal remarks, "is not in summer when the fruit is fresh on the tree, but from October to February, inclusive, during which months three-fourths of its fruit eating is done. From this it appears that fruit is really the winter food of the bluebird, tiding it over until insects are again abundant and taking the place of seeds eaten by so many birds at this season."[1] This authority determines, indeed, that 68 per cent of the Bluebird's food consists of insects, and that of these, Orthoptera (grasshoppers, crickets, and katydids), Lepidoptera (caterpillars), and Coleoptera (beetles) constitute by far the largest part. Anyone who has ever watched a bluebird for any length of time must have noticed its adeptness in catching insects on the wing; dashing out from its perch, flycatcher-like, it picks them off one by one. In addition to their cheery presence and song, their beautiful plumage, and their interesting habits, bluebirds in the orchard or garden are a valuable economic asset. The charges leveled against the Robin in no way apply to the Bluebird; its work is almost all to the good, and it deserves the fullest encouragement and protection.

"Bluebird" Wied, *Reise in Innere Nord-America*, 1839, 1:131 (near Ebensburg, Cambria Co., September)—Enty, *Ornithologist and Oölogist*, 1885, 10:78 (Templeton, Armstrong Co., migration)—Wickham, *Oölogist*, 1888, 5:92 (Beaver, Beaver Co., migration)—Stone, *Cassinia*, 1906, 9:44 (McConnellsburg, Fulton Co., June)—Pitcairn, *Bird-Lore*, 1907,

[1]U. S. Department of Agriculture, *Bulletin*, no. 171, 1915, p. 24.

9:155 (Riverview Park, Allegheny Co., nesting)—Burleigh, *Oölogist*, 1911, 28:156 (Harmarville, Allegheny Co., nesting)—Burleigh, *Oölogist*, 1913, 30:281 ([Aspinwall], Allegheny Co., winter)—McConnell, *Bird-Lore*, 1916, 18:27; etc. (McKeesport, Allegheny Co., December)—Burleigh and McGrew, *Bird-Lore*, 1916, 18:28 (Harmarville, Allegheny Co., December)—Boulton, *Bird-Lore*, 1916, 18:123 (Beaver, Beaver Co., nesting)—McConnell, *Oölogist*, 1918, 35:152 ("Christy Park," Allegheny Co., breeding)—Miller (R. F.), *Oölogist*, 1919, 36:157 (State College, Centre Co., nesting)—Dickey, *Oölogist*, 1919, 36:67 (Waynesburg, Greene Co., nesting)—Scoville, *Atlantic Monthly*, 1920, 126:37 (Treaster Valley, Centre Co., March)—McConnell, *Bird-Lore*, 1920, 22:32; etc. (Emsworth, Allegheny Co., December)—Blair, *In the Open*, July, 1920, 10:22 ([Plains Church], Butler Co., nesting)—Keesler, *Oölogist*, 1921, 38:170 (Harrisville, Butler Co., nesting)—McClelland, *Am. Mid. Nat.*, 1922, 8:36 (Washington, Washington Co., summer; migration)—Hoffman, *et al.*, *Bird-Lore*, 1923, 25:23 (Grove City, Mercer Co., December)—Street, *Cassinia*, 1923, 24:19 (Greencastle to Ft. Loudon, Franklin Co., June)—Sutton, *Bird-Lore*, 1924, 26:189 (Pittsburgh, Allegheny Co., migration, *fide* Blair), 418 (Greenville, Mercer Co., fall migration, *fide* Homer)—Christy, *Cardinal*, 1924, v. 1, no. 4, p. 10 (Big Traverse Valley, Beaver Co., June)—Lehman, *Bird-Lore*, 1925, 27:245 ([Chambersburg, Franklin Co.], nesting)—Christy and Hegner, *Bird-Lore*, 1924, 26:30; etc. (Raccoon Creek Valley, Beaver Co., December)—Eastwood, *Bird-Lore*, 1926, 28:402 (Coraopolis, Allegheny Co., October); 1927, 29:56 (Logan's Ferry, Allegheny Co., October; Thompsonville, Washington Co., November, *fide* Ellair), 127 (Ingram, Allegheny Co., February, *fide* Floyd); 197 (Springs, Somerset Co., migration, *fide* Miller)—Boulton, *Bird-Lore*, 1928, 30:196 (Pittsburgh region, March, migration; Baden, Beaver Co., March, *fide* Auerswald)—Miller (A. B.), *Bird-Lore*, 1932, 34:47 (Springs, Somerset Co., December).

Sialia sialis Teulon, *Jour. Boston Zoöl. Soc.*, 1882, 1:49 (Bradford, McKean Co.)—Townsend, *Proc. Acad. Nat. Sci. Philadelphia*, 1883, 60 (Latrobe, Westmoreland Co., nesting)—Jacobs, *Nat. Companion*, 1886, 2:58 (Waynesburg, Greene Co., summer; few in winter)—Dwight, *Auk*, 1892, 9:141 (Cresson, Cambria Co., June)—Todd, *Auk*, 1893, 10:41 (Two Lick, Indiana Co., June), 46 (Coalport, Clearfield Co., June)—Jacobs, *Summer Birds Greene Co., Pa.*, 1893, 14 (Greene Co., nesting)—Kirkpatrick, *Auk*, 1895, 12:309 (Meadville, Crawford Co., seasonal occurrence)—Baily, *Auk*, 1896, 13:297 (Williamsville, Elk Co., June–July)—Jacobs, *Gleanings from Nature*, 1898, 1:10, 13, 20 (Greene Co., nesting)—Todd, *Ann. Carnegie Mus.*, 1904, 2:593 (Erie and region, Erie Co., summer)—Todd, in Bausman, *Hist. Beaver Co., Pa.*, 1904, 2:1202 (Beaver Co., resident)—Keim, *Cassinia*, 1905, 8:41 (Port Allegany, McKean Co., summer)—Forrest, *Oölogist*, 1911, 28:115 (Washington, Washington Co., breeding).

Sialia sialis sialis Harlow, *Auk*, 1912, 29:477 (southern Centre Co., breeding)—Christy, *Cardinal*, 1923, v. 1, no. 1, [p. 15] (Sewickley, Allegheny Co., breeding; occasional in winter)—Burleigh, *Wilson Bull.*, 1923, 35:147 (Allegheny Co., nesting; scarce in winter); 1924, 36:74; and 1931, 43:54 (State College, Centre Co., migration; nesting)—Christy and Sutton, *Cardinal*, 1928, 2:75 (Cook Forest, Clarion Co., summer)—Sutton, *Ann. Carnegie Mus.*, 1928, 18:239 (Crawford Co. localities, summer; occasional in winter)—Burleigh, *Cardinal*, 1932, 3:79 (Chestnut Ridge, near Uniontown, Fayette Co., summer).

OLD WORLD WARBLERS

FAMILY SYLVIIDAE

THE FAMILY SYLVIIDAE is composed mainly of Old World Warblers, which in details of form are quite unlike the Wood Warblers of the New World. The American Ornithologists' Union *Check-List* assigns the Kinglets and the Gnatcatchers to this family, although some systematists believe that both should be removed therefrom.

The Kinglets (Subfamily Regulinae) are among the tiniest of all our birds. They have short, straight, slender bills and relatively short tails, and are mainly olive green in color. In habits they resemble the Wood Warblers, with which they are often found, searching industriously for insect food among the treetops. They breed in the northern parts of both continents, as well as southward in the mountains.

The Gnatcatchers (Subfamily Polioptilinae—a single genus) are truly American birds and occur principally in Central and South America. Of the seven forms in the United States, only one reaches our latitude. They are small, active, bluish-gray birds, with relatively long tails that show much white in flight.

BLUE-GRAY GNATCATCHER (Plate 16)

POLIOPTILA CAERULEA CAERULEA (Linnaeus)

Description—A very small bird, no larger than the Ruby-crowned Kinglet, but with a relatively longer tail. General color grayish blue above, whitish below, with a faint wash of bluish gray. Wings dusky, with bluish-gray edgings; tail black in the middle, white on the sides. A narrow white eye-ring, and a short black line over the eye. *Female* not so brightly colored in general as the male and without the black line over the eye.

Range—Our Blue-gray Gnatcatcher is an outlying and necessarily migratory representative of a generic group characteristic of the American tropics. The breeding range of the species is transcontinental, and in its summer distribution the eastern race is normally limited by the Carolinian Fauna, although like several other birds of this fauna it seems to be gradually working its way farther north. It is a rather common summer resident in the typically Carolinian country from the Ohio and lower Allegheny rivers southward, and eastward to the base of Chestnut Ridge. While I

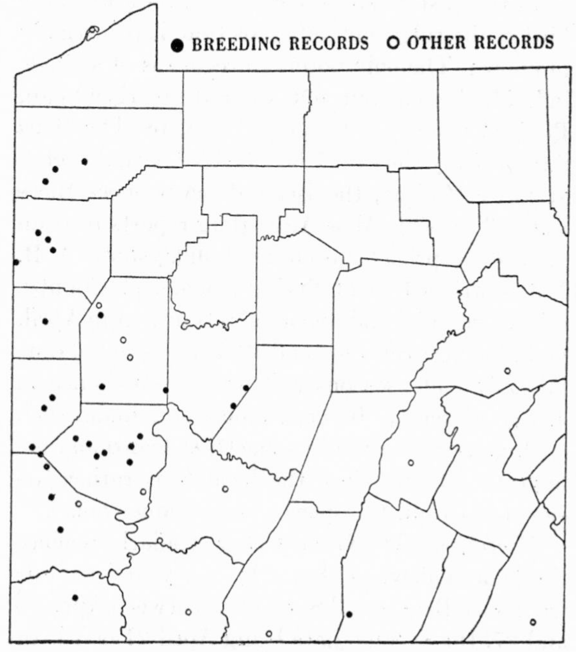

LOCAL RANGE OF THE BLUE-GRAY GNATCATCHER

have seen it only once (on May 22, 1896) in the Buffalo Creek region of Butler and Armstrong counties, I have traced it all the way to the eastern boundary of the latter county (Idaho and near Gastown), where I found it in June associated with the Black-throated Green Warbler. From this circumstance I would judge that it follows the Allegheny Valley at least to Venango County, but I have no information to that effect. Through Lawrence and Mercer counties, however, it has been traced to several points in Crawford County, where it is now known as a breeding bird. Although not nearly so common in that region as it is in Beaver County, it seems to occur there regularly. How much farther north it breeds is not certainly known. In Erie County it has been detected on Presque Isle in May, August, and September, but not under conditions conclusively indicative of breeding. The individuals seen there may have been on their way to or from southern Ontario. Across the Pennsylvania border in Ashtabula County, Ohio, the bird is a rare summer resident (Hicks), but it does not reach the lake shore plain regularly until it enters Lorain County (Jones). In western New York it is scarcely more than accidental.

In eastern Pennsylvania the Blue-gray Gnatcatcher is rare or casual (Stone). Thus is explained the fact that it does not invade the mountains from the east to any great extent. As a breeding bird in the ridge and valley section, it is virtually unknown. The only potential record is of a single individual seen, but not secured, at Hyndman, Bedford County, on June 1, 1898, by Thaddeus Surber. Only since 1927 has the bird been detected at State College; the isolated occurrences there were all in May. Miss A. E. Berg reports it as an occasional spring transient at Hollidaysburg. A. B. Miller writes that at Springs, Somerset County, it is an irregular and uncommon transient in April, and that between 1908 and 1927 it was noted during only eight seasons and usually only once in any given season. Its occurrence there under such circumstances certainly suggests a transmontane migration route, since the locality is rather too elevated to suit the species as a summer home.

Migration—The Gnatcatcher regularly reaches the Ohio Valley, as shown by ten years' records from both Beaver and Sewickley, between April 15 and 27, the average date being April 21 or 22. In 1912 T. D. Burleigh saw it at Pittsburgh on April 14, and in 1924 it was reported from Deer Creek, Allegheny County, on April 12 (Elliott, *et al.*). In an early season it may arrive in Greene County, according to S. S. Dickey, as early as April 12, but the average date of arrival there is April 15. Within a few days, or a week at most, the species attains its normal numbers for the summer, and nesting is under way. Less is known about its movements in the fall migration, as it is very inconspicuous at that season. Seldom is it seen after August. I positively identified it at Beaver on September 6, 1905, and again on September 5, 1910, and think that these dates approximate its average time of departure. (A published record of mine for September 24, 1888, is questionable.) Mr. Burleigh saw one bird at Pittsburgh on September 6, 1927. Undoubtedly the species is an early migrant in the fall.

Habits—Several writers imply that their finding of the Blue-gray Gnatcatcher in western Pennsylvania was a new discovery, but an examination of the list of references cited below will serve to dispel such an idea. As long ago as 1886, indeed, J. W. Jacobs wrote a brief account of the nesting of this species in Greene County, and in 1892 I published a more extended notice based on my own experience in Beaver County. The following account is condensed from this article.

The Gnatcatcher arrives during the third week in April, when pleasant weather has become fairly established and the orchard and forest trees are just beginning to burst into new life. Dry and rather open woods, especially if on a hillside, are its chosen haunts. There the birds may be found by following up their peculiar filing note, *chee-e-e-chee-e-e-chee-e-e*, which cannot possibly be confounded with that of any other species, although it bears some resemblance to the song of the Golden-winged Warbler. But this note is feeble compared with the Gnatcatcher's true song; for the bird has exquisite vocal powers, though they are not often exercised. As the song is heard for only a week or two after the species' arrival, it is not generally familiar even to professed ornithologists. It is not so full and clear as the vivacious song of the Ruby-crowned Kinglet (which migrates at the same time), but it is more exquisitely modulated, more expressive, and sweeter.

The gnatcatchers are invariably paired on their arrival, and they lose little time in selecting nesting sites. The location is always in the immediate vicinity of last year's nest and is frequently in the same tree. After the spot has been chosen, work on the nest is begun immediately. Construction requires between one and two weeks of constant labor on the part of the female; the male, so far as I have observed, never assists her, although he always remains near at hand and takes a great interest in the work. The nest is occasionally fixed in the crotch of an upright branch, but as a rule it is saddled on a horizontal limb, preferably of an oak, at an elevation of from twenty to fifty feet. Frequently it is placed directly under another limb and is thus partially protected from the disintegrating effect of rain. The elegant and elaborate structure is a credit to its tiny owner, whose labor is so patiently expended upon it. Though reminding one strikingly of the nest of the Hummingbird, with which it vies in intricacy of design and beauty of finish, it is much larger; in fact, it is very large in proportion to the size of its builder.

A nest that was collected on May 19, 1890, may be regarded as typical. It is composed of the delicate stalks of certain small weeds; fine strips of inner bark; bits of dry mullein leaf; down from the thistle, milkweed, and various other plants; and pieces of cocoons. There is no special lining other than the regular material used for the body of the nest, but the outside is completely and neatly stuccoed with bluish-gray lichens fastened on by a lavish use of cobwebs. The cavity is deeper than it is wide, and the brim is much constricted. The nest may easily be mistaken for a knot on the limb, and the birds often place it on a lichen-covered branch, the better to conceal it. This soft and perishable structure is loosely attached to its branch and never outlasts the season for which it was intended. Although it is so well hidden, finding it is in reality an easy matter, as the birds never stray far from home and are always certain to return sooner or later. When the female begins to incubate she occasionally answers the calls of her mate with reassuring notes, thus disclosing the position of her nest. When their territory is invaded, the birds become bold and fearless and often come within a yard of the observer, scolding and protesting vigorously. The female of a nesting pair that came to my attention was accidentally killed when the nest was nearly completed; the male in the course of a few days secured another mate, which built a new nest at a little distance, using the material of the old nest in its construction.

Certain authors have stated that the eggs are pure white in ground-color, but this is a mistake, though it is barely possible that some bleached or abnormally light-colored specimens may appear white. I have yet to see any specimens that differ much, except in density of marking, from the following pattern: light bluish green, marked with clearly defined spots of a light rufous color, which are distributed rather more thickly about the larger end. The eggs average .56 by .43 inches. According to my experience at Beaver, a set usually consists of five eggs, and they are very delicate and fragile. The young are abroad with their parents sometime in June, and family groups are commonly found lingering in or near their old haunts until late in August, when they depart for their winter quarters beyond the southern limits of the United States.

Later studies serve in general to confirm the above observations. In Greene County, where the species is so abundant that Dr. Dickey has found more than eighty nests in one season, it prefers white oak trees, but uses also red oak, walnut, white ash, elm, yellow locust, sugar maple, sycamore, and even apple trees. The earliest record for nest-building is April 22, and for a full set of eggs, May 5. Dr. Dickey has also found that birds that abandon first nests rebuild in a new location. Concerning the haunts and abundance of the Gnatcatcher, he says (1915): "The larger woods—several acres in extent—may contain as many as five or six pairs of the birds—during the past season I noticed fully six pairs in a woods of some ten acres. Not always are the birds found in woods but frequently [they] resort to groves of oaks, hickories, etc., small clusters of trees or saplings, and rarely to apple orchards. At times I have known the birds to make their homes in rather isolated trees, standing some distance from either wood, grove, or thicket. Prior to nest building the gnatcatchers flit about the higher branches of the trees where they secure the bulk of their insect food."

Polioptila cærulea Townsend, *Proc. Acad. Nat. Sci. Philadelphia*, 1883, 60 (Latrobe, Westmoreland Co.)—Jacobs, *Hoosier Nat.*, 1886, 2:30 (Waynesburg, Greene Co., nesting) —Jacobs, *Bay State Oölogist*, 1888, 1:46 (Waynesburg, Greene Co., nesting)—Warren, *Birds Pa.*, ed. 2, 1890, 323 (Washington Co., transient, *fide* Compton, *et al.*; Allegheny Co., breeding, *fide* Hazzard)—Todd, *Ornithologist and Oölogist*, 1892, 17:73 (Beaver, Beaver Co., nesting; habits)—Jacobs, *Summer Birds Greene Co., Pa.*, 1893, 14 (Greene Co., nesting)—Todd, *Ann. Carnegie Mus.*, 1904, 2:592 (Presque Isle, Erie Co., August)—Todd, in Bausman, *Hist. Beaver Co.. Pa.*, 1904, 2:1202 (Beaver Co., summer).

"Blue-gray Gnatcatcher" Jacobs, *Hawkeye Ornithologist and Oölogist*, 1888, 1:88 (Waynesburg, Greene Co., April)—Pitcairn, *Bird-Lore*, 1907, 9:155 (Riverview Park, Allegheny Co., breeding)—Burleigh, *Oölogist*, 1911, 28:156 (Harmarville, Allegheny Co., nesting)—Cooke, *Bird-Lore*, 1915, 17:201 (Beaver, Beaver Co., and Waynesburg, Greene Co., migration)—McConnell, *Oölogist*, 1918, 35:152 (Long Run, near McKeesport, Allegheny Co.)—McClelland, *Am. Mid. Nat.*, 1922, 8:36 (Washington, Washington Co., summer)—Blair, *Bull. Audubon Soc. W. Pa.*, 1923, 1:42 (Little Sewickley Creek, Allegheny Co., nesting)—Burleigh, *Wilson Bull.*, 1923, 35:79, 145 (Allegheny Co., nesting; migration) —Sutton, *Bird-Lore*, 1924, 26:190 (Deer Creek, Allegheny Co., *fide* Elliott, *et al.*, April)—Christy, *Cardinal*, 1924, v. 1, no. 4, p. 10 (Big Traverse Valley, Beaver Co., June)—Eastwood, *Bird-Lore*, 1925, 27:254 (Murdocksville, Washington Co., April, nesting), 262 (Pittsburgh region, Allegheny Co., April); 1926, 28:272 (Deer Creek, Allegheny Co., *fide* Blair and Squier; Raccoon Creek, Beaver Co., *fide* Reiter), 343 (Dixmont, Allegheny Co., July, *fide* Auerswald)—Wood, *Wilson Bull.*, 1932, 44:238 (State College, Centre Co., spring).

Polioptila cærulea cærulea Dickey, *Oölogist*, 1915, 32:67 (Waynesburg, Greene Co., nesting; habits)—Harlow, *Auk*, 1918, 35:146 (Greene, Washington, and Allegheny Co., summer)—Christy, *Cardinal*, 1923, v. 1, no. 1, [p. 15] (Sewickley, Allegheny Co., summer)—Burleigh, *Wilson Bull.*, 1923, 35:145 (Allegheny Co., nesting)—[Editor], *Cassinia*, 1926, 25:35 (Greencastle, Franklin Co., April, *fide* Ziegler)—Sutton, *Ann. Carnegie Mus.*, 1928, 18:235 (Meadville, Crawford Co., nesting, *fide* Kirkpatrick; Crystal Lake, Crawford Co., May)—Burleigh, *Cardinal*, 1929, 2:120 (Allegheny Co., fall migration)—Burleigh, *Cardinal*, 1932, 3:79 (Chalk Hill, Fayette Co., September).

EASTERN GOLDEN-CROWNED KINGLET (Plate 16)

REGULUS SATRAPA SATRAPA Lichtenstein

Description—A bird resembling a warbler, but much smaller than any of these. The *crown* has *two broad black lateral stripes*, enclosing a *median stripe* that is plain *yellow* in the female and *yellow, orange-centered*, in the male; there is a pale stripe over the eye and another underneath, but the eyelids are black; general color above, dull olive green, grayish on the upper back; edgings of tail and wings also dull olive green, the latter crossed by two pale bars; underparts plain dull grayish white.

Range—The Golden-crowned Kinglet is a close relative of the Old World Goldcrest, *Regulus cristatus*, and by some authors is ranked as a subspecies thereof. The eastern race breeds in the Canadian Fauna and winters thence southward to northern Florida. Its breeding range includes the Adirondack and Catskill Mountains in New York, the Pocono and North Mountain region of northeastern Pennsylvania, and the spruce belt of West Virginia and North Carolina. This southward extension along the Appalachian highlands is paralleled in the ranges of various other species of boreal origin and affinities, such as the Red-breasted Nuthatch, the Brown Creeper, and the Winter Wren; and all these have been found breeding in our region at an appropriate elevation. The Golden-crowned Kinglet, however, has not been so reported; and it seems incredible that it could have been overlooked. True, to this general statement there is one exception; for the species is marked "rare" and "casual" in Balliet's and Van Fleet's manuscript lists of the breeding birds of DuBois. The one locality where it might be expected is Tamarack Swamp in Clinton County, yet in a painstaking search during five different seasons, I failed to discover it there. Investigation of other parts of the plateau region has thus far proved equally fruitless. At Warren the species is known to R. B. Simpson only as a winter visitant, much more numerous in migration, and this is its status throughout our region in general. It is possible that further search in the northern and more elevated counties, however, may yet reveal breeding stations. Such a discovery will be awaited with interest.

Migration—Not until toward the end of September, after most of the warblers have come and gone, does the Golden-crowned Kinglet appear. I have never observed it at Beaver earlier than September 22 (1910), and it usually arrives about a week later and becomes common sometime in October. The transients depart about the first of November, leaving behind the normal small numbers of wintering birds. Early fall arrival dates from other stations correspond in general: Presque Isle, September 25, 1900 (Todd); Wilkinsburg, September 28, 1897 (Atkinson); Sewickley, September 30, 1928 (Christy); Dixmont, Allegheny Co., September 30, 1928 (Reiter); Shingletown Gap, Centre Co., September 25, 1915 (Burleigh). At Warren, however, Mr. Simpson has not detected the Golden-crown earlier in the season than October 9 (1894); and October 8 (1902) is the earliest fall date in the Renovo records of A. K. Pierce.

The spring migration begins early in April with an influx of birds from the South. The increase in numbers is very noticeable after the comparative scarcity of this bird during the winter months. It continues for about three weeks, and sometime during this period there is always a day or two of great movement, when the birds fairly swarm in the orchards and woodland. The last leave before the warblers arrive in force. At Beaver my records of "last-seen" birds were made on April 23 in 1888, 1889, and 1891; on April 28 in 1890; on April 29 in 1910; on May 1 in 1911; and on May 5 in 1909. Other comparable records for this season are: Washington, April 26, 1894 (Nease); Sewickley, April 26, 1903 (Christy); Pittsburgh, April 28, 1914 (Burleigh); Hartstown, April 29, 1922 (Sutton); Wilkinsburg, April 28, 1893 (Atkinson); State College, April 30, 1917 (Burleigh); Renovo, April 27, 1907 (Pierce); Presque Isle, April 30, 1900 (Todd); Warren, May 3, 1892 (Simpson); Sandy Lake, Mercer County, May 6, 1928 (Freni and Stanton). It must be borne in mind that this species is an earlier spring migrant than the Ruby-crowned and very rarely lingers beyond the last of April, while the other is sometimes common in the first half of May.

Habits—Although it is the smallest of our Passerine birds, this diminutive species is not therefor the most inconspicuous. In the winter it is a frequent component of the mixed flocks of small birds that go trooping through the woods. It usually works among the terminal twigs of the trees for insect fare, but it often descends to shrubbery and bushes at lower levels. It is partial to conifers of all kinds, and a grove of hemlocks naturally offers special attractions. It is not at all shy and may often be approached very closely. In general habits and behavior the Golden-crown is warbler-like, but it has a peculiar and characteristic way of fluttering in the air before alighting on a twig. It will then often shift its position so that its head markings are brought into prominence. The presence of the Kinglet in a company of winter birds is always revealed by its thin, feeble note, a sort of prolonged chirp, which is repeated almost constantly as the bird actively gleans among the branches. In days of great movement in the spring, when hundreds of birds are calling all around, the effect is very pleasing. Seldom have I heard the Golden-crown's true spring song in our region; it is a feeble, hesitating effort that is apparently usually reserved until the nesting grounds are reached. A friendly, sociable, harmless little bird, this kinglet comes and goes unmolested, doing its share in diminishing the hordes of insects that yearly threaten our forest, orchard, and shade trees. It is said to build a pensile nest of moss and similar substances, in coniferous trees, and to lay from six to nine eggs.

Regulus satrapus Teulon, *Jour. Boston Zoöl. Soc.*, 1882, 1:50 (Bradford, McKean Co.).

Regulus satrapa Townsend, *Proc. Acad. Nat. Sci. Philadelphia*, 1883, 60 (Latrobe, Westmoreland Co., transient)—Todd, *Ann. Carnegie Mus.*, 1904, 2:591 (Presque Isle, Erie Co., transient; winter)—Todd, in Bausman, *Hist. Beaver Co., Pa.*, 1904, 2:1202 (Beaver Co., winter).

"Golden-crowned Kinglet" Miller, *Bird-Lore*, 1908, 10:32; etc. (Springs, Somerset Co., December)—Pitcairn, *Bird-Lore*, 1908, 10:32 (West View, Allegheny Co., December)—Burleigh, *Oölogist*, 1913, 30:281 (Harmarville, Allegheny Co., winter)—Cooke, *Bird-Lore*, 1915, 17:118 (Beaver, Beaver Co., and Renovo, Clinton Co., migration)—McConnell, *Oölogist*, 1918, 35:152 ("Christy Park," Allegheny Co., transient)—Nicholson, *Bird-Lore*, 1921, 23:18 (Grove City, Mercer Co., December)—McClelland, *Am. Mid. Nat.*, 1922, 8:35 (Washington, Washington Co., winter)—Warfield, *Bird-Lore*, 1923, 25:23 (Chambersburg, Franklin Co., December)—Jones, *et al.*, *Bird-Lore*, 1923, 25:25 (Deer Creek, Allegheny Co., December)—Blair, *Bull. Audubon Soc. W. Pa.*, 1923, 1:42 (Wildwood, Allegheny Co., winter)—Sutton, *Bird-Lore*, 1923, 25:194 (Huntingdon, Huntingdon Co., March–April); 1924, 26:418 (Greenville, Mercer Co., fall migration, *fide* Homer)—Christy and Hegner, *Bird-Lore*, 1924, 26:30 (Raccoon Creek Valley, Beaver Co., December)—Eastwood, *Bird-Lore*, 1925, 27:407 (Emsworth, Allegheny Co., October); 1926, 28:207 ([McKinley Park],

Allegheny Co., April, *fide* Grimm)—MATUSZAK, *Bird-Lore*, 1926, 28:29 (Hyde Park, Westmoreland Co., December)—EASTWOOD, *Bird-Lore*, 1927, 29:56 (Butcher Run, Butler Co., November, *fide* Reiter)—CHRISTY and SUTTON, *Cardinal*, 1928, 2:75 (Cook Forest, Clarion Co., winter)—BOULTON, *Bird-Lore*, 1928, 30:271 (Sandy Lake, Mercer Co., May, *fide* Freni and Stanton), 401 (Dixmont, Allegheny Co., September, *fide* Reiter)—ELLIOTT, *Cardinal*, 1934, 3:171 (Raccoon Creek, Beaver Co., December).

"Kinglet" VALENTINE, *Bird-Lore*, 1908, 10:32 (Bellefonte, Centre Co., December)—SIMPSON, *Oölogist*, 1912, 29:248 (Warren, Warren Co., winter)—STONE, *Cassinia*, 1919, 22:37 (Altoona, Blair Co., winter, *fide* McGraw).

Regulus satrapa satrapa CHRISTY, *Cardinal*, 1923, v. 1, no. 1, [p. 15] (Sewickley, Allegheny Co., transient; occasional in winter)—BURLEIGH, *Wilson Bull.*, 1923, 35:145 (Allegheny Co., migration); 1924, 36:131 (State College, Centre Co., winter)—[Editor], *Cassinia*, 1926, 25:35 (Greencastle, Franklin Co., January, *fide* Ziegler)—BURLEIGH, *Cardinal*, 1929, 2:120 (Allegheny Co., December).

Regulus regulus satrapa SUTTON, *Ann. Carnegie Mus.*, 1928, 18:234 (Crawford Co. localities, winter).

EASTERN RUBY-CROWNED KINGLET (Plate 16)

CORTHYLIO CALENDULA CALENDULA (Linnaeus)

Description—A very small, warbler-like bird. Upperparts dull olive green, the head with a grayish cast; the wings and tail have yellowish-olive edgings, and the wings are crossed by two pale bars; underparts dull buffy white; eye-ring pale. The *male* has a *bright scarlet median crest*, more or less concealed; the *female* lacks this decoration.

Range—The range of this kinglet, like that of the Golden-crowned, is transcontinental and boreal. In general, however, this species summers farther north and winters farther south. It is unknown as a breeding bird in New York and in New England, except in northern Maine. In western Pennsylvania, as elsewhere in the same latitude, it is merely a transient visitant in spring and fall (at times very common) and a casual or accidental winter resident. Strays have been found in winter at Wilkinsburg and Sandy Creek, Allegheny County (December 28, 1894, and January 14, 1897, respectively—Atkinson), and at State College (January 4–9, 1917—Burleigh, 1924); but all such occurrences must be considered extraordinary.

Migration—Probably most of the kinglets of this species that pass through our region winter in the Gulf states. Thence they push north in April, and seldom arrive here earlier than about the third week in that month. The arrival dates in nine seasons' records at Beaver lie between April 12 (1890) and 23 (1901), while the average is April 17. On March 25, 1928, B. H. Christy saw and heard a ruby-crown at Clinton Pond, Allegheny County, but this unseasonably early date suggests that the bird may have been a wintering individual rather than a new arrival. This record is paralleled by A. B. Miller's for March 28, 1921. Some other unusually early records are: "Patton's Point," Beaver County, April 7, 1929 (Christy); near Entriken, Huntingdon County, April 8, 1921 (Sutton); Altoona, April 5, 1919 (McGraw); Erie, April 9, 1933 (Guynes); Pittsburgh (Schenley Park), April 9, 1921 (Boulton); Meadville, April 9, 1913 (First); State College, April 8, 1919 (Burleigh). The fact remains, however, that in a normal season the Ruby-crown may not be expected before the middle of April. While its migration period overlaps that of the Golden-crown to some extent, the latter species is an earlier migrant, and by the time the Ruby-crown has become common, the other has usually gone. Moreover, the Ruby-crown remains well into May, and the stragglers that bring up the rear may linger into the third week of that month. My records of "last-seen" birds in the spring migration at Beaver run from May 3 (1899) to as late as May 22 (1923), and the average date in thirteen years' records is May 12.

In the fall, however, the respective migration periods of the two species of kinglets coincide rather closely, although the Ruby-crown tends to arrive a little earlier. In 1900 the first fall migrants were noted at Presque Isle on September 18, and in 1888, on September 22. The latter date is also my earliest one for Beaver (1910), but T. D. Burleigh once recorded the species on September 12 (1916) at McKinley Park, Allegheny County. An examination of the original records of A. K. Pierce proves that the October dates cited for Renovo by W. W. Cooke (1915) are wrong and misleading. September 19 (1918) is Mr. Pierce's earliest fall record. The migration of the Ruby-crown is in full swing in October, and before the end of that month almost all the birds have passed through. October 21 is the average date of departure at Beaver, although on November 3, 1908, I saw a single belated migrant at Raccoon Creek; and Mr. Burleigh saw one at Pittsburgh on November 2, 1913, and one at State College on November 1, 1916.

Habits—Similar as the two species of kinglets are in general appearance, haunts, and habits, they exhibit certain differences in their behavior that facilitate their identification in the field. The Ruby-crown is by all odds the more active, nervous, and irascible of the two, as it is also the more musical. It does not manifest the same partiality for conifers, and it also tends to keep nearer the ground. It has a characteristic way of flirting its wings with a sudden jerking motion; otherwise its actions while exploring the trees and bushes for its minute insect food are warbler-like.

The males are in full song by the time they arrive in the spring, and one soon becomes aware of their presence. As a musician the Ruby-crown takes high rank. It is indeed astonishing that such a tiny bird can sing so loudly. On a still morning in April, with few other birds moving, the clear notes of the Ruby-crown are audible at a considerable distance. Its exquisite song compares favorably, in my opinion, with that of the Winter Wren—a species that migrates at the same time. It is a brilliant, vivacious effort, beginning, according to G. M. Sutton, "with a series of fine notes like those of the Black and White Warbler, then bursting into a repeated phrase of four descending notes, and either stopping or else continuing with a further phrasing suggesting that of the Mourning Warbler. Sometimes it repeats the first part of the song several times before continuing. The bird sings and hunts for food at the same time, and will break a song in two if it finds something to eat, and resume it after the interruption."

After the first few days of May this song is seldom heard, since the later migrants are all females. These have only an odd chattering, snapping, scolding note, which, once learned, will always serve to distinguish this kinglet from the Golden-crowned species. The same note is heard again in the fall. On one occasion at this season, I heard a male singing its full spring song.

Regulus calendulus TEULON, *Jour. Boston Zoöl. Soc.*, 1882, 1:50 (Bradford, McKean Co., spring).

Regulus calendula TOWNSEND, *Proc. Acad. Nat. Sci. Philadelphia*, 1883, 60 (Latrobe, Westmoreland Co., transient)—(Secretary), *Abstr. Proc. Delaware Valley Orn. Club*, 1900, 3:8 ([Round Island], Clinton Co., October, *fide* Rhoads)—TODD, *Ann. Carnegie Mus.*, 1904, 2:591 (Presque Isle, Erie Co., transient)—TODD, in Bausman, *Hist. Beaver Co., Pa.*, 1904, 2:1202 (Beaver Co., transient)—FORREST, *Oölogist*, 1911, 28:115 (Washington, Washington Co., transient).

"Ruby-crowned Kinglet" COOKE, *Bird-Lore*, 1915, 17:121 (Beaver, Beaver Co., and Renovo, Clinton Co., migration)—MCCONNELL, *Oölogist*, 1918, 35:152 ("Christy Park," Allegheny Co., transient)—EASTWOOD, *Bird-Lore*, 1925, 27:407 ([McKinley Park], Allegheny Co., September, *fide* Grimm); 1926, 28:403 (McKees Rocks, Allegheny Co., October); 1927, 29:273 (Springs, Somerset Co., April, *fide* Miller)—BOULTON, *Bird-Lore*, 1928, 30:196 ("Slack Hollow," Allegheny Co., April, *fide* Grimm; Raccoon Creek, Beaver Co., April, *fide* Squier and Reiter).

Regulus calendula calendula CHRISTY, *Cardinal*, 1923, v. 1, no. 1, [p. 15] (Sewickley, Allegheny Co., transient)—BURLEIGH, *Wilson Bull.*, 1923, 35:145 (Allegheny Co., migration); 1924, 36:131 (State College, Centre Co., migration).

Corthylio calendula calendula SUTTON, *Ann. Carnegie Mus.*, 1928, 18:235 (Meadville, Conneaut Lake, and Pymatuning Swamp, Crawford Co., transient).

WAGTAILS, PIPITS

FAMILY MOTACILLIDAE

THE NORTH AMERICAN PIPITS are dull-colored, terrestrial birds that in habits resemble the Larks. Their legs and feet are long and slender, with the hind claw much lengthened and straightened. Pipits inhabit open, treeless country, and they walk or run, rather than hop, over the ground. They are easily identified by their tail-wagging habit.

There are over 125 species and subspecies in this family, which is widely distributed, particularly in the Old World. Only one representative occurs in our region, and it is but an irregular transient.

AMERICAN PIPIT (Plate 17)

ANTHUS SPINOLETTA RUBESCENS (Tunstall)

Description—A small brownish bird with a walking gait. Smaller than the Prairie Horned Lark and more slenderly proportioned; bill very small and slender. *Spring plumage:* upperparts dull grayish brown; two pale bars on the wings; tail black, the outer feathers extensively white; underparts, together with a conspicuous line over the eye and a small spot below it, dull reddish buff or clay-color, the breast and sides showing obscure dusky streaks. *Fall and winter plumage:* similar to the spring dress, but underparts not so deep in color, and streaks on breast and sides heavier.

Range—This species of pipit ranges across the entire North American continent from the Atlantic coast to the Pacific; it breeds in the Arctic and Hudsonian life zones and winters southward to the Gulf states and Mexico. In western Pennsylvania, as elsewhere in the middle states, it is a transient only, and while at intervals it doubtless occurs as such throughout our region, it is common and regular only along the shores of Lake Erie, where conditions are unusually favorable. In the Pymatuning region of Crawford County it has been observed in recent years in gradually increasing numbers, and H. C. Kirkpatrick has seen good-sized flocks near Meadville in the fall. Reports from the interior counties, however, all designate the species as a rather rare and decidedly irregular visitor. This is its status at Warren, at Beaver, at State College, and at Hollidaysburg. For Allegheny County there are but two records: two birds shot out of a flock at Duquesne on October 26, 1896, by D. A. Atkinson; and one seen at Frick Park, Pittsburgh, on April 5, 1931, by P. P. Malley. F. L. Homer shot a male at New Hamburg, Mercer County, on April 22, 1888; and H. H. Elliott saw a flock near Jamisonville, Butler County, on October 24, 1939. A. B. Miller has one record from Springs, Somerset County, for March 30, 1908; and G. M. Sutton, one from Huntingdon for March 18, 1921. Apparently many skilled observers have overlooked this bird.

Migration—Collation of the available records shows that the migration of the Pipit is a long-drawn-out affair, both in spring and in fall. S. N. Rhoads claims to have seen the species at Beaver in the fall as early as August; and in 1900 I saw it on Presque Isle on September 8. Ordinarily, however, it arrives somewhat later in that month and stays through October and into November: November 15, 1900—Erie; November 17, 1900—Warren; November 28, 1916—State College. There is no evidence of its wintering within our limits, although it has been observed at State College as early as February 28 (1917) by T. D. Burleigh and was once seen at Warren on March 28 (1893) by R. B. Simpson. In the spring movement it seems to be most frequent in May, and probably the majority of birds pass through then. Late spring dates are: May 5, 1901—Warren; May 12, 1900—Erie; May 14, 1917—State College; May 14, 1932—Hartstown. Mr. Rhoads's suggestion that the Pipit might breed in the northwestern part of the state is entirely fantastic.

Habits—The American Pipit resembles the Horned Lark in certain respects. Gregarious habits; an erratic, jerky flight; weak call notes; a walking gait; and a predilection for open ground, are all characteristic of both species. At times, indeed, the two may be found together, but the association is likelier to be fortuitous than otherwise, and for the most part they keep in separate flocks. The Pipit is partial to the river beaches and to the shores of lakes and ponds, where it runs about, sandpiper-fashion, along the water's edge in search of its food. At Erie, where I have found it oftener than elsewhere in the state, it frequents the muddy flats at the mouth of Mill Creek, the outside beach of Presque Isle, or occasionally the shores of the bay. It is fond as well of working over plowed grounds and barren lands. Sometimes it occurs singly, but oftener in small groups, and occasionally even in fairly large flocks. On November 4, 1890, near Beaver, I saw two flocks that must have consisted of at least five hundred birds each; these were the largest flocks I have ever seen.

The Pipit is a restless bird; it is constantly rising at some real or fancied alarm to realight at a distance. Its general grayish-brown coloration blends so well with its surroundings that when the bird is at rest it is often hard to discern. On the ground its movements are graceful, involving a constant up-and-down tilting of the tail, after the fashion of the birds of this family. The only note that I have ever heard is a weak, two-syllabled chirp, given on the wing. Mr. Burleigh states that he has seen the Pipit alight in the top of a tree, as it is known to do at times on its breeding grounds.

Anthus pensilvanicus Rhoads, *Auk*, 1899, 16:313 (Beaver Co., transient)—Todd, *Ann. Carnegie Mus.*, 1904, 2:588 (Erie and Presque Isle, Erie Co., transient)—Todd, in Bausman, *Hist. Beaver Co., Pa.*, 1904, 2:1201 (Beaver Co., transient).

"Titlark" Simpson, *Oölogist*, 1911, 28:143; and 1912, 29:247 (Presque Isle, Erie Co., September and May).

Anthus rubescens Burleigh, *Wilson Bull.*, 1924, 36:130 (State College, Centre Co., migration)—Bergstrom, *Cardinal*, 1928, 2:107 (near Pymatuning Swamp, Crawford Co., November).

Anthus spinoletta rubescens Sutton, *Ann. Carnegie Mus.*, 1928, 18:224 (Meadville and Shermansville, Crawford Co., fall transient)—Bergstrom, *Cardinal*, 1930, 2:186 (Stewart's Corners, Crawford Co., November)—Elliott, *Cardinal*, 1933, 3:149 (Hartstown, Crawford Co., May); 1940, 5:71 (Center Tp. [near Jamisonville], Butler Co., October).

WAXWINGS

FAMILY BOMBYCILLIDAE

THE WAXWINGS are not brightly colored, but the blended tones of their trim plumage place them among the most beautiful birds of the Northern Hemisphere, to which they are exclusively confined. The family consists of a single genus (*Bombycilla*) with three species: one (*garrulus*) occurs in the northern parts of both the Old and the New World; one (*cedrorum*) is peculiar to North America; and one (*japonica*) is found only in Japan. In western Pennsylvania the Cedar Waxwing is common at all seasons; the Bohemian is a rare and irregular visitor.

Waxwings are small, arboreal birds that travel about in flocks, feeding on fruit and berries as well as on insects. Their heads bear long, pointed crests. Crimson, waxlike appendages often adorn the wings and occasionally the tail feathers; but these are not always present, nor are they peculiar to age or sex. The long, pointed wings have ten primary feathers, the outermost of which are much reduced; the bill is short, slightly hooked and notched at the tip; the nostrils are almost concealed by dense, velvety feathers. A weak, monotonous, lisping note is the only vocal accomplishment. The sexes are alike; the young differ from the adults in having a streaked plumage.

BOHEMIAN WAXWING

BOMBYCILLA GARRULA PALLIDICEPS Reichenow

Description—Similar in general to the Cedar Waxwing, but larger; *wings marked with white and yellow;* under tail coverts cinnamon rufous.

Range and local status—The Bohemian Waxwing, as its name implies, is mainly an Old World species. The American race summers in the mountains of western Canada; in the winter, however, it often wanders far to the eastward and invades the northern United States. In Pennsylvania it is an exceedingly rare and irregular visitant. Warren says (1890) that he had a specimen that was captured from a flock of twenty birds in a pine forest in the northern part of Elk County in midwinter. He also refers, in his usual casual manner, to the species' occurrence in Clinton and Allegheny counties, on the strength of reports from certain correspondents. Corroborative records from both these counties can now be cited. A specimen that is in the Carnegie Museum was shot by D. A. Atkinson from a small flock of ten or twelve birds, near Natrona, Allegheny County, on December 24, 1897. Dr. Atkinson stated that "they were in a small thicket, and were quite noisy." On March 5, 1912, near Renovo, A. K. Pierce came upon a flock of twelve Bohemian waxwings, feeding on frozen apples still hanging on the trees of an old orchard. In a letter to W. W. Cooke on June 30, Mr. Pierce wrote, "They appeared to be quite numbed by the cold and did not mind my presence at all, though I stood nearly under the tree. They seemed to be a little larger than the Cedarbird, with white markings on the wings and black on the throat; all had wax-tipped wings."

Four other occurrences complete the records for our region. R. L. Keesler saw a single Bohemian waxwing at close range at Forestville, Butler County, on February 1, 1921. S. J. Seiple writes that he identified one at "Kidds Mill," Mercer County, on April 5, 1936. R. B. Simpson states that he saw two birds on Presque Isle on January 11, 1939, and succeeded in approaching them rather closely. L. M. Peterson saw a group of four near Bradford, McKean County, on February 11, 1940. They came to a tree about ten feet from a window of his home and remained in plain sight for two minutes. Observers should watch for this species among the flocks of the Cedar Waxwing that are present in the winter.

Ampelis garrulus WARREN, *Birds Pa.*, ed. 2, 1890, 258 (Elk Co., winter; Clinton Co., *fide* Van Fleet; [?]Allegheny Co., *fide* Wrenshall).

CEDAR WAXWING (Plate 17)

BOMBYCILLA CEDRORUM Vieillot

Description—About the size of the Bluebird; *conspicuously crested.* General color *pale brown;* wings dusky gray, with narrow pale edgings and sometimes with red waxen tips to the secondaries; *tail* dusky grayish, *tipped with yellow;* a *broad black stripe on the forehead* extends backward through the eyes; *chin and upper throat, blackish* (with a white streak on either side); lower throat and breast, pale brown, this color merging into the dull greenish yellow of the abdomen; under tail coverts dull whitish. *Immature birds* are much duller and lack the blackish throat; the *underparts* are whitish, *streaked with dull olive brown.*

Range—The Cedar Waxwing is a distinctively North American species and has an extensive transcontinental range, which is limited to the northward, generally speaking, by the Canadian Life Zone. In the winter it reaches the southern United States, Mexico, and Central America, but many individuals elect to pass that season in the northern states. Forty and fifty years ago it was common in western Pennsylvania in the summer and was by no means infrequent in the winter, but it is now decidedly less numerous. The reason for the decrease in its numbers is not understood. It seems to be no more partial to one section than to another, and it has been reported from many stations in our region.

Migration—This is an erratic species, and its movements are uncertain and irregular. Because we frequently see it in the winter months, we are tempted to consider it a permanent resident wherever found; yet beyond question an influx takes place in the spring and an exodus in the fall. May marks the former movement, as all observers agree, while the latter probably occurs in October. No dates, however, can be given for either season.

Habits—Ever since the summer of 1886, when I found my first cedar waxwing's nest in an apple tree near my home, this bird has been one of my favorites. In the years that followed, I paid it considerable attention, became better acquainted with its habits, and collected several sets of its eggs. Trim, neat, and distinguished-looking, as well as mild-mannered and soft-voiced, it is an interesting subject for study. No pen picture that I might draw could equal the one from the facile pen of Elliott Coues, whose account is reproduced here in greater part:

"At any time of the year, in almost any part of the country, one may hear some curious wheezing, lisping notes, and, on looking about him, may see a dozen or a hundred little birds in sight, flying in an easy, rather undulating course, to alight in a compact body on the nearest tree, where they remain silent and motionless for a few moments, drawn up to their full heights, displaying their long top-knots; then they begin to move about and feed, unless some alarm sends them off to another tree. When the cedar ripens its glaucous-blue berries, these same birds are sure to be found there, gorging themselves on this fruit till they are literally choke-full—the last few berries sticking in their capacious throats for want of room below. These gourmands grow extremely fat at times; they are commonly called Cedar-birds, and their flesh is accounted a delicacy. They are also named Cherry-birds, from their fondness for cherries; and might with equal propriety be known as Gum-birds, or Huckleberry-birds, or by any other set of names indicating that they feed on a great variety of edible small-fruits. Naturally, the horticulturists dislike to see these silky-feathered fruiterers come trooping as 'thick as thieves,' and kill so many that in some sections their numbers become noticeably reduced. But we should always remember that at certain seasons these indolent, easy-going gormandizers display more agility and address in bug-catching than might be expected from them, destroying vast numbers of noxious insects. Let the irate gardener remember this when he goes for his gun; and let us all hope that people will learn, in the course of time, that the indiscriminate slaughter of birds, even of such noted thieves as Crows and Blackbirds, necessarily turns a well-poised balance in favor of insect-pests and by so much against the true interests of agriculture.

"Like most well-fed persons, our satiny Waxwings offset their gluttony and indolence with some nice, amiable traits. They are tender-hearted, affectionate birds, fond of each other, and quite capable of showing a degree of heroism in their devotion to one of their number who may be in difficulty. They make pleasant cage-birds, sleek and jaunty in their general bearing, with a certain *nonchalance*, which, however, it would be indiscreet in a fly to presume on so far as to enter their cage. They are either very innocent or unsuspicious birds, for they suffer themselves to be killed or captured when a little wit would have saved them. Their habitual indifference extends even to their courtships and housekeeping; they make cool love, seem in no hurry about it, and not much concerned for its consequences. You may see them loitering about in flocks all through the summer; they scarcely nest until the season is half over, and sometimes postpone their domestic affairs until the fall. The migration is another irregular and desultory matter with them; they are not reliable passengers, for, as if rivalling their larger cousins, these lesser Bohemians roam at their convenience over the country, whenever food is plenty and accessible. They retire from more northerly and uninviting regions in the fall, but in most parts of the country some of them may be found at any time of the year, while others are off in Mexico, Central America, or the West Indies. . . .

"So they lead their idle, uneventful lives—these *débonnaire* birds, sociable but not domestic, even a trifle dissipated, good-natured enough to a friend in a scrape, very reliable diners-out, and fond of showing off their dressy top-knots, on which so much of their mind is fixed."[1]

A further note on the fruit-eating habits of the Cedar Waxwing is contained in the following extract from my journal, dated June 9, 1888: "Today I visited an orchard where there are a number of early cherry trees which are at present in full bearing. Considerable injury is being done to the crop by the depredations of the birds, particularly the Cedar Waxwings, a flock of which I observed in the trees at the time. Not only are many fruits eaten *in toto*, but others are mutilated to a greater or less extent, and still others are knocked off in the efforts of the birds to reach them. The resulting damage is by no means inconsiderable." Stomach examinations bear out these charges but show also that this bird depends mainly on wild fruits of various kinds, and that during the spring and summer months it eats a fair proportion of insects, among which are a number of destructive pests. One often sees the Waxwing perched in a treetop, flying out after passing insects in the manner of a true flycatcher. Mulberries, of which it is exceedingly fond, if planted near an orchard, will usually divert its attention from more useful kinds of fruit.

Orchard and shade trees are favorite nesting sites of the Cedar Waxwing, as are also willow and sycamore trees along streams. The nest itself is a rather rough affair, carelessly constructed of dry grasses, weed stalks, and leaves, and lined with finer and softer material of the same sort and often with horsehair and some feathers. Seen from below, the structure might be taken for a robin's nest, but it is usually placed on a smaller branch than would be chosen by a robin; moreover, there is often some woolly or cottony material on the outside. I have repeatedly noted waxwings surreptitiously abstracting material from the nests of such birds as the American Goldfinch and the Baltimore Oriole, in the owners' absence. Later examination showed that this stolen material was worked into the waxwing's own nest. The elevation of the nest varies from ten to thirty feet. The eggs are four or five in number, although

[1]*Birds of the Colorado Valley*, 1878, p. 472.

sometimes only three are laid. They are peculiar and unmistakable: their ground-color is of a nondescript and characteristic pale grayish (or sometimes bluish) shade, while the markings are black spots, well defined and more or less evenly but rather thinly disposed. Average measurements are .87 by .61 inches. The nesting season, as Dr. Coues intimates, is comparatively late and sometimes unduly prolonged. I have never taken a full set of eggs earlier in the season than June 9, but D. A. Atkinson reports once finding a set on May 18. This was certainly an exceptionally early nesting. On the other hand, nests with eggs may be found throughout July and until the end of August, or even in early September. Whether these late nestings are actually second efforts, or merely delayed first efforts, I cannot say.

Ampelis cedrorum Teulon, *Jour. Boston Zoöl. Soc.*, 1882, 1:52 (Bradford, McKean Co., nesting)—Townsend, *Proc. Acad. Nat. Sci. Philadelphia*, 1883, 62 (Latrobe, Westmoreland Co.)—Jamison, *Ornithologist and Oölogist*, 1888, 13:134; and Dwight, *Auk*, 1892, 9:138 (Cresson, Cambria Co., June)—Todd, *Auk*, 1893, 10:45 (Coalport, Clearfield Co., June)—Jacobs, *Summer Birds Greene Co., Pa.*, 1893, 12 (Greene Co., nesting)—Baily, *Auk*, 1896, 13:291, 295 (Williamsville, Elk Co., nesting)—Jacobs, *Gleanings from Nature*, 1898, 1:35 (Greene Co., nesting)—Cope, *Cassinia*, 1902, 5:17 (Clinton and Potter Co., June)—Todd, *Ann. Carnegie Mus.*, 1904, 2:578 (Erie and Presque Isle, Erie Co., resident)—Todd, in Bausman, *Hist. Beaver Co., Pa.*, 1904, 2:1200 (Beaver Co., resident)—Keim, *Cassinia*, 1905, 8:40 (Port Allegany, McKean Co., summer).

"Cedar Waxwing" Todd, *Oölogist*, 1887, 4:89 (Beaver, Beaver Co., February; nesting)—Harlow, *Oölogist*, 1911, 28:167 ([State College, Centre Co.], late nesting)—Burleigh, *Oölogist*, 1911, 28:168 (Uniontown, Fayette Co., late nesting)—McConnell, *Oölogist*, 1918, 35:151 (McKeesport, Allegheny Co.)—Miller, *In the Open*, June, 1920, 10:24 (Thornhill, Allegheny Co.)—McClelland, *Am. Mid. Nat.*, 1922, 8:35 (Washington, Washington Co., resident)—Street, *Cassinia*, 1923, 24:16 (Greencastle to Ft. Loudon, Franklin Co., June)—Christy, *Cardinal*, 1924, v. 1, no. 4, p. 10 (Big Traverse Valley, Beaver Co., June)—Eastwood, *Bird-Lore*, 1926, 28:402 (Aspinwall, Allegheny Co., September, *fide* Auerswald); 1927, 29:56 ([McKinley Park], Allegheny Co., October, *fide* Grimm; Logan's Ferry, Allegheny Co., October)—Chaney, *Bird-Lore*, 1932, 34:47 (Uniontown, Fayette Co., December)—Thompson, *Bird-Lore*, 1933, 35:320 (Erie, Erie Co., nesting).

"Cedarbird" Stone, *Cassinia*, 1906, 9:44 (McConnellsburg, Fulton Co., June)—Simpson, *Oölogist*, 1909, 26:170; and 1912, 29:370 (Warren, Warren Co., nesting and winter records).

Bombycilla cedrorum Harlow, *Auk*, 1912, 29:475 ([State College], Centre Co., nesting)—Christy, *Cardinal*, 1923, v. 1, no. 1, [p. 11] (Sewickley, Allegheny Co., resident)—Burleigh, *Wilson Bull.*, 1923, 35:97 (Allegheny Co., transient); 1924, 36:69; and 1931, 43:50 (State College, Centre Co., resident; nesting)—[Editor], *Cassinia*, 1926, 25:32 (Greencastle, Franklin Co., May–June, *fide* Ziegler)—Christy and Sutton, *Cardinal*, 1928, 2:73 (Cook Forest, Clarion Co., June)—Sutton, *Ann. Carnegie Mus.*, 1928, 13:198 (Meadville and Pymatuning Swamp, Crawford Co., resident)—Burleigh, *Cardinal*, 1932, 3:79 ([Summit], Fayette Co., nesting)—McClintock, *Cardinal*, 1933, 3:127 (Ligonier, Westmoreland Co., May).

SHRIKES

FAMILY LANIIDAE

Among the Passerine forms, the Shrikes are birds of prey. The family is best represented and most widely distributed in the Old World, where its members show much diversity both in size and in coloration. Two species only (both plainly colored) occur in North America, and none is found south of Mexico. In western Pennsylvania the Northern Shrike is a winter visitor from the North; the Migrant Shrike is a summer resident.

Shrikes are bold, tyrannical birds that often kill the smaller species for food. These they strike down with their strongly developed, raptorial bills, which are hooked as well as notched and toothed. Insects, small snakes, lizards, and injurious rodents, are also included in their diet. The feet of Shrikes are weak and unfitted for grasping the struggling prey, and this may explain the fact that victims are frequently impaled on thorns or sharp twigs. The Shrikes are solitary birds that choose lofty lookout perches in the open, from which to watch for prey. The soft, blended tones of their gray, black, and white plumage make them handsome and unmistakable figures. Their home is in the thicket; and the rude, bulky nest, fashioned of twigs, is generally hidden in a thornbush or other dense growth.

NORTHERN SHRIKE (Plate 17)

LANIUS BOREALIS BOREALIS Vieillot

Description—A bird the size of the Blue Jay. General color gray; a prominent black stripe through the eye; wings black, with a white spot about the middle; tail black, the ends of most of the feathers white; underparts gray, *with fine, wavy, darker crossbars;* bill blackish, flesh-colored below at base. In *young birds* in fall plumage, the *upperparts and underparts* are more or less *washed with brown.*

Range—Our Northern Shrike is the American counterpart of the Eurasian *Lanius excubitor*, with which some authors consider it conspecific. Its breeding range coincides with the Hudsonian Life Zone, but in the winter this shrike migrates as far south (in the East) as Virginia and Kentucky. Although its numbers apparently do not fluctuate from season to season in the erratic fashion of certain other of our winter visitants, such as the Pine Grosbeak and the White-winged Crossbill, the species is still far from being common at any time. As it happens, most of the reports concerning it come from the northern and the westernmost counties, but very likely it is equally distributed throughout the region. There are records from three localities in Erie County (Erie, Lake Pleasant, and Cherry Hill), but none in recent years. In Crawford and Mercer counties the Northern Shrike is also uncommon, although F. L. Homer used to see two or three in the course of a season at New Hamburg. In Beaver County I have observed it only five times, and not at all since 1901. It has been noted in past years at Washington (Nease), at Wilkinsburg (Atkinson), and at Jacobs Creek and Scottdale, Westmoreland County (Medsger). R. B. Simpson of Warren and A. K.

Pierce of Renovo have had more experience with this bird than have any other observers in our region.

Migration—Most of the reports of this shrike concern winter occurrences and hence are not migration records at all. In a series of ten seasons' observations at Renovo, made by Mr. Pierce, November 10 is the average fall arrival date, and October 24 is the earliest. As these dates correspond with those from adjoining regions, they are probably fairly representative. (A September record from Erie, which I published in 1904 on the authority of S. E. Bacon, almost certainly pertains to the Migrant Shrike.) After the middle of March the Northern Shrike begins its northward movement, which is virtually complete, so far as our region is concerned, by the end of that month. Late dates on which this species is said to have been seen are April 15, 1900—Renovo (Pierce); and April 19, 1884—Meadville (Sennett).

Habits—Seen at a little distance, the Northern Shrike, in its size, appearance in silhouette, and choice of a post for observation, suggests the Sparrow Hawk. It regularly perches in the top of a tree in an exposed position and commanding a good view in all directions. But as soon as the Shrike takes wing, the resemblance ends; for instead of flying with the swallow-like ease and grace of a hawk, it moves through the air in a seemingly hesitant and labored manner, often rather low over the ground. It is solitary by choice, and a given individual may remain in one locality for some time. It feeds on mice and small birds, which it captures by a surprise attack and carries to a convenient perch to devour at leisure. After eating as much of its prey as it requires, it impales the remainder on a thorn, or else fixes it in the fork of a small branch. Whether prey thus treated is eventually eaten is a debatable question, but that it is often left to decay is evident from the fact that whole bodies of mice and birds may generally be found hung up in the vicinity of the Shrike's haunts. Several observers report seeing this bird come into towns in pursuit of English sparrows. This circumstance should count in its favor, but the Shrike is not common enough in our region to be of economic importance one way or another.

Lanius borealis Townsend, *Proc. Acad. Nat. Sci. Philadelphia*, 1883, 62 (Latrobe, Westmoreland Co.)—Warren, *Birds Pa.*, ed. 2, 1890, 260 (Cameron, Potter, and Elk Co., winter)—Todd, *Ann. Carnegie Mus.*, 1904, 2:578 (Erie, Erie Co., winter)—Todd, in Bausman, *Hist. Beaver Co., Pa.*, 1904, 2:1200 (Beaver Co., winter)—Oberholser, *Bird-Lore*, 1918, 20:286 (Renovo, Clinton Co., and Erie, Erie Co., migration)—Christy, *Cardinal*, 1923, v. 1, no. 1, [p. 11] (Sewickley, Allegheny Co., January)—Sutton, *Ann. Carnegie Mus.*, 1928, 18:199 (Meadville, Crawford Co., winter, *fide* Kirkpatrick)—Bergstrom, *Cardinal*, 1928, 2:107 (Sadsbury Township, Crawford Co., November)—Sutton, *Cardinal*, 1929, 2:131 (Brookville, Jefferson Co., November).

"Northern Shrike" Simpson, *Oölogist*, 1907, 24:87; 1910, 27:100; and 1912, 29:248, 249 (Warren, Warren Co., winter)—Wood, *Wilson Bull.*, 1932, 44:238 (State College, Centre Co., spring, *fide* Large; fall, *fide* Curry).

MIGRANT SHRIKE (Plate 17)

LANIUS LUDOVICIANUS MIGRANS Palmer

Description—Similar in general to the Northern Shrike, but smaller (smaller than the Robin). Bill also weaker, entirely black; and *underparts* (in adult) *plain grayish white*, without darker wavy crossbars. This latter character, however, shows in the immature plumage. The smaller size will always serve to distinguish this species from the Northern Shrike.

Range—*Lanius ludovicianus migrans* is the interior and northern race of a species that has an extensive range in Mexico and the United States and northward into southern Canada. The range of *migrans*, as worked out by A. H. Miller,[1] includes the Mississippi Valley (except the southern part) as far west as the edge of the Great Plains, and the country northeastward to New England and Ontario. In western Pennsylvania, however, this shrike is mostly confined to the western tier of counties in the breeding season and is fairly common and regular only in the northernmost of these—Erie, Crawford, and Mercer. As it happens, I have seen it only once in Beaver County, but H. H. Wickham records (1887) the finding of a nest near Beaver. Allegheny County yields a number of records (mostly for recent years), but of these, only two are records of breeding: Sewickley and Homestead (Atkinson). J. W.

[1] *University of California Publications in Zoology*, 1931, 38:59.

Jacobs found a nest in Greene County in the spring of 1884, but no others have come to his notice. For some reason the rough country of the Ohio Valley does not attract this species as do the level stretches of the northwestern counties. It avoids the highlands, and while it has been seen at Warren in the summer, it is not actually known to breed there. The seasonal status of one bird seen at Port Allegany, McKean County, early in August (Keim, 1905) is uncertain, as is also that of an individual seen on August 30, 1915, at Somerset (Burleigh). These are the only reports from the plateau section, but there are several migration records from State College and vicinity (Burleigh, 1924) and from Hollidaysburg (Berg), as well as one nesting record from the latter locality (May 31, 1934—McGraw).

Migration—The Migrant Shrike does not usually appear in the spring until after the Northern Shrike has left, so that at that season there is not much risk of confusing the two species. In 1888 B. H. Christy saw a shrike, supposedly a Migrant, along Big Sewickley Creek in Allegheny County on March 10—certainly an early date. Rudyerd Boulton secured one near the mouth of Raccoon Creek in Beaver County on March 17, 1923. The same year one was seen at Greenville, Mercer County, on March 21, by Louis Homer. R. B. Simpson observed the species at Warren on March 21, 1894, and on March 28, 1893. The earliest record for Presque Isle is March 25 (1932—Christy and Todd), and the earliest for State College is March 24 (1916—Burleigh). Seldom does this shrike arrive later than the first week in April. In the fall it often remains quite late in the season —until October or November, or even December (Mr. Simpson shot one at Warren on December 6, 1900)—but the available dates from various localities show little agreement. D. A. Atkinson remarks the relative abundance of the species during September and early October in Allegheny County as compared with its numbers during the summer months.

Habits—There is nothing suggesting the recluse in the nature of the Migrant Shrike. In the Erie-Crawford district, where it is locally common, it affects wastelands grown up to hawthorn and wild crab-apple trees and finds in such situations ideal hunting and nesting grounds. There it may be encountered perched on some exposed branch in plain sight, whence it retires if pressed too closely, usually to descend and fly low over the ground from perch to perch. Telegraph poles and wires along the highway are favorite lookouts.

Stomach examinations made by S. D. Judd[1] show that insects, particularly the larger kinds, make up the bulk of the food of this shrike and that mice and small birds constitute a much smaller portion than they do in the fare of the northern species. Nevertheless, the depredations wrought in one season on the bird life of a given locality by a single pair of migrant shrikes must be considerable. The species is not particular in its choice of prey. S. E. Bacon refers to its killing such birds as the Yellow Warbler and the White-throated Sparrow, and Dr. Atkinson writes: "This species is hard on the smaller birds, for on two occasions I have observed it killing field sparrows, and I once found the remains of an indigo bunting on a fence rail where a shrike had been resting." If it could only be induced to confine its attentions to English sparrows! I have never actually seen the Migrant Shrike in pursuit of other birds and, in view of its ordinary clumsy flight and slow movements, have often wondered at its ability to capture them. Its success is incontestable, however, since dead bodies impaled on thorns or caught in the fork of a branch present obvious evidence. Insects and other prey are similarly treated. Why the Shrike should kill so much and make use of so little is not understood. Small birds generally seem not to fear shrikes as they do hawks and owls; perhaps they do not recognize them as killers. At any rate, I have never seen shrikes being mobbed by other birds, among which they seem to move with impunity.

Nest-building begins very shortly after the birds' arrival. Sets of eggs have been found at Erie as early as April 15 (Bacon); and near Hartstown, young nearly ready to leave the nest were discovered on May 16 (Sutton). Probably more than one brood is reared in a season, since Dr. Atkinson once found a nest with eggs at Sewickley as late as June 14. Warren gives a detailed account (1890) of several nests collected near Erie on May 20 and 21, 1889. Of his experience on May 20, he writes:

"Today Mr. Geo. B. Sennett and I drove out

[1]U. S. Department of Agriculture, Biological Survey, *Bulletin*, no. 9, 1898, p. 20.

about three miles east of the city; on the way shot three adult shrikes (two males and female), and secured their nests and young. Both nests were built in thorn trees; one nest in a field near the edge of a woods, contained four young, two or three days old, and two eggs. This nest was placed eight feet from the ground, and constructed of small twigs, dried grasses, and plant fibers with an abundance of feathers and cotton. The other nest was situated about four and a half feet from the ground, directly over a cow-path in a meadow; it had evidently been disturbed as it was insecurely placed, being partly turned over. This nest, containing two half fledged males, was composed almost entirely of plant-fiber and chicken feathers; a few small twigs only being on the outside; measures inside of cavity four and one-half inches wide and two and one-half inches in depth."

On the next day, three more nests were found: "All were built in thorn or wild crab apple trees along the roadside, and were from ten to twelve feet above the ground. One nest contained five fresh eggs; parent bird setting [*sic*] on nest. When I was securing this nest and eggs the old birds flew near me uttering sharp, rasping cries. The notes of the young shrikes are not unlike the squeak of a mouse. . . . When taking the nests of shrikes which contained young, the old birds were quite bold, and when the squeaky cries of the young were heard, they flew directly at my head, but after finding it impossible to drive me away by these attacks they alighted close by, and remained silent witnesses to the despoliation of their treasures."

Other observers report similar experiences. G. M. Sutton, referring to the nest he found near Hartstown, writes (1928): "When I approached this nest the parents flew at me briskly, calling in harsh tones and biting savagely at my hands when I reached in to touch the young birds, which so completely filled the nest that I could not easily determine the material of the lining, nor the depth of the cup. The young were silent, but squirmed a little when touched. The gray plumage of their heads and backs was distinctly edged with brownish. In the red-haw tree, where the nest was built, were numbers of dead beetles and grasshoppers, and remains of mice, small snakes, and a small bird, probably a Tennessee Warbler." Two nests found near Mercer by G. P. Elliott in May, 1885, "were placed in thick thorn bushes, in a large meadow, and were mainly constructed of grass, bark from the grape vine, roots, etc., and were warmly lined with wool, besides having an outer network of dead thorn-twigs, probably placed there for the better protection of the nests." A set of eggs, collected by R. L. Fricke for the Carnegie Museum on May 11, 1937, south of Linesville, came from a nest of this type in a hawthorn bush in an open field.

Six eggs seem to be the usual number laid by the Migrant Shrike in our region. They vary somewhat in shape, from oval to short ovate, but average about .97 by .72 inches. The ground-color is white, and the markings are spots, sometimes definite in outline, sometimes indeterminate, of a very characteristic grayish-olive color, inclining to drab. Generally they are clustered more thickly around the larger end of the egg.

I have never heard the song of this bird. Mr. Burleigh, who has heard it only in the fall of the year, describes it as a varied medley, consisting of warbles, trills, squawks, and whistles.

Lanius ludovicianus excubitorides Elliott, *Ornithologist and Oölogist*, 1886, 11:15 (Mercer, Mercer Co., nesting).

Lanius ludovicianus Jacobs, *Nat. Companion*, 1886–87, 2:82 (Waynesburg, Greene Co., occasional)—Dwight, *Auk*, 1889, 6:198 (Erie, Erie Co., breeding, *fide* Sennett)—Warren, *Birds Pa.*, ed. 2, 1890, 261 (Erie, Erie Co., nesting; Crawford, Lawrence, and Mercer Co., breeding)—Rhoads, *Auk*, 1890, 16:312 ([Fair Oaks], Allegheny Co.)—Jacobs, *Summer Birds Greene Co., Pa.*, 1893, 12 (Greene Co., nesting).

Lanius ludovicianus migrans Todd, *Ann. Carnegie Mus.*, 1904, 2:578 (Erie and Presque Isle, Erie Co., summer)—Todd, in Bausman, *Hist. Beaver Co., Pa.*, 1904, 2:1200 (Beaver Co., rare in summer)—Keim, *Cassinia*, 1905, 8:40 (Port Allegany, McKean Co., August)—Harlow, *Auk*, 1918, 35:140 (East Springfield, Erie Co., nesting)—Christy, *Cardinal*, 1923, v. 1, no. 1, [p. 11] (Sewickley, Allegheny Co., irregular transient)—Burleigh, *Wilson Bull.*, 1923, 35:97 (Pittsburgh, Allegheny Co., April); 1924, 36:129 (State College, Centre Co., migration)—Sutton, *Ann. Carnegie Mus.*, 1928, 18:199 (Crawford Co. localities, summer)—Burleigh, *Cardinal*, 1929, 2:118 (between Sharpsburg and Aspinwall, Allegheny Co., August)—(?)O'Neil, *Cardinal*, 1930, 2:234 (Sewickley Tp., Allegheny Co., March).

"Migrant Shrike" Sutton, *Bird-Lore*, 1923, 25:194 (Greenville, Mercer Co., March, *fide* Homer; Raccoon Creek, Beaver Co., March, *fide* Boulton)—Malley and Shoemaker, *Redstart*, 1937, 4:70 (Pittsburgh, Allegheny Co., April)—[Editor], *Cardinal*, 1940, 5:66, note (above Little Sewickley Creek, Allegheny Co., November; [Sewickley], Allegheny Co., nesting, *fide* Atkinson).

VIREOS

FAMILY VIREONIDAE

THE VIREOS, OR GREENLETS, are peculiar to America. Only a half-dozen representatives of almost 150 known species and subspecies reach our region. They are all active, arboreal birds, which feed principally on insects, and are therefore migratory in this latitude. Their bills resemble those of Shrikes in that they are hooked and notched, as well as surrounded by conspicuous bristles. Their toes are coherent at the base.

Vireos are plainly colored; the soft greens and grays, varied with white and yellow, blend with the birds' chosen haunts in high, open woods or in shade trees of parks and lawns. The sexes are indistinguishable. Stouter bodies, heavier bills, and more deliberate movements, distinguish the Vireos from the Warblers, which they resemble somewhat in appearance and with which they are often associated in migration. One style of nest is built: a rather slight, thin-walled, cup-like structure, suspended from the fork of a twig. The eggs are white, sparsely speckled with dark markings.

Elliott Coues writes: "Next after the warblers, the greenlets are the most delightful of our forest birds, though their charms address the ear and not the eye. Clad in simple tints that harmonize with the verdure, these gentle songsters warble their lays unseen, while the foliage itself seems stirred to music. In the quaint and curious ditty of the white-eye—in the earnest, voluble strains of the red-eye—in the tender secret that the warbling vireo confides in whispers to the passing breeze—he is insensible who does not hear the echo of thoughts he never clothes in words."[1]

[1]*Key to North American Birds*, ed. 4, 1894, p. 331.

WHITE-EYED VIREO

VIREO GRISEUS GRISEUS (Boddaert)[2]

Description—One of the smaller vireos. Olive green above; wings dusky green, with two prominent pale bars; underparts dull white; the breast, sides, and flanks strongly washed with greenish yellow; *iris white*.

Range and migration—The White-eyed Vireo is a relatively southern species; it does not advance northward beyond the Alleghanian Fauna and is commoner in the Carolinian and Austroriparian faunas. Although common and well known in southeastern Pennsylvania, it is unaccountably rare in the western part of the state. According to E. H. Eaton, it is similarly rare in western New York. The authentic records from our region are few indeed; not all those that have come to my notice are acceptable. In 1893 J. W. Jacobs listed this vireo as a rare summer resident in Greene County, where in recent years S. S. Dickey has also observed it several times in May and June. It is apparently becoming established there. In 1937 Dr. Dickey saw two birds near Mapletown on September 26 (not October 26, as published), and this is our only date for the fall migration. D. A. Atkinson supplies two Allegheny County records, based

[2]In the writer's opinion, the northern race should be called *Vireo griseus noveboracensis* (Gmelin). Compare *Auk*, 1933, 50:115.

respectively on specimens shot near Homestead on May 20, 1894, and near West Elizabeth on May 17, 1895. In over fifty years' experience in Beaver County I have observed this vireo only twice. On May 14, 1909, I discovered one bird on the wooded hillside along Two-mile Run near Beaver, where it led me a merry chase. Again on May 4, 1922, I found one in the willow growth fringing the same stream. Miss Ruth Trimble reports seeing a singing male at "Bushy Run Battlefield," Westmoreland County, on May 3, 1936. The dates of these latter occurrences must have been near the normal arrival time of the species. There are also two records for the Pymatuning region; one for May 30 is late enough to suggest breeding (Seiple; Elliott). It is possible that this bird may prove to be more numerous in the ridge and valley section, from which there are a few records.

Habits—The White-eyed Vireo is an active, nervous, "jumpy" little bird, not so deliberate in movement as are our other vireos. In its actions and general behavior it suggests a flycatcher rather than a vireo. Moreover, it prefers to keep fairly close to the ground in bushy growth and dense thickets, where it cannot be easily observed. Its song, too, is quite unlike those of the other vireos; it lacks their sweetness and continuity and suggests the vocal efforts of some of the wrens. I have never seen the nest of this species, but Mr. Jacobs has two records of nests with eggs, taken near Waynesburg on May 28, 1889, and in Wayne Township on June 2, 1899. Both these nests were built in low bushes near the ground, in the type of location usually chosen by the species, and held four eggs each. The eggs are of the usual vireo type—white, with some dark reddish-brown spotting at the larger end—and measure about .75 by .55 inches. Dr. Dickey describes (1938) an abandoned nest (attributed to this species) found near Brock, Greene County, as narrower and deeper than that of the Red-eyed Vireo and fashioned of different materials. The outside was "shingled perpendicularly with flakes of yellowish-brown inner tree bark held in place with spider-web. The upper portion is spotted with fine sprays of green cedar moss (*Hypnum* sp.?). The lining consists of shreds of brown grape-vine bark, the felted wall of a caterpillar's cocoon, and a few sprays of green moss." This nest was built only about four feet from the ground in a wild plum tree.

Other authors have remarked similar characteristics of the nest of this vireo, so that Dr. Dickey's identification seems valid. On only one other occasion has he obtained actual evidence of breeding: on June 15, 1936, he watched a pair of white-eyed vireos feeding a young cowbird, near Spraggs, Greene County. Concerning the haunts of the species, he says:

"In habitat the White-eyed Vireo shows partiality to swamps, swales, and glades; yet, in districts from which such features are lacking, it is found inhabiting old fields grown up in a variety of native vegetation. Favorites among areas so chosen seem to be those where the cover consists of saplings of maple and elm associations; or of small trees and shrubs such as wild plum, witch hazel, burning bush, and the dogwoods and willow, and even an alder stand. The ground cover may be of such growth as cat-briers (*Smilax* sp.), wild oats grass (*Danthonia spicata*), ground pine (*Lycopodium complanatum* var. *flabelliforme*), or other associated plants."

"White-eyed Vireo" (?)Enty, *Ornithologist and Oölogist*, 1885, 10:78 (Templeton, Armstrong Co., May)—Stone, *Cassinia*, 1906, 9:44 (McConnellsburg, Fulton Co., June)—Wood, *Wilson Bull.*, 1932, 44:238 (State College, Centre Co., spring, *fide* Large).

Vireo noveboracensis Jacobs, *Summer Birds Greene Co., Pa.*, 1893, 12 (Greene Co., nesting).

Vireo griseus Christy, *Cardinal*, 1930, 2:234 (near Patton's Point, Beaver Co., May)—Dickey, *Cardinal*, 1938, 4:158 (Greene Co. localities; nesting).

YELLOW-THROATED VIREO (Plate 17)

VIREO FLAVIFRONS Vieillot

Description—Somewhat smaller than the Red-eyed Vireo. Upperparts olive green, the rump grayish; *wings* dusky, *with two conspicuous white bars*, and whitish edgings on the inner feathers; tail dusky, with light-colored outer edgings; sides of head and of breast, olive green, as is the back; a dark spot in front of the eye, interrupting the yellow eye-ring; *throat and breast yellow*, in contrast with the *white belly;* bill dark.

Range—The Yellow-throated Vireo winters primarily in Central America and migrates northward to occupy the eastern United States and adjacent provinces of Canada in the summer. Zonally considered, it is characteristic of the Carolinian and Alleghanian faunas and barely enters the Canadian. In New York, according to E. H. Eaton, and southward into western Pennsylvania as well, it avoids the highlands. At Warren, near the western edge of the plateau section, R. B. Simpson calls it "rather scarce" as a summer resident, and it is entered on Van Fleet's manuscript list of the breeding birds of DuBois as "quite rare." It must be exceedingly rare at Renovo to have escaped the notice of A. K. Pierce, who apparently collected only one specimen and that in September. I have never encountered the species anywhere in all my travels through the northern plateau counties, and I believe that the records made by F. R. Cope, Jr. (1902), for Clinton and Potter counties are erroneous. He admittedly did not actually see the birds that he identified, and it is more than likely that they were of the Blue-headed species, which sings and behaves much like the Yellow-throated and which is common enough in these counties.

Not until we reach Somerset County, where latitude finally offsets altitude, do we find this vireo summering regularly in the highlands. I have seen it near New Lexington in June; R. V. Mostoller reports it during the same month from Shanksville; and A. B. Miller says that at Springs, close to the Maryland boundary, it is an uncommon summer resident. Across the Allegheny divide, however, in the ridge and valley section, the species is locally common in the lowlands. But it is in the western part of our region, and particularly in the northwestern counties, that the Yellow-throated Vireo reaches its maximum abundance. According to my experience, it is far more numerous in the woodlands of Crawford County than elsewhere, although still outnumbered by the Red-eyed species. In the Ohio Valley and in the region to the southward it is less numerous but still fairly common, even as far east as the western slope of Laurel Hill in Westmoreland and Fayette counties.

Migration—In the spring movement the Yellow-throated Vireo appears usually about a week later than the Blue-headed. I have noted its arrival at Beaver between April 26 (1889) and May 8 (1909), and I find that records from various other stations correspond with these limiting dates. The fall movement is not so well defined. It seems to begin about the middle of August, or else the species changes its usual haunts at about that time; for often there is a marked influx, and for two or three weeks the birds become noticeably conspicuous in orchards and among shade trees, where previously they were not present. Very few remain after the middle of September. I am now satisfied that I was in error in recording this vireo at Beaver as late as October (in W. W. Cooke, 1909); this sight record probably actually pertained to the Blue-headed Vireo. The latest authentic departure date that I can cite is September 28, 1899, when a bird was shot at Wilmerding, Allegheny County, by D. A. Atkinson.

Habits—All our vireos are arboreal in habit, and none is more strictly so than the Yellow-throated. It remains high in the treetops, and it prefers oak woods and maple groves to denser forest growth. Its movements while feeding among the terminal branches are leisurely and deliberate, and as it pauses at intervals to sing, it exhibits none of the nervous activity shown by the warblers. Its song may readily be distinguished from that of the Red-eyed species by its slower tempo, more disconnected phrasing, and generally less vivacious mode of expression, although it is richer in tonal quality. By these very tokens it closely resembles that of the Blue-headed Vireo; I am not now sure that I can tell the two species apart by their songs alone. Both have a peculiar, sharp, impatient, rasping note that is uttered at intervals, sometimes in the middle of the regular song; it somewhat suggests a similar note of the Ruby-crowned Kinglet, but is louder and more intense. The song period of the Yellow-throated Vireo, like that of the Red-eyed, lasts through the spring and summer months; it is interrupted only by the molt, and is occasionally resumed in September, just before the birds leave for the South.

G. M. Sutton says (1928) of some yellow-throated vireos that he observed, "Mated birds were found to be very much attached to each other, and it was quite unusual to see one bird by itself." The pairs lose little time after their arrival in choosing a nesting site and beginning a nest. J. W. Jacobs, in a circumstantial account of the nesting of this species, states that in Greene County he has found the nest almost completed as early as May 9. Both birds work on it. True to form, they usually select a high site well out toward the extremity of a branch, so that the nest is often virtually inaccessible. Oak, maple, and hickory trees are favored above others. The nest, in typical vireo style, is a compact structure, suspended from the fork of a small branch; it is composed of fine grasses, shreds of bark, and silky weed fibers, and is lined with finer material of the same sort. It is neatly and completely stuccoed on the outside with bits of lichen, cocoon silk, and flakes of light-colored wood, which give it an elegance comparable with that of the nests of the Wood Pewee and the Blue-gray Gnatcatcher. This covering must be purely ornamental, since it serves no purpose of concealment. After the trees are fully in leaf the nest is not easy to see from below. An average nest measures three inches in the outside diameter by two and one-half inches in depth, with a cavity one and six-tenths inches deep.

The parents defend their home pertinaciously. Both sexes share the labor of incubation, and the male sometimes sings on the nest, thus betraying its position to the interested observer. Three or four eggs are laid; these are ovate or elliptical ovate in shape, and average .81 by .58 inches. They are white or creamy white, sparsely spotted (chiefly about the larger end) with dark purplish brown, sometimes inclining to black. The markings tend to be larger and heavier than in the eggs of our other vireos. Sets are complete by the last week in May.

"Yellow-throated Vireo" ENTY, *Ornithologist and Oölogist*, 1885, 10:78 (Templeton, Armstrong Co., April)—BRUMBAUGH, *Wilson Bull.*, 1905, 12:100 (Wilkinsburg, Allegheny Co., July)—STONE, *Cassinia*, 1906, 9:44 (Big Cove Tannery, Fulton Co., June)—COOKE, *Bird-Lore*, 1909, 11:165 (Beaver, Beaver Co., migration)—SIMPSON, *Oölogist*, 1909, 26:26 (Warren, Warren Co., breeding)—MCCONNELL, *Oölogist*, 1918, 35:151 (McKeesport, Allegheny Co.)—STREET, *Cassinia*, 1923, 24:17 (Ft. Loudon, Franklin Co., June)—EASTWOOD, *Bird-Lore*, 1925, 27:262 (Raccoon Creek, Beaver Co., May, *fide* Jones).

Vireo flavifrons JACOBS, *Summer Birds Greene Co., Pa.*, 1893, 12 (Greene Co., nesting)—(?)COPE, *Cassinia*, 1902, 5:17 (Tamarack Swamp, Clinton Co., and Oleona, Potter Co., June)—JACOBS, *Wilson Bull.*, 1903, 10:17 (Waynesburg, Greene Co., nesting)—TODD, *Ann. Carnegie Mus.*, 1904, 2:579 (Erie and Presque Isle, Erie Co., summer)—TODD, in Bausman, *Hist. Beaver Co., Pa.*, 1904, 2:1200 (Beaver Co., summer).

Lanivireo flavifrons HARLOW, *Auk*, 1912, 29:475 (State College, Centre Co., nesting); 1918, 35:141 (Centre and Warren Co., nesting)—CHRISTY, *Cardinal*, 1923, v. 1, no. 1, [p. 11] (Sewickley, Allegheny Co., and Frankfort Springs, Beaver Co., nesting)—BURLEIGH, *Wilson Bull.*, 1923, 35:98 (Allegheny Co., summer); 1924, 36:73; and 1931, 43:50 (State College, Centre Co., migration; nesting)—SUTTON, *Ann. Carnegie Mus.*, 1928, 18:202 (Meadville and Pymatuning Swamp, Crawford Co., summer).

BLUE-HEADED VIREO (Plate 17)

VIREO SOLITARIUS SOLITARIUS (Wilson)

Description—A bird the size of the Red-eyed Vireo; general form stouter. Top and sides of the head, bluish gray, relieved by a prominent *white eye-ring and white lores;* general color above, olive green; tail dusky; *wings* dusky, *with two conspicuous white bars*, and broad whitish edgings on the inner feathers; *underparts white*, the sides and flanks *shaded with yellowish olive green;* bill and feet dark. The *female* resembles the male, but is slightly duller; *immature birds* in the fall are still duller, and the crown forms a less noticeable contrast with the back.

Range—*Vireo solitarius* has an extensive east-and-west range; it reaches British Columbia on the Pacific coast and Cape Breton Island on the Atlantic. In the West it breaks up into several well-marked races. The typical or eastern race is relatively northern in its general summer distribution, as it is one of the birds that are characteristic of the Canadian Fauna; it also ranges to some extent into the Alleghanian, where, however, it is of more or less local occurrence. In the state of New York its breeding range is confined almost entirely to the Adirondack and Catskill regions, although it includes a few outlying localities in the western part. Across the border in western Pennsylvania, in those parts where Canadian conditions largely prevail, this vireo is common as a summer resident. I have collected specimens at various points in all the northern counties of the plateau region except Jefferson. In this section the species ranges west at least to Tidioute, Warren County (Homer), and to Clarion and Mayport, Clarion County, where the elevation is but 1,200 feet or less. In Clinton County, A. K. Pierce has found it nesting in the Susquehanna Valley (West Branch) at Renovo, and I have seen it at Tamarack Swamp and at the head of Burns Run, southeast of Keating. I also found it very common at Weedville, Elk County, on June 20 and 21 in 1894. In Clearfield County it has been recorded from DuBois (Van Fleet) and Anderson Creek (Todd).

From the region south of these localities there is a gap in the records, but presumably there is none in the range. Cambria and Somerset counties, however, are sufficiently well "spotted," from Laurel Hill on the west to the crest of the Alleghenies on the east. But this species, unlike the Hermit Thrush and the Junco, with which otherwise it conforms in its local distribution, is not sharply limited by the Allegheny divide, but ranges into the ridge and valley section to the eastward and apparently occurs throughout. R. C. Harlow reports it as breeding at Charter Oak, in northern Huntingdon County, while G. M. Sutton saw several breeding pairs in early July in the valley of Standing Stone Creek, a few miles to the east—a circumstance proving that the other was no mere isolated occurrence. Moreover, I noted the species at Vail, Blair County, on June 28, 1898; and one bird was taken in the valley of

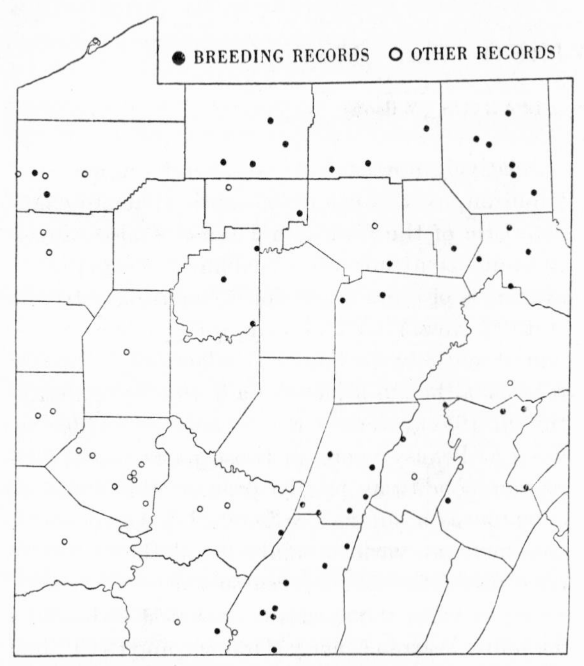

LOCAL RANGE OF THE BLUE-HEADED VIREO

Licking Creek, about three miles southeast of Newton Hamilton, Mifflin County, on July 17, 1895, by W. H. Phelps. Individuals were seen, though not taken, in the vicinity of Entriken, Huntingdon County, from June 3 to 6 in 1898 (Surber). These records suggest that the species must be a regular, although not a common, summer visitant throughout this general region. Miss A. E. Berg records it at Hollidaysburg, however, as a transient only.

In the region of Pymatuning Swamp this vireo reappears as a breeding bird (as attested by several observers) and thus confirms the boreal character of this locality. Through the western counties in general, and as far east as the Allegheny Valley and Chestnut Ridge, it is of course only a transient in the spring and fall, fairly common at certain times. It has been noted on Chestnut Ridge in Fayette County in late August (Burleigh), but in my opinion this occurrence cannot be treated as a breeding record.

Comparison of a series of specimens from Somerset County with another series from the northern counties shows that the southern birds have traces of grayish shading on the back; thus they are clearly intermediate in coloration between true *solitarius* and *alticola*, the race of the southern Appalachians.

Migration—The Blue-headed Vireo is the earliest of its tribe to appear in the spring and normally arrives sometime in April, before the trees are in leaf. I have seen it in Beaver County as early as April 19 (1889), but as a rule it does not come until the last week in the month, and in backward seasons it may even be delayed until May. This general statement applies to the adjacent counties as well. Some early spring records are: Wilkinsburg, April 23, 1895 (Atkinson); Frick Park, Pittsburgh, April 21, 1937 (Malley); Indiana, April 24, 1933 (Smyth); Pittsburgh, April 25, 1914 (Burleigh); Washington, April 26, 1883 (Nease). Corresponding dates come from the northwestern counties: "Kidds Mill," Mercer County, April 25, 1933 (Seiple); Hartstown, April 28, 1922 (Sutton); Presque Isle, April 26, 1902 (Simpson); Warren, April 18, 1901 (Simpson); Endeavor, Forest County, April 28, 1923 (Dickey). In the mountains, however, the van uniformly arrives somewhat earlier. A. B. Miller says that at Springs, Somerset County, this vireo comes between April

6 (1910) and 27 (1918), and that April 15 is the average date. This circumstance, in view of W. W. Cooke's observation (1909) that the race *alticola* reaches its breeding grounds about two weeks ahead of the migrants of the typical form, is significant, as it serves to confirm the intermediate tendency of the vireo population of this region. At State College, according to T. D. Burleigh, the case is much the same; April 20 is the average recorded date of arrival, and April 11 is the earliest. The only long series of migration records available is that supplied by Mr. Pierce for Renovo, which covers twenty-six seasons. His dates range from April 3 (1891) to May 2 (1912), but the average is April 22.

Where the Blue-headed Vireo is a transient only, it is usually in evidence until about the middle of May; its migration thus coincides with that of the warblers in general. Rudyerd Boulton reports seeing it at Raccoon Creek, Beaver County, as late as May 21 in 1922, and in 1923 I saw one bird at Beaver on May 24. In the fall migration it trails behind most of the warblers and does not reach the Ohio Valley until about the middle of September: September 14, 1898—Wilkinsburg (Atkinson); September 16, 1910—Beaver (Todd). It is sometimes very common at this season, even until its departure about the third week in October. Some late fall dates are: October 15, 1909 and 1910—Beaver (Todd); October 17, 1926—Cook Forest, Clarion County (Christy); October 19, 1916—State College (Burleigh); October 26, 1913—Pittsburgh (Burleigh); October 30, 1909—Renovo (Pierce). For the last-named locality, October 15 is the average "last-seen" date in a series of observations covering twenty-two years.

Habits—In its general habits and behavior this vireo resembles the Yellow-throated Vireo, which is, indeed, its closest relative. It is not so partial to the treetops, however, as is that species. It is rarely found away from woodland areas at any season. During migration it often associates with the warblers, among which it stands out by reason of its less hurried manner and its odd way of peering this way and that. At such times it may also be very conspicuous because of its frequent singing. The song is a characteristic, disconnected refrain, much resembling that of the Yellow-throated, and, like the song of that species, is occasionally interspersed with a peculiar, impatient, rasping note. Even in the fall, some individuals try to sing.

R. B. Simpson's full and interesting account (1914) of the nesting habits of this vireo in Warren County is reproduced here in substance. He says that in Warren County the species is a common summer resident in the wooded country away from the river valley and prefers heavy forest with plenty of hemlock. Here its presence is made known by its song, which strongly suggests that of the Red-eyed species, but is louder, richer, and fuller. Its scolding note is also deeper and harsher. It begins nesting rather early, and many pairs lay full sets of eggs before the other vireos and most of the warblers have fairly begun building. Mr. Simpson continues:

"I have frequently come upon females gathering nesting material and at such times they did not seem to be shy or show fear. I always found it an easy matter to keep the bird in sight until she reached the nest. The male frequently accompanies the female to and fro while nest building and at several nests where I spent some time watching operations I found that the male bird helped at times. In this vicinity they do not nest very high. I have never found one over twenty-five feet from the ground and have found several nests not over four feet up. The majority of nests are built in hemlocks. Occasionally a beech is chosen and I have found several close to the ground within hazel and other bushes on hardwood timbered ridges."

A vireo nest in a hemlock is certain to belong to the Blue-headed species. In size, make-up, and general appearance, however, the nest of this vireo so closely resembles that of the Red-eyed that Mr. Simpson doubts that it can always be distinguished, although individual examples vary considerably in structure and decorations. Some nests, indeed, are handsomely adorned on the outside with bits of lichen, cobwebs, and other decorative material, picked up in the deep and shady forests favored by the birds. A nest that was taken by Mr. Pierce at Kane, McKean County, and that is in the Carnegie Museum, is ornamented with bits of white paper. The incubating bird will permit close approach before finally leaving the nest. Four eggs are usually laid; sometimes only three. They average about .80 by .53 inches and are of the usual vireo type—white, sparsely spotted about the larger end with deep brown or black. They tend to be a little more heavily marked than are those of the Red-eyed Vireo, but are not always distinguishable therefrom. From the last week in May until the first week in June is about the time to look for full sets in Warren and McKean counties. Mr. Harlow tells of a nest that he found on May 24, 1913, in northern Huntingdon County, which contained young estimated to be about ten days old. This set of eggs must have been completed about May 2. He remarks on the fearlessness and unconcern shown by the parents at the time; and these same qualities have been noted by other observers who have had similar experiences.

Vireo solitarius TOWNSEND, *Proc. Acad. Nat. Sci. Philadelphia*, 1883, 62 (Latrobe, Westmoreland Co., transient)—WARREN, *Birds Pa.*, ed. 2, 1890, 265 (Blair, Centre, and Elk Co., summer)—DWIGHT, *Auk*, 1892, 9:133, 138 (Wopsononock Mountain, Blair Co., June)—BAILY, *Auk*, 1896, 13:291, 292, 295 (Straight Creek, near Williamsville, Elk Co., June–July)—RHOADS, *Auk*, 1899, 16:312 (Laughlintown, Westmoreland Co.; Cresson and Summit, Cambria Co.; Round Island, Clinton Co., breeding)—COPE, *Cassinia*, 1902, 5:17 (Tamarack Swamp, Clinton Co., and Oleona, Potter Co., June)—TODD, *Ann. Carnegie Mus.*, 1904, 2:580 (Presque Isle, Erie Co., transient)—TODD, in Bausman, *Hist. Beaver Co., Pa.*, 1904, 2:1200 (Beaver Co., spring transient)—SIMPSON, *Cassinia*, 1908, 11:81 (Warren, Warren Co., summer).

"Solitary Vireo" SIMPSON, *Oölogist*, 1906, 23:135; 1907, 24:134, 183; 1909, 26:119, 170 (Warren, Warren Co., nesting, etc.)—DICKEY, *Oölogist*, 1914, 31:171 ([Charter Oak], Huntingdon Co., nesting)—HARLOW, *Oölogist*, 1917, 34:165 ([Charter Oak], Huntingdon Co., nesting).

"Blue-headed Vireo" COOKE, *Bird-Lore*, 1909, 11:166 (Renovo, Clinton Co., migration)—MCCONNELL, *Oölogist*, 1918, 35:151 (Long Run, near McKeesport, Allegheny Co.)—EASTWOOD, *Bird-Lore*, 1925, 27:406 (Dixmont, Allegheny Co., fall, *fide* Reiter), 407 (Sandy Creek, Allegheny Co., *fide* Woodin); 1927, 29:56 (South Hills, Pittsburgh, Allegheny Co., October); 1927, 29:273 (Springs, Somerset Co., April, *fide* Miller)—BOULTON, *Bird-Lore*, 1928, 30:271 (Presque Isle, Erie Co., May, *fide* Reiter, *et al.*)—COPE and HAWKINS, *Forest Leaves*, 1934, 24:26 (E. Tionesta Forest Reserve, Warren and McKean Co., summer).

Lanivireo solitarius solitarius SIMPSON, *Oölogist*, 1914, 31:229 (Warren, Warren Co., nesting; habits)—BURLEIGH, *Wilson Bull.*, 1923, 35:98 (Allegheny Co., transient); 1924, 36:73 (State College, Centre Co., migration); 1931, 43:50 (Charter Oak, Huntingdon Co., summer)—CHRISTY and SUTTON, *Cardinal*, 1928, 2:73 (Cook Forest, Clarion Co., summer)—SUTTON, *Ann. Carnegie Mus.*, 1928, 18:203 (Crawford Co. localities, transient; rare in summer).

Vireo solitarius solitarius BURLEIGH, *Cardinal*, 1932, 3:79 (near Summit, Fayette Co., August).

RED-EYED VIREO (Plate 17)

VIREO OLIVACEUS (Linnaeus)

Description—Our largest vireo (larger than most warblers); bill about one-half inch long. Upperparts, as well as wings and tail, dull olive green; cap leaden gray, in strong contrast; underparts whitish, the under tail coverts with a faint yellowish tinge; superciliaries pale, conspicuous, and surmounted by a narrow black margin; a dark line through the eye, the *iris* of which is *red; no wing-bars.*

Range—This vireo ranges in summer over the eastern United States and southern Canada, and in the Northwest to the Pacific coast and southern Mackenzie. It winters in South America, from Colombia to Brazil. It is common and generally distributed in western Pennsylvania, wherever there is woodland.

Migration—The Red-eyed Vireo reaches our region at the same time as most of the warblers—late in April or during the first week in May. In 1889 I observed the first birds at Beaver on April 22, but have never since been able to match this record. My other dates of arrival fall between April 30 (1890) and May 11 (1911). In recent years the arrival of the species has apparently been retarded by unseasonably cold weather, to which it is sensitive. From other localities in the western tier of counties, the following early dates may be cited: April 27, 1902—Sewickley (Christy); April 24, 1894—Wilkinsburg (Atkinson); April 29, 1888—Waynesburg (Jacobs); April 26, 1895—Butler (Roth); May 5, 1922—Hartstown (Sutton); May 5, 1928—Johnstown (Canan). At Springs, Somerset County, this vireo has not been noted earlier than May 4, while the average date of arrival is May 10 (Miller). At Warren, near our northern border, it comes as a rule during the first week in May; May 3 (1899) is the earliest record (Simpson). For the ridge and valley section the records are fairly consistent: May 5, 1923—Hollidaysburg (Berg); May 4, 1919—Altoona (McGraw); May 7, 1915—State College (Burleigh). The only extensive series of migration records is that supplied by A. K. Pierce for Renovo. The dates he reports average decidedly earlier than those cited above and range from April 13 (in two years' records) to May 7 (one year), but I suspect that some of the records between 1894 and 1898 may have been based on erroneous identifications. After eliminating those that seem doubtful, I find that the average arrival date is April 28.

The Red-eyed Vireo begins its southward migration in September, even as early as September 7 (1903). The largest flights are accomplished in that month, but as a rule a few migrants are still in evidence in early October. Some late dates are: October 15, 1909—Beaver (Todd); October 3, 1913—Pittsburgh (Burleigh); October 3, 1900—Warren (Simpson); October 2, 1925—Shermansville, Crawford County (Bergstrom); October 6, 1894—Washington (Nease); October 8, 1904—Presque Isle (Simpson); October 20, 1909—Renovo (Pierce). The last is a remarkably late date.

Habits—The Red-eyed Vireo is a common and characteristic woodland bird; only occasionally does it enter orchards and small parks, which are the favorite haunts of the Warbling Vireo. Original forest, second growth, and open groves are all agreeable to the Red-eye. All summer long and at all hours of the day, one may hear its evenly modulated song, undiminished in hot weather and persisting after most of our other birds have ceased singing for the season. Not at all shy, it readily responds to "squeaking" and thus will often come up close enough to reveal its most distinctive field mark—the red iris. Like other vireos, it is rather deliberate and slow of movement, and when it comes to peer at the cause of the disturbance, it has an odd habit of stretching its head out to look from one side to the other. Its alarm-note is a long-drawn-out filing sound, somewhat suggesting that of the Catbird. All vireos are preeminently insectivorous, and this species is known to consume large quantities of caterpillars, beetles, bugs, and ants. In September and October it feeds to some extent on wild fruits but does not touch cultivated kinds. Thus it is a highly useful species, although it does not ordinarily come in contact with agricultural interests.

Nidification begins shortly after the birds arrive and settle for the summer. The nest is a cup-shaped structure, suspended by the brim from a forked twig, usually near the end of a branch. It is neatly and compactly built of strips of bark (usually from the grapevine), grasses, weed fibers, and leaves, and is lined with finer material, such as weed stalks, bits of inner bark, or pine needles. The outside is frequently ornamented with pieces of cocoons or hornet nests, bits of paper, and the like, but never to the same extent as are the nests of the Yellow-throated and Blue-headed species. Cobwebs are used outside to hold the nest firmly in shape. It is so well and solidly built that it outlasts the nesting season and becomes a conspicuous and easily recognizable object in the leafless woods in wintertime. It is deeply cupped and thus affords good protection to the eggs when their cradle is rocked in the wind. A typical nest measures three inches wide (outside) by two and one-fourth inches deep, with a cavity two by one and three-fourths inches. The elevation varies greatly, but the majority of the nests that I have examined were not over fifteen feet from the ground, while some were as low as four feet. D. A. Atkinson, however, reports finding one nest forty feet up in an elm tree. The eggs are three or four in number and are pure white, with a few specks or small spots of purplish or blackish brown, mostly about the larger end. They average about .85 by .55 inches. Full sets have been found in our region as early as May 15, but the first week in June is the more usual time. This is one of the birds most frequently victimized by the Cowbird.

Vireo olivaceus Teulon, *Jour. Boston Zoöl. Soc.*, 1882, 1:52 (Bradford, McKean Co.)—Townsend, *Proc. Acad. Nat. Sci. Philadelphia*, 1883, 62 (Latrobe, Westmoreland Co.)—Jamison, *Ornithologist and Oölogist*, 1888, 13:134; and Dwight, *Auk*, 1892, 9:138 (Cresson, Cambria Co., June)—Todd, *Auk*, 1893, 10:40 (Two Lick, Indiana Co., June), 45 (Coalport, Clearfield Co., June)—Jacobs, *Summer Birds Greene Co., Pa.*, 1893, 12 (Greene Co., nesting)—Baily, *Auk*, 1896, 13:295 (Williamsville, Elk Co., June–July)—Cope, *Cassinia*, 1902, 5:17 (Clinton and Potter Co., June)—Todd, *Ann. Carnegie Mus.*, 1904, 2:578 (Erie and Presque Isle, Erie Co., summer)—Todd, in Bausman, *Hist. Beaver Co., Pa.*, 1904, 2:1200 (Beaver Co., summer)—Keim, *Cassinia*, 1905, 8:40 (Port Allegany, McKean Co., summer)—Burleigh, *Cardinal*, 1932, 3:79 ([Summit], Fayette Co., summer).

"Red-eyed Vireo" Enty, *Ornithologist and Oölogist*, 1885, 10:79 (Templeton, Armstrong Co., May)—Jacobs, *Hawkeye Ornithologist and Oölogist*, 1888, 1:88 (Waynesburg, Greene Co., April)—Stone, *Cassinia*, 1906, 9:41, 44 (McConnellsburg, Fulton Co., June)—Pitcairn, *Bird-Lore*, 1907, 9:155 (Riverview Park, Allegheny Co., nesting)—Cooke, *Bird-Lore*, 1909, 11:80 (Beaver, Beaver Co., migration)—Simpson, *Oölogist*, 1911, 28:161; and 1914, 31:229 (Warren, Warren Co., nesting)—Dickey, *Oölogist*, 1914, 31:171 ([Charter Oak],

Huntingdon Co., June)—McConnell, *Oölogist*, 1918, 35:151 (McKeesport, Allegheny Co.)—Street, *Cassinia*, 1923, 24:17 (Greencastle, Franklin Co., nesting; Ft. Loudon, Jordan's Knob, and Horse Valley, Franklin Co., June)—Christy, *Cardinal*, 1924, v. 1, no. 4, p. 10 (Big Traverse Valley, Beaver Co., June); 1931, 3:44 (["Patton's Point"], Beaver Co., May)—Eastwood, *Bird-Lore*, 1925, 27:263 (Pittsburgh region, Allegheny Co., migration); 1926, 28:273 (Rector, Westmoreland Co., May, *fide* Knauz), 402 (Pittsburgh region, Allegheny Co., fall, *fide* Grimm).

Vireosylva olivacea Harlow, *Auk*, 1912, 29:475 (southern Centre Co., summer)—Christy, *Cardinal*, 1923, v. 1, no. 1, [p. 11] (Sewickley, Allegheny Co., nesting)—Burleigh, *Wilson Bull.*, 1923, 35:97 (Allegheny Co., nesting); 1924, 36:73; and 1931, 43:50 (State College, Centre Co., migration; summer)—Christy and Sutton, *Cardinal*, 1928, 2:73 (Cook Forest, Clarion Co., summer)—Sutton, *Ann. Carnegie Mus.*, 1928, 18:200 (Meadville and Pymatuning Swamp, Crawford Co., summer)—Christy, *Cardinal*, 1930, 2:191 (Schenley Park, Allegheny Co., nesting).

PHILADELPHIA VIREO (Plate 17)

VIREO PHILADELPHICUS (Cassin)

Description—Smaller than the Red-eyed Vireo, which it closely resembles in general coloration; the *underparts*, however, are more *decidedly* and *uniformly tinged with yellow*, especially in fall plumage.

Range—The Philadelphia Vireo is usually considered one of the rarer species, but it is actually commoner than is generally supposed. It is a species characteristic of the Canadian Life Zone and breeds from northern New England west to Alberta, but it is not known to follow southward along the mountains in the summer. Only lately, in fact, has it been detected in the Adirondack region of New York at that season. In view of these circumstances, the capture of a bird of this species at Waterford, Erie County, on July 6, 1895, is of some interest. The specimen in question (now in the United States Biological Survey collection) was shot by F. L. Homer on the edge of a low, swampy tract just northeast of the town. The significance of the record is not clear: this bird may have been a nonbreeding individual that had failed to get any farther north, or it may actually have been breeding at the time. Van Fleet included this vireo in his list of the breeding birds of DuBois and in 1892, answering a request by C. H. Merriam for further information, wrote as follows: "*Vireo philadelphicus* was seen twice during the breeding season on open slopes. On one occasion I was within eight feet of what seemed to be a brooding female. No specimens were taken, but I consider the identification reasonably certain." This information is given for what it may be worth.

All the other known records for this vireo from western Pennsylvania unquestionably pertain to transient individuals. Most of these records come from the counties north of the Ohio River, and from Clinton County in the east, but this circumstance does not necessarily imply that the species is not evenly distributed throughout. Unpublished records are at hand from Warren (Simpson), Renovo (Pierce), Verona (Atkinson), Harmarville (Trimble), and Hollidaysburg (Berg).

Migration—The winter home of the Philadelphia Vireo is in Central America. Its northward migration is late in getting under way, and the movement is correspondingly rapid. The species does not usually reach our region until the last, or next to the last, warbler wave in May; it remains for a few days only and soon passes on northward. During the height of its migration there is often a day or two when it is fairly common. In the spring of 1900 I noted it on Presque Isle between May 14 and 23. In the region of Pymatuning Swamp it has been observed from May 16 (1925) until as late as May 31 on two occasions (Sutton, 1928). My dates for Beaver range from May 15 (1908) to 22 (1923), and various records from neighboring localities correspond in general. The return movement takes place in September, but fall records are few and scattered. Early dates are: September 6, 1900—Presque Isle; September 7, 1925—Crystal Lake, Crawford County (Sutton); September 8, 1898—Renovo. Late dates are: September 25, 1900—Presque Isle; September 27, 1909—Beaver; October 2, 1906—Renovo. Thus the fall movement coincides with the height of the warbler migration. My experience has been that this vireo is fully as numerous at that season as in the spring, but not so easily observed.

Habits—The Philadelphia Vireo is by no means shy; on the contrary, it may often be approached rather closely and at times even seems to reciprocate the curiosity of an onlooker. In general appearance and in song, it is so similar to the Red-eyed Vireo that it must often escape detection. Its smaller size and brighter coloration, however, serve to distinguish it from that species. Its song, too, is slower, much more deliberate, with longer pauses between the phrases; the difference is clearly perceptible when both kinds happen to be singing at the same time. During the brief period of its spring visit, the Philadelphia Vireo does not sing nearly so much nor so constantly as does the Red-eyed; on the other hand, it not infrequently gives its full song in the fall. It is distinctively a woodland bird and as a rule keeps rather near the ground, in shrubbery and bushy growth, where its more deliberate movements distinguish it from the warblers, with which it is wont to associate.

Vireo philadelphicus OLIVER, *Auk*, 1902, 19:206 (Shields, Allegheny Co., transient; Pittsburgh, Allegheny Co., *fide* Link; Industry, Beaver Co., *fide* Todd)—TODD, *Ann. Carnegie Mus.*, 1904, 2:579 (Erie, Erie Co., transient)—TODD, in Bausman, *Hist. Beaver Co., Pa.*, 1904, 2:1200 (Beaver Co., transient).

"Philadelphia Vireo" SIMPSON, *Oölogist*, 1911, 28:144 (Erie, Erie Co., September)—SUTTON, *Bird-Lore*, 1923, 25:260 (Beaver, Beaver Co., May, *fide* Todd)—EASTWOOD, *Bird-Lore*, 1925, 27:407 (Sandy Creek, Allegheny Co., September, *fide* Woodin); 1926, 28:274 (Sandy Lake, Mercer Co., May, *fide* Squier)—BOULTON, *Bird-Lore*, 1928, 30:271 (Squaw Run, Allegheny Co., May, *fide* Fricke)—WOOD, *Wilson Bull.*, 1932, 44:238 (State College, Centre Co., fall, *fide* Curry).

Vireosylva philadelphica SUTTON, *Ann. Carnegie Mus.*, 1928, 18:201 (Crawford Co. localities, transient).

EASTERN WARBLING VIREO (Plate 17)

VIREO GILVUS GILVUS (Vieillot)

Description—Smaller than the Red-eyed Vireo, and duller in general coloration. Upperparts dull olive gray, the crown scarcely different; wings and tail similar; a pale streak over the eye; underparts white, the sides faintly shaded with dull greenish yellow. *No wing-bars* and no distinct markings except the superciliary stripe.

Range—The eastern race of the Warbling Vireo breeds from Saskatchewan east to Nova Scotia and south to Texas and North Carolina. In its northward range it is mainly restricted to the Alleghanian Fauna, and even in New York it avoids the Adirondack and Catskill regions. Its distribution in western Pennsylvania is similar and may be briefly summarized by the statement that the species is a summer resident of fairly common distribution in the western counties (east to the Allegheny Valley and Laurel Hill), rare or absent in the plateau section, and more or less common again in the ridge and valley section. It is not uncommon at Renovo, and I have traced it up the valley of Sinnemahoning Creek as far as Driftwood, Cameron County; but I have yet to find it anywhere in McKean, Potter, or Elk counties. I saw it at Punxsutawney, Jefferson County, in June, 1893, and Van Fleet calls it common at DuBois. It is rare or local, however, south of these points. I have found it in June at New Lexington and Centerville, Somerset County; but for Springs, in the same county, A. B. Miller has only two records (May 26, 1920, and June 6, 1922), both of which, however, suggest its breeding in that locality. It was once seen at Johnstown in May (Canan). In the upper Allegheny Valley it is known at Tionesta and Tidioute (Homer) and is also a regular summer resident at Warren, although more numerous in migration and confined to the river valley. According to my experience in Beaver County, it is not nearly so common and generally distributed now as it formerly was.

Migration—The winter range of the Warbling Vireo has not been fully determined, but it is known to include Guatemala. W. W. Cooke (1909) thinks that the species follows the Appalachian Mountains as its line of travel to and from New England. Such a supposition does not exactly accord with the bird's avoidance of the highlands in the breeding season. It reaches our region in the spring a little ahead of the Red-eyed Vireo. In a series of thirteen years' records from Beaver, the arrival dates lie between April 19 (1889) and 29 (1902), and April 26 is the average. The few similar existing records from neighboring counties, from Armstrong on the east to Greene on the south, also fall within these limits. At Warren, however, this vireo does not arrive until the first week in May, the earliest record being May 1 (1903), and in the mountains also it is a late comer. It has been observed at Hollidaysburg on May 5 (1923—Berg) and at State College not earlier than April 28 (1915—Burleigh). May 4 (1895) is the earliest date reported by A. K. Pierce for Renovo, and May 14 (1904) is the latest. If these dates are correct, a considerable retardation of the northward movement is indicated for the mountain regions.

This vireo leaves for the South during the third week in September. My dates for Beaver cover seven years and range from September 14 (1888) to 26 (1891), the average being September 19. D. A. Atkinson noted a late migrant at Wilkinsburg on September 27, 1894, and T. D. Burleigh saw one at State College on September 25, 1912. Other late dates are September 21, 1888—Erie (Sennett), and September 19, 1925—Crystal Lake, Crawford County (Sutton).

Habits—My acquaintance with the Warbling Vireo dates from a sunny day late in April, 1888, which I spent in tramping the woods and fields near Beaver. During the day my attention was repeatedly attracted by a certain bird that I kept hearing in the shrubbery and trees along a small stream. Its song was a continuous warble, without any special form or pattern, but sweet and pleasing, suggesting the song of the Purple Finch. In later years I became better acquainted with this diminutive songster and learned where to look for its nest. As it haunts the treetops, this plainly colored bird might easily elude notice, were it not for its marked musical ability. It is the only species of vireo that prefers orchards and the shade trees of towns to maples, elms, and sycamores along streams. Of its haunts and habits Elliott Coues writes:

"The Warbling Vireo is no less agile a bird than his cousin the Red-eye, and equally tireless in the pursuit of his insect prey; both these birds sing as they go, with an unconscious air, as if in a reverie; but the easy and wonderfully skillful modulation of the former's flowing song contrasts to great advantage with the Red-eye's abrupt and somewhat jerky notes. Both are among the most persistent of our musicians; in the Middle States, for example, their notes are heard from the latter part of April until far into September, and at all hours of the day. But much as we may admire Gilvus in the agreeable sentiment which his song inspires, we owe him a higher and more respectful consideration for the good services he renders us in a very practical way. Inhabiting by choice our parks, lawns, and orchards, and even the shade trees of our busiest streets, rather than the untried depths of the forest, these birds collectively render efficient service by ridding us of unnumbered insects, whose presence is a pest, as well as a continuous annoyance to sensitive persons. They take a foremost place among the useful birds for whose good services in this regard we have reason to be grateful."[1]

All the nests of this species that I have examined have been in orchards. A Rambo apple tree is always preferred if available, and the distance from the ground varies from ten to thirty feet. If built in an elm or sycamore, however, the nest may be at a still higher elevation. It is a pensile structure, hung from a fork near the end of a branch, and is thus often hard to reach. A typical nest is composed of dry grasses, glistening fiber from the milkweed, and perhaps bits of wool and string, fastened together with cobwebs on the outside and lined with fine weed stalks and plant down. One nest that I examined was composed almost entirely of the broad blades of a certain kind of grass. The outside of a typical nest measures about three inches in diameter by two inches in depth. The brim is often more or less constricted, to give greater security to the contents. Four eggs are usually laid, but sometimes only three; they are white, with a few small, scattered spots of grayish brown, and are scarcely different in color from those of the Red-eyed Vireo. They are smaller, however, measuring about .72 by .52 inches. As a rule they are laid toward the end of May or early in June.

My experience has shown that this vireo ceases to sing for a time after the breeding season but becomes vocal again in September. Were this not the case, its time of departure for the South would certainly be difficult to determine, since the bird is inconspicuous in the fall.

"Warbling Vireo" Jacobs, *Hawkeye Ornithologist and Oölogist*, 1888, 1:88 (Waynesburg, Greene Co., April)—Stone, *Cassinia*, 1906, 9:44 (McConnellsburg, Fulton Co., June)—Cooke, *Bird-Lore*, 1909, 11:79 (Beaver, Beaver Co., migration)—Simpson, *Oölogist*, 1909, 26:26 (Warren, Warren Co., nesting)—McConnell, *Oölogist*, 1918, 35:151 (McKeesport,

[1] *Birds of the Colorado Valley*, 1878, p. 503.

Allegheny Co.)—MILLER, *Oölogist*, 1919, 36:156 (State College, Centre Co., nesting)—McCLELLAND, *Am. Mid. Nat.*, 1922, 8:36 (Washington, Washington Co., summer; migration)—STREET, *Cassinia*, 1923, 24:17 (Greencastle to Ft. Loudon, Franklin Co., June)—EASTWOOD, *Bird-Lore*, 1925, 27:263 (Pittsburgh region, Allegheny Co., migration); 1926, 28:343 (Edgewood, Allegheny Co., July, *fide* Jones).

Vireo gilvus TODD, *Auk*, 1893, 10:40 (Two Lick, Indiana Co., June)—JACOBS, *Summer Birds Greene Co., Pa.*, 1893, 12 (Greene Co., nesting)—TODD, *Ann. Carnegie Mus.*, 1904, 2:579 (Erie, Erie Co., summer)—TODD, in Bausman, *Hist. Beaver Co., Pa.*, 1904, 2:1200 (Beaver Co., summer).

Vireosylva gilva gilva HARLOW, *Auk*, 1912, 29:475 (Boalsburg and State College, Centre Co., summer)—CHRISTY, *Cardinal*, 1923, v. 1, no. 1, [p. 11] (Sewickley, Allegheny Co., nesting)—BURLEIGH, *Wilson Bull.*, 1923, 35:98 (Allegheny Co., summer); 1924, 36:73; and 1931, 43:50 (State College, Centre Co., migration; nesting)—SUTTON, *Ann. Carnegie Mus.*, 1928, 18:202 (Hartstown and Meadville, Crawford Co., nesting).

WOOD WARBLERS

FAMILY COMPSOTHLYPIDAE

THE WOOD WARBLERS are found only in the New World and are the second largest bird family in North America. There are about two hundred species and subspecies, many of which are confined to the tropics. Seventy-three visit the United States, and thirty-six have been recorded from western Pennsylvania. Of this latter number, twenty-seven are summer residents and nine are transients in spring and fall.

The warblers are small, brightly colored birds; the sexes are usually unlike in coloration, and the changes of plumage with age and season are strongly marked. Diagnostic characters of the family are the slender, generally sharp-pointed bill, the nearly even tail, and the rather pointed wings with nine primaries. In spite of their name, most warblers have weak voices and exhibit no musical proficiency. Their habits are described by Elliott Coues:

"They come out of the South, pass on, return, and are away again, their appearance and withdrawal scarcely less than a mystery; many stay with us all summer long, and some brave the winters in our midst. Some of these slight creatures, guided by unerring instinct, travel true to the meridian in the hours of darkness, slipping past 'like a thief in the night,' stooping at day-break from their lofty flights to rest and recruit for the next stage of the journey. Others pass more leisurely from tree to tree, in a ceaseless tide of migration, gleaning as they go; the hardier males, in full song and plumage, lead the way for the weaker females and the yearlings. With tireless industry do the warblers befriend the human race; their unconscious zeal plays due part in the nice adjustment of Nature's forces, helping to bring about that balance of vegetable and insect life without which agriculture would be in vain. They visit the orchard when the apple and pear, the peach, plum, and cherry are in bloom, seeming to revel carelessly amid the sweet-scented and delicately-tinted blossoms, but never faltering in their good work. They peer into the crevices of the bark, scrutinize each leaf, and explore the very heart of the buds, to detect, drag forth, and destroy those tiny creatures, singly insignificant, collectively a scourge, which prey upon the hopes of the fruit-grower, and which, if undisturbed, would bring his care to nought. Some warblers flit incessantly in the terminal foliage of the tallest trees; others hug close to the scored trunks and gnarled boughs of the forest kings; some peep from the thicket, the coppice, the impenetrable mantle of shrubbery that decks tiny water-courses, playing at hide-and-seek with all comers; others more humble still descend to the ground, where they glide with pretty mincing steps and affected turning of the head this way and that, their delicate flesh-tinted feet just stirring the layer of withered leaves with which a past season carpeted the ground. We may seek warblers everywhere in their season; we shall find them a continual surprise; all mood and circumstance is theirs."[1]

Warbler migration in the fall is betrayed by faint, lisping voices from the treetops, where throngs of the tiny creatures are foraging for food. At this season no songs signalize their identity, and the skill of the bird student is tried in naming accurately these flitting forms—immature birds in obscure dress and adults in the subdued colors of the winter plumage.

R. L. Keesler's published record for Bachman's Warbler (*Vermivora bachmani*) (*Oölogist*, 1921, 38:170) is erroneous. The Sycamore Warbler (*Dendroica dominica albilora*) is a species that should be looked for in the spring in our western counties; B. H. Christy, indeed, believes that he saw this bird in southern Beaver County (see F. M. Chapman, *Warblers of North America*, 1907, p. 181). Kirtland's Warbler (*Dendroica kirtlandi*) must also migrate across our region.

[1]*Key to North American Birds*, ed. 4, 1894, p. 288.

BLACK AND WHITE WARBLER

MNIOTILTA VARIA (Linnaeus)

Description—A warbler of medium size, *streaked with black and white*, and having a rather long and slender bill. *Adult male: black prevailing;* median crown-stripe and superciliary stripe, white; *two white bars* on the *wings*, and white spots on the tail at the tip of the outer feathers; throat more or less "solid" black, and sides and flanks streaked with black, leaving only the middle of the abdomen pure white. *Adult* and *immature female: underparts white*, with few or no dusky streaks on the throat and breast. *Immature male:* similar to the adult female, but streaks on underparts black instead of dusky, and more pronounced.

Range—This warbler nests in the eastern United States and southern Canada and thence to southern Mackenzie; it winters in peninsular Florida, the West Indies, and from southern Mexico to Colombia and Venezuela. In western Pennsylvania it shows no faunal preferences and breeds throughout the region wherever suitable forest conditions exist. Some observers report it to be more numerous as a transient than as a summer resident.

Migration—Exclusive of the Louisiana Water-Thrush, this species is the earliest warbler to arrive in the spring. In a series of arrival records for Beaver covering thirteen seasons, the dates range from April 15 (1891) to May 1 (1910), and April 24 is the average. Available records from near-by counties correspond with these, and the records from the Erie-Crawford district yield dates only a day or two later. Even in the mountains the northward movement is not seriously retarded. The average date of arrival at Springs, Somerset County, is April 25 (Miller); at State College, April 23 (Burleigh); and at Renovo, April 28 (Pierce). R. B. Simpson of Warren is the only observer who reports no earlier date than May 1. The early migrants, it may be noted, are few in number; for the majority of birds do not come until a week or ten days later.

The southward movement of this warbler is known to begin very early, even in July, but is scarcely evident with us before September. The warbler waves of that month usually contain a certain proportion of this species. My latest fall date for it at Beaver is September 28 (1890). Occasionally it remains a little later: Renovo, October 4, 1897; Wilkinsburg, October 5, 1896.

Habits—The Black and White is one of the easiest warblers to distinguish in life. Its striped color pattern sets it apart, as does also its habit of keeping to the trunks and larger branches of the forest trees, where it creeps about in nuthatch-fashion, sometimes head downward, in search of its insect food. It is partial to woodland but not necessarily to heavy timber, as it is frequently found in second growth and shrubbery; but it is very seldom seen in orchards or about shade trees. Its regular song is a lisping note repeated a number of times rather rapidly and in the same key. This simple ditty may be altered on occasion by variations in both the tempo and the pitch of the notes, so that it becomes a more complicated and less distinctive performance. The male is in full song on its arrival in the spring and continues singing through June; sometimes it even recommences for a brief period in August.

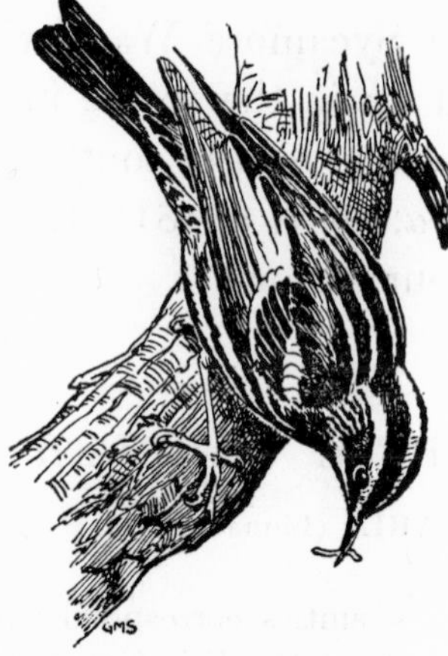

The nest of the Black and White Warbler is not easy to find, and to many observers it is unknown. The only two nests that I have found were discovered quite by accident, when the incubating birds were flushed. J. W. Jacobs published a full account (1899) of the nesting of the species in Greene County, where he considers it to be somewhat locally distributed in the breeding season. According to his observations, the bird is "very partial to mixed timber on the hillsides and secluded woodland cut up by numerous ravines whose steep sides are littered with leaves of the previous year. In such places the nest is to be found, sunken in the soft dirt or in a drift of leaves, and nearly always sheltered by a fallen branch, twig, or the base of a small sapling. Sometimes it is sunken in the base of a bank of leaves which have lodged against a twig or small sprout.

"The materials used in the construction of the nest seem to vary but little outwardly. Dry crumply leaves—many of which are skeletonized—form the outer walls, which are inlaid with abundance of grass, weed fiber and tendrils, and occasionally bark-strips. This is more or less heavily lined with horse and cow hair."

A nest containing one egg was found by Mr. Jacobs as early as May 7 in 1896. A week later the nest held four eggs of the rightful owner and one of the Cowbird, all slightly incubated. "These eggs are white with a perceptible creamy tint, marked with hazel, vinaceous-rufous and rich heliotrope purple, chiefly on the larger end, where, on one, a distinct wreath is seen. The majority of the markings are small dots and minute specks, but large showy blotches are also quite numerous; some of which measure over 0.15 inch diameter—one reaching 0.26 x 0.12 inch.

"The nest was composed of leaves and lined with tendrils and horse hair, and measured outwardly: 4.5 in diam. by 2.8 inches deep, and on the inside, 2.0 in diam. by 1.5 inches deep."

The same author describes the solicitude of a pair of these warblers for a young cowbird, and adds: "Four eggs is the largest number I have ever found in a single nest, while sets of two and three were common. But as all these small sets contained one or more eggs of *Molothrus ater* [the Cowbird], the laying was probably incomplete. Incubation, however, was allowed to start in all such sets to make sure that no more eggs would be laid.

"A series of eggs of this species, now before me, exhibit considerable variations, chiefly in point of markings and their distribution, the prevailing type being moderately marked, chiefly on the larger end, where a more or less well-defined wreath is discernible. The set taken May 15, 1896, and described above, is one of the more heavily marked sets. The most lightly marked set of the series is speckled all over with minute dottings of hazel, vinaceous-cinnamon and faint heliotrope purple. The ground color throughout is white or creamy tinted. Twenty-seven eggs in the series average: 0.67 x 0.53 inch."

Sets of five eggs have been found by R. C. Harlow, S. S. Dickey, A. K. Pierce, and myself, and are not so unusual as Mr. Jacobs implies. Mr. Harlow adds that in the Pocono Mountains he has on two occasions found nests in cavities in rotten stumps, fully two feet above the ground. May 20 is about the time to look for full sets.

Mniotilta varia Teulon, *Jour. Boston Zoöl. Soc.*, 1882, 1:50 (Bradford, McKean Co.)—Townsend, *Proc. Acad. Nat. Sci. Philadelphia*, 1883, 61 (Latrobe, Westmoreland Co., summer)—Dwight, *Auk*, 1892, 9:138 (Cresson, Cambria Co., June)—Todd, *Auk*, 1893, 10:40 (Chestnut Ridge, near Two Lick, Indiana Co., June), 45 (Coalport, Clearfield Co., June)—Jacobs, *Summer Birds Greene Co., Pa.*, 1893, 12 (Greene Co., summer)—Baily, *Auk*, 1896, 13:295 (Williamsville, Elk Co., June–July)—Jacobs, *Osprey*, 1899, 3:71 (Waynesburg, Greene Co., nesting)—Cope, *Cassinia*, 1902, 5:17 (Tamarack Swamp, Clinton Co., and upper Kettle Creek

Valley, Potter Co., June)—TODD, *Ann. Carnegie Mus.*, 1904, 2:580 (Presque Isle, Erie Co., summer)—TODD, in Bausman, *Hist. Beaver Co., Pa.*, 1904, 2:1201 (Beaver Co., summer)—COOKE, *Bull. Biol. Surv.* no. 18, 1904, 18 (Beaver, Beaver Co., migration)—KEIM, *Cassinia*, 1905, 8:40 (Port Allegany, McKean Co., summer)—HARLOW, *Auk*, 1912, 29:475 ("Stone Valley" [Charter Oak], Huntingdon Co., nesting)—CHRISTY, *Cardinal*, 1923, v. 1, no. 1, [p. 11] (Sewickley, Allegheny Co., summer)—BURLEIGH, *Wilson Bull.*, 1923, 35:98 (Allegheny Co., summer); 1924, 36:73; 1931, 43:50 (State College, Centre Co., migration; summer)—CHRISTY and SUTTON, *Cardinal*, 1928, 2:73 (Cook Forest, Clarion Co., summer)—SUTTON, *Ann. Carnegie Mus.*, 1928, 18:204 (Crawford Co. localities, summer)—BURLEIGH, *Cardinal*, 1932, 3:80 (Chestnut Ridge, near Uniontown, Fayette Co., summer).

"Black and White Creeper" VAN FLEET, *Ornithologist and Oölogist*, 1884, 9:108 (DuBois, Clearfield Co.).

"Black-and-white Warbler" COOKE, *Bird-Lore*, 1905, 7:203 (Beaver, Beaver Co., and Renovo, Clinton Co., migration) —STONE, *Cassinia*, 1906, 9:44 (Scrub Ridge, west of McConnellsburg, Fulton Co., June)—SIMPSON, *Oölogist*, 1909, 26: 170; and 1914, 31:119 (Warren, Warren Co., nesting, etc.); 1912, 29:330 (head of Tionesta Creek, Warren Co., summer) —HARLOW, *Oölogist*, 1914, 31:95 ("Stone Valley" [Charter Oak], Huntingdon Co., nesting)—DICKEY, *Oölogist*, 1914, 31:171 ([Charter Oak], Huntingdon Co., nesting)—MCCONNELL, *Oölogist*, 1918, 35:151 (McKeesport, Allegheny Co.) —MCCLELLAND, *Am. Mid. Nat.*, 1922, 8:37 (Washington, Washington Co., transient)—BOULTON, *Oölogist*, 1922, 39: 71, 73 (near Beaver, Beaver Co., May)—STREET, *Cassinia*, 1923, 24:17 (Little Cove Creek and Jordan's Knob, Franklin Co., June)—CHRISTY, *Cardinal*, 1924, v. 1, no. 4, p. 9 (Big Traverse Valley, Beaver Co., June)—EASTWOOD, *Bird-Lore*, 1925, 27:263, 338, 407 (Pittsburgh region, Allegheny Co., migration; nesting, *fide* Jones and Grimm), 407 (Stoops Ferry and Dixmont, Allegheny Co., August–September, *fide* Blair); 1926, 28:273 (Rector, Westmoreland Co., May, *fide* Knauz); 1927, 29:273 (Springs, Somerset Co., April, *fide* Miller)—COPE and HAWKINS, *Forest Leaves*, 1934, 24:26 (E. Tionesta Forest Reserve, Warren and McKean Co., summer).

PROTHONOTARY WARBLER

PROTONOTARIA CITREA (Boddaert)

Description—Male: whole head, neck, and underparts (except white under tail coverts), bright yellow; back yellowish green; rump, wings, and tail, bluish gray; tail showing white spots; bill black. *Female* much duller: head merely a little yellower than the back; underparts dull yellow.

Range—The Prothonotary Warbler is a relatively southern species, characteristic of the forested bottomlands along the rivers of the South Atlantic and Gulf states. Farther north it is less common but has been recorded regularly from the Mississippi and Ohio valleys as far north as Minnesota, Michigan, and Ohio. In the last-named state, according to L. E. Hicks, it is local but has been found as a summer resident in twenty-nine scattered counties, including a number in the Lake Erie drainage area. Moreover, since 1931, it has been found breeding in the vicinity of Buffalo, New York.[1] Clearly it is an austral species that is gradually pushing its range northward. While western Pennsylvania as a whole lies beyond its normal summer range, this warbler has recently been found breeding in Erie County, as might have been expected in view of the records from the adjoining states. The exact locality is Lake Le Bœuf, where the species was seen in July, 1938, and where two nests were discovered in 1939, as detailed below. Mrs. F. G. Andrews, who supplied the 1938 record, writes that she also noted a male prothonotary warbler "in a tall chestnut tree" on the shore of Erie Bay on May 30, 1938—a date that certainly suggests breeding. From the same locality there is another record of a bird studied at close range on September 6, 1918, by T. L. McConnell and L. F. Savage, who have published (1919) a full and circumstantial account of the occurrence.

Migration—Elsewhere in our region this warbler is merely a casual migrant, and the records are few and scattered. A male (now in the Carnegie Museum collection) was taken at Ben Avon, Allegheny County, on May 17, 1892, by D. A. Atkinson, who discovered it in a small flock of migrating warblers along the bank of the Ohio River. I have examined a bird shot by A. K. Pierce on May 17, 1911, on "Stout's Island" in the West Branch of the Susquehanna River opposite Renovo. A third report, although a sight record, seems credible; it pertains to a bird observed and watched for some time on May 10, 1923, at Hollidaysburg, by Miss A. E. Berg, who writes: "I saw a warbler dart ahead of me, in and out of the holes in the bank (it was along the river), acting like a wren. To my aston-

[1] C. S. BEARDSLEE, *Auk*, 1932, 49:91.

ishment it was a prothonotary." The same observer saw another late fall migrant on October 4, 1918. A more recent record is supplied by P. P. Malley, who identified a male of this species in Frick Park, Pittsburgh, on May 18, 1938.

Habits—I became acquainted with the Prothonotary Warbler in western Florida, where it is common along the small streams. Drifting along in a boat, I often flushed the birds from the water's edge, where the brilliant yellow of their plumage stood out against the leafy background like a flash of gold.

At the northern limit of its range the Prothonotary Warbler frequents the same type of swampy location. During the first week in July, 1938, F. G. Andrews and a friend were trolling along the south shore of Lake Le Bœuf when they came upon a family group of this warbler—a male, a female, and one, or possibly two, young birds. Mrs. Andrews writes: "It was unmistakably a prothonotary, for no other warbler has a deep orange-yellow breast in combination with slaty-blue wings and rump. This pair must have nested there, for the situation is ideal. The shores of the lake on that side are very swampy; they are inaccessible to the ordinary hiker and difficult to penetrate without high boots." The circumstances and time of year clearly indicate that the birds must have bred.

The next season, on June 26, 1939, this indication was confirmed by J. J. Palmer of Erie, who discovered a nest in a house-wren box that had been nailed to a tree. Mr. Palmer writes: "The box was not more than fifteen feet from the ground. The hole had been made much larger than the usual wren entrance. The parent birds were busy feeding young, although the nest was within a few feet of the water and of the path to the boat landing, where people were using the boats and working. Repeatedly we saw the birds within twenty-five feet. We also saw in a decayed post near by, in a knothole, a nest that, according to the keeper of the boats, had just been abandoned two days before. There were still two eggs in it. We saw other birds of this species in the surrounding trees." The eggs number from five to seven and measure about .69 by .56 inches; they are white, rather coarsely spotted with several shades of brown.

W. E. Dilley accompanied Mr. Palmer on his initial visit to this spot, and also saw the birds and heard them sing. The song is a simple monotone trill consisting of about four notes. Future developments concerning this little colony of prothonotary warblers will be awaited with interest.

Protonotaria citrea Rhoads, *Auk*, 1899, 16:312 ([Ben Avon], Allegheny Co., May, *fide* Atkinson).

"Prothonotary Warbler" McConnell and Savage, *Bird-Lore*, 1919, 21:242 ("Waldameer Park," Erie, Erie Co., September).

WORM-EATING WARBLER

HELMITHEROS VERMIVORUS (Gmelin)

Description—A warbler of medium size, with a rather stout, pointed bill. Upperparts (including wings and tail), olive green; *head buffy, with four broad black stripes* (two on the crown and one through each eye); sides of head (below the eye), throat, and rest of *underparts, dull buffy* (usually paler in the middle); feet pale.

Range—This is a relatively southern warbler. It winters mainly in the West Indies and Central America and migrates northward for the summer, reaching southern New England, the lower Hudson Valley in New York, and northern Illinois. It is a species of the Carolinian Fauna, and its breeding range in western Pennsylvania is discontinuous, comprising two separate areas on either side of the Allegheny Plateau. It proves to be a rather common summer resident (as warblers go) in Beaver County, and thence southward to Greene County, where J. W. Jacobs and S. S. Dickey have found many nests in past years. I have traced it east to Chestnut Ridge (in the gaps of the Kiskiminetas and Loyalhanna creeks), and northward to the mouth of Redbank Creek in Clarion County. In Indiana County it was noted on June 19, 1935, near Gaibleton by a party from the Carnegie Museum (Trimble). Warren claims to have observed it in Venango County but does not state the exact locality. Crawford County seems to be about the northern limit of its range, although it has not been known to breed there. G. M. Sutton noted two birds, presumably near Hartstown, in May, and S. J. Seiple has seen the species during the same month two miles south of Adamsville. In the adjoining state of Ohio, according to L. E. Hicks, it is not known to breed at the present time north of Mahoning County, which borders Lawrence County in Pennsylvania.

The Worm-eating Warbler is as common in the ridge and valley section as it is in the woodlands of the southwestern counties. I first discovered it there in June, 1895, while tramping from McVeytown, Mifflin County, to State College. It was observed not only in the valley country near the head of Standing Stone Creek in Huntingdon County, but also on Jacks Mountain, and again on Broad Mountain. Later experience in other parts of this general region has confirmed an earlier impression that this warbler, although rightly a species of the Carolinian Fauna, is actually unaffected by elevation in this section and ranges directly over the several mountain ridges. Here it lives side by side with such relatively northern birds as the Canadian, Black-throated Blue, and Blackburnian warblers. In view of the fact that in New England, for instance, it shows little if any tendency to invade the Alleghanian Fauna, this deviation is of interest.

This warbler has also been noted at Renovo, on the West Branch of the Susquehanna River, at rare intervals during the month of May and once in September, as recorded in the notes of A. K. Pierce and attested by the capture of at least one specimen (now in the Carnegie Museum). The status of the species in that region is uncertain. Probably the several records pertain to birds that overshot their normal limits in migration, as often happens. The species is also included in Van Fleet's manuscript list of the breeding birds of DuBois, but this unusual record requires confirmation.

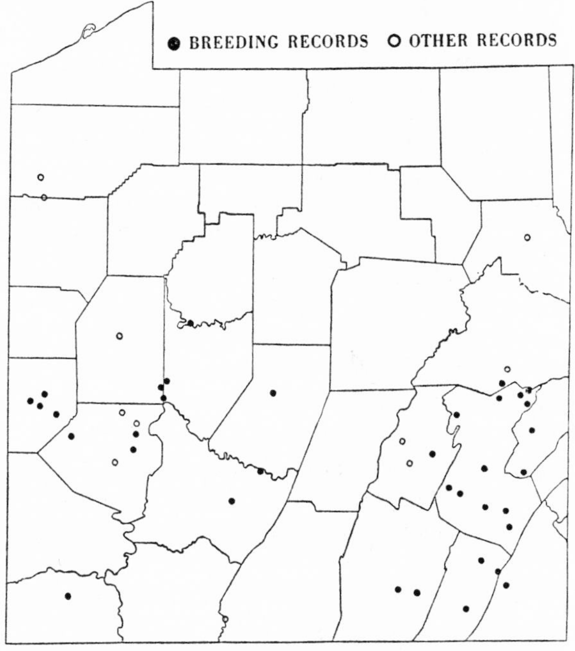

LOCAL RANGE OF THE WORM-EATING WARBLER

Migration—There are not many migration records for the Worm-eating Warbler. During six years its arrival at Beaver varied between April 29 and May 8, and May 4 was the average date. Since the few early dates from other sections lie within these limits, we are justified in expecting this species during the first week in May. I have never seen it at Beaver later in the season than the middle of August (August 16, 1888; August 17, 1908). In comparing records from other states, I am led to believe that this is the usual time of its departure for the South. An unusually late date, September 5 (1914), is reported by T. D. Burleigh for Pittsburgh.

Habits—Warblers as a class are among the most active of birds; in the season of migration they are so constantly on the move that it is often no simple matter to keep a given individual in sight long enough to identify it. The Worm-eating Warbler, however, is a comparatively easy-going species; it is rather slow and sedate in its movements and hops leisurely from branch to branch in its search for food. Its name has no actual significance, since so far as is known its food does not differ particularly from that of other species of similar haunts and habits. Wooded slopes are its chosen abodes, the shadier and cooler the better. It used to be fairly common on the steep hillside facing the Ohio River opposite the town of Beaver, where the northern exposure and the luxuriant forest growth combined to produce ideal conditions. Deep ravines, down which trickle little streams, and the slopes of which support good stands of deciduous trees, with plenty of shrubbery and bushes for cover, are favorite resorts. In such damp and shady retreats one may hear during May and June a simple bird song consisting of a single note, trilled for several seconds at a time. It is not quite so loud as that of the Chipping

Sparrow, perhaps, but is otherwise similar enough to justify the remark, "If you hear a chipping sparrow in the woods, it is a worm-eating warbler." By exercising a little caution, one may presently catch sight of the singer as it travels from bush to tree and back again, occasionally descending to a fallen log or to the ground, where it works among the low plants of the forest floor. Rather quiet and unobtrusive, clad in a modest garb of olive and buff, this bird somehow suggests a vireo as much as a warbler.

Year after year a given pair, or their successors, will return to the same spot to nest. After the usual courtship period, during which the male chases all rivals from his chosen territory, the nest is begun. It is built on the ground, in a location similar to that affected by the Black and White Warbler. I found a nest near Industry, Beaver County, on May 28, 1890, on the side of a steep bank formed by some projecting rocks—a type of site not infrequently selected. Dr. Dickey, who has published an interesting account of this warbler, says that in Greene County the nest is usually placed at the base of a sapling (with its brim flush with the accumulated dry leaves), or else beneath the sheltering roots of some larger tree. He describes a typical nest as "composed of a foundation of dead leaves, while the interior was lined with red flower-stalks of moss, *Polytrichum commune* and *Funaria*, fine grass blades, and a few green sprays of moss." The nests I have found in Beaver County conform to this description. It is often possible to discover the nest by systematically brushing over all likely ground with a switch made from a leafy branch and thus flushing the incubating bird. Often she will feign lameness and flutter off down the slope in an effort to draw attention from the nest.

The eggs are white, more or less evenly spotted with reddish brown. The markings vary considerably in quantity but are usually dots or specks rather than blotches. Average measurements are .69 by .53 inches. Five eggs are usually laid, but a smaller number is not uncommon, particularly when the Cowbird invades the nest, as it not infrequently does. Dr. Dickey has found several sets of six eggs each. He has found full sets of fresh eggs in Greene County at dates that range between May 15 and 31.

Helmitherus vermivorus Warren, *Birds Pa.*, ed. 2, 1890, 268, 274 (Clarion and Venango Co.; Franklin Co., September)—Todd, *Auk*, 1891, 8:397, 399 (near Beaver, Beaver Co., nesting; Buffalo Creek region, Armstrong and Butler Co., summer)—Jacobs, *Summer Birds Greene Co., Pa.*, 1893, 12 (Greene Co., nesting)—Jacobs, *Gleanings from Nature*, 1898, 1:9, 32 (Waynesburg, Greene Co., nesting)—Rhoads, *Auk*, 1899, 16:312 (Pittsburgh, Allegheny Co., *fide* Link).

Helmitheros vermivorus Todd, in Bausman, *Hist. Beaver Co., Pa.*, 1904, 2:1201 (Beaver Co., summer)—Cooke, *Bull. Biol. Surv.* no. 18, 1904, 28 (Beaver, Beaver Co., migration)—Harlow, *Auk*, 1918, 35:141 (Allegheny, Greene, Huntingdon, and Centre Co., breeding)—Christy, *Cardinal*, 1923, v. 1, no. 1, [p. 11] (Sewickley, Allegheny Co., summer)—Burleigh, *Wilson Bull.*, 1923, 35:98 (Allegheny Co., nesting); 1924, 36:73 (State College, Centre Co., migration); 1931, 43:51 (Charter Oak, Huntingdon Co., breeding)—Dickey, *Oölogist*, 1914, 31:96 (Waynesburg, Greene Co., nesting)—Sutton, *Ann. Carnegie Mus.*, 1928, 18:204 (Pymatuning Swamp, Crawford Co., May)—Dickey, *Cardinal*, 1934, 3:179 (Waynesburg, Greene Co., and Charter Oak and Spruce Creek, Huntingdon Co., nesting).

"Worm-eating Warbler" Cooke, *Bird-Lore*, 1906, 8:27 (Beaver, Beaver Co., migration)—Burleigh, *Oölogist*, 1911, 28:156 (Harmarville, Allegheny Co., nesting); 1914, 31:191 (Allegheny Co., May)—Harlow, *Oölogist*, 1914, 31:98 ([Charter Oak], Huntingdon Co., nesting)—Dickey, *Oölogist*, 1914, 31:170 ([Charter Oak], Huntingdon Co., nesting)—Street, *Cassinia*, 1923, 24:17 (Jordan's Knob, Franklin Co., June)—Eastwood, *Bird-Lore*, 1925, 27:263; and 1926, 28:272 (Pittsburgh region, Allegheny Co., May).

GOLDEN-WINGED WARBLER

VERMIVORA CHRYSOPTERA (Linnaeus)

Description—A warbler of average size, with a straight, sharp bill. *Adult male:* general color above, *grayish blue;* tail above and *wings*, similar, the latter crossed by *two yellow bars* (sometimes fused into one yellow spot); *crown yellow, and sides of head black*, bordered above and below with a white line; *throat black*, and rest of underparts grayish white; tail showing large white spots on the outer feathers. *Adult female:* in general similar to the male, but coloration duller, and the black of the *throat* replaced by *dull gray*, a little darker than the rest of the underparts; wings (externally) often tinged with yellowish green.

Range—In winter this warbler ranges from Central America to Colombia and Venezuela. Its summer home is in the eastern United States and southern Ontario. Although mainly a species of the Alleghanian Fauna in summer, it ranges beyond this zonal limit at many points and invades the upper part of the Carolinian Fauna, as well as the lower edge of the Canadian. The extension of its range into the latter fauna may be due to deforestation, since this species is one that tends to come in after the original coniferous forest has been cut and deciduous second growth has taken its place. The status and the relative abundance of the Golden-winged Warbler bear a curious complementary relationship to those of its cousin, the Blue-winged. While the latter is on the whole a more southerly bird, the respective ranges of the two overlap. It is the rule, however, that wherever both species occur, they are not equally common; one always outnumbers the other. Thus, in southern Connecticut, New Jersey, and on the Atlantic slope in general, the Blue-winged is the common species and the Golden-winged is correspondingly rare. West of the mountains, however, exactly the reverse is true. The exception to this general statement actually proves the rule. There is a restricted area in Crawford County where the Blue-winged is a common breeding bird, and there the Golden-winged is comparatively rare.

The published records for this warbler give an imperfect idea of its wide distribution in our area. But when the localities they refer to are plotted on a map in conjunction with the localities supplied in available manuscript records (most of which are my own), a fuller picture emerges. The Golden-wing seems to be most numerous in the southwestern quarter of our region, especially in the Carolinian Fauna. It is certainly common in Beaver, Butler, Allegheny, and Greene counties, and east as far as Indiana County (Two Lick) and the Ligonier Valley in Westmoreland County (Idlewild and Laughlintown). In Somerset County it seems to have ascended the valley of the Casselman River and has been reported from Casselman (Shufeldt), Rockwood (Todd), near Stoyestown (Mostoller), Savage Mountain, near Meyersdale (Preble), and Springs (Miller). In my opinion its appearance in this region at the elevation indicated is comparatively recent and is a direct result of deforestation. From the northern part of the plateau region there are only a few locality records. Van Fleet called the species "very rare" at DuBois, and in June, 1895, I encountered it at Kane and at Howard Hill (near Mount Jewett), McKean County. Although I found it common also near Tiona, Warren County, during the same season, the veteran observer of that county, R. B. Simpson, considered it only rare or casual at Warren until a few years ago. Lately, however, it has become more regular, although still far from common, and Mr. Simpson has been successful in finding its nest. It also occurs occasionally at Renovo, according to A. K. Pierce, and has been reported from Round Island, in the same county (Clinton), by S. N. Rhoads, in late May.

The status of the species in Erie County is not clear. I was surprised when I did not find it on Presque Isle in 1900, but L. E. Hicks has since recorded it there in August, and W. M. Guynes has reported it in July.

East of the Allegheny divide, the Golden-winged Warbler reappears, but it is not common. There are a few odd records for all the counties in that section except Franklin.

Migration—The Golden-winged Warbler arrives in our region during the first week in May, or even a little earlier if weather conditions permit. The exact dates for Beaver range from April 24 (1902) to May 8 (1911, 1923), but the average arrival date in thirteen seasons is May 3. Earliest dates for some other localities are: Waynesburg, April 20, 1893 (Jacobs); Sewickley, April 27, 1902 (Christy); Renovo, April 27, 1897 (Pierce); Springs, Somerset County, April 29, 1914 (Miller). Although it appears with the other warblers in the spring, this species is one of the first to depart in the fall. In fact, since it is seldom seen after July, it must begin its southward movement in August, after the postnuptial molt has been completed. In 1909 I saw it at Beaver on August 30, and in 1910, on September 1. D. A. Atkinson reports seeing one bird at Wilkinsburg on September 4, 1896. G. M. Sutton saw a male near Atlantic, Crawford County, on the unusually late date of September 17 (1925). J. W. Jacobs has one record for September 21, and several for the preceding week.

Habits—Heavy timber has no attraction for the Golden-winged Warbler. It is a bird that likes the edges of the woods, or tracts of scattered trees, preferably where the ground beneath is choked with brush and briers. Old clearings, or fields that have run to waste, especially if on the outskirts of woods, are favorite haunts. In Greene County, according to Mr. Jacobs (1904), "a field of fifteen acres, bordering an undergrowth woods and having other favorable conditions is almost certain to be the home of one pair. Smaller tracts do not always possess a nesting pair, but here and there a very small favorable nook of less than a quarter acre, in the edge of a woods is selected, and two such places entirely surrounded by woods were inhabited annually until the undergrowth crowded out the grass. . . . I have never found a nest in the creek bottom lands, but always well up the side or on top of a hill." In such locations the male makes his presence known by a characteristic song, a feeble effort consisting of one syllable, repeated from three to six times—*zee-zee-zee-zee*. It has an insect-like character and is not audible at any great distance. The singer perches near the top of a low tree or performs while moving about near the tips of the branches in search of food. Mr. Jacobs adds: "I have several times heard the song continued to the middle of July, and again on still sultry days in August. At this time, however, it is not so strong and complete as during the early summer. While emitting this song, the bird stands quite erect, stretched up to its full height, throat extended until the feathers ruffle. The head pointing about 70 degrees upward when the first syllable is uttered, is turned farther upward at the close of the song."

Concerning the food of this warbler, the same author writes: "This bird must be a great destroyer of leaf lice and small caterpillars that infest the tips of branches and the underside of leaves, for they are continually searching and picking at the opening buds and waxen leaves at the ends of new twigs, the male pausing frequently to sing. At times their actions remind one of the Gnatcatcher in flitting hither and thither snatching up small winged mites."

As soon as the birds are paired and settled for the season, nest-building is begun. For this task two days seem to be ample, and Mr. Jacobs has more than once found an egg in a nest on the second day after construction was started. A nest that I found near Beaver on June 1, 1910, was rather large and bulky and was not sunk in the ground but placed several inches above; it was supported by a clump of weeds and was in plain sight when these were parted. Its foundation was of dry leaves, and it was composed of grapevine bark and weed stalks, lined with finer material of the same kind.

In location and composition this nest was entirely similar to those described by Mr. Jacobs. He says that although nest-building does not occupy very much of the bird's time, the nest when completed is fairly compact and neatly cupped, although rather bulky for so small a bird. The base is composed of oak and beech leaves or any other kinds that dry hard and glossy without crumpling. On top of this heap is set a more compact structure, in which leaves are placed with the points downward. These are followed by a goodly supply of strips of grapevine bark and shreds of inner tree bark, so placed that the rough ends extend above the rim of the nest. The lining consists of fine grass stems and sometimes long horsehair. A lining is not always made, however, since some birds lay the eggs on the grapevine bark and a few intermingling grass stems. Although constructed of coarse materials, the inside of the nest presents a neat appearance; the long shreds of bark and grasses cross diagonally and resemble basketwork. The nest is almost always near some substantial supports such as weeds, briers, or elder shrubs, not sufficiently thick to hinder a good growth of grass. One nest in a marshy place was three inches above the ground in a clump of ironweed.

In Greene County the height of the laying season is from May 14 to 24. Sets of fresh eggs have been taken in Warren County on May 31 and June 2. The normal number of eggs varies from three to six. Six are very rare, however, and four are commoner than five. As a result of the Cowbird's interference, a smaller number may be laid —three, or only two. The eggs are white, with a faint shading of creamy buff, and are marked with spots of various shades of brown and with lighter-colored shell-markings. In the usual type there are only a few small spots, mainly about the larger end, as in vireos' eggs, while in other examples the markings are larger and more or less irregular. The eggs of this warbler are among the most sparsely marked of the entire group. They average .64 by .50 inches. Incubation requires fourteen days, and in ten days after hatching, the young are strong enough to leave the nest.

Helminthophila chrysoptera WARREN, *Birds Pa.*, ed. 2, 1890, 276 (Armstrong and Beaver Co., July)—TODD, *Auk*, 1891, 8:397, 399 (Beaver, Beaver Co., and Buffalo Creek region, Armstrong and Butler Co., summer); 1893, 10:40 (Two Lick, Indiana Co., June)—JACOBS, *Summer Birds Greene Co., Pa.*, 1893, 12 (Greene Co., nesting)—RHOADS, *Auk*, 1899, 16:312 (Allegheny, Beaver, and Westmoreland Co.)—JACOBS, *Gleanings*, no. 3, 1904, 1–30 (Waynesburg, etc., Greene Co., nesting)—TODD, in Bausman, *Hist. Beaver Co., Pa.*, 1904, 2:1201 (Beaver Co., summer)—COOKE, *Bull. Biol. Surv.* no. 18, 1904, 35 (Beaver, Beaver Co., and Waynesburg, Greene Co., migration)—FAXON, *Mem. Mus. Comp. Zoöl.*, 1911, 40: 76, pl., fig. 2 (Beaver, Beaver Co., description of young).

"Golden-winged Warbler" COOKE, *Bird-Lore*, 1904, 6:92 (Beaver, Beaver Co., and Waynesburg, Greene Co., migration) —SIMPSON, *Oölogist*, 1911, 28:165; and 1914, 31:119 (Warren, Warren Co., May, July)—DICKEY, *Oölogist*, 1914, 31:99 ([Charter Oak], Huntingdon Co., nesting)—MCCONNELL, *Oölogist*, 1918, 35:151 (Long Run, near McKeesport, Allegheny Co., breeding)—MILLER, *Oölogist*, 1919, 36:156 (Charter Oak, Huntingdon Co., nesting)—MCCLELLAND, *Am. Mid. Nat.*, 1922, 8:37 (Washington, Washington Co., spring)—CHRISTY, *Cardinal*, 1924, v. 1, no. 4, p. 10 (Big Traverse Valley, Beaver Co., June); 1925, v. 1, no. 6, p. 23 (Little Traverse Creek, Beaver Co., May)—EASTWOOD, *Bird-Lore*, 1925, 27:262 (Raccoon Creek, Beaver Co., May, *fide* Jones), 263; and 1926, 28:272 (Pittsburgh region, Allegheny Co., May).

Vermivora chrysoptera HARLOW, *Auk*, 1912, 29:475 (Monroe Furnace, Huntingdon Co., June); 1918, 35:142 ([Charter Oak], Huntingdon Co., summer; Greene and Allegheny Co.) —STONE, *Cassinia*, 1919, 22:35; and 1920, 23:36 (Altoona, Blair Co., May, *fide* McGraw)—CHRISTY, *Cardinal*, 1923, v. 1, no. 1, [p. 12] (Sewickley, Allegheny Co., breeding)—BURLEIGH, *Wilson Bull.*, 1923, 35:98 (Harmarville, Allegheny Co., nesting); 1924, 36:73; and 1931, 43:51 (State College, Centre Co., migration; breeding)—SUTTON, *Ann. Carnegie Mus.*, 1928, 18:206 (Crawford Co. localities, summer)—BURLEIGH, *Cardinal*, 1929, 2:118 (Allegheny Co., August)—ARTHUR, *Cardinal*, 1932, 3:55 (Lowrie Run and Harmarville, Allegheny Co., nesting).

BREWSTER'S WARBLER. *Vermivora leucobronchialis* Brewster

Description—Upperparts *bluish gray; crown and patch on wing coverts, bright yellow;* a dark stripe through the eye; *underparts white*, sometimes washed with yellow; tail showing white spots on the outer feathers. Plumage variable, scarcely any two specimens being exactly alike.

Remarks—This is not a "good" species, but either a color phase of the Blue-winged Warbler, as some authorities insist, or a hybrid between that species and the Golden-winged. It occurs wherever the two are found together, as for instance in southern New England, where most of the specimens on record have been taken. In our region, specimens have been collected only in Beaver and Crawford counties. One was secured by G. M. Sutton on the south bank of the Ohio River nearly opposite the town of Beaver on May 7, 1921, and another was taken by him at Hartstown on August 29, 1925. Both these specimens are now in the collection of the Carnegie Museum. The same observer also records a nest found at Hartstown by J. G. Thomas on June 6, 1922, which held three eggs in an advanced stage of incubation, and two young. The male parent was a typical white-throated bird, while the female was markedly yellowish below. S. J. Seiple observed a single bird southeast of Greenville on May 8, 1927, and another on May 11, 1928. B. H. Christy saw and positively identified a bird of this species on May 17, 1925, at the mouth of Little Traverse Creek in southern Beaver County.

On June 3, 1937, R. M. Edeburn and S. S. Ristich took me to a point on the highway about a mile and a half east of Green Garden, Beaver County, and showed me a male Brewster's warbler. Its song was precisely like that of the Golden-winged Warbler. These observers report that this bird (presumably the same one) was present at the same spot in the spring of 1938.

Vermivora leucobronchialis CHRISTY, *Cardinal*, 1923, v. 1, no. 1, [p. 12] ("Raccoon Creek" [Beaver], Beaver Co., May)—SUTTON, *Ann. Carnegie Mus.*, 1928, 18:206 (Hartstown, Crawford Co., nesting, *fide* Thomas).

"Brewster's Warbler" CHRISTY, *Cardinal*, 1925, v. 1, no. 6, p. 23 (Little Traverse Creek, Beaver Co., May).

LAWRENCE'S WARBLER. *Vermivora lawrencei* (Herrick)

Description—A bird resembling the Blue-winged Warbler, but with the characteristic black or dusky throat and head markings of the Golden-winged Warbler. Upperparts bright olive green; forehead, crown, chin, wide cheek-stripe, and *underparts, yellow;* black ear-patch extending below the eye to the bill; *throat and upper breast, black*, this color forming a triangular patch, pointed at the chin; wings bluish gray with two white bars; tail also bluish gray, the inner webs of the outer tail feathers mostly white.

Remarks—Lawrence's Warbler, like Brewster's Warbler, is a hybrid, resulting from the interbreeding of the Blue-winged and the Golden-winged warblers where these two species occur together. Lawrence's Warbler is much rarer than Brewster's Warbler, since its color pattern seems genetically to be a pure recessive. Maurice Broun, summarizing the theories advanced by J. T. Nichols,[1] Walter Faxon,[2] and others concerning the interesting and puzzling relationships of these birds, says: "Thus, briefly, when pure *pinus* mates with pure *chrysoptera*, the result should be a homogeneous brood of *leucobronchialis*, a Mendelian so-called dominant hybrid; when impure *pinus* is

[1] *Auk*, 1908, 25:86.

[2] *Memoirs Museum Comparative Zoölogy*, 1910, p. 57; 1911 p. 68; 1913, p. 311–316.

mated with pure *chrysoptera*, the progeny should be *chrysoptera* and *leucobronchialis* in equal numbers; pure *pinus* when paired with impure *chrysoptera* should give birth to *pinus* and *leucobronchialis* in equal numbers, while a mixed impure parentage of *pinus* and *chrysoptera* should produce equal numbers of *pinus, chrysoptera, leucobronchialis* and *lawrencei;* the last named manifests the recessive character of *lawrencei*, and its proportionately greater rarity is thus explained."[1]

The only record of Lawrence's Warbler in western Pennsylvania is one supplied by R. L. Fricke, who collected an adult male about five miles south of Linesville, Crawford County, on May 12, 1939. His attention was called to this unusual warbler by John Heron, who says that its song resembled that of the blue-winged warblers with which it was associated. The specimen is on display in the Carnegie Museum.

Vermivora lawrencei Fricke, *Cardinal*, 1939, 5:47 (near Linesville, Crawford Co., May).

[1]In E. H. Forbush, *Birds of Massachusetts*, 1929, 2:216.

BLUE-WINGED WARBLER

VERMIVORA PINUS (Linnaeus)

Description—A bird resembling the Golden-winged Warbler in size and proportions. *Male: bright yellow*, the back greenish yellow; a *short black streak through the eye; wings bluish gray, with two white bands* (sometimes fusing into one white patch); tail bluish gray, with large white spots on the outer feathers. *Female* rather duller than the male, and *young* still duller, the crown colored like the back.

Range—As worked out by W. W. Cooke,[1] the breeding range of this species corresponds rather closely with the limits of the Carolinian Fauna. In its local distribution and in its relative abundance, the Blue-winged Warbler seems to complement the Golden-winged. East of the Appalachian Mountains, where the latter species is decidedly rare, the Blue-winged is one of the commoner warblers; but in western Pennsylvania generally, where the Golden-winged is the prevailing form, the other is unaccountably rare. Not until we reach the flat country northwest of the terminal moraine do we find the Blue-winged common as a summer resident. The favorable ecological conditions there are a continuation of those just across the Pennsylvania boundary in Ohio, where the species is likewise fairly common. The extent of its local breeding area, however, remains to be determined. While Warren explicitly states that he personally saw or heard this warbler in summer in all the westernmost counties from Erie to Washington inclusive, he unfortunately cites no exact localities; he gives the impression, however, that it breeds sparingly throughout. It is certainly common in the vicinity of Pymatuning and Conneaut swamps in Crawford County, and thence south to Sharon and the Big Bend region of the Shenango River in Mercer County (McQuiston). It has also been traced east to Slippery Rock (Raney) and Jamisonville (Elliott) in Butler County.

These records tend partly to confirm Warren's observations. But in the hill country farther south, the Blue-winged is indeed one of the rarest of the warblers. It does not appear in J. W. Jacobs' list of the summer birds of Greene County, and in Beaver County it is so rare that in more than fifty years' field experience I have taken but two specimens (both during spring migration). I once saw this warbler, however, in June along the Ohio River, where it has also been noted in May by others (Boulton, 1922). S. S. Ristich sends two May and June (1938) records from Beaver County. On May 23, 1920, B. H. Christy and G. M. Sutton actually found a nest along Wheeling Creek, about two miles southeast of West Finley, on the southern border of Washington County. This breeding station is apparently an eastward extension of the Wheeling, West Virginia, breeding area. In view of the demonstrated rarity of the species in Beaver County, I am inclined to view the sight records from the adjoining county of Allegheny with suspicion; there is in existence, however, a spring specimen taken by D. A. Atkinson near Wilkinsburg. P. P. Malley, moreover, claims to have identified the Blue-wing in early May and late August in Frick Park, Pittsburgh. S. N. Rhoads's record of "two or three pairs" found breeding in the foothills of Laurel Hill, near Laughlintown, Westmoreland County, in June, 1898, is possibly correct, but it is unfortunately not supported by specimens. Warren's published record from Clarion County is almost certainly an error.

Migration—The Blue-winged Warbler reaches

[1]U. S. Department of Agriculture, Biological Survey, *Bulletin*, no. 18, 1904, p. 32.

our latitude early in May, in company with many others of this family. My dates for Beaver are May 2 (1891) and May 3 (1909). Farther north the species has been noted at Greenville on May 4 (1926—Seiple) and at Hartstown on May 3 (1922—Sutton). The above-mentioned specimen shot by Dr. Atkinson on April 23, 1894, constitutes an early spring record. At Pymatuning the fall movement is under way in August, and in 1925 the last bird was noted on September 19. The record for State College made by Merrill Wood[1] can scarcely be credited, since its sole basis is an observation made on October 13, a date much too late in the season to have applied to this species.

Habits—My own experience with this warbler has been somewhat limited. I completely overlooked it at Pymatuning Swamp during my earlier visits, and it remained for Dr. Sutton to discover that this locality was indeed a favored spot, as I have more recently learned for myself. He writes (1928): "Today it is unquestionably one of the most abundant, widely distributed, and characteristic members of its family in the region. But its occurrence seems to depend quite definitely on a certain type of low bushy growth, which occurs along the border of the Swamp, particularly near the dying tamaracks and at the margins of the lakes and streams. In every spring visit we have made to the Swamp its monotonous un-birdlike song has always greeted us, and the little brush-covered valleys and upgrown edges of the woodlands nearly always were found to harbor these delightful birds."

The blue-wings must begin nesting very soon after their arrival; at any rate, two pairs were found building on May 17. Dr. Sutton continues: "During the building of the nests the males in particular were often combative, and would chase each other about through the black raspberry-bushes, or through the dense willows. From all sides came their odd, droning songs, like the murmur of great bees. . . .

"The songs of the Blue-wing were found to merit close study. The characteristic performance of the arriving birds, as noted, was always the well known 'ee-zee' with the inhalant-exhalant quality mentioned by Chapman (*Birds of Eastern North America*, 1914, 442) and other authors. By May 29 a second song was characteristic. This song has also been noted by students. But a third song, unlike either, was often heard, particularly during the building of the nest, an elaborate and broken up rendition of the simple 'eee-zeee,' or 'swee-chee' (as Chapman has written it) which somewhat resembles the song of the Nashville Warbler. The song might be written 'swee, pit, chi chi chi,' the latter three notes with an exhalant quality. On September 1, 1925, a male was heard singing 'chi chi chi chi chi chi chi-zeee.' "

A nest that Miss Ruth Trimble and I found on May 25, 1934, contained four nearly fresh eggs of the Blue-winged Warbler and one of the Cowbird. We stumbled across it while traversing the dense alder and willow growth along Conneaut Outlet about two miles from Conneaut Lake. Built in the center of a skunk-cabbage clump, it was raised several inches from the ground and was a rather bulky structure, with a thick foundation of dry leaves. The nest proper was composed of dry grasses, with finer material of the same sort for lining. Nests found at Pymatuning by Dr. Sutton were very similar in location and composition and in both respects closely resembled those of the Golden-winged Warbler. The eggs, however, tend to be less heavily marked than those of that species; they are white, with a few small reddish-brown or purplish specks or spots, mostly about the larger end. They are usually four or five in number, and they average .62 by .50 inches.

Helminthophila pinus Warren, *Birds Pa.*, ed. 2, 1890, 275 (Crawford, Erie, Mercer, Lawrence, Beaver, and Washington Co., summer; [?]Clarion Co., breeding)—Todd, *Auk*, 1891, 8:397 (Beaver, Beaver Co., May); 1893, 10:209 (Beaver, Beaver Co., June)—Rhoads, *Auk*, 1899, 16:312 ([?]Beaver, Beaver Co.; [?]Laurel Hill, near Laughlintown, Westmoreland Co., breeding; [Wilkinsburg], Allegheny Co., April, *fide* Atkinson)—Todd, in Bausman, *Hist. Beaver Co., Pa.*, 1904, 2:1201 (Beaver Co., summer).

"Blue-winged Warbler" Boulton, *Oölogist*, 1922, 39:71 (Beaver, Beaver Co., May)—(?)Sutton, *Bird-Lore*, 1923, 25:260 (Allegheny Co., May)—Christy, *Cardinal*, 1923, v. 1, no. 1, [p. 12] ([near West Finley], Washington Co., nesting)—(?)Eastwood, *Bird-Lore*, 1926, 28:272 (Pittsburgh region, Allegheny Co., May)—Fricke, *Cardinal*, 1939, 5:46 (near Linesville, Crawford Co., May).

Vermivora pinus Sutton, *Ann. Carnegie Mus.*, 1928, 18:204 (Pymatuning Swamp, Crawford Co., nesting; song).

[1]*Wilson Bulletin*, 1932, 44:238.

TENNESSEE WARBLER (Plate 18)

VERMIVORA PEREGRINA (Wilson)

Description—A rather small, plainly colored warbler, with *unmarked wings and tail.* (The white spot on the latter is not obvious in life.) *Adult male in spring: head and upper back, gray; rest of upperparts,* including wing- and tail-edgings, *bright olive green,* but the edgings of the primaries inclining to gray; a short pale superciliary stripe, and below this a *dark stripe through the eye; underparts plain grayish white. Adult female:* similar, but duller, the crown washed with green and the underparts with yellow. *Immature birds in fall:* crown and upperparts in general, bright olive green; underparts white, with some olive-yellow shading, especially on the throat, sides, and flanks; a dark streak through the eye, and a paler one above it. Some individuals in this plumage show a faint pale bar on the wings.

Range—This warbler breeds in the Canadian Life Zone from Newfoundland to the upper Yukon Valley in Alaska, migrates through the Mississippi Valley, and winters from southern Mexico through Central America to Venezuela. Although it breeds regularly as far south as the higher Catskills in New York, there are no mountains in Pennsylvania high enough to accommodate it. Here it occurs only as a somewhat irregular transient, although it is often fairly common in both spring and fall, at least in the western tier of counties. During the fall migration there may be days of great movement, when the Tennessee Warbler is almost as numerous as the Black-poll. It has not been observed in the plateau section, except at Springs, Somerset County, where A. B. Miller finds it common in the spring. R. B. Simpson considers it one of the rare warblers at Warren and has never seen it away from the river valley. At Renovo it must also be rare, as there are only two specimens in the A. K. Pierce collection. In the ridge and valley section it has been recorded from State College (Burleigh) and from Altoona and Hollidaysburg (McGraw; Berg). It is an inconspicuous species, especially in the fall, and has doubtless been overlooked by many observers.

Migration—The Tennessee Warbler is one of the late migrants among this group and seldom reaches our latitude before the second week in May. My arrival dates at Beaver run from May 5 to 14, and the average date in eleven seasons is May 10. The earliest spring record for Springs is May 4 (1913), and for Warren, May 15 (1913). The movement continues for about two weeks. The "last-seen" records for Beaver vary between May 19 and 28, and yield May 23 as an average date. The species has been recorded from Warren as late as May 30 (1907) and from Frankfort Springs, Beaver County, on June 1 (1924—Christy). In 1935 I saw one bird on Presque Isle on May 30.

The fall movement is more extended than the spring migration and lasts a month or more. Available records are scarce, but allowance must be made for the difficulty of satisfactorily identifying the species at this season. It has been noted at Beaver as early as September 2 (1908) and was seen on September 5 (1925) at Crystal Lake, Crawford County, where it became abundant two days later (Sutton). The indications are that the first week in September marks its normal autumnal appearance in our region, although many of the actual records are considerably later. "Last-seen" dates for Beaver range from October 2 (1889) to 11 (1890); one unusually late record is that for October 26 (1909).

Habits—Coming after the trees are partially in leaf, the Tennessee Warbler may easily be overlooked by all but the practiced observer. Its plain coloration, its habit of keeping high in the terminal foliage of the forest trees, and its deliberate movements while feeding, make it difficult to detect. The song of the male, however, is penetrating and distinctive and when once learned is a sure clue to the presence of this bird. The song makes up in insistence and delivery for what it lacks in melody. It consists of a single penetrating note, repeated slowly at first, then more rapidly and in higher pitch, and ending in a still higher key, with a strong upward inflection. In the fall the species is silent, save for a low chirp, in no way distinctive. At this season it is likely to be found in bushes and shrubbery and along the edges of the woods, in company with other warblers of similar haunts and habits.

Helminthophila peregrina Warren, *Birds Pa.*, ed. 2, 1890, 278 (western Pa., transient)—Todd, *Auk*, 1891, 8:398 (Beaver, Beaver Co., transient)—Todd, *Ann. Carnegie Mus.*, 1904,

2:581 (Presque Isle, Erie Co., spring transient)—TODD, in Bausman, *Hist. Beaver Co., Pa.*, 1904, 2:1201 (Beaver Co., transient)—COOKE, *Bull. Biol. Surv.* no. 18, 1904, 42 (Beaver, Beaver Co., migration).

"Tennessee Warbler" COOKE, *Bird-Lore*, 1905, 7:239 (Beaver, Beaver Co., migration)—SIMPSON, *Oölogist*, 1907, 24:134; and 1914, 31:121 (Warren, Warren Co., transient)—MCCLELLAND, *Am. Mid. Nat.*, 1922, 8:37 (Washington, Washington Co., transient)—CHRISTY, *Cardinal*, 1924, v. 1, no. 4, p. 11 (Big Traverse Valley, Beaver Co., May)—EASTWOOD, *Bird-Lore*, 1925, 27:407; 1926, 28:272; and 1927, 29:272 (Pittsburgh region, Allegheny Co., migration), 273 (Springs, Somerset Co., May, *fide* Miller).

Vermivora peregrina STONE, *Cassinia*, 1920, 23:37 (Altoona, Blair Co., May, *fide* McGraw)—CHRISTY, *Cardinal*, 1923, v. 1, no. 1, [p. 12] (Sewickley, Allegheny Co., spring transient)—BURLEIGH, *Wilson Bull.*, 1923, 35:99 (Allegheny Co., May); 1924, 36:129 (State College, Centre Co., migration)—SUTTON, *Ann. Carnegie Mus.*, 1928, 18:207 (Meadville and Pymatuning Swamp, Crawford Co., transient).

ORANGE-CROWNED WARBLER (Plate 18)

VERMIVORA CELATA CELATA (Say)

Description—One of the smaller and more plainly colored warblers; *no wing-bars or tail-spots*. General color *dull greenish yellow*, paler below, with obscure streaks; a paler streak (not well marked) over the eye, and a *short darker streak through the eye;* crown sometimes with an orange-brown spot, usually concealed in life; no white on the under tail coverts. The *greenishness* of the coloration in general, and of the under tail coverts in particular, serves to distinguish this species from the Tennessee Warbler and the Nashville Warbler.

Range—Four races of this species are recognized, of which three are confined to the western part of the continent. The typical eastern race breeds in the Canadian and Hudsonian life zones from Hudson Bay to Alaska and winters from the South Atlantic and Gulf states to Mexico. While it occurs in our region as a transient in spring and fall, it is accounted one of the rarer warblers. It may really be much commoner, however, than it seems to be, not only in western Pennsylvania, but also throughout the eastern United States at large. Although I searched assiduously for this species in Beaver County, I did not finally detect it until the fall of 1909, when I secured two specimens. I collected two more in the spring of 1910 and subsequently have taken a few others. Meanwhile, the species had been observed and collected at several widely separated localities, as indicated in the records below. Later records fill in some of the remaining gaps and suggest that this warbler may be expected to occur in all parts of our region.

Migration—The limited data available concerning the spring migration of the Orange-crowned Warbler show that it passes through western Pennsylvania during the first two weeks in May, with most of the other species of this family. May 3 is the earliest recorded date, and May 19 is the latest. In the fall it is one of the later migrants and does not arrive until the middle of September. Most of the records lie in the first half of October; judging by reports from neighboring states, it may sometimes linger even later.

Habits—On May 12, 1910, I shot a male orange-crowned warbler under unusual circumstances. Before shooting, I identified it solely on the basis of its song, which was at once recognized as different from that of other warblers and was established by elimination as belonging to this species—the only warbler on our local list with whose song I was unfamiliar. This song is in general similar to those of the Nashville and the Tennessee warblers and might be described as intermediate between the two. The bird that I identified was singing from the top of a tall forest tree, although the usual habitat of the species is in lower growth. In fact, all the other orange-crowns that I have seen were skipping actively about in shrubbery and bushes. G. M. Sutton remarks on this warbler's partiality for the alder areas in Pymatuning Swamp, which is quite in keeping with its known preferences in the breeding season. In the fall its small size and dull greenish coloration distinguish it from the Myrtle Warbler and other species that migrate at the same time. Its only note at this season is a low chirp, in no way distinctive.

Helminthophila celata TODD, *Ann. Carnegie Mus.*, 1904, 2:580 (Presque Isle, Erie Co., fall transient).

"Orange-crowned Warbler" HARLOW, *Auk*, 1911, 28:268 ("State College," Centre Co., May)—HARLOW, *Cassinia*, 1912, 15:20 (Center Furnace Swamp, Centre Co., spring)—SIMPSON,

Oölogist, 1914, 31:121 (Warren, Warren Co.)—Sutton, *Bird-Lore*, 1923, 25:260 ([near Aspinwall], Allegheny Co., May; Raccoon Creek, Beaver Co., *fide* Boulton).

Vermivora celata Todd, *Cardinal*, 1925, v. 1, no. 5, p. 20 (Beaver, Beaver Co., October).

Vermivora celata celata Sutton, *Ann. Carnegie Mus.*, 1928, 18:207 (Crystal and Lower lakes, Crawford Co., May and September)—Malley, *Wilson Bull.*, 1936, 48:311 (Frick Park, Pittsburgh, Allegheny Co., May).

Additional records: Beaver, Beaver Co., taken October 9 and 15, 1909, and May 12 and 19, 1910; seen September 17, 1910, and May 10, 1911 (Todd); one seen May 13, 1924 (Boulton)—Warren, Warren Co., taken September 28, 1900, and May 14, 1906 (Simpson)—Turtle Creek, Allegheny Co., taken October 5, 1897 (Atkinson)—Renovo, Clinton Co., taken October 3, 1904, September 27 and October 12, 1906 (Pierce collection)—St. Marys, Elk Co., seen September 29, 1928 (Sutton).

NASHVILLE WARBLER (Plate 18)

VERMIVORA RUFICAPILLA RUFICAPILLA (Wilson)

Description—A rather small warbler, with yellow underparts and a whitish eye-ring, but *no wing-bars or tail-spots. Adult in spring: upperparts* (including wings and tail) *yellowish olive*, noticeably *brighter on the rump* and passing into *slaty gray on the head* (top and sides); the crown has a concealed spot of chestnut (not usually apparent in life); *eye-ring white; underparts yellow*, with some greenish shading on the flanks. *Females* are somewhat duller than males. *Immature birds in autumnal plumage:* similar to the spring male, but duller and browner, the head ashy brown, and the underparts washed with buff. In any plumage this species may readily be identified by the combination of characters just cited: the unmarked wings and tail, obvious white eye-ring, yellow underparts, and grayish or ashy-brown head, contrasting with the brighter, yellowish or greenish-yellow rump.

Range—Of this species, W. W. Cooke wrote (1904): "The breeding range of the Nashville warbler extends from Massachusetts and Connecticut westward to northern Illinois, and northward to Saskatchewan (Cumberland House) in the west and Cape Breton and Gaspé Bay in the east. The species is a rare visitor to Newfoundland. The southern limit of the breeding range coincides quite closely with the southern boundary of the Alleghenian zone. The bird breeds more commonly in New England than elsewhere in the United States, becoming less and less common to the westward." It winters mostly in southern and eastern Mexico and is rare in migration on the Atlantic slope south of Maryland. West of the mountains, however, it is a regular and common transient. This appears to be its status throughout western Pennsylvania at large, so far as the vast bulk of the species is concerned. As a summer resident it is represented by comparatively few scattered pairs. Warren was the first to note its presence in the breeding season, although he fails to give any exact localities.

Were we solely dependent upon the published records, the local breeding range of this warbler would still be mostly guesswork, and while my notes and those of certain other observers serve to fill the gaps to some extent, they are not so complete as one could wish. By the capture of a male near Hartstown (not Linesville, as erroneously stated by G. M. Sutton, 1928) on June 16, 1898, I satisfied myself that the species must be breeding in Pymatuning Swamp. In the same month it

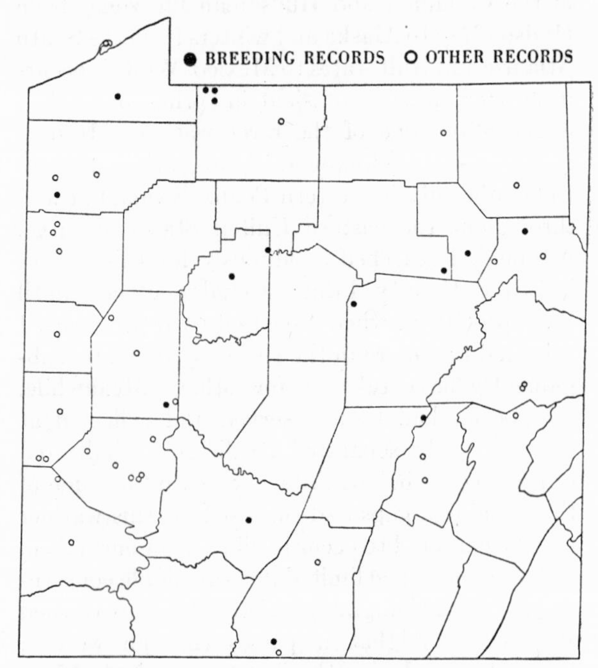

LOCAL RANGE OF THE NASHVILLE WARBLER

happened that I saw or secured specimens at three other widely separated points: Tamarack Swamp, Clinton County (where I had also shot one in June, 1895); Bear Lake, Warren County; and the summit of Chestnut Ridge, near Kingston, Westmoreland County. Thaddeus Surber also took a specimen on June 7, 1898, at Lloydville, Cambria County. In June, 1893, I had taken the species at Clarion Junction, Clarion County, and in June, 1894, at Driftwood, Cameron County. Again in 1907, on June 17, I identified it at Sarversville, Butler County, where I have no doubt it must have been breeding. S. S. Dickey reports having observed it at Tamarack Swamp in Erie County, in June, and also in the swamp of the same name in northeastern Warren County, north of Columbus. It appears as well on Van Fleet's manuscript list of the breeding birds of DuBois.

With these definite breeding localities fixed, we may now, reasoning by analogy, sketch in a distribution for this species corresponding in general with that of the Black-throated Green Warbler—although the two birds admittedly have little in common otherwise. Nor is it yet certain that their respective ranges coincide east of the Allegheny divide, since there are no June records for the Nashville Warbler from that region, and in fact not many for other seasons. The species is suggested as a subject for further research from the standpoint of its local distribution. It probably should be rated as a form of the Alleghanian Fauna, as Cooke suggests, insofar at least as its southern limit is concerned. In particular it should be looked for in summer in Somerset County, where A. B. Miller reports having observed three singing males on June 8, 1928, on the summit of Negro Mountain, at an elevation of 3,100 feet. Additional records are needed from the northern counties, too. Beyond our limits, the species is said to be a rare summer resident in western New York (Eaton) and also in Ashtabula County, Ohio (Hicks). Southward from Beaver County and thence eastward, presumably to Chestnut Ridge, it is known only as a spring and fall transient, but it has either been overlooked by many observers, or else confused with other species.

Migration—The Nashville Warbler appears during the flood tide of the warbler migration in both spring and fall and is sometimes inordinately abundant. Its spring arrival has been observed at Beaver during twelve seasons on dates ranging from April 25 to May 6, while April 30 is the average. Some early dates for other localities are: Wilkinsburg, April 21, 189_ (Atkinson); Pittsburgh, April 26, 1914 (Burleigh), and April 26, 1921 (Sutton); Springs, Somerset County, April 24, 1913 (Miller); Greenville, April 27, 1927 (Seiple). In 1915 the species was recorded on April 28 at both State College (Burleigh) and Renovo (Pierce), although most of the arrival records from the latter locality fall in the first or second week of May. At Warren, R. B. Simpson calls it irregular and uncommon and has not seen it earlier in the season than May 1 (1903). Except in its local breeding range as above outlined, it passes through the region as a rule before May 20, although I once noted it at Beaver on May 30 (1911), and B. H. Christy has seen it even in early June at Sewickley and also at McDonald Reservoir, Washington County. Doubtless these particular records pertain to belated migrants rather than to potential breeding birds.

On its way southward the species sometimes reappears as early as the latter part of August and commonly by the first week in September. The earliest recorded fall arrival dates are: Oakland, Pittsburgh, August 19, 1932 (Blair); Pittsburgh, August 26, 1927 (Burleigh); Sewickley, August 26, 1922 (Christy); and Beaver, August 27, 1916 (Boulton). By the end of September most of the migrants have left, but in some years a few linger into October (Beaver, October 15, 1909; Renovo, October 12, 1906; Sewickley, October 11, 1903).

Habits—The Nashville Warbler, as we see it in migration, is a bird of the woodland and is especially fond of tracts of bushes and scrub growth. Wild crab-apple thickets are favorite resorts. Almost every spring there is a day or two of decided movement, when the species is very common and on occasion exceedingly abundant. On May 3, 1901, I witnessed a remarkable flight at Beaver. That morning the woods everywhere were full of Nashville warblers, to the exclusion of almost all other kinds. I counted a dozen in one tree. They kept mostly in the treetops and were singing very little. This flight must have been an extensive one, as it was observed by Mr. Simpson at Warren on the same date. Similar flights have occurred in the fall as well.

The summer habitat of the species is on the outskirts of the forest among bushy growth and shrubbery. I have seen and taken the bird in the spruce area of Tamarack Swamp in Clinton County and also in the tamaracks of Pymatuning Swamp, where the conditions approximate those prevailing in the north country. It seeks no heights but occasionally mounts to the lower branches of trees, and during the month of June it is in full song. Its distinctive notes betray its presence, although the singer may be well hidden in the thick shrubbery. The song begins hesitantly, with a lisping note similar to that of the Black and White Warbler; this is repeated several times but changes abruptly into a lively twitter.

No nests of this warbler have been reported from our region. They should be looked for on the ground, among grasses or other vegetation. The eggs are said to number from three to five, and are white, with brownish spotting.

Helminthophila ruficapilla WARREN, *Birds Pa.*, ed. 2, 1890, 268 (Cameron, Elk, Cambria, and Blair Co., summer).

Helminthophila rubricapilla COOKE, *Bull. Biol. Surv.* no. 18, 1904, 37 (Beaver, Beaver Co., and Renovo, Clinton Co., migration)—TODD, *Ann. Carnegie Mus.*, 1904, 2:580 (Presque Isle, Erie Co., transient)—TODD, in Bausman, *Hist. Beaver Co., Pa.*, 1904, 2:1201 (Beaver Co., transient).

"Nashville Warbler" COOKE, *Bird-Lore*, 1905, 7:237 (Beaver, Beaver Co., and Renovo, Clinton Co., migration)—HARLOW, *Auk*, 1911, 28:268 (State College, Centre Co., May)—HARLOW, *Cassinia*, 1912, 15:20 (Center Furnace Swamp, Centre Co., spring)—SIMPSON, *Oölogist*, 1914, 31:121 (Warren, Warren Co., transient)—SCOVILLE, *Cassinia*, 1920, 23:20 ([Charter Oak, Huntingdon Co.], May)—MCCLELLAND, *Am. Mid. Nat.*, 1922, 8:37 (Washington, Washington Co., transient)—CHRISTY, *Cardinal*, 1924, v. 1, no. 4, p. 11 (Big Traverse Valley, Beaver Co., May)—EASTWOOD, *Bird-Lore*, 1926, 28:272; and 1927, 29:272 (Pittsburgh region, Allegheny Co., May)—BOULTON, *Bird-Lore*, 1928, 30:271 (Sewickley, Allegheny Co., May, *fide* Christy)—[CHRISTY, ed.], *Cardinal*, 1933, 3:150 (Pittsburgh, Allegheny Co., August, *fide* Blair)—FRICKE, *Cardinal*, 1939, 5:47 (near Linesville, Crawford Co., May).

Vermivora ruficapilla STONE, *Cassinia*, 1920, 23:37 (Altoona, Blair Co., May, *fide* McGraw).

Helminthophila rubricapilla rubricapilla CHRISTY, *Cardinal*, 1923, v. 1, no. 1, [p. 12] (Sewickley, Allegheny Co., transient)—BURLEIGH, *Wilson Bull.*, 1923, 35:99 (Allegheny Co., transient); 1924, 36:129 (State College, Centre Co., spring transient).

Vermivora ruficapilla ruficapilla CHRISTY and SUTTON, *Cardinal*, 1928, 2:73 (Cook Forest, Clarion Co., summer)—SUTTON, *Ann. Carnegie Mus.*, 1928, 18:206 (Crawford Co. localities, transient; occasional in summer).

Vermivora rubricapilla rubricapilla BURLEIGH, *Cardinal*, 1929, 2:118 (Allegheny Co., fall migration).

NORTHERN PARULA WARBLER (Plate 18)

COMPSOTHLYPIS AMERICANA PUSILLA (Wilson)

Description—A small warbler, with conspicuous white wing-bars, and a distinct greenish-yellow area on the back. *Male in spring:* upperparts grayish blue, the *back* with a large *patch of olive yellow; wings* blackish, edged with grayish blue and crossed by *two broad white bars;* tail feathers blackish, with slight edgings of blue, the outer feathers blotched with white near the tips; sides of head and of throat dull blue, as is the crown, but the region in front of the eye blackish; under eyelid white, and above the eye a small white spot; *throat* (in the middle) *dull yellow, tinged with orange-brown;* below this a dusky or brownish smudge (usually not well defined) separating the throat-patch from the orange-brown and yellow of the breast; rest of underparts white, the sides more or less washed with orange-brown. *Female in spring:* similar to the male but much duller, especially below, and usually lacking the dark band across the breast, which is an almost uniform dull yellow, continuous with the yellow of the throat. *Young birds* in the fall are still duller, and the upperparts are more or less greenish-tinged; the colored areas of the head and underparts are somewhat indefinite and blended.

Range—The other members of this genus are all tropical in their distribution and sedentary in habit. This species is migratory; it winters in the West Indies, Mexico, and Central America and pushes northward in the spring to occupy the eastern United States and southern Canada, as far north as the Gulf of St. Lawrence. The southern-breeding birds differ a little from those nesting in the north and are now recognized as a separate race. But the two races are so similar in color, and there is so much individual variation in the characters of birds from intermediate localities, that many Pennsylvania specimens could be referred to one race as properly as to the other.

The Parula Warbler in our region is decidedly a bird of the hemlocks and accordingly favors those areas where these trees abound. It is common throughout the high country of the Allegheny Plateau and also in the valleys and ravines of the ridge and valley section wherever hemlocks remain. In Crawford and Erie counties, too, it is locally common as a summer resident. But in Beaver and Allegheny counties—a region where its favorite tree is mostly confined to deep ravines and steep slopes—it has been found in the breeding season at only one locality (Big Traverse Creek), and seems to be extremely local as a summer resident, although it is fairly regular during migration. In the Buffalo Creek region of Butler and Armstrong counties, however, it reappears as a breeding species. Although not known in summer from the immediate neighborhood of Waynesburg, it has been discovered at that season at three localities near the southern border of Greene County (Dickey). Its apparent avoidance of the region to the northward must be due to local conditions and has thus no particular significance from a faunal standpoint.

Migration—With ten seasons' records of the arrival of this warbler at Beaver now on file (instead of the four available to W. W. Cooke in 1906), I find that the extremes are April 27 and May 12, and the average is May 6. While the main flight does not reach our region as a rule until the second week in May, the van of the species may come considerably earlier; but since these early migrants are so few in number, their arrival is easy to overlook. Thus it is possible that my Beaver records, which are later than those from other counties, are inaccurate. I have observed this warbler as early as April 19 (1900) at Erie and on April 24 (1899) in the Buffalo Creek region, while it has been reported from Springs, Somerset County, on April 19 (1925—Miller) and from Pittsburgh on April 26 (1914—Burleigh). R. B. Simpson's earliest spring date for Warren is May 1 (1903), and this is also the average date of arrival at Renovo, as indicated in twenty-four years' records. Migrants may commonly be seen as late as the last week in May; any birds present at a later date are presumably settled for the season. Nevertheless, I once took a male at Beaver, where the species is not known to breed, as late as June 2.

B. H. Christy's record of August 26 (1922) for southern Beaver County suggests that the fall movement begins during the latter part of that month, but I have never detected the bird before the first week in September, nor later than October 4 (1910). The latter is the average "last-seen" date at Renovo, according to the records of A. K. Pierce, which cover twenty-one seasons.

Habits—In the spring of 1889, when I began my study of the bird life of the Buffalo Creek region, I kept hearing a bird song that puzzled me not a little. It was a fine, wiry, humming song, suggesting the wheezy buzz of the cicada; but, try as I might, I could catch no glimpse of its author. Far up in the thick, bushy tops of the highest hemlocks, the singer remained concealed from sight. Although I naturally had my suspicions of its identity, it was not until one day late in May, when I chanced to see it fly from a hemlock into a hickory and was able to bring it down, that I was finally certain that the unknown was the Parula Warbler. Since that time I have encountered the species in many other places and have become more familiar with its ways—as familiar as anyone can be with a bird that persistently haunts the treetops and contrives to keep well hidden from view. It is one of the smallest and daintiest of the family and is easily recognized in life by the bluish back with greenish-yellow middle, the dark blotch on the breast, and the white-barred wings. During the season of migration, the Parula associates with other warblers and with them may even descend nearer the ground in deciduous woodland. It is unobtrusive in its habits and without any striking peculiarities, excepting of course its distinctive song, which is heard only in the spring. It is therefore often overlooked. Its name of "Parula" (a little titmouse) was suggested by its habit of feeding at times in an upside-down position.

All observers agree that it is difficult to find the nest of this bird. Watching the female while she is gathering nesting material is in fact the only sure way, and for this, much patience is necessary. The nest itself is usually so well hidden among the dense branches that it is virtually invisible from below. In New England and in the north country generally, this warbler is fond of placing its nest in the growth of usnea moss with which the forest trees are often festooned. A bunch of this hanging moss is fashioned into a pouch-shaped or ball-like structure and lined with similar but finer material; an entrance is left on one side or from above. Naturally such a bunch is concealed from casual observation. Because usnea moss is rare in western Pennsylvania, most of the parula warblers that pass the summer here are forced to choose other nesting sites. Both Mr. Simpson and Dr. Dickey have found nests in thick hemlock branches. From Springs, Somerset County, A. B. Miller writes: "As a breeding species this warbler seems confined to large hemlocks along streams and to Norway spruces growing near houses. On our home grounds, where we have a number of large Norway spruces, this bird is a regular summer visitor, and two or three pairs nest each year. The nests I have found were all built in the drooping branches of these trees, and were rather loosely constructed."

On occasion, however, a deciduous tree is chosen. H. C. Kirkpatrick describes a nest constructed of usnea moss that was placed forty feet from the ground in a maple. A nest that is now in the Carnegie Museum was collected by Mr. Pierce near Renovo on June 3, 1916. The label bears the information that the nest had been built in a bunch of rubbish left in a tree by the spring flood. It is open at the top and is soft and flimsy in construction, for it is composed almost entirely of usnea moss, with a few leaves and weed stalks added, and a little horsehair in the lining. Four eggs were found in this nest, but clutches are known to vary from three to five. The eggs are delicate and very small, averaging .67 by .48 inches. They are white, marked with small spots or dots of a brownish-red color, sparsely and rather evenly distributed. They resemble certain types of eggs laid by the Black-capped Chickadee. Full sets are to be expected during the first or second week in June.

Parula americana Teulon, *Jour. Boston Zoöl. Soc.*, 1882, 1:50 (Bradford, McKean Co., May).

"Blue Yellow-Back Warbler" Van Fleet, *Ornithologist and Oölogist*, 1884, 9:108 (DuBois, Clearfield Co.).

Compsothlypis americana Warren, *Birds Pa.*, 1888, 245 (Crawford Co., breeding, *fide* Sennett; (?)Centre Co., summer, *fide* Roberts)—Todd, *Auk*, 1891, 8:398 (Buffalo Creek region, Armstrong and Butler Co., summer; Beaver, Beaver Co., spring transient); 1893, 10:40 (Two Lick, Indiana Co., June), 45 (Coalport, Clearfield Co., June)—Baily, *Auk*, 1896, 13: 295 (Williamsville, Elk Co., June–July)—Todd, *Ann. Carnegie Mus.*, 1904, 2:581 (Erie and Presque Isle, Erie Co., summer)—Cooke, *Bull. Biol. Surv.* no. 18, 1904, 45 (Beaver, Beaver Co., and Renovo, Clinton Co., migration).

Compsothlypis americana usneæ Cope, *Cassinia*, 1902, 5:18 (Tamarack Swamp, Clinton Co., and Galeton and Kettle Creek, Potter Co., June)—Todd, in Bausman, *Hist. Beaver Co., Pa.*, 1904, 2:1201 (Beaver Co., transient)—Harlow, *Auk*, 1912, 29:478 (Bear Meadows, Centre Co., June, *fide* Musgrave); 1918, 35:142 (Huntingdon and Warren Co., breeding)—Christy, *Cardinal*, 1923, v. 1, no. 1, [p. 12] (Sewickley, Allegheny Co., transient; Big Traverse Creek, Beaver Co., breeding)—Burleigh, *Wilson Bull.*, 1923, 35: 99 (Allegheny Co., transient); 1924, 36:73 (State College, Centre Co., migration).

"Parula Warbler" Cooke, *Bird-Lore*, 1906, 8:168 (Beaver, Beaver Co. [in part], and Renovo, Clinton Co., migration) —Simpson, *Oölogist*, 1912, 29:276; and 1914, 31:121 (Warren, Warren Co., nesting); 1912, 29:330 (head of Tionesta Creek, Warren Co., summer)—Dickey, *Oölogist*, 1914, 31:170 ([Charter Oak], Huntingdon Co., breeding), 207 (Cresson, Cambria Co., June); 1919, 36:33 ([Charter Oak and Spruce Creek], Huntingdon Co., nesting)—McClelland, *Am. Mid. Nat.*, 1922, 8:37 (Washington, Washington Co., transient)—Sutton, *Bird-Lore*, 1924, 26:266 (Pittsburgh, Allegheny Co., and State College, Centre Co., spring)—Christy, *Cardinal*, 1924, v. 1, no. 4, p. 10, 12 (Big Traverse Valley, Beaver Co., June)—Eastwood, *Bird-Lore*, 1925, 27:263 (Pittsburgh region, Allegheny Co., May).

"Northern Parula Warbler" Harlow, *Auk*, 1911, 28:268 (State College, Centre Co., May)—Eastwood, *Bird-Lore*, 1926, 28:272 (Pittsburgh region, Allegheny Co., May)—Cope and Hawkins, *Forest Leaves*, 1934, 24:26 (E. Tionesta Forest Reserve, Warren and McKean Co., summer).

Compsothlypis americana pusilla Sutton, *Ann. Carnegie Mus.*, 1928, 18:208 (Meadville, Crawford Co., nesting, *fide* Sennett and Kirkpatrick; Pymatuning Swamp, Crawford Co., breeding)—Burleigh, *Wilson Bull.*, 1931, 43:51 (Charter Oak, Huntingdon Co., nesting)—Burleigh, *Cardinal*, 1932, 3:80 ([Summit], Fayette Co., summer).

EASTERN YELLOW WARBLER

DENDROICA AESTIVA AESTIVA (Gmelin)

Description—A warbler of medium size and *general yellow coloration; tail largely yellow. Adult male:* dull greenish yellow above, bright yellow below, with more or less distinct rufous streaks; crown and sides of head bright yellow like the underparts; wings and tail dusky, with broad yellow edgings. *Adult female:* similar but much duller and greener, the crown little if any brighter, and the streaks on the underparts faint. *Young birds* in the fall are still duller but may always be recognized by the extensive yellow area on the tail.

Range—No other warbler, not even the Maryland Yellow-throat, can boast such a wide distribution in North America as this species. Its east-and-west range is from coast to coast; toward the north it nearly reaches the limit of trees; and one of its several geographic races is confined to Mexico. The eastern race, which alone concerns us, winters in Central and South America and moves northward in the summer to occupy the greater part of eastern North America. It is common during that season throughout western Pennsylvania, where it is one of the best-known and most numerous of the warblers.

Migration—This species usually arrives with the first wave of warblers in the latter part of April, although the exact date depends upon weather conditions. A forward spring may cause it to appear at Beaver as early as April 18 (1891), while a backward season may delay it even until May 4 (1931). The average date of arrival in twenty-six seasons at this place is April 26. Some early spring dates for other places are: Wilkinsburg, April 16, 1891 (Atkinson); Waynesburg, April 17, 1896 (Jacobs); Pittsburgh, April 21, 1912 and 1916 (Burleigh); Greenville, April 24, 1927 (Seiple); Erie, April 26, 1902 (Simpson); Warren, April 27, 1891 (Simpson). The movement tends to lag a little in the mountains, since the average date of arrival is April 29 at Springs, Somerset County (Miller), and May 1 at Renovo (Pierce). The van is a populous one, and it is only a few days until the normal summer numbers are reached. While the spring arrival of the Yellow Warbler has thus been satisfactorily observed and recorded, the circumstances attending its departure for the South are of an entirely different order. It slips away unobtrusively in August, and only a few laggards—migrants from farther north, perhaps—are ever seen in September. My fall records for Beaver cover only six seasons, as it happens, and range from August 16 (1910) to 30 (1889).[1] T. D. Burleigh has noted the species at Pittsburgh as late as August 20 (1927), and in 1900 W. W. Worthington took a specimen on Presque Isle on August 31. G. M. Sutton (1928) cites a few occurrences at Pymatuning Swamp from September 16 to 21, 1925, and remarks that "in every instance these birds were alone, and not part of a flock of warblers." D. A. Atkinson says of this warbler in Allegheny County: "In the fall the Yellow Warbler leaves us about the last week of August, and it is usually scarce after August 25. September 3, 1898, is my latest fall record for this species, but John Watson shot a male from a flock of migrating warblers near Aspinwall on September 20, 1892."

Habits—The original habitat of the Yellow Warbler must have been the willow and alder growths

along streams, and these are still its chosen haunts wherever primitive conditions persist, as they do in the north country, for instance. In western Pennsylvania the species, while by no means averse to such locations, is more partial to orchards and shade trees and seldom takes to the woods, save at intervals during the season of migration. At Pymatuning Swamp, however, according to Dr. Sutton, it found congenial surroundings and was an abundant summer resident even in the wildest portions. No other bird to my mind so ideally embodies the spirit of the spring season as does the Yellow Warbler. Coming when all Nature is responding anew to the warming touch of the returning sun, it seems to bring with it the very air of the tropics. A flash of yellow against the green, as the dainty creature explores among the opening buds and blossoms, pausing only to give voice to its exuberance in sweet and lilting song—and the spell is cast. Thus to eye and ear does the Yellow Warbler carry the same message as that borne by the subtle fragrance of the orchard trees laden with bloom.

May finds the birds mated and busily engaged

[1]The record cited by W. W. Cooke (1905) for "September 30, 1888," is an error.

in building their nests. This labor falls wholly to the female, but the male is never far away. If the nest is placed in an orchard tree, or in a willow or an elm along a stream, it may be over thirty feet from the ground, but if in an elderberry bush (a not infrequent location), it may be as low as three or four feet. Wild crab-apple trees are also favorites, as their thick and almost thorny branches afford just the sites that this bird prefers, and a thicket of such trees is almost certain to harbor one or more pairs. No other warbler builds so neat and compact a nest. Its foundation is of fine strips of bark, grasses, and weed stalks, often supplemented by bits of wool, string, cloth, and other accessible substances. The outside is covered with plant down and milkweed fiber, which give the nest a characteristic whitish or cottony appearance. Inside it is lined with soft materials—down from the thistle, milkweed, and dandelion; delicate plant stalks; horsehair; and perhaps feathers. The surrounding branches are woven into the structure to give it stability. Outwardly it looks much like the nest of the American Goldfinch, but it is more deeply cupped; it may even measure as much as three inches in depth. On one occasion I detected a female yellow warbler stealing material from the unfinished nest of a chipping sparrow and carrying this to its own nest at a little distance. Like most thieves, it was a coward and a sneak, and although repeatedly driven away by the sparrow, it kept returning in the latter's absence.

Eggs of this warbler have been found by Dr. Atkinson as early as May 9 and thence until June 8. Dates later than this probably represent deferred or delayed nestings, since only one brood is ever reared in a season. The fourth week in May is about the time for full sets of eggs. Out of forty-three nests that Dr. Sutton found in one season at Pymatuning Swamp, only eight contained five eggs, and most of them not less than four. The eggs vary considerably, both in ground-color and in markings. In some examples the former is virtually pure white, but in most there is a grayish-green cast, more or less decided. The markings run from small spots, rather evenly distributed, to blotches and marbling about or around the larger end, and there is every conceivable intermediate condition. The color of these markings varies quite as much as their character—from blackish through deep purplish brown to dull drab. Some eggs are heavily marked, and others but lightly; those in a given set may vary among themselves in this respect, but not in the type of marking, which is uniform. Average measurements are .70 by .50 inches.

The Yellow Warbler is one of the species most frequently victimized by the Cowbird, and it is also one of the few that are known to do something resourceful about it. Unable to throw the strange egg out, it will often build a second story to its nest, burying the egg in the bottom. Three- and even four-story nests of this warbler have been recorded—the results of repeated invasions by the parasite. Would that this ruse were oftener practiced!

After the young are on the wing, the species usually forsakes the orchards and parks and retires to the shrubbery along streams and to areas of low second growth. It becomes quiet and inconspicuous and thus easily escapes observation until the time of its departure.

Dendrœca æstiva Teulon, *Jour. Boston Zoöl. Soc.*, 1882, 1:51 (Bradford, McKean Co., nesting)—Townsend, *Proc. Acad. Nat. Sci. Philadelphia*, 1883, 61 (Latrobe, Westmoreland Co., summer).

"Yellow Warbler" Enty, *Ornithologist and Oölogist*, 1885, 10:78 (Templeton, Armstrong Co., April)—Jacobs, *Hawkeye Ornithologist and Oölogist*, 1888, 1:88 (Waynesburg, Greene Co., migration)—Cooke, *Bird-Lore*, 1905, 7:32 (Beaver, Beaver Co., Waynesburg, Greene Co., and Renovo, Clinton Co., migration)—Stone, *Cassinia*, 1906, 9:44 (McConnellsburg, Fulton Co., June)—Pitcairn, *Bird-Lore*, 1907, 9:155 (Riverview Park, Allegheny Co., summer)—Simpson, *Oölogist*, 1909, 26:170; and 1914, 31:121 (Warren, Warren Co., summer)—Burleigh, *Oölogist*, 1910, 27:147; and 1911, 28:156 (Harmarville, Allegheny Co., nesting); 1913, 30:55 (Pittsburgh, Allegheny Co., nesting)—McConnell, *Oölogist*, 1918, 35:151 (McKeesport, Allegheny Co., breeding)—Miller, *Oölogist*, 1919, 36:156 (Charter Oak, Huntingdon Co., nesting)—McClelland, *Am. Mid. Nat.*, 1922, 8:36 (Washington, Washington Co., summer)—Street, *Cassinia*, 1923, 24:17 (Greencastle and Ft. Loudon, Franklin Co., June)—Christy, *Cardinal*, 1924, v. 1, no. 4, p. 9 (Big Traverse Valley, Beaver Co., June)—Eastwood, *Bird-Lore*, 1925, 27: 263; 1926, 28:272; and 1927, 29:272 (Pittsburgh region, Allegheny Co., migration); 1926, 28:273 (Millvale, Allegheny Co., nesting, *fide* Auerswald; Rector, Westmoreland Co., May, *fide* Knauz; Springs, Somerset Co., breeding, *fide* Miller)—Boulton, *Bird-Lore*, 1928, 30:271 (Millvale, Allegheny Co., April, *fide* Auerswald).

"Summer Yellowbird" Todd, *Oölogist*, 1887, 4:89 (Beaver, Beaver Co., nesting).

Dendroica æstiva Dwight, *Auk*, 1892, 9:138 (Cresson, Cambria Co., June)—Todd, *Auk*, 1893, 10:40 (Two Lick, Indiana Co., June), 45 (Coalport, Clearfield Co., June)—Jacobs,

Summer Birds Greene Co., Pa., 1893, 13 (Greene Co., nesting)—BAILY, *Auk*, 1896, 13:295 (Williamsville, Elk Co., breeding)—COPE, *Cassinia*, 1902, 5:10, 18 (Clinton and Potter Co., June)—TODD, *Ann. Carnegie Mus.*, 1904, 2:582 (Erie and Presque Isle, Erie Co., nesting)—TODD, in Bausman, *Hist. Beaver Co., Pa.*, 1904, 2:1201 (Beaver Co., summer)—COOKE, *Bull. Biol. Surv.* no. 18, 1904, 52 (Beaver, Beaver Co., and Renovo, Clinton Co., migration)—KEIM, *Cassinia*, 1905, 8:40 (Port Allegany, McKean Co., summer)—FORREST, *Oölogist*, 1911, 28:115 (Washington, Washington Co., summer).

Dendroica æstiva æstiva HARLOW, *Auk*, 1912, 29:475 (southern Centre Co., summer)—CHRISTY, *Cardinal*, 1923, v. 1, no. 1, [p. 12] (Sewickley, Allegheny Co., breeding)—BURLEIGH, *Wilson Bull.*, 1923, 35:99 (Allegheny Co., nesting); 1924, 36:73; 1931, 43:51 (State College, Centre Co., migration; nesting)—CHRISTY and SUTTON, *Cardinal*, 1928, 2:73 (Cooksburg, Forest Co., summer)—SUTTON, *Ann. Carnegie Mus.*, 1928, 18:209 (Meadville and Pymatuning Swamp, Crawford Co., summer)—BURLEIGH, *Cardinal*, 1929, 2:118 (Allegheny Co., August)—BURLEIGH, *Cardinal*, 1932, 3:80 (Summit, Fayette Co., nesting).

MAGNOLIA WARBLER (Plate 18)

DENDROICA MAGNOLIA (Wilson)

Description—Adult male in spring: crown and nape, bluish gray, with a white line on either side from above the eyes; forehead and sides of head, black, with a white spot on the lower eyelid; back black, the *rump yellow*, in strong contrast; upper tail coverts and *tail*, black, the latter *with square white spots* near the center of all the feathers except the middle pair; wings dull blackish, with a large white area on the coverts; underparts mostly bright yellow, the throat and middle of the abdomen immaculate, the breast and sides showing heavy black streaks; under tail coverts pure white. *Adult female in spring:* similar to the male but generally duller, the black of the back not so "solid" but more or less mixed with olive green, and the streaks of the underparts not so heavy. *Immature birds in fall:* still duller, without the head markings; back dull greenish olive, which becomes ashy on the crown; rump yellow, and tail as in the adult; wings showing two whitish bars; underparts yellow, the breast paler and duller, and usually a few dark streaks on the flanks. In any plumage the species may always be identified by the *median position and square-cut shape of the white spots* on the tail feathers.

Range—The principal winter home of the Magnolia Warbler is in the Central American countries and southern Mexico. Its summer home lies mainly in the Canadian Life Zone, from Newfoundland west to the Rocky Mountains, with a southward extension along the Appalachian highlands as far as Virginia. Although now known to be comparatively common, this warbler was thought to be rare by the early generation of ornithologists, and it was a long time before its distribution was finally worked out. Indeed, the first really satisfactory account of its nesting habits, by William Brewster, did not appear until 1877. Elliott Coues, writing in 1878, suspected that the species summered southward in the mountains, but the first edition of the American Ornithologists' Union *Check-List* (1886) was silent on this point. Although two fugitive summer records had meanwhile been reported from western Pennsylvania and although H. C. Kirkpatrick had actually found a nest with eggs near Meadville, Crawford County (in May, 1880), the wide extent of this bird's breeding range in our region apparently remained entirely unsuspected. Warren in 1890 cited certain actual and potential breeding records (Mr. Kirkpatrick's among them, at second hand), but, little realizing the importance and significance of his statements, he failed to specify exact localities and dates.

Thus matters stood in 1891 when I published an account of the taking of a set of eggs (now in the Carnegie Museum) in the Buffalo Creek region of southeastern Butler County, in June, 1889 (my outstanding ornithological achievement up to that time). It was evident, therefore, that in the breeding season the Magnolia Warbler was not wholly confined to the northern and mountainous parts of western Pennsylvania, since I had found it nesting at as low an elevation as one thousand feet in the lower Allegheny Valley. My interest was thus aroused, and it has been my good fortune to accumulate, with the aid of other observers and correspondents, much data on the local distribution of this warbler.

Ecological factors have an important bearing on the local range of this bird. During migration the species is apt to be found almost anywhere, but in the breeding season it is virtually confined to the hemlocks, to which it is even more attached than is the Black-throated Green Warbler. In particular, it is fond of low, bushy, second-growth hemlock, and this is the environment that it prefers above all others for its nesting sites. West of the plateau region in our state, such growth is usually found in deep ravines or along steep banks with a northerly exposure. In these cool and shady retreats the summer temperature is low enough to be congenial to certain species of the Canadian Fauna. Here local conditions tend to offset the effect of low altitude and to attract certain boreal forms. There is of course a limit beyond which this attraction ceases to work. A comparison of the status of the Magnolia Warbler in two localities only forty miles apart is informative on this point. My 1889 find in the Buffalo Creek region was made in the valley of "Watson Run," a wooded ravine where season after season several pairs of this warbler still remain to nest. Similar ravines in Beaver County, however, harbor no individuals of this or any other boreal species, and the Carolinian influence prevails. Apparently this influence also persists for some distance to the northward; for in that direction we do not encounter the Magnolia Warbler as a breeding bird until we reach Sandy Lake, Mercer County (Homer). Beyond this region, in Crawford and Erie counties, as far as the lake shore, it is locally common, and it must have been generally distributed there before the hemlock was extirpated over wide areas. This breeding area is continued into Ashtabula County, Ohio (Hicks), and apparently also into the extreme western part of New York.

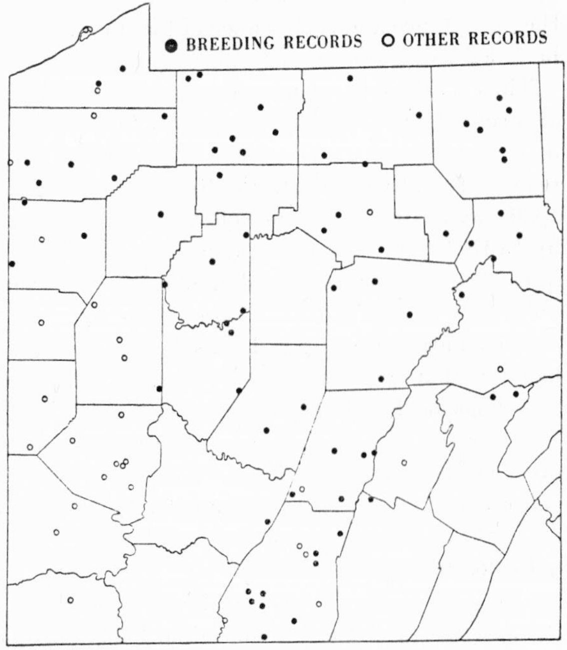

LOCAL RANGE OF THE MAGNOLIA WARBLER

Throughout Warren, McKean, and Potter counties, and southward across the highlands to Indiana, Cambria, and Somerset counties, the species has been traced as a common summer resident. It is not yet known from Chestnut Ridge south of Indiana County, but it appears again on the west slope of Laurel Hill near Laughlintown, Westmoreland County, and almost certainly follows that mountain into Maryland. To the eastward its range seems not to be so sharply limited by the crest of the Alleghenies as are those of certain other relatively northern forms. I have found this bird in northwestern Bedford County, west of Blue Knob, and on the east slope of the Alleghenies near Allegrippus, Blair County. It has been taken in June at Bear Meadows, Centre County (Buckhout), and is said to occur as well in northern Huntingdon County, south of the Seven Mountains. These extralimital records can probably be explained by local conditions, as can those in the west; at any rate, there is no evidence whatever for the occurrence in summer of this species in any other part of the ridge and valley section, although certain other species of Canadian affinities have regularly been found there.

Migration—Outside the area above described, the Magnolia Warbler is of course only a spring and fall transient, regular and rather common. It usually returns from the South with the second wave of warblers in early May, if the weather permits. In 1908 I saw it at Beaver on April 29, but during twelve other seasons it appeared between May 2 and 12; the average date is May 7. The migration lasts until about May 20 (the average of six years' records); in 1923 it continued until May 24. The few records from Allegheny County correspond with the above, as do also available dates from other counties in the western tier. At Renovo, where the species is a summer resident, observations made by A. K. Pierce during twenty-six spring seasons yield arrival dates from May 1 to 10, with May 6 as the average. At Springs, Somerset County, where this bird also breeds commonly, it arrives from April 26 to May 19, and the average date is May 5 (Miller).

The fall movement is not so easy to observe, since the birds are then more subdued in coloration and are songless. According to P. P. Malley, August 25 (1937) is the earliest fall date for Frick Park, Pittsburgh. In three different seasons I have noted this warbler at Beaver as early as August 30, and I have never recorded the first bird later than September 6. Latest dates range from September 27 to October 3. In the fall of 1900 I recorded the species on Presque Isle between August 30 and October 1. T. D. Burleigh says that he observed it in Allegheny County up to October 9 in the fall of 1913 and at State College until October 3 in 1916. Most of the late dates in Mr. Pierce's records for Renovo are in the last week in September, and one is as late as October 5 (1902). It may be concluded, therefore, that as a general rule the migration of the Magnolia Warbler through any given locality in our region where it is a transient visitant, requires about a month in both spring and fall.

Habits[1]—While it lacks the brilliant coloring of the Blackburnian Warbler, the Magnolia vies with the other for first place as the most beautiful of all our wood warblers. Its rich bluish-gray crown, bordered with white and contrasting vividly with the velvety black of the forehead and sides of the head; its bright yellow underparts, striped with black on breast and sides; its yellow rump and black tail, with a broad median crossbar of white, are all unmistakable color characters of the adult male. The vesture of the female is less spectacular, its colors being duller and more subdued, but the pattern is the same, as is also that of the young in autumn. This consistency makes the identification of the species easy at all seasons.

In mid-May, when this gaily colored visitor from the tropics suddenly appears among the sprouting shrubbery so recently bare, it invariably evokes a thrill akin to that of a new discovery. The pages of memory hold images of many individual magnolia warblers: in the willow thickets of the middle states—newly arrived from the tropics; in the hill country of New England—busy and anxious about their nests; beside the great lakes of the Mackenzie; and among the aspen glades of far-off British Columbia.

In the spring migration the Magnolia Warbler favors the woodland but often invades orchards and thickets adjoining forest areas. At this season it rather avoids the treetops and feeds instead in the lower branches and shrubbery; fruit trees in full bloom are favorite haunts. During the southward journey in the fall, the Magnolia follows the other warblers through the forest, or drops down occasionally to willow copses and bushy growths along woodland streams.

For its summer home this warbler chooses a hemlock thicket, and nesting begins soon after the birds have reached their breeding grounds. As a rule the nest is not more than ten or twelve feet from the ground. One that I found near Crumb, Somerset County, on June 12, 1893, was placed waist-high in a thick clump of hemlocks—a typical location, as confirmed by later experience and by other observers. This nest was small but loosely formed and was composed of fine hemlock twigs and grass stalks; it was lined with fine black rootlets and horsehair. All but one of more than fifty nests of this warbler that R. B. Simpson has examined near Warren were placed in hemlocks. One nest was at the exceptional height of thirty-five feet; another was only a foot from the ground in some low hemlock brush. Usually the nest is built in the bushy top of a small hemlock or on a horizontal branch of a larger one, where it is more or less concealed. The hemlock twigs that figure so prominently in its construction give it a characteristic blackish appearance and a durability that betray its identity long after the nesting season is over.

The Magnolia Warbler lays its eggs in late May or early June (from May 25 to June 6). They are usually four in number, although sets of three and five are occasionally found. The eggs are white, or faintly cream, speckled all over with light reddish brown; at the larger end the spots are denser and tend to form a wreath. The markings vary considerably in density, intensity, and arrangement, in different sets. Average measurements are .65 by .48 inches.

Words are futile as a medium for describing this warbler's song, which is often fittingly characterized as sprightly. It is commonly delivered in six syllables, given in pairs. One enthusiastic

[1]Account contributed by Edward A. Preble.

and accurate observer, Mrs. M. M. Nice, interprets it as *wichy, wichy, weé-sy*. But each one can transliterate it for himself and in describing individual songs will perhaps find it necessary to discard or add a syllable or two. Besides this regular song, the species has a peculiar, most unwarbler-like call note of two syllables, which reminds one of certain notes of the White-eyed Vireo. This note is common to both the male and the female in the nesting season.

Dendrœca maculosa Teulon, *Jour. Boston Zoöl. Soc.*, 1882, 1:51 (Bradford, McKean Co., summer).

"Black and Yellow Warbler" Van Fleet, *Ornithologist and Oölogist*, 1884, 9:108 (DuBois, Clearfield Co.).

Dendroica maculosa Warren, *Birds Pa.*, ed. 2, 1890, 269, 283 (Crawford and Somerset Co., breeding; Blair, McKean, and Cameron Co., summer)—Todd, *Auk*, 1891, 8:116, 398, 399 (Buffalo Creek region, Butler and Armstrong Co., nesting)—Dwight, *Auk*, 1892, 9:134, 139 (Cresson, Cambria Co., June)—Todd, *Auk*, 1893, 10:36, 37, 40 (Two Lick, Indiana Co., June), 42, 43, 45 (Coalport, Clearfield Co., June)—Baily, *Auk*, 1896, 13:292, 295 (Williamsville, Elk Co., nesting)—Cope, *Cassinia*, 1902, 5:10, 18 (Tamarack Swamp, Clinton Co., June)—Todd, *Ann. Carnegie Mus.*, 1904, 2:583 (Erie and Presque Isle, Erie Co., summer)—Todd, in Bausman, *Hist. Beaver Co., Pa.*, 1904, 2:1201 (Beaver Co., transient)—Cooke, *Bull. Biol. Surv.* no. 18, 1904, 65 (Beaver, Beaver Co., and Renovo, Clinton Co., migration).

"Magnolia Warbler" Warren, *Forest and Stream*, 1891, 37:83 (Kane, McKean Co., summer)—Simpson, *Nidiologist*, 1895, 2:164 (Warren, Warren Co., nesting)—Cooke, *Bird-Lore*, 1904, 6:200 (Beaver, Beaver Co., and Renovo, Clinton Co., migration)—Simpson, *Oölogist*, 1907, 24:183; 1909, 26:170; 1911, 28:161, 162, 201; 1912, 29:276, 277; and 1914, 31:121 (Warren, Warren Co., nesting, etc.); 1912, 29:330 (head of Tionesta Creek, Warren Co., summer)—Dickey, *Oölogist*, 1914, 31:170 ([Charter Oak], Huntingdon Co., nesting), 207 (Cresson, Cambria Co., nesting)—McConnell, *Oölogist*, 1918, 35:151 (McKeesport, Allegheny Co., transient)—Simpson, *Oölogist*, 1920, 37:142, 143 (Warren and Tionesta Creek, Warren Co., nesting)—McClelland, *Am. Mid. Nat.*, 1922, 8:37 (Washington, Washington Co., transient)—Christy, *Cardinal*, 1924, v. 1, no. 4, p. 11 (Big Traverse Valley, Beaver Co., May)—Eastwood, *Bird-Lore*, 1925, 27:263, 407; 1926, 28:272 (Pittsburgh region, Allegheny Co., May), 343 (Clarion River, Clarion Co., *fide* Elliott); 1927, 29:272 (Pittsburgh region, May), 273 (Springs, Somerset Co., breeding)—Cope and Hawkins, *Forest Leaves*, 1934, 24:26 (E. Tionesta Forest Reserve, Warren and McKean Co., summer).

Dendroica magnolia Harlow, *Auk*, 1912, 29:466, 475 (southern Centre Co., breeding); 1918, 35:142 (Blair and Centre Co. to Warren Co., breeding)—Christy, *Cardinal*, 1923, v. 1, no. 1, [p. 12] (Sewickley, Allegheny Co., transient)—Burleigh, *Wilson Bull.*, 1923, 35:139 (Allegheny Co., migration); 1924, 36:130 (State College, Centre Co., migration)—Christy and Sutton, *Cardinal*, 1928, 2:73 (Cook Forest, Clarion Co., nesting)—Sutton, *Ann. Carnegie Mus.*, 1928, 18:211 (Meadville and Pymatuning Swamp, Crawford Co., nesting)—Burleigh, *Cardinal*, 1929, 2:119 (Allegheny Co., fall migration).

CAPE MAY WARBLER (Plate 18)

DENDROICA TIGRINA (Gmelin)

Description—Adult male in spring: upperparts olive green mixed with black, the *rump abruptly yellow; crown black;* sides of head and a collar around the hindneck, yellow, with an *orange-brown spot on the ear coverts;* tail black, with large white spots; *wings* blackish, with olive-green edgings, the *coverts* largely *white, forming a spot;* underparts yellow, which becomes white on the abdomen; the lower throat, breast, and sides, streaked with black; bill and feet black. *Adult female:* dull greenish above, the crown grayish, the *rump yellowish;* underparts soiled whitish, the throat and breast washed with yellow, and the lower throat, breast, and sides, showing dusky streaks; tail showing white spots. *Immature male:* upperparts grayish olive green, the *rump yellowish;* wings dusky olive, with a whitish area on the coverts; sides of head yellow, clouded with gray; throat and underparts, yellow, which becomes white on the abdomen; the lower throat, breast, and sides, streaked with black and veiled with gray. *Immature female:* an obscure-looking warbler, dusky olive green above, the *rump yellowish;* wings and tail dusky, with olive-greenish edgings, the latter with white spots; underparts soiled whitish, with some yellow wash and with indistinct dusky streaks.

Range—The Cape May Warbler (so called because the first specimen that fell into Wilson's hands came from near Cape May, New Jersey) winters in the West Indies and migrates through the eastern United States to breed in the Canadian Life Zone, from Nova Scotia west to southern Mackenzie. Unlike certain other species of Canadian affinities, it does not continue southward into the Appalachian highlands, and it is unknown as a summer resident even in the Adirondacks.

Long considered to be one of our rarer transients, it is now known to be regular and fairly common in the fall migration and by no means so uncommon in the spring as had been supposed. Possibly it was overlooked in the earlier years of my bird studies, or else (more probably) it has actually become more numerous lately; at any rate I now consider it to be as common in Beaver County during the fall movement as the Black-throated Green Warbler. Records for our region are scattered but represent all sections. A. B. Miller writes that at Springs, Somerset County, this warbler may be rather common in some spring seasons, but that in other years it is rare or absent. He has not observed it in the fall, however; nor has R. B. Simpson seen it at that season at Warren.

Migration—Ordinarily we do not look for the Cape May Warbler before the first week in May, and often it does not appear until the second week. Mr. Miller says that he has observed it in southern Somerset County as early as April 26 (1913), but the average date of arrival is May 9. I have noted it at Beaver between May 8 (1923) and 14 (1908); the average arrival date there is May 11, and the "last-seen" dates are May 22 (1923) and May 19 (1924). Mr. Simpson has seen it at Warren as early as May 1 (1903). At Renovo it was not encountered by A. K. Pierce until the spring of 1912, when it was fairly common from May 12 to 16. In 1918 he saw it as late as May 26. In general, however, the bulk of the species passes through any given locality during the second and third weeks in May.

Fall migrants arrive early, often by the last of August, as indicated by the following records: Sewickley, August 28, 1896 (Atkinson, *fide* John Watson); Beaver, August 30, 1910 (Todd); Summit, Fayette County, August 30, 1916 (Burleigh); Frick Park, Pittsburgh, August 28, 1937 (Malley). According to my experience at Beaver, the species is common during September, and some birds are still passing through during the first part of the next month. My latest dates at this season are October 15, 1909; October 17, 1910; and October 13, 1924. P. P. Malley reports that in 1931 one bird remained at Homestead, Allegheny County, from October 15 to November 15 and haunted an ash-leaved maple on his property.

Habits—The Cape May Warbler, as we see it in transit, has no very striking peculiarities of habit to distinguish it from its congeners. A woodland species, it mingles freely with the other warblers of arboricole predilections and usually remains rather high in the trees. The male in the spring is a beautiful bird and may readily be recognized by its orange-brown ear coverts, but the females and the young birds are not so easily distinguished. The best clue to this warbler's presence is its song —a very simple effort consisting of a single note, repeated, without variation, three, four, or five times. It suggests that of the Black and White Warbler, but it is finer and lacks the lisping quality obvious in the song of that species. In the fall the Cape May has merely a low chirping note, in nowise distinctive. At this season I have seen as many as a dozen birds together in one isolated Norway spruce, to which they kept returning after excursions to the surrounding orchard trees. At least two of my correspondents have remarked upon this bird's curious and reprehensible habit of puncturing ripe grapes to drink the juice, but I cannot find that the injury done in this way is of more than local extent. Like other warblers, this species feeds mainly on small insects.

Dendroica tigrina Todd, *Auk*, 1891, 8:398 (Beaver, Beaver Co., transient)—Rhoads, *Auk*, 1899, 16:313 (Pittsburgh, Allegheny Co., *fide* Link; [Sewickley], Allegheny Co., *fide* Atkinson)—Todd, *Ann. Carnegie Mus.*, 1904, 2:581 (Presque Isle, Erie Co., transient)—Todd, in Bausman, *Hist. Beaver Co., Pa.*, 1904, 2:1201 (Beaver Co., transient)—Stone, *Cassinia*, 1915, 18:59 (State College, Centre Co., migration, *fide* Mason); 1919, 22:35; and 1920, 23:37 (Altoona, Blair Co., May, *fide* McGraw)—Christy, *Cardinal*, 1923, v. 1, no. 1, [p. 12] (Sewickley, Allegheny Co., spring transient)—Burleigh, *Wilson Bull.*, 1923, 35:99 (Allegheny Co., transient); 1924, 36:129 (State College, Centre Co., migra tion)—Sutton, *Ann. Carnegie Mus.*, 1928, 18:208 (Meadville and Pymatuning region, Crawford Co., transient).

"Cape May Warbler" Cooke, *Bird-Lore*, 1905, 7:275 (Beaver, Beaver Co., migration)—Simpson, *Oölogist*, 1910, 27:34; and 1914, 31:121 (Warren, Warren Co., spring transient) —Miller, *In the Open*, Dec., 1912, 3:41 (McKinley Park, Allegheny Co., transient)—McConnell, *Oölogist*, 1918, 35:151 (McKeesport, Allegheny Co., transient)—Boulton, *Oölogist*, 1922, 39:71, 73 (near Beaver, Beaver Co., May)—McClelland, *Am. Mid. Nat.*, 1922, 8:37 (Washington, Washington Co., transient)—Sutton, *Bird-Lore*, 1923, 25: 260; and 1924, 26:266 (Pittsburgh region, Allegheny Co., spring)—Eastwood, *Bird-Lore*, 1926, 28:272 (Pittsburgh region, Allegheny Co., May).

BLACK-THROATED BLUE WARBLER (Plate 18)

DENDROICA CAERULESCENS CAERULESCENS (Gmelin)

Description—Male: general color above, *dark blue,* the wings and tail nearly black, with dark blue edgings; the wings have a *large white spot at the base of the primaries,* and the tail also has prominent white spots near the tips of the outer feathers; *sides of head and whole throat, black,* which continues down the sides of the neck and belly; rest of underparts white. *Female* very different: dull olive green above, with a short white stripe over the eye and a *small white spot at the base of the primaries;* underparts dull buffy greenish or buffy yellowish; the white spots on the tail are indistinct or absent. *Immature birds* resemble the adults, but are usually duller.

Range—This warbler is a distinctly eastern species. It winters in the West Indies and migrates through the eastern United States, scarcely going beyond the Mississippi River. In summer it ranges from New England to Minnesota and southward in the Appalachian highlands to northern Georgia. Its range does not conform to zonal boundaries, since it is found in only the southern half of the Canadian Fauna and in the adjoining northern half (or more) of the Alleghanian. In New York, for example, it occurs as a breeding bird not only in the Adirondack and Catskill Mountains, but also, if less commonly, in most of the western counties. Across the boundary in Pennsylvania, as the general elevation increases, the Black-throated Blue Warbler becomes a common summer resident, and this is its status throughout the greater part of the western half of the state. It is not confined to the mountains, as intimated in the American Ornithologists' Union *Check-List,* nor even to the plateau region proper, but ranges all the way to the Allegheny River in Clarion and Venango counties and descends to an elevation of about eight hundred feet. Its reported occurrence in the Buffalo Creek region of Butler and Armstrong counties requires confirmation, as does also a report from Slippery Rock Creek (McConnell's Mills) in Lawrence County. If it really breeds at either of these two points, the records should doubtless be considered as extralimital and outlying.

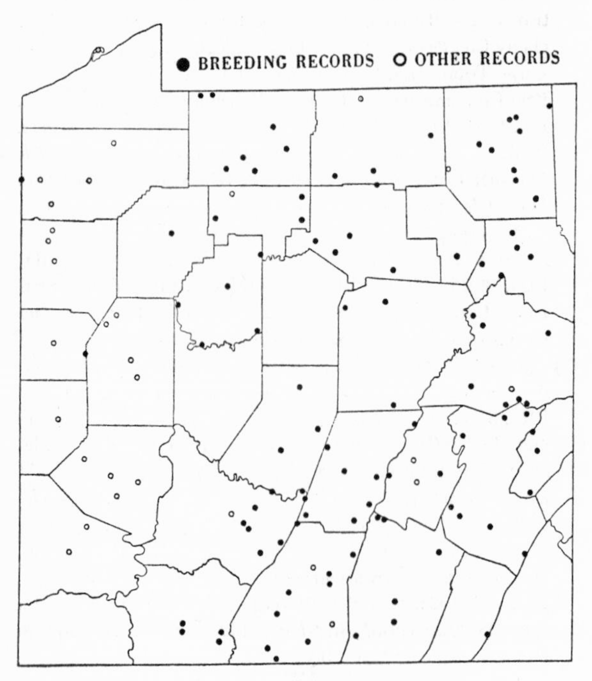

LOCAL RANGE OF THE
BLACK-THROATED BLUE WARBLER

In general, the species is a common transient in spring and fall in the western tier of counties, thence east to the Allegheny River and, toward the south, to the base of Chestnut Ridge. Warren states that it breeds in Crawford County and quotes H. C. Kirkpatrick to that effect, but the latter observer writes that his report was a mistake. G. M. Sutton failed to find it breeding in the Pymatuning region, but L. E. Hicks saw it on Hemlock Island in June, 1931, and found a nest in the Ohio portion of the swamp. S. S. Dickey noted it three miles east of Cambridge Springs, Crawford County, on May 31, 1926—a date suggesting breeding. It is not known to breed anywhere in Erie County, although I have found it just across the Warren County line at Bear Lake and at Tamarack Swamp. It is certainly common in the other northern counties and thence southward into Maryland. I have traced it southward along both Chestnut Ridge and Laurel Hill but have no record of its presence in the Ligonier Valley. It is one of several relatively northern species that range over the ridge and valley section indiscriminately, not keeping to the mountain ridges, but appearing as well in the valley country, wherever local conditions are suitable. There it mingles with a number of species whose Carolinian affinities are unquestioned. From a faunal standpoint this assemblage of species is odd.

The recognition of a southern race (*cairnsi*) of this warbler, as advocated by certain authors and allowed in the *Check-List*, is in my opinion questionable. The amount of black spotting on the back of the male, on which this supposed subspecies has mainly been based, is certainly variable, and I cannot avoid the impression that when present it merely signifies high plumage. Robert Ridgway's remarks on this point (1902), based on the examination of specimens from our region (collected by myself and others), are significant, as they indicate that the characters of *cairnsi* are inconstant in its supposed range. I have been unable to consult a satisfactory series of specimens from the southern Alleghenies, however, and it may be that the females would afford more stable characters, as some authorities claim.

Migration—The Black-throated Blue comes with the main wave of warblers in the first week in May. At Beaver the average date of arrival in thirteen seasons is May 7, with extremes of April 27 (1908) and May 10 (1909 and 1910). At Endeavor, Forest County, Dr. Dickey saw the species in 1923 on April 28. Fifteen seasons' records from Warren County made by R. B. Simpson, however, lie between May 5 and 13. Although these dates correspond in general with others from the western counties, they are later than those reported from Ohio and Michigan, and are doubtless misleading. A. B. Miller states that May 1 is the average date of arrival at Springs, Somerset County, while at Renovo the average in twenty-six years' records by A. K. Pierce is May 3, and the extremes are April 27 (1902, 1908) and May 9 (1895, 1917). The species is never very common during the spring movement, and its migration is rather hurried. On only one occasion (May 12, 1910) have I ever observed anything even approaching a flight. In the spring of 1923 I saw the last bird at Beaver on May 24, but I do not ordinarily expect to find many after the middle of May. A belated migrant was noted at Frick Park, Pittsburgh, on June 5, 1938, by P. P. Malley.

In 1889 I shot a bird of this species at Beaver on August 28—my earliest fall date. My other arrival records at this season fall mostly in the first week in September. The autumnal movement at this point covers a longer period than does the spring movement; for, while most of the transient individuals have passed through by the end of September, laggards have been encountered as late as October 17 (1891). At Warren, Mr. Simpson has observed this warbler as late as October 10 (1900). At Renovo the "last-seen" dates for nineteen seasons range from September 26 (1908) to October 11 (1897), and October 3 is the average. Most observers consider the species somewhat commoner and more regular in fall than in spring.

Habits—The male Black-throated Blue Warbler is readily identified by its striking color pattern, which is virtually the same at all seasons, and the female may always be recognized by the distinctive white spot at the base of the primaries. As a transient species this bird is confined to woodland, where it prefers shrubbery and the smaller trees and is thus easy to observe. Mr. Simpson writes that in Warren County the first migrants are seen in the river valley and that the birds do not appear in the uplands until a little later, when settling for the season. In nesting time the Black-throated Blue prefers deep woods with much undergrowth, the thicker the better. Rhododendron swamps are favorite resorts; indeed, this warbler is one of the characteristic birds of such areas. Mixed forests of hemlock and hardwood, where there is plenty of shade, are also favored. Time and again, however, I have found this species in deciduous woodland on mountain slopes, where conditions were otherwise suitable, and even in brushy second growth. From the base to the summit of Blue Knob, Bedford County, for instance, it proved to be common in early July, 1895.

On its breeding grounds the male spends most of its time high in the shrubbery, singing at frequent intervals. Its regular song is distinctive and consists of two or three syllables, the last of which is somewhat prolonged and has a decided upward swing. The general husky or wheezy quality is a marked characteristic, although it varies somewhat with the individual and the occasion. One of these variations somewhat resembles the usual song of the Blue-winged Warbler. The female is rather shy and silent and as a rule hugs the ground in the brushy growth, where her nest is always built. The nest is not easy to locate, as it is well concealed by foliage. On one occasion I found one in a low bush along the Youghiogheny River near Ohiopyle, Fayette County; another that I examined near Port Allegany, McKean County, must have belonged to this species. In the collection of the Carnegie Museum are several nests with eggs, taken by Mr. Pierce at Kane and Renovo. Mr. Simpson has supplied a full account of the nesting of this warbler in Warren County, where it is a rather common breeding species.

Two-thirds of the nests found by this observer were in rhododendron bushes, and most of the others were in brushy hemlocks. Several that Mr. Pierce found were in beech saplings. Wherever built, the nest is near the ground; it is usually from ten to twenty-four inches up, rarely more, and sometimes not over six inches. Says Mr. Simpson (1910): "The nests are compact and cup-shaped and sometimes are beautiful structures. The handsomest warblers' nests I have ever seen were of this species.

"The favorite materials are grape vine bark, fine strips of yellow and white birch bark and rotten wood. . . . For lining, fine black rootlets and fine grasses are used." All the nests that I have examined fit this description; their uniformly light-colored appearance is due of course to the materials used in their construction. So characteristic is this appearance that it will serve to identify the nest of this species as surely as the dead hemlock twigs do that of the Magnolia Warbler. Four is the usual number of eggs, but occasionally there are only three; while in the Pierce series there is one set of five. The eggs are white, usually with a faint creamy tint, and are marked with small but irregular spots of cinnamon color. Mr. Simpson writes: "All sets I have found were well wreathed, but they vary greatly in extent of markings. Some are simply wreathed and some sets are heavily marked all over." Average measurements are .66 by .51 inches. The first week in June is about the time to expect full sets, although one set in the Pierce collection was taken as early as May 18. In Potter County I have found young out of the nest on June 22.

Dendrœca cœrulescens Teulon, *Jour. Boston Zoöl. Soc.*, 1882, 1:51 (Bradford, McKean Co., May)—Townsend, *Proc. Acad. Nat. Sci. Philadelphia*, 1883, 61 (Latrobe, Westmoreland Co., transient).

"Black-throated Blue Warbler" Van Fleet, *Ornithologist and Oölogist*, 1884, 9:108 (DuBois, Clearfield Co.)—Cooke, *Bird-Lore*, 1906, 8:203 (Renovo, Clinton Co., and Beaver, Beaver Co., migration)—Simpson, *Oölogist*, 1910, 27:64; 1911, 28: 162, 201; and 1914, 31:121 (Warren, Warren Co., nesting; habits, etc.); 1912, 29:330; and 1920, 37:143 (head of Tionesta Creek, Warren Co., nesting)—Dickey, *Oölogist*, 1914, 31:171 ([Charter Oak], Huntingdon Co., May), 207 (Cresson, Cambria Co., nesting)—Miller (R. F.), *Oölogist*, 1919, 36:156 (Shingletown, Centre Co., nesting)—McConnell and Savage, *Bird-Lore*, 1919, 21:242 (Presque Isle, Erie Co., September)—McClelland, *Am. Mid. Nat.*, 1922, 8: 37 (Washington, Washington Co., transient)—Eastwood, *Bird-Lore*, 1925, 27:263, 407; 1926, 28:272 (Pittsburgh region, Allegheny Co., migration), 343 (Cooksburg, Forest Co., July, *fide* Elliott); 1927, 29:272 (Pittsburgh region, Allegheny Co., May), 273 (Springs, Somerset Co., summer, *fide* Miller)—Cope and Hawkins, *Forest Leaves*, 1934, 24:26 (E. Tionesta Forest Reserve, Warren and McKean Co., summer).

Dendroica cœrulescens Warren, *Birds Pa.*, ed. 2, 1890, 269 (Clinton Co., *fide* Van Fleet, Crawford Co., *fide* Kirkpatrick [error], and Warren Co., *fide* Greenlund, breeding), 281 (Clarion and Clearfield Co., breeding, *fide* Van Fleet)—Todd, *Auk*, 1891, 8:398 (Beaver, Beaver Co., August)—Dwight, *Auk*, 1892, 9:133, 134, 138 (Cresson, Cambria Co., June)—Homer, *Ornithologist and Oölogist*, 1893, 18:61 (Elmer, Potter Co., June)—Todd, *Auk*, 1893, 10:36, 37, 40 (Two Lick, Indiana Co., June), 42, 43, 45 (Coalport, Clearfield Co., June)—Baily, *Auk*, 1896, 13:292, 295 (Williamsville, Elk Co., June–July)—Ridgway, *Bull. U. S. Nat. Mus.* no. 50, part 2, 1902, 541 (Bedford, Cambria, Clinton, Fayette, Huntingdon, Mifflin, Somerset, and Warren Co., breeding) —Cope, *Cassinia*, 1902, 5:10, 18 (Tamarack Swamp, Clinton Co., and Oleona, Potter Co., June)—Todd, *Ann. Carnegie Mus.*, 1904, 2:582 (Presque Isle, Erie Co., transient)—Todd, in Bausman, *Hist. Beaver Co., Pa.*, 1904, 2:1201 (Beaver Co., transient)—Cooke, *Bull. Biol. Surv.* no. 18, 1904, 57 (Renovo, Clinton Co., migration)—Keim, *Cassinia*, 1905, 8:40 (Port Allegany, McKean Co., summer).

Dendroica cœrulescens cairnsi Ridgway, *Bull. U. S. Nat. Mus.* no. 50, part 2, 1902, 545 (Somerset, Clarion, Fayette, Bedford, and Centre Co., breeding; critical).

Dendroica cœrulescens cœrulescens Harlow, *Auk*, 1912, 29:475 ("Stone Valley" [Charter Oak], Huntingdon Co.; and Bear Meadows, Centre Co., summer); 1918, 35:142 (Huntingdon to Fayette Co., and Warren Co., breeding)—Christy, *Cardinal*, 1923, v. 1, no. 1, [p. 12] (Sewickley, Allegheny Co., spring transient)—Burleigh, *Wilson Bull.*, 1923, 35:138 (Allegheny Co., migration); 1924, 36:73; 1931, 43:51 (State College and vicinity, Centre Co., migration; summer)—Christy and Sutton, *Cardinal*, 1928, 2:73 (Cook Forest, Clarion Co., summer)—Sutton, *Ann. Carnegie Mus.*, 1928, 18:210 (Meadville and Pymatuning Swamp, Crawford Co., transient)—Burleigh, *Cardinal*, 1929, 2:119 (Allegheny Co., fall migration)—Burleigh, *Cardinal*, 1932, 3:80 ([Summit], Fayette Co., nesting).

MYRTLE WARBLER (Plate 18)

DENDROICA CORONATA (Linnaeus)

Description—A rather large warbler, with four distinct areas of *yellow:* on the *crown, rump, and either side of the breast. Adult male in spring:* upperparts bluish gray, the back with black stripes, the rump and the center of the crown, bright yellow; wings dusky, with paler edgings and two white crossbars; tail dusky, the outer feathers with large white spots; sides of head black, surmounted by a white stripe above the eye; below the eye a small white spot; throat and abdomen white; breast and sides black, sometimes "solid," but usually varied with white; on either side of the breast a large patch of yellow; bill and feet black. *Adult female:* similar, but much duller, the upperparts brownish, and the black of the underparts more extensively interrupted by white. *Fall and winter birds* are more or less "solid" brown above, the dark stripes being reduced to a minimum; the yellow spot on the crown is mostly concealed, and the other head markings are merely indicated; the underparts are buffy white, with dusky markings on the breast and sides; the yellow lateral spots are much smaller and sometimes scarcely evident, but the *yellow rump is always conspicuous.*

Range—The breeding range of this warbler is in the Hudsonian and Canadian life zones, from Alaska to Newfoundland and southward to British Columbia and northern New England. In New York it is a regular summer resident only in the higher elevations of the Adirondack and Catskill Mountains and is not known to range regularly any farther south along the Appalachian highlands. Warren claims to have identified summering birds of this species in western Pennsylvania on three separate occasions— in Cameron, McKean, and Clinton counties, respectively. He specifies exact dates but not exact localities. One hesitates to discredit these records, for which Warren himself was responsible, but there is absolutely no confirming evidence from other sources.[1] Warren's own observations may generally be trusted; most of his errors arose from accepting the reports of his correspondents at their face value. Observers generally throughout our region consider this warbler a common transient in spring and fall, but at Presque Isle it winters regularly, and it has been noted in winter in Allegheny and Washington counties, and at Hollidaysburg in Blair County. It is the hardiest of the warblers, and in the East it is known to winter in New Jersey and even in southern New England, and thence southward to the West Indies. Its wintering in the North, however, is determined by the availability of suitable food and cover.

Migration—Since the Myrtle Warbler winters so far north, it might be expected to appear in our region before the other warblers, but several species ordinarily arrive sooner. Usually the Myrtle makes its appearance at Beaver during the last week in April (once as early as April 22), and never later than May 3 (1911). G. M. Sutton reports a still earlier arrival date (April 16, 1921) for Pittsburgh; otherwise, most of the records now available for Allegheny and the adjacent counties fall within the above limits. Farther north, in Erie, Crawford, and Warren counties, the arrival dates are about the same. The earliest date for New Castle is April 19 (1932—Raney), and for Conneaut Lake, April 18 (1926—Seiple). At Springs, Somerset County, A. B. Miller has seen the species as early as April 8 (1907). At State College it has been noted on April 19 (1917—Burleigh), but at Renovo it has not appeared before April 27 (several years —Pierce). The movement at any given place lasts about two weeks. I have never seen this warbler at Beaver after May 15, but R. B. Simpson writes that in the spring of 1907 (a very late season) he saw stragglers at Warren on May 30 and June 6.

After all the other warblers have come and most of them have gone, the Myrtle puts in a tardy appearance on its return journey in the fall. October 1 is the average time of arrival in the region of the Ohio Valley, although much earlier dates are on record. Indeed, in 1900 the species reached Presque Isle on September 18 and in about a week outnumbered all other warblers. Nevertheless, it is the tardiest of its family at this season, and the majority of birds do not pass through until

[1]Compare, however, *Cassinia*, 1923, 24:59, in which the presence of this species in the breeding season in the Pocono Mountains of northeastern Pennsylvania is affirmed.

October. Almost every year a few late stragglers are in evidence during the first few days of November and occasionally even later. T. D. Burleigh saw one at Harmarville, Allegheny County, on December 31, 1914; and in December, 1930, a few were seen near the same place by several other observers. Early in January, 1939, William Montagna observed a single myrtle warbler at a feeding shelf in Canonsburg, Washington County, and was told that it had been there for some time.

Habits—The Myrtle Warbler (or the Yellow-rumped, as I still prefer to call it) stands out from its fellows of the same family not only because of its larger size and striking coloration, but also because of certain characteristic habits. Its sharp chirp is distinctive; and its yellow rump-patch, always conspicuous in flight, is an excellent field mark. In the spring, when the species often invades orchards and shade trees, the male has also a low, soft, pleasing warble, suggesting that of the Warbling Vireo but more variable and not so long. At this season, although not disdaining the society of other warblers, the Myrtle is often seen in straggling companies of its own kind, traversing the treetops and feeding on insects. In the fall, when it is at times abundant, it is less exclusive and frequently forsakes its regular woodland haunts to join the Junco and the Field, Chipping, and Song sparrows in waste fields, hedgerows, tracts of high weeds, and other places where seeds are plentiful. A scattered flock in a bushy thicket behaves much like a flock of the sparrows with which these warblers mingle on terms of amity. Seeds constitute the bulk of their fare at this season, and this item in their food is the factor that enables them to prolong their stay in the fall and even to remain throughout the winter. On Presque Isle, where alone in our region there is an abundance of bayberries (*Myrica carolinensis*), the Myrtle Warbler is able to pass the winter, subsisting on the wax derived from the berries of this bush, and finding shelter in the thick evergreens growing there in profusion.

Dendrœca coronata Teulon, *Jour. Boston Zoöl. Soc.*, 1882, 1:51 (Bradford, McKean Co., spring)—Townsend, *Proc. Acad. Nat. Sci. Philadelphia*, 1883, 61 (Latrobe, Westmoreland Co., transient).

Dendroica coronata Warren, *Birds Pa.*, ed. 2, 1890, 269 (Cameron, McKean, and Clinton Co., summer)—Todd, *Ann. Carnegie Mus.*, 1904, 2:582 (Presque Isle, Erie Co., transient and winter resident)—Todd, in Bausman, *Hist. Beaver Co., Pa.*, 1904, 2:1201 (Beaver Co., transient)—Cooke, *Bull. Biol. Surv.* no. 18, 1904, 61 (Renovo, Clinton Co., and Beaver, Beaver Co., migration)—Christy, *Cardinal*, 1923, v. 1, no. 1, [p. 12] (Sewickley, Allegheny Co., transient)—Burleigh, *Wilson Bull.*, 1923, 35:138 (Allegheny Co., transient; rare in winter); 1924, 36:129 (State College, Centre Co., transient)—Elliott, *Cardinal*, 1930, 2:202 (Harmarville, Allegheny Co., December; Metcalf, Westmoreland Co., March).

"Myrtle Warbler" Cooke, *Bird-Lore*, 1906, 8:61 (Renovo, Clinton Co., migration)—Simpson, *Oölogist*, 1907, 24:134; and 1914, 31:121 (Warren, Warren Co., transient)—McConnell, *Oölogist*, 1918, 35:151 (McKeesport, Allegheny Co., transient)—McClelland, *Am. Mid. Nat.*, 1922, 8:36 (Washington, Washington Co., transient)—Christy, *Cardinal*, 1924, v. 1, no. 4, p. 11 (Big Traverse Valley, Beaver Co., May)—Sutton, *Bird-Lore*, 1924, 26:418 (Greenville, Mercer Co., October, *fide* Homer)—Eastwood, *Bird-Lore*, 1925, 27:262; 1926, 28:272; and 1927, 29:272 (Pittsburgh region, Allegheny Co., migration), 56 (Logan's Ferry, Allegheny Co., October), 273 (Springs, Somerset Co., April, *fide* Miller)—Boulton, *Bird-Lore*, 1928, 30:14 (Guys Run, Allegheny Co., November, *fide* Reiter, *et al.*), 271 (Sandy Lake, Mercer Co., April, *fide* Reiter, *et al.*)—Taylor and Manley, *Bird-Lore*, 1930, 32:35 (Deer Creek [Harmarville], Allegheny Co., December)—Upson, *et al.*, *Bird-Lore*, 1933, 35:27; and Beal and Peterson, *Bird-Lore*, 1934, 36:33 (Presque Isle, Erie Co., December).

Dendroica coronata coronata Sutton, *Ann. Carnegie Mus.*, 1928, 18:210 (Meadville and Pymatuning Swamp, Crawford Co., transient).

BLACK-THROATED GREEN WARBLER (Plate 19)

DENDROICA VIRENS VIRENS (Gmelin)

Description—A warbler of medium size, with green upperparts, *yellow cheeks and superciliaries*, and conspicuous *white wing-bars. Adult male:* upperparts (including top of head), bright yellowish green; *sides of head and of throat, bright yellow*, relieved by a dull greenish area behind and below the eye; *wings* dusky, *with two white bars;* tail dusky, the outer feathers largely white; underparts white (sometimes yellow-tinged), except the *throat* (medially), *breast, and stripes on the sides and flanks, which are black. Adult female:* similar in general to the male, but the black of the throat and breast is less "solid" and is more or less overlaid with lighter color. *Young male:* similar to the adult male, but the black of the underparts is veiled with pale feather-tipping. *Young female:* similar to the young male, but the throat and the breast are dull yellowish white, with a faint darker stripe on either side, and the streaks on the sides and flanks are much less distinct. *Juvenal plumage:* upperparts dull olive green; underparts yellowish white, with dusky streaks.

Range—This warbler winters south of the United States (mainly in Mexico and Central America) and breeds in the Alleghanian and lower Canadian faunas from Alberta eastward to Newfoundland, and southward in the Appalachian highlands to northern Georgia and Alabama. In western Pennsylvania it occurs as a summer resident not only in the highlands, but also in the ridge and valley section to the east, without regard to elevation. West of the highlands it ranges to Chestnut Ridge, the Allegheny River Valley, and the northwestern district in general, as far south as Lawrence and Butler counties. Its local breeding range is correlated rather closely with the distribution of the white pine and the hemlock. Where these conifers prevail, the Black-throated Green appears, although in the mountains it is by no means averse to hardwood timber, if high and dense. It is a common breeding bird in the Buffalo Creek region of Armstrong and Butler counties and thus ranges within twenty-five miles of Pittsburgh. From the Ohio and lower Allegheny valleys southward, it is known only as a transient, common in spring and fall. Three observers have found it breeding at McConnell's Mills, in extreme eastern Lawrence County; and H. H. Elliott writes that it breeds occasionally near Jamisonville, in central Butler County. In Mercer County, according to H. M. McQuiston, it occurs in the vicinity of Sharon as a regular summer resident and has been noted also near Big Bend on the Shenango River. It is very common in Pymatuning Swamp and elsewhere in Erie and Crawford counties wherever any stands of white pine and hemlock remain.

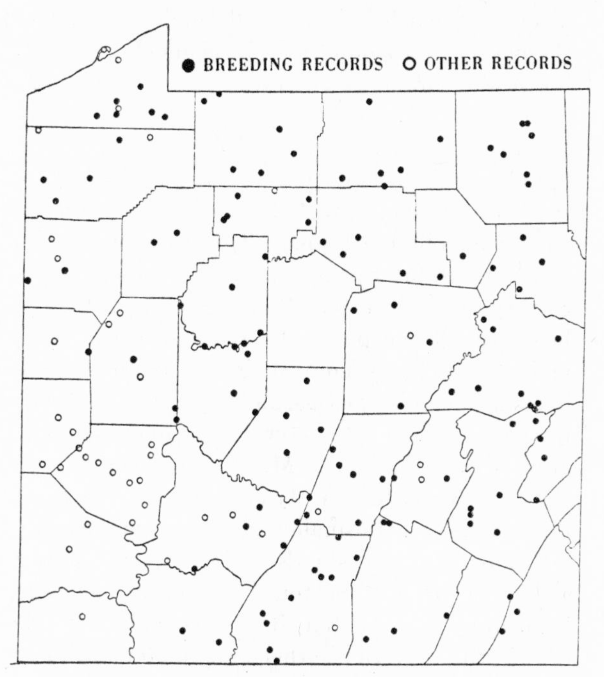

LOCAL RANGE OF THE
BLACK-THROATED GREEN WARBLER

Migration—April 30 is the average date of arrival for this warbler at Beaver, and I have never noted it there earlier than April 22 (1909). A study of the dates from neighboring localities reveals that the end of April is a fair average for this region, although some earlier records have been made. The species was reported from Frick Park, Pittsburgh, on April 17, 1938, by P. P. Malley. On April 19, 1900, I was greatly surprised to find a lone black-throated green warbler near Erie. B. H. Christy saw one near Sewickley on this same date in 1925, and A. B. Miller also cites April 19 as an early record from Springs, Somerset County. This observer considers April 23 the average date of arrival at that locality, while T. D. Burleigh gives April 27 for State College. A. K. Pierce's records for Renovo, covering twenty-six seasons, yield April 29 as the average date, April 22 (1900) as the earliest, and May 8 (1911) as the latest. The migratory movement at any one place seldom continues more than two or three weeks; I have seen migrants at Beaver, however, as late as May 26 (1921) or 27 (1910)—a time when most of the local breeding pairs are settled for the season.

In the fall the species begins its southward movement during the last week of August: Presque Isle, August 24 (1900); Frick Park, Pittsburgh, August 20 (1937); and Sewickley, August 27 (1905). At Beaver it appears and becomes more or less common during the first week in September.

The movement continues through that month and well into the next. I have seen this warbler at Beaver as late as October 13 (1910) and 16 (1909). Late dates from other places are: Pittsburgh, October 13, 1912 (Burleigh); Washington, October 14, 1894 (Nease); State College, October 18, 1914 (Burleigh); Renovo, October 17, 1907 (Pierce). Most of the departure dates from the last-named locality lie in the first and second weeks in October.

Habits—As a transient the Black-throated Green Warbler has no striking peculiarities to distinguish it from its arboricole allies. It is essentially a bird of the woodland and seldom invades orchards and shade trees in the course of its migration. Keeping high in the trees and moving actively about, it is not an easy bird to study during its hurried visits in spring and fall. At the latter season it has only a chirping note, which seems to me a little sharper than that of any other warbler; but in the spring it may readily be identified by the distinctive song of the male, which when once learned is easy to recognize. This song ordinarily consists of five notes, the third and fourth of which are slurred, emphasized, and pitched higher in the scale. The song is susceptible of several variations, however, one of which is decidedly less metallic in timbre —more wheezy, so to speak. One bird watched by G. M. Sutton (1928) "began his song with two downward notes; these were followed by two ascending notes, and the song was finished by a droning buzz which is usually the next to the last syllable in the normal song."

On its breeding grounds the Black-throated Green Warbler shows a marked preference for coniferous woods; I have found it, however, among the oaks and chestnuts of Chestnut Ridge and in the hardwood forest on the slopes and summit of Blue Knob in Bedford County. Dr. Sutton says that at Pymatuning Swamp it was almost sure to be found "wherever tall black birches and equally tall, slender hemlocks grew side by side." The higher the trees, the better the bird is suited. It delights to feed and to sing among the thick tops of the very tallest hemlocks, where it is often practically invisible from below and might escape notice were it not for its slender filing notes, which come sifting down through the maze of branches and are a sure clue to its presence. The female, having no song, is hard to discern and harder still to follow; hence her nest is difficult to locate. My latest attempt to find a nest of this warbler was made on May 24, 1935. With a party from the Carnegie Museum, I repaired to "Watson Run," a small stream entering Buffalo Creek from the north, on the line between Butler and Armstrong counties. I had worked in this same ravine in the spring of 1889, and at that time the Black-throated Green Warbler was common there, as it is now. Although the males were singing all around and although we scanned the treetops carefully with the glass and even climbed several of the trees, no sign of a nest could we discover. In all this time only one female was seen, and she eluded us completely.

R. B. Simpson, although he has successfully located several nests at Warren, confesses that he, too, has frequently been baffled in his efforts. One nest that he discovered was fully sixty-five feet from the ground in a tall yellow birch and was invisible from below, while another was at a height of only fifteen feet in a small hemlock. Most of the nests he has found were in hemlocks, built on horizontal branches at rather high elevations. Other observers report much lower locations—as low even as six feet. The only nest that I ever found was about twenty feet from the ground in a small white pine, near its top and well out on the end of an oblique branch. This was on June 8, 1934, at Sulphur Spring, on the edge of Tamarack Swamp in northwestern Warren County; the nest held eggs at the point of hatching. Small, neat, and rather deeply cupped, it was built of birch bark, thin hemlock twigs, and fine grasslike stems; it was reinforced with cobwebs and lined with fine grasses and horsehair. Mr. Simpson finds considerable variation in style, however; the nests built in birches are smaller and neater and usually contain many fine shreds of birch bark. A nest described by Dr. Sutton "was very deep and beautifully constructed, its lining including bits of hair, fur, and soft feathers, and its foundational material consisting chiefly of slender and uniform twigs of dead hemlock." Four eggs constitute the usual set; they are white, with rather small, irregular reddish-brown spots. Average measurements are .65 by .51 inches. By June 1 the sets are usually complete in Warren County, but Mr. Simpson has taken eggs between May 23 and June 20.

Dendrœca virens TEULON, *Jour. Boston Zoöl. Soc.*, 1882, 1:51 (Bradford, McKean Co., summer)—TOWNSEND, *Proc. Acad. Nat. Sci. Philadelphia*, 1883, 61 (Latrobe, Westmoreland Co., transient).

"Black-throated Green Warbler" VAN FLEET, *Ornithologist and Oölogist*, 1884, 9:108 (DuBois, Clearfield Co.)—WARREN, *Forest and Stream*, 1891, 37:83 (Kane, McKean Co., summer)—COOKE, *Bird-Lore*, 1904, 6:57 (Beaver, Beaver Co., and Renovo, Clinton Co., migration)—SIMPSON, *Oölogist*, 1911, 28:201; and 1914, 31:121 (Warren, Warren Co., nesting, etc.); 1911, 28:39 (Presque Isle, Erie Co., April); 1912, 29:330; and 1920, 37:143 (head of Tionesta Creek, Warren Co., nesting)—DICKEY, *Oölogist*, 1914, 31:171 ([Charter Oak], Huntingdon Co., May); 1919, 36:43 ([Spruce Creek, Huntingdon Co.], June)—MCCONNELL, *Oölogist*, 1918, 35: 151 (McKeesport, Allegheny Co., transient)—MILLER, *Oölogist*, 1919, 36:156 (Charter Oak, Huntingdon Co., nesting)—MCCLELLAND, *Am. Mid. Nat.*, 1922, 8:37 (Washington, Washington Co., transient)—STREET, *Cassinia*, 1923, 24:10, 17 (Little Cove Creek, near Foltz; and Jordan's Knob, Franklin Co., June)—SUTTON, *Bird-Lore*, 1924, 26:266 (Pittsburgh region, Allegheny Co., May), 337 (Wattsburg, Erie Co., summer, *fide* Allen)—CHRISTY, *Cardinal*, 1924, v. 1, no. 4, p. 11 (Big Traverse Valley, Beaver Co., May)—EASTWOOD, *Bird-Lore*, 1925, 27:263; 1926, 28:272; and 1927, 29: 272 (Pittsburgh region, Allegheny Co., April–May); 1925, 27:406 (Dixmont, Allegheny Co., September, *fide* Reiter); 1927, 29:273 (Springs, Somerset Co., breeding)—BOULTON, *Bird-Lore*, 1928, 30:271 (Deer Creek, Allegheny Co., April, *fide* Auerswald, *et al.*)—COPE and HAWKINS, *Forest Leaves*, 1934, 24:26 (E. Tionesta Forest Reserve, Warren and McKean Co., summer).

Dendroica virens WARREN, *Birds Pa.*, ed. 2, 1890, 270, 289 (Clinton and Clearfield Co., breeding, *fide* Van Fleet; Crawford Co., breeding, *fide* Sennett and Kirkpatrick)—TODD, *Auk*, 1891, 8:398, 399 (Beaver, Beaver Co., transient; Buffalo Creek region, Butler and Armstrong Co., June)—DWIGHT, *Auk*, 1892, 9:133, 139 (Cresson, Cambria Co., June)—TODD, *Auk*, 1893, 10:37, 41 (Two Lick and Chestnut Ridge, Indiana Co., June), 42, 43, 45 (Coalport, Clearfield Co., June)—BAILY, *Auk*, 1896, 13:292, 296 (Williamsville, Elk Co., June–July)—COPE, *Cassinia*, 1902, 5:10, 18 (Clinton and Potter Co., June)—COOKE, *Bull. Biol. Surv.* no. 18, 1904, 87 (Beaver, Beaver Co., and Renovo, Clinton Co., migration)—TODD, *Ann. Carnegie Mus.*, 1904, 2:584 (Erie and Presque Isle, Erie Co., transient)—TODD, in Bausman, *Hist. Beaver Co., Pa.*, 1904, 2:1201 (Beaver Co., transient)—KEIM, *Cassinia*, 1905, 8:40 (Port Allegany, McKean Co., summer)—HARLOW, *Auk*, 1912, 29:476 ("Stone Valley," Huntingdon Co.; Bear Meadows and Bald Knob, Centre Co., summer); 1918, 35:143 (Fayette and Huntingdon Co., breeding)—CHRISTY, *Cardinal*, 1923, v. 1, no. 1, [p. 13] (Sewickley, Allegheny Co., transient)—BURLEIGH, *Wilson Bull.*, 1923, 35: 140 (Allegheny Co., migration); 1924, 36:73; 1931, 43:51 (State College and region, Centre Co., migration; breeding) —BURLEIGH, *Cardinal*, 1929, 2:119 (Allegheny Co., fall migration)—HARTUNG, *Cardinal*, 1934, 3:200 (McConnell's Mills, Lawrence Co., breeding).

Dendroica virens virens CHRISTY and SUTTON, *Cardinal*, 1928, 2:73 (Cook Forest, Clarion Co., summer)—SUTTON, *Ann. Carnegie Mus.*, 1928, 18:214 (Meadville and Pymatuning Swamp, Crawford Co., summer)—BURLEIGH, *Cardinal*, 1932, 3:80 (Summit, Fayette Co., nesting).

CERULEAN WARBLER (Plate 18)

DENDROICA CERULEA (Wilson)

Description—Adult male: general color above, *deep blue*, brightest on the crown; back streaked with black; an irregular dark stripe on either side of the crown; *wings* externally, dull blue, *with two conspicuous white bars;* tail black, externally bluish, with white spots on the outer feathers; underparts white, with a *band of deep blue* (sometimes inclining to black) *across the breast*, and irregular stripes of the same color on the sides and flanks. *Adult female:* upperparts dull bluish green, unmarked; underparts greenish white, with faint darker streaks on the sides and flanks; a buffy-white stripe over the eye; wing and tail markings as in the male. *Young birds* of both sexes resemble in general the adult female and lack the dark collar on the breast; females at this stage are greener above and yellower below than males.

Range—This warbler winters in South America and migrates northward in the spring to the eastern United States, mainly west of the Allegheny Mountains. It is a species of decidedly Carolinian predilections and barely reaches southern Ontario, whence it ranges into western New York, in the region south of Lake Ontario. In Ohio, according to Lynds Jones, it is not so common now as it was formerly. In West Virginia it is common in the Ohio Valley, and this area of relative abundance extends into western Pennsylvania. My first direct encounter with the Cerulean Warbler was in the spring of 1889, and soon thereafter I determined that in Beaver County it was common as a migrant and fairly common as a summer resident. I consider it less numerous there now, however, than it once was. In recent years I have traced it north to Lake Erie, east to Chestnut Ridge and southern Clarion County, and south to the West Virginia boundary. In Greene County, where it was at first overlooked by J. W. Jacobs, it has proved to be one of the most characteristic breeding birds. How far it regularly ascends the Allegheny Valley is uncertain, but it may reach Venango County, inasmuch as it has been noted at Meadville by H. C. Kirkpatrick since 1892. At Warren its occurrence is purely accidental. In more recent years sundry observers (including myself) have detected it in the Pymatuning region, and its breeding there has been definitely established.

The occurrence of this warbler in Somerset County (New Lexington) and Clinton County, as attested by Warren on the authority of two of his correspondents, certainly requires confirmation. East of the Allegheny divide, however, indisputable evidence of its presence is provided by the specimen collected on July 2, 1895, by W. H. Phelps, at the foot of Tussey Mountain, some two miles southeast of Charlesville, Bedford County. E. A. Preble saw one bird on the lower edge of the Alleghenies near New Paris in the same county in early June, 1893, but failed to obtain it. C. W. G. Eifrig also reports a single bird at Johnsburg, Somerset County, on August 1, 1903. The species appears as a transient on Miss A. E. Berg's list of the birds of Hollidaysburg.

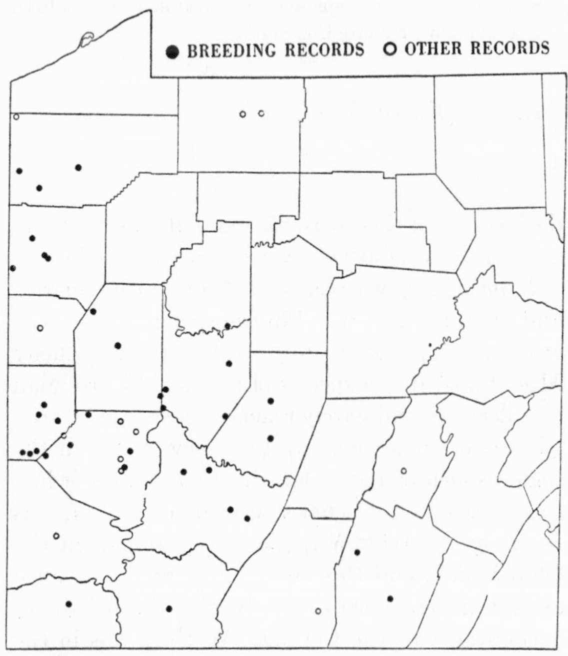

LOCAL RANGE OF THE CERULEAN WARBLER

Migration—The Cerulean Warbler reaches western Pennsylvania about the first of May in the migration wave that carries so many other species of this family on their northward way. Exact dates for Beaver lie between April 26 (1913) and May 11 (1911); May 3 is the average in fifteen seasons' observations. The few scattered arrival dates from other sources also lie within these limits. The fall movement begins very early, sometimes even in July. W. W. Cooke (1906) quotes me as authority for a late fall record (September 14, 1889) of this species at Beaver. The bird in question was unfortunately not secured, and in the light of later experience I am inclined to believe that it was probably some other species—the Parula, perhaps. At any rate, I have never satisfactorily identified this warbler at Beaver later than August 25 (1890). It has been known to remain a little later, however (September 3, 1897), at Wilkinsburg (Atkinson).

Habits—Ever since that day in May, 1889, when I first held in my hand a specimen of this dainty warbler, reputed to be so rare and so decidedly southern in its faunal affinities, and realized that I had indeed secured a "new" bird for western Pennsylvania, the Cerulean Warbler has been one of my favorites. Its tasteful pattern of blue and white blends as well with the green of the upper foliage of the trees as with the hue of the sky, and were the tiny bird not an indefatigable singer, it might easily pass unnoticed. During migration, and also in the breeding season, the species is partial to high, open, oak woods, as well as to low and damp beech woodland, and generally avoids smaller growth. Inhabiting the terminal foliage of the highest forest trees and seldom descending to the lower branches, it might easily elude even the most careful observer were it not for its characteristic song, which may readily be distinguished from that of any other warbler. This song is a modest effort and in its whirring, husky quality suggests in a measure that of the Parula Warbler. It usually consists of three or four notes, all in one key, followed by one that is strongly burred. The song is given incessantly until the end of June but only intermittently in July and very rarely in August.

Finding and collecting the nest of this warbler in 1890 was one of my earliest ornithological exploits and attracted the attention of C. E. Bendire, then curator of oölogy in the United States National Museum. Until that year, authentic instances of its nesting had been few indeed, although many valid accounts have since appeared. Keeping in mind what I had previously learned of the bird's haunts and habits, I began my quest on May 24. I quote from my article published in 1891: "Proceeding to a patch of woodland where I had previously located two pairs, I quickly discovered one of the males, and in the course of half an hour his mate appeared, whereupon I transferred my attention to her. After an hour's patient watching she at last was seen to go to her nest, which was thus discovered to be saddled on the fork of a horizontal branch of a certain kind of tree [basswood], far out from the trunk, and fully 50 feet from the ground. The only way it could possibly be reached was by climbing a tall, slim butternut tree adjacent, thus enabling one to scoop out the eggs [one by one] by means of a net attached to the end of a pole. However, on May 26 the plan was successfully carried out, though not without considerable risk; in addition the nest was secured and the female bird shot, thus putting the identification beyond question. The male came about at the time, but apparently manifested little concern.

"The nest was a small, neat structure, tightly fastened to its branch, and composed mainly of weed stalks and strips of bark, though the outside, whose texture was rendered firmer by means of a plentiful supply of saliva and cobwebs, presented a decidedly white appearance, owing to the color of the stems composing it as well as to the bits of paper and hornets' nest added. The lining was simply finer weed stalks. It contained three eggs of the Warbler and one of the Cowbird, all fresh, so that the set was probably incomplete. In color they almost exactly resemble a set of American Redstarts in my collection, differing only in being slightly shorter. The ground-color is white, with a rather decided suggestion of bluish green, spotted over, in the style of most Warblers, with reddish-brown, the spots tending to aggregate at and around the larger end."

S. S. Dickey has published (1920) an account of the nests found by him in Greene County from 1905 to 1914. These were substantially similar to the nest described above. Four eggs apparently constitute the usual set for first layings; they average .64 by .50 inches. From May 20 to May 27 is the time to look for full sets. One nest that Dr. Dickey found was only eighteen feet from the ground, but the others were considerably higher. The nests that I have located in later years have all been built in oaks at high elevations. I have found young on the wing as early as July 10. After the cessation of song, the Cerulean Warbler becomes inconspicuous and so remains until its departure for the South.

Dendroica cærulea Warren, *Birds Pa.*, ed. 2, 1890, 269, 284 (Somerset Co., summer, *fide* Moore; Clinton Co., breeding[?], *fide* Van Fleet)—Todd, *Auk*, 1891, 8:238 (Beaver, Beaver Co., nesting); 1893, 10:38, 41 (Two Lick, Indiana Co., June)—Rhoads, *Auk*, 1899, 16:313 (Pittsburgh, Allegheny Co.; Beaver, Beaver Co.; and Ligonier, Westmoreland Co., breeding).

Dendroica cerulea Cooke, *Bull. Biol. Surv.* no. 18, 1904, 69 (Beaver, Beaver Co., migration)—Todd, in Bausman, *Hist. Beaver Co., Pa.*, 1904, 2:1201 (Beaver Co., summer)—Chapman, *Warblers N. Am.*, 1907, 170 (Waynesburg, Greene Co., nesting, *fide* Jacobs)—Harlow, *Auk*, 1918, 35:142 (Allegheny Co.; Greene Co., nesting)—Dickey, *Oölogist*, 1920, 37:88 ([Greene Co.], Pa., nesting; range; habits)—Christy, *Cardinal*, 1923, v. 1, no. 1, [p. 12] (Sewickley, Allegheny Co., breeding)—Burleigh, *Wilson Bull.*, 1923, 35:139 (Allegheny River and Deer Creek, Allegheny Co., nesting)—Sutton, *Ann. Carnegie Mus.*, 1928, 18:211 (Meadville and Hartstown, Crawford Co., summer)—Burleigh, *Cardinal*, 1929, 2:119 (Deer Creek, Allegheny Co., August).

"Cerulean Warbler" Brumbaugh, *Wilson Bull.*, 1905, 12:100 (Wilkinsburg, Allegheny Co., July)—Cooke, *Bird-Lore*, 1906, 8:204 (Beaver, Beaver Co., migration)—Miller, *In the Open*, Dec., 1912, 3:41 (McKinley Park, Allegheny Co., transient)—Dickey, *Oölogist*, 1912, 29:302 (Waynesburg, Greene Co., nesting)—Simpson, *Oölogist*, 1914, 31:121 (Warren, Warren Co., May)—McClelland, *Am. Mid. Nat.*, 1922, 8:37 (Washington, Washington Co., transient)—Sutton, *Bird-Lore*, 1923, 25:260 (Beaver Co., spring)—Christy, *Cardinal*, 1924, v. 1, no. 4, p. 9 (Big Traverse Valley, Beaver Co., June); 1931, 3:44 (["Patton's Point"], Beaver Co., May)—Eastwood, *Bird-Lore*, 1925, 27:263; 1926, 28:272; and 1927, 29:272 (Pittsburgh region, Allegheny Co., April–May)—Arthur, *Country Rambler*, 1934, 105 (Deer Creek, Allegheny Co., nesting).

BLACKBURNIAN WARBLER (Plate 19)

DENDROICA FUSCA (Müller)

Description—Adult male in spring: upperparts black, with some irregular white stripes; wings dark, with a *large white spot on the coverts;* tail black, the outer feathers with large white areas; the median crown-spot, the broad superciliaries, a spot under the eye, and the *sides of the neck, throat, and breast, are flame-orange;* lores and ear coverts black; rest of underparts white, yellow-tinged anteriorly, the sides and flanks streaked with black. In the fall the pattern is the same, but the colors are blended and more subdued. *Adult female:* similar to the adult male, but general coloration duller; the black of the upperparts is more or less overspread with an olivaceous tinge, the throat is duller orange, and all the markings are less distinct. *Young male:* similar to the adult male in the fall, but much duller; more olivaceous above and more uniformly yellowish below, with less conspicuous streaks. *Young female:* still duller; dull olive above and buffy yellowish below, the lateral streaks barely indicated. The yellow superciliaries, in contrast with the dark-colored sides of the head and the yellow or yellowish throat, will serve to distinguish the species at this stage from the Black-poll and Bay-breasted warblers, which it otherwise resembles.

Range—The principal winter home of the Blackburnian Warbler is in northern South America. Its summer home is in the forest region stretching from Manitoba and Minnesota eastward to New England and Nova Scotia and thence southward in the Appalachian highlands to northern Georgia. From a zonal point of view it is a species of the lower Canadian Fauna that ranges rather far into the Alleghanian. The first suggestion that this warbler might breed in western Pennsylvania came from Warren (1890), but his statements lack precision and are unsatisfactory. In the next few years absolute evidence of its presence in the breeding season at several different localities in the highlands came to light and enabled the sketching of an outline of its local range. Now, largely because of my own researches (1892–99) and the work of other observers, it is possible to complete the picture with a fair degree of accuracy. In view of our present knowledge, the statement of W. W. Cooke (1904) that "in the Allegheny Mountains a few Blackburnian Warblers breed in Pennsylvania" is misleading; for as a matter of fact the species breeds commonly almost everywhere above 1,500 feet.

The Blackburnian Warbler is a common transient in the western counties of our region as far east as Laurel Hill and the Allegheny Valley. It is known as a common summer resident in the northern and more elevated interior counties, as well as in the mountain ridges of the southeastern section. It seems in general to be more northern in its local predilections than is the Black-throated Blue Warbler. The latter species breeds on Chestnut Ridge, where it has been recorded at several points, but the Blackburnian does not seem to occur in summer west of Laurel Hill, at least south of the Conemaugh River. North of this stream the species is known from Two Lick (Todd) and Gaibleton (Trimble), Indiana County; Clarion (Todd); and Tidioute, Warren County (Homer). Thence it ranges westward over the eastern and higher parts of Crawford and Erie counties, where it has been found at Spartansburg (Todd), Lake Pleasant

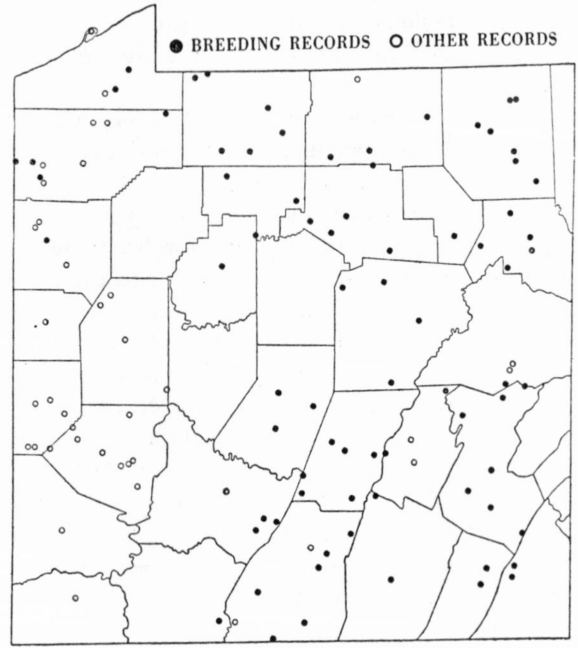

LOCAL RANGE OF THE BLACKBURNIAN WARBLER

(Todd), and Waterford (Homer). S. S. Dickey has seen it near Cambridge Springs, Crawford County, as late as May 31—a date that strongly suggests breeding. At Pymatuning Swamp it is a regular although not common summer resident, but whether this breeding area is an isolated one or is in fact connected with the main range of the species to the eastward, is not known. The fact that so much of the forest has been removed from this area has given rise to many such distributional problems.

Migration—A few days before or after the first of May, a large wave of warblers invariably includes the Blackburnian. Exact dates at Beaver have been found to range between April 29 (1908 and 1935) and May 10 (1911), while May 4 is the average. Early dates from some other localities are: Springs, Somerset County, April 25; State College, April 26; Pittsburgh (Frick Park), April 25; Meadville, April 29; Warren, May 1. In twenty-four seasons' records from Renovo the dates lie between April 25 (1897) and May 11 (1917), and May 2 is the average. During the course of the spring migration there are often a few days of excessive movement, when the species is inordinately common. T. D. Burleigh refers to a flight that took place at Pittsburgh on May 16 and 17, 1914; and from May 15 to 17, 1925, G. M. Sutton (1928) "saw literally hundreds" in the hemlocks five miles north of Hartstown. The spring movement lasts three weeks or more; I have seen migrants at Beaver as late as May 25 (1923) and 27 (1910), while B. H. Christy has seen them at Frankfort Springs, Beaver County, on June 1 (1924)—a date on which eggs have been found in Warren County.

The fall movement begins early in the season, but its onset is of course perceptible only outside the local breeding area. Out of nine arrival records for this warbler at Beaver, three are in August (August 28 to 31), and none is later than September 9. The species was recorded on Presque Isle in 1900 from August 21 until October 2. According to Mr. Burleigh, August 24 (1927) is the earliest fall date for Pittsburgh. D. A. Atkinson has noted the Blackburnian Warbler at Wilkinsburg as early as August 26 (1893) and as late as October 12 (1899). The latter date is exceptional, since most of the birds leave in September and the whole movement at this season seldom lasts more than a month. One specimen was taken at New Hamburg, Mercer County, on August 20, 1895 (Homer). In 1911 and in 1918, A. K. Pierce recorded this warbler at Renovo on September 28, but most of his "last-seen" dates are considerably earlier. The species has been noted at Warren as late as October 8 (Simpson).

Habits—In a family in which beauty is the general rule, the Blackburnian Warbler is nevertheless outstanding, and it is considered by many the loveliest of all the warbler tribe. There is surely nothing in the bird world that surpasses in brilliance the fiery orange of its throat and breast, set off by the glossy black of its upperparts and glowing like a wisp of flame as the bird turns to and fro in the morning sun. Pre-eminently a forest warbler, the Blackburnian haunts the treetops and the terminal foliage and rarely descends close to the ground. During migration it prefers the high woods, deciduous and evergreen alike, and seldom comes into orchards and bushy growth unless, perhaps, under stress of adverse weather. In the summer, when settled on its nesting grounds, it shows a decided partiality for conifers—hemlocks and white pines—the higher the better. In Tamarack Swamp, Clinton County, I found it in the spruce area also. If conifers are scattered or absent in a given breeding territory, however, the Blackburnian Warbler does not scorn deciduous timber that is sufficiently high and otherwise suitable. Although it is common in the somber shade of the hemlocks of the northern counties and the highlands in general, it is by no means rare in the hardwood forest of the mountains east of the Allegheny divide. At Springs, Somerset County, A. B. Miller writes that it is not confined to hemlocks but inhabits also high deciduous woods and especially maple groves.

The Blackburnian, like the other warblers of its class, is a bird of action, and under ordinary circumstances it is ceaselessly "on the go" in quest of its small insect prey. But sometimes in the nesting season, presumably while the female is incubating, the male may be observed to remain perched for a long time in one spot, perhaps near the top of a tall hemlock, leisurely preening his plumage, turning this way and that, and singing at frequent intervals. His song is a rather weak and vacillating effort, which begins with a series of wheezy, chipping notes resembling those of the

Black and White Warbler; these are followed by a rather musical trill ending in one or two high squeals. Not a loud song, it may easily escape notice, and in dense woodland it is hard to trace. Ferreting out the location of the nest is still more difficult. Having had no experience myself in this matter, I recount that of R. B. Simpson of Warren, whose energy, patience, and persistence have yielded tangible results with so many elusive species of the local avifauna.

Mr. Simpson rightly considers the nest of the Blackburnian Warbler the most difficult to locate of those of the warblers of his region. Like the nest of the Black-throated Green Warbler, it is as a rule built high in a tree and can seldom be discovered save by detecting the female at work on its construction. One female that he watched gathered most of the material from the ground, sometimes at a distance from the nesting site. Mr. Simpson remarks that the male accompanied her on many trips but did not assist her. With one exception all the nests he has found (including several not recorded in his articles in the *Oölogist*) were in hemlocks, at elevations varying from twenty to fifty feet. The exceptional nest was in a large chestnut, sixty feet from the ground. The nests were in every instance saddled on a horizontal branch, well out from the trunk. They resembled nests of the Magnolia Warbler but were if anything a little looser in construction and generally bulkier. They were built mostly of dead hemlock twigs and were decorated to some extent with cobwebs. The female, according to Mr. Simpson, is a close sitter, but the male is seldom if ever in evidence near the nest. The eggs when fresh have a decidedly greenish ground-color and are thus altogether different from those of the Magnolia Warbler. They are more or less heavily spotted, or even blotched, with two shades of brown, and the markings are densest around the larger end. Average measurements are .68 by .50 inches. Of nine nests found by Mr. Simpson, six contained four eggs (or young); two held five; and one, only three. These nests were discovered on dates varying from May 26 to June 6, except for one that was found on June 25 (probably a second nesting).

Dendrœca blackburniæ Teulon, *Jour. Boston Zoöl. Soc.*, 1882, 1:51 (Bradford, McKean Co., May)—Townsend, *Proc. Acad. Nat. Sci. Philadelphia*, 1883, 61 (Latrobe, Westmoreland Co., spring transient).

"Blackburnian Warbler" Van Fleet, *Ornithologist and Oölogist*, 1884, 9:108 (DuBois, Clearfield Co.)—Warren, *Forest and Stream*, 1891, 37:83 (Kane, McKean Co., summer)—Stone, *Cassinia*, 1906, 9:41, 44 (Scrub Ridge, west of McConnellsburg, Fulton Co., June)—Simpson, *Oölogist*, 1912, 29:330 (head of Tionesta Creek, Warren Co., summer); 1914, 31:91, 121; 1920, 37:142; and 1922, 39:86 (Warren, Warren Co., nesting, etc.)—Harlow, *Cassinia*, 1912, 15:20 (Center Furnace Swamp, Centre Co., spring)—Harlow, *Oölogist*, 1914, 31:98 ([Charter Oak], Huntingdon Co., spring)—Dickey, *Oölogist*, 1914, 31:171 ([Charter Oak], Huntingdon Co., nesting); 1919, 36:43 ([Spruce Creek, Huntingdon Co.], June)—McConnell, *Oölogist*, 1918, 35:151 ("Olympia Park," McKeesport, Allegheny Co., transient)—McClelland, *Am. Mid. Nat.*, 1922, 8:37 (Washington, Washington Co., transient)—Street, *Cassinia*, 1923, 24:17 (head of Horse Valley, and near Metal, Franklin Co., June)—Sutton, *Bird-Lore*, 1924, 26:266 (Pittsburgh region, Allegheny Co., May)—Christy, *Cardinal*, 1924, v. 1, no. 4, p. 11 (Big Traverse Valley, Beaver Co., May)—Eastwood, *Bird-Lore*, 1925, 27:263, 407; 1926, 28:402; and 1927, 29:272 (Pittsburgh region, Allegheny Co., May, September, and October, *fide* Grimm); 1926, 28:273 (Rector, Westmoreland Co., May, *fide* Knauz); 1927, 29:273 (Springs, Somerset Co., breeding, *fide* Miller)—Cope and Hawkins, *Forest Leaves*, 1934, 24:26 (E. Tionesta Forest Reserve, Warren and McKean Co., summer).

Dendroica blackburniæ Warren, *Birds Pa.*, 1888, 245 (Crawford and Erie Co., breeding, *fide* Sennett); ed. 2, 1890, 287 (Clinton and Clearfield Co., breeding, *fide* Van Fleet; Centre and McKean Co., June, August; Fayette Co., transient)—Todd, *Auk*, 1891, 8:398 (Beaver, Beaver Co., transient; Buffalo Creek region, Butler Co., June 1, 1889)—Dwight, *Auk*, 1892, 9:133, 134, 139 (Cresson, Cambria Co., June)—Todd, *Auk*, 1893, 10:36, 37, 41 (Two Lick, Indiana Co., June), 42, 43, 45 (Coalport, Clearfield Co., June)—Baily, *Auk*, 1896, 13:292, 296 (Williamsville, Elk Co., June–July)—Cope, *Cassinia*, 1902, 5:10, 18 (Tamarack Swamp, Clinton Co., and Oleona, Potter Co., June)—Todd, *Ann. Carnegie Mus.*, 1904, 2:584 (Presque Isle, Erie Co., transient)—Todd, in Bausman, *Hist. Beaver Co., Pa.*, 1904, 2:1201 (Beaver Co., transient)—Cooke, *Bull. Biol. Surv.* no. 18, 1904, 80 (Beaver, Beaver Co., migration)—Keim, *Cassinia*, 1905, 8:40 (Port Allegany, McKean Co., summer)—Chapman, *Warblers N. Am.*, 1907, 175 (Beaver, Beaver Co., and Renovo, Clinton Co., migration)—Simpson, *Oölogist*, 1909, 26:163 (Warren, Warren Co., habits; nesting).

Dendroica fusca Harlow, *Auk*, 1912, 29:476 (southern Centre Co., summer); 1918, 35:143 (Huntingdon Co., north to Warren Co.)—Christy, *Cardinal*, 1923, v. 1, no. 1, [p. 13] (Sewickley, Allegheny Co., transient)—Burleigh, *Wilson Bull.*, 1923, 35:139 (Allegheny Co., migration); 1924, 36:73 (State College, Centre Co., migration); 1931, 43:51 (mountains near State College, Centre Co., breeding)—Christy and Sutton, *Cardinal*, 1928, 2:73 (Cook Forest, Clarion Co., nesting)—Sutton, *Ann. Carnegie Mus.*, 1928, 18:214 (Pymatuning Swamp, Crawford Co., nesting; Meadville, transient)—Burleigh, *Cardinal*, 1929, 2:119 (Allegheny Co., fall migration).

CHESTNUT-SIDED WARBLER (Plate 19)

DENDROICA PENSYLVANICA (Linnaeus)

Description—A warbler of medium size, with *pure white underparts*, chestnut sides, a conspicuous yellow crown, and *yellow wing-bars*. In the *adult male* a black stripe runs from the bill over the eye, and another stripe below the eye extends to the *chestnut of the sides;* ear coverts and sides of the neck, white; back black, varied with greenish yellow, in striped pattern; *wings* and tail dark, the former *with two yellow bars*, the latter with the outer feathers extensively white. *Adult female* similar, but duller, the chestnut sides less prominent. Adults in the fall lack the black-and-white head pattern, while the crown is greenish yellow like the back; the chestnut of the sides is less extensive. *Immature birds* are still more greenish above and show only a trace of chestnut on the flanks, or none at all. In this plumage the species may always be recognized by the *white underparts* in combination with the *yellow wing-bars*.

Range—This warbler winters in Central America, whence it migrates across the Gulf of Mexico and through the southern states to occupy its summer range farther north. It is a common breeding bird in New England and New York and thence westward, in forested country, to Saskatchewan and eastern Nebraska. It ranges much farther south, however, along the Allegheny Mountains and their outlying spurs and foothills. Its faunal affinities are decidedly Alleghanian, although it invades the lower part of the Canadian Fauna at many points. As might be expected from this general statement, its breeding range in western Pennsylvania is extensive; it includes all except the portion west and south of the Monongahela and Ohio rivers, where the species is only a transient. In Fayette County this warbler is not known to breed west of Chestnut Ridge, but just north of that county its range swings off to the west to include Mount Pleasant, Westmoreland County (Preble), and Turtle Creek, Allegheny County (Atkinson), at which places nests have been found. The species breeds also in the northern part of Allegheny County; it has been found at lower Deer Creek (Atkinson, *fide* J. Watson), at North Park, and north of Sewickley (Christy). I feel safe in asserting that it does not breed in the parts of Beaver County that I have worked; I believe, however, despite the lack of positive records, that it probably does occur in summer in the northern section and thence northward through Lawrence County. Its breeding range in this area thus closely parallels the Veery's. East of the main Allegheny divide, the latter species is local, while the warbler is very common—as it is also throughout the plateau region and the northwestern counties in general.

● BREEDING RECORDS ○ OTHER RECORDS

LOCAL RANGE OF THE CHESTNUT-SIDED WARBLER

Migration—Members of this species make up a large proportion of the warbler flight or "wave" that comes as a rule during the first week in May. My arrival dates for Beaver, ranging from April 29 (1908) to May 8 (several years), with May 4 as an average, correspond with similar records from adjoining counties. They also coincide with the A. K. Pierce records covering twenty-five years at Renovo, in which the average date is May 3. I have known this warbler to remain at Beaver as late as May 28 (1910)—a date on which nests have been found on its breeding grounds. A. B. Miller has observed the species as early as April 21 (1916) at Springs, in Somerset County, and

R. B. Simpson once saw it on Presque Isle on April 26 (1902). These are both exceptional records.

Observers in areas outside the local breeding range of this warbler report that it is one of the earliest migrants in the fall. At Beaver I always look for it in August, and I suspect that it has arrived there earlier than my earliest date (August 18, 1888) would indicate, since T. D. Burleigh once saw it in Pittsburgh on August 12. Although beginning so early, the migration is not in full swing until September, and for two or three weeks during the flood tide of the movement, the species is very numerous indeed. The last migrants have been noted at Beaver on October 1, 1890 (Todd); at Pittsburgh on October 3, 1926 (Grimm); and at Renovo on October 4, 1896 (Pierce).

Habits[1]—In Warren County this pleasing little songster is one of the commoner migrant warblers during the first half of May. At this time, however, it is found almost entirely in the valleys of the Allegheny River and its larger branches; for the vegetation is much farther advanced there than in the uplands. Sometimes severe storms of wind and rain during this period force the Chestnut-sided Warbler to take shelter in the fruit and shade trees of the towns, although it prefers the woodlands. Later in May, when the wooded hillsides turn green, the species may be found settled for the nesting season in suitable localities in highlands and lowlands alike. Avoiding the heavy timber, it chooses for a summer home a region grown up to briers and low brush. The cut-over forests or "slashings," where the tangle of brush and briers is dense, are favorite nesting grounds. Many pairs also build along roadsides, near the margins of woods, and in old fields. When nesting near farms or clearings, and along roadsides, they are frequently imposed upon by the Cowbird.

During the entire nesting period the male spends much of his time singing; he selects for his perch a lone tree or one on the edge of the woods that overlooks his domain. Here he stays for minutes on end, singing at frequent intervals. His song always sounds to me like *dis-dis-dis-dismiss-you*, with a strong accent on the penultimate syllable.

Nest-building begins at Warren about the last week in May. I have found many nests of this warbler, and my experience has been that the first week in June (unless the season happens to be very late) is the time to look for full sets of fresh eggs. My earliest dates are May 23 (1928) and May 25 (1930); on the first-mentioned day I found five fresh eggs, and on the second, four. Dates for other years, covering a long period, range from May 29 to June 10. In the spring of 1910 (a very late season) the first full set was not found until June 6. On June 22 of that year I found a nest with four eggs; this is my latest record for fresh eggs of this species. Most of the nests that I have seen were built in blackberry canes, the rest in low brush of various kinds. As a rule they were placed at an elevation of from two to four feet, and I have never seen one more than five feet from the ground. Small and neat, the nests are composed of fine, dry grasses, strips of weeds, and other vegetable fibers; they are lined with fine rootlets and grasses and are sometimes thickly decorated with cobwebs and plant down.

The eggs are usually four in number, but sets of five are not uncommon, and occasionally there are only three. They are white, often tinged with pale green, and are irregularly spotted with grayish brown. These markings are more or less confluent at or around the larger end. Heavily marked sets are sometimes spotted with umber brown. Average measurements are .69 by .50 inches.

Dendrœca pensylvanica Teulon, *Jour. Boston Zoöl. Soc.*, 1882, 1:51 (Bradford, McKean Co., May).

"Chestnut-sided Warbler" Van Fleet, *Ornithologist and Oölogist*, 1884, 9:108 (DuBois, Clearfield Co.)—Warren, *Forest and Stream*, 1891, 37:83 (Kane, McKean Co., summer)—Cooke, *Bird-Lore*, 1904, 6:163 (Beaver, Beaver Co., and Renovo, Clinton Co., migration)—Stone, *Cassinia*, 1906, 9:41, 44 (Scrub Ridge, west of McConnellsburg, Fulton Co., June)—Simpson, *Oölogist*, 1909, 26:170; 1912, 29:277; and 1914, 31:121 (Warren, Warren Co., nesting, etc.); 1912, 29:330 (head of Tionesta Creek, Warren Co., summer)—Dickey, *Oölogist*, 1914, 31:171 ([Charter Oak], Huntingdon Co., nesting)—McConnell, *Oölogist*, 1918, 35:151 (McKeesport, Allegheny Co.)—McClelland, *Am. Mid. Nat.*, 1922, 8:37 (Washington, Washington Co., transient)—Street, *Cassinia*, 1923, 24:17 (Jordan's Knob, Franklin Co., June)—Christy, *Cardinal*, 1924, v. 1, no. 4, p. 11 (Big Traverse Valley, Beaver Co., May)—Eastwood, *Bird-Lore*, 1926, 28:272 (Pittsburgh region, Allegheny Co., May), 273 (Rector, Westmoreland Co., May, *fide* Knauz), 402 (South Hills district, Pittsburgh, Allegheny Co., October, *fide* Grimm); 1927, 29:272 (Pittsburgh region, Allegheny Co., May), 273 (Springs, Somerset Co., breeding, *fide* Miller)—Hegner and Christy, *Cardinal*, 1931, 3:22 (North Park, Allegheny Co., May)—Cope and Hawkins, *Forest Leaves*, 1934, 24:26 (E. Tionesta Forest Reserve, Warren and McKean Co., summer).

[1]Account contributed by Ralph B. Simpson.

Dendroica pensylvanica WARREN, *Birds Pa.*, 1888, 245 (Crawford and Erie Co., breeding, *fide* Sennett); ed. 2, 1890, 284 (Blair, Mercer, Cameron, and McKean Co., summer)—TODD, *Auk*, 1891, 8:398, 399 (Beaver, Beaver Co., transient; Buffalo Creek region, Armstrong and Butler Co., nesting)—DWIGHT, *Auk*, 1892, 9:133, 139 (Cresson, Cambria Co., and Wopsononock Mt., Blair Co., June)—TODD, *Auk*, 1893, 10:37, 41 (Two Lick, Indiana Co., June), 42, 43, 45 (Coalport, Clearfield Co., June)—BAILY, *Auk*, 1896, 13:291, 292, 296 (Williamsville, Elk Co., June–July)—COPE, *Cassinia*, 1902, 5:18 (Galeton, Potter Co., June)—TODD, in Bausman, *Hist. Beaver Co., Pa.*, 1904, 2:1201 (Beaver Co., transient)—TODD, *Ann. Carnegie Mus.*, 1904, 2:583 (Presque Isle, Erie Co., summer)—COOKE, *Bull. Biol. Surv.* no. 18, 1904, 71 (Beaver, Beaver Co., and Renovo, Clinton Co., migration)—KEIM, *Cassinia*, 1905, 8:40 (Port Allegany, McKean Co., summer)—HARLOW, *Auk*, 1912, 29:476 (State College, Centre Co., summer); 1918, 35:142 (Fayette and Franklin Co., etc.)—CHRISTY, *Cardinal*, 1923, v. 1, no. 1, [p. 12] (Sewickley, Allegheny Co., transient; northern Allegheny Co., summer)—BURLEIGH, *Wilson Bull.*, 1923, 35:139 (Allegheny Co., transient); 1924, 36:73; 1931, 43:51 (State College, Centre Co., migration; summer)—CHRISTY and SUTTON, *Cardinal*, 1928, 2:73 (Cook Forest, Clarion Co., summer)—SUTTON, *Ann. Carnegie Mus.*, 1928, 18:212 (Meadville and Pymatuning Swamp, Crawford Co., nesting)—BURLEIGH, *Cardinal*, 1932, 3:80 ([Summit], Fayette Co., nesting).

BAY-BREASTED WARBLER (Plate 19)

DENDROICA CASTANEA (Wilson)

Description—Adult male: crown chestnut; forehead and sides of head, black, contrasting with a buffy-white spot on either side of the neck; upperparts dull grayish, with black stripes; *wings* dusky, *with two white bars;* tail dusky, with large white spots on the outer feathers; *throat, breast, and sides, rich chestnut brown;* rest of underparts buffy white. *Adult female:* the chestnut of the crown duller, sometimes wanting; sides of the head merely dusky or grayish, so that the characteristic head pattern is lost; chestnut brown of the underparts much restricted and usually in evidence only on the sides of the throat and body; otherwise resembling the male. *Young birds* in the fall: bright olive green above, with some indication of black streaks on the back; dull buffy yellowish below, unstreaked. In this plumage the species closely resembles the Black-poll Warbler of similar age, but may usually be identified by the dark feet, the lack of any streaks below, and the slight tinge of bay color on the flanks (not always in evidence). The wings and tail are marked as in the adult.

Range—So strictly is the Bay-breasted Warbler confined to the Canadian Fauna in the breeding season that it does not range southward along the Appalachian highlands, as do many of its associates. It is not known to breed in the Catskill Mountains in New York and is rare and local even in the Adirondacks. Its predilections are thus decidedly more northern than are those of some of our other warblers. It winters in Panama and Colombia and crosses the Gulf of Mexico in its migrations. In western Pennsylvania it appears as a transient visitant, fairly common in both spring and fall, but more or less irregular.

Migration—The Bay-breasted Warbler is one of the later arrivals in the spring and seldom reaches our latitude until the second week in May. Only once (in 1904) have I seen it at Beaver as early as May 8, and most of my arrival dates are five or six days later, as are those of several other observers from near-by counties. R. B. Simpson gives May 3 (1899) as his earliest spring date for this warbler at Warren, and adds that it is very irregular, appearing in some seasons in large flights, and in others not at all. The last transients do not leave for the north until toward the end of May or sometimes even later. I have never recorded the species at Beaver later than May 25, which is probably a fair average date of departure. In the spring of 1924 (a backward season) laggards were noted at Frankfort Springs, Beaver County, and Linesville, Crawford County, on June 1 (Christy; Sutton), and at Warren on June 10 (Simpson). In 1935 the species was still fairly common on Presque Isle on May 30. A. K. Pierce's records covering twenty-one seasons at Renovo show arrival dates mostly in the second and third weeks in May; May 10 (1912) is the earliest arrival record, and May 29 (1907) is the latest date of departure. A single individual seen and identified at close range in "Slack Hollow," south of Pittsburgh, on July 30, 1925, by W. C. Grimm, must have been a stray that had failed to reach its breeding grounds.

Fall records are neither so numerous nor so satisfactory. The species probably always reaches us in

August, as does the Black-poll Warbler. This conclusion is suggested by G. M. Sutton's capture of a young bird near Hartstown on August 22, 1925; by T. D. Burleigh's report of one seen at Pittsburgh on August 30, 1927; and by P. P. Malley's record from Frick Park, Pittsburgh, for August 20, 1937. All other "first-seen" records at this season are in September, which is the month of the main movement. The Bay-breasted Warbler leaves as a rule long before the Black-poll; I have never seen it at Beaver later than September 27 (1909), and the latest fall date among Mr. Pierce's records for Renovo is October 8 (1902).

Habits—There was a time when I considered the Bay-breasted Warbler to be somewhat of a *rara avis*, but later experience has prompted me to modify this opinion. In the spring I find the species moving through the woods in loose bands or scattered companies, not avoiding the other warblers, but more or less independent of them. A tract of woodland may be full of many kinds of migrating warblers, but the Bay-breasts, if present, will be found concentrated in one restricted area. Unless an observer happens to encounter the flight, he is likely to assume that the species is not present. On the other hand, a large flight naturally produces the impression of extraordinary numbers. Thus may be explained the conflicting testimony of observers concerning the status of this warbler. The bird seems rather partial to beech woodland in the spring and customarily remains in the treetops. Its song is a lisping effort, not unlike the Redstart's. In the fall the Bay-breast associates freely with the Black-poll and other species migrating at the same time, and has no especial peculiarities of behavior. Because of its close resemblance in immature dress to the Black-poll, it is easily overlooked.

Dendrœca castanea Townsend, *Proc. Acad. Nat. Sci. Philadelphia*, 1883, 61 (Latrobe, Westmoreland Co., spring).

Dendroica castanea Todd, *Auk*, 1891, 8:398 (Beaver, Beaver Co., rare spring transient)—Todd, in Bausman, *Hist. Beaver Co., Pa.*, 1904, 2:1201 (Beaver Co., transient)—Todd, *Ann. Carnegie Mus.*, 1904, 2:583 (Presque Isle, Erie Co., May)—Stone, *Cassinia*, 1919, 22:35; and 1920, 23:37 (Altoona, Blair Co., May, *fide* McGraw)—Christy, *Cardinal*, 1923, v. 1, no. 1, [p. 12] (Sewickley, Allegheny Co., transient)—Burleigh, *Wilson Bull.*, 1923, 35:139 ([McKinley Park], Allegheny Co., migration); 1924, 36:130 (State College, Centre Co., migration)—Cooke, *Bull. Biol. Surv.* no. 18, 1904, 74 (Beaver, Beaver Co., and Renovo, Clinton Co., migration)—[Editor], *Cassinia*, 1926, 25:33 (Greencastle, Franklin Co., May, *fide* Ziegler)—Sutton, *Ann. Carnegie Mus.*, 1928, 18:213 (Crawford Co. localities, transient)—Burleigh, *Cardinal*, 1929, 2:119 (Allegheny Co., fall migration).

"Bay-breasted Warbler" Cooke, *Bird-Lore*, 1904, 6:162 (Renovo, Clinton Co., migration)—Simpson, *Oölogist*, 1907, 24:134; 1914, 31:121; and 1920, 37:142 (Warren, Warren Co., transient)—McConnell, *Oölogist*, 1918, 35:151 (McKeesport, Allegheny Co., transient)—Miller, *In the Open*, June, 1920, 10:24 (Thornhill, Allegheny Co.)—McClelland, *Am. Mid. Nat.*, 1922, 8:37 (Washington, Washington Co., transient)—Sutton, *Bird-Lore*, 1924, 26:266, 336 (Pittsburgh, Allegheny Co.; Warren, Warren Co., migration, *fide* Simpson and Granquist)—Christy, *Cardinal*, 1924, v. 1, no. 4, p. 11 (Big Traverse Valley, Beaver Co., May)—Eastwood, *Bird-Lore*, 1925, 27:263, 407 (Pittsburgh region, Allegheny Co., May and September, *fide* Grimm), 337 ("Slack Hollow," Allegheny Co., July, *fide* Grimm); 1926, 28:272 (Pittsburgh region, Allegheny Co., May).

BLACK-POLL WARBLER (Plate 19)

DENDROICA STRIATA (Forster)

Description—*Adult male in spring:* general coloration black and white; *whole crown black;* across the nape a whitish band, joining the white areas on the sides of the head below the eyes; back streaked with black on a grayish-brown ground; *wings* dusky, *with* narrow greenish edgings and *two broad white bars;* tail dusky, the outer feathers with white spots; *underparts white, the sides with black streaks,* which extend forward to the chin, leaving only the middle of the throat white; *feet pale. Adult female:* much duller; the crown and nape streaked with black on a greenish ground, as are the rest of the upperparts; head pattern indistinct or merely indicated; underparts more or less shaded with green, and the streaks reduced in extent and less distinct. *Immature:* general color of upperparts (including crown), bright olive green, with usually some indication of dusky streaks; wings darker, with two yellowish-white bands; sides of head (around the eye) decidedly yellowish; underparts pale yellowish olive, inclining to whitish on the abdomen and under tail coverts, and usually with a decided suggestion of darker streaks on the sides. *Adult birds in the fall* resemble the immature birds but are more distinctly streaked with black above and below. The tail pattern is the same at all stages. The pale feet, general greenish coloration, well-marked wing-bars, faint streaks below, and the tendency to white on the crissum, are good field marks in the fall.

Range—The Black-poll Warbler is notable among our Passerine birds for its rather unusual migration route. It breeds throughout the Canadian and Hudsonian life zones—even to the limit of trees—from Alaska to Newfoundland and southward in the mountains of the West to Colorado. In the East, however, it ranges no farther south in summer than the Catskills and does not go much below four thousand feet. Its winter home is in northern South America, which it reaches by way of the Bahamas and Cuba. Since it has such an extensive breeding area, the total number of individuals must be very large; and the species is one of the commonest and best-known warblers in the northeastern United States. In western Pennsylvania it is common in the spring and abundant in the fall, when it outnumbers all the other warblers combined and constitutes the bulk of the smaller migrants in the woods. Farther south along the Appalachians, it seems to be rare in the fall.[1]

Migration—In the spring the Black-poll regularly brings up the rear of the warbler hosts. As Elliott Coues says, "When the Black-polls appear in force, the collecting-season is about over!" This warbler is in fact one of the latest transients and is usually the last to leave. A single bird taken at Beaver on May 6, 1899, was an unseasonably early arrival. On the other hand, there have been seasons, such as the spring of 1910, when the species has not appeared until May 20. May 14 is the average arrival date in the Ohio Valley, but in the mountains, May 20 is nearer the time of first appearance, as shown by the A. K. Pierce records from Renovo. Migration at any one place lasts about two weeks. The Black-poll is the only transient warbler that regularly remains until June. Often it is still common during the last of May, when all the other warblers have gone. Late transients have been noted at Springs, Somerset County, on June 12, 1919 (Miller); at Wilkinsburg on June 4, 1892 (Atkinson); at Warren on June 12, 1907 (Simpson); and at several other localities on June 1.

The return movement begins in August, sometimes as early as the third week (Wilkinsburg, August 18, 1894—Atkinson), but usually about the end of the month. The first week in September finds the Black-poll common and at times even incredibly numerous. Its numbers are undiminished in the early part of October, and the last birds do not ordinarily leave until the third week of that month. The species has been reported from Wilkinsburg on October 28 (1894—Atkinson) and from Renovo on October 30 (1904—Pierce); and I once shot a belated straggler at Beaver on November 2 (1899). Thus the migration in the fall covers a period of nine or ten weeks—much longer than in the spring.

Habits—Arriving late in the season, after most of our warbler visitors have come and gone and after the trees are in blossom or partially in leaf, the plainly colored Black-poll Warbler might easily be passed over by the unobservant. Primarily a bird of the woodland, where it seeks the terminal foliage of the trees, it nevertheless, during its brief spring sojourn with us, often comes into orchards and the shade trees and parks of towns. Its song has a sibilant, lisping, hissing sound, not loud, but with an insistent, penetrating quality that is distinctive. It consists of a single note, repeated from six to twelve times, slowly and hesitantly at first, then more rapidly, and again falling off toward the end—giving a distinct *crescendo e diminuendo* effect. The song is not always easy to trace to its source, as it has a certain ventriloquistic character that is deceiving. The bird itself is rather deliberate in its actions and is difficult to see against the foliage. In the fall, when it appears in unwonted numbers, it is likely to be found almost anywhere—in the deep woods or in bushy growth, in orchards or in high weeds, or in our gardens and about our shade trees. At this season its ordinary note is a short chirp, in nowise distinctive; on at least one occasion in the fall, however, I have heard it give its spring song.

Dendrœca striata Townsend, *Proc. Acad. Nat. Sci. Philadelphia*, 1883, 61 (Latrobe, Westmoreland Co., transient).

"Black-poll Warbler" Van Ostrand, *Osprey*, 1896, 1:38 (Morganza, Washington Co., fall; food)—Cooke, *Bird-Lore*, 1905, 7:204 (Beaver, Beaver Co., and Renovo, Clinton Co., migration)—Simpson, *Oölogist*, 1911, 28:161; 1914, 31:121; and 1920, 37:142 (Warren, Warren Co., transient; migration)—

[1] T. D. Burleigh, *Wilson Bulletin*, 1934, 46:142–147.

McConnell, *Oölogist*, 1918, 35:151 (McKeesport, Allegheny Co., transient)—Miller, *In the Open*, June, 1920, 10:24 (Thornhill, Allegheny Co.)—McClelland, *Am. Mid. Nat.*, 1922, 8:37 (Washington, Washington Co., transient)—Christy, *Cardinal*, 1924, v. 1, no. 4, p. 11 (Big Traverse Valley, Beaver Co., May)—Eastwood, *Bird-Lore*, 1925, 27: 263; 1926, 28:272, 402; 1927, 29:56 (Pittsburgh region, Allegheny Co., migration), 273 (Springs, Somerset Co., May, *fide* Miller)—[Christy, ed.], *Cardinal*, 1933, 3:150 (Pittsburgh, Allegheny Co., October, *fide* Blair).

Dendroica striata Todd, *Ann. Carnegie Mus.*, 1904, 2:583 (Presque Isle, Erie Co., transient)—Todd, in Bausman, *Hist. Beaver Co., Pa.*, 1904, 2:1201 (Beaver Co., transient) —Cooke, *Bull. Biol. Surv.* no. 18, 1904, 76 (Beaver, Beaver Co., migration)—Christy, *Cardinal*, 1923, v. 1, no. 1, [p. 13] (Sewickley, Allegheny Co., transient)—Burleigh, *Wilson Bull.*, 1923, 35:139 (Allegheny Co., migration); 1924, 36:130 (State College, Centre Co., migration)—Sutton, *Ann. Carnegie Mus.*, 1928, 18:213 (Meadville and Pymatuning Swamp, Crawford Co., transient).

NORTHERN PINE WARBLER (Plate 19)

DENDROICA PINUS PINUS (Wilson)

Description—A rather large, plainly colored warbler. *Adult male:* upperparts uniform dull yellowish green; underparts brighter, more decidedly yellow, with faint dusky-greenish streaks or shading on the sides, but no decided markings anywhere; *wings* dusky or grayish, *with two prominent whitish bars;* tail dusky, with white spots on the outer feathers. *Adult female:* a dull-looking warbler; dull olive greenish above and soiled whitish below, with a tinge of greenish yellow on the breast, and the wing and tail markings inconspicuous. *Young birds* in the fall are duller than adults of the same sex; the young female is brownish olive above and buffy yellowish below. In *juvenal plumage* the upperparts are dull umber brown and the underparts are soiled grayish white with a brownish-buffy wash.

Range—Compared with certain other species of warblers under consideration, the Pine Warbler has a wide latitudinal range, extending from the Gulf of Mexico to southern Canada. It is a resident species in approximately the southern third of this range, but in the northern part, including Pennsylvania, it is a summer resident only. The Pine Warbler is a good example of a bird whose presence is regulated by definite ecological conditions. It is common in the South and northward along the Atlantic slope as far as New England, inhabiting pine lands throughout. It invades our ridge and valley section presumably from this direction and finds there the habitat it prefers—areas grown up to yellow[1] and pitch pine (*Pinus echinata* and *P. rigida*). There are parts of Fulton, Huntingdon, and Centre counties where such growth invites the Pine Warbler in goodly numbers. I have found it particularly abundant, for example, in the Tussey Mountain Barrens of southern Huntingdon County and at Wells Tannery, Fulton County; it is said to be very common also on Scrub Ridge in the latter county. In Centre County I have encountered it among pitch pines on the summit of the Alleghenies above Port Matilda and at Sandy Ridge, but nowhere in the high country to the southward.

In some parts of the northern United States the Pine Warbler is addicted to forests and growths of white pine (*Pinus Strobus*), but not in western Pennsylvania. True, our white pine is now nearly all gone, and there remain here and there only small tracts of second growth and isolated areas of older trees. None of these is now known to harbor any pine warblers, and, indeed, I have failed to detect the species anywhere in the plateau area (outside Centre County), and I doubt if it ever occurred there in strictly white-pine country. Van Fleet lists this warbler as a rare summer resident at DuBois, but its occurrence there must have been purely local. East of the Allegheny divide, as we have seen, the species favors the pitch pine and yellow pine, but west of the divide it is virtually confined to tracts of red pine (*Pinus resinosa*). As these are now few and scattered, the Pine Warbler is correspondingly localized as a breeding bird. I discovered it in June, 1893, in a tract of red pines less than a mile south of Clarion Junction, Clarion County, and revisited the spot a year later to secure additional specimens. On June 15, 1894, I met the species near Mayport, in the same county, under similar conditions. In Clinton County it is common and characteristic in the red pines on the summit of

[1]Or short-leaved pine.

the mountain divide south of the West Branch of the Susquehanna River. These are my only records for this part of the country. Farther north, R. B. Simpson reports the Pine Warbler as a rare summer resident in the neighborhood of Warren, and L. E. Hicks observed it at Heart's Content, Warren County, on July 5, 1931.

West of the Allegheny River this warbler is exceedingly rare; in fact it is one of the rarest of the family. In over fifty years' experience at Beaver I have seen and taken it only once, and there are but two records for Allegheny County (East Pittsburgh—Atkinson; Frick Park—Malley). R. L. Keesler writes that he saw two birds at Barmore Lake, Mercer County, on May 7, 1926. Warren quotes Sennett as his authority for the statement that this warbler occurred in the Erie-Crawford district; it is, however, exceedingly rare. G. M. Sutton saw one bird near Shermansville, Crawford County, late in April, 1922, and Professor Hicks reports that he saw a male on Hemlock Island, in the same county, on June 12, 1931. The date would imply breeding. On Presque Isle the species has been noted on two occasions in the spring and at least once in the fall.

Migration—The Pine Warbler is one of the hardiest of the tribe and in this respect resembles the Myrtle Warbler. It arrives early in the season and leaves late (for a warbler), but there are few actual records. It has been noted seven miles south of Huntingdon on April 7 (1921—Sutton; Dickey); at East Pittsburgh on April 4 (1900—Atkinson); and at Renovo on April 6 and April 10 (1903, 1905—Pierce). Mr. Simpson, however, does not look for it at Warren until after April 20, and my spring records for Presque Isle are for April 24 and 28. These dates suggest that the birds do not complete their northward movement until about the first week in May. P. P. Malley reports seeing one at Frick Park, Pittsburgh, on April 22, 1936. A. B. Miller's only record for Springs, Somerset County, is for May 3, 1909. Only two fall occurrences are on record: one bird seen at Erie on October 1, 1933 (Guynes); and one taken by myself at Beaver on October 14, 1909.

Habits—My acquaintance with this warbler began in June, 1893, when I met it in a stand of fine old red pines near Clarion Junction. Upon entering this grove I heard a junco-like trill, the source of which puzzled me at first, since the sound did not seem to come from any one spot in particular and I could not descry the birds high up in the dense pine leaves. At last, however, I caught sight of a small bird passing from one tree to the next and succeeded in bringing it down for identification. The attachment of this warbler to the pines is persistent and pronounced. Working mostly among the leaf clusters and smaller branches, the bird is hard to see even under ideal circumstances, as, for example, when the males are in full song. During migration it may at times be found in deciduous woodland. Mr. Simpson is the only observer in our region who has found the nest of this species. The first nest that he located (on May 14, 1902) held four eggs and was seventy feet from the ground in the top of a tall pine. It was built on a slanting limb and was composed of fine bark strips, pine needles, fine grasses, and other vegetable fibers, and was thickly lined with milkweed-down and thistledown, in the manner of a yellow warbler's nest. The eggs measure about .70 by .52 inches; they are grayish white, spotted with reddish brown of several shades, more densely at or around the larger end. The markings are usually heavier and more sharply defined than in most warblers' eggs.

Dendroica vigorsii Warren, *Birds Pa.*, ed. 2, 1890, 291 (Crawford and Erie Co., transient, *fide* Sennett; Clinton and Clearfield Co., transient, *fide* Van Fleet)—Todd, *Ann. Carnegie Mus.*, 1904, 2:585 (Presque Isle, Erie Co., transient)—Harlow, *Auk*, 1912, 29:476 (southern Centre Co., summer); 1918, 35:143 (Mifflin, Centre, and Warren Co., summer; Huntingdon Co., nesting)—Burleigh, *Wilson Bull.*, 1924, 36:73; 1931, 43:51 (State College, Centre Co., migration; nesting).

"Pine Warbler" Cooke, *Bird-Lore*, 1904, 6:21 (Renovo, Clinton Co., migration)—Stone, *Cassinia*, 1906, 9:44 (Scrub Ridge, west of McConnellsburg, Fulton Co., June)—Jackson, *Cassinia*, 1909, 12:12 (Warren, Warren Co., May)—Simpson, *Oölogist*, 1914, 31:121 (Warren, Warren Co., breeding).

Dendroica pinus pinus Sutton, *Ann. Carnegie Mus.*, 1928, 18:216 (Shermansville, Crawford Co., April).

NORTHERN PRAIRIE WARBLER

DENDROICA DISCOLOR DISCOLOR (Vieillot)

Description—A rather small warbler. Upperparts olive yellow, the *back with a band of chestnut spots,* partly concealed; wings duller, with two paler bands; tail blackish, with large white spots on the feathers; a line above the eye and a spot below the eye, bright yellow; a small spot before the eye and a broken line on each side of the throat, black; *underparts bright yellow,* the *sides streaked with black. Females* are duller than males, and *young birds* are similar, but the chestnut spots on the back are better concealed.

Range—The Prairie Warbler (so-called) is one of the common breeding birds of the Atlantic coast as far north as Massachusetts. In the interior it breeds locally north to central Michigan and west to eastern Kansas and Nebraska. It is thus principally a bird of the Carolinian Fauna, but it invades the Alleghanian to some extent. W. W. Cooke states (1904) that "a few breed . . . in western Pennsylvania," and the 1931 edition of the American Ornithologists' Union *Check-List* narrows the territory to "southwestern Pennsylvania." The grounds for this allocation are unknown to me. Professor Cooke's statement, however, seems to have been based on a manuscript record by a local observer at Titusville, Crawford County—a record that I cannot accept. Certainly the Prairie Warbler is exceedingly rare west of the mountains—rarer even than the Pine Warbler. Not one of the published records cited below is above question—not even my own! In September, 1890, at Beaver, I observed a few birds that I believed to be of this species, but as I was unable to secure them or to duplicate the observations, I now feel that the identification was probably erroneous. On the basis of analogy, it is almost certain that W. C. McClelland's record for Washington falls in the same category. Since there are no specimens in the Sennett Collection to support Warren's assertion that the species occurs as a transient in the Erie-Crawford district, his statement is without any corroboration whatever.

Thus there is no satisfactory published record for the Prairie Warbler from anywhere in our whole region. Moreover, I can cite only three authentic occurrences in southwestern Pennsylvania; all of them were in Allegheny County. One bird (now in the Carnegie Museum) was shot by D. A. Atkinson near Wilkinsburg on May 22, 1896; another was secured by John Watson near Avalon on September 21, 1893; and P. P. Malley advises me that he satisfactorily identified a single bird of this species in Frick Park, Pittsburgh, on April 29, 1936, and heard it sing. A. B. Miller reports having observed a prairie warbler at Springs, Somerset County, on May 2, 1926, but this occurrence must have been exceptional indeed, since the altitude of the locality is much above one thousand feet, which is the usual limit for this species. Another exceptional occurrence is reported by R. B. Simpson, who saw and studied at close range a single male along the Allegheny River at Warren on May 8, 1932.

There is nevertheless one part of western Pennsylvania where the Prairie Warbler is a common and characteristic breeding bird—the pine barrens of Fulton County, where the yellow pine[1] (*Pinus echinata*) is the prevailing forest tree. In the course of a collecting trip through this county, made at my instance in June, 1895, W. H. Phelps took a single bird near Licking Creek, about two miles from the village of Needmore. The capture of this specimen was the first intimation that this warbler might breed anywhere in our region. Accordingly, when I traversed this section in June, 1899, I watched for it, and was pleased to find it locally common. I saw the first bird at Hustontown on June 7 and later saw others on the west slope of Sideling Hill, about two miles beyond West Dublin. The next day I encountered the species in the barrens just south of Wells Tannery and secured a few specimens, all in worn breeding plumage. I failed to find it, however, in Bedford County farther west; nor did I ever meet it in Huntingdon County, even where the Pine Warbler, a frequent associate, was abundant. Its local breeding range is probably much restricted and coincides in general with the distribution of the yellow pine, which enters the state from the Potomac drainage area along our southern border. H. A. McGraw, however, writes that on July 2,

[1]Or short-leaved pine.

1938, he discovered two males in the Pine Barrens near Scotia, Centre County, where they were undoubtedly breeding. R. C. Harlow also reports one at State College on May 8, 1909. Farther north the Prairie Warbler is only a casual visitant. A. K. Pierce secured a single specimen (now in the Carnegie Museum), unrecognized at the time, at Renovo on May 5, 1907.

Migration—All that is known concerning the local movements of this species is limited to the dates of its occurrence already specified. It arrives during the first week in May and departs in the latter half of September.

Habits—As has already been implied, the Prairie Warbler is as exclusively addicted to the pines as the Pine Warbler itself. Where it is common it may even outnumber the latter, and it is certainly more conspicuous; for it chooses a lower and more exposed perch and is not nearly so active nor so continuously on the move. The male will often sit for minutes in one spot and sing at short intervals. His song is distinctive and differs decidedly from that of any other warbler with which I am familiar; in timbre and general make-up it suggests that of the Parula Warbler, but the notes grow successively higher in pitch and inflection and produce a peculiar effect. There is no information from any local source concerning the nesting habits of this species. The nest, however, is built in a bush or sapling. Three to five eggs constitute a set, and they are white with brown spots.

Dendroica discolor (?)Warren, *Birds Pa.*, ed. 2, 1890, 293 (Erie and Crawford Co., transient, *fide* Sennett)—(?)Todd, *Auk*, 1891, 8:398 (Beaver, Beaver Co., fall, rare)—(?)Todd, in Bausman, *Hist. Beaver Co., Pa.*, 1904, 2:1201 (Beaver Co., transient)—(?)Cooke, *Bull. Biol. Surv.* no. 18, 1904, 96 (western Pa., breeding)—(?)Sutton, *Ann. Carnegie Mus.*, 1928, 18:217 (Crawford Co., *fide* Sennett *ex* Warren).
"Prairie Warbler" (?)McClelland, *Am. Mid. Nat.*, 1922, 8:37 (Washington, Washington Co., transient).

WESTERN PALM WARBLER (Plate 19)

DENDROICA PALMARUM PALMARUM (Gmelin)

Description—A warbler of medium or average size, with *white tail-spots, yellow under tail coverts*, and *no decided wing-bars. Adult male in spring:* top of *head, chestnut*, with a yellow stripe on each side over the eye; sides of head brownish, as is also the back, brightening to dull greenish yellow on the rump and upper tail coverts; wings brownish like the back, and *tail* dusky black *with large white spots on the outer feathers;* underparts more or less yellow, mixed with sordid white, and showing some darker (brownish-red) streaks on the breast and sides. The yellow below varies greatly in extent and is sometimes restricted to the throat, but is never so "solid" nor so deep as in *Dendroica palmarum hypochrysea*. The *adult female* has less yellow below and less chestnut in the cap. *Young birds* in the fall lack the cap, the head being dull brownish like the back; the yellow below is only a wash, except on the under tail coverts. The species is an obscure-looking warbler at this season, but notable features are the slightly brighter (greenish) rump, the white tail-spots, the lack of any definite wing-bars, and in particular the bright yellow under tail coverts.

Range—There are two well-marked races of the Palm Warbler. One breeds in eastern Canada and migrates along the Atlantic slope to winter in the Gulf states. The other breeds in the Hudson Bay region and migrates through the interior to winter in southern Florida and the West Indies. The species as a whole is characteristic in summer of the Canadian Life Zone. In migration each race stays in its particular route, and only rarely do strays ever wander outside the appointed path. In general, the Allegheny Mountains (using the name in the broad sense) serve to keep the two races apart during migration. True *palmarum* is the form found west of the mountains, while *hypochrysea*, the Yellow Palm Warbler, occurs only to the east. As a matter of fact, *hypochrysea* seems to be rather closely restricted to the Atlantic coastal plain, and there is no evidence that it ever invades western Pennsylvania at all, although it might occur in Franklin County. The only acceptable evidence will be specimens actually in hand. Certain observers in the western counties have recorded the Yellow Palm Warbler through a misconception of the range and status of the two forms. Others who believe that they have seen the Yellow Palm in life in our region are admittedly unfamiliar with its distinctive characters. The species is a fairly regular transient, less common in the spring than in the fall. But it is not nearly so rare as some observers suppose.

Migration—The Palm Warbler arrives with most of the other warblers about the first week in May, sometimes even earlier. April 29 (1935) is my earliest date for Beaver, and May 4 (1919), the earliest given by B. H. Christy for Sewickley; with these dates the records of other observers largely agree. But T. D. Burleigh has recorded the species at Pittsburgh on April 25 (1913) and at State College (once) on April 15 (1919). At Springs, Somerset County, where it is reported to be regular, it arrives between April 23 and May 4, the average date being May 1 (Miller). In 1900 it appeared on Presque Isle on April 30, was common for a few days only, and disappeared on May 7. It seldom remains at any one locality after the middle of May. One bird was seen at Lower Lake, Crawford County, on May 16, 1925 (Sutton).

In the fall, the species reappears during the first week in September, as proved by a multiplicity of records from Presque Isle, Pymatuning Swamp, Beaver, and Wilkinsburg. Its autumnal migration is not so hurried, and its stay is often prolonged into October. I have repeatedly found it at Beaver during the first half of that month, and in 1909 it remained until October 16. The great majority of the transients, however, seem to pass through during the latter part of September. The bird is hardy, but no instance of its wintering in our region has been reported.

Habits—"Palm Warbler" is scarcely an appropriate name for this bird in our latitude; it might better be called "Red-poll Warbler," in allusion to its coloration, or "Brush Warbler," indicating its favorite habitat. One of the less common warblers in the spring, inconspicuous in coloration and not given to singing insistently, it passes through our region quickly and quietly. Its song is a simple junco-like trill, hard to tell from that of the Pine Warbler. The peculiarity of the Palm Warbler that serves to distinguish it from its congeners in life is its habit of constantly wagging its tail up and down. The Oven-bird has precisely the same habit but is so much larger and so differently colored that there is no risk of confusing the two species.

Sometimes the Palm Warbler takes to the woods with the other warblers, but oftener it comes into orchards, old fields, and brushy places. On Presque Isle we used to find it among the shrubbery and low bushes in open places, and even along the margins of the ponds. It is sparrow-like in its haunts and habits, particularly in the fall, and frequently mingles with the Song, Field, White-throated, White-crowned, and other sparrows as they work through the brushy growth and high weeds along fences, at the edges of woods, and in waste fields. The Myrtle Warbler at times manifests the same sparrow-like habit, and then the two species are occasionally found together.

Dendroica palmarum Warren, *Birds Pa.*, ed. 2, 1890, 292 (west of Alleghenies, transient)—Todd, *Ann. Carnegie Mus.*, 1904, 2:585 (Presque Isle, Erie Co., transient)—Todd, in Bausman, *Hist. Beaver Co., Pa.*, 1904, 2:1201 (Beaver Co., transient)—Cooke, *Bird-Lore*, 1905, 7:276 (Beaver, Beaver Co., migration).

Dendroica palmarum palmarum Christy, *Cardinal*, 1923, v. 1, no. 1, [p. 13] (Sewickley, Allegheny Co., May)—Sutton, *Ann. Carnegie Mus.*, 1928, 18:216 (Conneaut Lake and Pymatuning Swamp, Crawford Co., transient)—Christy, *Cardinal*, 1929, 2:131 (near Frankfort Springs, Beaver Co., October).

"Palm Warbler" Simpson, *Oölogist*, 1914, 31:121 (Warren, Warren Co., transient)—Eastwood, *Bird-Lore*, 1926, 28:272 (Pittsburgh region, Allegheny Co., May), 403 (Clinton and vicinity, Allegheny Co., October); 1927, 29:272 (Pittsburgh region, May)—Boulton, *Bird-Lore*, 1928, 30:401 (Deer Creek, Allegheny Co., October, *fide* Manley, *et al.*).

"Yellow Palm Warbler" (error) Burleigh, *Oölogist*, 1914, 31: 191 (Allegheny Co., May)—Eastwood, *Bird-Lore*, 1926, 28:403 (Clinton and vicinity, Allegheny Co., October, *fide* Squier).

Dendroica palmarum hypochrysea (error) Cooke, *Bull. Biol. Surv.* no. 18, 1904, 95 (Beaver, Beaver Co., September) —Burleigh, *Wilson Bull.*, 1923, 35:140 (Allegheny Co., spring transient); 1924, 36:130 (State College, Centre Co., migration).

"Western Palm Warbler" Wood, *Wilson Bull.*, 1932, 44:238 (State College, Centre Co., spring).

OVEN-BIRD (Plate 20)

SEIURUS AUROCAPILLUS (Linnaeus)

Description—A large warbler, superficially resembling a miniature thrush. Upperparts (including wings and tail), olive green; *head showing two black lateral stripes, enclosing an area of russet brown;* sides of head similar to the back, but eye-ring whitish; underparts white, with a black stripe on either side of the throat, and the breast and sides streaked with black; throat, middle of abdomen, and under tail coverts, pure white. The fall plumage is practically the same. No tail-spots.

Range—Generally speaking, this warbler is a species of the eastern United States, but it ranges north in the summer to Newfoundland and Hudson Bay. It winters in the West Indies, Mexico, and Central America. Under suitable forest conditions it is a common and generally distributed summer resident at all elevations throughout western Pennsylvania at large.

Migration—Usually the Oven-bird appears a little in advance of the majority of the warblers. Arrival dates at Beaver range from April 23 to May 3, and I always expect it there about April 28—a date corresponding with the available records from Sewickley, Wilkinsburg, and other places in Allegheny County. T. D. Burleigh, however, reports seeing one bird on April 14 (1912) and one on April 19 (1914), and G. M. Sutton recorded one on April 22 (1921). Certainly these must have been enterprising and early migrants; for various odd arrival records from several other southwestern counties correspond with the later dates. In the Erie-Crawford district the species arrives a day or two later, while at Warren it does not appear until after the first of May. In the mountains, too, its arrival is slightly retarded; at Renovo, for example, April 27 (1908) is the earliest spring record.

Probably our summer-resident oven-birds depart in August and are replaced by migrants from farther north. At any rate, the species is sometimes very common in September, when the other warblers are moving southward. It has been noted at Beaver as late as October 6 (1910), and even later at other places: Pittsburgh, October 9, 1912 (Burleigh); State College, October 18, 1914 (Burleigh); Queen, Bedford County, October 22, 1916 (McGraw); Renovo, October 16, 1906 (Pierce).

Habits—Entering almost any tract of woodland in the summer season—quietly, but with eyes and ears alert—one may presently espy a small, thrush-like bird casually picking its way over the dry leaves of the forest floor. It walks with pretty, mincing steps as it slowly and unobtrusively goes about its business of searching for insect food. Its modest coloration harmonizes with the subdued tints of the shadowy recesses of the forest where it dwells. So composed is it in its demeanor and so decidedly terrestrial in its habits that at first glance it suggests a thrush rather than a warbler, but the resemblance is purely superficial. Most of its time is passed on the ground, but often, especially if its haunts are invaded, it will fly to a low branch for a better look at the intruder; walking along in easy, graceful fashion, it chirps vigorously. Sometimes the male sings from the ground, but more frequently it mounts to a higher elevation to deliver its springtime chant.

John Burroughs' description of this song is appropriate: "Satisfied that I have no hostile intentions, the pretty pedestrian mounts a limb a few feet from the ground, and gives me the benefit of one of his musical performances, a sort of accelerating chant. Commencing in a very low key, which makes him seem at a very uncertain distance, he grows louder and louder till his body quakes and his chant runs into a shriek, ringing in my ear with a peculiar sharpness. This lay may be represented thus: 'TEACHER, TEACHER, TEACHER, TEACHER, TEACHER!'—the accent on the first syllable and each word uttered with increased force and shrillness."[1] Some later writers have found fault with this interpretation, claiming that the song is subject to considerable individual variation in accent, pitch, and tempo. My own experience long ago led me to a similar conclusion, and I now find that R. T. Moore, after an intensive study of the songs of this species, which he has recorded in musical notation, fully corroborates my views. He says:

"No two birds sing the same song and most individuals during hours of repetition change their productions considerably. There is not one song-property that does not sometime or other vary or vanish. Even the tone-quality, generally a thick breathy whistle, is subject to some variation. . . . Still more in the other song-properties is variation common. The rate of speed is slow or rapid, the pitch is high or low, the couplets alter in number from three to eleven, the position of the accent shifts here and there, the unaccented note ('er') is sometimes dropped completely and that famous crescendo, to which so many have pinned their faith as to an immutable ear-mark of identification, exhibits the extreme limits of deviation possible to a musical expression."[2]

[1] *Wake-Robin*, 1913 edition, p. 57.
[2] *Cassinia*, 1914, 17:17–24; pl. 2.

In further reference to the crescendo effect, Mr. Moore remarks: "As far as my experience goes, it is the most tremendous crescendo in the bird-world, quite capable of astounding the blasé intruder into its region of high oaks and beeches. There from the bush-free earth out of the heaps of restless leaves will swell that voice, which in the time of three seconds will surge from distant wood to his very feet. No musician can render it with more precision! Heard at a distance it is free of all vagaries and has that confident ring, which at once claims the woods and dominates all other songs, however much finer musically. Other birds have conceived some value in crescendo and have employed it more or less effectively, particularly the Screech Owl, who has pushed it to the extreme in the service of mystery, and the Flicker, whose product is as harsh as the Ovenbird's is soothing, but neither of them has caught the full conception of its noblest power, the ability to express unbounded exultation by one mighty surge to climax, as has this great Accentor, wee of form, but gigantic in voice."

But the male Oven-bird has also another and very different song—a surprise song—which he reserves for special occasions. Under the influence of his excitement, he flies into the air and bursts into a wild jumble and medley of musical notes, without form or pattern. Burroughs says:

"Mounting by easy flights to the top of the tallest tree, he launches into the air with a sort of suspended, hovering flight, like certain of the finches, and bursts into a perfect ecstasy of song,—clear, ringing, copious, rivaling the goldfinch's in vivacity, and the linnet's in melody. This strain is one of the rarest bits of bird melody to be heard, and is oftenest indulged in late in the afternoon or after sundown. Over the woods, hid from view, the ecstatic singer warbles his finest strain. In this song you instantly detect his relationship to the water-wagtail,—erroneously called water-thrush,—whose song is likewise a sudden burst, full and ringing, and with a tone of youthful joyousness in it, as if the bird had just had some unexpected good fortune. For nearly two years this strain of the pretty walker was little more than a disembodied voice to me, and I was puzzled by it as Thoreau by his mysterious night-warbler, which, by the way, I suspect was no new bird at all, but one he was otherwise familiar with. The little bird himself seems disposed to keep the matter a secret, and improves every opportunity to repeat before you his shrill, accelerating lay, as if this were quite enough and all he laid claim to. Still, I trust I am betraying no confidence in making the matter public here. I think this is preëminently his love-song, as I hear it oftenest about the mating season. I have caught half-suppressed bursts of it from two males chasing each other with fearful speed through the forest."

Once I detected a female oven-bird singing. On May 19, 1910, I had shot a bird in the act of singing an odd, nondescript song that had attracted my attention, and I expected to pick up, instead of an oven-bird, some species new and strange to me. On dissection the specimen proved to be a female.

The name "Oven-bird," which properly belongs to a Neotropical family (Furnariidae), has been adopted for this species because of the odd architecture of the bird's nest. Ground-nesting birds usually contrive to conceal their nests under a fallen branch or a drift of leaves among thick growth; but the Oven-bird builds its own blind, so to speak. Its nest is sunk level with the ground and is then domed over; an entrance is left on one side. Even when built in a perfectly open place in the forest, as it often is, the nest cannot be noticed except from directly in front, so well do the dry leaves and other materials composing it match their surroundings. The lining is of finer stuff of the same sort, but the nest proper is a rather loose structure. Four to six eggs are the usual complement; they are white, plentifully sprinkled and spotted with reddish brown, more thickly at and around the larger end. Average measurements are .79 by .63 inches. The last week in May and the first week in June mark the height of the nesting season in our region.

Siurus auricapillus TEULON, *Jour. Boston Zoöl. Soc.*, 1882, 1:49 (Bradford, McKean Co., nesting)—TOWNSEND, *Proc. Acad. Nat. Sci. Philadelphia*, 1883, 61 (Latrobe, Westmoreland Co., nesting).

"Golden-crowned Thrush" ENTY, *Ornithologist and Oölogist*, 1885, 10:79 (Templeton, Armstrong Co., May).

Seiurus aurocapillus JAMISON, *Ornithologist and Oölogist*, 1888, 13:134; and DWIGHT, *Auk*, 1892, 9:139 (Cresson, Cambria Co., June)—TODD, *Auk*, 1893, 10:41 (Two Lick, Indiana Co., June), 45 (Coalport, Clearfield Co., June)—JACOBS, *Summer Birds Greene Co., Pa.*, 1893, 13 (Greene Co., nesting)—BAILY, *Auk*, 1896, 13:296 (Williamsville, Elk Co.,

June–July)—COPE, *Cassinia*, 1902, 5:18 (Tamarack Swamp, Clinton Co., and Little Kettle Creek, Potter Co., June)—TODD, *Ann. Carnegie Mus.*, 1904, 2:585 (Erie, Erie Co., summer)—TODD, in Bausman, *Hist. Beaver Co., Pa.*, 1904, 2:1201 (Beaver Co., summer)—COOKE, *Bull. Biol. Surv.* no. 18, 1904, 99 (Beaver, Beaver Co., migration)—HARLOW, *Auk*, 1912, 29:476 (southern Centre Co., breeding)—CHRISTY, *Cardinal*, 1923, v. 1, no. 1, [p. 13] (Sewickley, Allegheny Co., breeding)—BURLEIGH, *Wilson Bull.*, 1923, 35:140 (Allegheny Co., nesting); 1924, 36:73; 1931, 43:51 (State College, Centre Co., migration; summer).

"Oven-bird" BRUMBAUGH, *Wilson Bull.*, 1905, 12:100 (Wilkinsburg, Allegheny Co., nesting)—COOKE, *Bird-Lore*, 1906, 8:100 (Beaver, Beaver Co., and Renovo, Clinton Co., migration)—STONE, *Cassinia*, 1906, 9:41, 44 (Scrub Ridge, west of McConnellsburg, Fulton Co., June)—PITCAIRN, *Bird-Lore*, 1907, 9:155 (Riverview Park, Allegheny Co.)—SIMPSON, *Oölogist*, 1912, 29:330 (head of Tionesta Creek, Warren Co., summer); 1914, 31:122 (Warren, Warren Co., summer)—DICKEY, *Oölogist*, 1914, 31:171 ([Charter Oak], Huntingdon Co., nesting)—MCCONNELL, *Oölogist*, 1918, 35:151 (McKeesport, Allegheny Co.)—MILLER, *Oölogist*, 1919, 36:156 (Charter Oak, Huntingdon Co., nesting)—MCCLELLAND, *Am. Mid. Nat.*, 1922, 8:36 (Washington, Washington Co., summer)—STREET, *Cassinia*, 1923, 24:17 (Conococheague Creek, Mercersburg; Little Cove Creek, Foltz; and Jordan's Knob, Franklin Co., June)—CHRISTY, *Cardinal*, 1924, v. 1, no. 4, p. 9 (Big Traverse Valley, Beaver Co., June)—EASTWOOD, *Bird-Lore*, 1925, 27:263; and 1926, 28:272 (Pittsburgh region, Allegheny Co., April–May), 273 (Rector, Westmoreland Co., May, *fide* Knauz); 1927, 29:272 (Pittsburgh region, Allegheny Co., May), 273 (Springs, Somerset Co., April, *fide* Miller).

Seiurus aurocapillus aurocapillus CHRISTY and SUTTON, *Cardinal*, 1928, 2:73 (Cook Forest, Clarion Co., nesting)—SUTTON, *Ann. Carnegie Mus.*, 1928, 18:217 (Meadville and Pymatuning Swamp, Crawford Co., summer; nesting)—BURLEIGH, *Cardinal*, 1932, 3:80 ([Summit], Fayette Co., nesting).

NORTHERN WATER-THRUSH (Plate 19)

SEIURUS NOVEBORACENSIS NOVEBORACENSIS (Gmelin)

GRINNELL'S WATER-THRUSH

SEIURUS NOVEBORACENSIS NOTABILIS Ridgway

Description—A large warbler, the size of the Oven-bird. Upperparts, including wings and tail, and a band through the eye, brownish olive; a creamy-buff stripe over the eye; *underparts* white, more or less tinged with *naphthalene-yellow*, and streaked with olivaceous black, lightly on the throat, more heavily on the breast and sides, leaving the abdomen (medially) and the under tail coverts nearly or quite unspotted.

The sexes are alike, but there is considerable variation in the intensity and extent of the streaks on the underparts. Fall specimens are more richly colored, as in spring and summer the yellow tinge fades out almost to white and the whole plumage becomes much worn. There is often an indication of a median crown-stripe of buff, suggesting affinity to *Seiurus aurocapillus*.

Grinnell's Water-Thrush, *Seiurus noveboracensis notabilis*, the western race of the species, is a little darker above and paler below (on an average) than the typical form; the bill is slightly longer. The two forms cannot be distinguished from each other in life.

Range—This species is characteristic of the Canadian Life Zone; it ranges northward in summer to Newfoundland and Labrador along the Atlantic coast and to Hudson Bay in the interior. In the Allegheny Mountains it goes south to West Virginia. It is well known as a breeding bird in the northern and more elevated parts of the New England states, as well as throughout the Adirondack and Catskill Mountains in New York. It has been recorded also from sundry localities in the latter state just north of the Pennsylvania boundary. These extralimital records constitute an extension of its breeding area in western Pennsylvania. In our region the species inhabits the highlands extending from Warren County on the west through McKean and Potter counties and thence eastward beyond our geographical limits, wherever any suitable forest remains. South of these counties its range gradually contracts, since it is sharply defined on the east by the crest of the Allegheny Mountains and probably on the west by Laurel Hill; where it passes into Maryland, therefore, it is apparently restricted to a narrow strip in Somerset County between the Allegheny divide and Negro Mountain.

There are no records to show that this species ever occurs with *Seiurus motacilla*, the Louisiana

Water-Thrush, in the breeding season, although the two sometimes approximate each other, and the latter is known to ascend the Casselman River as far as Rockwood, Somerset County, and on occasion to even higher elevations in the same county. A. B. Miller writes that he has found *motacilla* in the lower reaches of the streams draining Glade Mountain toward the west, while *noveboracensis* is (or was) the prevailing form higher up. The latter is likewise the prevailing form on the crest of the Alleghenies at Cresson, Cambria County, but S. S. Dickey has traced *motacilla* to a point near the summit on the eastern slope. At the present time it is not possible to outline with exactness the eastern limit of the range of *noveboracensis* north of Cambria County, because of the lack of precise information regarding the avifauna of the upper valley of the West Branch of the Susquehanna River. Nor are there as yet any records from Cameron County. There is a belt of considerable width through Indiana, Jefferson, Clarion, and Forest counties where neither species of water-thrush has been observed, although almost certainly one or the other must occur. In this case, as in others involving similar considerations, I believe that the range of this species is, or at least was, approximately coincident with that of the Slate-colored Junco, and I have so indicated it on the distribution map.

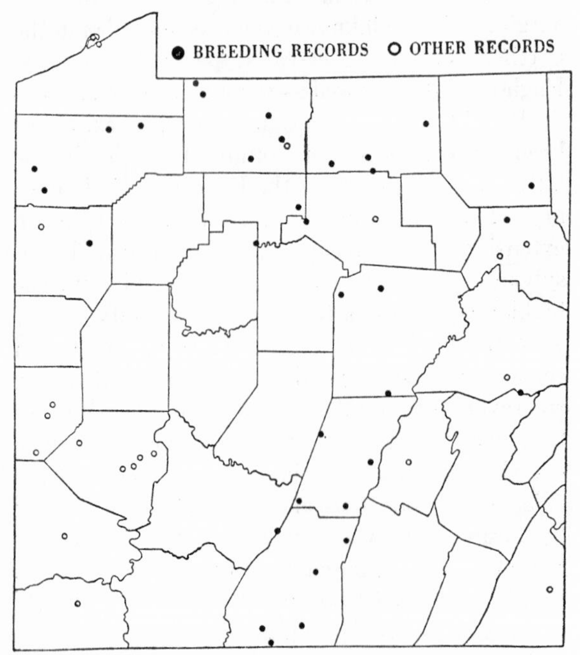

LOCAL RANGE OF THE NORTHERN WATER-THRUSH (INCLUDING GRINNELL'S WATER-THRUSH)

Warren quotes Sennett as his authority for the statement that the Northern Water-Thrush breeds in the woods and tamarack swamps of Crawford County, and the latter's observations to this effect have been abundantly confirmed. The species is certainly one of the commonest and most characteristic birds in the cool depths of Pymatuning Swamp, where it associates with other boreal forms of bird life in this island of the Canadian Life Zone. But I was not a little surprised to find it also along the wooded western shore of Canadohta Lake, in Crawford County, where it seemed to be decidedly out of place. Possibly it was the lone survivor of a former Canadian association at this point. Dr. Dickey has also found it breeding near Cambridge Springs, in the same county, and it has even been found at Sandy Lake, Mercer County, under similar conditions (Sutton, 1928). It should be looked for in Conneaut Swamp, Crawford County, and in Tamarack Swamp, Erie County.

Beyond a doubt these latter records represent outlying islands, so to speak, in the breeding range of the species; these are determined entirely by peculiar local conditions. But the most surprising discovery in this connection is that the breeding birds of these swamp areas belong to the western race of the species, *notabilis*, and not to the typical eastern form, as hitherto supposed.[1] This conclusion is borne out by a comparison of a series of specimens from Pymatuning Swamp with specimens from western Canada and from the Atlantic coast region. Moreover, all the available specimens that were shot during migration in the western counties proved to be *notabilis*, and I have seen at least one specimen of the latter race from Renovo. On the other hand, breeding birds from the northern counties and from the highlands in general, as far south as Somerset County, are just as clearly referable to typical *noveboracensis*. No attempt has been made to segregate the records of the two races in the list of references or on the distribution map, and in the following account the two subspecies are treated as one. Some interesting questions regarding the geographical history of this species and its com-

[1]This discovery was made by the writer in 1925 but was not announced at the time. In the meanwhile the fact has been fully confirmed by several Ohio observers.

ponent races naturally arise at this point, but their discussion will have to be postponed.

There are clear indications of increasing local restriction in the breeding areas of the Northern Water-Thrush—a restriction due primarily to deforestation and the consequent destruction of the bird's natural haunts. Some of our northern birds seem able to survive the destruction of their forest environment, but this species apparently cannot. For example, in 1889, H. J. Roddy (as quoted by Warren) reported *S. noveboracensis* as a breeding bird at Bear Meadows, Centre County. But when I visited this locality in 1895 I found only *S. motacilla*. The place had been laid waste in the meantime by lumbermen, and only a few odd spruce and balsam-fir trees remained. But there was nothing remarkable in the presence of *noveboracensis* there at the time of Professor Roddy's visit, before these trees were cut out; in fact, it would have been more remarkable had he not found the bird. I judge that *motacilla* must have come in since that time, following up the streams from the lower levels, where it is very numerous. Similar replacements seem to be in progress in Warren and Somerset counties, according to R. B. Simpson and Mr. Miller, and are doubtless also taking place in many other sections.

It is to be remarked that the area occupied by this species in Pennsylvania and southern New York, considered as a whole, is entirely disconnected from its main breeding range to the northward.

Migration—Outside the breeding area just defined, the Northern Water-Thrush (both races collectively) is of course merely a transient. It is a later migrant in the spring than the Louisiana Water-Thrush and as a rule does not arrive until about the first of May or even later. My earliest spring date for Beaver is May 1 (1911), while April 30 (1932) is the earliest for Waynesburg (Dickey). Some earlier dates, however, are on record: Pittsburgh, April 27 (1921—Sutton), and April 26 (1937—Malley); Sandy Lake, Mercer County, April 22 (1928—Reiter, *et al.*); State College, April 24 (1917—Burleigh); Warren, April 25 (1892—Simpson). Arrival records earlier than these may possibly pertain to the other species. S. J. Seiple, however, writes that he is certain that a water-thrush that he saw at "Kidds Mill," Mercer County, on April 5, 1936, was *noveboracensis* and not *motacilla*. For localities within the species' breeding area, some average dates of first appearance are: Renovo, May 6 (Pierce); Warren, May 2 (Simpson); Cambridge Springs, Crawford County, May 2 (Dickey); Springs, Somerset County, May 5 (Miller). In 1922 the first birds were observed at Pymatuning Swamp on April 28 (Sutton). The species has been seen at Beaver as late as May 27 (1907) and at State College on the same date (1916)—a time when breeding birds should be laying eggs.

In the fall migration this warbler is one of the earliest to appear south of its breeding grounds. Migrants have been noted at Pittsburgh on August 12 (1914) and at Beaver on August 17 (1899), and more numerously toward the end of that month and in September. Two late fall records are: State College, October 14, 1916 (Burleigh); and Renovo, October 15, 1918 (Pierce). Migration records for both species of water-thrush must be received with caution, as the risk of confusion is great.

Habits—During the season of migration, the Northern Water-Thrush haunts the shrubbery and thick herbage along streams, skulking among the reedy growths and seldom coming into plain sight unless called up by "squeaking." Then it will sometimes appear at close range with startling suddenness, to peer at the cause of the disturbance for a moment and then dart back into the depths of the thicket. Along the Ohio River and Raccoon Creek in Beaver County, I have repeatedly come upon it in the willow growth fringing the banks, but so well does it contrive to keep out of sight that I have seldom been able to secure specimens. In fact, it might easily escape detection in the spring (as it often does in the fall) were it not for its song, which is distinctive. In its general character and sequence of notes it is obviously like that of the Louisiana Water-Thrush, but it is more hurried in delivery, less musical, and shorter, and it lacks the wild ring that comes at the end of the song of the other species. Not only is the song delivered in fast time, as if the bird were in great haste, but it also has a pronounced explosive quality. According to G. M. Sutton (1928), "Mr. Langdon hit upon a most fortunate rendition of the song of this species when he wrote it 'Hurry, hurry, hurry, pretty, pretty, pretty.' " Transient birds are by no means the constant singers that they become on their nesting grounds. In the fall movement they are silent save for a harsh call note, which by a trained ear may be distinguished from that of any other species, with the possible exception of the Louisiana Water-Thrush. At this season of the year it is unusual to see more than one bird at a time.

Although the Northern Water-Thrush regularly frequents the willow fringes along streams in more or less open situations, it may also be found about marshes and stagnant pools wherever there is sufficient cover. It has even been observed occasionally in orchards and about lawns. On its breeding grounds, where it is somewhat less shy and retiring in its behavior, its preference for stagnant water is notable. In this respect it differs decidedly from the Louisiana Water-Thrush, which is never found away from running water in shady woodland. It is true that at higher altitudes the Northern Water-Thrush is sometimes found along swift mountain streams, but as a general rule it favors isolated pools of standing water in the woods—the kind of habitat that does not attract the other species at all. Rhododendron swamps are favorite haunts. Nowhere have I found this bird more numerous than in Pymatuning Swamp, which seems exactly suited to its needs, and in Tamarack Swamp in Clinton County, where conditions were very similar. Where the birds are plentiful it is a simple matter to call them up by "squeaking." They fly in to alight on a near-by branch, where they seem to balance, as it were precariously, constantly bobbing the tail up and down in their peculiar and characteristic manner, as do the birds of the wagtail family. When undisturbed they seem to spend much of their time feeding on various insects at the edge of the water. The flight of the species is swift and darting, and usually low.

The nest of this water-thrush is always well hidden under overhanging banks or roots. Once at Pymatuning Swamp I watched a pair for a long time without discovering their secret. On a later occasion, however (May 23, 1934), I flushed an incubating female from her nest under the exposed roots of a tree in the midst of the swamp. F. R. Cope, Jr., writes (1902) of finding a nest with four eggs near Oleona, Potter County, on June 26, 1900: "The nest was beautifully situated among the roots of a large beech tree on the banks of what, in spring, must be a beautiful little mountain torrent, and although it was not collected, I feel no doubt of the identity. Indeed this whole locality was admirably suited to the habits of this bird, and doubtless a more thorough search would have revealed it as not an uncommon breeder." A nest found by W. L. Baily near Williamsville, Elk County, in June, 1894, was also placed under the roots of a tree. Another nest (now in the Carnegie Museum), taken by A. K. Pierce at Tamarack Swamp, Clinton County, on May 28, 1907, is made of green moss, a few small twigs, and fine rootlets, and is lined with horsehair; it was very cleverly concealed from view beneath the exposed roots of a witch-hazel bush in a mound of green moss.

Dr. Dickey has supplied me with an account of several nests found by him in Warren and Crawford counties, and he remarks that the favorite site is in the upturned roots of a fallen tree. "In the absence of these, the bird hides its nest in a moss-padded cranny of a decayed stump, in a mossy mound at the base of swamp shrubbery, in a decaying log, and now and then beneath the rooflike, undercut root system of a forest tree at the very edge of a stream. The nest itself is a neat and pleasing structure, its foundation consisting of crumbling skeleton leaves, leaf petioles, rootlets, and mosses (*Hypnum*, *Sphagnum*, *Funaria*, and *Polytrichum*). Its usual lining consists of the red flower stalks of the moss, which give it a certain gaudy aspect, and there are sometimes bits of yellowish grass, pieces of horsetail (*Equisetum*), and animal hair of various kinds. A typical nest is about five inches high by two and one-half inches deep, with a cavity two inches by one and one-half inches." Mr. Simpson finds that the nesting period in Warren County extends from May 14 to June 10. Four or five eggs are laid. They are scarcely distinguishable from those of the Ovenbird, and they measure .77 by .60 inches. They are white, speckled, spotted, or occasionally even blotched, with grayish brown; the markings are densest at or around the larger end.

Seiurus noveboracensis Warren, *Birds Pa.*, ed. 2, 1890, 271, 294 (Clinton and Clearfield Co., breeding, *fide* Van Fleet; Bear Meadows, Centre Co., July, *fide* Roddy; Crawford Co., breeding, *fide* Sennett)—Dwight, *Auk*, 1892, 9:133, 134, 139 (Cresson, Cambria Co., nesting)—Todd, *Auk*, 1893,

10:45 (Coalport, Clearfield Co., June)—BAILY, *Auk*, 1896, 13:296 (Williamsville, Elk Co., nesting)—COPE, *Cassinia*, 1902, 5:18 (Oleona, Potter Co., nesting)—TODD, *Ann. Carnegie Mus.*, 1904, 2:585 (Erie and Presque Isle, Erie Co., transient)—TODD, in Bausman, *Hist. Beaver Co., Pa.*, 1904, 2:1201 (Beaver Co., transient)—COOKE, *Bull. Biol. Surv.* no. 18, 1904, 102 (Renovo, Clinton Co., migration)—CHRISTY, *Cardinal*, 1931, 3:43 (McDonald Reservoir, Washington Co., May).

"Large-billed Water-Thrush" (error) WARREN, *Forest and Stream*, 1891, 37:83 (Kane, McKean Co., summer).

"Northern Water-Thrush" COOKE, *Bird-Lore*, 1906, 8:101 (Renovo, Clinton Co., migration)—SIMPSON, *Oölogist*, 1920, 37:142 (head of Tionesta Creek, Warren Co., May)—McCLELLAND, *Am. Mid. Nat.*, 1922, 8:37 (Washington, Washington Co., transient)—BOULTON, *Bird-Lore*, 1928, 30:271 (Sandy Lake, Mercer Co., April, *fide* Reiter, *et al.*)—COPE and HAWKINS, *Forest Leaves*, 1934, 24:26 (E. Tionesta Forest Reserve, Warren and McKean Co., summer).

"Water-Thrush" SIMPSON, *Oölogist*, 1912, 29:330 (head of Tionesta Creek, Warren Co., summer); 1914, 31:122 (Warren, Warren Co., summer)—BURLEIGH, *Oölogist*, 1914, 31: 191 (Allegheny Co., May)—CHRISTY, *Cardinal*, 1924, v. 1, no. 4, p. 11 (Big Traverse Valley, Beaver Co., May)—EASTWOOD, *Bird-Lore*, 1926, 28:272 (Pittsburgh region, Allegheny Co., May), (?)274 (Sandy Lake, Mercer Co., May, *fide* Squier).

Seiurus noveboracensis noveboracensis HARLOW, *Auk*, 1918, 35: 143 (Warren, Clinton, and Cambria Co., breeding)—CHRISTY, *Cardinal*, 1923, v. 1, no. 1, [p. 13] (Sewickley, Allegheny Co., spring transient)—BURLEIGH, *Wilson Bull.*, 1923, 35:140 Pittsburgh, Allegheny Co., migration); 1924, 36:130 (State College, Centre Co., migration)—CHRISTY and SUTTON, *Cardinal*, 1928, 2:74 (Thom's Run, Clarion Co., summer)—SUTTON, *Ann. Carnegie Mus.*, 1928, 18:218 (Pymatuning Swamp and vicinity, Crawford Co., and Sandy Lake, Mercer Co., summer).

LOUISIANA WATER-THRUSH (Plate 19)

SEIURUS MOTACILLA (Vieillot)

Description—A large warbler, the size of the Oven-bird. Upperparts, including wings and tail, dark olive, as is also a band through the eye; a white stripe over the eye; *underparts* white, *more or less shaded with buff*, especially on the sides and under tail coverts; the breast and sides prominently streaked with olive brown, the streaks continuing in a more or less interrupted stripe, leaving the throat unspotted (generally). *Juvenal plumage:* similar to the adult, but the general coloration duller, and the streaks below less distinct. Fall birds are somewhat more richly colored than those of spring, but in any plumage the species may be distinguished from the Northern Water-Thrush by the more or less *buffy* (instead of yellowish) tinge of the *underparts*, while the streaks are more strictly confined to the breast and sides, leaving the throat (usually) and the abdomen mostly unmarked. The bill, too, is longer, but this difference is not noticeable in life.

Range—Properly speaking, the Louisiana Water-Thrush is a bird of the Carolinian Fauna. It reaches its northern breeding limit in southern Connecticut, the lower Hudson Valley, and southern Michigan and ranges thence into southern Ontario and western New York, where, however, it is rather rare and local. Its breeding range in western Pennsylvania, like those of other Carolinian birds, is discontinuous; it comprises two distinct areas, separated by the Allegheny divide and the plateau region in general, where *Seiurus noveboracensis* is the prevailing form. As explained in the discussion of the latter species, at no point are the two known to occur together, although in Crawford, Warren, and Somerset counties they come very close to each other. Their respective ranges are in fact mutually complementary, although there is a belt of country where thus far neither species has been recorded.

I have traced *S. motacilla* far up the eastern slopes of the Allegheny Mountains above Port Matilda, Centre County; and S. S. Dickey has observed it at a similar elevation in Blair County, east of Cresson. Unquestionably the crest of this ridge constitutes the eastern dividing line between the respective ranges of the two species in our section. East of the Allegheny divide, in the ridge and valley section, the Louisiana Water-Thrush is one of the most characteristic summer-resident birds. It haunts the wooded valleys and the ravines and ascends the streams almost to their heads. It is particularly numerous, for instance, in the rhododendron growth along Tatman Run, in southern Huntingdon County, and along Detweiler Run and other small streams in the extreme northern part of the same county. Evidently it has reached this general region from the east, by way of the drainage systems of the Susquehanna and

Potomac rivers, and has found the broken and irregular mountain ridges there no barrier to its spread. At any rate, it has succeeded in ascending the West Branch of the Susquehanna River for a considerable distance—probably farther than the available records indicate (Burns Run, Clinton County)—and its range there may interdigitate with that of *noveboracensis*.

West of the mountains, the Louisiana Water-Thrush has obviously come in from the Ohio Valley, and it is now generally distributed in the western counties, especially south of the Ohio River. There are few wooded ravines in Beaver, Allegheny, Washington, and Greene counties that are without one or more pairs of this species. Thence it ranges eastward in almost undiminished numbers, across Chestnut Ridge and up the western flank of Laurel Hill. It even seems to have passed this latter ridge through the gap of the Youghiogheny River and also by way of the Casselman River, which it has ascended as far as Rockwood and the eastern slope of Negro Mountain near the Maryland border. It has been reported several times in June from the vicinity of Johnstown; these reports, could they be substantiated, would indicate that the species has passed as well through the gap of the Conemaugh River below that point.[1] In Indiana County its range approximates that of *noveboracensis* to within a few miles, and in southern Clarion County it has been traced as far up Redbank Creek as Mayport (Todd). Farther north it has been noted at Endeavor, Forest County, in June (Dickey) and at Warren as a rare summer resident (Simpson), but it is almost certainly a recent immigrant in both these localities.

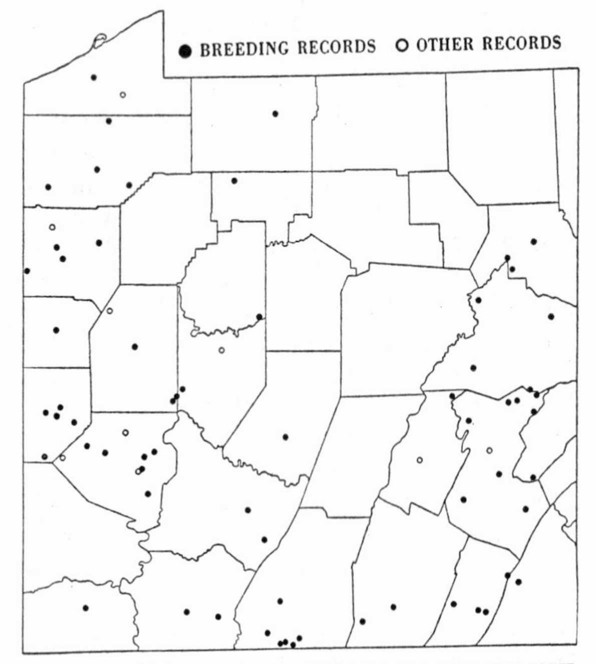

LOCAL RANGE OF THE LOUISIANA WATER-THRUSH

The status of *motacilla* and *noveboracensis* in the northwestern counties is peculiar and interesting. Certain correspondence that I have examined between Sennett and H. C. Kirkpatrick suggests that there was some confusion and uncertainty in the past as to which species was breeding in Crawford County. The fact of the matter is that both species breed in the county, but never together in exactly the same habitat. Unquestionably, *motacilla* is the commoner and more generally distributed breeding form there; for it has been recorded from Sugar Lake (Homer), from near Meadville (Kirkpatrick), from Cambridge Springs (Dickey), and, as stated by G. M. Sutton, from several small streams in the vicinity of Pymatuning Swamp. On the other hand, *noveboracensis* is confined to definitely restricted localities, such as Pymatuning Swamp itself and Canadohta Lake, which, faunally considered, are boreal islands. Recently *motacilla* has been traced in the breeding season to certain streams flowing down the lake shore plain in Erie County (Perry; Guynes), where, however, it is far from common.

The outstanding feature in the distribution of this water-thrush is the species' tendency to extend its local range by ascending streams to their headwaters and thus to reach an elevation comparable with that at which the other species normally occurs. At Bear Meadows, Centre County, the Louisiana seems actually to have supplanted the Northern Water-Thrush since the destruction of the original forest. Probably it is progressively encroaching upon the breeding range of the latter species as forest conditions change. Certainly there is good reason to believe that its range has been widening, while that of the Northern species has become more restricted. For instance, R. B. Simpson, whose field experience at Warren covers many years, could cite but a single accidental

[1] So many sight records for both species of water-thrush are contradictory and unsatisfactory that it seems best to ignore them for the present, in the absence of better evidence.

record for *S. motacilla* until 1903, but now finds it a regular although still uncommon summer resident. It seems to have gained a foothold there in recent years, as have several other austral species. Thus is the faunal aspect of the country being gradually altered.

Migration—The winter home of the Louisiana Water-Thrush is in Mexico and Central America. It is one of the earliest of the warbler tribe to reach us in the spring and precedes even those species that have much shorter distances to come. My arrival records for Beaver, covering twelve seasons, lie between April 9 (1933) and 19 (1923), while the average date is April 14. That these dates are fairly representative is indicated by their close agreement with records from neighboring counties. On rare occasions, however, the species has been known to appear much earlier, and it has even been reported in March. T. D. Burleigh observed one bird at Pittsburgh on April 6, 1914, and P. P. Malley saw one on April 3, 1936. Dr. Dickey reports seeing one along the Juniata River at Spruce Creek, Huntingdon County, on April 5, 1921. In 1913 B. H. Christy saw the first bird at Sewickley on March 30, and in 1923 Dr. Sutton saw one near Huntingdon on the same date. Unusually mild weather is of course the reason for such early occurrences. A series of arrival records made at Renovo by A. K. Pierce yield April 23 as the average date and April 11 (1901) as the earliest.

This water-thrush apparently leaves for the South very early in the season. I have never seen it at Beaver after the third week in August, and Mr. Burleigh's latest record for Allegheny County is August 20 (1927)—a fact that makes me very suspicious of the September records cited by W. W. Cooke from Renovo, on the authority of Mr. Pierce. Even as conscientious an observer as he, could easily have mistaken one species for the other at this season. Since the Louisiana Water-Thrush is known to reach its winter quarters in Central America by the middle of August, its continued presence in our latitude in late September or October would indeed be surprising.

Habits[1]—What is there about the song challenge of the Louisiana Water-Thrush that so vividly calls to mind his home in the cool ravine? Has he listened so long to the soliloquy of the shaded stream, as it slips down its shaly bed and wanders past damp roots and bowing ferns, that he has imitated its boldest mood? Or have the quiet shadows and the dark leaf mold led him to compose a song that will startle the silence of the woodland where he dwells?

Three distinctly repeated notes introduce this striking volley, which is entirely unlike the song of other warblers and much stronger and more prolonged than that of the species' near relative, the Northern Water-Thrush. It is delivered either from the ground or from a tree, and sometimes even during flight. The head of the singer is thrown well back, his whole body is shaken with energy, and his usually restless tail is for the moment allowed to hang at an easy, downward angle. The alarm-note is a loud, somewhat metallic *chink*.

Intrusion in the bird's haunts is heralded by a rich outburst of song. Yet even in the very home of the elusive songster we rarely see him save as he shoots by in his rapid, dashing flight. I have spent many hours in chasing this "song" up and down a wooded glen, to be rewarded only by a hurried glimpse of a modestly colored bird nervously teetering on the wet rocks, wading through the shallow water, hastily snatching at an insect in the mud, walking the length of a fallen limb, balancing on a fern stalk, and eyeing me suspiciously. All the while he bobs his tail; the movement gives the impression that the tail is held up by a spring and that he is continually trying to press it down. Mark his streaked sides and white eye-line quickly, for soon he is gone.

The evening flight song, as I have heard it in Greene County, is a memorable performance. In the gathering dusk the singer himself is not seen. The song seems to be dashing here and there. It sweeps downward in jerking stages as the final measures decrease in volume. It is prolonged, and the latter half is a repetition of tinkling notes that fade away to nothingness as the bird plunges back into the darkness whence he came.

Once I saw two birds, probably a mated pair, in a quarrel at the water's edge. They dashed about, struck the surface of the water several times, scrambled over the dead leaves between the weeds, and finally, to my utter amazement, came to terms in a brilliant duet. Since that time I have ascertained that the female does sing, although less frequently than the male.

If the bird itself seems difficult to observe, at-

[1]Account contributed in part by George M. Sutton.

tempt to find the nest! Increased agitation and boldness on the part of the parents usually indicate that the nest is somewhere close at hand, and careful search may reveal it under an overhanging bank or among the exposed roots of a tree. One nest that I found was hidden behind a great rock held in place by the bare roots of a beech tree. Another was built in a cavity under a low bank about ten feet from the edge of a stream. Leading to the nests were neat pavements of dry leaves, arranged with considerable care.

The young are much like their parents in color and bearing, and they early acquire the bobbing habit, although at first their tails are not long enough to be noticeable. One youngster that I caught bobbed so hard that I wondered that he did not fall over on his head each time he raised the ludicrous stub. When liberated he flew swiftly, for so young a bird, and crouched among the stalks of a stand of May apples, nor could I startle him a second time.

Rarely indeed is the Louisiana Water-Thrush ever seen, even in migration, near quiet, woodland pools or among the weeds along larger streams—haunts that the Northern Water-Thrush customarily frequents. At Pymatuning Swamp I have found the two species nesting within a few hundred yards of each other, the former along a shallow, rapidly descending stream that flowed into the swamp, and the latter among the black birches, hemlocks, and ferns that grew about the sphagnum-lined pools.

Dr. Sutton's account ends here, but a few notes on the nesting habits of the species should be added. The nests that I have found have all fitted his description and were concealed under the overhanging banks of small streams in the woods. J. W. Jacobs and Dr. Dickey have found many nests in Greene County. According to their observations, five eggs comprise the average set, but sometimes only four are laid, and occasionally six. They state that the species is a frequent victim of the Cowbird's parasitic habit. Nests have been found containing five eggs of the Water-Thrush and four of the Cowbird. One nest that held three eggs of the Cowbird and none of the rightful owner had been deserted by the builders. Nidification ordinarily begins about April 25 in Greene County, and sets of eggs are often complete as early as the first week, and usually by the second week, in May. I have seen young on the wing in Beaver County as early as May 28. The eggs are white or creamy white, irregularly spotted with soft shades of brown, gray, and lilac; the markings are sometimes distributed more or less evenly, but often are clustered in the form of a wreath or zone about the larger end. Average measurements are .77 by .61 inches.

Siurus motacilla Townsend, *Proc. Acad. Nat. Sci. Philadelphia*, 1883, 61 (Chestnut Ridge, Westmoreland Co.).

(?)"Water-Thrush" Enty, *Ornithologist and Oölogist*, 1885, 10:78 (Templeton, Armstrong Co., April).

"Long-billed Water Thrush" Jacobs, *Hawkeye Ornithologist and Oölogist*, 1888, 1:88 (Waynesburg, Greene Co., April).

Seiurus motacilla Warren, *Birds Pa.*, ed. 2, 1890, 271, 295 (Meadville, Crawford Co., summer, *fide* Sennett)—Todd, *Auk*, 1893, 10:41 (Yellow Creek, near Two Lick, Indiana Co., June)—Jacobs, *Summer Birds Greene Co., Pa.*, 1893, 13 (Greene Co., nesting)—Brown, *Abstr. Proc. Delaware Valley Orn. Club*, 1900, 3:13 (Laurel Hill Creek, Somerset Co., nesting)—Todd, in Bausman, *Hist. Beaver Co., Pa.*, 1904, 2:1201 (Beaver Co., summer)—Cooke, *Bull. Biol. Surv.* no. 18, 1904, 106 (Beaver, Beaver Co., and Renovo, Clinton Co., migration)—Harlow, *Auk*, 1912, 29:476 (Laurel Run, Huntingdon Co., nesting); 1918, 35:143 (Greene, Allegheny, Centre, Huntingdon, and Mifflin Co., nesting)—Dickey, *Oölogist*, 1913, 30:135 (Waynesburg, Greene Co., nesting; habits)—Christy, *Cardinal*, 1923, v. 1, no. 1, [p. 13] (Sewickley, Allegheny Co., summer)—Burleigh, *Wilson Bull.*, 1923, 35:140 (Allegheny Co., nesting); 1924, 36:73 ("State College" [Bear Meadows and Shingletown Gap], Centre Co. [and Charter Oak, Huntingdon Co.], migration); 1931, 43:51 (Laurel Run, Huntingdon Co., nesting)—Sutton, *Ann. Carnegie Mus.*, 1928, 18:219 (Meadville and vicinity of Pymatuning Swamp, Crawford Co., nesting)—Burleigh, *Cardinal*, 1929, 2:119 (Allegheny Co., August)—Burleigh, *Cardinal*, 1932, 3:80 (Chestnut Ridge, near Uniontown, Fayette Co., summer).

"Louisiana Water-Thrush" Brumbaugh, *Wilson Bull.*, 1905, 12:100 (Wilkinsburg, Allegheny Co., July)—Stone, *Cassinia*, 1906, 9:44 (Big Cove Tannery, Fulton Co., June)—Cooke, *Bird-Lore*, 1906, 8:102 (Waynesburg, Greene Co., and Renovo, Clinton Co., migration)—Simpson, *Oölogist*, 1914, 31:122 (Warren, Warren Co., August)—Dickey, *Oölogist*, 1914, 31:171 ([Charter Oak], Huntingdon Co., nesting), 207 ([east of] Cresson, Cambria Co., June)—Carter, *Oölogist*, 1914, 31:231 (Waynesburg, Greene Co., nesting)—McConnell, *Oölogist*, 1918, 35:151 (McKeesport, Allegheny Co., breeding)—Miller, *Oölogist*, 1919, 36:156 (Charter Oak, Huntingdon Co., nesting)—Scoville, *Cassinia*, 1920, 23:20 ([Charter Oak, Huntingdon Co.]; song)—Sutton, *Bird-Lore*, 1923, 25:194 (Huntingdon, Huntingdon Co., March; Clinton Pond, Allegheny Co., April, *fide* Christy)—Street, *Cassinia*, 1923, 24:10, 18 (Jordan's Knob and Horse Valley, Franklin Co., June)—Sutton, *Bird-Lore*, 1924, 26:190 (Wildwood, Allegheny Co., *fide* Homer; Beaver, Beaver Co., April, *fide* Todd)—Christy, *Cardinal*, 1924, v. 1, no. 4, p. 9, 11 (Big Traverse Valley, Beaver Co., April, June)—Eastwood, *Bird-Lore*, 1925, 27:263; and 1926, 28:272 (Pittsburgh region, Allegheny Co., April), 274 (Sandy Lake, Mercer Co., May, *fide* Squier).

KENTUCKY WARBLER (Plate 20)

OPORORNIS FORMOSUS (Wilson)

Description—One of the larger warblers. Plain *olive green above* (including wings and tail) and *bright yellow below;* top and sides of head black, this color extending a little way on the sides of the neck; a *bright yellow line* runs from the base of the bill over and *almost around the eye;* feet pale; *no wing-bars.* In the *female* the black areas of the head are more restricted and are more or less veiled with olive green.

Range—The Kentucky Warbler is a species of decidedly austral affinities and distribution. Judged by its northern limit, it is almost typically Carolinian. On the Atlantic slope it reaches the lower Hudson Valley and is common over much of southeastern Pennsylvania. Its range skirts the Appalachians generally, swinging around their southern extremity to spread west over the central Mississippi and Ohio valleys to the limit of the forest region. In southwestern Pennsylvania this warbler is one of the common and characteristic summer residents. From the West Virginia border it ranges eastward to Chestnut Ridge, and it has even ascended the valley of the Youghiogheny River on the other side of the ridge as far as Ohiopyle, Fayette County (Preble). It is common as well, according to my own experience, in the woods at the "Packsaddle," where the Conemaugh River cuts through the ridge, and it has been reported in June by R. V. Mostoller from the vicinity of Johnstown ("Saint Clair Dam") at an altitude of 1,450 feet. Almost certainly this last record represents a recent extension of range. The northern limit of its range in this general region seems to run from Indiana (Trimble) to the Buffalo Creek region in Butler and Armstrong counties; to Jamisonville, Butler County (Elliott); and thence to Beaver. The species is unreported from any point north of this line,[1] save for a single recent record from H. M. McQuiston. He discovered a singing male near the Big Bend of the Shenango River, in Mercer County, during the last week in June, 1935, but was unable to approach closely enough for a full view. No other valid records exist for the northwestern counties or for the adjacent section of Ohio.

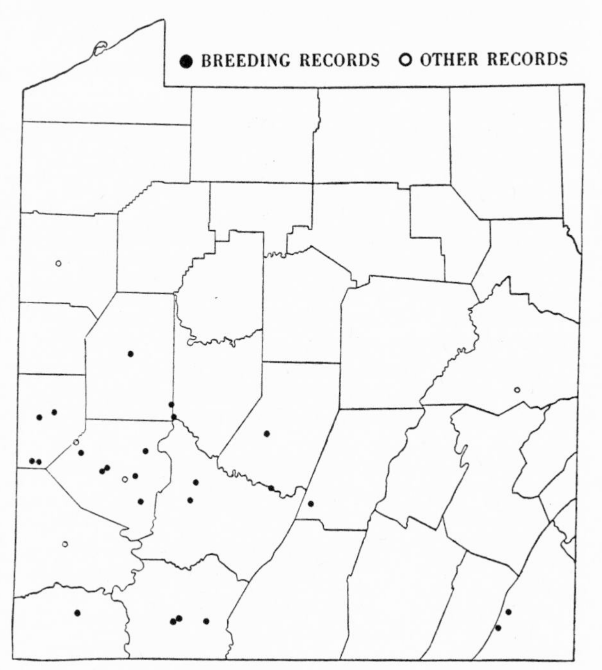

LOCAL RANGE OF THE KENTUCKY WARBLER

The Kentucky Warbler barely enters the ridge and valley section. I could not find it in Franklin County during the short time at my disposal in 1899, but in June, 1920, J. F. Street and his party observed it at two different localities on the edge of the mountains. At State College it is merely an accidental visitant.

Migration—This warbler usually arrives with the bulk of the family during the first week of May. Odd records from Allegheny County by sundry observers confirm this conclusion, while my earliest date at Beaver is April 30 (1902). In the fall movement the species is one of the earlier migrants and in fact is rarely seen after the middle of August. Some late dates that have been reported are: Beaver, September 13, 1888, and September 10, 1910; Sewickley, September 13, 1903; Pittsburgh, September 8, 1914. The species is particularly difficult to observe and identify satisfactorily in the fall. It goes to Central America for the winter and migrates directly across the Gulf of Mexico.

Habits—The Kentucky Warbler (so-called be-

[1]Warren's ascription of this species to Clarion, Clinton, and Clearfield counties is a palpable error, probably due to some transposition in his notes.

cause it was discovered in Kentucky) is a lover of damp, shady woods. On the bottomlands and along the lower slopes of the adjacent hillsides, wherever any tracts of this type remain, it is in evidence and, under favorable conditions, may even be abundant. It delights to skulk and hide in woodland where there is some underbrush or a rank growth of green plants. Almost as much of a ground warbler as the Oven-bird itself, it habitually works over the forest floor and among the lush herbage in its quest for food. If alarmed it may hop into the lower branches of a tree, there to display the rich colors of its plumage for a brief moment before dropping back into concealment. The green of its upperparts so closely matches the foliage that when on the ground the bird is not so easy to descry as one might suppose. In its partiality for thick covert it recalls the Maryland Yellow-throat, but in its habits and behavior it is more like the Oven-bird.

The males are in full song on their arrival in early May and at that season may sometimes be seen chasing each other about in disputed territory. They are persistent songsters until near the last of June. The song is a clearly whistled call of two syllables, repeated four or five times. It seems to me to resemble that of the Oven-bird, but it is monotone in character, without the inflection so prominent in the song of the latter species. It compares to some extent with certain vocal performances of the Carolina Wren but is not nearly so loud. Often the song is delivered from a perch in a low tree, but the birds frequently sing from the ground while searching for food. The ordinary call note is a soft, musical chirp.

Courting and mating require little time. The work of constructing the nest falls mainly to the female, but the male seldom strays far away while she is building. Like the Golden-winged Warbler but unlike most ground-nesting birds, the Kentucky Warbler always builds its nest above the ground level. The nests that I have found have been placed either in the base of a tuft of weeds, supported by the diverging stems, or between the ground forks of a small sapling. Areas grown up to May apple are often favored. Wherever placed, the nest is well screened from above. Usually it is rather bulky, because of the quantity of dry leaves used in the foundation. The nest proper is composed of dry leaves, fine twigs, and weed stalks, and is lined with finer material of the same sort or with rootlets, horsehair, or tendrils. Four or five eggs are normally laid, but I once found a nest with only two eggs, which were being incubated. The eggs are white, spotted or flecked, densely or sparsely, with rufous cinnamon or occasionally with a deeper shade of brown; the markings are usually confluent at or around the larger end; they vary considerably, even in the same set. Average measurements are .74 by .58 inches. The last week in May marks the height of the nesting season, but fresh sets have been taken in Greene County from May 18 to June 10. The eggs of a set taken by E. A. Preble and myself at "Pine Grove," near Industry, Beaver County, on June 19, 1893, were nearly fresh.

Oporornis formosa Jacobs, *Hawkeye Ornithologist and Oölogist*, 1889, 2:38 (Waynesburg, Greene Co., nesting).

Geothlypis formosa (?)Warren, *Birds Pa.*, ed. 2, 1890, 296 (Clarion Co., nesting; Clinton and Clearfield Co., transient, *fide* Van Fleet)—Todd, *Auk*, 1891, 8:398; and 1893, 10:209 (Beaver, Beaver Co., nesting)—Jacobs, *Taxidermist*, 1892, 1:108 (Waynesburg, Greene Co., nesting)—Jacobs, *Summer Birds Greene Co., Pa.*, 1893, 13 (Greene Co., nesting)—Jacobs, *Gleanings from Nature*, 1898, 1:5, 19, 26 (Waynesburg, Greene Co., nesting)—Eifrig, *Auk*, 1904, 21:248 (Pittsburgh, Allegheny Co., breeding)—Todd, in Bausman, *Hist. Beaver Co., Pa.*, 1904, 2:1201 (Beaver Co., summer)—Cooke, *Bull. Biol. Surv.* no. 18, 1904, 108 (Beaver, Beaver Co., migration).

"Kentucky Warbler" Cooke, *Bird-Lore*, 1905, 7:135 (Beaver, Beaver Co., and Waynesburg, Greene Co., migration)—Brumbaugh, *Wilson Bull.*, 1905, 12:100 (Wilkinsburg, Allegheny Co., July)—Dickey, *Oölogist*, 1912, 29:302 (Waynesburg, Greene Co., nesting; habits)—McConnell, *Oölogist*, 1918, 35:151 (McKeesport, Allegheny Co.)—McClelland, *Am. Mid. Nat.*, 1922, 8:37 (Washington, Washington Co., transient)—Street, *Cassinia*, 1923, 24:10, 18 (Little Cove Creek, [above] Foltz, Fulton Co., and Jordan's Knob, Franklin Co., June)—Christy, *Cardinal*, 1924, v. 1, no. 4, p. 9 (Big Traverse Valley, Beaver Co., June)—Eastwood, *Bird-Lore*, 1925, 27:263; 1926, 28:272; and 1927, 29:272 (Pittsburgh region, Allegheny Co., April and May)—Wood, *Wilson Bull.*, 1932, 44:238 (State College, Centre Co., May, *fide* Ross).

Oporornis formosus Dickey, *Oölogist*, 1914, 31:118 (Greene Co., nesting)—Christy, *Cardinal*, 1923, v. 1, no. 1, [p. 13] (Sewickley, Allegheny Co., breeding)—Burleigh, *Wilson Bull.*, 1923, 35:141 (Harmarville, Allegheny Co., nesting; migration)—Burleigh, *Cardinal*, 1929, 2:119 (Allegheny Co., fall migration)—Burleigh, *Cardinal*, 1932, 3:81 (Chestnut Ridge, near Uniontown, Fayette Co., summer).

CONNECTICUT WARBLER (Plate 20)

OPORORNIS AGILIS (Wilson)

Description—One of the larger warblers; general coloration olive and yellow; *wings plain. Male in spring:* upperparts, including wings and tail, plain olive green, the *head grayish;* a conspicuous *white eye-ring; throat and breast grayish;* rest of underparts dull yellow; feet pale brownish. *Female* similar but duller. *Young in fall:* similar to the spring adult, but the crown is brownish, the *eye-ring is buffy white,* and the *throat and breast are buffy brown.* (Not to be confused with the Maryland Yellow-throat in the same stage.)

Range—The Connecticut Warbler is a comparatively rare and little-known species, since its secretive habits and the nature of its haunts combine to shield it from observation. It was a long time before its breeding grounds were discovered, but they were finally located in Manitoba and the adjacent parts of Minnesota, in typically Canadian Fauna territory. This warbler winters in South America, which it reaches by flying eastward to the Atlantic coast and thence southward by way of the West Indies. Its northward migration, on the contrary, is by way of the Mississippi Valley.[1] On theoretical grounds, therefore, it should be much more regular and numerous in our region in the fall than in the spring, when its main route lies farther west. This condition actually obtains; for, while several observers report the species as an irregular transient in the fall, dependable spring records are scarce. Sight records must always be received with reservations, if for no other reason than that this species bears a close resemblance to the much commoner Mourning Warbler. The reasons for querying certain references on the list below will presently appear.

Migration—In the spring, besides being exceedingly rare, the Connecticut Warbler is a late migrant. The earliest authentic date of its appearance is May 18 (1922), when it was observed at Crystal Lake, Crawford County, by G. M. Sutton. I noted one bird in Pymatuning Swamp, north of Hartstown, in the same region, on May 22, 1933, but failed to secure it. My only spring specimen was shot on May 25, 1900, on Presque Isle, where I also saw single birds on May 22 and 29. D. A. Atkinson secured a specimen (now in the Carnegie Museum) at Wilkinsburg on May 22, 1896; and, according to S. N. Rhoads, G. A. Link, Sr., took a specimen in the vicinity of Pittsburgh on June 4, 1894.[2] One bird was identified at Tamarack Swamp, Clinton County, on May 28, 1907, by A. K. Pierce; this is his only spring record for this species. The most recent records concern: an individual observed by B. H. Christy on May 28, 1933, in southeastern Beaver County; one seen by P. P. Malley at Frick Park, Pittsburgh, on May 22, 1936; and one noted by S. J. Seiple near Shenango, Mercer County, on May 25, 1937. These records, conforming with those available from adjoining states, suggest that published references bearing April and early May dates should be rejected.

In the fall this warbler is irregular. In some seasons it appears in small numbers; in others, not at all. It comes early in September; my records of its arrival at Beaver were made on September 3, 1908; September 4, 1905; and September 5, 1899. Mr. Pierce secured specimens at Renovo on September 7, 1906, and at Kane on September 8, 1896. The migration movement continues through September and occasionally into the following month. Exact records are: Beaver, September 23, 1905, and September 24, 1924 (Todd); Pittsburgh, September 22, 1911 (Burleigh); Warren, September 21, 1902 (Simpson); Presque Isle, September 24, 1900 (Todd); State College, September 30, 1915 (Burleigh); Renovo, September 25, 1893, and October 8, 1901 (Pierce).

Habits—The Connecticut Warbler is perhaps the most secretive bird of its family and is certainly one of the most difficult to observe. So closely, indeed, does it keep under cover that sight identifications by inexperienced observers should rightly be questioned. One may hear the bird readily enough, and recognize it by its song, but seeing it is another matter entirely. W. W. Worthington and I once encountered one of these warblers on Presque Isle ensconced in a dense growth of bushes, where for almost two hours it successfully evaded our attempts to capture it. It remained so well

[1]Compare W. W. Cooke, in U. S. Department of Agriculture, *Bulletin*, no. 185, 1915, p. 21, fig. 7.

[2]The female to which Mr. Rhoads also refers is actually a Mourning Warbler.

concealed that we had but one or two fleeting glimpses of it, although it was within a few feet of us, as evidenced by its singing. The song of this warbler is quite loud and clear and bears a striking resemblance to those of the Mourning and Kentucky warblers, but it also has a peculiar explosive quality heard to some extent in the notes of the Canada Warbler and the Water-Thrush. It is susceptible of three or four variations but is perfectly distinctive.

During its spring sojourn the Connecticut Warbler keeps in the shelter of low brush and thick undergrowth, especially in swampy places. Rarely does it venture more than a few feet above the ground, and it pays little or no attention to "squeaking." In the fall it often visits the dense willow growth along streams and is also partial to stands of ragweed or jewelweed, which grow in close formation and afford good protection. Occasionally it is possible to decoy a bird to the edge of such a growth for a moment or two. At this season its only note is a sharp chirp, easily recognized when once learned. On one occasion in the fall I heard the spring song given in a subdued key.

Geothlypis agilis Warren, *Birds Pa.*, ed. 2, 1890, 297 (Erie Co., September; Clinton Co., transient, *fide* Van Fleet)—Rhoads, *Auk*, 1899, 16:313, part (Allegheny Co., June, *fide* Link)—Todd, *Ann. Carnegie Mus.*, 1904, 2:586 (Presque Isle, Erie Co., transient)—Todd, in Bausman, *Hist. Beaver Co., Pa.*, 1904, 2:1201 (Beaver Co., transient).

"Connecticut Warbler" Simpson, *Oölogist*, 1914, 31:122 (Warren, Warren Co., September)—(?)McConnell, *Oölogist*, 1918, 35:151 (McKeesport, Allegheny Co., transient)—(?)Eastwood, *Bird-Lore*, 1925, 27:263 (Pittsburgh region, Allegheny Co., April [error]); (?)1926, 28:273 (Ridgway, Elk Co., May, *fide* Alsop)—(?)Boulton, *Bird-Lore*, 1928, 30:401 (Millvale, Allegheny Co., October[?], *fide* Auerswald).

Oporornis agilis Burleigh, *Wilson Bull.*, 1923, 35:141 ([Pittsburgh], Allegheny Co., September); 1924, 36:130 (State College, Centre Co., September)—Todd, *Cardinal*, 1925, v. 1, no. 5, p. 20 (Beaver, Beaver Co., September)—Sutton, *Ann. Carnegie Mus.*, 1928, 18:220 (Crystal Lake and Lower Lake, Crawford Co., May and September)—Christy, *Cardinal*, 1934, 3:176 (Big Sewickley Creek [west side], Beaver Co., May).

MOURNING WARBLER (Plate 20)

OPORORNIS PHILADELPHIA (Wilson)

Description—A warbler larger than the average, resembling the Connecticut Warbler in general, but without any eye-ring; breast of male distinctly black. *Adult male:* upperparts, *wings* (*plain*), and tail, olive green; head (all around) gray, the lores blackish; *throat gray*, this color *deepening into black on the breast;* rest of underparts bright yellow, shaded with green on the sides; feet pale. *Adult female:* similar in general to the adult male, but *throat and breast ashy gray*, without black. *Young in the fall* resemble the adult female, but the head is greenish, as is the back, and the throat and breast are tinged with buff or yellow.

Range—The Mourning Warbler winters in the tropics from Nicaragua to Ecuador and Venezuela, whence it migrates across the Gulf of Mexico and the southern United States to reach its summer home, which lies in a belt mainly included in the Canadian Fauna and stretching from Newfoundland westward to the foothills of the Rocky Mountains in Alberta. In the summer, like many other species with the same general distribution, it ranges southward in the Appalachian highlands to West Virginia, where it appears at an elevation of three thousand feet. In the western counties of Pennsylvania, as well as in the ridge and valley section, it is merely a transient, not very common or well known, and has been reported by only a few observers. Its local breeding range is confined to the highlands and has been determined with precision only toward the north and the south. I found this bird common in June in Potter County some years ago, when much original forest still remained. As deforestation does not necessarily prove disastrous to this particular species, because of the nature of its habitat, it is probably just as numerous there now as it ever was.

This area of comparative abundance, so to speak, extends westward through McKean County and most of Warren, and southward through Forest, Elk, and Cameron counties to northern Clearfield County. Bear Lake, Warren County, where I found the species in June, 1898, is the western limit of its local range, and at Tidioute, in the same county, it occurs at an elevation of only about 1,100 feet (Homer). This circumstance would suggest a local distribution coextensive with that of the Hermit Thrush, but, in the absence of definite records from

Forest (except the extreme eastern part), Clarion, Jefferson, and Indiana counties, the western limit of the range in this intermediate region remains conjectural. The species reappears, however, along the crest of Laurel Hill in Cambria and Somerset counties, and farther south on Negro Mountain. The Allegheny divide is definitely its eastern limit in these two counties. It should be looked for farther north, in Clearfield County and on the summit of the mountain ridge southeast of the West Branch of the Susquehanna River, where conditions seem well suited to its needs.

Migration—In spring the Mourning Warbler is irregular both in numbers and in time of appearance. It must be counted one of the rarer warblers at this season, and in some years it may even escape notice altogether. Among the later migrants, it seldom reaches our latitude before the second week in May, and it is always commoner during the latter half of that month. May 6 (1902) is my earliest spring date for Beaver, and May 28 (1910), my latest. Dates from other localities in the western counties fall mostly within these extremes. A specimen taken at Erie by Sennett on June 4, 1875, was a belated migrant. An even more unusual record is that of a singing male observed by B. H. Christy near Sewickley on June 17, 1928; this bird may have been left behind in the migration. At Warren, where the species is a common summer resident, R. B. Simpson has recorded it as early as May 3 (1899) and 4 (1902), but most of his dates of arrival are considerably later. In a series of records made by A. K. Pierce at Renovo, on the edge of this warbler's breeding area, the earliest date is May 4 (1896); in four different years the species was first noted there on May 8, and the average arrival date in twenty-four years is May 12.

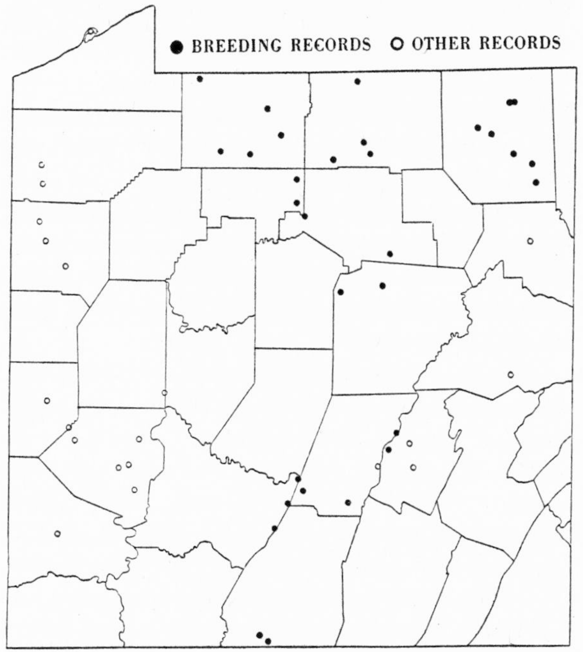

LOCAL RANGE OF THE MOURNING WARBLER

In the fall the Mourning Warbler is exceptionally rare—or perhaps it would be more accurate to say that it is very rarely observed. Only twice have I noted it at Beaver at that season: on September 11, 1899, and on August 28, 1908. A specimen was secured on each occasion, so that identification was proved beyond question. T. D. Burleigh supplies a sight record for Pittsburgh for August 14, 1913. G. M. Sutton observed the species at Pymatuning Swamp on September 11 and 12, 1925, and L. E. Hicks saw it at Presque Isle as late as September 25 in 1930. No other fall records have been reported.

Habits—Of all the warblers, with the exception of the Connecticut, this species is the most difficult to see and study during migration. By comparison, the arboricole kinds, however high in the trees they may elect to stay, are easy to identify. In the fall, indeed, identification of the Mourning Warbler is almost impossible; for then the rank growth of herbage among which it delights to hide effectively screens it from view. In the spring the species, usually remaining near the ground, seeks the cover of briery thickets and dense tangles, brush piles in the woods, and thick undergrowth. A blackberry thicket on the edge of a woods, impenetrable except at some cost, is a favorite resort. At this season, however, males may easily be recognized by their song, which is entirely distinctive. It consists of a gurgling trilled note, rapidly repeated several times; in my opinion, it resembles in a measure the song of the Maryland Yellowthroat (a not-distant relative). It is fairly loud (for a warbler's song), so that its general direction is easy to trace, but to catch a glimpse of the performer, successfully concealed in the underbrush, is by no means so easy. Later in the season, after the birds are settled on their nesting grounds, they may often be "squeaked up" by the usual method.

Large areas of country in the northern counties, once covered by heavy forest, have been denuded of their merchantable timber. These cut-over lands or "slashings," now grown up to briers and bushes, with brake fern beneath and a scrubby second growth beginning amid fallen logs and brush left from the first clearing, are ideal nesting grounds for the Mourning Warbler. These haunts it shares with the Maryland Yellow-throat, with which it has much in common. I have at times encountered it in the deep woods, but never far from the edge. In Potter County, along the hilltop highway between Sweden Valley and Cherry Spring, it was common in June, 1898; there it haunted the briers and bushes by the roadside, where good cover was flanked by forest growth on either side. In Warren County, according to Mr. Simpson, it is found not only in the "slashings" and barrens of the hilltops, but also in the bottomlands along the Allegheny River, where there are rank growths of skunk cabbage and tangles of vines. The birds usually keep well hidden in the low brush and rarely try a higher perch for more than a moment. The males occasionally mount to the lower branches of a tree to sing, but upon the slightest alarm they dive into the thicket to continue their song.

Mr. Simpson considers the female Mourning Warbler one of the most secretive birds in our region, and I fully endorse this opinion. He has found it almost impossible to detect her in the act of building, but later in the season, after the young are out of the nest, she is always more in evidence. The nests he has examined were found by a systematic search of the area where the males were singing. The following account of the nesting of the species is quoted from an article by T. H. Jackson (1909), which was based on his experience in Warren County in 1908:

"The first nest of the Mourning Warbler that we located was on a bunch of ferns in an open space in the woods, close beside the stream. We saw and heard the birds there frequently, but it (the nest) was not completed, and was possibly abandoned because of our frequent presence in the vicinity. Another nest with one egg was found on the edge of the cemetery in a clump of briars. It was placed very close to the ground, and though we watched for the bird each time we were near the nest, only at the last visit did we get a sight of her sufficient to make her identity sure. The nest still contained but a single egg, apparently well incubated.

"About a mile below the town, and close beside the river, there is a grove of scattering trees covering perhaps six to eight acres of lowland that is subject to overflow at times. Over this entire tract there is a dense growth of nettles, briars, and a variety of rank weeds that covered the ground from two to three feet deep. Two pairs of Mourning Warblers were known to be located somewhere in this jungle, although on that morning, June 5th, we did not hear their song once; we decided to give the ground a thorough search, and from eight to eleven o'clock worked hard to cover every possible hiding place where the nest might be concealed. Mosquitoes, gnats, and nettles did not add perceptibly to the pleasure of the search, but as one of our main objects in coming to Warren County was to see and hear the Mourning Warbler in its summer home, no trouble or discomfort was considered in accomplishing this end. . . .

"As we were about to give up the search, Mr. Simpson walked round to the edge of the thicket where it merges into a grass field, and there at the very edge, among the tall weeds, he flushed a bird from the nest. She was off and out of sight too quickly to determine her identity, but as I was photographing the nest she gradually became bolder, and finally both birds came into plain view, proving beyond doubt the identity of our prize. It [the nest] had the appearance of having originally been placed on the ground, but by the rapid growth of the weeds with which it was entangled had been raised about six inches. The outside of the nest was made of coarse weed-stalks and stems; so arranged that the nest was much broader one way than the other, the greatest width over all being nine inches, while its shortest diameter was but six inches. It was four inches in depth over all, while the cup was two and a quarter inches deep. The second layer was composed of dry oak leaves, and next came a substantial layer of grape-vine bark in strips, some of them a foot long and one-eighth to one-quarter inch in width. The inside lining was a thin layer surrounding the entire cup of the nest, and consisting of strong, hair-like filaments of a reddish color, not unlike in appearance the fruit stalks of the hair-moss, used by the Worm-eating Warbler for the same purpose, excepting that they are much longer and tougher than that material.

"The eggs were four in number and measured .81 x .52, .80 x .55, .79 x .55 and .78 x .52 (in hundredths of an inch). The ground color is pearl, three of them having obscure lilac markings wreathed about the greater end, with a few bolder spots of reddish-brown, the fourth egg being thickly spotted with the brown shade evenly over the entire surface, similar to the eggs of the White-breasted Nuthatch. All of the eggs are quite pointed."

Several nests in the Carnegie Museum that were taken by Mr. Pierce at Kane between June 5 and 15, resemble in general the one described above. They are much like those of the Maryland Yellow-throat but are bulkier. These were all found in clumps of beech sprouts and were several inches from the ground. The eggs (four in every nest) closely resemble those of the Oven-bird, even in their variations, but are smaller. Both Mr. Simpson and S. S. Dickey have several times found sets of five eggs, from June 1 on. The nesting habits of this species merit further study and investigation.

Geothlypis philadelphia TEULON, *Jour. Boston Zoöl. Soc.*, 1882, 1:50 (Bradford, McKean Co., summer)—WARREN, *Birds Pa.*, ed. 2, 1890, 297 (Renovo, Clinton Co., summer, *fide* Van Fleet)—TODD, *Auk*, 1891, 8:240, 398 (Beaver, Beaver Co., rare spring transient)—DWIGHT, *Auk*, 1892, 9:133, 134, 139 (Wopsononock Mountain, Blair Co., June)—RHOADS, *Auk*, 1899, 16:313 (Laurel Hill, near Laughlintown, Westmoreland Co., breeding)—COPE, *Cassinia*, 1902, 5:11, 18 (between Oleona and New Bergen, Potter Co., June)—TODD, *Ann. Carnegie Mus.*, 1904, 2:586 (Presque Isle, Erie Co., transient)—TODD, in Bausman, *Hist. Beaver Co., Pa.*, 1904, 2:1201 (Beaver Co., transient)—COOKE, *Bull. Biol. Surv.* no. 18, 1904, 112 (Renovo, Clinton Co., migration)—STONE, *Cassinia*, 1905, 8:59 (Kittanning Point, Blair Co., June).

"Mourning Warbler" WARREN, *Forest and Stream*, 1891, 37:83 (Kane, McKean Co., summer)—COOKE, *Bird-Lore*, 1905, 7:169 (Beaver, Beaver Co., and Renovo, Clinton Co., migration)—SIMPSON, *Oölogist*, 1907, 24:134; 1909, 26:26, 170; 1911, 28:201; and 1914, 31:91, 122; (Warren, Warren Co., nesting, etc.); 1912, 29:330 (head of Tionesta Creek, Warren Co., summer)—SHARPLES, *Oölogist*, 1908, 25:121 (Warren Co., nesting)—JACKSON, *Cassinia*, 1909, 12:9 (Warren, Warren Co., nesting)—MCCONNELL, *Oölogist*, 1918, 35:151 (McKeesport, Allegheny Co., transient)—MCCLELLAND, *Am. Mid. Nat.*, 1922, 8:37 (Washington, Washington Co., transient)—SUTTON, *Bird-Lore*, 1923, 25:260 (Raccoon Creek, Beaver Co., *fide* Elliott, *et al.*)—EASTWOOD, *Bird-Lore*, 1926, 28:272 (Pittsburgh region, Allegheny Co., May)—BOULTON, *Bird-Lore*, 1928, 30:271, 337 (Guys Run and Sewickley, Allegheny Co., May, June, *fide* Auerswald and Christy)—COPE and HAWKINS, *Forest Leaves*, 1934, 24:26 (E. Tionesta Forest Reserve, Warren and McKean Co., summer)—MALLEY and SHOEMAKER, *Redstart*, 1937, 4:70 (Pittsburgh, Allegheny Co., migration).

Geothlypis agilis (error) RHOADS, *Auk*, 1899, 16:313, part ("Leetsdale" [Fair Oaks], Allegheny Co., May [Seager]).

Oporornis philadelphia STONE, *Cassinia*, 1919, 22:36 ("Altoona," Blair Co. [Laurel Gap, Cambria Co.], May, *fide* McGraw)—CHRISTY, *Cardinal*, 1923, v. 1, no. 1, [p. 13] (Sewickley, Allegheny Co., May)—BURLEIGH, *Wilson Bull.*, 1923, 35:141 (Allegheny Co., August); 1924, 36:130 (State College, Centre Co., May)—SUTTON, *Ann. Carnegie Mus.*, 1928, 18:221 (Pymatuning Swamp, Crawford Co., transient).

MARYLAND YELLOW-THROAT (Plate 20)

GEOTHLYPIS TRICHAS TRICHAS (Linnaeus)

Description—A yellow and olive-green warbler of medium size, with *plain wings. Adult male:* upperparts, including wings and tail, olive green; a *black "mask"* across the forehead, reaching back to the ear coverts and bordered on the top by ashy gray; throat and breast yellow, and rest of underparts buffy, suffused with yellow, particularly the under tail coverts; bill black. *Adult female:* dull olive green; no black "mask," but the head olive like the back, or washed with brown; underparts much duller than in the male. The *young male* in the fall is similar to the adult female but usually shows a trace of black on the sides of the head. The *young female* in the fall is a nondescript-looking warbler, without any distinct markings; upperparts olive green, the head brownish; underparts buffy, the throat, breast, and under tail coverts suffused with yellow.

Range—In one form or another the Yellow-throat ranges from Florida and Mexico to Canada, and from the Atlantic coast to the Pacific. According to the American Ornithologists' Union *Check-List*, the form inhabiting "northern Pennsylvania" is *brachidactyla*, the Northern Yellow-throat, while typical *trichas* is said to breed in "southern Pennsylvania." Insofar as specimens from the western half of the state are concerned, I must admit my inability to distinguish two races; the birds from the northern and the southern counties look alike to me. In our region this species is a summer resident, common and universally distributed. It winters in the West Indies and Central America.

Migration—The first week in May marks the vernal appearance of the Maryland Yellow-throat in our latitude; the species is then easily observed and identified, and many notes on its arrival are available. In my records for Beaver covering twenty-one different seasons, arrival dates range from April 28 (1908) to May 11 (1911), and May 4 is the average. These dates are confirmed by scattered records from neighboring counties. A series of records covering twenty-three years at Renovo, made by A. K. Pierce, yields dates ranging from April 27 (1908) to May 12 (1899, and other years); May 6 is the average. This bird was reported at Hollidaysburg as early as April 26 in 1921 (Berg) and on the same date at Springs, Somerset County, in 1913 (Miller).

Although this warbler is not difficult to observe in the fall, its movements at that season are mostly unrecorded. It is in evidence as a rule through most of September when the other warblers are migrating, and laggards are not infrequently seen in early October. Late dates are: Beaver, October 8, 1910 (Todd); Wilkinsburg, October 8, 1894 (Atkinson); State College, October 10, 1915 (Burleigh); Presque Isle, October 13, 1900 (Todd); and Renovo, October 24, 1903 (Pierce). Whether the yellow-throats that summer in our region go to Central America or to the West Indies for the winter has not been determined; in the latter event their route would take them across the mountains.

Habits—Even those amateur bird students who confess themselves puzzled by the warblers as a group, usually know the Maryland Yellow-throat. The black mask of the male, seen as he hops at intervals to an exposed spray above the general level of his haunts, is a good field mark, and his song is likewise distinctive and easily recognized. This song consists of three syllables, very rapidly given, and repeated several times. It may be transliterated thus: *whit-i-shee, whit-i-shee, whit-i-shee;* or *witch-i-ty, witch-i-ty, witch-i-ty.* The exact rendering varies with different individuals. All through May and June the Yellow-throat sings constantly, and its song may frequently be noted in the fall as well. It has also a "flight song," which I have heard several times. In delivering it, the bird mounts into the air in a wild, excited fashion, singing a jumble of odd notes, interspersed with those of its regular song. The ordinary call note of both sexes has a peculiar quality or timbre that is highly characteristic.

The Yellow-throat likes thick cover, especially if this grows on swampy ground. It is partial to the shrubbery, bushes, and weedy growth fringing the banks of streams, large and small, but it is by no means confined to the lower levels and often affects the uplands, wherever there are high weeds, brush, and scrub. In the northern counties it finds the briery growth of the cut-over timber lands congenial. It was very common at Tamarack Swamp, Clinton County, on my several visits to that locality; indeed, it was one of the few birds that preferred the tamarack area proper. According to G. M. Sutton (1928), it is "particularly abundant among the cat-tails, high grass, and rank weeds of Pymatuning." On Presque Isle, where conditions are similarly favorable, it is a common inhabitant of the bushes and shrubbery surrounding the ponds. It is a nervous, active little bird, suggesting a wren in its behavior and in some of its poses. Although keeping under cover for the most part, it will almost always respond to "squeaking," and it often comes to the edge of the bushes of its own accord, where it can easily be observed. Thus it lacks the innate shyness of such warblers as the Kentucky, the Mourning, and particularly the Connecticut, which in general favor the same or similar locations.

In Greene County the nesting period is from May 18 to June 2 (Jacobs); farther north it averages a little later and lasts until the middle of June. According to T. D. Burleigh, two broods are generally reared, the eggs for the second brood being laid about the middle of July. The nest of this warbler is not easy to find, and systematic search may be rewarded less often than desultory wandering in the birds' chosen haunts. Built in a bunch of weeds, in the base of a small bush, or in a clump of tall grass, the nest is always raised a little above the ground. One that D. A. Atkinson found was in a bush at a height of four feet. Nests found at Pymatuning Swamp by Dr. Sutton were built among the dead cattails. One that I discovered at Tamarack Swamp, Warren County, was in a low huckleberry bush in the open bog, in plain sight from above. Always a rather bulky structure for so diminutive a bird, the nest is supported by a foundation of dry leaves; it is composed of dry weed stalks, shreds of grapevine bark, and similar material, and is neatly lined with fine grasses and (sometimes) horsehair. Four or five eggs comprise the usual set, but sometimes only three are laid, particularly when the Cowbird interferes. They are white, with a few spots, and sometimes fine lines, of purplish brown, all usually rather well defined, and confluent around the larger end. The eggs are not often heavily marked; generally the spotting is as sparse as in the eggs of the vireos. The shape, however, is different, inclining to rounded ovate. Average measurements are .71 by .54 inches.

Geothlypis trichas Teulon, *Jour. Boston Zoöl. Soc.*, 1882, 1:50 (Bradford, McKean Co., May)—Townsend, *Proc. Acad. Nat. Sci. Philadelphia*, 1883, 61 (Latrobe, Westmoreland Co., summer)—Jacobs, *Hawkeye Ornithologist and Oölogist*, 1889, 2:27 (Waynesburg, Greene Co., nesting)—Dwight, *Auk*, 1892, 9:139 (Cresson, Cambria Co., June)—Todd, *Auk*, 1893, 10:41 (Two Lick, Indiana Co., June), 46 (Coalport, Clearfield Co., June)—Jacobs, *Summer Birds Greene Co., Pa.*, 1893, 13 (Greene Co., nesting)—Baily, *Auk*, 1896, 13:296 (Williamsville, Elk Co., June–July)—Jacobs, *Gleanings from Nature*, 1898, 1:26 (Waynesburg, Greene Co., nesting)—Rhoads, *Auk*, 1899, 16:313 (Allegheny and Beaver Co.; Laughlintown, Westmoreland Co., breeding)—Palmer, *Auk*, 1900, 17:221, 234 (western Pa.; critical)—Cope, *Cassinia*, 1902, 5:19 (Clinton and Potter Co., June)—Keim, *Cassinia*, 1905, 8:40 (Port Allegany, McKean Co., summer)—Forrest, *Oölogist*, 1911, 28:115 (Washington, Washington Co., breeding)—Christy, *Cardinal*, 1923, v. 1, no. 1, [p. 13] (Sewickley, Allegheny Co., breeding).

"Maryland Yellow-throat" Hazzard, *Ornithologist and Oölogist*, 1884, 9:23 ("Allegheny," Allegheny Co.)—Cooke, *Bird-Lore*, 1905, 7:277 (Beaver, Beaver Co., and Renovo, Clinton Co., migration)—Stone, *Cassinia*, 1906, 9:44 (McConnellsburg, Fulton Co., June)—Simpson, *Oölogist*, 1909, 26:170; 1914, 31:122; and 1920, 37:43 (Warren, Warren Co., nesting)—Simpson, *Oölogist*, 1912, 29:330 (head of Tionesta Creek, Warren Co., summer)—Dickey, *Oölogist*, 1914, 31:171 ([Charter Oak], Huntingdon Co., nesting)—McClelland, *Am. Mid. Nat.*, 1922, 8:36 (Washington, Washington Co., summer)—Boulton, *Oölogist*, 1922, 39:71 (near Beaver, Beaver Co., May; song)—Street, *Cassinia*, 1923, 24:18 (Conococheague Creek, near Mercersburg, and Ft. Loudon, Franklin Co., June)—Christy, *Cardinal*, 1923, v. 1, no. 2, [p. 17] (Clinton Pond, Allegheny Co., May); 1924, v. 1, no. 4, p. 9 (Big Traverse Valley, Beaver Co., June)—Eastwood, *Bird-Lore*, 1925, 27:262 (Raccoon Creek, Beaver Co., May, *fide* Jones); 1926, 28:272; and 1927, 29:272 (Pittsburgh region, Allegheny Co., May).

"Maryland Warbler" Eastwood, *Bird-Lore*, 1925, 27:263 (Pittsburgh region, Allegheny Co., May).

Geothlypis trichas brachidactyla Todd, *Ann. Carnegie Mus.*, 1904, 2:586 (Erie and Presque Isle, Erie Co., nesting)—Todd, in Bausman, *Hist. Beaver Co., Pa.*, 1904, 2:1201 (Beaver Co., summer).

"Northern Yellow-throat" Pitcairn, *Bird-Lore*, 1907, 9:155 (Riverview Park, Allegheny Co., summer)—McConnell, *Oölogist*, 1918, 35:151 (McKeesport, Allegheny Co.).

Geothlypis trichas trichas Harlow, *Auk*, 1912, 29:476 (southern Centre Co., summer)—Burleigh, *Wilson Bull.*, 1923, 35:141 (Allegheny Co., migration; nesting); 1924, 36:73; 1931, 43:52 (State College, Centre Co., migration; summer)—Christy and Sutton, *Cardinal*, 1928, 2:74 (Cook Forest, Clarion Co., summer; critical)—Sutton, *Ann. Carnegie Mus.*, 1928, 18:221 (Meadville and Pymatuning Swamp, nesting)—Burleigh, *Cardinal*, 1932, 3:81 (Chestnut Ridge, near Uniontown, Fayette Co., summer).

YELLOW-BREASTED CHAT

ICTERIA VIRENS VIRENS (Linnaeus)

Description—About the size of the Cedar Waxwing. *Adult male:* upperparts (including wings and tail), olive green; underparts bright yellow, except the abdomen and under tail coverts, which are white; a white stripe from the bill to above the eye, a white spot below the eye, and an elongated white spot or stripe at the base of the lower mandible; lores blackish, and ear coverts grayish; bill black. *Female:* similar but duller. *Young:* brownish olive above, buffy olive below.

Range—The summer range of the Chat (both races collectively) is transcontinental and is mainly included within the limits of the United States. The species winters in Mexico and Central America. The eastern or typical race has long been considered a bird of the Carolinian Fauna insofar as its northern limit is concerned. W. W. Cooke, writing in 1904, adopts this view, and the 1931 edition of the American Ornithologists' Union *Check-List* does not dissent. But one has only to consult the state distribution maps for Massachusetts and New York, made by E. H. Forbush and E. H. Eaton respectively, to discover the inadequacy of this concept. The fact is that in the East the Yellow-breasted Chat regularly ranges over much of the Alleghanian Fauna as well.[1] Whether it has actually extended its range

[1]Farther west the distributional status of the Chat is different. T. S. Roberts, for example, says that the species is extremely rare in Minnesota (*Birds of Minnesota*, 1932, 2:273).

in later years, or was overlooked in this area by the early writers, is not clear. It is hard to believe that this species was present on the crest of the Alleghenies (where it has been repeatedly detected in recent years) under primitive conditions, before deforestation had changed the environment. Unfortunately no early records have come down to us from this part of the country, but if we may believe Audubon, the Chat had been observed "as far as the borders of Lake Erie in Pennsylvania" more than a century ago, and this early record is validated by some of more recent date.

Whatever the situation may be, the local range of the Yellow-breasted Chat, as it appears from the records plotted on the accompanying map, is most peculiar and does not lend itself to ready interpretation. The species is common in two distinct and separated areas—the Ohio Valley and the ridge and valley section—as are also most of our recognized Carolinian birds. But it is not confined to these sections, as they are. It has invaded Clinton County from the east, ascending the West Branch of the Susquehanna River and the valleys of its tributaries. The extent of this penetration is suggested by a late June record from Clearfield, made by S. S. Dickey. Farther north, in Potter County, the species was identified at Galeton in June, 1900, by F. R. Cope, Jr. A nesting pair

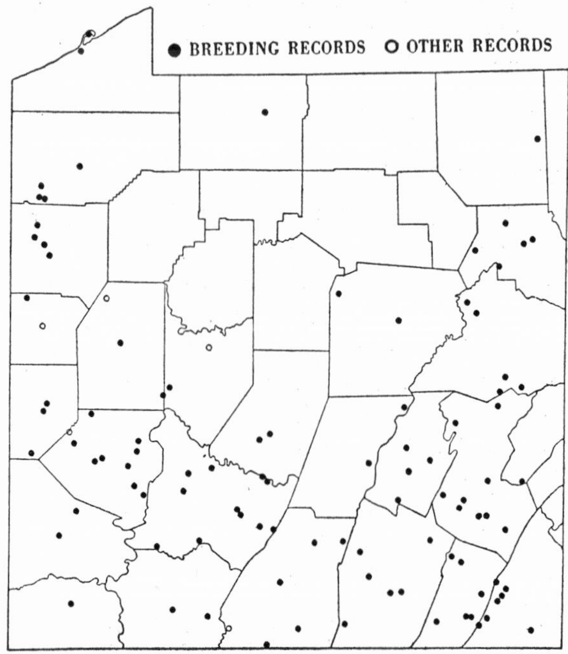

LOCAL RANGE OF THE YELLOW-BREASTED CHAT

found along Conewango Creek in 1903 by F. L. Homer, and another pair found in 1911 by R. B. Simpson, constitute the only known records for the vicinity of Warren. The species is listed by Van Fleet as a "not common" breeding bird at DuBois; in view of the records just cited, this statement may be accepted.

My impression is that the Chat is not so common in the Ohio Valley as it was forty or fifty years ago. It is still numerous, however, in the southwestern counties, but much less so northward. In Crawford County it is regular but uncommon, while in Erie County, along the lake shore, it is rare. Its status across the border in Ohio is virtually the same. Greater interest attaches to the distribution of the bird in the higher parts of our southern counties. Unlike certain Carolinian species, it has apparently found neither Chestnut Ridge nor Laurel Hill an effective barrier to its spread over Somerset County—which indeed it may have invaded from the east as well. The Chat has been seen and taken on the crest of the Alleghenies at Lloydville and Cresson, Cambria County (Surber; Jamison, 1888), and at Crumb and Keystone Junction (near Meyersdale), Somerset County (Preble). The latter observer reported it also from Hooversville and Somerset; and at Springs, close to the Maryland border, A. B. Miller calls it a regular but not common summer resident. This would seem to be its status throughout Somerset County generally, regardless of altitude. In short, the Yellow-breasted Chat seems to be peculiarly sensitive to the effects of environment and is always ready to take advantage of any change in its favor and to extend its range accordingly.

Migration—The Chat usually arrives at Beaver during the first week in May, or, according to the record, between April 27 (1908) and May 10 (1924). The average date in fourteen seasons is May 3. Available records from neighboring counties, supplied by other observers, correspond. According to a series made by A. K. Pierce over a period of twenty-five years, April 24 (1915) and May 7 are respectively the earliest and average dates of arrival at Renovo. This observer has reported the species' departure in the fall from the same locality at dates ranging from September 1 to 21 and 22. The latter dates seem very late indeed, since this bird is an unusually early migrant at this season and is rarely seen after August. I think, however, that I saw a chat on September 13, 1890, at Beaver, and D. A. Atkinson gives September 16, 1898, as his latest fall record for Wilkinsburg. Miss Alice Greves found a dead chat at Greensburg on September 22, 1939. The Chat is so exceedingly difficult to observe and identify satisfactorily except during its song period that the only acceptable evidence of its occurrence at any other time is a specimen in the hand. Naturally I feel that any records made as late as October 10[1] are questionable.

Habits[2]—Some bird names are misnomers. The Turkey Buzzard, for instance, is not a buzzard at all. The latter is a British hawk of large size and soaring habit. Some early colonist or explorer, familiar with the English name for a soaring bird of large size, called the American Turkey Vulture a "Buzzard," and the misnomer held fast. Likewise, the Meadowlark is of the blackbird-oriole tribe and not a lark at all. But the Yellow-breasted Chat, commonly called "Chat," is most appropriately named, although Chat ought to come first, as in Hungarian and Chinese family nomenclature; for, ten to one, you will hear his conversation and listen spellbound—yes, spellbound—many times when you will not see him at all.

First of all, he lives in the jungle—usually a bramble or grapevine thicket in our region. Here, among the dense foliage of a thick and almost impenetrable blackberry clump the stout, recurved prickles of which penetrate all but the heaviest clothing, where even a marauding cat will hesitate to venture, Madam Chat hides her nest.

Early on a spring morning after the middle of May and before the middle of June, you are strolling up one of those ravines that come down from the tillable highlands to a rough and rocky gorgelike valley. Or perhaps you have traveled the ridge road and are coming down across a prospective hay meadow or a dewberry tangle. While yet a hundred yards or more from an old rail fence that runs along the margin of the wood, you are startled by a whistled call of two or three notes of the same tone. You might say they are pitched at high C of the musical scale, or even lower, but each slides off slightly after the fashion of the conversational tone of a "musical" voice. Immediately there follows a deep single note; then come several more on a still different key—and "the chat is on," in whistles, calls, chuckles, cackles, croaks, and even near groans. It may last from five to fifteen minutes. Stand there, twist your neck up and down, to right and to left, then straight ahead, and try to locate the speaker from the direction of his chatter. It is all disconcerting; the sound is now here, now there, and the foliage is so heavy and the bird so wary that perhaps, indeed most probably, he escapes your search altogether. When you think that at last you have located him on this buttonball branch at your

left, he flies in jerky, almost tumbling fashion from the tip of an elm limb on your right. He has no set speech. His tones are not difficult to imitate if you have any knack at all in whistling, so that you may, if you please, indulge for some minutes in a conversation which your friend will carry on with verve and vigor. You may arouse his resentment; in that event, when he drops from his perch (he almost invariably sings from a lofty position) you may observe him shaking himself as though with indignation and then turn, falter, tumble, hover, and perform diverse curious antics on his way to the tangle below.

I recall a recent experience. Four of us were leaving the road in a wooded valley and ascending the side of a little ravine. As we reached the clearing, which, like other similar clearings in western Pennsylvania, passes from woodland to open field by way of a blackberry jungle, we were listening to the voices and calls of the early morning convocation, naming this and that bird as we recognized it. Directly I heard the distant chatter of a flock of crows and remarked, "Well, there is no mistaking that sound"; and my companions readily assented. Then a chat was heard. We replied and for a minute or two carried on a conversation that we, for our part, could not in the least

[1]Compare S. K. Eastwood, *Bird-Lore*, 1926, 28:403.
[2]Account contributed by Edmund W. Arthur.

understand. Again the crows called softly from the distant hill. Up spoke our friend the chat, tacking on a few phrases that were unmistakably from the same source as the "crow talk," and down he went into the silent jungle. The bird is not only a ventriloquist; he is also an arrant and skillful imitator. If birds can recognize and take delight in human perplexity, that chat must have had a lot of fun in listening to my friends and me as we guessed at the probable location of a flock of crows, and in noting our confusion when he revealed himself as the impersonator.

Not only is this bird an irrepressible "chat," but he is obviously "yellow-breasted," so that his name fits him like wax. His color is splendid and splendidly protective. Among the leaves of a buttonball tree on a sunny May morning, a chat may work in plain sight within fifty yards of you, and so effective is his yellow-and-green attire and his streaked countenance that you may search with all your skill and fail to see him until he flies. And the plumage of the female blends so well with the green of brambles and bindweed that grow about the location of her nest that you will have to be alert to distinguish her as she lies low over her eggs. Although much more retiring and less noisy than her rollicking mate, she is nevertheless very much on the job.

The Yellow-breasted Chat, that brilliant jewel of our spring woodlands, is the largest of the wood warblers. While not abundant, it is nevertheless not rare among the hills and river valleys of our region. Where you find a pair this year, you will very likely find the same or another pair next year. Probably few runs or creeks flowing into the Allegheny, Monongahela, or Ohio rivers, where there are old brambly fields or hawthorn-bordered pastures, are without a pair or more of these birds.

The nest is a rather bulky structure of grapevine bark, heavy grasses, leaves, and like material, with an interior cushion of fine grass. While brier thickets are favorite nesting sites, stumps or snags covered with grapevine or climbing bindweed also provide the necessary seclusion. The first nest I ever saw was in a heavy canopy of hedge bindweed (*Convolvulus repens*) covering a snag of sapling locust or thorn on a sunny knoll. It was in the midst of a rather close growth of wild crab-apple, hawthorn, and other shrubby trees. When we found the nest, the bird was off, and we did not see her. Although we waited for some time in concealment, she did not return. On our next visit, I approached from one side of the shelter, and my companion from the opposite side. I made the final advance. The ruse worked; W. S. Thomas, a careful and accurate observer, had the satisfaction of seeing the bird skulk from the foliage on the side away from me. It paused for a brief instant but long enough for proper identification, which was subsequently confirmed by observation of the eggs and young.

The eggs of the Chat show wide variation in markings; the white ground-color may be evenly speckled with reddish brown and lilac, or it may be blotched and spotted, the color deepening at the larger end. The average size is .90 by .66 inches. The usual time of laying is during the latter half of May and in early June; three to five eggs comprise a set, with four the commoner number.

The food of this species consists chiefly of insects. The large, heavy bill indicates a capacity for beetles; since the Chat also feeds upon various berries, this instrument may likewise be of service in cracking frail seeds.

To its human friends the Chat is always an attraction and a novelty. Whether it performs as a songster, a conversationalist, or a clownish acrobat, its coloratura phrases, "wisecracks," and aerial stunts, are alike entertaining, refreshing, and surprising.

Icteria viridis Audubon, *Orn. Biog.*, 1834, 2:223 (Lake Erie, Pa.).

"Yellow-breasted Chat" Enty, *Ornithologist and Oölogist*, 1885, 10:79 (Templeton, Armstrong Co., May)—Jacobs, *Hawkeye Ornithologist and Oölogist*, 1888, 1:88 (Waynesburg, Greene Co., migration)—Stone, *Cassinia*, 1906, 9:44 (McConnellsburg, Fulton Co., June)—Burleigh, *Oölogist*, 1911, 28:156 (Harmarville, Allegheny Co., nesting)—Miller (M. H.), *In the Open*, Dec., 1912, 3:41 (McKinley Park, Allegheny Co., summer)—Dickey, *Oölogist*, 1914, 31:171 ([Charter Oak], Huntingdon Co., nesting)—McConnell, *Oölogist*, 1918, 35: 152 (Long Run, near McKeesport, Allegheny Co.)—Miller (R. F.), *Oölogist*, 1919, 36:156 (Charter Oak, Huntingdon Co., nesting)—Christy, *Cardinal*, 1924, v. 1, no. 4, p. 9 (Big Traverse Valley, Beaver Co., June)—Eastwood, *Bird-Lore*, 1925, 27:262 (Raccoon Creek, Beaver Co., May, *fide* Jones), 338 (Pittsburgh, Allegheny Co., May, nesting, *fide* Jones); 1927, 29:272 (Pittsburgh region, Allegheny Co., May).

Icteria virens Jamison, *Ornithologist and Oölogist*, 1888, 13:134 (Cresson, Cambria Co., June)—Todd, *Auk*, 1891, 8:398 (Beaver, Beaver Co., summer); 1893, 10:37, 38, 41 (Two

Lick, Indiana Co., June)—JACOBS, *Summer Birds Greene Co., Pa.*, 1893, 13 (Greene Co., nesting)—JACOBS, *Gleanings from Nature*, 1898, 1:19, 27, 35, 36 (Waynesburg, Greene Co., nesting)—COPE, *Cassinia*, 1902, 5:19 (Galeton, Potter Co., June)—TODD, *Ann. Carnegie Mus.*, 1904, 2:587 (Presque Isle, Erie Co., summer)—TODD, in Bausman, *Hist. Beaver Co., Pa.*, 1904, 2:1201 (Beaver Co., summer)—COOKE, *Bird-Lore*, 1904, 6:23 (Beaver, Beaver Co., and Renovo, Clinton Co., migration)—COOKE, *Bull. Biol. Surv.* no. 18, 1904, 120 (Beaver, Beaver Co., Waynesburg, Greene Co., and Renovo, Clinton Co., migration).

Icteria virens virens HARLOW, *Auk*, 1912, 29:476 ([Pine Grove Mills, Centre Co.], nesting); 1918, 35:144 (Bald Knob, Centre Co., breeding)—DICKEY, *Oölogist*, 1914, 31:156 ([Greene Co.], nesting)—STONE, *Cassinia*, 1919, 22:36 (Altoona, Blair Co., summer, *fide* McGraw)—CHRISTY, *Cardinal*, 1923, v. 1, no. 1, [p. 13] (Sewickley, Allegheny Co., breeding)—BURLEIGH, *Wilson Bull.*, 1923, 35:141 (Allegheny Co., nesting); 1924, 36:73; and 1931, 43:52 (State College, Centre Co., migration; nesting)—SUTTON, *Ann. Carnegie Mus.*, 1928, 18:222 (Meadville and Pymatuning Swamp, Crawford Co., nesting)—BURLEIGH, *Cardinal*, 1932, 3:81 (Chestnut Ridge, near Uniontown, Fayette Co., summer).

"Chat" SIMPSON, *Oölogist*, 1909, 26:153 (Erie, Erie Co., July); 1911, 28:165; and 1914, 31:122 (Warren, Warren Co., nesting)—SCOVILLE, *Cassinia*, 1920, 23:20 ([Charter Oak, Huntingdon Co.], May)—MCCLELLAND, *Am. Mid. Nat.*, 1922, 8:36 (Washington, Washington Co., summer)—STREET, *Cassinia*, 1923, 24:10, 18 (Greencastle to Ft. Loudon, Jordan's Knob, and Horse Valley, Franklin Co., June).

HOODED WARBLER (Plate 20)

WILSONIA CITRINA (Boddaert)

Description—Adult male: upperparts bright olive green, the *wings plain*, a little duller; *underparts bright yellow;* head and throat black, with a *broad band or "mask" of bright yellow* across the forehead and sides of the head; tail dusky, the feathers edged with bright olive green, the outer feathers with large white areas; feet pale. *Adult female:* similar, but the black area of the head and throat reduced or wanting, these parts being colored to correspond with the upperparts and underparts, respectively. *Young birds* are in general similar to adults, but the markings are less distinct. In any plumage the unbarred wings, yellow underparts, and white tail-spots are the best field marks.

Range—This species is peculiar to the eastern United States in summer, but it winters in Mexico and Central America. Of the three members of its generic group it has the most southern breeding range, which extends southward to the shores of the Gulf of Mexico. The northern limit of this range is decidedly irregular and seems to be fluctuating. It conforms for the most part to the accepted northern boundary of the Carolinian Fauna; but there are now many records of this bird's casual occurrence farther north, and they apparently justify the suspicion that an extension of range is in progress. There seems to be a constant tendency for birds of this species to overshoot the mark, so to speak, in the spring migration—a tendency in itself likely to produce such an extension. On the Atlantic coast the Hooded Warbler is not known to breed beyond southern Connecticut, and in western New York it is locally distributed, especially in the vicinity of Lake Erie and Lake Ontario, and avoids the highlands altogether. In western Pennsylvania it is also found in the region of Lake Erie, but it becomes more numerous southward, in the direction of the Ohio Valley, where it is a common summer resident. Thence it invades the mountains to the eastward and inhabits the woods on both

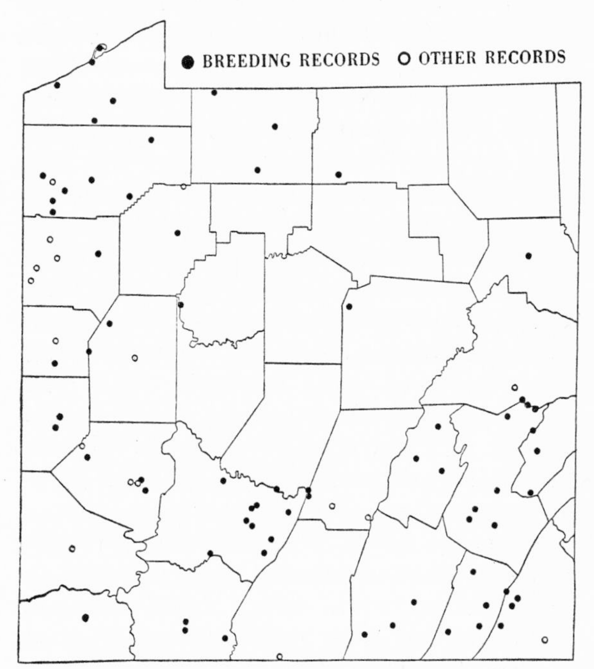

LOCAL RANGE OF THE HOODED WARBLER

Chestnut Ridge and Laurel Hill from base to summit. For the highlands of Somerset County, however, there are as yet no breeding records, although A. B. Miller, in listing the species at Springs as a rare migrant, remarks that he has two June records.

Throughout the ridge and valley section the Hooded Warbler is likewise common, not only in the valley country, but at the higher elevations as well. Oddly enough, at Bear Meadows, in southern Centre County, the Hooded and Canada warblers are closely associated. The former may possibly have been a recent immigrant, and the latter a relict of primitive conditions. The status of the Hooded Warbler in the region east of the Allegheny divide parallels that of several other supposedly Carolinian species; but the bird's occurrence in the plateau region is puzzling and difficult to reconcile with known laws. I myself have never observed the species anywhere in that section, nor in fact closer thereto than Bear Lake, in northwestern Warren County. At Warren, however, it breeds regularly, although not commonly, and remains chiefly in the uplands; it has also been recorded in summer near the head of Tionesta Creek, in the same county (Simpson), and in the East Tionesta Forest Reserve (Cope and Hawkins, 1934). Moreover, its nests and eggs have repeatedly been taken by A. K. Pierce at Kane (a locality from which it had first been reported by Warren as early as 1891), at an elevation of over two thousand feet. The species also appears on both Balliet's and Van Fleet's lists of the breeding birds of DuBois, where local conditions could scarcely have been any different from those originally prevailing at Kane.

Although Mr. Pierce found the Hooded Warbler at Renovo almost every spring between 1892 and 1922, he did not find it in the breeding season until 1912 and did not discover a nest until 1914. In the season of 1915 he located no fewer than twelve breeding pairs. Thus one receives the impression that in Clinton County, at least, this bird has been a comparatively recent immigrant. It seems to be a species that, regardless of elevation, is always ready to invade and settle in a new region as soon as the local conditions become favorable.

Migration—In both 1899 and 1902 I recorded the arrival of this warbler at Beaver as early as April 29. In 1908 and 1911, however, it was not noted until May 11 and May 9, respectively. Otherwise my "first-seen" dates are in the first week of May, which I consider the average time of arrival in the Ohio Valley. Farther north the bird tends to be a few days later and at Warren is delayed until the second week in May. The only long series of records is from Renovo and covers eighteen seasons. The dates range from May 4 to 18, the average being May 9. Mr. Miller has not observed the species at Springs, Somerset County, near our southern boundary, earlier than May 7 (1921). Although this warbler is not so difficult as some others to identify in the fall, few records for that season are available. The southward movement is under way in September, and most of our summer residents have gone before the end of that month. Some late dates are: Beaver, September 25, 1890, September 28, 1930, and October 3, 1891 (Todd); Pittsburgh, September 19, 1912 (Burleigh); State College, September 19, 1915 (Burleigh); Renovo, October 4, 1900, and October 3, 1902 (Pierce). By October the earliest migrants have already reached their winter quarters in Central America.

Habits[1]—Although not the commonest of the warblers that breed in western Pennsylvania, the Hooded Warbler is certainly one of the most striking. Were it not for the fact that it is generally found only in regions well removed from human habitation, its livery of gold, green, and jet, together with its loud, clear song, would undoubtedly make it one of our best-known warblers.

This bird exhibits several anomalous ecological preferences. In a suitable habitat it may be really abundant, as for example at McConnell's Mills on Slippery Rock Creek in Lawrence County, where in July of 1927 I found no fewer than ten singing males in two miles along the creek bottom. In Beaver County it occurs regularly in laurel thickets and in the luxuriant bottomlands of streams tributary to the Ohio and Beaver rivers. In the northern part of the state its preference for evergreen shrubs is evidenced in its frequent association with rhododendron, while on the series of ridges of the Allegheny Mountains it occurs in hardwood timber. It is apparently dependent on moist, rich woodland that supplies an abundance of secluded, leafy song-perches from which the males may pro-

[1]Account contributed by Rudyerd Boulton.

claim their territory. It also requires plenty of ground cover and forest-floor herbage, from which it collects most of its food.

The nest is invariably placed near the ground, generally at no greater height than three feet. It is often located in blackberry tangles, although laurel bushes and suckers from stumps are sometimes selected. The nest itself is a neat cup of dry grasses and weed stalks, with a foundation and periphery of dead leaves, and it is sometimes partially suspended from supporting twigs. June is the month of greatest breeding activity, and in the first week the eggs are laid. The normal number is four, but three or five sometimes comprise a set. They are white, lightly spotted with brown, purple, and lavender, and the markings tend to form a wreath about the large end. In size the eggs average about .71 by .51 inches.

During the nesting season the Hooded Warbler is a persistent singer, although an intruder in his territory is apt to silence him, at least temporarily. The song is penetrating and distinctive and can easily be heard at a distance of more than a hundred yards. On one occasion, while quietly watching a singing male on the palisades of the Ohio River opposite Beaver, I had an opportunity to observe closely the singing behavior. A bare twig within fifteen feet of my head was one of the perches. This was quite within the canopy of the forest and was not an exposed site, although the bird obviously had an extensive view of its surroundings. For ten minutes or so it sang at intervals of about forty-five seconds and then flew to another song-perch a hundred yards away. Its position was slightly more erect than in the normal pose, and between songs it was motionless on the twig except for occasional flirts of the tail, which caused the white areas to flash into view.

Like most birds, the Hooded Warbler has a number of songs, but to me the most characteristic is a series of three double syllables, with a pronounced accent on the first half of the last phrase. It can be written *peet-to, peet-to, weet-two.* Others have syllabized it as follows: *pea-ry, pea-ry, pea-ah* (Eifrig); *tsu-e, tsu-e, tsu-e, tsu-wee-tsu* (Dawson); *whee-whee-whee-a-wheer* (Allison). The call note is a sharp *chip* that becomes metallic and staccato when the bird is alarmed.

Once I was amazed to find myself eye to eye, as it were, with an adult male of this species. The bird was sitting quietly on a low branch of a leafy maple and must have flown in while my attention was directed elsewhere. Brilliant sun shining through the young leaves made some of them appear as yellow as the bird's breast, while the green tones of its back were matched by other leaves in the shadow. The black markings of the head and throat were, in this instance at least, true "ruptive markings," since it was some moments before I could clearly see the outline of the bird, although it was in plain view and in good light. When examining specimens in the laboratory, it is difficult to think of the Hooded Warbler as protectively colored. I suspect the truth is that at some time and under some circumstances every bird or animal is seen with difficulty, both by man and by its natural predators. It is in the nature of things that if the sum total of these occasions gives a species even an infinitesimal advantage, the combinations of color that contribute to that survival-value will become genetically fixed.

On one occasion Norman McClintock and I set up a photographic blind six feet from a hooded warbler's nest that had been discovered just above the "Elm Rocks" on lower Raccoon Creek in Beaver County. For about half an hour both parents were much disturbed by the great pyramid of canvas that was suddenly reared before their home, and they raced about the forest floor like little mice. Eventually their alarmed chirpings became quieter and they began to search half-heartedly for insects. All this time the fledglings, which were about ready to leave the nest, twisted and squirmed about in order to follow with their eyes the comings and goings of their parents. Finally the female darted to the nest, tucked into a capacious throat a consignment of small insects that looked like plant lice, and the normal routine of feeding was soon resumed. Both adults frequently visited the nest, but the male was hurried in his actions, compared to his more deliberate mate. In two hours of observation, during which a splendid motion-picture record was made, the young were fed several times with small insects of the type mentioned, once with green geometrid larvae, and three times with large pale moth millers. The wings of the moths were folded and tucked and jammed into the mouths of the youngsters, the tips sometimes protruding for some minutes. Once, while standing on the edge of the nest, the female dropped a moth, but she neatly retrieved it in the air before it had fallen the eighteen inches to the ground.

As we dismantled the blind, the nest "exploded," all four of the young birds leaving as by a signal. Three were escorted by the male, while the smallest and weakest was followed by Mr. McClintock and me, as well as by the female; it settled on a dead branch five feet from the ground, where the parent continued to feed it.

Sylvania mitrata Warren, *Birds Pa.*, ed. 2, 1890, 271, 300 (Clinton and Clearfield Co., breeding, *fide* Van Fleet; Erie Co., *fide* Sennett; Centre Co., *fide* Roddy; Elk, Cameron, Somerset, Blair, and Cambria Co., summer)—Todd, *Auk*, 1891, 8:399; and 1893, 10:209 (Beaver, Beaver Co., breeding)—Jacobs, *Summer Birds Greene Co., Pa.*, 1893, 13 (Greene Co., nesting)—Rhoads, *Auk*, 1899, 16:313 (Beaver, Beaver Co., May; Laughlintown, Westmoreland Co., June; and "Leetsdale" [Fair Oaks], Allegheny Co., May).

"Hooded Warbler" Warren, *Forest and Stream*, 1891, 37:83 (Kane, McKean Co., summer)—Cooke, *Bird-Lore*, 1904, 6:22 (Renovo, Clinton Co., and Beaver, Beaver Co., migration)—Stone, *Cassinia*, 1906, 9:41, 44 (Scrub Ridge, west of McConnellsburg, Fulton Co., June)—Simpson, *Oölogist*, 1909, 26:170; 1914, 31:91, 122 (Warren, Warren Co., nesting, etc.); 1912, 29:250 (Erie, Erie Co., June), 330 (head of Tionesta Creek, Warren Co., transient)—Miller (M. H.), *In the Open*, Dec., 1912, 3:41 (McKinley Park, Allegheny Co., summer)—Miller (R. F.), *Oölogist*, 1919, 36:156 (Charter Oak, Huntingdon Co., nesting)—McClelland, *Am. Mid. Nat.*, 1922, 8:37 (Washington, Washington Co., transient)—Street, *Cassinia*, 1923, 24:10, 18 (Little Cove Creek above Foltz, Jordan's Knob, and Horse Valley, Franklin Co., June)—Eastwood, *Bird-Lore*, 1926, 28:272 (Pittsburgh region, Allegheny Co., May)—Cope and Hawkins, *Forest Leaves*, 1934, 24:26 (East Tionesta Forest Reserve, Warren and McKean Co., summer).

Wilsonia mitrata Todd, *Ann. Carnegie Mus.*, 1904, 2:587 (Erie, Erie Co., summer)—Todd, in Bausman, *Hist. Beaver Co., Pa.*, 1904, 2:1201 (Beaver Co., summer)—Cooke, *Bull. Biol. Surv.* no. 18, 1904, 123 (Renovo, Clinton Co., and Beaver, Beaver Co., migration)—Stone, *Cassinia*, 1905, 8:59 (Brush Mountain, Blair Co., June).

Wilsonia citrina Harlow, *Auk*, 1912, 29:476 ("Stone Valley" [Charter Oak], Huntingdon Co.; Shingletown Gap, Centre Co., summer); 1918, 35:144 (Franklin, Centre, Huntingdon, Mifflin, Juniata, Clinton, and Warren Co.)—Stone, *Cassinia*, 1920, 23:38 (Altoona, Blair Co., May, *fide* McGraw)—Christy, *Cardinal*, 1923, v. 1, no. 1, [p. 13] (Sewickley, Allegheny Co., breeding)—Burleigh, *Wilson Bull.*, 1923, 35:141 (Allegheny Co., September); 1924, 36:73; 1931, 43:52 (State College, Centre Co., migration; nesting)—[Editor], *Cassinia*, 1926, 25:34 (Greencastle, Franklin Co., May, *fide* Ziegler)—Sutton, *Ann. Carnegie Mus.*, 1928, 18:222 (Meadville and Pymatuning Swamp, Crawford Co., nesting)—Burleigh, *Cardinal*, 1929, 2:119 (Pittsburgh, Allegheny Co., August)—Burleigh, *Cardinal*, 1932, 3:81 ([Summit], Fayette Co., summer).

WILSON'S WARBLER (Plate 20)

WILSONIA PUSILLA PUSILLA (Wilson)

Description—One of the smaller warblers. *Adult male:* upperparts (including wings and edgings of tail), yellowish green; *underparts bright yellow; cap black;* forehead, eye-ring, and line over eye, bright yellow; sides of head yellow, shaded behind with green. *Adult female:* in general similar to the male, but duller, and black cap smaller. In the *young male* in the fall, the black cap is veiled with green, while in the *young female* the crown is colored like the back.

Range—As stated by W. W. Cooke (1904), "The combined breeding and migration ranges of the eastern and western forms of the Wilson Warbler cover the greater part of the North American continent. The eastern subspecies scarcely nests south of the Canadian life zone." In the breeding season this bird is the most northern of the three species of its generic group, and proceeds far beyond the limits of our region. It is thus merely a transient with us, fairly regular, but common only at odd intervals. It has been reported from various sections of western Pennsylvania by different observers and is probably no more or no less numerous in one part than in another.

Migration—From its winter home in Central America this warbler migrates northward, probably across the Gulf of Mexico, to reach the southern states in April. One of the later warbler migrants, it seldom reaches the latitude of western Pennsylvania before the second week in May, while the full tide of the migration comes still later. I have not noted it at Beaver earlier than May 8 (1889; 1913), and most of my arrival records show dates considerably after that time; in 1910 I recorded it on May 28. In 1895 it was seen at Renovo on the exceptionally early date of May 1, and in 1907 it was noted there as late as May 31 (Pierce). At Springs, Somerset County, it has arrived between May 14 and 25, the average date being May 20 (Miller). May 10 (1902) is the earliest date for Warren (Simpson). I saw one bird on Presque Isle on May 30 in 1935. Laggards may even remain until June.

In the fall migration this warbler often appears late in August, although the main movement is in September. August 28 (1937) is an early record for Frick Park, Pittsburgh (Malley). I have noted it at Beaver at various times between August 30 (1910) and September 21 (1910). Corresponding dates for the Pymatuning region of Crawford County in 1925 were August 28 and September 22 (Sutton), and for Presque Isle in 1900, August 30 and September 21. At Renovo, A. K. Pierce observed the species as late as September 24 in 1900, and one specimen was secured by D. A. Atkinson at Wilkinsburg on September 25, 1898. The latest fall record is supplied by T. D. Burleigh, who saw one bird at Pittsburgh on October 1 in 1913.

Habits—This dainty little warbler does not appear as a rule until the shrubbery and bushes are sufficiently leafed to conceal its brightly colored plumage. Thickets of hawthorn or wild crab-apple trees, in full bloom at the time of its arrival, are its favorite haunts; in the absence of these, it may choose thickets of bushes and briers, or alders and low willows along streams. It passes most of its time industriously gleaning among the blossoms and will occasionally betray its presence by its characteristic song. This song, which is suggestive of the Nashville Warbler's, begins with a series of several notes, all in the same key, and ends with a twitter. The ordinary call note is a lisping chirp. In the fall this warbler often works in high weeds, such as jewelweed and ragweed. It is an active, sprightly little bird, with a habit of twitching its tail up and down at intervals; in some of its actions it suggests a flycatcher.

Wilsonia pusilla TODD, *Ann. Carnegie Mus.*, 1904, 2:587 (Presque Isle, Erie Co., transient)—TODD, in Bausman, *Hist. Beaver Co., Pa.*, 1904, 2:1201 (Beaver Co., transient)—COOKE, *Bird-Lore*, 1904, 6:58 (Beaver, Beaver Co., and Renovo, Clinton Co., migration)—COOKE, *Bull. Biol. Surv.* no. 18, 1904, 126 (Beaver, Beaver Co., and Renovo, Clinton Co., migration).

"Wilson Warbler" SIMPSON, *Oölogist*, 1914, 31:122 (Warren, Warren Co., transient)—MCCLELLAND, *Am. Mid. Nat.*, 1922, 8:37 (Washington, Washington Co., transient)—CHRISTY, *Cardinal*, 1924, v. 1, no. 4, p. 2 (Big Traverse Valley, Beaver Co., May)—EASTWOOD, *Bird-Lore*, 1925, 27:263; 1926, 28: 272 (Pittsburgh region, Allegheny Co., May)—WOOD, *Oölogist*, 1932, 49:106 (State College, Centre Co., May).

Wilsonia pusilla pusilla CHRISTY, *Cardinal*, 1923, v. 1, no. 1, [p. 13] (Sewickley, Allegheny Co., transient)—BURLEIGH, *Wilson Bull.*, 1923, 35:142 (Allegheny Co., fall transient); 1924, 36:130 (State College, Centre Co., migration)—SUTTON, *Ann. Carnegie Mus.*, 1928, 18:223 (Meadville and Pymatuning Swamp, Crawford Co., transient)—BURLEIGH, *Cardinal*, 1929, 2:120 (Allegheny Co., fall migration).

CANADA WARBLER (Plate 20)

WILSONIA CANADENSIS (Linnaeus)

Description—A warbler of average size, with the upperparts (except the head), wings, and tail, uniform in color. *Adult male:* upperparts (including wings and tail), slaty gray, the forehead and crown more or less varied with black; eye-ring, lores, and underparts, bright yellow; a *broad necklace of black spots* on the breast is joined in front to a black area on the sides of the neck and head reaching as far as the eyes; feet pale. *Female:* similar, but the black markings of the head and breast are less distinct and more dusky olive in color. *Young birds* in the fall resemble the adult female but are still duller, with all the markings less distinct.

Range—The summer range of the Canada Warbler stretches from Newfoundland westward to the base of the Rocky Mountains and southward along the Appalachian highlands to northern Georgia. It is one of the few birds that attracted Audubon's notice when he crossed the Pennsylvania mountains. On the north, its range impinges upon that of Wilson's Warbler; on the south, upon that of the Hooded. Although in the main it is a species characteristic of the Canadian Fauna, it invades the Alleghanian at many points. In western New York, according to E. H. Eaton, it breeds in the highlands of the southern counties; across the border in western Pennsylvania, it occupies all the plateau region, and in the Allegheny Valley drops down to an elevation of one thousand feet or even lower. My record from Freeport, Armstrong County, where several pairs along

Buffalo Creek were apparently settled for the season in June, 1894, brings the breeding range within twenty-five miles of Pittsburgh. In the southwestern counties in general, as far east as Chestnut Ridge, the species is known only as a regular and fairly common transient in spring and fall.[1] It has been found in the breeding season at several points along Chestnut Ridge: Two Lick and Yellow creeks, Indiana County (Trimble; Smyth); the "Packsaddle" and Kingston, Westmoreland County (Todd); and Summit, Fayette County (Burleigh; Dickey). No breeding records are available from the Ligonier Valley, although there are some from Laurel Hill and from Somerset and Cambria counties as far east as the crest of the Alleghenies.

East of the main divide, a peculiar situation exists. In this region, where the several mountain ridges frequently attain an elevation of two thousand feet, and to which such northerly inclined birds as the Black-throated Blue Warbler and the Blackburnian Warbler are so partial in summer, one would naturally expect to find the Canadian Warbler also. Yet it apparently avoids this section, except for an isolated area centering in the so-called "Seven Mountains" of Centre and Huntingdon counties, where it has been found summering by R. C. Harlow, S. S. Dickey, T. D. Burleigh, and myself. That its presence there is not primarily dependent upon altitude may be inferred from the fact that it occurs in the valleys of the streams as well as in the highlands. Farther west I have encountered it in June in the eastern foothills of the Alleghenies near Port Matilda, Centre County, and also, surprisingly, along Bald Eagle Creek at Vail, Blair County. At Hollidaysburg and Altoona, however, it is known only as a transient (Berg; McGraw).

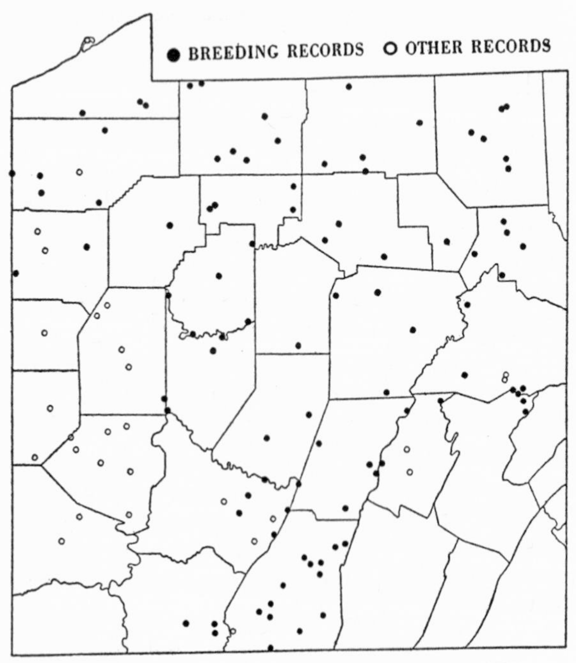

LOCAL RANGE OF THE CANADA WARBLER

The status of the species in the northwestern counties has not yet been fully determined. In the region of Pymatuning Swamp, it is, as would be expected, a regular but not very common summer resident; according to H. M. McQuiston, it also breeds near Sharon. To the north and east, its presence in June near Cambridge Springs and Hydetown, Crawford County, and at Union City, Erie County, is vouched for by Dr. Dickey, while F. L. Homer found it common at Edinboro, Erie County, in July, 1895. The latter observer found a family group near Sandy Lake, Mercer County, during the same season. These various records tend to fill the gap between those from Pymatuning Swamp, on the one hand, and those from Warren County, on the other, and suggest that the species originally ranged continuously across this region, where now it is of only local and isolated occurrence. This arm of its breeding area extends westward into Ashtabula County, Ohio (Hicks). From Mercer County southward, as well as along the lake shore plain in Erie County, the species is a transient only.

Migration—The Canada Warbler goes to South America for the winter. In its northward migration it does not reach our latitude until the first, or often the second, week in May. No April dates are on record. I have noted its arrival at Beaver between May 3 and 13. (Later dates are probably erroneous.) The average arrival date there is May 7; and I have recorded its (presumed) departure from May 18 to 28. In the neighboring county of Allegheny it has been seen between May 4 and 24 (Burleigh). Generally speaking,

[1]An apparent exception to this general statement may be noted. In 1924 B. H. Christy was surprised to find a singing male always at the same place along Big Traverse Creek, Beaver County, until June 15. The next year he again found one (probably the same bird) there on July 5. If this particular bird was breeding, the occurrence was certainly exceptional and sporadic.

these limiting dates coincide with those from other parts of our region and indicate the usual period of migration. At Renovo, where the species breeds, the arrival records of A. K. Pierce for twenty seasons range from May 4 to 14, and the average date is May 8—one day later than at Beaver. Some early arrival dates from other localities are: Butler, May 4, 1895 (Roth); Greenville, May 5, 1922 and 1929 (Seiple); Springs, Somerset County, May 4, 1914 (Miller); Warren, May 6, 1899 (Simpson).

The fall movement begins very early—long before there is any apparent necessity for the birds to migrate. Mr. Burleigh has reported this warbler from Pittsburgh on July 27, 1912, and on July 25, 1913. Such early dates seem remarkable but are understandable in view of the fact that the species breeds at no great distance from this locality. Other observers report it in August: Johnsburg, Somerset County, August 1, 1903 (Eifrig); Morganza, Washington County, August 14, 1896 (Van Ostrand); Frick Park, Pittsburgh, August 17, 1937 (Malley); New Hamburg, Mercer County, August 18, 1888 (Homer); Sewickley, August 27, 1919 (Christy); Beaver, August 27, 1891 (Todd). As a rule it is less numerous in fall than in spring, and the majority of the birds evidently pass through our region before September. Indeed, most of the "last-seen" dates for Renovo in the A. K. Pierce records fall in August, and the latest is September 11 (1913). The species was seen at Pymatuning Swamp on September 12 in 1925 (Sutton). In 1889 I saw it at Beaver on September 7, and Mr. Burleigh supplies an extraordinarily late record—October 3 (1913)—for Pittsburgh. By that time the vanguard of the species has reached Costa Rica.

Habits—Concerning this warbler, Gerald Thayer writes: "The Canadian is a sprightly, wide-awake, fly-snapping Warbler, vivid in movement and in song; clearly marked and brightly colored. In actions it is like the Wilson's, a sort of mongrel between a *Dendroica*, an American Redstart, and a true Flycatcher. It darts after flying insects like one of the Tyrannidæ, and its bill may sometimes be heard to 'click' when it seizes something; it has much of the Redstart's insistent nervousness of motion, but is a less airy 'flitter'; and, finally, it glides and gleans among leaves and twigs like a true gleaning Warbler."[1]

During migration this bird chooses shrubbery, bushy growths, and the lower branches of forest trees; it seldom ascends into the treetops with the other warblers. In the spring I have occasionally seen it gleaning among the blossoms of orchard trees. At this season the male is a persistent singer; his twittering song is characteristic, but hard to describe. It is rapidly delivered and, if it were louder, might sound a little like a fragment of the song of the American Goldfinch. The bird often sings from a low perch and will dart under cover if disturbed. On its nesting grounds the species is like the Black-throated Blue Warbler in its partiality for rhododendron thickets, where it is sometimes very common. Nowhere have I found it more numerous during June than in the rhododendron growth of Tamarack Swamp, Clinton County, and of Bear Meadows, Centre County. In the Buffalo Creek region of Armstrong and Butler counties it inhabits woodland thickets, especially those growing along the smaller streams and the banks of the creek itself, in the shade of the hemlocks. Although wont to keep under cover, it readily responds to "squeaking," and a pair may often be decoyed to within a few feet of an observer. Their anxiety will betray the proximity of a nest or young.

Sundry workers have found nests of this warbler in various parts of western Pennsylvania. Of two that I discovered at Anderson Creek, Clearfield County, on June 10, 1899, one was placed in a cranny among the upturned roots of a fallen tree, the other in a hole in the rotten wood of a mossy log, just under a projecting knot. Both types of location, according to the observations of others, are favorite sites. R. B. Simpson, who has found many nests at Warren, reports that they are also placed under the projecting banks of streams and among the ferns and moss on the sides of large rocks and ledges. One nest referred to by Mr. Burleigh was built in a mass of dry leaves at the base of a huckleberry bush; the brim was flush with the ground. Wherever located, the nest is a more or less bulky, formless structure; it is composed of dry (often skeletonized) leaves, shreds of bark, dry grass, and weed stalks, with a lining of finer vegetable fibers, among which the black rootlets of the maidenhair fern (*Adiantum*) are a conspicuous element. Often the cavity of the nest

[1]In F. M. Chapman, *Warblers of North America*, 1907, p. 283.

is off center, because of the configuration of the nest-hole. Four or five eggs compose the set; they are laid late in May or early in June. In shape they tend to rounded ovate, and they average .67 by .52 inches. The ground-color is white, with a slight creamy tint, and the markings are speckles or spots of reddish brown, more evenly distributed than is usual with warblers' eggs in general.

Muscicapa canadensis AUDUBON, *Orn. Biog.*, 1834, 2:18 (Allegheny Mts., western Pa.).

Myiodioctes canadensis TEULON, *Jour. Boston Zoöl. Soc.*, 1882, 1:51 (Bradford, McKean Co., July)—TOWNSEND, *Proc. Acad. Nat. Sci. Philadelphia*, 1883, 61 (Latrobe, Westmoreland Co., transient)—VAN FLEET, *Ornithologist and Oölogist*, 1884, 9:108 (DuBois, Clearfield Co.).

Sylvania canadensis WARREN, *Birds Pa.*, ed. 2, 1890, 271, 301 (Clinton Co., *fide* Van Fleet; McKean Co., *fide* Teulon; Centre Co., *fide* Roddy, breeding)—TODD, *Auk*, 1891, 8:399 (Beaver, Beaver Co., transient; Buffalo Creek region, Butler and Armstrong Co., summer)—DWIGHT, *Auk*, 1892, 9:133, 134, 139 (Cresson, Cambria Co., June)—TODD, *Auk*, 1893, 10:42, 46 (Coalport, Clearfield Co., June)—BAILY, *Auk*, 1896, 13:291, 292, 296 (Williamsville, Elk Co., June–July).

"Canadian Flycatcher" WARREN, *Forest and Stream*, 1891, 37:83 (Kane, McKean Co., summer).

"Canadian Warbler" COOKE, *Bird-Lore*, 1904, 6:59 (Beaver, Beaver Co., and Renovo, Clinton Co., migration)—SIMPSON, *Oölogist*, 1909, 26:170; 1911, 28:162; 1912, 29:276; and 1914, 31:122 (Warren, Warren Co., nesting, etc.); 1912, 29:330 (head of Tionesta Creek, Warren Co., summer)—MILLER (M. H.), *In the Open*, Dec., 1912, 3:41 (McKinley Park, Allegheny Co., transient)—HARLOW, *Oölogist*, 1914, 31:98 ([Charter Oak], Huntingdon Co., spring)—DICKEY, *Oölogist*, 1914, 31:171 ([Charter Oak], Huntingdon Co., June), 207 (Cresson, Cambria Co., June)—MILLER (R. F.), *Oölogist*, 1919, 36:156 (Shingletown, Centre Co., nesting)—MCCLELLAND, *Am. Mid. Nat.*, 1922, 8:37 (Washington, Washington Co., transient)—CHRISTY, *Cardinal*, 1924, v. 1, no. 4, p. 10 (Big Traverse Valley, Beaver Co., June)—EASTWOOD, *Bird-Lore*, 1925, 27:263; 1926, 28:272 (Pittsburgh region, Allegheny Co., May), 273 (Rector, Westmoreland Co., May, *fide* Knauz).

Wilsonia canadensis COPE, *Cassinia*, 1902, 5:10, 19 (Tamarack Swamp, Clinton Co., and Potter Co., June)—TODD, *Ann. Carnegie Mus.*, 1904, 2:587 (Presque Isle, Erie Co., transient)—TODD, in Bausman, *Hist. Beaver Co., Pa.*, 1904, 2:1201 (Beaver Co., transient)—COOKE, *Bull. Biol. Surv.* no. 18, 1904, 129 (Beaver, Beaver Co., and Renovo, Clinton Co., migration)—KEIM, *Cassinia*, 1905, 8:40 (Port Allegany, McKean Co., summer)—HARLOW, *Auk*, 1912, 29:466, 476 (Bald Knob and region, Centre Co., nesting); 1918, 35:144 (Fayette, Juniata, Huntingdon, Centre, and Warren Co., breeding)—CHRISTY, *Cardinal*, 1923, v. 1, no. 1, [p. 13] (Sewickley, Allegheny Co., transient)—BURLEIGH, *Wilson Bull.*, 1923, 35:142 (Allegheny Co., migration); 1924, 36:73; and 1931, 43:52 (State College and vicinity, Centre Co., migration; nesting)—CHRISTY and SUTTON, *Cardinal*, 1928, 2:74 (Cook Forest, Clarion Co., summer)—SUTTON, *Ann. Carnegie Mus.*, 1928, 18:223 (Pymatuning Swamp, Crawford Co., breeding; Meadville, transient)—BURLEIGH, *Cardinal*, 1932, 3:81 (Summit, Fayette Co., nesting).

"Canada Warbler" EASTWOOD, *Bird-Lore*, 1927, 29:273 (Springs, Somerset Co., breeding, *fide* Miller)—HEGNER and CHRISTY, *Cardinal*, 1931, 3:22 (North Park, Allegheny Co., May)—COPE and HAWKINS, *Forest Leaves*, 1934, 24:26 (E. Tionesta Forest Reserve, Warren and McKean Co., summer).

AMERICAN REDSTART (Plate 20)

SETOPHAGA RUTICILLA (Linnaeus)

Description—A warbler of medium size, with an orange or yellow area on either side of the breast; the tail has a similarly colored, square-cut area and a broad black tip. *Adult male:* upperparts, head, throat, and *breast*, black, the latter with a *large orange spot* on either side, extending under the wings; rest of underparts white; *wings* black, with a *large dull orange area in the middle; tail* black in the middle and at the tip, the rest *pale orange;* bill black. *Adult female:* similar to the male in color pattern only; top and sides of head grayish; rest of upperparts dull olive, the wings and tail darker, and the colored areas yellow, brighter on the sides of the breast; underparts dull white, the spot on the sides of the breast dull orange or yellow. *Immature male* (second year): resembles the adult female, but there are usually some black feathers intermixed on the head and underparts; the sides of the breast more orange. (The bird breeds in this plumage.) *Young birds* in the fall are still duller than the adult female, and the wing-spot is often reduced to a mere trace.

Range—Only a few warblers have a more extensive breeding range than that of the American Redstart. It covers the greater part of the northern United States and a large area in Canada from the Gulf of St. Lawrence north and west to the valley of the Mackenzie River. The total number of individuals must be very large. The species does not reach the Pacific coast; in the East it ranges southward to North Carolina and (in the mountains) to northern Alabama. Its winter range is likewise extensive and includes the West Indies, southern Mexico, Central America, and northern South America. Western Pennsylvania thus lies in the midst of its general breeding range, but its local range within the area is decidedly "spotty." Although known as a common summer resident in Beaver County, it is listed as rare at Bethany, West Virginia, not many miles away. It is common also in all the western counties as far east as the mountains, as well as in the ridge and valley section in general. I have never found it, however, in the plateau region except at Port Allegany, McKean County, and at Cranberry Swamp, Warren County. Although there are a few records (published and otherwise) from various parts of this area, the species is apparently much less numerous there than in the lower country on either side. I found it abundant in June, 1898, on the lower slopes of Chestnut Ridge along the gap of Loyalhanna Creek, but on my traverse of Cambria and Indiana counties in 1893 I did not see a single bird. Some records from that region, however, have since been received.

Migration—At Pittsburgh in the spring of 1916, the first redstart of the season was observed by T. D. Burleigh on April 21. This was an unusually early date; ordinarily we do not look for this bird until about the first of May, and in backward seasons it may not come until a week or so later. My arrival records for Beaver range from April 26 (1899) to May 10 (1910); the average date is May 4. R. B. Simpson reports the species' arrival at Warren from May 1 (1903) to 12 (1893). In the A. K. Pierce records for Renovo, covering twenty-five seasons, the dates vary from April 29 (1914) to May 14 (1901), and the average is May 4—as it is also at Beaver. On days of special movement in the spring migration, large flights sometimes occur. In the fall these flights are of regular occurrence, and in September the Redstart becomes especially prominent among the hosts of kindred species that throng our woodlands. The bulk of the Redstart population summers north of our region, and the southward migration begins very early. Migrants from the North are in evidence in August, but the great influx does not occur until September. By the middle of that month most of the birds have passed through, but almost every year laggards may be seen at intervals until early October. Late fall records are: Beaver, September 30, 1890 (Todd); Pittsburgh, October 3, 1937 (Shoemaker), and September 27, 1912 and 1913 (Burleigh); Wilkinsburg, September 29, 1897 (Atkinson); State College, October 4, 1916 (Burleigh); Renovo, September 30, 1906, and October 16, 1903 (Pierce). Besides these, there are two records of single birds that seem to have been left behind by their companions: B. H. Christy saw a redstart at Sewickley on November 28, 1926, and H. A. McGraw found another on December 25, 1918, at Lakemont, Blair County. One wonders how so delicate a bird withstands the cold weather and further how it is able to find sustenance. In any event, it is very doubtful whether these individuals could have survived the winter.

Habits[1]—From the Redstart of Europe to the American bird of the same name is a far cry. The first is a small kind of thrush; the second, a somewhat aberrant species of the strictly New World family of wood warblers. Indeed, about the only thing that the two birds have in common is a habit of flirting the tail and exposing the differently colored outer feathers. The plumage of the male, with its contrast of black, white, and orange, places the Redstart among our more brilliantly colored birds, yet the species often escapes the eyes of the uninitiated.

When we regard a color plate of the American Redstart, we may wonder why this dazzling creature is so easily overlooked in the woods. But when in some sun-flecked coppice we at length discover the Redstart as the source of the shrill and simple song that we have been hearing, we are ready to acknowledge the value, to this bird, at least, of protective coloration.

Audubon, following the suggestion of Edwards, has pictured the Redstart dashing in a burst of fury upon a wasp that is portrayed with an impossibly outthrust sting. He has displayed the bird's plumage to advantage, it is true, and, in a day of lifeless delineation, the vivacity of his portrayal must have been refreshing; but as a presentment of the actual, living creature, Audubon's work is exaggerated and unreal.

The Redstart is active, quick of movement, and not easy to follow with the eye as it flits through the forest. When the male is singing, however, he commonly perches on a dark and naked branch,

[1]Account adapted largely from a manuscript supplied by Bayard H. Christy.

within the dome of foliage of some young tree. Dappled sunlight falls all about him, sifting down through the leafy canopy overhead. He does not move, except when from time to time he raises his head to sing. Although he may perch in full view, he is so well concealed from below that the searching eye scarcely spots him before he is off again, darting to another leafy apartment. Sometimes, to be sure, he will perch and sing from some dead, blackened stub against the sky; even so, his identity is all but lost, and he seems to be no more than a touch of sun upon some glistening point.

The song of the Redstart has been likened to those of several other species of this family group—the Yellow, Chestnut-sided, and Magnolia warblers. It bears a close resemblance, in both form and delivery, to that of the Bay-breasted Warbler, but it is softer and more sibilant. It is variable both in length and in emphasis. The young males of the second year also sing, but in a feebler manner. The peculiar quality of the Redstart's song is hard to describe; it is like a friend's voice that is recognized at once, although wherein it differs from a thousand others is hard to say.

Like most of its family, the Redstart is a bird of the forest. In the Ohio Valley it is fond of the damp, rich woods of the bottomlands and of the glades and hillsides along the smaller streams. In Mercer and Crawford counties, where the country is flatter, it frequents open forests on swampy land. In the Pymatuning region, according to G. M. Sutton (1928), it is "common as a summer resident only in the deciduous woods of the uplands, principally among the slender saplings of birch, maple, aspen, and beech." In Warren County, Mr. Simpson reports it common in summer in hardwood growths and also in suitable places along the river valley. Although it is of arboreal habit, it often descends to lower growth and bushes near the ground. It is a typical "flycatching" warbler, securing a fair proportion of its insect prey by dashing out into the air, but it is also an industrious gleaner among the leaves and branches.

After the birds' arrival, no more than a week or so elapses before nest-building begins. This labor falls to the female. Some observers report finding nests only two or three feet from the ground, but these low sites are exceptional. Mr. Simpson, who has found many nests in past years, writes that the majority were five or six feet from the ground, and none was over twenty. I have found some nests, however, at considerably higher elevations—perhaps in the crotch of a sapling or far out near the end of a lower limb of a tree. Mr. Christy once found a nest in an elderberry bush; and one that I discovered in 1890 was built in a dead branch caught in a tangled mass of grapevines—a curious and rather insecure location. Otherwise this nest was typical. It was composed of grayish-white, glistening plant fibers (probably from the milkweed), intermixed with fine strips of bark and bits of weed stalks; the brim was firm and compact, and the lining was composed of fine weed stalks and flaxlike fibers. The weathered appearance of the outside of the nest may be due in part to the source from which it comes. Late in May, 1935, at Presque Isle, I watched two female redstarts gathering nesting material from old vireo nests in the vicinity.

Dr. Sutton (1928) describes the nests of the Redstart found in the Pymatuning region as "always beautifully constructed, saddled deeply into the crotch of a slender trunk, or built upon a dead protruding limb like a knot. The walls of some of the nests were so thin that when removed from their crotch great holes appeared in the sides where no lining had been placed. In one case a nest had been built over the abandoned structure of a previous year. Only one nest was over twenty feet from the ground. Most of them were from six to twelve feet up. The females were often quite tame and one allowed me to stroke her back. As a rule they fluttered off slowly, however, with vivid wings and tail spread widely. Sets of eggs usually numbered four; but four nests with five eggs or young were found. No Cowbird eggs were found in any of the nests." In other sections the Redstart is a frequent victim of this parasite.

The eggs of this species are white, with a faint greenish tint, and are more or less heavily speckled, spotted, or sometimes blotched, with grayish brown, usually more densely at or around the larger end. They measure about .63 by .48 inches. May 25 is about the time for full sets in our region, but they have been found as early as May 18 and as late as June 26. The latter date almost certainly indicates a second attempt at nesting (Atkinson). Young are usually on the wing by the end of June.

Setophaga ruticilla TEULON, *Jour. Boston Zoöl. Soc.*, 1882, 1:51 (Bradford, McKean Co., nesting)—TOWNSEND, *Proc. Acad. Nat. Sci. Philadelphia*, 1883, 61 (Latrobe, Westmoreland Co.) —WARREN, *Birds Pa.*, ed. 2, 1890, 302 (Erie, Crawford, Blair, Centre, Potter, and McKean Co., breeding)—TODD, *Auk*, 1891, 8:399 (Beaver, Beaver Co., summer)—JACOBS, *Summer Birds Greene Co., Pa.*, 1893, 13 (Greene Co., nesting)—BAILY, *Auk*, 1896, 13:296 (Clarion River, near Williamsville, Elk Co., June–July)—TODD, *Ann. Carnegie Mus.*, 1904, 2:588 (Erie and Presque Isle, Erie Co., summer)—TODD, in Bausman, *Hist. Beaver Co., Pa.*, 1904, 2:1201 (Beaver Co., summer)—COOKE, *Bull. Biol. Surv.* no. 18, 1904, 132 (Beaver, Beaver Co., and Renovo, Clinton Co., migration)—KEIM, *Cassinia*, 1905, 8:40 (Port Allegany, McKean Co., summer)—HARLOW, *Auk*, 1912, 29:478 (southern Centre Co.)—CHRISTY, *Cardinal*, 1923, v. 1, no. 1, [p. 14] (Sewickley, Allegheny Co., nesting)—BURLEIGH, *Wilson Bull.*, 1923, 35:142 (Allegheny Co., nesting); 1924, 36:73; 1931, 43:52 (State College and vicinity, Centre Co., migration; summer) —CHRISTY, *Cardinal*, 1927, 2:18 (Sewickley, Allegheny Co., November)—CHRISTY and SUTTON, *Cardinal*, 1928, 2:74 (Cook Forest, Clarion Co., summer)—SUTTON, *Ann. Carnegie Mus.*, 1928, 18:223 (Pymatuning Swamp, Crawford Co., nesting).

"Redstart" SIMPSON, *Nidiologist*, 1895, 2:164 (Warren, Warren Co., nesting)—SIMPSON, *Oölogist*, 1912, 29:330 (head of Tionesta Creek, Warren Co., summer); 1920, 37:142 (Warren, Warren Co., nesting)—DICKEY, *Oölogist*, 1914, 31:171 ([Charter Oak], Huntingdon Co., May)—MCCONNELL, *Oölogist*, 1918, 35:152 (Long Run, near McKeesport, Allegheny Co., breeding)—MCGRAW, *et al.*, *Bird-Lore*, 1919, 21:37 ("Altoona" [Lakemont], Blair Co., December)—BOULTON, *Oölogist*, 1922, 39:71 (near Beaver, Beaver Co., May)—MCCLELLAND, *Am. Mid. Nat.*, 1922, 8:36 (Washington, Washington Co., summer)—BLAIR, *Bull. Audubon Soc. W. Pa.*, 1923, 1:41 (West View, Allegheny Co., nesting)—CHRISTY, *Cardinal*, 1924, v. 1, no. 4, p. 11 (Big Traverse Valley, Beaver Co., May)—SUTTON, *Bird-Lore*, 1924, 26:337 (Pittsburgh region, summer)—EASTWOOD, *Bird-Lore*, 1926, 28:272 (Pittsburgh region, Allegheny Co., May), 402 (Aspinwall, Allegheny Co., September, *fide* Auerswald).

"American Redstart" COOKE, *Bird-Lore*, 1903, 5:189 (Beaver, Beaver Co., and Renovo, Clinton Co.; migration)—BURLEIGH, *Oölogist*, 1911, 28:156 (Harmarville, Allegheny Co., nesting)—SIMPSON, *Oölogist*, 1914, 31:122 (Warren, Warren Co., summer)—EASTWOOD, *Bird-Lore*, 1927, 29:272 (Pittsburgh region, Allegheny Co., May).

TROUPIALS

FAMILY ICTERIDAE

THIS LARGE family of decidedly tropical affinities is confined to the New World. Only 18 of more than 150 known species occur north of Mexico. Of these, 11 are found in western Pennsylvania. The Bobolink, Eastern Meadowlark, Eastern Redwing, Orchard Oriole, Baltimore Oriole, Bronzed Grackle, Purple Grackle, and Cowbird, are common summer residents; the Yellow-headed Blackbird and the Western Meadowlark are accidental visitors; and the Rusty Blackbird is a transient that breeds farther north.

The Icteridae are closely related to the Fringillidae. Characters common to both families are nine-primaried wings, and bills that are angulate at the base. With most of the Icteridae, however, the bill is sharper, less conical, and without bristles.

Members of this family occupy a wide variety of habitats. Some, such as the orioles, nest and feed among the treetops; the grackles feed on the ground, walking about with stately mien; the blackbirds nest in reedy marshes, usually in large colonies; others, such as the Meadowlark and the Bobolink, prefer dry meadows or plains; the Cowbird is parasitic and lays its eggs in the nests of other birds. The food depends largely upon the niche that a particular species occupies; it includes fruit, seeds, insects, and grain. Some species are gifted songsters; others have only rough, harsh notes. The plumage varies from black (sometimes with a metallic sheen) to showy combinations of yellow, orange, scarlet, and black. The sexes are usually quite dissimilar, the female being smaller and duller-colored than the male.

BOBOLINK

DOLICHONYX ORYZIVORUS (Linnaeus)

Description—A bird with a heavy, finchlike bill and pointed tail feathers. *Adult male in breeding plumage:* black, with white or buffy areas on the nape, shoulders, and lower back. *Adult female* very different: upperparts dull olive buff, streaked with brown; underparts dull buff, with some streaks on the sides and flanks. *Adult and immature birds in fall plumage:* similar to the adult female in spring, but more heavily suffused with buff, especially below.

Range—The summer home of the Bobolink comprises the larger part of the northern United States and southern Canada as far west as Montana and the plains of Saskatchewan, with isolated colonies still farther west. Its winter home is in South America, in the pampas of Bolivia and Brazil. Thus it has a long migration route, which has been traced by W. W. Cooke, to whose article the interested reader is referred.[1] Obviously, the center of abundance of the Bobolink was originally in the prairies of the upper Mississippi Valley, and the species' advent in the East must have been

[1] U. S. Department of Agriculture, *Bulletin*, no. 185, 1917, p. 37, fig. 1.

comparatively recent. One can scarcely conceive of this bird, with its decided liking for open country, as a prehistoric inhabitant of the vast area now comprised in the New England and Middle Atlantic states, where once the forest reigned supreme. Although the Bobolink is properly a bird of the Alleghanian Fauna, its local range in western Pennsylvania is naturally governed by prevailing conditions. It is most numerous in the northwestern counties, where the country is flatter and opener. There was a time when it was also a common summer bird at Beaver, where in recent years it has become scarce and local. It is said, however, to be still fairly common and generally distributed in the Ligonier Valley in Westmoreland and Fayette counties.

Observers from various parts of the state agree that since the early twenties there has been a marked falling off in the numbers of this species. Excessive shooting of the birds during migration has had its effect, so that scarcely a tithe of their original numbers remains. A. B. Miller suggests that at Springs, Somerset County, the early mowing of hayfields has been a deterrent factor: "As a boy, I rarely knew hayfields to be mown until after July 4, by which time most young bobolinks were probably fledged; but now, mowing commonly begins by June 15 or even earlier. The young birds are newly hatched and helpless, and even should the nest and its contents escape the mower, it cannot hope to escape the horse rake which shortly follows. This custom of early mowing is good economy for the farmer and secures a better quality of hay, but it is disastrous for the Bobolink. If widespread, as it probably is, it may account in part for the decrease of the species."

Even during the period of its general abundance, the Bobolink was rare as a summer resident in Washington and Greene counties, where today it is virtually only a transient. S. S. Dickey, however, writes that it has bred for several years in a meadow above Ten-mile Creek, northeast of Jefferson, in Greene County, where a nest with eggs has been found. It has always been rather rare and local in the plateau region, from which there are only a few scattered records. In June, 1898, I found several pairs established in a meadow some two miles from Sweden Valley, Potter County, but I have never encountered the species in summer at any other point in the highlands of the northern and central counties, except at Bear Lake, Warren County. R. B. Simpson, however, lists it as common near Warren, and it appears on Van Fleet's list of the breeding birds of DuBois as "rather scarce and local." Although there are a few published records for McKean, Elk, and Clarion counties, as listed below, it is significant that A. K. Pierce found this bird only once in Clinton County, and then during migration. In Somerset County, however, it has been found summering near Somerset (Preble), Stoyestown (Canan), and Springs (Jacobs, 1933); and in Cambria County, near Johnstown (Freer; Mostoller). Why the Bobolink should thus favor the southern part of the plateau region and avoid the northern part is not apparent—but perhaps this condition is after all less real than it seems. In the ridge and valley section the species is known to breed at only a few places: the vicinity of State College (Burleigh); Hollidaysburg and near Altoona (Berg; McGraw); and Mercersburg, Franklin County (Phelps).

Migration—The Bobolink leaves its southern winter quarters in March and reaches the middle states two months later. In some seasons a bird or two may be seen in our region toward the end of April, but as a rule the first arrivals are noted during the first week of May, when the warbler migration is at its height. Often the first intimation one has of their presence is the characteristic tinkling song, heard as the birds pass overhead in the early morning hours. Eleven years' records from Beaver lie between April 29 (1910) and May 10 (1908), the average date being May 4. These dates apply as well to other parts of our region, even as far north as Erie County. April 26 is the earliest date of arrival on record; it applies alike to Springs, Somerset County (Miller), and to Meadville (First). The vernal movement at any given place requires about two weeks. The males always precede the females. Signs of the return movement are in evidence during the latter part of August, when the wandering flocks are increased by accessions from the north. September is a month of more or less steady movement, and the last stragglers may linger until the following month. The species was noted at Shermansville, Crawford County, as late as October 10 in 1925 (Bergstrom).

Habits[1]—A merry madcap in Harlequin garb

[1]Account contributed by RUTH TRIMBLE.

of black and white is the Bobolink. His Columbine, in less fanciful dress of streaked brown and yellow, resembles so closely the weed stalks and grasses of summertime meadows that she frequently passes unnoticed. Not so her gallant mate, who wears his pied garment contrariwise. A neat black waistcoat right up to his chin, and on his back and shoulders patches of white that flash in the sunlight, make of him a striking anomaly in the bird world.

Like a gay gypsy band, the bobolinks troop into our meadows in May and settle for a brief time to engage in the serious business of raising their families. This occupation, laggardly undertaken and quickly dispatched, seems to fill but a short interlude in their carefree existence. The males arrive first and reconnoiter for summer quarters. Bobolinks are not common throughout our region but occur in isolated bands, gypsy-fashion, in the broad, flat fields that are replicas of their ancestral prairies. On a morning in early May, in one of their favored haunts, a tinkle of fairy music, like the strains of an old Greek harp, seems to come from the sky and may be traced to a company of male bobolinks, circling on fluttering wings high above. While you watch, the tinkling notes descend earthward, and an exuberant male sinks to a swaying weed stalk; with tail spread, wings partly opened, and the feathers of his nape ruffled, he concludes his song with a few enchanting notes addressed to the mate he is wooing. Up she darts from the grasses to engage him in lively chase, and in a flash he is off again in pursuit—an ardent troubadour, serenading his lady as he follows her; at times, seemingly forgetting her, he mounts skyward, his throat fairly bursting with the ecstatic melody that bespeaks his *joie de vivre.* No other bird courtship exhibits such reckless abandon. None is attended by such a flood of joyous music bubbling forth irrepressibly, with never a plaintive strain. No other wooing seems so delightfully spontaneous and gay. This wanton frolic may continue for a week or more before nest-building is actually begun and the female assumes responsibility for her family.

Although bobolinks usually arrive during the first week of May, nests with eggs are seldom found much before the end of that month or early June. Some dates are: Meadville, May 22 and May 25 (Kirkpatrick); State College, May 30 (Harlow); Hartstown, June 1 (Sutton); near Greensburg, June 2 (Fricke); Verona, June 16 (Atkinson); Warren, June 11 (Simpson). The nest is a frail, cup-shaped structure, fashioned from grasses and rootlets and placed on the ground in a meadow, where it is usually so skillfully hidden by long grass that it is difficult to find. The eggs number from four to six; they are extremely variable in color and may be either dull white or ashy blue, spotted and blotched with brown and lilac. The female alone incubates the eggs, but the male attends not far away. At the approach of an intruder, he flutters about and "chinks" resentfully, while the female slips quietly from the nest and flushes some distance beyond, to join the male in protest. The young are fed on grasshoppers, crickets, and other insects.

By the end of July the young bobolinks are fully fledged and the adult birds have assumed their autumnal dress. The rapturous song of courtship days has ceased, and the only note at this season is a metallic "chink," which is commonly heard from the damp meadows and grainfields where the birds congregate in large numbers preparatory to the southward flight. They feed by day in wheat, oat, and buckwheat fields and continue their flight by night, when their calls may be heard as they pass overhead. In the fall plumage, the male cannot be distinguished from the female or from the young. This, as F. M. Chapman writes, "is the 'Reed-bird' plumage. It is worn until the following spring when, late in February and early in March, before leaving its winter home in northern Argentina and southwestern Brazil, the bird undergoes a complete molt, including the wings and tail. This creates no change in the general appearance of the female, but the male undergoes a striking transformation. So far as feathers are concerned, he is the bird we know in early summer, but the body-feathers are all so widely fringed with yellowish, those of the nape with brownish, and those of the scapulars, rump, and upper tail-coverts with dusky grayish, that it is difficult to believe the bird can pass into the shining black, buff, and white breeding plumage without losing or gaining a single feather. But during the northward migration in March and April, the yellow, brown, and gray tips gradually wear away, the plumage of the nape, rump, upper tail-coverts, and scapulars apparently fades, the bill turns from brownish to blue-black, and by the time the bird reaches its nesting-ground few traces of what one might call its traveling cloak remain."[1]

In western Pennsylvania the bobolinks are recognized as desirable and beneficial bird-citizens that reserve their finest livery and sweetest song for their sojourn in this region. In the South, on the contrary, they are known as "Reed-birds" or "Rice-birds," because in their leisurely fall migration they invade the rice fields in vast companies. Waxing fat at the expense of the planters, they mar their otherwise creditable reputation. To prevent serious damage to the crops it is necessary to engage watchers to kill or scare away the birds. In recent years, however, rice-growing has been practically abandoned in the South Atlantic states, and the Bobolink menace has correspondingly lessened. A part of the decrease in the numbers of bobolinks in the East is attributed to their wholesale slaughter in the South in former years. Not only economic necessity but also epicurean delight was served in this yearly massacre; for the "Reed-bird" was considered a great delicacy and was killed by the thousands for food. Federal protection of migratory birds now saves the bobolinks from this disaster, and it is only when they infringe seriously upon the rights of man that they pay with their lives. Nevertheless, the Bobolink remains a veritable pest in one region and a welcome and cherished visitor in another.

Dolichonyx oryzivorus Townsend, *Proc. Acad. Nat. Sci. Philadelphia*, 1883, 63 (Latrobe, Westmoreland Co., summer)—Warren, *Birds Pa.*, 1888, 240 (Crawford and Erie Co., breeding, *fide* Sennett)—Jacobs, *Summer Birds Greene Co., Pa.*, 1893, 8 (Greene Co., nesting)—Baily, *Auk*, 1896, 13: 294 (Williamsville, Elk Co., July, *fide* Reese)—Rhoads, *Auk*, 1899, 16:312 (southwestern Pa., summer; Potter Co., nesting, *fide* Larrabee)—Todd, *Ann. Carnegie Mus.*, 1904, 2:566 (Erie, Erie Co., breeding)—Todd, in Bausman, *Hist. Beaver Co., Pa.*, 1904, 2:1200 (Beaver Co., summer)—Keim, *Cassinia*, 1905, 8:39 (Port Allegany, McKean Co., summer) —Harlow, *Auk*, 1912, 29:478 (Boalsburg, Centre Co., June, *fide* Todd); 1918, 35:136 (Fayette Co.; Warren, Warren Co., and State College and Oak Hall, Centre Co., nesting)—Stone, *Cassinia*, 1919, 22:33 (Altoona, Blair Co., breeding, *fide* McGraw)—Oberholser, *Bird-Lore*, 1920, 22:213 (Beaver, Beaver Co., migration)—Christy, *Cardinal*, 1923, v. 1, no. 1, [p. 8] (Bakerstown, Allegheny Co., and Hanover Tp., Beaver Co., nesting)—Burleigh, *Wilson Bull.*, 1923, 35:90 ([Harmarville], Allegheny Co., nesting); 1924, 36:71; and 1931, 43:45 (State College, Centre Co., migration; nesting) —Christy and Sutton, *Cardinal*, 1928, 2:71 (Scotch Hill, Clarion Co., June)—Sutton, *Ann. Carnegie Mus.*, 1928, 18:161 (Meadville and Pymatuning Swamp, Crawford Co., summer)—Christy, *Cardinal*, 1930, 2:218 (Sewickley Tp., Allegheny Co., nesting)—Burleigh, *Cardinal*, 1932, 3:81 (Uniontown, Fayette Co., summer; Chalk Hill, Fayette Co., August)—McClintock, *Cardinal*, 1933, 3:127 (Ligonier, Westmoreland Co., summer).

"Bobolink" Enty, *Ornithologist and Oölogist*, 1885, 10:79 (Templeton, Armstrong Co., May)—Jacobs, *Hawkeye Ornithologist and Oölogist*, 1888, 1:88 (Waynesburg, Greene Co., April) —Simpson, *Oölogist*, 1911, 28:201 (Warren, Warren Co., breeding)—McConnell, *Oölogist*, 1918, 35:150 (McKeesport, Allegheny Co., breeding)—Miller, *In the Open*, June, 1920, 10:23 (Thornhill, Allegheny Co., May)—McClelland, *Am. Mid. Nat.*, 1922, 8:37 (Washington, Washington Co., May)—Eastwood, *Bird-Lore*, 1925, 27:263 (Pittsburgh region, Allegheny Co., April); 1926, 28:273 (Rector, Westmoreland Co., May, *fide* Knauz)—Jacobs, *Auk*, 1933, 50:119 (Springs, Somerset Co., nesting).

[1] *Bird-Lore*, 1920, 22:217.

EASTERN MEADOWLARK

STURNELLA MAGNA MAGNA (Linnaeus)

Description—About the size of the Robin. Upperparts streaked with black and brown; head showing two black lateral stripes, with a pale one between; sides of head grayish white, with a yellow spot before the eye and a black stripe behind; tail mostly dark, the outer feathers on either side white; *underparts bright yellow*, with a *broad crescent of black across the breast* and some dark stripes on the sides and flanks; under tail coverts mostly buffy. *Female* similar to the male, but smaller, and the breast-crescent not so broad. In the fall the general color above is a much richer brown, while the yellow below is duller and the black of the breast is veiled with buff.

Range—The Meadowlark is remarkable in that its range as a species not only covers a large part of the eastern United States and southern Canada, but extends also across Mexico and Central America to include the northern part of the South American continent. The species varies somewhat geographically, and several races are now recognized. Like the Bobolink, the Meadowlark has undoubtedly profited from the clearing of the country in the northeastern sections of the United States and has modified its range accordingly. The Eastern Meadowlark is a common summer resident throughout western Pennsylvania, and it likewise occurs occasionally and irregularly in winter, not only in the Ohio Valley, but also as far north as Warren and Erie, and in the mountains as well. Indeed, winter occurrences of this bird have been noted since the time of Wilson; they are not a development of recent years. The species is hardy and can withstand the cold if food is available.

Migration—The Meadowlark is one of the earliest migrants to appear in the spring and arrives shortly after the Robin and the Bluebird. Since it winters sporadically in our region and regularly just to the southward, it never has very far to come; mild days may induce its arrival as early as the latter part of February, but as a rule it does not appear until sometime in the following month. Twenty seasons' arrival records from Beaver range from February 25 to March 24, but the great majority lie in the second and third weeks in March, while the average date of all is March 13. Not until toward the last of that month, however, does the species reach its normal summer numbers. These are maintained until the latter part of September, when they seem to be augmented by an influx from the north. October is a month of considerable movement, and while most of the birds have left by the first of November, some may linger until the end of the month, and a few may even remain through the winter. Similar conditions prevail in other parts of our region. A few birds are said to winter almost every year at State College, where in 1916 the earliest migrants appeared on February 13 (Burleigh). At Renovo, not much farther north, the average and earliest dates of arrival are respectively March 26 and March 13 (Pierce). The dates already quoted for Beaver, however, hold good for the western tier of counties in general, although there is considerable variation from year to year.

Habits—When the clear, ringing whistle of the Meadowlark is first heard in the land, it is a sure sign that spring is on the way, reluctant and elusive though its advent may be at times. On a frosty March morning, with a meadowlark calling from the top of a tree at the edge of a field, dull of sense and of spirit must he be who does not thrill to the sweet strains, with their haunting undertone of plaintive wistfulness. As a vocalist the Meadowlark is without a peer in its own class, although its repertoire is limited. It is fond of singing from an elevated perch—the very top of a tree or of a telegraph pole by the roadside—but it often sings from the ground, too, in the interludes of feeding. In a genetic sense, the Meadowlark is of course far removed from the true larks; it is instead a troupial which has adopted a terrestrial mode of life and as a result has become somewhat modified. On the ground it has a graceful walking gait, and the striped coloration of its upperparts blends so well with its surroundings that when at rest the bird is not easy to see.

Like the Bobolink, the Meadowlark is characteristically a species of the open fields and meadows. When disturbed while feeding in such resorts, it flies off with a harsh, rattling alarm-note, to alight farther away or to seek a perch in a tree commanding a view of the situation. In flying, it proceeds by vigorously flapping its wings and then sailing for a distance (in a manner not unlike that of the Bob-white), exposing the white feathers in its tail. Most of its food is picked up from the ground. Grasshoppers are favorite tidbits; in August, when these insects are abundant, they constitute over two-thirds of the total diet. Surprising as it may seem, meadowlarks shot in the winter months have been found to contain the dead and dried remains of grasshoppers picked up in the fields. Thus, economically, the species is outstandingly useful.

The Meadowlark is fond of the company of its own kind and prefers to travel in flocks, small or large. In the wintertime particularly, it inhabits unmown or waste fields, where there is plenty of cover and where the snow is likely to be less solid. Flocks in the spring are seldom large, and in a few weeks they break up into mated pairs, which are soon busy with housekeeping duties. The nest is well concealed and very hard to find; in all my experience I have stumbled across only a very few. As a rule it is sunk in the ground and is more or less domed over by the same material that composes its side walls: dry stems of grasses, clover, and other plants. It is a bulky and rather formless affair but is always well sheltered from above by the high grasses among which it is built. The eggs are four or five in number, rarely six, and occasionally only three; they measure about 1.15 by .80 inches. The ground-color is white, and the markings, of a reddish or vinaceous-brown color, vary from flecks to spots of fair size. Sometimes the spotting is more or less uniformly distributed, but mostly it is clustered about or around the larger end. Full sets have been found in Greene County during the first week in May, and in other sections, throughout that month and the next. Almost certainly two broods are sometimes raised. A set of eggs in the Carnegie Museum was collected at Washington on July 25, 1899; and in August, in Allegheny County, D. A. Atkinson has found young unable to fly.

Alauda magna Wilson, *Am. Orn.*, 1811, 1:20 (near Somerset, Somerset Co., February).

Sturnella magna Townsend, *Proc. Acad. Nat. Sci. Philadelphia*, 1883, 63 (Latrobe, Westmoreland Co., breeding; occasional in winter)—Dwight, *Auk*, 1892, 9:136 (Cresson, Cambria Co., June)—Todd, *Auk*, 1893, 10:39 (Two Lick, Indiana Co., June), 44 (Coalport, Clearfield Co., June)—Jacobs, *Summer Birds Greene Co., Pa.*, 1893, 9 (Greene Co., nesting)—Baily, *Auk*, 1896, 13:294 (Williamsville, Elk Co., June–July)—Chapman, *Bull. Am. Mus. Nat. Hist.*, 1900, 13:297, (316) (Erie, Erie Co.)—Cope, *Cassinia*, 1902, 5:16 (Clinton and Potter Co., June)—Todd, *Ann. Carnegie Mus.*, 1904, 2:567 (Erie, Erie Co., summer; occasional in winter) —Todd, in Bausman, *Hist. Beaver Co., Pa.*, 1904, 2:1200 (Beaver Co., summer)—Keim, *Cassinia*, 1905, 8:39 (Port Allegany, McKean Co., summer).

"Meadowlark" Enty, *Ornithologist and Oölogist*, 1885, 10:78 (Templeton, Armstrong Co., March)—Jacobs, *Hoosier Nat.*, 1887, 2:78 (Waynesburg, Greene Co., winter)—Wickham, *Oölogist*, 1888, 5:92 (Beaver, Beaver Co., February)—Stone, *Cassinia*, 1906, 9:43 (McConnellsburg, Fulton Co., June)—Simpson, *Oölogist*, 1908, 25:171 (Warren, Warren Co., albinistic specimen)—Jackson, *Cassinia*, 1909, 12:12 (Warren, Warren Co., May)—Harlow, *Cassinia*, 1912, 15:20 (Center Furnace Swamp, Centre Co., winter)—Burleigh, *Oölogist*, 1913, 30:281 (Allegheny Co., winter)—Oldys, *Cassinia*, 1915, 18:28 (Washington, Washington Co., song)—McConnell, *Oölogist*, 1918, 35:150 (McKeesport, Allegheny Co., breeding)—Warfield, *Bird-Lore*, 1919, 21:37 (Chambersburg, Franklin Co., December)—McGraw and Hays, *Bird-Lore*, 1920, 22:31 (Altoona and vicinity, Blair Co., December)—Street, *Cassinia*, 1923, 24:14 (Greencastle to Ft. Loudon, Franklin Co., June)—Sutton, *Bird-Lore*, 1923, 25:132, 194 (Pittsburgh region, Allegheny Co., winter); 1924, 26:56, 122 (Greenville, Mercer Co., February, *fide* Homer; Sharpsburg, Allegheny Co., February, *fide* Stephan)—Eastwood, *Bird-Lore*, 1926, 28:273 (Rector, Westmoreland Co., May, *fide* Knauz); 1927, 29:196 (Pittsburgh region, Allegheny Co., March), 197 (Springs, Somerset Co., March, *fide* Miller)—Savage, *et al.*, *Bird-Lore*, 1928, 30:41 (McKeesport, Allegheny Co., December)—Boulton, *Bird-Lore*, 1928, 30:127 (Buffalo Creek, Armstrong Co., December, *fide* Reiter, *et al.*), 195 (Raccoon Creek, Beaver Co., February)—Christy and Hegner, *Bird-Lore*, 1929, 31:38 (Frankfort Springs to Clinton, Allegheny Co., December)—Miller, *Bird-Lore*, 1932, 34:47 (Springs, Somerset Co., December)—Auerswald, *et al.*, *Bird-Lore*, 1940, 42:87 (near Pittsburgh, Allegheny Co., December)—Johnson, *Bird-Lore*, 1940, 42:88 (Warren, Warren Co., December).

Sturnella magna magna Harlow, *Auk*, 1912, 29:473 (southern Centre Co., summer)—Oberholser, *Bird-Lore*, 1921, 23:79 (Renovo, Clinton Co., and Beaver, Beaver Co., migration) —Christy, *Cardinal*, 1923, v. 1, no. 1, [p. 8] (Sewickley, Allegheny Co., breeding; occasional in winter)—Burleigh, *Wilson Bull.*, 1923, 35:91 (Allegheny Co., summer; January); 1924, 36:71; and 1931, 43:46 (State College, Centre Co., migration; nesting)—Christy and Sutton, *Cardinal*, 1928, 2:71, 75 (Cook Forest, Clarion Co., summer and winter)—Sutton, *Ann. Carnegie Mus.*, 1928, 18:167 (Crawford Co. localities, summer; occasional in winter)—Bergstrom, *Cardinal*, 1930, 2:186 (Pymatuning Swamp, Crawford Co., January)—Burleigh, *Cardinal*, 1932, 3:81 (near Uniontown, Fayette Co., summer).

WESTERN MEADOWLARK

STURNELLA NEGLECTA Audubon

Description—Similar to the Eastern Meadowlark, but the general coloration is paler, and the yellow of the throat invades the malar region.

Range—As its name implies, the Western Meadowlark is a western bird, although its range overlaps that of the Eastern Meadowlark to some extent. Its occurrence as far east as Pennsylvania is of course purely fortuitous, and its breeding there, if established, would be still more remarkable. The single occurrence on record seems to rest on a sound basis, since the species was identified by its song, which is strikingly dissimilar to that of its eastern congener.

Habits—H. H. Elliott's note (1936) on this species is of peculiar interest: "On June 9, 1935, in a meadow by the roadside just south of Hartstown, Mr. [O. C.] Reiter and I came upon a Western Meadowlark, *Sturnella neglecta* Audubon. It was my first encounter with the species, and I was at the time puzzled that a bird of the appearance of the meadowlark should be singing a song so strange and beautiful. It seemed to stand out from the familiar songs about us. The notes were loud, clear, flute-like, and the performance more voluminous than that of our familiar bird. We stopped and watched for some time, and, noting that the bird was occupied in carrying food and in singing, we inferred that it was one of a nesting pair. The *chuck* note also that it uttered in flight was unlike any note of the eastern bird."

Sturnella neglecta ELLIOTT, *Cardinal*, 1936, 4:72 (Hartstown, Crawford Co., June).

YELLOW-HEADED BLACKBIRD

XANTHOCEPHALUS XANTHOCEPHALUS (Bonaparte)

Description—Male: very nearly as large as the Bronzed Grackle. General color black; *head (all around,* except chin and region around eye) *and breast, yellow;* a white area at the base of the wing. *Female:* much smaller and duller; general color brown; *throat and breast yellow,* and some yellow on the sides of the head. In fall birds, the crown and the nape are more or less veiled with black.

Range and local status—The Yellow-headed Blackbird is distinctly a western bird; it breeds in marshes as far east as the Mississippi Valley but during migration is casual or accidental farther east in the United States and Canada. The few comparable records from our region are listed below. Warren (1890) quotes H. C. Kirkpatrick as follows: "I had the good fortune to get a fine pair of Yellow-headed Blackbirds on March 25, 1890, the first I have ever observed around here." It seems, however, that the birds in question were only seen and not secured—a fact that forms a significant commentary on the dependability of Warren's report. D. A. Atkinson shot one bird at Wilkinsburg on April 26, 1895, from a flock of Red-wings, and S. E. Bacon took a single bird (now in the Carnegie Museum) on Presque Isle on August 22, 1896. A record referring to a male seen by G. E. Welshons at Turtle Creek, Allegheny County, on April 13, 1928, and reported by G. M. Sutton, was later questioned. It does not seem possible, however, that any observer, amateur or otherwise, could mistake a bird as striking as the male Yellow-headed Blackbird.

Xanthocephalus xanthocephalus WARREN, *Birds Pa.*, ed. 2, 1890, 212 (Meadville, Crawford Co., March, *fide* Kirkpatrick)—RHOADS, *Auk*, 1899, 16:312 (Wilkinsburg, Allegheny Co., *fide* Atkinson)—TODD, *Ann. Carnegie Mus.*, 1904, 2:566 (Presque Isle, Erie Co., August, *fide* Bacon)—SUTTON, *Ann. Carnegie Mus.*, 1928, 18:163 (Meadville, Crawford Co., March, *fide* Kirkpatrick)—SUTTON, *Auk*, 1929, 46:119 (Turtle Creek, Allegheny Co., April, *fide* Welshons)—HOLT, *Auk*, 1929, 46:390 (Turtle Creek, Allegheny Co.; critical).

EASTERN RED-WING

AGELAIUS PHOENICEUS PHOENICEUS (Linnaeus)

Description—Much smaller than the Bronzed Grackle; sexes unlike. *Adult male in breeding plumage:* black; *on the wing coverts a large crimson spot* bordered with buff. *Adult female:* smaller than the male; upperparts dark brown, with some pale streaks; a pale stripe over the eye; underparts striped with black and dull white, the throat usually paler (pinkish buff); crimson spot on wing coverts scarcely or not obvious. *Immature males* in the fall are heavily mottled with rusty buff above and with buffy white below; the colored area on the wing coverts is much duller and is mixed with dusky tones. Young birds of both sexes *(juvenal plumage)* resemble the female but are generally darker above and tinged with buff below.

Range—The Red-wing has an extensive range. In one form or another it is found from the Atlantic coast to the Pacific and from Costa Rica to

Canada. The typical or eastern race[1] is common throughout western Pennsylvania as a summer resident, and on several occasions has even been found wintering. It abounds in the Pymatuning region of Crawford County and in other swampy areas, large and small, in the open country. While it always prefers wet areas, it can and does get along very well in high grass of any kind, such as the Bobolink inhabits; in fact, the two species are often found together in the upland meadows. Although the Red-wing is still common in its chosen haunts, I believe that it is by no means as numerous as it once was, and some other observers agree with this conclusion. Not all the available breeding areas are occupied—as once they were—nor are so many and such large flocks seen during migration as formerly. But the species is probably in no danger of extinction; it is eminently able to adapt itself to changing conditions.

Migration—A hardy species, wintering not far beyond our southern border, the Red-wing is an early migrant in the spring; it usually appears in our region after the Bronzed Grackle but before the Meadowlark. The exact date of its arrival varies considerably and depends largely on weather conditions, which in recent years have been most variable. In the spring of 1891 I saw a small flock flying southward at Beaver on February 26, the premature advance having evidently been turned into a retreat by the "second winter" that season. On the other hand, in the spring of 1934, which was an exceptionally late and backward season, the species was not noted until April 1. The average date of arrival at Beaver (in twenty-eight seasons' records) is March 13, and more than half the records lie between March 7 and 17.[2] Since the records of various other observers substantially correspond with these, they may be considered applicable to western Pennsylvania at large.

The southward movement begins in October, when the transients pass through in enormous flocks. By the end of that month most of these have gone, but a few birds usually linger into November. Some late fall dates are: Beaver, November 10, 1923, and November 26, 1890 (Todd); Pittsburgh, November 16, 1912 (Burleigh); State College, November 14, 1916 (Burleigh); Warren, November 28, 1900 (Simpson); Erie, November 12, 1900 (Todd); Renovo, November 14, 1910 (Pierce). Several winter records are also at hand: Meadville, a flock of twenty-five, December 27, 1896 (Kirkpatrick); Forestville, Butler County, December 25, 1927 (Keesler); Wilkinsburg, "one remained all winter near an ice pond with a flock of English Sparrows" (Atkinson); Verona, Allegheny County, January 8, 1899 (Atkinson); "Denny Pond," Allegheny County, December, 1923 (Elliott, *et al.*); Raccoon Creek, about five miles south of Beaver, winter of 1935–36, a group of seven (Ristich). All these dates are of course exceptional in this latitude.

Habits[3]—The male Red-wing, in coat of shining black with conspicuous epaulettes of crimson and buff, is a fine-looking figure. Since he is no musician, his is not a bandmaster's uniform; by a process of exclusion, we ascribe to it a military significance. When the hosts gather in late summer, we naturally think of an "army." A convocation of these blackbirds in the meadow bottom, excitedly squeaking and jabbering in their curious jargon, seems all confusion, and yet this vast concourse, at some signal which neither you nor I would observe, rises, wheels, and turns, with a military precision that is little short of marvelous.

In the early spring, usually toward the middle of March, or after the frost has left the ground, the arrival of the red-wings is announced by a chorus of convulsive squeaks, explosive calls, and wheezing sounds. The early arrivals are bands of males, and evidently they are birds of passage. Later, the summer birds appear among a great host of migrants, including grackles, starlings, cowbirds, and rusty blackbirds. They fly by day and drop into the marshes in endless file in the evening to rest and feed. Those that elect to remain lose no time in staking out their claims to territory. The conversational bickering and chattering of noisy travelers is replaced by the musical tones of the red-wings that are awaiting mates. Swaying on a dead cattail, the male spreads his wings and tail, puffs out his feathers, and raises his flaming shoulder-patches, as he chants his *quong, quong, quee!* Red-wings are bold and quarrelsome in de-

[1]*Agelaius phoeniceus arctolegus*, the Giant Red-wing of western Canada, has been collected in West Virginia (Alexander Wetmore, *Proceedings U. S. National Museum*, 1937, 84:433; Karl Haller, *Auk*, 1938, 55:677) and may be expected in western Pennsylvania as well.

[2]The average date, "March 9," cited by H. C. Oberholser (1922) is an error.

[3]Account adapted largely from a manuscript by Edmund W. Arthur.

fense of their territories, and roving suitors are quickly routed. One male usually has two, and sometimes even three, mates. The females, quieter in manner and dress, build the nests and incubate without assistance from their showy consorts, to which our attention is first and perhaps most steadily attracted.

The colonizing that is to some extent characteristic of this species may be a matter of the convenience or availability of group nesting sites; at any rate red-wings display the family tendency to be gregarious. It is their nature to seek membership in large associations of their kind. Enter a cattail or an elderberry meadow in early spring, and immediately, from here, there, and everywhere, you will hear the staccato *chack, chack, chack* of the male, who perches sentinel-like upon a cattail top or other convenient station. One is tempted to believe that he is fully conscious of the impression he conveys of a dark-skinned scout in full uniform, whose divers duties as sentry and buffoon compel him at times to occupy a curious but interesting dual role.

The first nests are built in May, usually between the tenth and the twenty-fifth. June and July nestings indicate second broods. Like their oriole cousins, the red-wings are skillful builders; they weave their nests of grasses and sedges into the upright forks of willow trees or of elder shrubs, or between the cattail rushes in the marsh. So securely is the fabric lashed to its support that the nest cannot be collected without the framework. The average red-wing swamp contains a number of "fool nests." Some of these are only partly finished; others are completely finished but never occupied. Whether these are built because the birds are fickle in their choice of sites, or fastidious about the pattern of their nests, or particular about their structural engineering, or are providing against peering eyes or prying hands, is uncertain.

A ubiquitous species, the Red-wing has adapted itself to a variety of habitats. D. A. Atkinson writes: "It may be found nesting in the swamp in low, marshy fields, in the elders along streams and ponds, and sometimes in thickets or even in grassy meadows far from water. Sometimes the nest is placed in a bunch of grass, practically on the ground, and on two occasions I have found nests in willow trees at a height of more than thirty feet; the usual height in rushes is eighteen inches, and in saplings or bushes, three or four feet." Three to five eggs comprise a set, and four is the common number. They are pale blue in color, peculiarly scrawled, spotted, and blotched with black, dark brown, and purple, chiefly at the larger end; they measure 1.04 by .72 inches. The young are hatched in eleven days and leave the nest in ten or eleven more. They are fed almost entirely upon insects. The diet in the late summer and fall for young and old alike consists mainly of weed seeds and grain. Enormous congregations of blackbirds in ravening hordes plunder the grainfields and cornfields and thus offset in a large measure the good they do in destroying weeds and insects. The large flocks retire at night to roost in certain swamps or reed-grown river bars and low islands, and leave in the morning to forage over the adjacent territory.

In the Allegheny River, north of Pittsburgh, a roost has recently come under the protection of the Audubon Society of Western Pennsylvania. A. D. Kirk, who was responsible for establishing the sanctuary, describes the activities of the birds:

"After the first brood is on the wing about the middle of June, the old males and the young birds fly nightly to the little island. They arrive about sundown, and the early flocks are small. Later in the season the flocks gradually increase in size, and in July I have observed ten to fifteen thousand birds settling for the night. From high in the air they nose-dive to the weedy growth that covers the island. In the wild sunflower, golden glow, elder, and scrubby black willow, they perch and preen or fly back and forth in small flocks. Occasionally some assemble on the shore line, where they seem to be picking sand or grit. As the shadows lengthen, the flocks take refuge among the weed stalks, and the fluttering and chattering gradually cease as the birds settle for the night. Before dawn, the robins and song sparrows call, and at the break of light the red-wings come forth and stream away from the island between 5:30 and 6:00 A.M. Few remain during the day, and I have seen no evidence of nests on this site. About August 1 the red-wings begin to leave the vicinity, and from then until September 1 only small, scattered flocks are observed at night."

H. C. Kirkpatrick describes another roost in Crawford County: "One of the largest roosts in the county is the extensive marsh bordering Conneaut Lake on the west, which has been a favorite resort for many years. The red-wings and the bronzed grackles of the surrounding country for miles congregate here in the evenings in immense numbers, like a black cloud, while the sound of their wings as they suddenly rise en masse from the cattails resembles distant thunder."

In October, migration is well under way, and the transients pass over in flocks of thousands; by the end of the month most have gone, but it will be November or later before the last laggard red-wings hurry through to their winter home in the southern states.

Agelæus phœniceus TOWNSEND, *Proc. Acad. Nat. Sci. Philadelphia*, 1883, 63 (Latrobe, Westmoreland Co., breeding)—TEULON, *Jour. Boston Zoöl. Soc.*, 1883, 2:9 (Bradford, McKean Co.)—WARREN, *Forest and Stream*, 1891, 37:183 (Presque Isle, Erie Co., and Conneaut Lake, Crawford Co., fall).

Agelaius phœniceus DWIGHT, *Auk*, 1892, 9:136 (Cresson, Cambria Co., June)—TODD, *Auk*, 1893, 10:39 (Two Lick, Indiana Co., June)—JACOBS, *Summer Birds Greene Co., Pa.*, 1893, 9 (Greene Co., nesting)—BAILY, *Auk*, 1896, 13:294 (Williamsville, Elk Co., breeding)—COPE, *Cassinia*, 1902, 5:15 (Kettle Creek Valley and New Bergen, Potter Co., June)—TODD, *Ann. Carnegie Mus.*, 1904, 2:566 (Presque Isle, Erie Co., summer)—TODD, in Bausman, *Hist. Beaver Co., Pa.*, 1904, 2:1200 (Beaver Co., summer)—KEIM, *Cassinia*, 1905, 8:39 (Port Allegany, McKean Co., summer).

"Red-winged Blackbird" FORREST, *Oölogist*, 1901, 18:137; 1910, 27:134 (Washington, Washington Co., nesting; albino)—STONE, *Cassinia*, 1906, 9:43 (McConnellsburg, Fulton Co., June)—BURLEIGH, *Oölogist*, 1911, 28:156 (Harmarville, Allegheny Co., nesting)—HARLOW, *Cassinia*, 1912, 15:22 (Center Furnace Swamp, Centre Co., nesting)—SIMPSON, *Oölogist*, 1912, 29:249, 350 (Presque Isle, Erie Co., nesting)—SIMPSON, *Oölogist*, 1913, 30:50 (Warren, Warren Co., March)—ROGERS, *Bird-Lore*, 1914, 16:183 (near Pittsburgh, Allegheny Co., migration)—CARTER, *Oölogist*, 1914, 31:231 (Waynesburg, Greene Co., nesting)—MCCONNELL, *Oölogist*, 1918, 35:150 (McKeesport, Allegheny Co.)—MILLER (R. F.), *Oölogist*, 1919, 36:155 (Lemont, Centre Co., nesting)—MILLER (M. H.), *In the Open*, June, 1920, 10:24 (Thornhill, Allegheny Co., nesting)—STREET, *Cassinia*, 1923, 24:14 (Greencastle to Fort Loudon and Conococheague Creek, Franklin Co., June)—CHRISTY, *Cardinal*, 1923, v. 1, no. 2, [p. 17] (Clinton Pond, Allegheny Co., nesting); 1924, v. 1, no. 4, p. 10 (Big Traverse Valley, Beaver Co., June)—ELLIOTT, *et al.*, *Bird-Lore*, 1924, 26:30 ("Denny Pond," Allegheny Co., December)—EASTWOOD, *Bird-Lore*, 1926, 28:207 (Pittsburgh region, Allegheny Co., March), 273 (Rector, Westmoreland Co., May, *fide* Knauz); 1927, 29:196 (Pittsburgh region, Allegheny Co., March), 197 (Springs, Somerset Co., March, *fide* Miller)—BOULTON, *Bird-Lore*, 1928, 30:195 (Baden, Beaver Co., March, *fide* Auerswald, *et al.*)—CHRISTY, *Cardinal*, 1931, 3:43 (McDonald Reservoir, Washington Co., May)—MCCLINTOCK, *Cardinal*, 1933, 3:128 (Ligonier, Westmoreland Co., June).

"Red-wing" MCCLELLAND, *Am. Mid. Nat.*, 1922, 8:36 (Washington, Washington Co., summer)—HOLT, *Cardinal*, 1925, v. 1, no. 6, p. 24 (Pymatuning Swamp, Crawford Co., nesting; etc.).

Agelaius phœniceus phœniceus HARLOW, *Auk*, 1912, 29:473 (southern Centre Co., breeding)—CHRISTY, *Cardinal*, 1923, v. 1, no. 1, [p. 8] (Sewickley, Allegheny Co., breeding)—BURLEIGH, *Wilson Bull.*, 1923, 35:91 (Allegheny Co., nesting); 1924, 36:71; and 1931, 43:46 (State College, Centre Co., migration; nesting)—BURLEIGH, *Cardinal*, 1932, 3:81 (Lake Seaton, Fayette Co., nesting).

Agelaius phœniceus predatorius OBERHOLSER, *Bird-Lore*, 1922, 24:85 (Beaver, Beaver Co., and Renovo, Clinton Co., migration)—CHRISTY and SUTTON, *Cardinal*, 1928, 2:71 (Cook Forest, Clarion Co., summer)—SUTTON, *Ann. Carnegie Mus.*, 1928, 18:164 (Meadville, Conneaut Lake, and Pymatuning Swamp, Crawford Co., summer; habits).

ORCHARD ORIOLE

ICTERUS SPURIUS (Linnaeus)

Description—Decidedly smaller than the Baltimore Oriole. *Adult male: black and chestnut.* Head (all around), upper back, tail, throat, and upper breast, black; rest of underparts and lesser wing coverts, chestnut; wings dusky brownish, with some white edgings to the feathers; bill dark. *Young male* (second year): dull olive green above; dull yellowish green below, the *throat sharply black;* wings dusky, with some white bars and edgings. *Female:* upperparts dull olive green, brighter on the head, rump, and tail; underparts plain dull yellow; wings dusky, with whitish bars and edgings. In *juvenal plumage* the young bird resembles the adult female.

Range—In general, the Orchard Oriole is more southerly in the breeding season than the Baltimore. It barely reaches southeastern Ontario and is rare in New England, especially north of Massachusetts. Either the center of abundance in the North has shifted in recent years, or the species has decreased materially in numbers. Never so common or so generally distributed as the Baltimore Oriole in western Pennsylvania, it was nevertheless once a regular and well-known summer resident in many sections where now it is extremely rare. In 1891 I considered it "fairly common" in Beaver County and thereafter recorded its arrival from year to year until 1913, but since that season my records have been scanty. D. A. Atkinson listed it as a "fairly abundant summer resident" in Allegheny County in the nineties, whereas T. D. Burleigh, whose field work in that county did not begin until 1910, seems never to have encountered it there at all. H. H. Elliott has had no breeding records from Jamisonville, Butler County, since 1914. Other observers report a similar scarcity. The species enters the plateau region very sparingly, and it is probably a newcomer there. R. B. Simpson, a competent observer, omits it from his list of the birds of Warren County, and A. K. Pierce supplies but one record for Clinton County (Renovo, April 29, 1896). I observed this oriole, however, at Punxsutawney, Jefferson County, in June, 1893, and at Weedville, Elk County, in June, 1894; and Van Fleet includes it in his manuscript list of the breeding birds of DuBois. At Springs, Somerset County, according to A. B. Miller, it is very rare but was observed during the breeding season in 1914 and 1920. There are also several records (some of them recent) for the ridge and valley section, as far north as State College. Nevertheless, the species seems to be recessive throughout our entire region; the reason for this recession is not obvious.

Migration—The Orchard Oriole winters from southern Mexico through Central America to Colombia—as does also the Baltimore Oriole. The two species reach western Pennsylvania at about the same time; seldom do they arrive more than a few days apart. The appearance of the Orchard Oriole has been recorded at Beaver from April 22 to May 8 (Todd); at Wilkinsburg from April 26 to May 7 (Atkinson); and at Sewickley from April 27 to May 15 (Christy). The last date seems unusually late. At Washington the species has been observed as early as April 26 (Nease); at Shermansville, Crawford County, on May 4 (Bergstrom); at Butler, on May 5 (Roth); and at State College, on May 6 (Burleigh). Usually it arrives with the first large wave of warblers. The fact that it leaves for the South remarkably early is proved by its appearance in Guatemala during the latter part of July and in early August. I have never noted it in our region later than August, but can cite no exact dates of departure. Dr. Atkinson gives September 7 (1899) as his latest fall date at Wilkinsburg. Probably few of the birds of this species remain on their breeding grounds more than ten weeks.

Habits—As its common name implies, this species is partial to orchards (although no more so than the Baltimore Oriole); it is also not averse to shade trees and woodland trees along roadsides. Much more plainly garbed than the Baltimore Oriole, shier and more retiring in disposition, and much less common, it is not so well known as the other species. In fact, many observers have overlooked it entirely. The males are in full song on their arrival and continue to sing throughout the nesting season; then they become silent and easily escape notice. The song of the Orchard Oriole obviously resembles that of the Baltimore, but it conforms more closely to one pattern or theme, is less musical, and is more hurried in delivery. The singing male often selects a perch in the very top of a tree. The birds hunt their insect food in the terminal foliage and very rarely descend to the ground; they are active but rather solitary.

Nest-building begins within a week or two after the birds' arrival and progresses so efficiently that full sets of eggs have been taken in Allegheny County as early as May 20 (Atkinson), and even a little earlier in Greene County (Jacobs). Generally speaking, however, the end of May is the height of the nesting season, although nests with eggs have been found a month later. Perhaps these were the second efforts of pairs whose first attempts had failed. It is usually easy to find the nest; one has only to make a careful search of the group of trees frequented by the male bird. The nests I have found were all in Rambo apple trees, about twenty feet from the ground, but various observers report finding them in other kinds of trees and as low as six feet. In its situation, shape, and composition, the nest of the Orchard Oriole is perfectly characteristic, and it is not likely to be confounded with that of any other bird. It is generally placed near the extremity of a branch, but often on a short limb near the top of the tree. It is a basket-shaped structure, suspended by the brim to the fork of a branch and sometimes steadied by an attachment to a twig below. Seldom is it more than three inches deep, and the outside diameter is about the same. It is thus a much shallower structure than that built by the Baltimore Oriole; moreover, it is composed almost wholly of green, well-cured grass blades, interwoven into a resistant fabric and firmly bound to the supporting branch by strands of grass. Often there is no special lining except a layer of finer grass, but in some nests, soft, cottony materials are used—bits of wool, down from the dandelion and the milkweed, rabbit fur, and other hair. Four or five eggs are laid. They are noticeably smaller than the eggs of the Baltimore Oriole, measuring (on an average) only .79 by .58 inches. They are white, irregularly spotted and scrawled, or slightly clouded, with dark umber brown or black; the markings tend to be denser at the larger end.

The Orchard Oriole's habit of occupying the same tree as the Kingbird has been remarked in the discussion of the latter species. This arrangement must be of the Oriole's seeking and is perhaps made to secure itself against marauders by soliciting the Kingbird's protection; but it seems to be mutually satisfactory.

Icterus spurius Townsend, *Proc. Acad. Nat. Sci. Philadelphia*, 1883, 63 (Latrobe, Westmoreland Co.)—Jacobs, *Summer Birds Greene Co., Pa.*, 1893, 9 (Greene Co., nesting)—Todd, *Ann. Carnegie Mus.*, 1904, 2:567 (Erie, Erie Co., summer)—Todd, in Bausman, *Hist. Beaver Co., Pa.*, 1904, 2: 1200 (Beaver Co., summer)—Harlow, *Auk*, 1912, 29:473; 1918, 35:137 (southern Centre Co., breeding)—Oberholser, *Bird-Lore*, 1923, 25:119 (Beaver, Beaver Co., migration) —Christy, *Cardinal*, 1923, v. 1, no. 1, [p. 8] (Sewickley, Allegheny Co., summer)—Burleigh, *Wilson Bull.*, 1924, 36:71; 1931, 43:46 (State College, Centre Co., migration; nesting)—Sutton, *Ann. Carnegie Mus.*, 1928, 18:167 (Meadville and Pymatuning Swamp, Crawford Co., summer)—Burleigh, *Cardinal*, 1932, 3:81 (Chalk Hill, Fayette Co., nesting)—Christy, *Cardinal*, 1939, 5:21 (Pymatuning Lake, near Linesville, Crawford Co., May).

"Orchard Oriole" Jacobs, *Hawkeye Ornithologist and Oölogist*, 1888, 1:88 (Waynesburg, Greene Co., April)—Stone, *Cassinia*, 1906, 9:43 (McConnellsburg, Fulton Co., June)—McClelland, *Am. Mid. Nat.*, 1922, 8:36 (Washington, Washington Co., summer)—Street, *Cassinia*, 1923, 24:14 (Greencastle to Ft. Loudon, Franklin Co., June)—Eastwood, *Bird-Lore*, 1926, 28:273 (Oakdale, Allegheny Co., May, *fide* Portman; "Coraopolis Heights," Allegheny Co., May, *fide* Frederick; and Industry, Beaver Co., May, *fide* Elliott).

BALTIMORE ORIOLE

ICTERUS GALBULA (Linnaeus)

Description—Adult male: head (all around) and upper back, black, this color extending to the breast in apical pattern; wings black, with white edgings; tail black centrally, orange-yellow laterally; lower back, lesser wing coverts, and *rest of underparts, bright orange;* bill bluish black. *Adult female:* similar to the male in color pattern but much duller; the black areas mottled with green, and the orange areas more saffron yellow; tail not distinctly bicolor. *Immature:* upperparts (including tail), yellowish brown, the upper back rather duller and darker; wings dusky, with whitish edgings; underparts saffron orange, brightest on the breast and under tail coverts, palest on the throat. (At this stage males are usually more brightly colored than females.) The *juvenal plumage* resembles the immature but is still duller.

Range—The Baltimore Oriole has about the same winter range as the Orchard Oriole (from southern Mexico to Colombia), but in the breeding season it goes a little farther north than that species; it ranges from Alberta to Nova Scotia and thence southward to northern Georgia and central Louisiana. Thus the two species are found together over much of the eastern United States. The Baltimore Oriole barely reaches the Canadian Life Zone; it is properly a species of the Transition and Upper Austral life zones. In New York, according to E. H. Eaton (1914), it is rare in the wooded parts of the Adirondack and Catskill Mountains, where its advent has followed the clearing of the country. Clearing of the land may also explain its presence in western Pennsylvania. It is hard to conceive of the Baltimore Oriole as a primitive inhabitant of the coniferous forest that once covered the plateau region; and it is still uncommon enough there to be considered a newcomer. I did not encounter it during my traverse of the wilds of western Cambria County in June, 1893, until I had emerged from the forest and entered the cleared areas in Indiana County. For the northern counties there are a few scattered summer records; most of the records made at that season, however, come from the region west of the Allegheny River and Laurel Hill. In the ridge and valley section the species is common and seems to range (unchecked by the Allegheny divide) across Somerset County; for it has been reported at Springs (Miller) and at Stoyestown (Mostoller). My impression is that this oriole is not nearly so common now, however, as it was forty years ago, although its present numbers still far exceed those of the Orchard Oriole.

Migration—Many reports on the spring movements of this species are available, since its arrival is easily determined. Twenty-five years' "first-seen" records from Beaver lie between April 19 (1889) and May 4 (1934), the average date being April 28. In recent years the trend is toward later, rather than earlier, arrival, because of the increasing backwardness of the seasons. B. H. Christy's records from Sewickley cover about the same range, as do also those of other observers in the Ohio Valley. In the mountains the species does not appear as a rule until the first of May or later. In the A. K. Pierce records from Renovo, covering twenty-five years, May 5 is the average date, and the earliest is April 30 (1903). Thus it seems that the northward advance is retarded in the mountainous country. This is understandable on the assumption that the movement is from southwest to northeast. Sometimes the Oriole is common from the very day it arrives, and it always reaches its maximum numbers within a few days thereafter.

In comparison with the spring migration, the southward movement in the fall is accomplished quickly and quietly. August finds the Oriole's numbers already on the wane, and by the end of that month the last birds have usually gone, although in some seasons a few stragglers linger into September. August 31 is in fact the average "last-seen" date in series of records from both Beaver and Renovo, while the latest date for the former place is September 10 (1921—Sutton). Late records for other places are: Sewickley, September 4, 1922 (Christy); Pittsburgh, September 8, 1927 (Burleigh); Crystal Lake, Crawford County, September 4, 1928 (Sutton); State College, September 16, 1915 (Burleigh); Renovo, September 21, 1899 (Pierce). Any record made after the first week in September is notable.

Habits—The orange, black, and white of this beautiful oriole were the colors of Lord Baltimore's coat of arms. Among the most brilliant and gaudy of its tribe, the species comes to us from the tropics, flashing on our view a fleeting glimpse of their gorgeous and varied bird life. The coming of the Oriole always proclaims sunny skies and balmy air, bursting buds and blossoming fruit trees, the humming of insects and the subtle fragrance of spring flowers. The warbler hosts, pushing north at about the same time, might pass through unnoticed by the casual observer, despite their variety, abundance, and bright colors. Not so the Baltimore Oriole, whose arrival is well advertised to both eye and ear. The male Oriole, as he works among the terminal branches of the trees, is especially conspicuous; for his brilliant hues form a sharp contrast to his surroundings. He seems to take delight in displaying his charms for all to see and in calling attention to himself by his volubility. As a musician he ranks high, and his rich, mellow notes, ringing out full and clear from orchard or grove, carry with them a suggestion of tropical verdure and exuberance. His repertoire ranges from a single loud note to a longer song with elaborate variations, delivered with a swing and fullness most pleasing to the ear. In the early days I used to listen to an oriole that seemed to say: "Are you *very* hard of hearing?" In driving off a rival from his territory, or an intruder from the vicinity of his nest, the male uses a harsh, scolding note, rapidly repeated. The female has precisely the same note.

The Baltimore Oriole is primarily partial to

orchards, especially old orchards where the trees are of full growth. It is at home also in the shade trees along the streets and in the parks of our towns and villages—wherever the trees are high enough to be safe as nesting sites. Many pairs, however, still cling to their original haunts in the trees along streams and about the edges of woods. Often an isolated group of large trees in a field, or sometimes a single tree, will be appropriated as a home by a pair of orioles. While the Oriole is strictly arboreal in its haunts and habits, and while it requires good-sized trees for nesting, it is content with a rather restricted feeding range and accordingly has been able to adapt itself to the changed conditions brought about by deforestation. If a few large trees are left, or if orchards become available, the Oriole can survive.

As a destroyer of noxious insects, this species stands near the head of the list. Caterpillars form the largest percentage of its food; these are supplemented by beetles, bugs, grasshoppers, and ants. Although the Oriole spends a great deal of its time searching for these insects among leaves and branches, it is not exclusively insectivorous. In the fruit season it takes its toll of cherries, blackberries, and raspberries. I once watched a single cherry tree to which, in the course of an hour, six orioles (adult and young) came to feed upon the ripe fruit. It is but fair to say that the fruit of this particular tree was worth very little. The damage done to the cherry crop by the Oriole, however, is not to be compared with that inflicted by the Robin, and it is more than offset by the species' destruction of noxious insects.

A colorful and brilliant member of the bird world, a pleasing songster, and a valuable economic asset, the Baltimore Oriole has yet another claim to distinction. Its pouch-shaped nest, suspended from the tip of a drooping branch, beyond reach of harm from man or beast, and swaying freely in the summer breeze, is a truly admirable example of bird architecture. There are indeed other birds, such as the vireos and the Orchard Oriole, that build hanging nests, but theirs are much less elaborate in design and workmanship. Of the many nests that I have found, I have examined only a few, since most of them were practically inaccessible. According to my observation, the species prefers an apple tree of the Rambo variety (now nearly extinct) and, failing that, an elm, a pear, a sycamore, some other variety of apple, and a walnut, in the order named. The female does most or all of the work on the nest, although the male usually accompanies her on her trips back and forth for materials and seems to enjoy inspecting its construction. She begins by firmly fastening a number of long strands upon the supporting twigs. These strands are then caught together at the bottom and, as more are added, are looped and interwoven, until the final result, after days of labor, is a long bag-shaped structure, rather constricted at the mouth, with the lower part rounded and enlarged. It is composed of a fabric thick and strong enough to withstand the stress of ordinary wind and weather. Vegetable fibers of any kind that may be available are utilized in fashioning this framework. Bits of string or yarn picked up here and there are often incorporated, and I saw one nest built almost entirely of horsehair. Within this foundation is set a lining of finer and softer materials, such as plant down, bits of wool and cotton, hair, or grass stems. The nest is so substantially built that it usually outlasts the season for which it was intended, and a tree may hold the dilapidated remains of several old nests.

Nest-building is usually well under way by the second week in May, and full sets of eggs may be found from the middle of that month until about June 10. Later nestings are doubtless second attempts. Four or five eggs are laid, or occasionally as many as six. They tend to be rather long ovate, measuring about .91 by .61 inches. In color they are white, often with a slight creamy tint, and are spotted and scrawled in irregular fashion, but more thickly about the larger end, with blackish brown and lighter shell-markings. The markings are distinct, although not dense. The eggs may easily be distinguished from those of any other Pennsylvania bird.

Both parents are assiduous in caring for the young, which usually leave the nest sometime in June. The molting season for the adults follows directly. The jubilant song of the male bird is hushed—only by an occasional musical call note does he betray his presence—and the female and the young are not any more vociferous. In August, however, having assumed fine fresh plumage, the Oriole again becomes noisy and conspicuous, although less so than in the spring. Amid the dense foliage of the trees the birds often elude observation, despite their brilliant colors. The urge to migrate presently becomes irresistible, and soon all are on their southward way to the tropics from which they came, and whence they will return as another spring season rolls around.

Icterus baltimore TEULON, *Jour. Boston Zoöl. Soc.*, 1883, 2:9 (Bradford, McKean Co., spring).

Icterus galbula TOWNSEND, *Proc. Acad. Nat. Sci. Philadelphia*, 1883, 64 (Latrobe, Westmoreland Co., nesting)—COOKE, *Auk*, 1885, 2:58 (New Lexington, Somerset Co., migration)—TODD, *Auk*, 1893, 10:39 (Two Lick, Indiana Co., June), 44 (Coalport, Clearfield Co., nesting)—JACOBS, *Summer Birds Greene Co., Pa.*, 1893, 9 (Greene Co., nesting)—COPE, *Cassinia*, 1902, 5:16 (Clinton and Potter Co., June)—TODD, *Ann. Carnegie Mus.*, 1904, 2:567 (Erie and Presque Isle, Erie Co., summer)—TODD, in Bausman, *Hist. Beaver Co., Pa.*, 1904, 2:1200 (Beaver Co., summer)—PITCAIRN, *Oölogist*, 1907, 24:41 (Riverview Park, Allegheny Co.)—HARLOW, *Auk*, 1912, 29:473 (southern Centre Co., nesting)—OBERHOLSER, *Bird-Lore*, 1922, 24:339 (Beaver, Beaver Co., and Renovo, Clinton Co., migration)—CHRISTY, *Cardinal*, 1923, v. 1, no. 1, [p. 8] (Sewickley, Allegheny Co., summer)—BURLEIGH, *Wilson Bull.*, 1923, 35:92 (Pittsburgh, Allegheny Co., nesting); 1924, 36:71; and 1931, 43:46 (State College, Centre Co., migration; nesting)—SUTTON, *Ann. Carnegie Mus.*, 1928, 18:168 (Crawford Co. localities, summer)—BURLEIGH, *Cardinal*, 1929, 2:118 (Allegheny Co., fall migration)—SUTTON, *Cardinal*, 1929, 2:121 (Crystal Lake, Crawford Co., September)—SEMPLE, *Cardinal*, 1932, 3:69 (western Pa., nesting)—BURLEIGH, *Cardinal*, 1932, 3:81 (Chalk Hill, Fayette Co., nesting).

"Baltimore Oriole" ENTY, *Ornithologist and Oölogist*, 1885, 10:78 (Templeton, Armstrong Co., April)—JACOBS, *Hawkeye Ornithologist and Oölogist*, 1888, 1:88 (Waynesburg, Greene Co., April)—"C. S. L.," *Oölogist*, 1888, 5:60 (Warriorsmark, Huntingdon Co., nesting)—BRUMBAUGH, *Wilson Bull.*, 1905, 12:100 (Wilkinsburg, Allegheny Co., July)—STONE, *Cassinia*, 1906, 9:43 (McConnellsburg, Fulton Co., June)—PITCAIRN, *Bird-Lore*, 1907, 9:155 (Riverview Park, Allegheny Co., nesting)—SIMPSON, *Oölogist*, 1909, 26:170 (Warren, Warren Co., nesting)—BURLEIGH, *Oölogist*, 1911, 28:156 (Harmarville, Allegheny Co., nesting)—HARLOW, *Oölogist*, 1912, 29:308 (Center Furnace Swamp, Centre Co., nesting)—ROGERS, *Bird-Lore*, 1914, 16:274 (Pittsburgh, Allegheny Co., migration)—MCCONNELL, *Oölogist*, 1918, 35:150 (McKeesport, Allegheny Co.)—MCCLELLAND, *Am. Mid. Nat.*, 1922, 8:36 (Washington, Washington Co., summer)—STREET, *Cassinia*, 1923, 24:14 (Greencastle to Ft. Loudon, Franklin Co., June)—CHRISTY, *Cardinal*, 1924, v. 1, no. 4, p. 10 (Big Traverse Valley, Beaver Co., June)—EASTWOOD, *Bird-Lore*, 1925, 27:263 (Pittsburgh region, Allegheny Co., April), 337 (Bradford Woods, Allegheny Co., August, *fide* Frederick); 1926, 28:273 (Rector, Westmoreland Co., May, *fide* Knauz); 1927, 29:273 (Springs, Somerset Co., April, *fide* Miller).

RUSTY BLACKBIRD (Plate 21)

EUPHAGUS CAROLINUS (Müller)

Description—About the size of the Eastern Redwing; bill slender; iris pale yellow. *Adult male in spring:* wholly black, with a slight dark greenish gloss. *Adult female in spring:* plumbeous blackish, the wings and tail somewhat darker and glossier. *In the adult and immature males in the fall,* the black of the body plumage is more or less obscured by the *broad rusty-buff edgings of the feathers. Female in fall:* upperparts deep rusty buff (most pronounced on the head); underparts similar but paler; a buffy stripe over the eye and a darker one below it; wings blackish with rusty-buff edgings; tail black.

Range—Of its family, the Rusty Blackbird is the most northern species and, in fact, the only Pennsylvania species that passes beyond our limits to breed. In the summer it ranges through the Canadian and Hudsonian life zones from Alaska to Newfoundland and south to the Adirondacks in New York. In our section it is mainly a transient, more or less uncommon and irregular everywhere except at Pymatuning Swamp, where favorable local conditions attract it in considerable numbers both in spring and in fall. The main winter range of this blackbird lies to the southward, but it is a hardy species and has repeatedly been observed at various points in western Pennsylvania during the cold season. On December 6, 1889, I saw a small group at the mouth of the Beaver River, and on December 10, 1919, I found a flock of about a dozen birds along the Ohio River at Economy, Beaver County. The species has been noted at Springs, Somerset County, during December (Miller); at State College on January 6, 1917 (Burleigh); and at Jamestown, Mercer County, on February 1, 1934 (Dilley). At Hollidaysburg it was found "all winter" in 1920–21 (Berg). While these are exceptional records, they seem to be more than merely accidental in their significance.

Migration—Ten of these birds in a flock found near Beaver on February 22, 1888 (Wickham), may have been either winter residents or exceptionally early migrants. March 12 (1892) is the same observer's next earliest date for that locality.

Early spring records from some other places are: Indiana, February 17, 1933 (Greenberg); Meadville, March 2, 1892 (Kirkpatrick); State College, March 4, 1919 (Burleigh). These dates to the contrary, the species does not as a rule appear until the middle or end of March (depending on the weather) and does not become common (if ever) until April, when most of the birds pass through. Stragglers do not all leave until May. Late migrants have been recorded at "Patton's Point," Beaver County, on May 6, 1928 (Christy); at Chambersburg, Franklin County, on May 7, 1925 (Sutton); at Hartstown, Crawford County, on May 13, 1922 (Sutton); and at Erie on May 17, 1902 (Bacon). Thus the migration period in the spring is unusually long. In the fall it is somewhat shorter. Seldom does the Rusty Blackbird arrive before the last week in September or the first week in October. It was reported at Renovo on September 14, 1903 (Pierce); at Hartstown on September 22, 1925 (Sutton); and at Erie on September 27, 1893 (Bacon). October is the month of greatest movement, and November finds many birds still present; but by the end of that month most of them have gone, and only a few stragglers remain for the winter. Some actual "last-seen" dates are: Warren, November 9, 1905 (Simpson); Raccoon Creek, Beaver County, November 12, 1923 (Boulton); Kane, November 10, 1897 (Pierce); Meadville, November 14, 1908 (Kirkpatrick); Cherry Hill, Erie County, November 14, 1900 (Bacon); Renovo, November 16, 1897 (Pierce); Presque Isle, November 18, 1902 (Simpson); State College, November 20, 1914 (Burleigh); Forestville, Butler County, November 25, 1921 (Keesler); Pittsburgh, November 23, 1913, and November 26, 1914 (Burleigh). The later dates thus merge with the known winter records and may actually pertain to prospective winter residents. To estimate the average date of departure therefore seems impracticable.

Habits—For the most part the Rusty Blackbird belies its name; for it is only in the fall that its body plumage is veiled with rust color. In behavior, haunts, and habits, the species is a true grackle, rather than a marsh troupial. During its sojourn in our region it often associates with both the Bronzed Grackle and the Red-wing, and even with the Cowbird. It prefers swampy lands, with an abundance of bushy growth, to open marshes or high trees. Small groups are the rule in the spring, except at Pymatuning Swamp, where large flocks are common. G. M. Sutton writes (1928): "These flocks stopped in the dense alder thickets north of Hartstown. Their squealing, spluttering jargon was musical at a distance. They fed mostly on the ground, and more than once I was able to approach them closely enough to observe them walking rapidly about, pecking here and there at the roots, and wading through the water up to their bellies, like sandpipers." In April, 1935, I found rusty blackbirds very numerous not far from Linesville; they were in loose flocks in the woods along the edge of the swamp, and they kept in one general direction as they drifted through the treetops or the lower growth. Their wheezy, gurgling notes were not unpleasing to the ear.

"In the fall," according to Dr. Sutton, "much more noticeably than in the spring, the Rusty Blackbirds mingle with the Red-winged Blackbirds and Cowbirds." Along the Ohio River at the former season they commonly frequent the willow growth; their call notes are harsher, more grackle-like, than in the spring, but the birds are quieter and travel in more compact flocks.

Scolecophagus ferrugineus Townsend, *Proc. Acad. Nat. Sci. Philadelphia*, 1883, 64 (Latrobe, Westmoreland Co.).

Euphagus carolinus Todd, *Ann. Carnegie Mus.*, 1904, 2:568 (Erie and Presque Isle, Erie Co., transient)—Todd, in Bausman, *Hist. Beaver Co., Pa.*, 1904, 2:1200 (Beaver Co., transient)—Oberholser, *Bird-Lore*, 1921, 23:295 (Pittsburgh, Allegheny Co., and Renovo, Clinton Co., migration)—Christy, *Cardinal*, 1923, v. 1, no. 1, [p. 8] (Sewickley, Allegheny Co., transient)—Burleigh, *Wilson Bull.*, 1923, 35:92 (Allegheny Co., transient); 1924, 36:77 (State College, Centre Co., migration)—Sutton, *Ann. Carnegie Mus.*, 1928, 18:169 (Meadville, Conneaut Lake, and Pymatuning Swamp, Crawford Co., transient).

"Rusty Blackbird" Harlow, *Cassinia*, 1912, 15:20 (Center Furnace Swamp, Centre Co., spring)—Eastwood, *Bird-Lore*, 1926, 28:207; 1927, 29:196, 197 (Pittsburgh region, Allegheny Co., March)—Boulton, *Bird-Lore*, 1928, 30:13 (Rector, Westmoreland Co., November, *fide* Fricke), 195 (upper Deer Creek, Allegheny Co., March), 271 (Raccoon Creek, Beaver Co., May, *fide* Christy).

PURPLE GRACKLE (Plate 21)

QUISCALUS QUISCULA QUISCULA (Linnaeus)

Description—Larger than the Robin; the tail rounded. General coloration black. The *head* (*all around*) and the *breast are glossed with dark steel blue or steel green*, the wings and tail, with purple, and the upperparts and underparts (except as aforesaid), with green or purple, in broken, iridescent bars. The *female* is decidedly smaller and duller, and the *young bird* in first plumage is almost uniformly dusky black.

Range—According to the American Ornithologists' Union *Check-List*, the Purple Grackle, *Quiscalus quiscula quiscula*, is the form that inhabits the Atlantic slope from Long Island to Georgia. I have provisionally retained this arrangement, but F. M. Chapman, who has made a special study of this group of conspecies, transfers the name *quiscula* to the Florida Grackle and calls the Atlantic slope form *stonei*.[1] He uses the name *ridgwayi* for the intergrades (or hybrids?) between *stonei* and *aeneus* (the Bronzed Grackle). The area where these two forms meet is a wide strip that extends southward from New York along the Appalachian mountain chain. While *stonei* is found mostly east of this chain and *aeneus* mostly to the west thereof, in the mountains themselves a curious situation exists. Here both forms nest side by side and interbreed so freely that the only way to identify a given set of eggs is to collect the parent birds. At least this has been the experience of R. C. Harlow and T. D. Burleigh at State College. A. K. Pierce claimed that both forms were breeding in Clinton County, but his identifications, since they were based in part on an assumed difference in nesting habits, are questionable. The necessary data for establishing the exact range of (so-called) *quiscula* in western Pennsylvania are lacking, but the assumption is that this form occupies the entire ridge and valley section as far west as the Allegheny divide, beyond which it is replaced by *aeneus*.[2] Each form, however, invades the territory of the other, as already pointed out, and occasional individuals appear far beyond their proper limits. Thus, a specimen in the Carnegie Museum (No. 8296), taken at Wilkinsburg on April 20, 1894, is clearly "*quiscula*," although it comes from the region where *aeneus* alone would be expected to occur. I am inclined to believe that these two forms are distinct species rather than geographical races as they are classified in the 1931 edition of the *Check-List*.

Migration—Like its western cousin, the Bronzed Grackle, this bird is one of the hardiest of the Icteridae; it comes north to occupy its nesting grounds in March and departs in October or early November. Very few records of its movements are available. It was reported from Hollidaysburg on March 9 in 1921 (Berg) and from Huntingdon on March 8 in 1925 (Truman). It has been noted late in December near Chambersburg (Warfield, 1919) and probably winters at times in that section of western Pennsylvania.

Habits—The general habits of the Purple Grackle are so similar to those of the Bronzed that one account will suffice for both. (The reader is referred to the account of the latter species.) The two forms can be distinguished in life only under the most favorable circumstances and only by observers who are equally familiar with both. Sight records made in disputed territory must therefore be accepted with reservations.

Quiscalus quiscula DWIGHT, *Auk*, 1892, 9:136, part (Cresson, Cambria Co., and Altoona, Blair Co., June)—CHAPMAN, *Bull. Am. Mus. Nat. Hist.*, 1892, 4:14 (Centre Co.).

"Purple Grackle" STONE, *Cassinia*, 1906, 9:43 (McConnellsburg, Fulton Co., June)—HARLOW, *Cassinia*, 1912, 15:20 (Center Furnace Swamp, Centre Co., spring)—WARFIELD, *Bird-Lore*, 1919, 21:37 (Chambersburg, Franklin Co., December)—STREET, *Cassinia*, 1923, 24:15 (Greencastle to Ft. Loudon, Franklin Co., June).

Quiscalus quiscula quiscula HARLOW, *Auk*, 1912, 29:473 (southern Centre Co., nesting); 1918, 35:137 (western Pa.)—BURLEIGH, *Wilson Bull.*, 1924, 36:72; 1931, 43:46 (State College, Centre Co., migration; nesting).

Quiscalus quiscula ridgwayi OBERHOLSER, *Auk*, 1919, 36:552 (central Pa., in range).

[1] *Auk*, 1936, 53:405–417.

[2] As I did not realize the importance of collecting specimens of grackles at the time, my contribution to the subject is relatively small in proportion to the extensive field work I have done in this region. A few years ago G. M. Sutton undertook to investigate the question, but was unable to complete his work, and the material he collected was subsequently lost.

BRONZED GRACKLE (Plate 21)

QUISCALUS QUISCULA AENEUS Ridgway

Description—General color black. *Adult male:* head (all around) and breast glossed with deep violaceous blue, the wings and tail, with purple, and the *upperparts and rest of the underparts, with bronze* (nearly uniformly). *Female:* smaller and duller, the bronzy gloss scarcely evident below. *Young:* dusky black, without gloss. Bill (in both sexes) black; eyes yellow.

Range—In general, the range of the Bronzed Grackle is much more extensive than that of the Purple Grackle. It reaches from the Appalachian Mountains westward to the Rockies, northward to the Gulf of St. Lawrence and Great Slave Lake, and southward to the Gulf of Mexico. Over this vast region the characters of this form are remarkably constant; only toward the southeast, where its range meets that of "*quiscula*," do they approach those of the latter form. The Bronzed Grackle, and not the Purple, is the prevailing form over most of western Pennsylvania, west and north of the Allegheny divide. Just how much farther east the former regularly extends has not been determined. Both, however, are found at State College (Harlow; Burleigh), where they not infrequently interbreed, and a similar condition probably exists in other parts of the ridge and valley section. This condition strongly suggests that the two birds are distinct although closely allied species.

Migration—The Bronzed Grackle regularly winters in the southern part of its general range, but there are a few records of its occurrence in the winter months in the upper Ohio Valley and even as far north as Crawford County. Mild and open winters, such as those that have prevailed in recent years, naturally have no terrors for this hardy species, which presses northward on the heels of winter and often appears in late February, following or even anticipating the Robin and the Bluebird. Early records for Beaver are: February 22, 1888 (Wickham); February 22, 1890 (Todd); February 24, 1891 (Wickham); February 17, 1917 (Boulton). Later dates, however, are far more usual; they range from March 4 to 20, the exact time depending on the weather. The species was noted at Sewickley on February 27 in 1890 and 1921 (Christy). Otherwise, Allegheny County arrival dates correspond with the normal time of arrival at Beaver: Wilkinsburg, March 9–14 (Atkinson); Sewickley, March 1–19 (Christy). In the mountains the species tends to be later; at Renovo, March 19 is the average date, as compared with March 8 at Beaver. By the first of April at the latest, all the summer-resident birds are settled on their breeding grounds.

The great flocks of grackles that gather in August and September begin to move southward in October. The big flights continue almost unabated during the first week of that month, and scattered flocks and laggard birds often remain two or three weeks longer. Indeed, it is hard to fix a time for the autumnal departure of this species, because of the irregular stragglers in the rear of the migratory movement—some of which are destined to remain through the winter. As a rule, however, there is a marked diminution in numbers after the first week in November.

Habits—"Crow Blackbird" would be a more appropriate if less precise name for this species. Certainly it is crow-like, not only in its general coloration, but also in its bold demeanor, its omnivorous diet, and its gregarious disposition. Appearing as it does in vast flocks, which by their very size attract the attention of the casual beholder, it is a species whose potentialities for good or ill cannot be lightly ignored. Its arrival in the spring is usually delayed until the snow is practically gone, and is heralded by the appearance, in their old haunts, of noisy flocks or small groups, perched in the treetops in some conspicuous place. These earliest comers are usually few in number (a small flock at most), but in about a week, migrating flocks of from a hundred to two or three thousand birds make their appearance. Most of these pass on northward, while others rove about the country for a month or so before dispersing to breed. Grackles are fond of wet meadows and the vicinity of streams, but not to the same extent that Red-wings are.

The Grackle finds most of its food on the ground. An unseasonable snowfall naturally handicaps the search and drives the birds to the waterside or sometimes to garbage heaps, where they consort with English sparrows and starlings. No sooner does the spring plowing begin than the grackles congregate and follow in the wake of the plowman, proceeding at an easy, walking gait, their glossy coats glistening in the spring sunshine. From the freshly turned earth they pick up quantities of insects, particularly beetles and grubs, among which cutworms and the larvae of the May beetle (*Lachnosterna*) figure prominently. Grasshoppers are another important article of diet. Stomach examinations prove that the work of this bird during the spring months is, from an economic standpoint, largely beneficial. Insects in great numbers are required to feed the growing young, and many harmful kinds are thus kept in check. But even at this season, not all the Grackle's activities can be construed as helpful. It has been accused of robbing the nests of other birds and of pulling sprouting corn. Of both these charges it is admittedly guilty, but in what degree is not easy to say. Having repeatedly seen grackles being chased by robins, I judge that the latter are frequent victims of the former's nest-robbing tendencies. As it builds an open nest, the Robin naturally invites such attention, and it may not always be able to defend its home against aggression. But as in my opinion there are too many robins, the actual harm done is probably exaggerated. The second charge can likewise be substantiated. I can certify that the Grackle pulls sprouting corn, as I have myself observed it in the act. In Butler County in May, 1889, it was responsible for more damage than the Crow. I doubt, however, whether the habit is widespread and universal. Injury to a crop is easy to prevent by tarring the seed before planting.

After the young are on the wing, family groups may often be seen searching for aquatic forms of life along the edges of larger streams; the young are querulous; the parents, busy and preoccupied. It is not long before these groups join with others to form flocks of greater or less size, which presently betake themselves to the cornfields. There trouble begins in earnest. The ears of corn, now "in the milk," are greedily devoured by the hordes of grackles and red-wings that descend upon the fields in a mighty host and leave devastation behind them. The birds are easily able to strip the green husks from the ears in order to reach the growing grain, and what they do not destroy is left exposed to the weather to dry or rot. Many a farmer knows to his sorrow what terrible damage to his crop a large flock of these birds can inflict. If driven from one part of the field, they will congregate in another, as bold and persistent as ever. There seems to be no way, short of a constant guard, to circumvent this thievery, although it might be interesting to test the efficacy of using a trained falcon or other hawk. Corn (ripened grain) likewise constitutes a large proportion of the food of the Grackle during the fall months; and although some mast and weed seeds are eaten, very few insects are consumed. Nevertheless, if their nest-robbing proclivities are left out of account as an unknown and variable quantity, the grackles appear to do more good than harm. F. E. L. Beal concludes that "the local ravages they commit are usually due to overcrowding in a restricted area, and when this occurs there is no doubt that their numbers should be reduced."[1]

To the dispassionate observer the courtship performance of the male grackle is decidedly grotesque and ludicrous. If perched in the top of a tree with a company of his fellows (similarly engaged), he puffs out his plumage, partly opens his wings, spreads his tail, and emits a hoarse, raucous, squawky "song" that may be pleasing enough to the object of his attention but that certainly grates on human ears. The ordinary call note of both sexes is similarly harsh and unpleasant, especially when heard in chorus. During the mating season the male carries his tail in a boat-shaped position, with the central feathers depressed. By April most of the birds are paired, and nesting is under way.

In primeval times the species probably nested, as the Rusty Blackbird does now, in bushes and shrubbery near the water, and it is interesting to find a few pairs still following the ancestral custom. H. C. Kirkpatrick writes that some years ago he knew of a small swampy area, densely grown up to shrubbery (mostly buttonbush, *Cephalanthus occidentalis*), where year after year a colony of grackles nested. Twenty-two nests were found in this small area, which was only about a hundred feet by fifty. And G. M. Sutton (1928) says that in May, 1925, he "found two nests, each with a full set of eggs, among the cat-tails at the head of Conneaut Lake, in what appeared to be a very

[1]U. S. Department of Agriculture, Biological Survey, *Bulletin*, no. 13, 1900, p. 69.

unusual situation. These nests were less than a foot above the surface of the water."

The vast majority of our grackles, however, have adapted themselves to the conditions brought about by civilization and have taken up their abodes in orchards and shade trees. They manifest a strong partiality for conifers. Even in nesting time the communal habit is strong, and it is not unusual to find several nests in a group. T. D. Burleigh (1931) once found as many as fifteen nests in a large isolated white pine near State College. In the old days the Beaver cemetery, which was planted with Norway spruces, was a favorite breeding spot; hundreds of pairs nested there —often two or three in the same tree. Climbing to a nest always brought angry and excited protests from all the birds within hearing; they gathered around the intruder and by sheer force of numbers tried to drive him away. In some parts of the country the Grackle regularly builds its nest in holes in trees, and both Mr. Burleigh and D. A. Atkinson have found nests in such situations. Nests have also been found under the eaves of buildings. In recent years the Grackle has manifested a tendency, remarked by several observers from various parts of the country, to nest in the steelwork of bridges.

Wherever placed, the nest is a rather large, bulky, and well-built structure, composed of small twigs, dry grasses, and weed stalks and lined with finer material of the same sort. It is deeply cupped, with thick walls, and is sometimes reinforced with mud, in the manner of the Robin's. Four, five, or sometimes even six eggs, constitute the complement. The markings in different sets vary greatly, but the ground-color is usually a pale greenish white, often more or less overlaid with pale brownish clouding, which produces a soiled effect. The eggs are spotted, blotched, and scrawled, in irregular but characteristic fashion, with brownish black, more thickly around the larger end. Average measurements are 1.14 by .82 inches. According to my experience, they are usually laid between (about) April 20 and May 10.

The post-breeding activities of the Grackle have already received some attention. It travels in flocks, sometimes of enormous size, which fly in compact formation. The noise produced by the many wings passing overhead sounds like that made by a strong wind. During the day these flocks scatter and wander over a considerable area in search of forage, but in the evening they converge toward some favorite roost. For several years the Beaver cemetery was used as a grackle roost from August to November. Red-wings also assembled there in large numbers. Toward evening an observer stationed near this place would see flock after flock of both species coming in to settle for the night, amid indescribable din and confusion. As daylight faded, the birds became quiet, save for a few sporadic outbursts from time to time. In later years this particular spot was abandoned as a roost. Immense fall flights, such as those observed in 1888, are unknown today. The Grackle may not be a wholly desirable bird citizen, but it is one that might be sorely missed were it wiped out. E. H. Forbush writes that in Colonial days the "maize thieves," as the grackles were called, were persecuted for their depredations to the point of extermination. "The war against the birds was so successful that in 1749 locusts, cutworms and other grass-destroying pests so completely ruined the grass crop of the New England states that the farmers were obliged to send to England and Pennsylvania to obtain hay enough to feed their cattle through the winter."[1] In due course the colonists saw their mistake and repented of their folly; let us not now repeat that mistake.

Quiscalus versicolor Teulon, *Jour. Boston Zoöl. Soc.*, 1883, 2:9 (Bradford, McKean Co.).

Quiscalus purpureus (error) Townsend, *Proc. Acad. Nat. Sci. Philadelphia*, 1883, 64 (Latrobe, Westmoreland Co.)—Homer, *Ornithologist and Oölogist*, 1889, 14:88 (New Hamburg, Mercer Co., nesting).

"Crow Blackbird" Enty, *Ornithologist and Oölogist*, 1885, 10:78 (Templeton, Armstrong Co., March).

Quiscalus quiscula (error) (?)Jamison, *Ornithologist and Oölogist*, 1888, 13:134 (Cresson, Cambria Co., June)—(?)Jacobs, *Summer Birds Greene Co., Pa.*, 1893, 10 (Greene Co., summer).

"Purple Grackle" (error) Wickham, *Oölogist*, 1888, 5:92 (Beaver, Beaver Co., February)—Simpson, *Oölogist*, 1913, 30:51 (Warren, Warren Co., March)—Burleigh, *Oölogist*, 1913, 30:55 (Pittsburgh, Allegheny Co., nesting).

Quiscalus quiscula æneus Warren, *Birds Pa.*, 1888, 241; ed. 2, 1890, 224 (western Pa.)—Todd, *Auk*, 1893, 10:39 (Two Lick, Indiana Co., June)—Jacobs, *Summer Birds Greene Co., Pa.*, 1893, 10 (Greene Co., nesting)—Baily, *Auk*, 1896, 13:294 (Williamsville, Elk Co., nesting)—Todd, *Ann. Carnegie Mus.*, 1904, 2:568 (Erie, Erie Co., summer)—Todd, in Bausman, *Hist. Beaver Co., Pa.*, 1904, 2:1200 (Beaver Co., summer)—

[1]*Birds of Massachusetts*, 1927, 3:458.

Keim, *Cassinia*, 1905, 8:39 (Port Allegany, McKean Co., summer)—Forrest, *Oölogist*, 1911, 28:114 (Washington, Washington Co., summer; January, one record)—Harlow, *Auk*, 1912, 29:474 (southern Centre Co., nesting); 1918, 35: 137 (Pa. west of Allegheny Mountains)—Oberholser, *Auk*, 1919, 36:554 (southwestern Pa., in range)—Oberholser, *Bird-Lore*, 1921, 23:192 (Beaver, Beaver Co., and Renovo, Clinton Co., migration)—Christy, *Cardinal*, 1923, v. 1, no. 1, [p. 8] (Sewickley, Allegheny Co., breeding; rare in winter)—Burleigh, *Wilson Bull.*, 1923, 35:92 (Pittsburgh, Allegheny Co., nesting)—Christy and Sutton, *Cardinal*, 1928, 2:71 (Cook Forest region, Clarion Co., summer)—Sutton, *Ann. Carnegie Mus.*, 1928, 18:169 (Crawford Co. localities, summer; occasional in winter)—Burleigh, *Wilson Bull.*, 1931, 43:46 (State College, Centre Co., nesting)—Burleigh, *Cardinal*, 1932, 3:82 (Uniontown and Chalk Hill, Fayette Co., summer).

Quiscalus æneus Chapman, *Bull. Am. Mus. Nat. Hist.*, 1892, 4:3, 8 (Erie, Erie Co., breeding; Meadville, Crawford Co., breeding, *fide* Sennett), 12 (Centre Co., *fide* Warren).

"Bronzed Grackle" Harlow, *Cassinia*, 1912, 15:20 (Center Furnace Swamp, Centre Co., spring)—Harlow, *Oölogist*, 1917, 34:64 (State College, Centre Co., nesting)—McConnell, *Oölogist*, 1918, 35:150 (McKeesport, Allegheny Co.) —Miller, *Oölogist*, 1919, 36:156 (State College, Centre Co., nesting)—Stahl, *et al.*, *Bird-Lore*, 1921, 23:18 (Deer Creek[?], Allegheny Co., December)—Christy, *Cardinal*, 1923, v. 1, no. 2, [p. 17] (Clinton Pond, Allegheny Co., nesting)—Sutton, *Bird-Lore*, 1923, 25:132 (Pittsburgh region, Allegheny Co., winter); 1924, 26:122 (Greenville, Mercer Co., February, *fide* Homer), 190 (Pittsburgh, Allegheny Co., nesting)—Eastwood, *Bird-Lore*, 1927, 29:196 (Pittsburgh region, Allegheny Co., March), 197 (Springs, Somerset Co., March, *fide* Miller).

EASTERN COWBIRD

MOLOTHRUS ATER ATER (Boddaert)

Description—Smallest of our blackbirds; bill heavy, sparrow-like. *Male:* glossy black with steel-blue reflections; *head deep brown* (all around). *Female:* grayish brown, paler below; throat whitish, with some obscure streaks on the underparts. *Young in first plumage:* similar to the female, but paler below; throat whiter, and the streaks on the underparts more pronounced.

Range—The Cowbirds as a group are mainly characteristic of tropical America. Only one species enters the northern United States and southern Canada; it is a migrant and winters in the southern part of its general range. This species is a common summer resident in western Pennsylvania, especially in the opener parts of the country and away from the mountains. It is a hardy bird, and there are several records of its wintering in Allegheny and certain other counties, even as far north as Warren.

Migration—The Cowbird may be expected in our region in March, unless the weather conditions then are extremely unfavorable. It comes at about the same time as the Mourning Dove and the Meadowlark; the average arrival date for the Ohio Valley is March 20. At Warren, however, it does not appear until early in April (Simpson). Some February dates have been recorded, but these almost certainly pertain to winter-resident birds. An early comer in the spring, the Cowbird is also a laggard in the fall. It leaves sometime after the middle of October or even later: Beaver, October 17, 1910 (Todd); Wilkinsburg, October 19, 1899 (Atkinson); Shermansville, Crawford County, October 20, 1925 (Bergstrom); State College, November 2, 1916 (Burleigh); Renovo, November 16, 1894 (Pierce). The November dates may possibly pertain to prospective winter residents.

Habits—The Cowbird is so called because of its fondness for pastures, which it supposedly frequents to feed on the insects stirred up by the cattle. In its ambulatory gait and gregarious tendencies it resembles the Grackles, from which, however, it differs by reason of its parasitic egg-laying habit. As our only regularly parasitic bird, it has a unique place in our avifauna and merits more than merely perfunctory notice. Occasionally it is found singly or in small groups, but oftener in companies of a dozen or more, and not infrequently, during the season of migration, in flocks of from one to several hundreds, which behave much like flocks of the Bronzed Grackle and frequent the same kind of habitat. Its courtship display, too, somewhat resembles that of the Grackle: the male fluffs out his feathers, spreads his wings and tail, and bows forward in a ludicrous fashion, while uttering a series of nondescript gulping notes.

Studies of the Cowbird's food made by F. E. L. Beal[1] fail to show any connection between the bird's actual diet and its association with cattle, but do show that from an economic standpoint it

[1]U. S. Department of Agriculture, Biological Survey, *Bulletin*, no. 13, 1900, p. 22–30.

is a valuable species, not only because it destroys many insects (especially in the summer months), but also because it consumes the seeds of noxious weeds in large quantities. Fruit does not enter into its diet, and the grain it takes is mostly waste. Were there no other factor than its food habits to be considered, the verdict would be in its favor; but when the harm done to other birds by its parasitic habit is taken into account, the matter appears in a different light.

As is well known, the European Cuckoo builds no nest of its own but imposes its eggs on other birds, which hatch them and rear the young. This is also the custom of the American Cowbird (although otherwise these two species have little in common). The list of birds imposed upon by the Cowbird is a long one and comprises practically all our Passerine kinds except the larger Corvidae, the Laniidae, and species that nest in cavities, such as the nuthatches, titmice, and wrens. Even birds of this latter group are occasionally victimized. The Cowbird always prefers to lay in nests of species smaller than itself, such as those of warblers, sparrows, vireos, and the like, and the alien egg naturally receives more warmth from the body of the incubating bird. Also, it regularly hatches sooner than the other eggs, so that the young interloper gets off to a better start than its nest companions. The period of incubation for the egg of the Cowbird has been determined to be ten days —from two to four days less than that of most small Passerine birds. Sometimes a female cowbird will deposit an egg in a new but empty nest, often causing the rightful owners to desert. Some birds, notably the Yellow Warbler, attempt to outwit the intruder by adding another story to the nest and burying the egg beneath the new material. Three-, four-, and five-story nests of the Yellow Warbler have been found. Some larger birds—the Robin and the Catbird, for instance—heave the odd-colored egg out of the nest. But, as a rule, if the cowbird's egg appears after one or two of the birds' own have been laid, the hosts accept the addition and proceed as if nothing had happened —with disastrous results to their own offspring.

How the Cowbird finds and parasitizes so many nests has always been a puzzle to me. Authors generally, including Elliott Coues in 1874, give the impression that the species is polygamous or promiscuous and that the female leaves the flock only when under pressure of finding a nest in which to lay. But Herbert Friedmann, in his admirable monograph of this group of birds,[1] has shown that the Cowbird is monogamous (although not strictly so) and that each mated pair confines its activities to a given territory during the breeding season, precisely as do other birds. He believes that the small flocks that one sees at this time are composed of nonbreeding individuals. The males outnumber the females in the proportion of about three to two. According to his account, "The Cowbird ordinarily finds the nests it victimizes by watching the birds build. Frequently I have noted Cowbirds perched almost motionless for an hour or more watching vireos, warblers, and sparrows carrying nesting material . . . the female when ready to lay flew to a perch overlooking the intended nest until the egg was just ready to be laid when she flew directly to the nest. There was no hesitation in her actions, she apparently knew in advance the location of the nest."

It seems, therefore, that the available nests within the territory of a given pair are located in advance by intensive study and are parasitized in turn. It has been supposed that one female may lay as many as ten or twelve eggs in the course of a season, but Dr. Friedmann feels certain that a single bird lays only four or five—no more than the number normally laid by other species of this family. Usually, but not always, only one egg is laid in any one nest by the same bird. It may also happen that more than one female may lay in the same nest—a circumstance indicated by the obvious differences in the coloration of the eggs. This could not occur if each female adhered strictly to her own chosen territory; but the territorial limits sometimes overlap, and the males are often lax in defending them. The largest number of cowbird eggs that I have ever found in any nest was in that of a scarlet tanager; it contained four of the cowbird and three of the tanager. Seldom does a

[1] *The Cowbirds. A Study in the Biology of Social Parasitism.* Springfield, Ill., and Baltimore, 1929.

nest parasitized by the Cowbird contain a full set of the rightful owner. On this point the testimony is abundant and explicit, but we do not yet know what happens to the missing eggs. Time and again I have located a nest with a full set of eggs, to find on a later visit that a cowbird's egg had been added and that one or more of the original eggs had disappeared. Once or twice I have found the latter lying outside the nest, but whether they had been ejected by the cowbird intentionally, or only accidentally, through clumsiness, was impossible to say. Very often the introduction of the strange egg entails a reduction in the normal set of the host.

Dr. Friedmann supplies a long list of species that have been reported as hosts of the Cowbird; some of them, however, are very infrequent victims. As already stated, the vireos, warblers, sparrows, and some of the smaller flycatchers, are the kinds oftenest imposed upon. "The five birds most frequently parasitized by the Cowbird in New York State are the Red-eyed Vireo, Redstart, Yellow Warbler, Chipping Sparrow, and Song Sparrow. In the next group of five should be placed the Ovenbird, Maryland Yellowthroat, Towhee, Indigo Bunting, and Yellow-breasted Chat. This group is closely followed by the Warbling Vireo, Yellow-throated Vireo, Chestnut-sided Warbler, Phoebe, and Veery, while the Wood Thrush and Field Sparrow are next in frequency of being parasitized. At Ithaca the Redstart and Red-eyed Vireo were about tied for first place, followed in order by the Chipping Sparrow, Phoebe, Song Sparrow, Veery, Maryland Yellowthroat, and Louisiana Water Thrush." J. W. Jacobs, writing of his experience in Greene County (1924), lists thirty-two species as victims of the Cowbird. Concerning the extent of the imposition, he states that out of a total of 2,700 sets taken between 1891 and 1922, 234 contained one or more eggs of the parasitic species. Inasmuch as at first he passed over many sets that seemed to be incomplete, the actual percentage of parasitized nests must have been much larger. "The total number of Cowbirds' eggs with the sets collected was 308. These were found in the nests of thirty-two different species. Warblers, Vireos, and Buntings stood the brunt of this imposition."

Mr. Jacobs further writes that in Greene County the Kentucky Warbler is the species most frequently imposed upon by the Cowbird. Forty-seven nests of this species yielded fifty-six eggs of the parasite. Receiving the next greatest amount of attention was the Yellow-breasted Chat—a species that according to Dr. Friedmann is highly intolerant of the Cowbird and usually deserts its nest after invasion. The Louisiana Water-Thrush was another favorite victim, with a record of forty-nine eggs from seventeen nests. My own observations in Beaver County have been very similar. So large a proportion of the nests of small birds that I have found have been invaded by the Cowbird that I have often wondered how these birds contrive to hold their own in point of numbers. From Warren County, R. B. Simpson sends a list of twenty-one victimized species, including among others the Least Flycatcher, the Bobolink, and the Pine Siskin. Within their respective ranges, the Cardinal and the Towhee, the eggs of which somewhat resemble those of the parasite, are also frequently duped. At Pymatuning Swamp, according to G. M. Sutton (1928), the Red-wings refuse to tolerate the presence of a cowbird on their breeding grounds. Dr. Sutton saw "a flock of Red-wings once pursue a female Cowbird until she was utterly exhausted and plunged into the water to escape. Her pursuers chased her to the edge of the Swamp then headed her off and forced her back to the opposite bank." Not only is the Pymatuning Red-wing thus immune from this parasite, but other marsh-inhabiting species, such as the Swamp Sparrow and the Maryland Yellow-throat, are also incidentally benefited.

The egg of the Cowbird is white, profusely speckled with brown, the exact shade of which varies somewhat. Usually the markings are denser toward the larger end, around which they sometimes tend to form a wreath. The average size of the eggs is .84 by .65 inches. Those laid by the same female are more or less alike, so that one can often tell by inspection whether or not the eggs in a given nest were laid by the same bird. The laying period varies with different individuals but as a whole covers May and most of June—the time when the victims are also breeding. The trouble begins after the eggs hatch. The young cowbird usually comes out a day or two ahead of his nest-mates and usurps the advantage from the start. He is larger, lustier, and louder-voiced than they; he demands and receives more food and attention from his foster parents; and he grows so fast that he soon fills the whole nest, smothering or crowding out the rightful occupants. Seldom can a pair of birds succeed in raising any of their own offspring after a cowbird has invaded their nest. Instead, they supinely accept the situation and rear the young cowbird as their own. One often sees a warbler or vireo feeding an insistent young cowbird much larger than itself. After the young bird is able to care for itself it joins its own kind, preparatory to the fall flocking.

Every single cowbird in existence must thus have been raised at the expense of a nestful of other and more desirable birds. Indeed, the Cowbird is unquestionably a serious check upon the increase of these species. Yet its favorite hosts, such as the Red-eyed Vireo, Oven-bird, Redstart, Yellow Warbler, and Louisiana Water-Thrush, seem to be just as numerous as ever. Dr. Friedmann, in discussing this question, thinks that "the Cowbird is one of the most efficient single checks on the undue increase of a large number of species" of birds, which otherwise might become an economic menace. He continues: "The danger of the Cowbird lies with the uncommon species. Birds of low numerical status are, in a sense, the failures of nature. Some of them may be slowly dying out; others may be just holding their own, but to these species the Cowbird can become a very real source of danger. These birds should be helped by man and Cowbird eggs or young indiscriminately destroyed when found in their possession. Of course uncommon birds are relatively uncommonly parasitized, but in the case of rare species each individual nest is a matter of far more importance than a number of nests of an abundant one."

Dr. Friedmann concludes that the Cowbird is a sort of necessary evil, one of nature's schemes of checks and balances, to be dispensed with locally if necessary, but not to be generally outlawed. With these conclusions I agree theoretically. But my practice is to destroy every cowbird egg that I find in a nest; for I feel that the Cowbird is far too numerous in our region for the good of the native avifauna. To several species it is certainly a real menace. Its numbers could well be reduced 75 per cent or even more, with resulting advantage to many of our small birds whose presence is desirable from an economic or aesthetic point of view. Better more warblers and fewer cowbirds. Certainly the latter have increased unduly with the clearing and cultivation of the country, and the former have enough difficulty in maintaining themselves without the menace of the Cowbird superadded. I favor the removal of all legal protection from this bird and an effort to reduce its numbers (but not, of course, to exterminate the species).

Molothrus pecoris Teulon, *Jour. Boston Zoöl. Soc.*, 1883, 2:9 (Bradford, McKean Co.).

Molothrus ater Townsend, *Proc. Acad. Nat. Sci. Philadelphia*, 1883, 63 (Latrobe, Westmoreland Co., summer)—Dwight, *Auk*, 1892, 9:136 (Cresson, Cambria Co., June)—Todd, *Auk*, 1893, 10:39 (between Two Lick and Homer City, Indiana Co., June)—Jacobs, *Summer Birds Greene Co., Pa.*, 1893, 9 (Greene Co., summer)—Todd, *Ann. Carnegie Mus.*, 1904, 2:566 (Erie, Erie Co., summer)—Todd, in Bausman, *Hist. Beaver Co., Pa.*, 1904, 2:1200 (Beaver Co., summer)—Keim, *Cassinia*, 1905, 8:39 (Port Allegany, McKean Co., summer).

"Cowbird" Jacobs, *Hoosier Nat.*, 1886, 2:31 (Waynesburg, Greene Co., parasitic habit)—Jacobs, *Hawkeye Ornithologist and Oölogist*, 1888, 1:88 (Waynesburg, Greene Co., April)—Jacobs, *Gleanings from Nature*, 1904, 3:23 (Waynesburg, Greene Co., June)—Stone, *Cassinia*, 1906, 9:43 (McConnellsburg, Fulton Co., June)—Pitcairn, *Bird-Lore*, 1907, 9:155 (Riverview Park, Allegheny Co., breeding)—Burleigh, *Oölogist*, 1912, 29:395 (Pittsburgh, Allegheny Co., fall)—Harlow, *Auk*, 1912, 29:473 (southern Centre Co., breeding)—McConnell, *Oölogist*, 1918, 35:150 (McKeesport, Allegheny Co.)—Miller (R. F.), *Oölogist*, 1919, 36: 155 (Lemont, Centre Co., breeding)—Miller (M. H.), *In the Open*, June, 1920, 10:23 (Little Sewickley Creek, Allegheny Co., June)—Stahl, *et al.*, *Bird-Lore*, 1921, 23:18 (Forest Hills to Deer Creek, Allegheny Co., December)—Warfield, *Bird-Lore*, 1923, 25:23 (Chambersburg, Franklin Co., December)—Street, *Cassinia*, 1923, 24:14 (Greencastle to Ft. Loudon, Franklin Co., June)—Sutton, *Bird-Lore*, 1923, 25:132 ([Squaw Run], Allegheny Co., December); 1924, 26:56 (Grove City, Mercer Co., December, *fide* Nicholson), 122 (Greenville, Mercer Co., February, *fide* Homer)—Elliott, *et al.*, *Bird-Lore*, 1924, 26:30 ("Denny Pond" to Deer Creek, Allegheny Co., December)—Christy, *Cardinal*, 1924, v. 1, no. 4, p. 10 (Big Traverse Valley, Beaver Co., June)—Jacobs, *Oölogist*, 1924, 41:52 (Greene Co., parasitic habit)—Eastwood, *Bird-Lore*, 1926, 28:58 (Pittsburgh, Allegheny Co., November), 402 (McKinley Park, Allegheny Co., October)—Arthur, *Country Rambler*, 1934, 43 (Guyasuta Run, Allegheny Co., winter).

Molothrus ater ater Oberholser, *Bird-Lore*, 1920, 22:343 (Beaver, Beaver Co., and Renovo, Clinton Co., migration)—Christy, *Cardinal*, 1923, v. 1, no. 1, [p. 8] (Sewickley, Allegheny Co., summer; occasional in winter)—Jacobs, *Oölogists' Record*, 1923, 3:18, 19 (Waynesburg, Greene Co., parasitic habit)—Burleigh, *Wilson Bull.*, 1923, 35:90 (Allegheny Co., summer); 1924, 36:71; and 1931, 43:43 (State College, Centre Co., migration; breeding)—Christy and Sutton, *Cardinal*, 1928, 2:71 (Sigel, Jefferson Co., summer)—Sutton, *Ann. Carnegie Mus.*, 1928, 18:162 (Meadville and Pymatuning Swamp, Crawford Co., summer; habits)—Burleigh, *Cardinal*, 1929, 2:118 (Squaw Run, Allegheny Co., December).

TANAGERS

FAMILY THRAUPIDAE

THE TANAGERS are an extensive tropical American family, notable for their brilliancy of plumage, as well as for marked sexual differences in color. They are most closely related to the Finches but are separated therefrom mainly by certain features of the bill, which is less angulate at the base and which in many species is notched near the tip. Like the Finches, they have only nine developed primary wing feathers.

There are more than five hundred species and subspecies of Tanagers, most of which are confined to the tropics. Of this large number, only five reach the United States. In western Pennsylvania one only (the Scarlet Tanager) is a common summer resident; the Summer Tanager, a more southern form, is a rare visitant. Tanagers are woodland birds that feed on insects and fruits and are thus migratory in temperate regions.

SCARLET TANAGER

PIRANGA ERYTHROMELAS[1] Vieillot

Description—Adult male in breeding plumage: bright scarlet; wings and tail black. *Adult male in fall:* olive green, rather brighter below; wings and tail black. *Young male in fall:* similar to the adult male at the same season, but the tail olive like the back, and the wings dusky greenish, black only at the base. *Adult female:* olive green, rather brighter below; wings a little darker. *Young female:* similar but generally duller. The *juvenal plumage* resembles that of the female but is duller and shows some streaks below.

Range—The Western Tanager in the West, and the Scarlet Tanager in the East, are two species that have pushed their respective ranges far beyond those of their tropical congeners. They are outlying species of a family group that is a large and conspicuous element in the avifauna of the tropics. The Scarlet Tanager breeds over most of the northeastern United States and the adjacent parts of Canada, mainly in the Alleghanian and Carolinian faunas, and does not invade the true Canadian Fauna (the spruce and fir area) to any great extent. Its range in western Pennsylvania covers our entire area and is conditioned only by suitable forest covert. The latter consideration, rather than that of elevation, is the deciding factor; for the bird is fully as common on the crest of the Allegheny Mountains as it is in the Ohio Valley. It is pre-eminently a bird of the forest and is especially partial to hemlock and beech woodland.

Migration—The Scarlet Tanager comes and goes with the warblers. It winters in South America and crosses the Gulf of Mexico in its migration flight back and forth.[2] May 1 is the average date of its arrival at Beaver, although there is a variation (depending on the advance of the season) of about a week either way. Allegheny County reports made by several different observers correspond in general with the Beaver records. The earliest available dates are April 17 (1891), for Waynesburg (Jacobs), and April 20 (1889), for Sewickley (Christy); both are exceptional. Farther north, in the mountains, the species usually arrives a few days later; the average date both at Renovo (Pierce) and at Warren (Simpson) is May 5. The females generally come a little later than the males, but after their arrival no time is lost before nest-

[1]In the writer's opinion, this should be written *erythromelaena*.
[2]Compare F. C. LINCOLN, U. S. Department of Agriculture, *Circular*, no. 363, 1935, p. 36.

building begins. G. M. Sutton reports finding a nest under way at Pymatuning Swamp as early as May 11 in 1922.

The spring arrival of the species is easy to observe, and accordingly there are many records, but its departure in the fall often passes unheralded. Before the birds leave, the males doff their gaudy colors and revert to an inconspicuous dull green dress much like that of the females. September finds the tanagers on their southward way, and by the end of that month nearly all have gone. Some "last-seen" dates are: Presque Isle, September 26, 1900 (Todd); Beaver, October 3, 1905 (Todd); Pittsburgh, October 4, 1913 (Burleigh); Renovo, October 13, 1901 (Pierce).

Habits[1]—A scarlet tanager is singing high in the maple tree above us. We peer upward, eager for a glimpse of the performer. We peer in vain, though the singing continues. The song is like the Robin's in pattern; but it has a certain huskiness and drawl and alto quality about it, and its melody is vaguely minor. How can the bird hide itself so completely? We know it is bright red, but we cannot find it even with our binocular. The singing stops. The leaves at the end of a long branch shake. There is a streak of dull red, then sudden fire as the bird flies out of the shadow across a patch of sunlight to the top of a beech close by.

The male Scarlet Tanager in nuptial plumage is always a thrilling sight. He is somehow most appealing when, having just returned from his winter home in northern South America, he finds himself in our somewhat chilly world searching for sluggish insects among the buds of early May. Summer has not yet come. The dominant tones of the woodland are gray and brown, with here and there a touch of new green or the white of bloodroot and trillium petals. Among these diffident and uncertain color harmonies the Tanager's bold red strikes a note of confidence. Moving from bough to bough, and even occasionally to the ground, it makes us think of a flame that is kindly and reassuring wherever it goes, bidding the young leaves spread themselves to the moist air and urging the bundled mandrake umbrellas to shove themselves upward through the loam.

The male, reaching his nesting ground somewhat in advance of his dull-colored mate, usually does not sing volubly on the day of his arrival but is content with spreading his feathers to the chary sun, with chasing the transient warblers about, and with scolding us if we follow him too closely. *Chip-purr!* he cries, as he turns quickly on a branch, flicks his black tail, and flashes off.

The plumage of the female is so dull in color that she and her mate scarcely seem of the same species. Moving among the leaves of the treetops she is very difficult to see, but we can hear the unmistakable *chip-purr* of her scolding whenever we invade her nesting territory.

As various observers have noted, there is a period of about two weeks in early May when the Scarlet Tanager is especially conspicuous in the woodlands of western Pennsylvania. This is partly because the bright males are selecting and defending their territories and announcing their desire for mates in fervent singing. Furthermore, the species is actually more abundant at this season than it is later in the summer; for numerous transient individuals, en route to more northerly nesting grounds, are present. By May 15 most of the scarlet tanagers of the northeastern United States and southern Canada have reached their summer home and the spring migration is over.

Nest-building begins promptly after courtship and mating are finished. The female does all the work of construction, and a nest may be built in a remarkably short time, frequently in little more than a day. She may work feverishly for periods of fifteen minutes or more, then apparently forget parental duties and devote herself to preening, bathing, or feeding. All the while, the male sings loudly, as if announcing repeatedly to his mate that he is ready to give battle the moment an enemy invades their chosen nesting grounds.

The nest is neither compact, strong, nor particularly neat. It is composed of slender weed stalks and stems of leaves and is lined with dry grasses and fine rootlets. The walls and bottom are often so thin that the faint blueness of the eggs shows from the side or from below. It is usually placed from twenty to forty feet from the ground in a large tree in the midst of the forest. Although hidden from the side by leafage, it may be surprisingly visible from the ground beneath the tree.

Sometimes the Scarlet Tanager nests in orchards or in relatively open woods. F. L. Homer once found a nest in an apple tree "only a short distance from a house" near New Hamburg, Mercer

[1]Account contributed by George M. Sutton.

County. On May 30, 1914, at Chalk Hill, Fayette County, T. D. Burleigh discovered a nest, with four slightly incubated eggs, six feet from the ground in a small tree at the side of a road "over five hundred yards from the nearest woods." The species usually prefers heavier woodland, however. At Pymatuning Swamp, Crawford County, I found it especially abundant in beech, swamp maple, black birch, and hemlock woods. D. A. Atkinson considers the beech the favorite nest-tree in Allegheny County. In Warren County, R. B. Simpson finds the species preferring hemlock and beech. W. E. C. Todd considers it an inhabitant of the deep woods and perhaps somewhat partial to tracts of hemlock in Beaver County. In Armstrong and Butler counties he found it abundant in the coniferous forest. E. A. Preble says that in Westmoreland County it is common in the oak and chestnut woods but also affects the hemlock to some extent. In various parts of Somerset County he observed it in oak, chestnut, and pine woods. Obviously, the Scarlet Tanager likes both deciduous and coniferous timber, providing the trees are large enough to furnish the proper temperature, humidity, light and shadow, and food—in short, the many and variously interrelated factors that compose the birds' summertime world.

The eggs, which are light greenish blue, spotted with reddish brown, usually number four, though five are sometimes laid. They resemble those of the Rose-breasted Grosbeak but are smaller, averaging .88 by .68 inches. The Cowbird frequently parasitizes the Scarlet Tanager. I recall finding a nest near Bethany, West Virginia, in which there were two tanager eggs and three cowbird eggs, with two more cowbird eggs buried in the lining. A nest that Mr. Todd collected in Beaver County on May 30, 1891, contained three slightly incubated eggs of the Tanager, together with four eggs of the Cowbird. So far as I have been able to determine, only one brood is reared in a season, although a new nest is built and a second set of eggs laid if the first eggs are destroyed.

Young scarlet tanagers just out of the nest (about two weeks old) are so heavily streaked below that they do not resemble either of their parents very closely. They wear this juvenal plumage for only a short time, however, and by September are much like the adult female. By this time the adult male, too, has changed his appearance. He has lost his nuptial plumage, feather by feather, and the scarlet of his head and body has been replaced by dull olive green and yellow. A few red blotches may remain, but the gay feathers drop out rapidly, and by the time he heads for the tropics he is an inconspicuous bird. Males in their first winter plumage have dull olive-green wings and tails (remnants of the juvenal plumage); but males that are two years old or older are black-winged and black-tailed in winter.

The postnuptial molt of the adults begins as soon as the young are safely on the wing. This means that we may find adult males with small patches of incoming winter plumage on the back or belly sometimes as early as late July or early August. Mr. Todd writes that certain specimens shot in August in Beaver County were irregularly patched with green, scarlet, and yellow and that they presented an unusual appearance. The molt may progress deliberately in some individuals, but it is usually over by mid-September. In this molt, all plumage, including that of the wings and the tail, is replaced. Whether certain individuals begin their southward migration while still in the postnuptial molt, I cannot say; but it is reasonable to suppose that migration can be accomplished only by birds that are in perfect physical condition, and that therefore no southward flight is attempted until the molt is finished.

The Scarlet Tanager is an eater of insects. The young are fed almost wholly on leaf-consuming caterpillars. Small fruits are taken when available, but the Tanager is all too infrequent a visitor to our gardens and orchards. Lover of the forest that he is, he does not seek our company. If we wish to make his acquaintance we must search for him among the beech trees, the oaks, the maples, and the hemlocks, that are his summer home.

Pyranga rubra (not of Linnaeus, 1758) TEULON, *Jour. Boston Zoöl. Soc.*, 1882, 1:52 (Bradford, McKean Co., summer)—TOWNSEND, *Proc. Acad. Nat. Sci. Philadelphia*, 1883, 61 (Latrobe, Westmoreland Co., summer)—JACOBS, *Nat. Companion*, 1886–87, 2:82 (Waynesburg, Greene Co., summer).

"Scarlet Tanager" VAN FLEET, *Ornithologist and Oölogist*, 1884, 9:108 (DuBois, Clearfield Co.)—ENTY, *Ornithologist and Oölogist*, 1885, 10:78 (Templeton, Armstrong Co., April)—JACOBS, *Hawkeye Ornithologist and Oölogist*, 1888, 1:88 (Waynesburg, Greene Co., April)—STONE, *Cassinia*, 1906, 9:44 (Scrub Ridge, west of McConnellsburg, Fulton Co., June)—BURLEIGH, *Oölogist*, 1911, 28:180; 1912, 29:363 (Uniontown, Fayette Co., nesting; feeding habits)—MCCONNELL, *Oölogist*, 1918, 35:151 (Long Run, near McKeesport, Allegheny Co., spring)—MILLER (R. F.), *Oölogist*, 1919, 36:156 (Charter Oak, Huntingdon Co., nesting)—MILLER (M. H.), *In the Open*, June, 1920, 10:24 (Thornhill, Allegheny Co.)—McCLELLAND, *Am. Mid. Nat.*, 1922, 8:36 (Washington, Washington Co., summer; migration)—STREET, *Cassinia*, 1923, 24:16 (Greencastle to Ft. Loudon and Jordan's Knob, Franklin Co., June)—CHRISTY, *Cardinal*, 1924, v. 1, no. 4, p. 10 (Big Traverse Valley, Beaver Co., June)—EASTWOOD, *Bird-Lore*, 1925, 27:263 (Pittsburgh region, Allegheny Co., May), 337 (Bradford Woods, Allegheny Co., August, *fide* Frederick); 1926, 28:273 (near Rector, Westmoreland Co., May, *fide* Knauz); 1927, 29:273 (Springs, Somerset Co., June, *fide* Miller)—MILLER (A. B.), *Bird-Lore*, 1934, 36:301 (Springs, Somerset Co., food)—COPE and HAWKINS, *Forest Leaves*, 1934, 24:26 (E. Tionesta Forest Reserve, Warren and McKean Co., summer).

Piranga erythromelas JAMISON, *Ornithologist and Oölogist*, 1888, 13:134; and DWIGHT, *Auk*, 1892, 9:138 (Cresson, Cambria Co., June)—TODD, *Auk*, 1893, 10:40 (Two Lick, Indiana Co., June), 45 (Coalport, Clearfield Co., June)—JACOBS, *Summer Birds Greene Co., Pa.*, 1893, 11 (Greene Co., nesting)—BAILY, *Auk*, 1896, 13:295 (Williamsville, Elk Co., June–July)—JACOBS, *Gleanings from Nature*, 1898, 1:31 (Waynesburg, Greene Co., nesting)—COPE, *Cassinia*, 1902, 5:17 (Kettle Creek Valley and Galeton, Potter Co.; Tamarack Swamp, Clinton Co., June)—TODD, *Ann. Carnegie Mus.*, 1904, 2:576 (Erie and Presque Isle, Erie Co., summer)—TODD, in Bausman, *Hist. Beaver Co., Pa.*, 1904, 2:1200 (Beaver Co., summer)—KEIM, *Cassinia*, 1905, 8:39 (Port Allegany, McKean Co., summer)—HARLOW, *Auk*, 1912, 29:474 (southern Centre Co. and "Stone Valley," Huntingdon Co., summer)—OBERHOLSER, *Bird-Lore*, 1918, 20:16 (Beaver, Beaver Co., and Renovo, Clinton Co., migration)—CHRISTY, *Cardinal*, 1923, v. 1, no. 1, [p. 10] (Sewickley, Allegheny Co., breeding)—BURLEIGH, *Wilson Bull.*, 1924, 26:72; 1931, 43:49 (State College, Centre Co., migration; breeding)—CHRISTY, *Cardinal*, 1931, 3:44 (["Patton's Point"], Beaver Co., nesting)—BURLEIGH, *Cardinal*, 1932, 3:82 (Chalk Hill, Fayette Co., nesting).

"Tanager" SIMPSON, *Oölogist*, 1911, 28:201 (Warren, Warren Co., nesting); 1920, 37:143 (head of Tionesta Creek, Warren Co., nesting)—BLAIR, *In the Open*, June, 1920, 10:22 (Butler Co., June).

Pyranga erythromelas BURLEIGH, *Wilson Bull.*, 1923, 35:96 (Allegheny Co., nesting).

Piranga olivacea CHRISTY and SUTTON, *Cardinal*, 1928, 2:72 (Cook Forest, Clarion Co., summer)—SUTTON, *Ann. Carnegie Mus.*, 1928, 18:193 (Crawford Co. localities, summer; nesting).

SUMMER TANAGER

PIRANGA RUBRA RUBRA (Linnaeus)

Description—About the size of the Scarlet Tanager. *Male:* uniform carmine red, including wings and tail. *Female:* dull greenish above and buffy yellowish below.

Range and local status—This species is much more austral in its general distribution than is the Scarlet Tanager; it seldom ranges beyond the Carolinian Fauna and is rare and irregular along the northern frontier of that fauna. It is fairly common in the vicinity of Washington, D.C., and should be looked for in Franklin County, Pennsylvania, where somewhat similar conditions obtain. In Ohio, according to L. E. Hicks, it is distributed over more than one-third of the state and ranges much farther north in the eastern part. Its regular northern limit there is Columbiana County, which adjoins Beaver County (Pennsylvania) on the west; notwithstanding the reasonable expectation thus engendered, I have failed to find the species in the latter county.

There are but three reports of the occurrence of this bird in our region; all are sight records but are probably trustworthy. S. N. Rhoads (1899) wrote that one summer tanager was seen by G. A. Link, Sr., in the South Side Cemetery, Pittsburgh, sometime in the nineties; and it so happens that Mr. Link once gave me the same information and added that the occurrence was in the spring. The second report is contributed by H. M. McQuiston, who writes that he observed a male near Sharon, Mercer County, on May 5 and 6, 1934, and watched it for some time on both occasions: "When first seen, the bird was sitting quietly, with his wings slightly drooped (the day was sultry), on the horizontal limb of a small dead tree. He was perched at an elevation of about fifteen feet. The tree was located at the bottom of a thinly wooded ravine, about half a mile northeast of town. After a while he flew to the lower branches of a tall tree on the top of a steep bank, and then traveled from one tree to another. The next day I observed him farther down the ravine, feeding on insects in a tall white oak. A male cardinal chased him away and I did not see him again." The locality is very close to Trumbull County, Ohio, from which stragglers of this species have been reported. The third record concerns a male seen by S. J. Seiple and Edward Mason at "Kidds Mill," Mercer County, on May 25, 1927.

Piranga rubra RHOADS, *Auk*, 1899, 16:312 (Pittsburgh, Allegheny Co., *fide* Link).

FINCHES

FAMILY FRINGILLIDAE

To the family Fringillidae belong all the Sparrows and the allied birds called Finches, Buntings, Grosbeaks, and Crossbills. This is in fact the largest of all bird families and is distributed throughout the world except in the Australian region. Thirty-six species occur in western Pennsylvania, and among them are some of our commonest and most familiar birds. Members of this family are extremely diversified in coloration, form, and habits. The brown, streaked, "sparrowy" members are mainly inhabitants of fields and build their nests on the ground. In this group, the sexes are similar. The more strikingly colored Finches and Grosbeaks are as a rule more arboreal. The plumage of the males is bright and attractive, and the females are more somberly garbed.

The birds of this family possess only nine primary wing feathers. The outstanding character of all the species is the stout, conical bill with the lower mandible turned abruptly down near the base; it is perfectly adapted for crushing seeds, which comprise almost three-fourths of the diet. Grosbeaks have bills that are large, thick, and rounded in outline; Sparrows and Finches have sharp, canary-like bills; and Crossbills, as their name implies, have the mandibles curiously crossed at the tips. In addition to the seeds and vegetable matter that form the bulk of their food, these birds feed on insects. The diet of the young birds consists almost exclusively of the latter.

In this varied group the types of nesting sites are numerous. Some species prefer the treetops or low bushes; some nest in undergrowth; others choose the grasses of meadow and marsh. Among the members of this family are found some of the most beautiful bird songs, as well as some of the most ineffectual.

EASTERN CARDINAL

RICHMONDENA CARDINALIS CARDINALIS (Linnaeus)

Description—Smaller than the Robin; *head crested;* bill short and heavy, reddish in both sexes. *Male:* carmine red, the head and underparts brighter, the "face" black. *Female:* dull brown (paler below); the crest, wings, and tail, tinged with carmine, the "face" dusky. The *young bird* resembles the female.

Range—The Cardinal is a species of austral origin and proclivities that has pushed its way northward to and beyond the Carolinian Fauna—an invasion that seems still to be in progress. A bird characteristic of the southern states, the Cardinal is regularly found as far north as the lower Hudson Valley on the Atlantic slope, and as far as northern Ohio and Indiana in the interior. Its local range in western Pennsylvania is peculiar and interesting. Like our other Carolinian species, this one is most numerous in the southwestern counties, from the Ohio Valley southward and eastward to the mountains. It is also common and generally distributed in the low country of the ridge and valley section as far as the Allegheny divide. Because the divide interrupts the ranges of most Carolinian species, one is wholly unprepared to find that it does not absolutely interrupt the range of the Cardinal in the southern counties. The species' approach to the higher ground has probably been from the west, across the Ligonier Valley (for which there are sundry records), and thence by way of the Conemaugh and Youghiogheny rivers into Cambria and Somerset counties. It is known to breed in the Johnstown region (Mostoller; Canan) and has been reported from several points in northern Somerset County (Mostoller). It is common all the year round at Confluence, in southern Somerset County (Trimble); and, according to A. B. Miller, it breeds regularly at Springs, in the same county, but at a higher elevation. This observer adds that "a few pairs are found along the Casselman River and at several other places; I think that the species, while still far from common, is slowly increasing in numbers." The presumed extension of range in these sections must be a comparatively recent development, induced doubtless by deforestation.

Farther north in the plateau region, the Cardinal is virtually unknown. Localities on the edge of the plateau at which summer occurrences have been recorded are Two Lick (Todd, 1893) and Gaibleton (Trimble, and others), Indiana County; and South Bethlehem, Armstrong County (Todd). In 1933 the species was found nesting at Warren

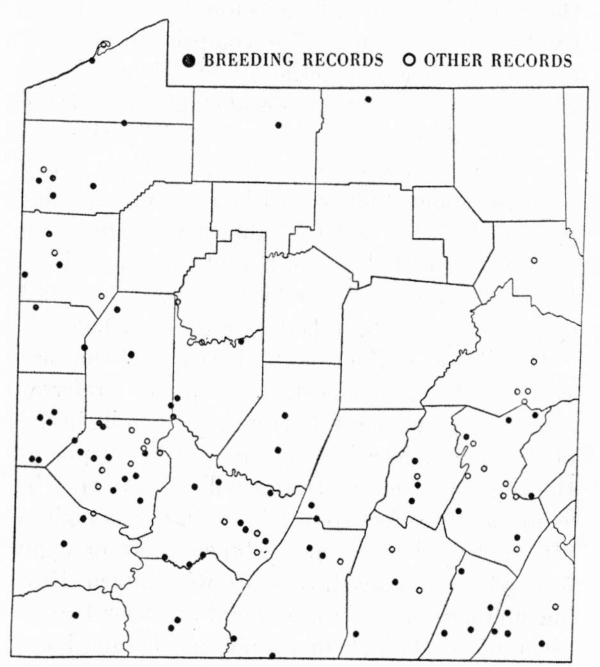

LOCAL RANGE OF THE EASTERN CARDINAL

(Simpson), where until that time it had been considered merely a straggler. Lloyd Scherer, Jr., writes me that L. M. Peterson found two pairs nesting in Bradford, McKean County, during past summers. Its status at Renovo, where it has been noted a few times in May by A. K. Pierce, remains undefined. West of the Allegheny River and north of the Ohio, it is by no means so common as it is south of the latter stream; nevertheless, it is now recognized as a component part of the avifauna as far north and west as the shores of Lake Erie. Today it occurs fairly regularly in the Erie-Crawford district, although it did not always do so. I saw no cardinals at Erie in 1900, but in my 1904 report I was able to cite a single breeding record by S. E. Bacon from that locality as an exceptional case. In recent years, however, I see this bird on Presque Isle every time I go there, and the local observers find it regularly.

In Crawford County the history of the Cardinal has been much the same as in Erie County. G. M. Sutton writes (1928): "Mr. Kirkpatrick noted a male and female at Meadville on December 25, 1884. So far as I have been able to determine, this is the earliest record for the species in this section of the State. At that time both Mr. Kirkpatrick and Mr. Sennett thought that this pair might be escaped cage-birds. Cardinals were not seen in any considerable numbers until 1897 when several pairs were observed. By 1903 they were fairly numerous and were often seen. Mr. Kirkpatrick says concerning its present status at Meadville: 'It has been noted every month in the year, except August, September, and October; it is more often seen during winter than at any other time, and during cold spells occasionally ventures into the residential districts of the city.' "

Dr. Sutton adds that in the Pymatuning region the number of cardinals apparently doubled between 1922 and 1924. It is thus fair to infer that in the northwestern counties generally, the species is increasing and replacing certain others that have retired because of the change in ecological conditions. It is significant that the first recorded appearances of this bird at any given place are nearly always in the winter. That its ultimate range is conditioned by winter, rather than by summer, temperatures seems, therefore, almost self-evident. Like other birds of similar tastes, the Cardinal may wander about more or less during the winter months in search of new feeding grounds, but it is not migratory in the usual sense of the word.

In the Ohio Valley and the southwestern counties in general, there has also been a marked increase in the number of cardinals during the past fifteen or twenty years. The species has proved to be most adaptable. Once confined largely to woodland or wild areas and extensively trapped for the cage-bird traffic, it has now become a chief beneficiary of the newly awakened interest in bird study. Today it is a well-known and carefully protected bird in the parks and gardens of towns and villages, and it has even been known to nest close to dwellings.

Habits[1]—A flash of red through the somber winter woods, a loud clear whistle on an early spring morning—these are the memories I have of the Cardinal as I first knew it in my boyhood days. It was indeed the first bird with which I could claim a reasonable familiarity. Almost the only brightly colored bird to be seen in winter, it is a universal favorite. To many species, the approach of winter means a long journey to a more hospitable clime; and for those of vivid plumage, it often entails a change to a drab, nondescript dress that affords better protection from the numerous enemies that make such a journey hazardous. The Cardinal, however, is an exception; for it has never felt the urge to migrate in the fall, and the striking plumage of the males remains unchanged throughout the year. When danger, real or fancied, threatens, the Cardinal seeks concealment in shrubbery or thickets, and wherever these retreats are available it readily accepts the proximity of man. In recent years it has invaded the parks and residential sections of Pittsburgh in gradually increasing numbers, and it is seemingly as much at home there as it is in the wooded ravines in the vicinity of the city. It eagerly partakes of seeds and bread crumbs put out to attract it during the winter months, and frequently it can be induced to linger in the spring and rear its young in rose arbors or barberry thickets. While not so sociable as other birds, the Cardinal is nevertheless not averse to the companionship of its own kind throughout the greater portion of the year, and, except during the nesting season, can be found in loose flocks of from six to a dozen or more individuals. Throughout the winter, especially when snow is on the ground, flocks can be found day after day in certain ravines or in short stretches of woods, and they have come to be accepted as a regular part of the winter landscape. Males and females occur together at this season of the year; the females are easily recognized by their brownish plumage that shows traces of red only on the wings and tail.

With the coming of the first warm days in late February, the loud, clear whistle of the males sounds from the tops of saplings or even of larger trees; and within a short time scattered pairs replace the small flocks previously encountered in the thickets and underbrush. Contrary to the usual rule in the bird world, the female is an accomplished singer; her song, usually given from a partially concealed location, is less vigorous than that of the male, but equally pleasing. Actual nesting is delayed until there is relatively little likelihood of a late snowfall or low temperatures, and it is the middle of April or later before full sets of eggs can be found. The normal set comprises three eggs, although four are sometimes laid. They are dull white, at times with a decided gloss, and are spotted and blotched over much of the entire surface with varying shades of reddish brown. They measure about 1.00 by .70 inches. A noticeable peculiarity is the fact that almost without exception one egg is strikingly different from the others, the spots being smaller and less numerous—almost as though it had been laid by another female.

In Allegheny County the location of the nest varies little; grapevine tangles are the preferred sites. Only once have I found a nest built in another type of location; it was in a brush pile at the edge of a field at Harmarville. Nests may be as low as three feet from the ground or as high as fifteen, but the average distance is six or eight feet; wherever placed, they are well hidden. During summers spent in the mountains near Uniontown, where the Cardinal is not uncommon, I saw

[1]Account contributed by THOMAS D. BURLEIGH.

nests built in the rhododendrons that bordered the streams. There can be little doubt that the species customarily raises two broods during the spring and summer months, although some pairs probably raise only one. I have found fresh eggs as early as April 16 (1910), but the majority of birds do not incubate full sets until the first week in May. Again in late June and early July, and not infrequently even later, nests holding but two eggs can be found, and these indicate second broods rather than belated attempts to rear young after the first nests had been destroyed.[1] Nests are at times somewhat bulky; loosely built of weed stems, dead leaves, bits of paper, and shreds of bark, they are well cupped and are lined with fine weed stems and rootlets.

Nestlings of both sexes resemble the female, but young males soon begin their postjuvenal molt and by late summer present a curious mottled appearance. It is usually September before the last trace of brown has disappeared. The young males then become practically indistinguishable from the adult males, in the company of which they can be found throughout the winter months.

"Red Bird" Wilson, *Am. Orn.*, Ord ed., 1828, 1: cvii (Ohio River, western Pa.).

Cardinalis virginiana Townsend, *Proc. Acad. Nat. Sci. Philadelphia*, 1883, 63 (Chestnut Ridge, Westmoreland Co., summer).

"Cardinal Grosbeak" Warrick, *Ornithologist and Oölogist*, 1883, 8:46 (Washington, Washington Co., nesting; habits) —Kirkpatrick, *Forest and Stream*, 1884, 21:474 (Meadville, Crawford Co., winter)—Jacobs, *Hoosier Nat.*, 1887, 2:78 (Waynesburg, Greene Co., resident; description nest and eggs)—Simpson, *Oölogist*, 1914, 31:80 (Warren, Warren Co., winter)—McClelland, *Am. Mid. Nat.*, 1922, 8:35, 38 (Washington, Washington Co., resident).

Cardinalis cardinalis Todd, *Auk*, 1893, 10:40 (Two Lick, Indiana Co., June)—Jacobs, *Summer Birds Greene Co., Pa.*, 1893, 11 (Greene Co., nesting)—Jacobs, *Gleanings from Nature*, 1898, 1:14, 25, 30, 31 (Waynesburg, Greene Co., nesting)—Todd, *Ann. Carnegie Mus.*, 1904, 2:575 (near Erie, Erie Co., nesting)—Todd, in Bausman, *Hist. Beaver Co., Pa.*, 1904, 2:1200 (Beaver Co., resident)—Surface, in *Ninth Ann. Report Pa. Dept. Agric., for 1903*, 1904, 178, 232 (Centre Co., November)—Forrest, *Oölogist*, 1911, 28: 114 (Washington, Washington Co., resident).

"Cardinal" Stone, *Cassinia*, 1906, 9:44 (McConnellsburg, Fulton Co., June)—Pitcairn, *Bird-Lore*, 1908, 10:32 (West View, Allegheny Co., December)—Miller (M. H.), *Bird-Lore*, 1909, 11:28; etc. (McKinley Park, Allegheny Co., December)—Miller (A. B.), *Bird-Lore*, 1910, 12:29; etc. (Springs, Somerset Co., December)—Burleigh, *Oölogist*, 1912, 29:316 (Harmarville, Allegheny Co., nesting; habits) —Gerberding, *Bird-Lore*, 1912, 14:29 (Greenville, Mercer Co., December)—Simpson, *Oölogist*, 1912, 29:370; and 1921, 38:135 (Warren, Warren Co., winter)—Burleigh, *Bird-Lore*, 1913, 15:29 (Aspinwall, Allegheny Co., December)—Burleigh, *Oölogist*, 1913, 30:55 ([Harmarville], Allegheny Co., nesting, etc.)—McGraw, *et al.*, *Bird-Lore*, 1919, 21:37; etc. (Altoona, Blair Co., December)—Warfield, *Bird-Lore*, 1919, 21:37; etc. (Chambersburg, Franklin Co., December) —Dickey, *Oölogist*, 1919, 36:67 (Waynesburg, Greene Co., nesting)—McConnell, *Bird-Lore*, 1920, 22:31; etc. (Emsworth, Allegheny Co., December)—Stahl, *et al.*, *Bird-Lore*, 1921, 23:18 ([Forest Hills to Deer Creek], Allegheny Co., December)—Nicholson, *Bird-Lore*, 1921, 23:18 (Grove City, Mercer Co., December)—Street, *Cassinia*, 1923, 24:16 (Greencastle to Ft. Loudon, Franklin Co., June)—Christy, *Cardinal*, 1924, v. 1, no. 4, p. 10 (Big Traverse Valley, Beaver Co., June)—Eastwood, *Bird-Lore*, 1925, 27:337 (Bradford Woods, Allegheny Co., August, *fide* Frederick); 1926, 28:58 (Ingram, Allegheny Co., *fide* McCracken), 343 (Dixmont and vicinity, Allegheny Co., July, *fide* Auerswald); 1927, 29:56 (Logan's Ferry, Allegheny Co., October; Thompsonville, Washington Co., November, *fide* Ellair)—Christy, *Cardinal*, 1926, v. 1, no. 8, p. 20 ("Waldameer Park," Erie Co., winter, *fide* Perry; near Redbank and Foxburg, Clarion Co.)—Matuszak, *Bird-Lore*, 1926, 28:29 (Hyde Park, Westmoreland Co., December)—Portman, *et al.*, *Bird-Lore*, 1926, 28:31 (Thompsonville, Washington Co., December)—Boulton, *Bird-Lore*, 1928, 30:196 (Pittsburgh region, spring song) —Berkheimer, *Bird-Lore*, 1933, 35:27; etc. (Osterburg, Bedford Co., December)—Beal and Peterson, *Bird-Lore*, 1934, 36:33 (Presque Isle, Erie Co., December)—(?)Cope and Hawkins, *Forest Leaves*, 1934, 24:26 (E. Tionesta Forest Reserve, Warren and McKean Co., summer)—Elliott, *Cardinal*, 1934, 3:170 (Raccoon Creek, Beaver Co., December)—Wright, *Cardinal*, 1935, 4:49 (Thornburg, Allegheny Co., nesting).

Cardinalis cardinalis cardinalis Harlow, *Auk*, 1912, 29:478 ("Stone Valley," Huntingdon Co., May); 1918, 35:139 (Centre and Greene Co., breeding)—Christy, *Cardinal*, 1923, v. 1, no. 1, [p. 10] (Sewickley, Allegheny Co., resident)—Burleigh, *Wilson Bull.*, 1923, 35:96 (Allegheny Co., nesting); 1931, 43:49 (near State College, Centre Co., resident) —[Editor], *Cassinia*, 1926, 25:32 (Greencastle, Franklin Co., resident, *fide* Ziegler).

Richmondena cardinalis cardinalis Sutton, *Ann. Carnegie Mus.*, 1928, 18:189 (Meadville and Pymatuning Swamp, Crawford Co., resident)—Burleigh, *Cardinal*, 1932, 3:82 (Chestnut Ridge, near Uniontown, Fayette Co., breeding).

Richmondena cardinalis Mercur, *Cardinal*, 1937, 4:122 (Pittsburgh, Allegheny Co., nesting).

[1][Two observers (Wright, 1935; Mercur, 1937) have found certain pairs raising three broods in a season, but whether or not this is a prevailing custom is uncertain.]

ROSE-BREASTED GROSBEAK

HEDYMELES LUDOVICIANUS (Linnaeus)

Description—A bird the size of the Cardinal; bill large and heavy. *Adult male in spring:* head (all around), upper back, and wings, black, the latter with white spots; tail black, with large white areas on most of the feathers; a *large spot of rose crimson on the breast* just below the black throat and extending in a wedge down the middle of the breast; rest of underparts white; under wing coverts rose pink; bill light-colored. *Adult female:* upperparts brown, streaked with paler brown; head dark brown and showing pale median and superciliary stripes; wings and tail dull brown, the former with some white spots; lower back also dull brown; underparts dull white, with dark streaks on the breast and sides; *under wing coverts saffron orange;* bill light-colored. In *fall plumage* the male is more or less brownish above; the black throat is absent or merely indicated; and the rosy patch on the breast is faint and poorly defined. The rosy under wing coverts, however, remain well marked.

Range—The Rose-breasted Grosbeak breeds in the northern United States and the adjacent parts of Canada from Nova Scotia and New England westward to the Dakotas and thence northward to Great Slave Lake. It migrates through the southern states and across the Gulf of Mexico to winter in southern Mexico, Central America, and northwestern South America. Its breeding range, zonally considered, covers the Alleghanian Fauna, the lower half (more or less) of the Canadian Fauna, and the upper half (approximately) of the Carolinian. This range comprehends nearly all of our region; there is indeed but one small section from which there are no summer records—Greene County, in the extreme southwestern part of the state. In Washington County the species is rare, as it is also in Beaver County, although about forty years ago it was one of the commonest summer residents there. In my journal for 1896 I referred to its "constantly increasing" numbers, especially in the environs of the town of Beaver, where now it is decidedly uncommon. Exactly when the decrease became marked my records do not show, but it seems to have been within the past fifteen or twenty years. The cause is obscure, but it may well be the Cowbird, which has increased disproportionately to other and more desirable species of our local avifauna.

The Grosbeak, however, is subject to shifting fluctuations in its numbers. E. H. Forbush writes that "fifty years ago the bird was far less common in New England than it has been since the twentieth century came in. . . . Its numbers, however, fluctuate; it may appear commonly for a few years in a section, and then suddenly become rare."[1] A. B. Miller says that at Springs, Somerset County, the species is common in some years and scarce in others. H. C. Kirkpatrick is quoted by G. M. Sutton (1928) to the effect that between 1875 and 1885 it was common at Meadville, Crawford County, where, according to all observers, it is now rare. Dr. Sutton writes: "Mr. Kirkpatrick believes that its disappearance may be accounted for by the demand for these songsters as cage-birds which developed at the time of their greatest abundance"; but this explanation to my mind is entirely unacceptable.

However common the Grosbeak may have been in the Ohio Valley and the western counties in general, it was no less common in the higher and mountainous sections. Its presence there was attested by numerous observations made personally during the nineties. Its present status as compared with that of earlier years, however, remains uncertain. If there is any locality in western Pennsylvania where rose-breasted grosbeaks are now as common as song sparrows, as stated by W. L. McAtee (1908), I do not know where it is.

Migration—The Rose-breasted Grosbeak is a rather delicate bird, and it does not arrive much earlier than the warbler advance that takes place about the last of April or the first of May. April 24 and May 8 are the extreme dates in my arrival records for Beaver (covering twenty-two years), and May 1 is the average. With these dates the records from Allegheny County (Sewickley and Wilkinsburg) closely correspond. In the Erie-Crawford district and in the mountains in general, the species tends to arrive a few days later; May 5 is the average date at Renovo. The birds become common (if at all) almost at once and, being con-

[1] *Birds of Massachusetts,* 1929, 3:114.

spicuous, are easily observed. In the fall when they are dull-colored, hard to see, and practically silent, exactly the reverse is true. Migration begins as early as August, but all the birds do not leave until September, and an occasional laggard may linger into the following month. Some late dates from various localities are: Erie, September 21, 1889 (Sennett); Crystal Lake, Crawford County, September 24, 1925 (Sutton); Beaver, October 3, 1905 (Todd); Renovo, October 8, 1908 (Pierce); State College, October 19, 1916 (Burleigh).

Habits—Led by divers authors to believe that the Rose-breasted Grosbeak was a *rara avis*, I was delightfully surprised in my boyhood to find it common near my home. The male is a handsome and conspicuous figure in his garb of black and white, enlivened by a breast-patch of rose red. Far from being a recluse, he seems to court attention, at least in the springtime when he is in full song and plumage, and he chooses a prominent position from which to deliver his vocal effusions. His song, repeated at frequent intervals during the height of the season, somewhat suggests the Robin's but is more varied and musical and much more richly modulated. Under the stress of unusual emotion he may rise to sublime heights. Rudyerd Boulton (1922) describes an interesting flight song that he once heard: "Suddenly, in the midst of an ordinary sequence of syllables, a gorgeous male burst into a rapturous cascade of double notes and flutings, and springing into the air, he fluttered and dangled his wings and legs much as a Yellow-breasted Chat would." Usually the male ceases to sing in July, with the onset of the annual molt, but with some birds there is a partial recrudescence of the song period in September before they leave for the South. I have repeatedly heard the full song given at this season, sometimes with all the fervor shown in the spring; but oftener it is toned down and abbreviated. The ordinary call or alarm-note (common to both sexes) is a loud clucking sound.

The forest was the original home of this species, and many pairs continue to inhabit their primitive haunts, especially in the more thinly settled areas. But the Grosbeak, unlike many forest birds (the Scarlet Tanager, for example), is an adaptable species and has been able to accommodate itself to the changed conditions brought about by deforestation. In large numbers it has invaded our orchards and parks, where the beauty of its song and plumage has made it a general favorite and a desirable and welcome addition to our dooryard birds. Under these circumstances, its economic status becomes of some importance. Careful studies of its food habits made by the United States Biological Survey some years ago (McAtee, 1908) show that it takes almost as much vegetable as animal food. Wild fruit is eaten in large measure, as are also weed seeds; and at times a little grain is taken. Complaints have been made that the Grosbeak eats green peas, but this reprehensible habit must be local; at any rate, there is no evidence that it ever indulges in this practice in our region. On the contrary, it has repeatedly been observed feeding on the Colorado potato beetle; and stomach examinations reveal that it destroys this and several other noxious insects in large numbers; it should consequently be rated high among the birds most beneficial to agriculture. Its virtual disappearance from regions where once it was common can therefore be regarded only as a misfortune.

The female Grosbeak is inconspicuous but not especially diffident. A few days after her arrival the birds pair off and begin nesting. They are not particular in their choice of site; almost any tree will do, provided that its branches are well above the ground. I once found a nest within six feet of the ground, but the location is usually higher, in a sapling or larger tree. The nest itself is a frail and flimsy structure, composed almost entirely of dry weed stalks and lined with finer material of the same sort; it is loosely constructed and so thin that it is usually possible to count the eggs from below. Four, or rarely five, eggs are laid, and occasionally only three. Full sets may be looked for from the middle to the end of May, but D. A. Atkinson reports finding a fresh set as late as June 29. Doubtless this was the result of a delayed nesting, since only one brood is raised in a season. The eggs are remarkably like those of the Scarlet Tanager in color, but are larger, averaging .90 by .69 inches. They are pale greenish blue, speckled or spotted with rufous or olive brown; the exact shade of the markings, as well as their size and density, varies considerably. The male takes his turn in incubating the eggs and, while thus engaged, often unwittingly betrays the position of the nest by singing. After the young birds hatch he works hard at the task of feeding them, and during this period his song is only intermittent.

Of the Rose-breasted Grosbeak, which delights both eye and ear and serves man well, I say: May its tribe again increase!

Guiraca ludoviciana TEULON, *Jour. Boston Zoöl. Soc.*, 1883, 2:9 (Bradford, McKean Co., nesting).

Zamelodia ludoviciana TOWNSEND, *Proc. Acad. Nat. Sci. Philadelphia*, 1883, 63 (Chestnut Ridge, Westmoreland Co., summer)—COPE, *Cassinia*, 1902, 5:17 (between Oleona and New Bergen, Potter Co., June)—TODD, *Ann. Carnegie Mus.*, 1904, 2:575 (Erie and Presque Isle, Erie Co., summer)—TODD, in Bausman, *Hist. Beaver Co., Pa.*, 1904, 2:1200 (Beaver Co., summer)—MCATEE, *Bull. Biol. Surv.* no. 32, 1908, 33 (western Pa.)—HARLOW, *Auk*, 1912, 29:478 ("Stone Valley," Huntingdon Co.); 1918, 35:139 (Warren, Clarion, Venango, and Allegheny Co., summer)—CHRISTY, *Cardinal*, 1923, v. 1, no. 1, [p. 10] (Sewickley, Allegheny Co., breeding)—BURLEIGH, *Wilson Bull.*, 1923, 35:96 (Allegheny Co., nesting); 1924, 36:129 (State College, Centre Co., migration).

"Rose-breasted Grosbeak" ENTY, *Ornithologist and Oölogist* 1885, 10:78 (Templeton, Armstrong Co., April)—TODD, *Oölogist*, 1887, 4:89 (Beaver, Beaver Co., nesting)—WARREN, *Forest and Stream*, 1891, 37:83 (Kane, McKean Co., summer)—VAN OSTRAND, *Osprey*, 1896, 1:38 (Morganza, Washington Co., fall; food)—SIMPSON, *Oölogist*, 1906, 23:135, and 1911, 28:162 (Warren, Warren Co., June)—PITCAIRN, *Bird-Lore*, 1907, 9:155 (Riverview Park, Allegheny Co., breeding)—BURLEIGH, *Oölogist*, 1911, 28:156 (Harmarville, Allegheny Co., nesting); 1912, 29:395 (Pittsburgh, Allegheny Co., nesting)—COOKE, *Bird-Lore*, 1912, 14:158 (Beaver, Beaver Co., and Renovo, Clinton Co., migration)—DICKEY, *Oölogist*, 1914, 31:207 (Cresson, Cambria Co., nesting)—MILLER, *In the Open*, July, 1915, 5:23 (McKinley Park, Allegheny Co., May)—MCCONNELL, *Oölogist*, 1918, 35:151 ("Christy Park," Allegheny Co., breeding)—SCOVILLE, *Cassinia*, 1920, 23:20 ([Charter Oak], Huntingdon Co., May)—MCCLELLAND, *Am. Mid. Nat.*, 1922, 8:36 (Washington, Washington Co., summer; migration)—BOULTON, *Oölogist*, 1922, 39:71 (near Beaver, Beaver Co., May; song)—BLAIR, *Bull. Audubon Soc. W. Pa.*, 1923, 1:41 (West View, Allegheny Co., nesting)—SUTTON, *Bird-Lore*, 1923, 25:260 (Pittsburgh, Allegheny Co., spring); 1924, 26:337 (Wattsburg, Erie Co., summer, *fide* Allen)—STREET, *Cassinia*, 1923, 24:16 (Conococheague Creek, Mercersburg, Franklin Co., June)—EASTWOOD, *Bird-Lore*, 1925, 27:262 (Pittsburgh region, Allegheny Co., migration), 337 ("Slack Hollow," Allegheny Co., July, *fide* Grimm), 338 (Pittsburgh region, Allegheny Co., nesting, *fide* Jones); 1926, 28:273 (Rector, Westmoreland Co., May, *fide* Knauz), 343 (Edgewood, Allegheny Co., July, *fide* Jones; Dixmont and vicinity, Allegheny Co., July, *fide* Auerswald); 1927, 29:273 (Springs, Somerset Co., summer, *fide* Miller)—COPE and HAWKINS, *Forest Leaves*, 1934, 24:26 (E. Tionesta Forest Reserve, Warren and McKean Co., summer).

Habia ludoviciana WARREN, *Birds Pa.*, ed. 2, 1890, 246 (Crawford and Erie Co., summer, *fide* Sennett)—DWIGHT, *Auk*, 1892, 9:138 (Cresson, Cambria Co.; near Altoona, Blair Co., June)—TODD, *Auk*, 1893, 10:40 (Two Lick, Indiana Co., June), 45 (Coalport, Clearfield Co., June)—BAILY, *Auk*, 1896, 8:295 (Williamsville, Elk Co., June–July).

Hedymeles ludoviciana CHRISTY and SUTTON, *Cardinal*, 1928, 2:72 (Thom's Run, Cook Forest, Clarion Co., May)—SUTTON, *Ann. Carnegie Mus.*, 1928, 18:190 (Crawford Co. localities, nesting; habits).

Hedymeles ludovicianus BURLEIGH, *Cardinal*, 1932, 3:82 (Chestnut Ridge, near Uniontown, Fayette Co., summer).

EASTERN BLUE GROSBEAK

GUIRACA CAERULEA CAERULEA (Linnaeus)

Description—A little smaller than the Cardinal; the bill not quite so heavy. *Male: blue;* the *wings* and tail duskier, the former with *two bands of cinnamon brown. Female:* cinnamon brown, paler and more buffy below; wings showing two pale bands.

Range and local status—The Eastern Blue Grosbeak belongs to the southern states and is rare or casual toward the northern part of the Carolinian Fauna. In Ohio it is virtually unknown, but on the eastern side of the Appalachians it occurs regularly, although rarely, as far north as Washington, D. C., and there are a few records also for southeastern Pennsylvania. That it occasionally reaches our section is scarcely open to doubt, although as yet no specimens have been taken. On June 18, 1920, J. F. Street saw a pair "flying across the west branch of the Conococheague Creek above the Mercersburg Road," on the extreme edge of our region in Franklin County. Miss A. E. Berg reports the species at Hollidaysburg on dates that indicate breeding (from May 25 to June 23). I once questioned her closely concerning these occurrences, and she insisted that they were based on valid identifications. Indeed, it would be difficult to confuse this species with any but the Indigo Bunting, and the smaller size of the latter would at once eliminate it.

A record from northern McKean County is surprising but apparently admissible. It is transmitted by Lloyd Scherer, Jr., on the authority of L. M. Peterson, who reported seeing two male blue grosbeaks in his dooryard at South Bradford from May

15 to May 17 in 1932. "They were seen each time in the same part of the yard, on the ground under an apple tree. Chickweed grows here and the birds seemed to be eating it. There was excellent opportunity for observation, since the birds permitted us to approach within twenty-five or thirty feet before flying into the near-by thicket, and as soon as we would withdraw they would emerge and resume their feeding. At first they were supposed to be indigo buntings, but subsequent and numerous examinations with glasses convinced us that they were blue grosbeaks. The brown wing-bars and the oversized beaks confirmed the identification, at least to our satisfaction." The occurrence of this species so far north is of course purely fortuitous.

"Blue Grosbeak" STREET, *Cassinia*, 1923, 24:10, 16 (Conococheague Creek, Mercersburg, Franklin Co., June).

INDIGO BUNTING

PASSERINA CYANEA (Linnaeus)

Description—A rather small but stocky finch. *Adult male: deep, rich blue,* most brilliant on the head and throat; wings and tail dusky, edged with blue. *Adult female:* upperparts dull brown, without decided markings; underparts soiled whitish, marked with brown and faintly striped. *Young birds* of both sexes at first resemble the adult female; young males later acquire some blue color above and below.

Range—*Passerina cyanea* is a species characteristic of the eastern United States and the adjoining Canadian provinces; it ranges westward to the edge of the Great Plains, where it is replaced by another species, *P. amoena.* It breeds plentifully in the Alleghanian, Carolinian, and lower Canadian faunas. It is accordingly found as a summer resident throughout our entire region, and where ecological conditions are suitable it is as common at the higher elevations in the mountains as it is in the river valleys. The species winters in Cuba, southern Mexico, and Central America generally, and migrates across the Gulf of Mexico.

Migration—As a rule the Indigo Bunting does not reach the latitude of western Pennsylvania until the first or sometimes even the second week in May, when the warbler migration is at its peak. Average dates of arrival are: Waynesburg, May 3; Beaver, May 6; Warren, May 7; Meadville, May 7; State College, May 6; Renovo, May 9. Unusually early dates are: Pittsburgh region, April 26 (1925); Waynesburg, April 29 (1891); Beaver, April 30 (1887); Renovo, May 2 (1902); Warren, May 4 (1902). The species becomes really common about a week after the first birds arrive. The southward movement gets under way in September but is so unobtrusively accomplished that there is a great dearth of records bearing on it. My latest fall record for Beaver is September 25 (1909), but observers in other sections have noted the species even later: State College, October 3 (1915—Burleigh); Renovo, October 19 (1903—Pierce). In general, however, most of the birds have left for the South by the first of October.

Habits[1]—To find the Indigo Bunting we must go to the clearings where there is a dense undergrowth of briers, ferns, scrub oak, and forest-tree sprouts or saplings, with an occasional dead or defective tree left as useless by the lumbermen. A habitat near water is preferred, even if the water is only a small mountain stream; but dry hillside thickets and even orchards are often chosen. Where the Towhee lives and breeds, there also will the Indigo Bunting be found. If, while traversing a path in the countryside, you accidentally scare a plain brown, sparrow-like bird from her nest in a bush, her *cheep* will be almost certain to bring into sight her brilliant blue mate, anxious over the welfare of his consort; then identification of the brown female is a simple matter. Not that he is always blue; for when he is between you and the sun he looks black, and he is not so conspicuous as one might infer from a color plate or a written description of him. The nest, placed about three feet from the ground in the crotch of a small sapling, consists mostly of dead leaves, with some grass and plant fiber, and is usually lined with hair. In it may be seen from three to five—but more commonly four—pale bluish-white eggs, measuring .73 by .57 inches. It may also hold a larger speckled

[1]Account contributed by HARRY A. MCGRAW.

egg, deposited there by the Cowbird; for this parasite frequently makes the Indigo Bunting one of its many victims.

Nest-building begins soon after the birds' arrival in May, and two broods are probably raised each year. Complete sets of eggs have been found in the latter part of that month and in early June; according to D. A. Atkinson, fresh eggs of the second laying may be found as late as August 9. Dr. Atkinson also says that at least on some occasions both sexes assist in incubation.

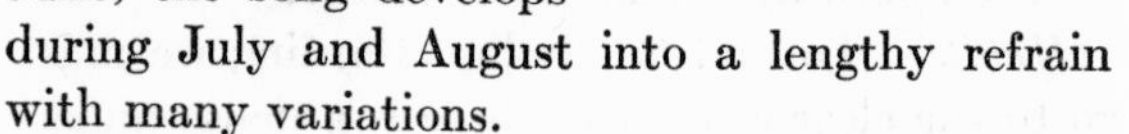

This bird is one of our most persistent singers, although it is not at its best on arrival; but the longer it stays, the longer its song grows, and the hotter the weather, the oftener it sings. From a few bars in May and June, the song develops during July and August into a lengthy refrain with many variations.

Unlike the Red-eyed Vireo, another constant singer that may be heard among the trees at the edges of the same thickets, the Indigo Bunting does not hunt its food while it sings. Instead, it seeks some prominent perch, such as an electric wire or a high branch of a dead tree—often the topmost one—from which to deliver its high-pitched, hurried warble. The song, which is loud and not particularly melodious, seems to me to consist of a series of bars; all the notes in each bar have the same pitch, but each phrase differs from the preceding one in pitch and in number of notes. It is repeated over and over with numerous additions and is sometimes given on the wing and occasionally at night. The song period lasts until mid-August, when the fall molt begins. Then the male assumes a plumage resembling that of the female. This change may account in part for the scarcity of fall records.

The Indigo Bunting spends most of its time on the ground or in low bushes. While it is no doubt comparatively safe there from hawks and other enemies, it is frequently killed, as are many other birds, by cars on the roads. While driving through a woodland not long ago, we saw a pair of indigo buntings in the middle of the road a short distance ahead, the male spreading his wings and dancing about the female. They paid no attention to the car, and, as we were too close to do more than slow down, the car passed right over them. When we looked back they were still in the same place and unhurt. I am afraid that many birds in similar situations are not so lucky.

It is sometimes said that the Indigo Bunting is frequently misidentified as the Blue Grosbeak. If one keeps in mind the larger size of the Grosbeak, there should be no difficulty in distinguishing the two species.

From an economic standpoint, this species is valuable. According to E. H. Forbush, it consumes large quantities of objectionable insects, such as grasshoppers, caterpillars, measuring worms, and beetles; it also eats seeds, many of which are those of weeds. Examination of the stomach contents of a few birds collected in an orchard infested with cankerworms, revealed that 78 per cent of the total food consisted of this pest.

Cyanospiza cyanea Teulon, *Jour. Boston Zoöl. Soc.*, 1883, 2:9 (Bradford, McKean Co.)—Cope, *Cassinia*, 1902, 5:17 (Germania, Potter Co., June)—Todd, *Ann. Carnegie Mus.*, 1904, 2:576 (Erie, Erie Co., summer)—Todd, in Bausman, *Hist. Beaver Co., Pa.*, 1904, 2:1200 (Beaver Co., summer)—Keim, *Cassinia*, 1905, 8:39 (Port Allegany, McKean Co., summer).

Passerina cyanea Townsend, *Proc. Acad. Nat. Sci. Philadelphia*, 1883, 63 (Latrobe, Westmoreland Co., summer)—Jamison, *Ornithologist and Oölogist*, 1888, 13:134 and Dwight, *Auk*, 1892, 9:138 (Cresson, Cambria Co., June)—Todd, *Auk*, 1893, 10:40 (Two Lick, Indiana Co., June), 45 (Coalport, Clearfield Co., June)—Jacobs, *Summer Birds Greene Co., Pa.*, 1893, 11 (Greene Co., nesting)—Baily, *Auk*, 1896, 13:295 (Williamsville, Elk Co., June–July)—Jacobs, *Gleanings from Nature*, 1898, 1:19, 25 (Greene Co., nesting)—Harlow, *Auk*, 1912, 29:474 (southern Centre Co., nesting)—Christy, *Cardinal*, 1923, v. 1, no. 1, [p. 10] (Sewickley, Allegheny Co., breeding)—Burleigh, *Wilson Bull.*, 1923, 35:96 (Allegheny Co., nesting); 1924, 36:72; and 1931, 43:49 (State College, Centre Co., migration; nesting)—Christy and Sutton, *Cardinal*, 1928, 2:72 (Cook Forest, Clarion Co., summer)—Sutton, *Ann. Carnegie Mus.*, 1928, 18:191 (Crawford Co. localities, summer; nesting)—Burleigh, *Cardinal*, 1932, 3:82 (Chestnut Ridge, near Uniontown, Fayette Co., summer).

"Indigo Bird" Enty, *Ornithologist and Oölogist*, 1885, 10:78 (Templeton, Armstrong Co., May)—Stone, *Cassinia*, 1906, 9:44 (McConnellsburg, Fulton Co., June)—Harlow, *Oölogist*, 1911, 28:167 (State College, Centre Co., nesting).

"Indigo Bunting" Jacobs, *Hawkeye Ornithologist and Oölogist*, 1888, 1:88 (Waynesburg, Greene Co., April)—Pitcairn, *Bird-Lore*, 1907, 9:155 (Riverview Park, Allegheny Co., breeding)—COOKE, *Bird-Lore*, 1911, 13:199 (Beaver, Beaver Co.; Waynesburg, Greene Co.; and Renovo, Clinton Co., migration)—BURLEIGH, *Oölogist*, 1911, 28:156 (Harmarville, Allegheny Co., nesting)—CUSHMAN, *Wilson Bull.*, 1916, 28:39 (North East, Erie Co., habits)—MCCONNELL, *Oölogist*, 1918, 35:151 (Long Run, near McKeesport, Allegheny Co.)—MILLER, *Oölogist*, 1919, 36:157 (Charter Oak, Huntingdon Co., nesting)—MCCLELLAND, *Am. Mid. Nat.*, 1922, 8:36 (Washington, Washington Co., summer; migration)—STREET, *Cassinia*, 1923, 24:16 (Greencastle, Ft. Loudon, Jordan's Knob, and Horse Valley, Franklin Co., June)—CHRISTY, *Cardinal*, 1924, v. 1, no. 4, p. 10 (Big Traverse Valley, Beaver Co., June)—EASTWOOD, *Bird-Lore*, 1925, 27:262 (Raccoon Creek, Beaver Co., May, *fide* Jones), 263 (Pittsburgh region, Allegheny Co., April); 1926, 28:273 (Rector, Westmoreland Co., May, *fide* Knauz)—COPE and HAWKINS, *Forest Leaves*, 1934, 24:26 (E. Tionesta Forest Reserve, Warren and McKean Co., summer).

"Indigo Finch" SIMPSON, *Oölogist*, 1909, 26:170 (Warren, Warren Co., nesting).

PAINTED BUNTING

PASSERINA CIRIS (Linnaeus)

Description—Similar to the Indigo Bunting in size and proportions. *Male:* top and sides of head, blue; upper back pale green; lower back red; wings and tail dark; entire underparts red. *Female:* dull greenish; underparts paler, the abdomen yellowish.

Range and local status—This brilliant finch belongs to the Lower Austral Life Zone of the southeastern United States, beyond which it is merely an accidental visitant. Escaped cage birds may be responsible for certain extralimital records; this possibility must always be kept in mind. The reference cited below is perhaps disputable on this ground. The author, Archibald Rutledge, writes: "On May 16, 1921, three miles due south of Mercersburg, Pa., on a country lane, I positively identified a male Nonpareil [Painted Bunting], in full plumage. The bird was first seen in a hedge of osage orange; thence it flew to a locust tree, where it was carefully observed. It behaved and looked like a wild bird and not like one that had escaped from captivity. With the Painted Bunting I have been familiar since boyhood, when I used to know it well at my home on the South Carolina coast."

The data concerning the only other occurrence reported in our region are given here for what they may be worth. In the museum of St. Vincent College, near Latrobe, Westmoreland County, there is a mounted male specimen of presumed local origin. I am greatly indebted to the Reverend Maximilian Duman, O.S.B., for his efforts to trace the history and authenticity of this specimen. Unfortunately the specimen itself bears no label with date or locality, and the persons directly concerned with its capture are now deceased. One of the older members of the St. Vincent community, the Reverend Louis Haas, however, remembers the circumstance very well; for he realized at the time that it was an exceptional record. It seems that the bird was collected in 1883 or 1884 by the Reverend Cornelius Eckl, O.S.B., on the Andrew Thomas farm near Donohoe, about four and a half miles west of Latrobe. Mr. Thomas came to the college and said that a very unusual bird was nesting in (or near) his orchard; and a few days later the Reverend Mr. Eckl collected the bird. There is nothing to indicate whether or not the nest was taken; at any rate, it is not now in evidence.

If authentic, this report constitutes the most northerly breeding record known for the Painted Bunting; but the bird's occurrence in our region is of course merely accidental.

Passerina ciris RUTLEDGE, *Auk*, 1921, 38:606 (near Mercersburg, Franklin Co., May).

DICKCISSEL

SPIZA AMERICANA (Gmelin)

Description—About the size of the English Sparrow. *Male:* back grayish brown, with darker streaks; a large chestnut patch at the bend of the wing; head greenish-tinged, the nape and ear coverts gray; a prominent yellow stripe over the eye, and a yellow spot at the base of the lower mandible; breast yellowish; a large black spot on the throat. *Female:* the color pattern as described for the male is merely indicated, but the yellow tinge on the breast is practically diagnostic.

Range and local status—Once a common species on the Atlantic slope, the Dickcissel for some inexplicable reason has virtually disappeared from that region, and even west of the Appalachians it seems gradually to be losing ground. A bird of the open country, it might be expected, with the passing of the forest, to spread eastward from the prairies of the Mississippi Valley, as certain other species have apparently done; instead, the indications are that its range in the eastern sections is shrinking year by year. Early records for our region are unfortunately lacking, but F. L. Homer's notes are enlightening. He wrote: "This bird is one that has certainly changed its summer range. Formerly it was not uncommon as a summer resident in this vicinity [New Hamburg, Mercer County]. I have in my collection an old mutilated skin of a bird that I shot one summer on my father's farm. This was about 1885. I distinctly remember the two birds (a pair) that stayed in a hayfield all summer, till one of them was shot. But since 1887 I have not actually seen a single bird anywhere in northwestern Pennsylvania, although a few years ago I thought I heard one about four miles east of here." The specimen referred to is now in the Carnegie Museum; it is also alluded to by G. M. Sutton (1928).

I have never seen this species in Beaver County, nor has J. W. Jacobs encountered it in Greene County. Several specimens shot by W. T. Warrick in East Washington, Washington County, were examined by J. S. Nease, in whose collection I remember seeing them many years ago. On the authority of S. E. Bacon, I included the species in my Erie list (1904) as a rare summer resident; but F. M. Chapman, commenting on this listing, remarked (1904) that Sennett "observed at least six individuals of this species which were evidently breeding near the city [of Erie]." This circumstance suggests that the bird was either commoner than Mr. Bacon had supposed, or else had been overlooked. No recent records from Erie County have been reported, although there are two from the adjoining county of Ashtabula in Ohio.[1]

Van Fleet includes the Dickcissel in his manuscript list of the breeding birds of DuBois, and Miss A. E. Berg states that she observed a single bird at Hollidaysburg on June 3, 1923. These reports complete the list of known records.

Spiza americana Todd, *Ann. Carnegie Mus.*, 1904, 2:576 (Erie, Erie Co., summer, *fide* Bacon)—Sutton, *Ann. Carnegie Mus.*, 1928, 18:192 ("Transfer" [New Hamburg], Mercer Co., spring, *fide* Homer).

"Dickcissel" Chapman, *Bird-Lore*, 1904, 6:170 (Erie, Erie Co., summer, *fide* Sennett).

[1]L. E. Hicks, *Wilson Bulletin*, 1933, 45:193.

EASTERN EVENING GROSBEAK

HESPERIPHONA VESPERTINA VESPERTINA (Cooper)

Description—About the size of the Rose-breasted Grosbeak; *bill short, very stout*, and yellowish in color. *Male:* dull olive yellow, the head brownish; forehead yellow, this color reaching back over the eyes and enclosing a black patch on the crown; primaries black; secondaries white; tail black. *Female:* grayish brown, paler below, with some yellow tinge on the neck, back, and sides of the breast; wings black, with white markings; tail and its upper coverts black, with white spots.

Range—The breeding range of the typical or eastern race of the Evening Grosbeak was long a matter of conjecture. In 1903 fledglings were discovered in western Alberta.[1] Since then the bird has been traced eastward in summer to northern Ontario and Michigan and even to Vermont (one record only).[2] Very probably the species originated in western North America, and its spread eastward was a later development—a natural and gradual outgrowth from the peculiar migration route that the present race often follows and that is paralleled in the cases of certain waterfowl and shore birds. Before the winter of 1889–90, the Evening Grosbeak had been virtually unknown east of Ohio and Ontario, but during that season an extensive invasion carried it to the New England states, and records accumulated from many localities. The cause of this invasion is obscure but may very well have been the failure of the food supply in the species' former wintering grounds. Since 1890, several seasons have been marked by more

[1]John Macoun, *Catalogue of Canadian Birds*, 1904, part 3, p. 416.

[2]R. M. Marble, *Auk*, 1926, 43:549.

or less extensive Grosbeak invasions, so that this bird is seemingly becoming a regular, instead of an erratic, visitor.

Western Pennsylvania records are still few in number. During the memorable winter of 1889–90, Warren noted this bird in eleven counties, but, with his usual lack of perspicacity, he failed to cite exact localities. From other sources, however, we learn that during this incursion the species was found at Erie (Bacon), Warren (Simpson), near Meadville (Kirkpatrick), and near Sewickley (Christy). In 1910, when another invasion occurred, R. B. Simpson saw a few grosbeaks at Warren. In February, 1914, some were seen by Warren in Bedford County, but again the exact locality is not given. According to H. A. McGraw, two were seen near the "ore-holes" at East Altoona, Blair County, on February 18, 1922, by H. B. Kinch. A bird shot at Hartstown by C. A. Bergstrom on March 8, 1926, is now in the Carnegie Museum. More recent records concern a small flock seen at State College in April, 1930, by Merrill Wood and W. S. Clarke, Jr., and two birds seen on Presque Isle on December 27, 1933, by C. M. Beal and R. T. Peterson. Lloyd Scherer, Jr., writes that the species was "very common" at Port Allegany, McKean County, during late winter and early spring in 1934, 1935, and 1936.

Migration—The peculiar east-and-west migration route of the Evening Grosbeak has been discussed by A. W. Butler[1] and by W. W. Cooke.[2] That it actually holds true with individual birds has been established by bird-banding.[3] During the 1889–90 invasion, the first birds were noted in December, and some were present as late as the middle of May. It is conceivable that these may have lingered so long that they were unable to reach their regular breeding grounds at the proper time and were thus led to breed in localities far to the eastward. G. M. Sutton mentions a single bird taken at Meadville on July 21, 1910 (by H. C. Kirkpatrick, not by Sennett, as erroneously stated); this must have been one that had failed to migrate.

Habits—The substance of Mr. Simpson's remarks concerning his experience with this bird at Warren in 1910 is reproduced herewith. On February 27 a friend told him of some strange birds seen in the town. "These birds had been about the lawns and trees in the main residence part of town for several days and because of their tameness and looks had attracted considerable attention." Mr. Simpson was surprised to find that they were evening grosbeaks. There were four males and two females, and one of the former was in very bright plumage. They kept rather closely in one vicinity, sometimes visiting bare places on the lawns, but staying mostly in the trees, feeding on maple buds and on frozen and dried apples. They were very tame and would permit approach within fifteen or twenty feet. The local residents soon learned their name and history and became quite interested in them. They were last seen on March 17.

Coccothraustes vespertina WARREN, *Birds Pa.*, ed. 2, 1890, 224 (Erie, Crawford, Warren, Elk, Cameron, Clinton, Venango, Beaver, Westmoreland, Somerset, and Washington Co., winter).

Hesperiphona vespertina TODD, *Ann. Carnegie Mus.*, 1904, 2: 568 (Erie, Erie Co., winter).

"Evening Grosbeak" SIMPSON, *Oölogist*, 1911, 28:102 (Warren, Warren Co., winter)—BEAL and PETERSON, *Bird-Lore*, 1934, 36:33 (Presque Isle, Erie Co., December)—CLARKE, *Bird-Lore*, 1930, 32:422 (State College, Centre Co., April).

Hesperiphona vespertina vespertina WARREN, *Auk*, 1914, 31:400 (Bedford Co., winter)—CHRISTY, *Cardinal*, 1923, v. 1, no. 1, [p. 8] (4 miles north of Sewickley, Allegheny Co., April)—SUTTON, *Ann. Carnegie Mus.*, 1928, 18:170 (Meadville and Hartstown [3 miles north], Crawford Co., *fide* Kirkpatrick and Bergstrom).

"Eastern Evening Grosbeak" WOOD, *Wilson Bull.*, 1932, 44: 238 (State College, Centre Co., April).

[1] *Auk*, 1892, 9:238–247.
[2] *Journal Washington Academy of Sciences*, 1912, 2:60–62.
[3] M. J. MAGEE, *Bulletin Northeastern Bird-Banding Association*, 1928, 4:56–59.

EASTERN PURPLE FINCH

CARPODACUS PURPUREUS PURPUREUS (Gmelin)

Description—About the size of the English Sparrow; bill heavy; tail emarginate. *Adult male: dull crimson*, which is brightest on the head, rump, and breast, is streaked with brown above, and fades into white on the lower abdomen and tail coverts; wings and tail brownish. *Adult female:* upperparts *brownish gray*, with paler streaks; a pale stripe over the eye, and a broad dark one behind it;

wings and tail uniform with the upperparts, but unmarked; underparts dull white, broadly streaked with brownish gray, but the abdomen (in the middle) and the under tail coverts, immaculate. *Immature male* (first year) similar to the adult female. Fall specimens are brownish.

Range—Our Purple Finch is a member of a generic group that is distributed through the boreal parts of both Eurasia and North America. The species has a transcontinental range, but the western birds belong to a different race. The eastern form is a bird of the Canadian and Alleghanian faunas in the breeding season. It winters mainly in the southern states and less numerously farther north, even in our latitude. While I have no winter records of my own from Beaver County (unless one made on March 9, 1889, might be so construed), other observers have been more fortunate, and winter dates from Allegheny County have also been reported. Farther north, in Crawford County, the species occurs irregularly in winter, and it has even been detected at Warren during some of the coldest weather ever known there (Simpson, 1914). At Springs, Somerset County, it is most irregular—abundant during some winters and entirely absent during others (Miller). It has been observed also at State College during the winter (Burleigh). Insofar as its status as a winter resident in our region is concerned, therefore, the Purple Finch resembles the other boreal finches in its general irregularity in numbers and appearance. Like them, too, it seems to be governed in its erratic wanderings over the country at this season by the shifts in food supply rather than by climatic conditions.

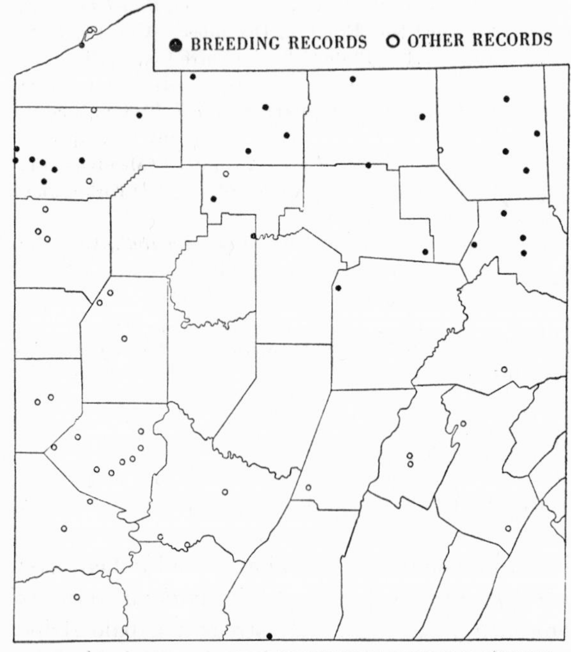

LOCAL RANGE OF THE EASTERN PURPLE FINCH

The summer range of the species is more clearly defined. The report of its breeding in the Erie-Crawford district made by Warren in 1888 (on Sennett's authority) has since been abundantly confirmed. My own researches in the northern counties have shown that it is a summer resident in the plateau section, north of the West Branch of the Susquehanna River. There are no breeding records south of this river except from Springs, where the species was found nesting on one occasion by A. B. Miller. There is every reason to believe that between Springs and DuBois (from which locality Van Fleet reports it present in June) its summer range is (or was) continuous, since it extends southward into the West Virginia mountains. But even in the northern counties this bird is only sparingly distributed, and Tamarack Swamp, Clinton County, is the only locality where I have ever found it at all common in summer. At Warren it is a regular but not common summer resident (Simpson). It has been noted also at Tionesta (Homer); at Canadohta Lake, Crawford County (Todd); and, more recently, at Tamarack Swamp, Warren County (Todd). These records serve to connect the main breeding area of the species in our region with the Pymatuning Swamp area and show that the range coincides with the former distribution of the white pine to the westward.

Migration—By far the greater part of the Purple Finch population winters south of our region and summers to the north. Consequently, the species is much more numerous during migration than at any other season. To most observers it is indeed known only as a transient visitant, but the problem of its movements in migration is not easily solved. As W. W. Cooke (1914) aptly remarks, "There is therefore a broad belt, covering at least a third of the entire range of the species, in which migration dates are unsatisfactory, because the records of real spring migration are so mixed with notes on birds that have wintered. The case is made more involved by the fact that the Purple Finch is normally a late migrant, so that there are, in reality, two sets of notes, one of birds that have wintered unnoticed in the deep woods and are recorded when they spread to the open country during the first warm days of spring, and the other of migrants from the south that arrive two to six weeks later." All March records for our region can pertain only to birds that must actually have wintered. These remarks apply with almost equal force to dates in the first three weeks of April. Not until April 20 at the earliest, and usually not until the last week in that month, are actual migrants from the South in evidence. They come with the warbler flight at that time, are common for a week or two, and disappear (at localities outside the breeding range) about the middle of May.

Fall migration records are few and unsatisfactory. I have seen the species at Beaver as early as September 10 (1910) and 17 (1921), and in other seasons have not seen it until October. It is much less common in the fall than in the spring.

Habits—The boreal finches as a group are all sociable with their own kind and tolerant toward others. Sometimes, it is true, we may come upon a lone purple finch, but far oftener it is a flock that attracts our attention, except of course in the breeding season, when singing males, each in its own territory, are conspicuous. Winter often finds the Purple Finch fraternizing with the American Goldfinch, the Bluebird, or even the Tree Sparrow. But the flocks of migrant purple finches that pass through in spring and fall are usually by themselves. High in the treetops of the forest, their forms dark silhouettes against the sky, they work among the terminal branches and are silent save for an occasional musical chirp. So quietly do they feed, indeed, that often the first intimation of their presence comes from the broken bits of buds falling from above. In the spring they are particularly fond of the succulent buds of the beech and the elm. Some writers maintain that they damage also the buds and flowers of orchard trees, but there is no local testimony to that effect. In summer, insects are included to some extent in their bill of fare, and in fall and winter they feed on wild fruits of various kinds.

Flocks vary in size, but from a dozen to a score of birds is a fair average. For some reason, females and young males always greatly outnumber the mature males. Both young and old males sing in desultory fashion during the spring migration and even as early as March, but they conserve their best efforts until they reach their breeding grounds. Perched on the very tip of an evergreen tree in full view of all beholders, with the morning sun falling on its crimson plumage, the adult male pours forth a song of singular beauty and power—a rich, melodious, rambling warble that is inferior only to that of its cousin, the Pine Grosbeak, and can be heard at a considerable distance in the still air. When several males are singing in concert, the effect is most pleasing. E. H. Forbush says that the male "pours out his gushing, ecstatic warble from the top of some tree, and when performing before his mate his musical efforts transcend his ordinary notes and he launches into the air, fluttering about with quivering wings in lowly emulation of the Skylark, pouring forth a continuous melody until, exhausted with this most remarkable vocal effort, he floats down with uplifted pinions toward the object of his affections."[1]

Purple finches were common in the spruce and tamarack areas of Tamarack Swamp, Clinton County, on the several occasions in June when I visited that interesting locality, but I could never find a nest; nor have I been more fortunate elsewhere. In the Pymatuning region of Crawford County, where the species nests in small numbers, G. M. Sutton (1928) says that "on May 16, 1925, a pair was found building a nest in a high, thinly leaved tamarack two miles below Linesville. The male sang ecstatically for minutes at a time and the female came with great mouthfuls of twigs and soft materials with which she worked energetically while weaving them into the nest. . . . Mr. Crumb has a single egg which was taken in a former year from a nest, which he found in a tree in an orchard about four miles west of Linesville."[2]

[1]*Birds of Massachusetts*, 1929, 3:11.

[2]The Meadville record of a nest with young, mentioned by Dr. Sutton, is an error, according to H. C. Kirkpatrick. Also, the specimen that I secured on June 16, 1897, to which he refers, was taken near Linesville, not Hartstown.

R. B. Simpson is the only other bird student in our region who has had any experience with this bird as a nesting species. He writes that at Warren it is common in the spring in flocks in the river valley and that some pairs remain to breed. In the breeding season it rather avoids the woods and prefers to nest in evergreen trees in cemeteries and even about houses in the town, or in evergreens growing in groups elsewhere in the valley. By watching the female in the act of building, he has found several nests, but he has collected only one set of (four) eggs; this came from a nest in the very top of a fifty-foot spruce in a cemetery, and was reached only with the greatest difficulty. The eggs of this finch are pale greenish blue, rather sparsely spotted, chiefly at and around the larger end, with grayish brown and black. They are thus very like some types of eggs of the Chipping Sparrow. Average measurements are .79 by .56 inches.

Carpodacus purpureus Teulon, *Jour. Boston Zoöl. Soc.*, 1882, 1:52 (Bradford, McKean Co.)—Townsend, *Proc. Acad. Nat. Sci. Philadelphia*, 1883, 62 (Latrobe, Westmoreland Co., spring)—Warren, *Birds Pa.*, 1888, 241; ed. 2, 1890, 227 (Erie and Crawford Co., breeding)—Cope, *Cassinia*, 1902, 5:16 (Tamarack Swamp, Clinton Co., and between Oleona and New Bergen, also Galeton, Potter Co., June)—Todd, *Ann. Carnegie Mus.*, 1904, 2:569 (Erie, Erie Co., breeding)—Todd, in Bausman, *Hist. Beaver Co., Pa.*, 1904, 2:1200 (Beaver Co., spring transient)—Baily, *Auk*, 1896, 13:292, 294 (Williamsville, Elk Co., June–July).

"Purple Finch" Simpson, *Oölogist*, 1906, 23:135 (Warren, Warren Co., breeding)—Gerberding, *Bird-Lore*, 1912, 14:29 (Greenville, Mercer Co., December)—Cooke, *Bird-Lore*, 1914, 16:21 (Renovo, Clinton Co., and Beaver, Beaver Co., migration)—Christy and Hegner, *Bird-Lore*, 1915, 17:34; etc. (Sewickley, Allegheny Co., December)—McConnell and Savage, *Bird-Lore*, 1917, 19:23 (McKeesport, Allegheny Co., December)—Warfield, *Bird-Lore*, 1920, 22:31 (Chambersburg, Franklin Co., December)—McClelland, *Am. Mid. Nat.*, 1922, 8:37 (Washington, Washington Co., spring)—Sutton, *et al.*, *Bird-Lore*, 1923, 25:24 (Monaca to Raccoon Creek, Beaver Co., December)—Sutton, *Bird-Lore*, 1923, 25:194 (Schenley Park, Pittsburgh, Allegheny Co., April, *fide* Blair; Mercer Co., *fide* Homer); 1924, 26:266 (Deer Creek, Allegheny Co., May, *fide* Frederick)—Eastwood, *Bird-Lore*, 1926, 28:402 (Clinton region, Allegheny Co., October); 1927, 29:196 (Pittsburgh region, Allegheny Co., March), 197 (Springs, Somerset Co., winter, *fide* Miller)—Boulton, *Bird-Lore*, 1928, 30:13 (Milltown, Allegheny Co., October, *fide* Auerswald, *et al.;* Sewickley, Allegheny Co., November, *fide* Christy); 1928, 30:195 (Johnstown, Cambria Co., February, *fide* Auerswald)—Elliott, *Cardinal*, 1934, 3:170 (Raccoon Creek, Beaver Co., December).

"Crimson Finch" Simpson, *Oölogist*, 1914, 31:54 (Warren, Warren Co., winter).

Carpodacus purpureus purpureus Harlow, *Auk*, 1918, 35:137 (Warren Co., breeding)—Christy, *Cardinal*, 1923, v. 1, no. 1, [p. 8] (Sewickley, Allegheny Co., transient)—Burleigh, *Wilson Bull.*, 1923, 35:92 (Allegheny Co., winter); 1924, 36:77 (State College, Centre Co., winter; migration)—Christy and Sutton, *Cardinal*, 1928, 2:71 (Cook Forest, Clarion Co., summer)—Sutton, *Ann. Carnegie Mus.*, 1928, 18:171 (Crawford Co. localities, resident).

"Eastern Purple Finch" Cope and Hawkins, *Forest Leaves*, 1934, 24:26 (E. Tionesta Forest Reserve, Warren and McKean Co., summer).

CANADIAN PINE GROSBEAK

PINICOLA ENUCLEATOR LEUCURA (Müller)

Description—A large finch with a stout, blackish bill. *Adult male: dull crimson red*, the wings with white markings; tail dusky; lower abdomen and under tail coverts, grayish. *Young male: grayish*, the crown and the rump tinged with dull brownish red; wings dusky, with grayish-white edgings. *Female:* similar to the young male, but head and rump tinged with green (instead of brown), this color sometimes spreading to the underparts.

Range—The Pine Grosbeak is a boreal species common to both Eurasia and North America; in both continents it divides up into several geographical races. In summer it ranges north to the limit of trees and south across the spruce and fir zone, but in the East it does not invade the Appalachian highlands proper and in fact does not go south of the White Mountains. In the winter it wanders irregularly farther south, occasionally reaching western Pennsylvania. There is a small, dark race, *eschatosus* (not yet formally recognized by the American Ornithologists' Union), which was originally described from Newfoundland but which actually ranges into the Maritime Provinces of Canada. It now seems that this is the race that commonly invades our region, although *leucura*, which summers in Canada directly to the northward, is the one that we would naturally expect. There is, however, only one indisputable record of this latter form; it is based on a male that was shot near East Pittsburgh, Allegheny County, on

January 1, 1900, by D. A. Atkinson. All other western Pennsylvania specimens thus far examined belong to *eschatosus*. Our Pine Grosbeak invasions, therefore, come mainly from the northeast. The species is one of those irregular winter visitants the occurrence of which is determined not by the onset of cold weather but by the failure of the usual food supply. It appears only at irregular intervals, and most of our records come from the northern and higher parts of the state, where coniferous trees are more in evidence. The years represented by these records lie between 1875 and 1939. The largest flight was in the season of 1906–7; the scattered occurrences since then have been purely sporadic. The most recent record pertains to several birds seen in the vicinity of Uniontown in late December, 1938, and in early January, 1939, by William Montagna.

Migration—The northeast-to-southwest migration flight of this species is as remarkable as the west-to-east route of the Evening Grosbeak. In the winter of 1903–4, there was a small flight at Warren, which lasted from November 26 to March 1. During this time, pine grosbeaks were likewise noted at several other points in Warren County (Starbrick, Thompson, Torpedo, and Donaldson) and also at Sheriff Run, Forest County. The big flight of 1906–7 began at Warren with two birds on November 29, reached its height in the last week in January, and ended on February 21. There have been no more flights since then, although two females were noted on December 11, 1918, and a pair was seen on May 25, 1923 (Simpson). The latter date is certainly extraordinary and suggests that the birds may have been breeding; if they were, the occurrence can be regarded only as accidental. At State College the species was present until March 30 in 1930 and as late as May 1 in 1926—another late spring record. The earliest fall date reported is October 22 (1917), when one bird, "which looked as if it were sick or exhausted," was noted at Hollidaysburg by Miss A. E. Berg. A. B. Miller sends a few records from Springs, Somerset County, but none for earlier in the season than December 16 (1907). Available data indicate that this grosbeak first reaches and spreads across the northern part of the state and thence passes southward over the highlands, rather avoiding the Ohio Valley.

Habits—The Pine Grosbeak, as I have come to know it in the north country, is a familiar, confiding, and at times rather conspicuous bird. Since I myself have never seen it in Pennsylvania, I condense the following account of its haunts and habits from R. B. Simpson's interesting articles, cited in the references below. He states that in the season of 1906–7 he saw two birds on November 26, while he was hunting hares in the hills back of Warren. Others were noted at intervals until December 21, when he found a flock of twenty-five feeding in a mountain ash. On January 23 he came across the main feeding ground—a grove of mountain ash at the base of a steep and heavily timbered hill. About seventy-five birds were scattered through this grove, and the snow was covered with their cuttings. A dark, stormy day prevented him from distinguishing the red males, but the next day, with the temperature 20° below zero, he came back and secured a few specimens. Only about one bird out of twelve or fifteen was an adult male. They were feeding on the berries of the mountain ash and to a lesser extent on the buds of the maple. While thus engaged they were quiet, and as long as food was within reach they remained on their perches. Those not feeding were noisy and restless and were constantly calling. Flocks were coming and going all the time. Some flocks would approach from the hillside while others would plunge straight down from above. Before dropping down into the mountain ash trees to feed, the flocks would almost always alight first in a tall hemlock or hardwood tree. Smaller flocks would often alight on the hemlocks (both dead and living), and at intervals some birds would burst into song, but it was difficult to say whether these were always red males. With the grosbeaks there were large numbers of both species of crossbills, but these kept entirely in the hemlocks.

Other observers have noticed the Pine Grosbeak feeding on the seeds of the hemlock and the jack pine and also on the berries of the red sumac. The call note of the species is a soft, clear, musical whistle, quite characteristic. O. W. Knight writes: "Soft, tender, ventriloquial and caressing at times, at others rising clear and loud but always full of trills and warbles, the song of the Pine Grosbeak easily places it on equal footing with any of our song birds."[1]

[1]*Birds of Maine*, 1908, p. 370.

Pinicola enucleator Rhoads, *Auk*, 1899, 16:312 (Emporium, Cameron Co., *fide* Larrabee; [East Pittsburgh], Allegheny Co., *fide* Atkinson).

Pinicola enucleator leucura Todd, *Ann. Carnegie Mus.*, 1904, 2:568 (Erie, Erie Co., winter)—Sutton, *Ann. Carnegie Mus.*, 1928, 18:171 (Meadville, Crawford Co., February, *fide* Huidekoper).

"Pine Grosbeak" Simpson, *Oölogist*, 1907, 24:86; and 1914, 31:53 (Warren, Warren Co., winter)—Hoffman, *et al.*, *Bird-Lore*, 1923, 25:23 (Grove City, Mercer Co., December).

"Canadian Pine Grosbeak" Wood, *Wilson Bull.*, 1932, 44:238 (State College, Centre Co., spring and winter).

Additional records: Bellevue, Allegheny Co., noted by E. M. Poole, January 14, 1898 (Atkinson)—Renovo, Clinton Co., three taken from a flock along Drury's Run on January 23, 1900 (Pierce)—State Game Refuge No. 1 (7 miles south of Renovo), Clinton Co., during the winter of 1915 a flock of twelve was fed by J. B. Ross (Sutton)—South Bethlehem, Armstrong Co., flock of six seen January 5, 1922 (Christy).

HOARY REDPOLL

ACANTHIS HORNEMANNI EXILIPES (Coues)

Description—Similar in general to the Common Redpoll, but *much lighter-colored* throughout, especially on the rump and underparts, where white prevails.

Range and local status—The Hoary Redpoll breeds in the arctic and subarctic regions from Alaska to Hudson Bay and winters irregularly southward to the northern United States. It is included in the Pennsylvania list on the basis of a single occurrence, which can scarcely be considered other than fortuitous. The bird was identified by C. S. Beardslee on January 9, 1934, on Presque Isle. It was easily singled out from a flock of common redpolls by its different coloration, and it was studied through a binocular at close range under exceptionally favorable conditions. What was doubtless the same bird was seen at the same place on January 28 by G. M. Cook. Both these observers are confident of the correctness of the identification.

COMMON REDPOLL

ACANTHIS LINARIA LINARIA (Linnaeus)

Description—About as large as the American Goldfinch; bill small and sharp; coloration streaked. *Adult male: dusky brown*, with paler streaks; *crown crimson;* wings showing two pale bars; *chin dusky*, and throat and underparts more or less tinged with pinkish crimson. *Adult female:* similar to the male, but without any pinkish tinge below. *Young:* similar to the adult female, but lacking the crimson crown.

Range—In summer the Redpoll inhabits boreal Eurasia and America. In the latter continent it is a species characteristic of the Hudsonian Life Zone, which comprises the more northerly part of the great coniferous forest stretching from Alaska to Labrador. In the winter it moves southward and reaches southern Canada and the northern United States; occasionally it goes even farther, but its movements are as erratic and irregular, at least in western Pennsylvania, as those of the other boreal finches. Like them it has been recorded most frequently in the northern and highland counties, but it is likely to occur anywhere during its southern incursions. The earliest invasion recorded took place in February, 1875, when Sennett secured several specimens at Erie. The species was noted at this same locality in March, 1893, by S. E. Bacon, but it was not seen again until the winter of 1933–34, when a large-sized flock stayed on Presque Isle and was noticed by several observers. The Redpoll reappeared there in February, 1937, and in March of that year one bird was taken in Allegheny County. R. B. Simpson noted a flock at Warren in December, 1887, but saw no others until the winter of 1908–9, when there was a notable flight of northern birds of several species. This incursion carried the Redpoll eastward to Centre County (State College) and southward to Somerset County (Springs). There was a considerable flight during the winter of 1911–12, and another during that of 1916–17, but for the years between and since, there are only a few scattered records. The species is rare in the Ohio Valley and southward.

Migration—A winter wanderer rather than a

regular migrant, the Redpoll conforms to no general rule in its comings and goings. In the winter of 1908 it did not appear at State College (or at least it was unobserved) before December 12, but there are several November records for other years and places, and on one occasion it was noted at New Hamburg, Mercer County, as early as October 13 (Homer). It is likelier to be common in the colder months of January and February than earlier or later in the season, but it often lingers until the last of March or even later. The latest spring date on record is April 25 (1912), reported by Mr. Simpson for Warren.

Habits—Although single birds are occasionally encountered, the Redpoll usually appears in flocks (sometimes of large size), which frequently include American goldfinches and pine siskins, its near relatives. T. D. Burleigh (1924) says that at State College during the winter of 1916–17 he repeatedly saw flocks of fully five hundred birds. "Invariably they were feeding on the seeds of weeds sticking above the snow that covered the ground, and when in large flocks were very restless and constantly shifting about." R. C. Harlow's vivid picture (1909) of an earlier flight at the same locality is reproduced herewith:

"It was on December 12, 1908, that the forerunners of the hosts which were to come were first observed. We were returning from a vain search for Ducks, and while beating our way across the fields, against a blinding snowstorm, suddenly a flock of small Finches flew rapidly by and settled on the drifting snow. In a moment I recognized the note of the Redpoll, and, all aglow, I hurried forward and watched them as they flitted nervously about over the surface of the snow, frequently feeding on the low weed-stalks which everywhere rose above the rapidly deepening mantle. But, surely, they could not be Redpolls! No, for there, as they scurried about, we frequently caught sight of pale yellowish wing-bars among the plainer pinions of the mass. And there, scattered amid the flock of perhaps thirty Redpolls, were probably twelve Pine Siskins. Well content, we left them, and, as we hurried home in the twilight, several other flocks took wing at our near approach. Evidently, the Redpolls were here after all!

"But these were only the smallest fraction of what was to come. All during the winter months, they were found in legions throughout the Nittany Valley. Not only in the fields, but, also, in the orchards, in the town, and even on the college campus did we hear their cheerful notes. As March drew near, every day I looked for their departure, yet they showed no signs of leaving. Not until the last of the month did they grow scarce, and the last stragglers lingered until April 10,—days after the arbutus and hepatica had burst their swelling buds.

"What impressed me most was their tameness. Repeatedly have I approached to within a few feet of a feeding flock, and they evinced no alarm. When they did fly, it was only to make a few undulating circles, and then return to the vicinity of their former feeding-place. Frequently, part of the flock would arise, and individuals would continue their search for seeds, totally unconcerned over their departing comrades. On near approach, the males could be easily distinguished from the females by their bright rosy breasts, varying in intensity of coloration as the ages of the birds.

"They fed indifferently on the snow or perched upon the weed-stalks, those below picking up the seeds shaken down by the more industrious gleaners. Many a field have I seen literally covered with a network of their dainty tracks in the new fallen snow; yet not all obtain their sustenance in this manner, for on several occasions, I have noticed them picking vigorously at the buds of the maples in early spring.

"Unceasingly, as they flew in undulating circles overhead, or fed companionably on the ground, we heard them call—a clear *per-chee* varying to a sharp *clee-e*—somewhat resembling the similar notes of the Goldfinch, yet distinct. But in early March the males began to sing, and I was privileged to add a new bird concert to my category. A vigorous, wild, Goldfinch-like melody it was, somehow bringing to me pictures of the cold, wind-swept barrens of northern Labrador, where these tireless bits of bird life would soon nest. Inspect, as I did at near view, thousands of Redpolls, yet not one was referable to any form other than *Acanthis linaria.*

"The Redpolls have gone, yet vividly, in my mind's eye, I see the flocks feeding before me in the bleak fields or hear them go calling overhead. And when the snow once more steals softly down and the winds bring cold blasts from the frigid north, I shall wait patiently to catch the first glimpse of my sociable winter companions,—the Redpolls."

Acanthis linaria TODD, *Ann. Carnegie Mus.*, 1904, 2:569 (Erie and Presque Isle, Erie Co., winter)—HARLOW, *Bird-Lore*, 1909, 11:121 (State College, Centre Co., winter).

"Redpoll" HARLOW, *Cassinia*, 1912, 15:20 (Center Furnace Swamp, Centre Co., winter)—SIMPSON, *Oölogist*, 1912, 29: 370 (Warren, Warren Co., winter)—BOULTON, *Bird-Lore*, 1918, 20:36 (Beaver, Beaver Co., December)—KEESLER, *Oölogist*, 1921, 38:171 ("Harrisville," [Forestville], Butler Co., winter)—EASTWOOD, *Bird-Lore*, 1926, 28:207 (Pittsburgh region, Allegheny Co., March); 1927, 29:55 (Sandy Lake, Mercer Co., November, *fide* Ross and Freni)—SKAGGS, *Wilson Bull.*, 1937, 49:294 (Presque Isle, Erie Co., February).

Acanthis linaria linaria STONE, *Cassinia*, 1923, 24:30 (Greencastle, Franklin Co., February, *fide* Ziegler)—BURLEIGH, *Wilson Bull.*, 1923, 35:92 ([Highland Park], Allegheny Co., November); 1924, 36:128 (State College, Centre Co., [and Charter Oak, Huntingdon Co.], winter)—SUTTON, *Ann. Carnegie Mus.*, 1928, 18:173 (Meadville, Crawford Co., fall).

Additional records: Renovo, Clinton Co., noted in January, February, and November, 1897; several specimens taken (Pierce)—Clarington, Forest Co., a flock in February, 1923 (A. R. Hillard)—Morganza, Washington Co., noted February 13, 1897 (Van Ostrand)—Raccoon Creek, Beaver Co., February 11, 1923 (Boulton)—Linesville, Crawford Co., November 8, 1926; Greenville, Mercer Co., March 7, 1930 (Seiple)—Hollidaysburg, Blair Co., occasional in fall and winter, in flocks (Berg)—Upper Talleycavey, Allegheny Co., March 31, 1937, one shot by R. L. Fricke (specimen in Carnegie Museum).

GREATER REDPOLL

ACANTHIS LINARIA ROSTRATA (Coues)

Description—Similar to the Common Redpoll, but *general coloration darker*, and *bill heavier*. The two races are not certainly distinguishable in life.

Range and local status—This race of the Redpoll breeds in Greenland and wanders irregularly southward in winter to eastern Canada and the northern United States. A single specimen (now in the collection of the United States Biological Survey) was shot from a small flock of redpolls on Presque Isle by S. E. Bacon on March 31, 1893.

Acanthis linaria rostrata TODD, *Ann. Carnegie Mus.*, 1904, 2:569 (Presque Isle, Erie Co., March; one record).

NORTHERN PINE SISKIN (Plate 21)

SPINUS PINUS PINUS (Wilson)

Description—A bird resembling the American Goldfinch, from which it may readily be distinguished by its *streaked plumage* (brown above, whitish below), with only a touch of yellow at the base of the wings and the tail. (No red spot on the crown, or black area on the throat, as in the Redpoll.)

Range—Our Pine Siskin is the American analogue of the Eurasian *Spinus spinus*. It has a wide transcontinental range in the United States and Canada, breeds mainly in the Canadian Life Zone, and winters southward. An outlying race inhabits the mountains of Mexico. The breeding range of the typical race in the East is not yet well understood; it seems indeed to vary from year to year, and it is unquestionably discontinuous. According to E. H. Eaton,[1] the species breeds sporadically in the Adirondack Mountains and possibly in the Catskills (although I can find no very recent records), and there are valid records of its breeding even in the lower Hudson Valley—far south of its proper zone. On the other hand, it has been found summering in the southern Appalachians, and from this circumstance one would infer that its range in the highlands, like those of other species of the Canadian Fauna, must follow the mountains all the way. This remains to be proved, however, and it is a long distance from northern Pennsylvania to western North Carolina.

June occurrences of most birds usually indicate breeding, but this is not necessarily true of the Pine Siskin, as will presently be shown. The authentic breeding records from our region are few and scattered, but they indicate a breeding range covering the plateau section (its northern part, at least) and extending thence westward to the Erie-Crawford district. The first suggestion that the species might breed in western Pennsylvania came from S. N. Rhoads (1899), who recorded it merely

[1]*Birds of New York*, 1914, 2:279.

as "breeding in the mountains of the northwest counties." As there are no mountains whatever in that section, the statement is meaningless. His field notebook, however, shows that he observed this bird at Round Island, Clinton County, between May 29 and June 1, 1896, and this observation is evidently the sole basis for his published record. His evidence is therefore purely presumptive. We now know that the Pine Siskin lays its eggs in March or early April and that the young are often on the wing by May. They go about in flocks composed of a number of family groups, and the roving instincts of the species might carry these flocks far from their nesting grounds by the end of May. A flock was found on Presque Isle on May 24, 1900 (Todd, 1904), but the circumstance is not proof that the birds comprising it were reared in the vicinity. In 1920, flocks were noted at Sewickley (Christy) and at Beaver (Todd) during the third week in May. Again in 1923, when the species was in evidence in our region generally, it was observed at Beaver, in flocks and otherwise, from February 22 until as late as May 13. Nevertheless, I cannot consider these occurrences as signs of breeding. Parallel cases from other localities might be cited.

There are, however, three indisputable breeding records for western Pennsylvania, based on the actual finding of nests. R. B. Simpson discovered the species nesting at Warren in 1912 and again in 1925. G. M. Sutton found a nest with young during the spring season of 1925 at Hull, Potter County, and several old nests in Pymatuning Swamp (near Hartstown). S. S. Dickey writes that he repeatedly observed pine siskins during March and April of that year at Drake's Mill, Crawford County, and that he believed them to be breeding at the time, although he found no nests. On April 4 he saw several birds two miles east of Erie. It would seem, therefore, that during the season of 1925 the Siskin must have been breeding throughout our northern counties and probably farther south in the highlands. But it is fairly clear that the species does not breed regularly in this section. Almost certainly its breeding range varies from year to year, possibly according to shifts in the food supply. It is probable, too, that not all birds breed every year; this explanation would account for the presence of the species at unexpected times. The Siskin is best known to our local observers as a winter resident, but it is erratic in appearance and irregular in numbers; it is common in some winters and entirely absent in others. There are records from numerous localities in western Pennsylvania.

Migration—Much remains to be learned about the movements of the Siskin. It is a winter wanderer rather than a true migrant. After the breeding season, old and young gather in flocks and rove over the country in search of food. Thus one is likely to encounter them almost anywhere during the summer, fall, and winter months. If there is any southward movement induced by stress of weather, it takes place in October and November, as indicated by records from Renovo (Pierce) and elsewhere. The return movement probably occurs in February. As already intimated, May dates can scarcely be considered true migration records.

Habits—If the Pine Siskin is a confirmed opportunist among birds, it is also a cheerful optimist. It travels in flocks, is sociable with its own kind, and often fraternizes with such kindred spirits as goldfinches, redpolls, and crossbills. It shares the modest fare of these species, their restless, wandering habit, and their general air of exuberance and irrepressible good cheer. Even while feeding, siskins are forever twittering and chattering among themselves in lively fashion, and sub-zero temperatures seem to put no damper on their spirits. Tame and trusting by nature, they will often permit close approach; at other times they seem restless, and a whole flock will rise at some fancied alarm to fly out of sight or perhaps to return after a circuitous flight. They are inordinately fond of hemlock and alder seeds and are often observed feeding thereon. Sometimes, however, they may be found in mixed woodland, in bushes and weeds, or even in orchards. A flock that I noted at Beaver during the spring of 1920 haunted the shade trees and gardens of the town. In their general behavior, their jerky, wavering manner of flight, and their volubility, they are remarkably like American goldfinches. Their call notes also resemble those of that bird but are rather harsher, more nasal, and more grating in character. Heard in chorus, they carry a long distance.

The unseasonably early nesting of the Siskin is as odd a fact as is the late nesting of its cousin, the Goldfinch, but it is a fact that is less generally known. So far as our region is concerned, the credit for the discovery of this eccentricity belongs to Mr. Simpson, whose timely article (1912) substantially cleared up the mystery concerning the nesting and seasonal status of this species. Had Dr. Sutton and I but remembered the substance of this article at the time, the significance of the abundance of this bird at Pymatuning Swamp in May, 1923, would not have escaped us. The accidental finding of a nest (with young ready to leave) in Potter County two years later supplied the clue. Dr. Sutton writes (1928):

"From February 18 to 21, 1925, Siskins were abundant everywhere in the hemlocks north of Hartstown and were roving about in noisy pairs, though strangely enough, I was at the time blind to the fact that they were mated. Over and over again I watched the busy birds stripping the fiber from the stalks of weeds and gathering wooly stuff from old buds and cocoons, and in my ignorance diagnosed their actions as a quest for food. All this time they were probably building nests. These nests would likely have been completed during the next two weeks, and eggs laid during the middle of March. Therefore the great flocks of birds seen on May 16 and 17, 1923, were probably young birds, which had been reared at the Swamp, together with their parents. I have at hand numerous old nests of the Siskin (taken from horizontal hemlock boughs, and which I had temporarily identified as those of the Goldfinch) which agree admirably with the nest from Potter County from which the young birds had flown."

The substance of Mr. Simpson's important paper on the Pine Siskin in Warren County is here reproduced. He remarks that "not a winter passes but a few flocks are about and at irregular intervals large flights occur. They make their appearance in November, and by the first of April have about all departed.

"They are found in flocks in hemlock woods in the mountains and when large flights occur, flocks numbering as high as 200 are to be met with. They feed almost entirely on the small cones of the hemlock and are noisy and restless. They no doubt breed sparingly every season [?] as at different times in summer I have seen small parties of them back in the mountains."

Throughout the winter of 1911–12 and as late as April, the birds were abundant in the vicinity of Warren and even appeared about the town, wherever there were evergreen trees in cemeteries, groves, or woodland. On April 14 a pair was discovered building a nest in a little clump of pines. Upon searching various tracts of evergreens, Mr. Simpson found many other birds, apparently mated pairs. "At this season they were feeding on the young buds of maples, etc., as well as in the conifers. They were very noisy and restless and their sharp notes, somewhat like [those of] a Goldfinch, could be heard on every hand. The males were in full song and singing constantly."

Mr. Simpson found ten nests between April 14 and May 3. Invariably they were in evergreen trees—white and yellow pine, hemlock, or spruce —and were placed on horizontal branches, sometimes well out from the trunk, at heights varying from six to thirty feet from the ground. On April 16 he found one that had just been started, and spent some time on several different days watching its construction. "The female did all the work, the male often accompanying her to and fro. The birds were constantly calling. The female frequently called while at the nest and the male was continually singing. April 29th the female began sitting on three eggs." Another nest found on April 28 contained three birds several days old. "The nests," Mr. Simpson continues, "were neat and pretty. They were well built and warmly lined. As soon as the young were hatched the old birds became very quiet and have remained so ever since. Occasionally I hear one sing a little or hear a few flying over or meet a little bunch along some road feeding in the grass or on the ground. At such times they are very tame and allow a person to approach within a few feet, before taking flight. I made one trip for nests back into virgin timber, but although the birds were common enough, I could not find a single nest. Possibly in the big timber they nested high up."

In the spring of 1925 the Siskin again nested at Warren, but much earlier in the season than in 1912. Between April 1 and 6, Mr. Simpson found two nests containing young and one that held eggs far advanced in incubation. (This was during the season that the species is believed to have bred in Crawford County, and the dates correspond.) Evidently the time of nesting, as well as the breeding area, is a variable quantity. According to Mr. Simpson, three eggs comprise a full set. They resemble those of the American Goldfinch in their pale greenish ground-color but are sparsely flecked with light reddish brown. The spots sometimes form a wreath around the larger end.

Spinus pinus Rhoads, *Auk*, 1899, 16:312 ("northwestern Pa.," breeding)—Todd, *Ann. Carnegie Mus.*, 1904, 2:570 (Erie, Erie Co., May)—Simpson, *Oölogist*, 1912, 29:372 (Warren, Warren Co., nesting)—Harlow, *Auk*, 1918, 35:138 (Centre Co., spring; Warren Co., nesting)—Christy, *Cardinal*, 1923, v. 1, no. 1, [p. 9] (Sewickley, Allegheny Co., winter)—Stone, *Cassinia*, 1923, 24:30 (Greencastle, Franklin Co., February, *fide* Ziegler)—Burleigh, *Wilson Bull.*, 1923, 35:93 (Allegheny Co., winter); 1924, 36:128 (State College, Centre Co., migration)—[Livingston, ed.], *Cassinia*, 1929, 27:28 (Ellisburg, Potter Co., February, *fide* Miller)—Christy, *Cardinal*, 1936, 4:98 (Big Traverse Valley, Beaver Co., November).

"Pine Siskin" Harlow, *Bird-Lore*, 1909, 11:121 (State College, Centre Co., December)—Cooke, *Bird-Lore*, 1910, 12:139 (Renovo, Clinton Co., migration)—Simpson, *Oölogist*, 1912, 29:330 (head of Tionesta Creek, Warren Co., summer), 370; 1914, 31:53; and 1921, 38:135 (Warren, Warren Co., winter)—Miller, *Bird-Lore*, 1917, 29:23 (Springs, Somerset Co., December)—Hoffman, *et al.*, *Bird-Lore*, 1923, 25:23 (Grove City, Mercer Co., December)—Christy and Hegner, *Bird-Lore*, 1923, 25:25 (Sewickley, Allegheny Co., December)—Jones, *et al.*, *Bird-Lore*, 1923, 25:25 (Deer Creek region, Allegheny Co., December)—Christy, *Bull. Audubon Soc. W. Pa.*, 1923, 1:12 (Allegheny Co., winter)—Sutton, *Bird-Lore*, 1923, 25:132 (Bakerstown, Allegheny Co., winter), 194 (Pittsburgh, Allegheny Co., winter; Huntingdon, Huntingdon Co., March)—[Christy], *Cardinal*, 1923, v. 1, no. 2, [p. 10] (Big Traverse Valley, Beaver Co., winter)—Eastwood, *Bird-Lore*, 1926, 28:207 (Pittsburgh region, Allegheny Co., spring), 402 (Clinton region, Allegheny Co., October); 1927, 29:56 (Butcher Run, Butler Co., November), 126 (Pittsburgh region, winter), 197 (Springs, Somerset Co., *fide* Miller)—Burleigh, *Cardinal*, 1929, 2:118 (Squaw Run, Allegheny Co., December)—Elliott, *Cardinal*, 1934, 3:170 (Raccoon Creek, Beaver Co., December).

"Pine Finch" Simpson, *Oölogist*, 1909, 26:26; and 1910, 27:100 (Warren, Warren Co., winter).

Spinus pinus pinus Sutton, *Ann. Carnegie Mus.*, 1928, 18:174 (Pymatuning Swamp, Crawford Co., and [Hull], Potter Co., breeding)—Bergstrom, *Cardinal*, 1930, 2:186 (Pymatuning Swamp, Crawford Co., winter).

EASTERN GOLDFINCH (Plate 21)

SPINUS TRISTIS TRISTIS (Linnaeus)

Description—Adult male in summer: bright yellow; cap black; wings and tail black, with white markings. *Adult female in summer:* dull yellowish olive above, brighter below; wings dusky, with white bars and edgings; tail dusky, with small white spots on the outer feathers. *Adult male in winter:* upperparts brownish; underparts soiled whitish, the throat tinged with yellow and the flanks with brown; wings and tail black, with white markings. *Adult female in winter:* similar to the same sex in summer plumage, but duller and browner. *Young birds* in the fall resemble the adults of either sex, but their plumage is suffused with brown and buff.

Range—The range of the American Goldfinch is transcontinental but not boreal. Primarily a bird of the Transition and upper Austral life zones, it does not invade the Canadian to any great extent. The eastern race winters over most of its breeding range and southward to the Gulf coast. It is generally distributed throughout western Pennsylvania and occurs at all seasons of the year, although not so commonly in the winter. Like the true boreal finches, it is irregular and somewhat erratic except in the breeding season, which begins in July.

Habits[1]—The Goldfinch always brings to mind the warm, drowsy days of early summer; for it is then, when other birds are quiet and inconspicuous, that this species is most in evidence. For reasons of its own, it delays domestic activities until late June or early July and roams about throughout the spring months in carefree flocks; only when the young of other birds are on the wing is nesting given any consideration. One can but theorize on the reason for this strange behavior, although it is possible that the late ripening of the thistle, on which the Goldfinch depends to a large extent for both nesting material and food for its young, is partly responsible. Be that as it may, it is late July before scattered pairs replace the flocks formerly encountered daily in the open fields. Any bird song is welcome at this time of the year, and the ecstatic outburst of the male as he circles overhead during the hot, dry days of August will, when once heard, always be remembered.

In western Pennsylvania the Goldfinch occurs throughout the year, although its presence during the winter months is, like that of others of its family, determined in some degree by the weather and the available food supply. In unusually severe winters relatively few birds will be seen, but in

[1]Account contributed by Thomas D. Burleigh.

milder seasons numerous flocks will be found almost daily after early November. Along Deer Creek, at Harmarville, Allegheny County, flocks have frequently been seen feeding in the sycamores; when a strong, bitter wind prevailed, it was not uncommon to find these birds feeding with the tree sparrows on the seeds of weeds sticking above the snow. At this season of the year the males are very similar to the females in appearance, since the bright yellow of their coats is replaced by a drab olive brown; were it not for their characteristic notes, the uninitiated observer would have difficulty in recognizing them. These notes are suggestive of the Canary's and have a cheery quality that emphasizes, during the bleak winter days, the happy-go-lucky disposition of these sociable little birds.

In late March and early April a gradual molt transforms the dull plumage of the males into the vivid yellow dress of the summer months. The females undergo little change, and after the first of May the sexes are easy to distinguish. For almost two months the birds continue to roam about in flocks, and the males, which are then in song, are often a rather conspicuous part of the landscape. In fact, if one comes within hearing distance of one of these flocks feeding in a willow or an elm, the general effect suggests the proximity of an aviary of no mean proportions.

Although it is possible at rare intervals to find a nest with fresh eggs early in July, the latter part of that month is a far more usual time. Decidedly exceptional is D. A. Atkinson's record of fresh eggs found on July 3 (1898) in Allegheny County. My earliest record for Fayette County is July 31 (1915), and W. E. C. Todd mentions having found a nest with eggs at Beaver on July 28 (1899); these can be considered average dates for this part of the state. It may be that two broods are reared by at least some of the birds, as fresh eggs are frequently found late in August and not infrequently during the first week in September. The number of eggs varies from four to six, and five comprises the average set. They are bluish white, unmarked when fresh; as incubation advances, the bluish tint fades somewhat. Average measurements are .65 by .48 inches. The situation of the nest varies considerably; although conifers are consistently shunned, practically all other trees and many shrubs are favored. In Fayette County, red haws growing in abandoned pastures were frequently chosen, and there the nests were within four feet of the ground. On the other hand, it was not unusual to find nests from twenty to thirty feet from the ground in chestnuts and various oaks standing in open woods. Maple trees in towns and in city parks are commonly used. The nest itself is compactly built of plant fibers, shreds of bark, plant down, and fine weed stems; it is well cupped and is almost invariably lined with thistledown. Horsehair was contained in the lining of one nest found in Centre County, but this is the only exception that I have noted in many years' experience with this species.

After the young have left the nest they can be seen in company with their parents until the first frosty mornings. Then there is a noticeable gathering into flocks that hints of winter days not far distant.

Astragalinus tristis Townsend, *Proc. Acad. Nat. Sci. Philadelphia*, 1883, 62 (Latrobe, Westmoreland Co., summer)—Teulon, *Jour. Boston Zoöl. Soc.*, 1883, 2:8 (Bradford, McKean Co., breeding)—Cope, *Cassinia*, 1902, 5:16 (Clinton and Potter Co., June)—Todd, *Ann. Carnegie Mus.*, 1904, 2:569 (Erie and Presque Isle, Erie Co., resident)—Todd, in Bausman, *Hist. Beaver Co., Pa.*, 1904, 2:1200 (Beaver Co., resident)—Keim, *Cassinia*, 1905, 8:39 (Port Allegany, McKean Co., summer)—Forrest, *Oölogist*, 1911, 28:115 (Washington, Washington Co., breeding).

"American Goldfinch" Todd, *Oölogist*, 1887, 4:89 (Beaver, Beaver Co., nesting)—Jacobs, *Hoosier Nat.*, 1887, 2:78 (Waynesburg, Greene Co., resident; description nest and eggs)—Wickham, *Oölogist*, 1888, 5:92 (Beaver, Beaver Co., winter)—Pitcairn, *Bird-Lore*, 1907, 9:155 (Riverview Park, Allegheny Co., breeding)—Miller, *Bird-Lore*, 1908, 10:32; etc. (Springs, Somerset Co., December)—Burleigh, *Oölogist*, 1911, 28:180 (Chestnut Ridge, near Uniontown, Fayette Co., nesting).

Spinus tristis Jamison, *Ornithologist and Oölogist*, 1888, 13:134; and Dwight, *Auk*, 1892, 9:137 (Cresson, Cambria Co., June)—Todd, *Auk*, 1893, 10:40 (Two Lick, Indiana Co., June), 44 (Coalport, Clearfield Co., June)—Jacobs, *Summer Birds Greene Co., Pa.*, 1893, 10 (Greene Co., resident; nesting)—Bailey, *Auk*, 1896, 13:291, 294 (Williamsville, Elk Co., breeding).

"Goldfinch" Stone, *Cassinia*, 1906, 9:43 (McConnellsburg, Fulton Co., June)—Pitcairn, *Bird-Lore*, 1908, 10:32 (West View, Allegheny Co., December)—Gerberding, *Bird-Lore*, 1912, 14:29 (Greenville, Mercer Co., December)—McConnell, *Oölogist*, 1918, 35:150 (McKeesport, Allegheny Co., resident)—McGraw, *et al.*, *Bird-Lore*, 1919, 21:37; etc. (Altoona, Blair Co., December)—Warfield, *Bird-Lore*, 1919, 21:37; etc. (Chambersburg, Franklin Co., December)—McConnell, *Bird-Lore*, 1920, 22:31; etc. (Emsworth, Allegheny Co., December)—Nicholson, *Bird-Lore*, 1921, 23:18

(Grove City, Mercer Co., December)—McClelland, *Am. Mid. Nat.*, 1922, 8:35 (Washington, Washington Co., resident)—Jones, *et al.*, *Bird-Lore*, 1923, 25:24; etc. (Deer Creek, Allegheny Co., December)—Street, *Cassinia*, 1923, 24:15 (Greencastle to Ft. Loudon, Franklin Co., June)—Christy, *Cardinal*, 1924, v. 1, no. 4, p. 10 (Big Traverse Valley, Beaver Co., June)—Christy and Hegner, *Bird-Lore*, 1925, 27:41; etc. (Raccoon Creek Valley and region, Beaver Co., December)—Eastwood, *Bird-Lore*, 1925, 27:337 (Bradford Woods, Allegheny Co., August, *fide* Frederick); 1926, 28:208 (Ridgway, Elk Co., March, *fide* Alsop), 273 (Rector, Westmoreland Co., May, *fide* Knauz)—Matuszak, *Bird-Lore*, 1926, 28:29 (Hyde Park, Westmoreland Co., December)—Eastwood, *Bird-Lore*, 1927, 29:56 (Logan's Ferry, Allegheny Co., October; Thompsonville, Washington Co., November, *fide* Ellair)—Scoville, *Runaway Days*, 1927, 226 (Seven Mts., Centre Co., March)—Chaney, *Bird-Lore*, 1932, 34:47 (near Uniontown, Fayette Co., December)—[Christy, ed.], *Cardinal*, 1933, 3:150 (Edgewood, Allegheny Co., *fide* Blair)—Berkheimer, *Bird-Lore*, 1933, 35:27; etc. (near Osterburg, Bedford Co., December)—Elliott, *Cardinal*, 1934, 3:170 (Raccoon Creek, Beaver Co., December).

Astragalinus tristis tristis Harlow, *Auk*, 1912, 29:474 (southern Centre Co., nesting)—Stone, *Cassinia*, 1919, 22:33 (Altoona, Blair Co., May, *fide* McGraw)—Christy, *Cardinal*, 1923, v. 1, no. 1, [p. 9] (Sewickley, Allegheny Co., resident)—Burleigh, *Wilson Bull.*, 1923, 35:93 (Allegheny Co., resident); 1931, 43:47 (State College, Centre Co., nesting)—Christy and Sutton, *Cardinal*, 1928, 2:72 (Cook Forest, Clarion Co., resident)—Sutton, *Ann. Carnegie Mus.*, 1928, 18:173 (Meadville and Pymatuning Swamp, Crawford Co., resident; nesting).

Spinus tristis tristis Burleigh, *Cardinal*, 1932, 3:82 (near Uniontown, Fayette Co., summer; nesting).

RED CROSSBILL

LOXIA CURVIROSTRA PUSILLA Gloger[1]

Description—A stocky bird somewhat larger than the English Sparrow, with the mandibles crossed near the tip. *Male: dull red*, brighter and purer on the rump; wings and tail dusky, unmarked. *Female: dull green*, the rump a little brighter; wings and tail plain dusky. *Young in juvenal plumage:* upperparts and underparts showing dusky streaks on a soiled greenish background; wings dull greenish dusky.

Range—The Red Crossbill, a vagrant species that wanders irregularly southward in the winter, inhabits the boreal regions of both Eurasia and America and breaks up into a number of geographic races in different parts of its range. It has recently been made the subject of careful study by Ludlow Griscom (1937), with interesting results. Although it was long known as a highly erratic species, its vagaries prove to be much more involved and paradoxical than had heretofore been supposed. Mr. Griscom finds that at least three distinct races occur in eastern North America, with possibly a fourth in the southern Appalachians. A large, dark race breeds in Newfoundland; it is exemplified by Gloger's type and must be called *pusilla*. A small, short-billed race, *minor*, is native in the humid northwestern Pacific coast district but has occasionally invaded the East. A third race, newly christened *neogæa*, has a wide breeding range in the Canadian Life Zone from New Brunswick as far west at least as Minnesota. At intervals (determined probably by failure of the food supply) the crossbills leave their established homes and adventure into new and strange regions, their wandering instincts often taking them far afield. The Newfoundland birds, for example, have been collected as far south as Florida and as far west as Kansas, and it is conceivable that they may have crossed western Pennsylvania en route. A tremendous eastern flight of the Pacific coast race, *minor*, occurred during the winter of 1887–88. At least one of the subsequent lesser invasions of this race (that of 1923) involved our region, as proved by specimens in the Carnegie Museum. But by far the largest percentage of specimens (summer and winter) from western Pennsylvania obviously belong to the race *neogæa*. Mr. Griscom believes that this race never breeds in the Appalachians south of New York except in the years following an incursion from the North, when some pairs remain behind. He claims that in the mountains of Pennsylvania "there is as yet no final evidence of a permanently resident population" of the Red Crossbill.

One must be cautious in approaching this subject, however. As in the case of the Pine Siskin, summer records are not *ipso facto* breeding records; for, on the one hand, the Crossbill is known to nest both very early and very late in the season, and on the other, it may pass the spring and early

[1]As shown herein, this name is misapplied in the American Ornithologists' Union *Check-List of North American Birds* (1931 edition).

summer months at a given place without making any attempt to nest. As yet there are no authentic records of nesting in our region; the few reports of breeding are based on presumptive evidence, such as the finding of young in the streaked (juvenal) plumage, accompanied by their parents. There is of course no way of telling how far such birds may have strayed from the place where they were hatched. The chances are that they have been raised in the general vicinity, although Mr. Griscom opines that only young not fully grown can safely be considered nonwanderers.

It is perhaps significant that our summer records for the Red Crossbill nearly all come from the highlands, where so many other relatively northern species occur in the breeding season. The Crossbill is indeed one of the few truly Canadian Life Zone birds that summer in our region. Warren (1890) records it as breeding in Clinton, Clearfield, and Cameron counties—presumably on the strength of reports received from his correspondents. He adds: "Dr. Van Fleet informs me they are found at all seasons about Renovo." The latter observer is doubtless also responsible for the Clearfield County record, since in his manuscript list of the breeding birds of DuBois, he says: "I have taken newly fledged young in February and May." The journals of A. K. Pierce fully substantiate Van Fleet's estimate of the status of the species at Renovo. On one occasion (March 30, 1897), Mr. Pierce even watched a female gathering nesting material, but unfortunately he failed to locate her nest. Moreover, on June 21, 1899, I myself encountered a family group of crossbills on the mountaintop south of Renovo and collected the adults and some full-grown young in the streaked plumage. Mr. Pierce also writes of having seen both old and young birds at Kane on April 24, 1903. He says that the gonads of a male shot there on February 20, 1894, were much enlarged.

In Warren County, according to R. B. Simpson, the status of the Red Crossbill as a breeding bird rests on similar presumptive evidence. At Springs, Somerset County, A. B. Miller has seen or heard the species a few times in June and July. There is also some evidence of its breeding in the mountains of southern Centre County. On March 26, 1916, R. C. Harlow and T. D. Burleigh happened on two mated pairs at Shingletown Gap; and H. A. Surface (1904) says that "in the summer of 1902 a pair of old birds accompanied by four of their young were seen for two days upon the State College campus." These had probably wandered from the mountains. The available records thus raise considerable doubt concerning Mr. Griscom's main contention, but the evidence is admittedly far from conclusive.

Migration—Outside the putative breeding range above outlined, the Red Crossbill is only an irregular winter visitor, uncertain and sporadic in its appearance and in the length of its stay. There are a few odd records for Washington, Allegheny, Beaver, Butler, Mercer, Crawford, and Erie counties, and one for Huntingdon County. Although the species presumably breeds in Warren County, it is much more numerous there, according to Mr. Simpson, as a winter visitant. He writes that during the winter of 1887–88 it "fairly swarmed" and that on one occasion he saw as many as five hundred birds together. (These must have belonged to the western race, *minor*.) Again in the winters of 1904–5 and 1906–7 there were large flights. On February 3, 1932, he saw a flock of about fifty, the first in several years. The last large flight to reach the western tier of counties occurred during the winter of 1922–23, when the Red Crossbill (the race *minor*) appeared with the White-winged Crossbill, but in much smaller numbers. At Wildwood, Allegheny County, both species remained until March 3. F. A. Hegner (1932) reports a flock of about a dozen birds at Sewickley Heights, Allegheny County, on April 3, 1932. In the fall, the Red Crossbill has been observed as early as October 25 (1919) at Brentwood, Allegheny County (Miller, 1920).

Habits—So largely does the Crossbill depend for its living on coniferous trees that its range and movements are conditioned thereby. Feeding mainly on their seeds and well fitted to withstand low temperatures, it is ordinarily able to pass the winter in the north country. But should there be a shortage or failure of the cone crop, as happens at intervals (for reasons not well understood), the birds must either migrate or perish. In the North they live largely on the seeds of the two species of spruce found there; in our latitude it is the hemlock cones upon which they depend, although those of the pine are not disregarded. The several invasions on record have always been in seasons when our hemlock trees were prolific. Certain other birds are likewise fond of the seeds of this conifer, but the Crossbill is more adept at securing them, as its bill is especially modified for this very purpose. The crossed mandibles, according to O. W. Knight, are used in feeding "with a quick prying twisting motion" to separate the scales of the cones and extract the seeds, which are then shelled to expose the edible kernels. A flock busily engaged in feeding is usually very quiet, and only an occasional musical chirp or a few falling cones or seed scales betray its presence. In attempting to reach the cones, the birds may assume every imaginable pose and often hang head-downward, parrot-like, to accomplish this end.

Except in the breeding season, the Crossbill travels in flocks, sometimes of large size but always more or less straggling in character. Restless but unafraid, it may often be closely approached. It is not absolutely confined to coniferous growths. Mr. Miller (1920) tells of a flock that once came to his garden to feed on sunflower seeds. Late in November, 1900, I found the species fairly common near Round Island, Clinton County, in second-growth woodland. The birds frequented an old camp, and there they descended from the treetops to alight on the ground, evidently in search of small scraps or salty fragments. Mr. Simpson writes of finding a large flock working on the ground in the snow.

The ordinary note of the Crossbill is a characteristic staccato *tic-tic-tic,* uttered mostly during flight. In the spring the male has a very beautiful song, which G. M. Sutton heard on one occasion (March 20, 1921) at Mill Creek, Huntingdon County, and thus describes: "The wonderful song was unusually long and much varied. It suggested that of the Purple Finch in a measure, but was of a much finer quality and was less reckless in range. At intervals there would be a long trill—very much like a canary's—given on one note and followed by a series of almost foreign-sounding whistles. Altogether it was one of the most beautiful songs I have ever heard."

Loxia curvirostra minor Warren, *Birds Pa.,* 1888, 241 (Warren Co., winter); ed. 2, 1890, 228 (Clinton, Clearfield, and Cameron Co., breeding)—Rhoads, *Auk,* 1899, 16:312 ([Round Island], Clinton Co., breeding; Allegheny Co., *fide* Atkinson)—Surface, in *Ninth Ann. Report Pa. Dept. Agric., for 1903,* 1904, 178, 232 (State College, Centre Co., summer)—Harlow, *Auk,* 1918, 35:137 ([Shingletown Gap], Centre Co., March)—Burleigh, *Wilson Bull.,* 1924, 36:128 ("State College" [Shingletown Gap], Centre Co., March).

"Crossbill" Simpson, *Oölogist,* 1906, 23:135 (Warren, Warren Co., summer); 1912, 29:329 (head of Tionesta Creek, Warren Co., summer), 370; 1921, 38:135 (Warren, Warren Co., winter)—McClelland, *Am. Mid. Nat.,* 1922, 8:37 (Washington, Washington Co., one record)—Christy, *Bull. Audubon Soc. W. Pa.,* 1923, 1:10 (Wildwood, Allegheny Co., etc., habits).

"American Crossbill" Simpson, *Oölogist,* 1909, 26:26; 1910, 27:100; and 1914, 31:53 (Warren, Warren Co., winter)—Arthur, *Country Rambler,* 1934, 37 ("Crouse's Run" [Wildwood], Allegheny Co., February; habits).

"Red Crossbill" Miller, *Bird-Lore,* 1920, 22:97 (Brentwood, Allegheny Co., October)—Sutton, *Bird-Lore,* 1923, 25:132, 194 (Wildwood, Allegheny Co., February–March; "Sewickley" [Frankfort Springs, Beaver Co.], *fide* Christy; Raccoon Creek, Beaver Co., *fide* Boulton).

Loxia curvirostra pusilla Sutton, *Ann. Carnegie Mus.,* 1928, 18:172 (Hartstown, Crawford Co., winter)—Hegner, *Cardinal,* 1932, 3:95 (Sewickley Heights, Allegheny Co., April).

Loxia curvirostra neogæa Griscom, *Proc. Boston Soc. Nat. Hist.,* 1937, 41:166 (Renovo, Clinton Co.; Erie Co.).

WHITE-WINGED CROSSBILL

LOXIA LEUCOPTERA Gmelin

Description—A bird resembling the American Red Crossbill, except that the male is pinkish red rather than deep dull red; the general plumage has a streaked effect; and the *wings have two white bands.*

Range—This is in general a more northern species than the Red Crossbill. Its breeding range comprises the coniferous forest belt of Canada and extends also into northern Maine; there are outlying colonies in the Adirondack and White Mountains. This crossbill does not range so far south in winter as the other, and its visits are more irregular and infrequent. The first invasion traceable in our region was in the winter of 1874–75, as indicated by specimens taken at Erie by Sennett. In the winter of 1904–5, according to R. B. Simpson, a very few birds of this species appeared at Warren with the Red Crossbill. But in the winter of 1906–7 there was a large and extensive flight involving both species, as well as the Pine Grosbeak. This flight was general over the northeastern United States. My first observation of it was at Ekastown, Butler County, when on December 23, 1906, I saw a flock of a dozen birds in some Norway spruces in a farmyard; again, on February 22, 1907, I encountered a small flock in the hemlocks along Four-mile Run, three miles below Beaver, in Beaver County. It was a surprise to meet with a similar small flock at the same place just two years later—on February 22, 1909. In 1916 three birds were noted on this same date at Reitz Gap, Centre County, by T. D. Burleigh; this was the only local record made during that year. In the early months of 1920, however, this crossbill was reported from Springs, Somerset County (where it had been first noted in 1907 by A. B. Miller), and from Waynesburg and Swarts, Greene County (Dickey). The next large flight, comparable to that of 1906–7, occurred in the early months of 1923 and brought the birds in great numbers to Allegheny County, where they were studied by several observers. They were also found during this same season at Pymatuning Swamp (Sutton, *fide* Hunter and others); at Lakemont, Blair County (McGraw); at Endeavor, Forest County (Dickey); and at Warren (a few only—Simpson). There is a 1933 record for Presque Isle (Beal and Peterson, 1934).

Migration—The movements of this species are so erratic and irregular that they scarcely merit the name of migrations. Mr. Simpson says that during the 1906–7 flight, the first white-wings appeared at Warren late in October, and by the middle of November the birds were abundant. In other years and places, they were not actually noticed until December. March usually finds them moving northward. In 1907, all had left Warren by the middle of that month; but Mr. Miller saw one at Springs that season as late as April 9. They remained at Erie in 1875 at least until March 22, and at Warren in 1923 until March 11; but the flocks at Wildwood, Allegheny County, disappeared on March 3.

Habits—A truly boreal species, fitted to withstand the severe cold of the northern latitudes, the White-winged Crossbill does not ordinarily need to come as far south as Pennsylvania for the winter. Why, then, should it appear at intervals in such numbers? Its sporadic incursions must be due to the occasional failure of its food supply in the north country. It depends largely on the seeds of conifers for food, and for some reason not well understood, the spruce and fir trees in the North at times fail to bear cones. Then the birds are forced southward to seek a substitute—which is provided by the cones of the hemlock. During their stay in our region, they frequent groves of this tree and wander about in flocks, which scatter out and recombine in divers permutations. More than one observer has seen flocks estimated to contain three hundred birds, but smaller groups are the rule. While feeding, the birds clamber about in the treetops or on the ends of the branches, assuming almost every conceivable position in their efforts to get at the cones and dislodge the seeds. Their actions at such times are parrot-like, as they often pose upside down at the end of a branch in order to reach some particular cone. The snow beneath these trees is always well littered with cones and scales. In March the crossbills may be observed hopping about on bare places on the ground. Their call is soft and musical, and their erratic and undulating flight resembles that of the American Goldfinch. Usually they are quite tame and easy to approach; Mr. Miller writes that he repeatedly picked them up and that they would eat suet while sitting on his hand.

G. M. Sutton's impressions of this species at Wildwood in 1923, as recorded in his field notes, are interesting: "January 20—a flock of White-winged Crossbills was seen at Wildwood, and a male and a young female were shot from a flock of about seven birds that were feeding on the lower outer branches of a hemlock. They also drank from the stream. When feeding unmolested, they were nearly silent, but they broke out into chirping before flying away. Later a flock of six was seen (possibly the same birds), and still later, a flock of perhaps twenty-five or thirty was noted.

"January 27—Messrs. Homer, Emerson, Lithgow, and I went to Wildwood to look for crossbills —and we were not disappointed! We started at about 10:30 A.M. and got back at 3 P.M. At Hart's Run a rather small flock of White-wings (presumably) was seen and heard. Homer and Emerson got a good look at them as they alighted in a tree near at hand. I heard them passing over but scarcely had any view of them at all. They swung about erratically through the air, apparently without any particular object or destination in view. In the deep valley at Wildwood we encountered scores of the birds (possibly three hundred or more) flying from tree to tree and busily engaged in feeding. Masses of them would leave one feeding ground for another and progress in a constant stream along the steep, hemlock-covered slope. They were not particularly wild, nor were they (as literature had led me to believe) especially tame. While the birds were feeding, there was a constant chattering going on; the notes were either double- or triple-syllabled and very sweet and musical, although not clear. Now and then could be heard a louder, somewhat clearer note, seeming to come from another species of bird; but the chances are that it was another note of one of the crossbills. The birds stayed entirely on the outer branches where the cones grew, and crawled about with occasional flutterings like scores of tiny parrots. Rarely would two of them come close together, but the whole flock might alight on a tree, fairly covering it for a time. In their actions, the two species (the Red and the White-winged) seemed to be alike. The crops of the specimens shot were filled with vegetable matter (presumably hemlock seeds)."

Loxia leucoptera Todd, *Ann. Carnegie Mus.*, 1904, 2:569 (Erie and Presque Isle, Erie Co., winter)—Burleigh, *Wilson Bull.*, 1924, 36:128 ([Reitz Gap, near] State College, Centre Co., February)—Sutton, *Ann. Carnegie Mus.*, 1928, 18:173 (Pymatuning Swamp, Crawford Co., winter, *fide* Hunter).

"White-winged Crossbill" Simpson, *Oölogist*, 1907, 24:86; and 1914, 31:53 (Warren, Warren Co., winter)—[Christy, ed.], *Cardinal*, 1923, v. 1, no. 2, [p. 10] (Wildwood and Sewickley, Allegheny Co., and Frankfort Springs, Beaver Co., winter)—Christy, *Bull. Audubon Soc. W. Pa.*, 1923, 1:10 (Wildwood and Sewickley, Allegheny Co.; Frankfort Springs, Beaver, and Raccoon Creek, Beaver Co., winter)—Sutton, *Bird-Lore*, 1923, 25:132 (Wildwood, Allegheny Co., winter; Sewickley, Allegheny Co., *fide* Christy; Raccoon Creek, Beaver Co., *fide* Boulton), 194 (Wildwood, Allegheny Co., winter)—Beal and Peterson, *Bird-Lore*, 1934, 36:33 (Presque Isle, Erie Co., December)—Arthur, *Country Rambler*, 1934, 37 ("Crouse's Run" [Wildwood], Allegheny Co., February; habits).

RED-EYED TOWHEE

PIPILO ERYTHROPHTHALMUS ERYTHROPHTHALMUS (Linnaeus)

Description—A bird of about the same size and proportions as the Cardinal, but with a much smaller bill. *Male:* throat, breast, and upperparts in general, black; a white spot and white edgings on the wings; *large white areas on the outer tail feathers*, showing conspicuously in flight; underparts white (in the middle) from the breast down, the sides and flanks bright rufous; iris red; bill dark. *Female:* similar to the male in color pattern, except that the black is replaced by rich brown. *Young in juvenal plumage:* upperparts brown; underparts buffy; dusky streaks throughout; wings and tail brown, the white areas more restricted.

Range—*Pipilo erythrophthalmus* is a distinctively eastern species and ranges only to the edge of the Great Plains; beyond that limit it is replaced by *P. maculatus*. Faunally considered, it shows decidedly austral predilections and does not invade the Canadian Life Zone to any great extent. In New York, according to E. H. Eaton, it avoids the Adirondack and Catskill Mountains, except along the river valleys and about settlements. There is reason to believe that its original range in western Pennsylvania was restricted to the lower country and that its advent in the highlands has been comparatively recent and occasioned by deforestation. If we bear in mind the type of habitat preferred by this species, it becomes obvious that since primeval times there has been a tremendous increase in the area suited to its needs, and that the increase in its numbers is a natural consequence thereof. At the present time, the Towhee ranges commonly and indiscriminately throughout our region, in the highlands and lowlands alike, and is one of our best-known summer residents.

In recent years a few towhees have shown a tendency to remain throughout the winter in favorable places, but whether these hardy birds are migrants from farther north or are locally reared is not known. The increasing mildness of our winters may be a contributing factor in this development, although even in the unusually severe season of 1935–36, reports of wintering towhees were received. J. W. Jacobs writes that in Greene County the species winters regularly in small numbers; and there are numerous winter records (listed in the references below) for Allegheny County. In Beaver County, D. E. Sollberger found a group of about fifty birds along the Raccoon Creek hillside near "Patton's Point" in January, 1934; and H. H. Elliott encountered smaller groups during five different seasons on his "Christmas Census" trips at a point a little below the mouth of the same stream. It was my privilege to be with Mr. Elliott on December 26, 1931; on this occasion we found about a dozen towhees, associated with cardinals and song sparrows. They were inhabiting a dense thicket of blackberry briers and wild-rose bushes, intergrown with tall weeds and tangled vines. It was an ideal shelter, with plenty of food at hand. The Towhee has been found in winter as far north as Crawford and Clarion counties (Sutton, 1928), and on one occasion (January 1, 1906) was identified in Warren County (Simpson); but the Ohio Valley constitutes the usual limit of its occurrence at that season.

Migration—The bulk of our summer-resident Towhee population winters in the southern states. March finds the birds on their northward way, and one learns to expect them in their old haunts shortly after the snow has disappeared. This statement holds true at any rate for the Ohio Valley. At Beaver I look for the Towhee any time from the middle to the end of March; March 13 (1908) is my earliest date, and it is also B. H. Christy's earliest for Sewickley (1921). March 23 is the average time of arrival at Greenville (Seiple). The species has been observed at Erie as early as March 10 (1894—Bacon) and at Cambridge Springs, Crawford County, on March 4 (1925—Dickey); but these dates are exceptional. A definite and marked retardation of the northward movement in the mountains becomes evident when arrival dates at Renovo, for example, are compared with those from the Ohio Valley. April 5 and April 23 are respectively the earliest and average dates for the former locality, according to the records of A. K. Pierce, which cover seventeen years. At Springs, Somerset County, close to our southern border and near the crest of the Alleghenies, April 10 is the average date of arrival, and March 20 and April 25 are the extremes (Miller). At Warren, on the western edge of the plateau region, the Towhee seldom appears until sometime in April, and the earliest date reported by R. B. Simpson for that locality is March 26 (1904). In the ridge and valley section the species was noted at Hollidaysburg on April 2, 1923 (Berg), and at State College on April 11, 1919 (Burleigh).

Not until October is there any perceptible diminution in the numbers of the Towhee. The majority of the birds leave around October 20, but laggards may remain until the end of that month or even into November. Some "last-seen" dates are as follows: Beaver, November 16, 1901 (Wickham); Sewickley, November 10, 1901 (Christy); Wilkinsburg, November 4, 1896 (Atkinson); State College, November 14, 1915 (Burleigh); Renovo, November 12, 1904 (Pierce); Altoona (five miles southwest), December 12, 1926 (McGraw). This last record may have pertained to a wintering bird.

Habits[1]—No furtive denizen of the forest, but an inhabitant of thickets and of open roadside woodlands, the energetic Towhee soon makes its presence known to the wanderer in its chosen haunts. Perhaps from the undergrowth along a path, you will hear a vigorous scratching or scuffling in the dry leaves. If you remain quiet and peer intently into the tangled growth, you will discover a small bird kicking the leaves aside in short, backward jumps as it searches for grubs and dormant insects. The long tail is jauntily elevated, and its flashy white spots advertise its owner's progress. If you betray your presence, the restless activity ceases and the towhee flies to a low limb to investigate. His annoyance is registered in an inquiring *che-wink, t'whee* as he moves about nervously and turns his ruby eye in the direction of the disturbance. His curiosity is great, and if perchance you have invaded a nesting territory, his mate will join him in scolding you.

The female Towhee is more retiring than the male; she seldom leaves the shelter of her thicket home and never aspires to the heights attained by the male as he delivers his spring song. On a bright morning in May, from the top of the tallest tree, as close to the sun as he can get, he pours out his characteristic song: *sweet' tow-hee-e-e-e; drink' your tea-e-e-e; chip'-per-chee-e-e-e; sweet' bird s-i-n-n-g.* Whatever transliteration you prefer,

[1]Account contributed by Ruth Trimble.

the character of the song is unmistakable: two sharp, clear notes, followed by a trill. This song has always seemed to me a little "tinny" in quality but pleasant because of its earnestness and exuberance. Sometimes, however, the Towhee achieves a mellifluous quality in a song that is clear, resonant, and almost thrushlike in tone.

In western Pennsylvania the towhees arrive early in the spring; some venturesome individuals,

indeed, may occasionally spend the winter here. The summer population usually moves in late in March, the males arriving first. When the females appear, the wooing begins with a lively chase through the thickets. The white-marked wings and tails flash impressively as they are rapidly spread and folded in the courtship display. First nests are ready in May as a rule, although eggs have been found as early as April 26 (Atkinson) and April 30 (Wickham); the average set consists of four, but three and five are not unusual. The Towhee rears two broods in a season. It builds the nest for the first brood on the ground, under the shelter of a small bush, stump, or bunch of weeds. The nest for the second family is generally placed from one to five feet above the ground in a low bush. The reason for this variation cannot easily be explained. It may be that in early spring a ground nest affords better concealment and that later in the season the thick, leafy vegetation provides the necessary security. The nest is a rather bulky affair, composed of dried leaves, weed stems, and strips of bark, and lined with fine grass, rootlets, or hair. Nests found in late June or in July and August are undoubtedly for second broods. Exceptionally late nesting dates are July 31 (Burleigh) and August 4 (Atkinson). The eggs are white, finely dotted all over with reddish brown; they measure .96 by .71 inches. The responsibility of incubation falls largely upon the female, but the male is said to assist; both are vigorous defenders when their domain is invaded. The young Towhee is an awkward, ungainly creature. Its streaked plumage is so unlike that of its parents that it almost seems an overgrown changeling as it teeters precariously on a low bush and calls insistently for food and attention. The young are fed chiefly on insects of various kinds—beetles, caterpillars, grasshoppers, or spiders. Although the adults feed partly on insects, their main diet consists of weed seeds, wild fruits, and berries.

The rich black-and-chestnut color of the male, together with a fancied resemblance to the Robin, has earned for the Towhee the name "Ground Robin." The species is not usually found around dwellings, unless the gardens are spacious enough to support some dense undergrowth to ensure a safe retreat. In the open woodland, in every thicket, on every shrubby slope, in wooded parks, and sometimes even in fields overgrown with weeds, we may expect to find the Towhee; and its restless, noisy activity suggests an animal a dozen times its size. It seeks the hills and the lowlands impartially, and it has the distinction of being the only bird that we observed on the very top of Negro Mountain (the highest point in the state) during a June visit to that place. Ubiquitous, bold, and conspicuous, the Towhee is one of the easiest species for the novice to identify.

Pipilo erythrophthalmus TOWNSEND, *Proc. Acad. Nat. Sci. Philadelphia*, 1883, 63 (Latrobe, Westmoreland Co.)—TEULON, *Jour. Boston Zoöl. Soc.*, 1883, 2:9 (Bradford, McKean Co.)—JAMISON, *Ornithologist and Oölogist*, 1888, 13:133, 134; and DWIGHT, *Auk*, 1892, 9:138 (Cresson, Cambria Co., June)—TODD, *Auk*, 1893, 10:40 (Two Lick, Indiana Co., June), 45 (Coalport, Clearfield Co., June)—JACOBS, *Summer Birds Greene Co., Pa.*, 1893, 11 (Greene Co., nesting)—BAILY, *Auk*, 1896, 13:291, 294 (Williamsville, Elk Co., June–July)—JACOBS, *Gleanings from Nature*, 1898, 1:30 (Greene Co., nesting)—COPE, *Cassinia*, 1902, 5:17 (between Cross Fork and Tamarack Swamp, Clinton Co., June)—TODD, *Ann. Carnegie Mus.*, 1904, 2:575 (Erie and Presque Isle, Erie Co., summer)—TODD, in Bausman, *Hist. Beaver Co., Pa.*, 1904, 2:1200 (Beaver Co., summer)—KEIM, *Cassinia*, 1905, 8:39 (Port Allegany, McKean Co., summer).

"Towhee Bunting" ENTY, *Ornithologist and Oölogist*, 1885, 10:78 (Templeton, Armstrong Co., April).

"Chewink" TODD, *Oölogist*, 1887, 4:89 (Beaver, Beaver Co, nesting)—JACOBS, *Hawkeye Ornithologist and Oölogist*, 1888, 1:88 (Waynesburg, Greene Co., April)—BOULTON, *Oölogist*,

1922, 39:71 (near Beaver, Beaver Co., nesting)—STREET, *Cassinia*, 1923, 24:15 (Greencastle to Ft. Loudon, and Jordan's Knob, Franklin Co., June).

"Towhee" STONE, *Cassinia*, 1906, 9:44 (Scrub Ridge, west of McConnellsburg, Fulton Co., June)—PITCAIRN, *Bird-Lore*, 1907, 9:155 (Riverview Park, Allegheny Co., breeding)—BURLEIGH, *Oölogist*, 1911, 28:168 (Chestnut Ridge, near Uniontown, Fayette Co., nesting)—COOKE, *Bird-Lore*, 1912, 14:287 (Beaver, Beaver Co., and Renovo, Clinton Co., migration)—BURLEIGH, *Oölogist*, 1913, 30:281 ([Guyasuta], Allegheny Co., winter)—HARLOW, *Oölogist*, 1914, 31:86 (Oil City, Venango Co., nesting)—BURLEIGH, *Bird-Lore*, 1915, 17:34 ([Guyasuta], Allegheny Co., December)—SAVAGE and MCCONNELL, *Bird-Lore*, 1918, 20:37 (McKeesport, Allegheny Co., December)—MCCONNELL, *Oölogist*, 1918, 35:151 ("Christy Park," Allegheny Co., breeding)—MCCLELLAND, *Am. Mid. Nat.*, 1922, 8:36 (Washington, Washington Co., summer)—MCCONNELL, *et al.*, *Bird-Lore*, 1922, 24:22 (Emsworth, Allegheny Co., December)—SUTTON, *Bird-Lore*, 1923, 25:132 (Aspinwall, Allegheny Co., December), 194 (Clinton Pond, Allegheny Co., March, *fide* Christy); 1924, 26:56 (Wildwood, Allegheny Co., November), 122 (Sharpsburg, Allegheny Co., February, *fide* Gnann)—CHRISTY, *Cardinal*, 1924, v. 1, no. 4, p. 10 (Big Traverse Valley, Beaver Co., June)—EASTWOOD, *Bird-Lore*, 1925, 27:337 (Bradford Woods, Allegheny Co., August, *fide* Frederick; and "Slack Hollow," Allegheny Co., July, *fide* Grimm); 1926, 28:207 (Pittsburgh region, Allegheny Co., March, *fide* Grimm), 273 (Rector, Westmoreland Co., May, *fide* Knauz); 1927, 29:126 (Thompsonville, Washington Co.; Industry, Beaver Co.; and Tom's Run, Allegheny Co., December; Bradford Woods, Allegheny Co., January), 197 (Springs, Somerset Co., March, *fide* Miller)—MILLER, *Bird-Lore*, 1925, 27:400 (Springs, Somerset Co., nesting)—ELLAIR, *et al.*, *Bird-Lore*, 1927, 29: 29 (Thompsonville and vicinity, Washington Co., December)—BOULTON, *Bird-Lore*, 1928, 30:127 (Oakdale and Millvale, Allegheny Co., winter, *fide* Portman and Auerswald)—CHRISTY and HEGNER, *Bird-Lore*, 1929, 31:38 (["Patton's Point"], Beaver Co., December)—MALLEY, *Bird-Lore*, 1932, 34:46 (near Pittsburgh, Allegheny Co., December)—ELLIOTT, *Cardinal*, 1934, 3:170 (Raccoon Creek, Beaver Co., December)—MALLEY, *Oölogist*, 1938, 55:43 (Frick Park, Allegheny Co., song)—STERE, *et al.*, *Bird-Lore*, 1940, 42:85 (Deer Creek region, Allegheny Co., December).

Pipilo erythrophthalmus erythrophthalmus HARLOW, *Auk*, 1912, 29:474 (southern Centre Co., nesting)—CHRISTY, *Cardinal*, 1923, v. 1, no. 1, [p. 10] (Sewickley, Allegheny Co., breeding, occasional in winter)—BURLEIGH, *Wilson Bull.*, 1923, 35:95 (Allegheny Co., nesting); 1924, 36:72; and 1931, 43:49 (State College and vicinity, Centre Co., migration; nesting)—CHRISTY and SUTTON, *Cardinal*, 1928, 2:72 and 75 (Cook Forest, Clarion Co., summer and January)—SUTTON, *Ann. Carnegie Mus.*, 1928, 18:189 (Crawford Co. localities, summer; occasional in winter)—BURLEIGH, *Cardinal*, 1932, 3:82 ([Summit], Fayette Co., nesting).

"Red-eyed Towhee" COPE and HAWKINS, *Forest Leaves*, 1934, 24:26 (E. Tionesta Forest Reserve, Warren and McKean Co., summer).

LARK BUNTING

CALAMOSPIZA MELANOCORYS Stejneger

Description—A fairly large sparrow, with a rather stout bill. *Male:* black, with a *large white spot on the wing;* tail feathers tipped with white. *Female* very different: sandy brown above and whitish below, with dusky streaks throughout; wings showing a large buffy-white spot on the coverts; tail tipped with white.

Range and local status—The Lark Bunting is characteristic of the central plains region; normally it does not range even as far east as the Mississippi River, but in migration it may accidentally reach the Atlantic coast. The credit for adding the bird to the Pennsylvania list belongs to F. L. Homer. He writes: "On June 9, 1896, I saw a male lark bunting along the road between 'Fruits Mill' and Clarksville [now Clarksboro], Mercer County. When first noticed it was in the roadway with other sparrows (chiefly Vesper). It flew up on the fence and then, as I approached, dropped down into the cornfield just beyond. It was very tame and allowed me to drive up almost opposite it. While perched on the fence it sang a song of five syllables, the first two of which were delivered slowly and the rest more rapidly. This song reminded me of that of the Vesper Sparrow but was shorter, softer, and not so silvery." This circumstantial account of an unmistakable species leaves little to be desired, and the record is therefore entirely credible.

EASTERN SAVANNAH SPARROW (Plate 21)

PASSERCULUS SANDWICHENSIS SAVANNA (Wilson)[1]

Description—A small, dull-colored, short-tailed, streaked sparrow, with yellowish superciliaries and without definite markings on the wings and tail. Upperparts dull grayish brown, with dusky streaks; underparts white, the breast, sides, and flanks showing dusky streaks, the throat faintly or not at all streaked, and the abdomen (medially) and under tail coverts immaculate. A dark stripe on either side of the head, and a paler one between; a *pale yellow stripe over the eye;* on either side of the throat a broken dark stripe, which does not quite reach the base of the bill. The streaked underparts, in conjunction with the yellowish superciliaries and plain tail, are always diagnostic. In fall plumage the colors are blended, and the underparts are suffused with buff. *Young birds* resemble the adults.

Range—In one form or another the Savannah Sparrow inhabits an immense area of country; its summer range extends from a little beyond the limit of trees southward through the northern United States (and farther south in the mountains of the West). In winter the species migrates to Mexico and the Gulf coast. The eastern race is a common summer resident in New England and in New York, except on Long Island. In New Jersey and southeastern Pennsylvania, it is a common transient. In western Pennsylvania, however, the Savannah Sparrow is only locally common as a summer resident, and outside its breeding range is unaccountably rare. Not until May, 1908, did I succeed in finding it in Beaver County, and I have but one later record, also made during the spring migration. B. H. Christy has encountered it twice near Clinton, Allegheny County—once in the spring and once in the fall; there is an April specimen from Wilkinsburg, in the same county, in the Carnegie Museum collection; and there are two sight records from Frick Park, Pittsburgh (Malley). These are the only available records from the upper Ohio Valley, but since the species is now known to breed just across the state line in Columbiana County, Ohio, and near Wheeling, West Virginia, the discovery of its breeding in this region may also be expected.

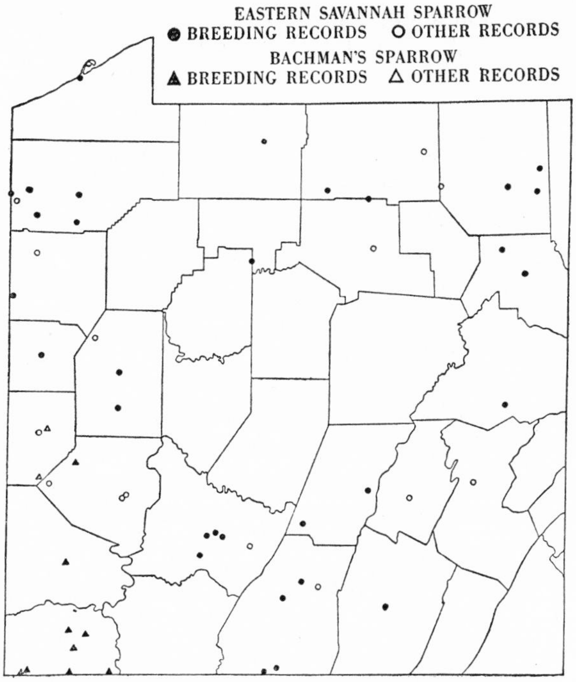

EASTERN SAVANNAH SPARROW
● BREEDING RECORDS ○ OTHER RECORDS
BACHMAN'S SPARROW
▲ BREEDING RECORDS △ OTHER RECORDS

LOCAL RANGES OF THE SAVANNAH SPARROW AND OF BACHMAN'S SPARROW

Crawford County, with its extensive acreage of marshland and flat country, is the metropolis, so to speak, for this sparrow in western Pennsylvania. There it is justly rated as a "fairly common and regular transient visitant and summer resident" (Sutton, 1928), as had been anticipated by Sennett, whom Warren quotes to the same effect. Very likely its status in Erie County is similar, although precise breeding records are scarce, as they are also in Mercer County. E. C. Raney, however, writes that the species is an uncommon summer resident near New Castle; and H. H. Elliott assigns it a similar status near Jamisonville, in central Butler County. Mr. Christy has also observed it in June at a point about six miles south of Butler. Farther south, we do not find it breeding until we reach certain flat, open areas just west of Chestnut Ridge in Westmoreland County; there it breeds in the same type of country as that favored by the Upland Plover. These various records define the western limit of the

[1]In a recent article, J. W. Aldrich restricts *savanna* to the breeding bird of Nova Scotia and sets up a new name, *mediogriseus*, for the Savannah Sparrow of the interior. (See *Ohio Journal of Science*, 1940, 40:4.)

known breeding range in our region. The Savannah Sparrow breeds locally throughout the highlands, as far east as Potter County (and beyond) and as far south as the Maryland boundary (Springs, Somerset County—Miller), and thence to West Virginia. Deforestation and cultivation have of course been the factors governing its appearance in this general region. It is a species that quickly takes advantage of changed conditions. In June, 1899, I found a pair established in a little clearing at Cherry Spring, Potter County, with forest on all sides. Apparently this sparrow breeds at suitable places throughout our ridge and valley section also, although only two records are available—one from State College (Harlow), and one from Bedford Springs (Rhoads). It is an Alleghanian species that seems to be pushing southward and that has already reached not only the highlands of West Virginia, but also the lower country in the Panhandle, and many counties in Ohio.[1]

Migration—Only a few migration records are available. The species has been reported in the spring from Huntingdon on March 19, 1921 (Sutton); from State College on March 25, 1916, March 27, 1917, and March 26, 1919 (Burleigh); from Linesville, Crawford County, on March 30, 1926 (Sutton); from Indiana on April 3, 1933 (Smyth); from Erie on April 6, 1934 (Guynes); and from Warren on April 5, 1928 (Granquist). The northward migratory movement continues until the first week in May (Beaver—May 5, 1908, and May 2, 1933). That the fall movement takes place in September is indicated by the records for Presque Isle of 1900. The latest fall date comes from State College: October 16 (1915—Burleigh).

Habits—The Savannah Sparrow, as its name implies, is a bird of the open country. Under primitive conditions in Pennsylvania, it must have been restricted to the rank growth of grasses fringing the marshes and perhaps also to the growth along the shores of lakes and ponds. These sites are still favorite resorts, especially during the season of migration, when wet, boggy meadows also offer peculiar attractions. While the Savannah Sparrow is thus partial to the vicinity of water, it is by no means averse to drier ground, and in the summer may often be found in upland fields and meadows. As it hops along the ground in search of food, it is rendered inconspicuous by its plain coloration, in exact harmony with its surroundings; when forced to fly, it does so in a weak, vacillating manner, as though making an effort. Its ordinary call note is a low *'tsip*. In the breeding season the male sings from a fence post, a tall weed, or even a hillock on the ground. Its song is a feeble refrain with a certain insect-like quality; it is introduced by three or four single *'tsips*, followed by a trill and then by a slurred *r* note that has a strong falling inflection and ceases abruptly. The song is so low that it cannot be heard more than a few rods away.

Savannah sparrows are very numerous in the neighborhood of Pymatuning Lake and Swamp, not only in the wet meadows, but also in the dry uplands. The birds lie very closely and will not flush until almost underfoot; they then fly in erratic fashion, to realight and run rapidly away, mouselike, through the grass. Sooner or later in that vicinity, one is bound to flush a bird from its nest; at least this was the experience of our party from the Carnegie Museum in 1934 and 1935. One nest that we found was in a tussock of marsh grass growing in the water; the others were all on drier ground. All were well concealed by overhanging vegetation. They were simply made, and consisted of dry weed stalks and grasses, with finer material in the lining. The eggs are four or five in number and vary so much in shade and in markings that no general description will answer. A pale greenish-blue ground-color is frequent, but some eggs are dull whitish. The markings range from fine dots to heavy blotches of various shades of brown, densely or sparsely distributed over the surface, but as a rule more heavily massed around the larger end. Average measurements are .78 by .56 inches. May 15 is about the time for full sets, although R. C. Harlow once found an incubated set at State College as late as July 11.

G. M. Sutton discovered young birds in fresh feather in August along the borders of Pymatuning Swamp, while the adults remained apart from the young in the upper fields, awaiting the completion of the molt.

Ammodramus sandwichensis savanna WARREN, *Birds Pa.*, 1888, 241 (Crawford Co., breeding, *fide* Sennett); ed. 2, 1890, 234 (Crawford and Erie Co., breeding, *fide* Sennett; Clinton Co., *fide* Van Fleet)—DWIGHT, *Auk*, 1892, 9:133, 137 (Cresson,

[1]Compare L. W. CAMPBELL, *Wilson Bulletin*, 1928, 40:223; L. E. HICKS, *Ohio State University Studies*, 1935, 40:177; and T. E. SHIELDS, *Wilson Bulletin*, 1935, 47:35.

Cambria Co., June)—BAILY, *Auk*, 1896, 13:294 (Williamsville, Elk Co., June–July)—RHOADS, *Auk*, 1899, 16:312 (Bedford Springs, Bedford Co., June)—COPE, *Cassinia*, 1902, 5:16 (Tamarack Swamp, Clinton Co., June; Germania and Galeton, Potter Co., June).

Passerculus sandwichensis savanna TODD, *Ann. Carnegie Mus.*, 1904, 2:571 (Erie and Presque Isle, Erie Co., summer?)—HARLOW, *Auk*, 1918, 35:138 (State College, Centre Co., and Warren, Warren Co., nesting)—BURLEIGH, *Wilson Bull.*, 1924, 36:72; 1931, 43:48 (State College, Centre Co., migration; nesting)—CHRISTY, *Cardinal*, 1926, v. 1, no. 7, p. 25 (Clinton, Allegheny Co., September)—CHRISTY and SUTTON, *Cardinal*, 1928, 2:72 (3 miles north of Cooksburg, Forest Co., June)—SUTTON, *Ann. Carnegie Mus.*, 1928, 28:177 (Crawford Co. localities, summer)—[LIVINGSTON, ed.], *Cassinia*, 1929, 27:28 (State College, Centre Co., nesting, *fide* Carter)—CHRISTY, *Cardinal*, 1932, 3:70 (Butler [6 miles south], Butler Co., and near Greensburg, Westmoreland Co., breeding).

"Savanna Sparrow" SIMPSON, *Oölogist*, 1906, 23:135; 1909, 26:26 (Warren, Warren Co., nesting)—HARLOW, *Oölogist*, 1912, 29:279 (State College, Centre Co., nesting)—EASTWOOD, *Bird-Lore*, 1927, 29:273 (Springs, Somerset Co., April, *fide* Miller)—BOULTON, *Bird-Lore*, 1928, 30:271 (Youngstown, Westmoreland Co., June)—MCCLINTOCK, *Cardinal*, 1933, 3:125 (Ligonier, Westmoreland Co., April).

EASTERN GRASSHOPPER SPARROW (Plate 21)

AMMODRAMUS SAVANNARUM AUSTRALIS Maynard

Description—A small, plainly colored sparrow, without any very distinctive markings. *Adult:* top of head showing two dark stripes enclosing a paler one; sides of head plain dull buffy brown; back mottled with chestnut and black; wings dull buffy brown with some black spots, the bend yellowish (this color not ordinarily visible in life); tail feathers narrow and pointed, gray and black; underparts dull white, the throat and breast strongly washed with buff. *Juvenal plumage:* in general similar to the adult, but the breast has a broad band of dusky spots, as in Henslow's Sparrow.

Range—*Ammodramus savannarum* is clearly a species of Neotropical origin, since it is represented by resident races in Florida, the West Indies, Central America, and even Colombia. The two northern races, which together occupy the full width of the continent, are migratory. The eastern form ranges northward in summer to New England and southern Ontario and winters in and beyond the southern states. It avoids the mountains in New York and, according to E. H. Eaton, does not ordinarily range above one thousand feet. Its distribution in western Pennsylvania, however, does not wholly fit this pattern, since in Cambria and Somerset counties, on the western flank of the Alleghenies proper, the species regularly occurs above two thousand feet wherever local conditions permit. It is obvious that its advent in that section has followed the clearing and cultivation of the country and has thus been comparatively recent. Undoubtedly the species has greatly increased in numbers during the past century, and it is interesting to find that in extending its range it has invaded territory far beyond its usual altitudinal and faunal limits. It is a common summer resident in the cultivated valleys of the ridge and valley section and in the western counties generally, but I have never detected it in the northern part of the plateau region, where the Savannah Sparrow seems in a measure to take its place. Significantly enough, it is not included in the records of A. K. Pierce from Clinton and McKean counties; and in Warren County, R. B. Simpson has noted it on only three occasions, all of which were in May and June. On the other hand, there are summer records for DuBois (Van Fleet), Clearfield (Dickey), and near Cooksburg, Forest County (Christy and Sutton, 1928).

Migration—At State College the Grasshopper Sparrow is said to be "always plentiful by the middle of April" (Burleigh, 1924); in 1919 it was noted there as early as April 8. Arrival dates from other parts of our region, however, are considerably later. Ten years' records from Beaver lie between April 20 and 30—an unusually short interval—and with these, nearly all the dependable dates from adjacent areas correspond, as do those from Ohio and Indiana, cited by W. W. Cooke.[1] Nevertheless, the species may sometimes come earlier. D. A. Atkinson writes that his arrival records for Wilkinsburg run from April 13 to 19, and B. H. Christy states that in Allegheny County he has seen this bird at Sewickley on April 16 (1921) and at Bakerstown on April 17 (1927). The time of the spring arrival is easy to establish, but

[1] *Bird-Lore*, 1910, 12:13.

the departure in the fall is more difficult to determine. G. M. Sutton recorded the species near Pymatuning Swamp until September 20 in 1925, and in 1898 Dr. Atkinson noted it until September 28 at Wilkinsburg. At State College, T. D. Burleigh observed single birds on October 7, 1915, and October 23, 1916. Since no specimens were collected, it is of course possible that some of these fall records may have been misidentifications. Miss Alice Greves, however, found a dead bird at Greensburg on October 31, 1938; this specimen is now in the Carnegie Museum.

Habits—During the earlier years of my ornithological activity, I was puzzled for a time by a grasshopper-like trilling that kept recurring in the hay meadows and waste fields. Finally I succeeded in dropping the singer with a long shot, and thus verified my suspicion that it was a grasshopper sparrow. The name is most appropriate; for there are few persons who, hearing these thin, buzzing notes for the first time, would suspect that they came from a bird. Through the hot days of summer, continuously at twilight, and at intervals in the night, this listless, monotonous song persists. To some ears it is inaudible unless close at hand, and at best it carries only a few hundred feet. The bird mounts a tall weed or a fence post to deliver its song; otherwise one would scarcely be aware of its presence. Ordinarily it keeps close to the ground among the thick grasses, and when flushed flies only a little way, in feeble, jerky fashion, before again taking cover. The customary song of the male follows the pattern above described, but a different refrain, reserved for special occasions, is longer and more musical and is separated into phrases. Probably this is the mating song.

The nest of this species, like those of most ground-nesting sparrows, is not easy to find. Persistent walking over a likely field, or dragging it with a rope, may result in flushing a sitting bird and thus discovering her nest, but nests are oftener found by accident. According to J. W. Jacobs (1893), "The female is a close sitter, not leaving her post until almost trampled upon." The nest itself is a flimsy structure, composed of dry grasses and weed stalks; it is sunk in the ground and is screened from observation from above by overhanging vegetation. The eggs, four or five in number, are pure white, speckled with reddish brown, which varies in shade from vinaceous cinnamon to burnt sienna. The markings are usually rather sparse, but in occasional sets are fairly heavy. On the whole, the eggs of this sparrow are not unlike those of certain warblers. They tend to be rounded or elliptical ovate in shape, and they measure about .73 by .54 inches. Complete sets have been found in Greene County from May 15 to July 21. These dates indicate an exceptionally long breeding season; unless, indeed, more than one brood is reared. After the males cease singing, the birds are very difficult to find, although they frequent their usual haunts until sometime in September.

Ammodramus savannarum passerinus WARREN, *Birds Pa.*, ed. 2, 1890, 235 (State College, Centre Co., summer; Crawford and Erie Co., summer, *fide* Sennett)—DWIGHT, *Auk*, 1889, 6:198 (Erie, Erie Co., breeding, *fide* Sennett); 1892, 9:137 (Cresson, Cambria Co., June)—TODD, *Auk*, 1893, 10:40 (Two Lick, Indiana Co., June)—JACOBS, *Summer Birds Greene Co., Pa.*, 1893, 10 (Greene Co., nesting)—BAILY, *Auk*, 1896, 13:294 (Williamsville, Elk Co., June–July).

Coturniculus savannarum passerinus TODD, *Ann. Carnegie Mus.*, 1904, 2:571 (Erie and Presque Isle, Erie Co., summer) —TODD, in Bausman, *Hist. Beaver Co., Pa.*, 1904, 2:1200 (Beaver Co., summer)—JACOBS, *Wilson Bull.*, 1905, 12:18 (Waynesburg, Greene Co., nesting).

"Grasshopper Sparrow" STONE, *Cassinia*, 1906, 9:44 (McConnellsburg, Fulton Co., June)—MILLER, *Oölogist*, 1919, 35: 156 (State College, Centre Co., nesting)—MCCLELLAND, *Am. Mid. Nat.*, 1922, 8:37 (Washington, Washington Co., summer)—STREET, *Cassinia*, 1923, 24:15 (Greencastle to Ft. Loudon, Franklin Co., June)—SUTTON, *Bird-Lore*, 1924, 26:337 (Wattsburg, Erie Co., *fide* Allen)—EASTWOOD, *Bird-Lore*, 1925, 27:262 (Pittsburgh region, Allegheny Co., April); 1926, 28:274 (Sandy Lake, Mercer Co., May, *fide* Squier), 343 (Dixmont region, Allegheny Co., July, *fide* Auerswald); 1927, 29:273 (Springs, Somerset Co., April, *fide* Miller).

Ammodramus savannarum australis DICKEY, *Oölogist*, 1913, 30:148 (Waynesburg, Greene Co., nesting)—HARLOW, *Auk*, 1912, 29:474 (southern Centre Co., nesting)—CHRISTY, *Cardinal*, 1923, v. 1, no. 1, [p. 9] (Sewickley, Allegheny Co., summer)—BURLEIGH, *Wilson Bull.*, 1923, 35:93 (Allegheny Co., summer); 1924, 36:72; and 1931, 43:48 (State College, Centre Co., migration, nesting)—CHRISTY and SUTTON, *Cardinal*, 1928, 2:72 (near Cook Forest, Clarion Co., summer)—SUTTON, *Ann. Carnegie Mus.*, 1928, 18:178 (Hartstown and Meadville, Crawford Co., nesting)—BAIRD, *Cardinal*, 1936, 4:73 (Sewickley Tp., Allegheny Co., nesting).

WESTERN HENSLOW'S SPARROW[1] (Plate 21)

PASSERHERBULUS HENSLOWI HENSLOWI (Audubon)

Description—A small sparrow, resembling the Grasshopper Sparrow in size and proportions, and with the tail feathers similarly narrow and pointed. Head and neck with a decided greenish cast; crown showing two dark stripes enclosing a paler one; *back chestnut with black spots;* wings reddish brown; underparts dull whitish, the *breast and sides with heavy black streaks.* (Not to be confused with the young of the Grasshopper Sparrow, which is similarly colored below.)

Range—The extremely local distribution and general inconspicuousness of this sparrow have created the impression that it is rare. It breeds in the Alleghanian and Carolinian faunas from the Great Plains to New England, but its small size, retiring disposition, and the nature of its habitat, combine to shield it from the attention of the uninitiated. Yet in areas where conditions are ideal, it is rather common, and it is by no means hard to discover in the breeding season. It is known as a summer resident from two widely separated areas in our region. The credit for adding this species to the western Pennsylvania list belongs to R. C. Harlow and S. S. Dickey, who found it nesting in a restricted section of extreme northern Huntingdon County in May, 1913. This remained the only local record until 1922, when G. M. Sutton found the bird breeding near Hartstown, Crawford County. Recent field work by parties from the Carnegie Museum has disclosed that Henslow's Sparrow is common not only in the neighborhood of Pymatuning Swamp and Lake, but in the outlying districts as well. B. H. Christy and I found it in early May near the "Jumbo Woods" in Beaver Township, Crawford County, while L. E. Hicks reports three breeding colonies between Albion and Springfield, Erie County. H. M. McQuiston has traced it south to the Big Bend of the Shenango River in Mercer County, and further research will undoubtedly prove that it breeds in suitable situations throughout Erie, Crawford, and Mercer counties. The fact that in Ohio it breeds south to Columbiana County,[2] which adjoins Beaver County on the west, is suggestive.

Migration—T. D. Burleigh recorded this species at Charter Oak, Huntingdon County, on April 28, 1917, and May 4, 1918; and on October 8, 1916, he reported it from Center Furnace, Centre County. These dates probably represent with fair accuracy the limits of its stay in our region. C. S. Beardslee reports one bird seen at Erie (Presque Isle?) on April 29, 1932. Outside its known breeding range, the species has not been observed in our region.

Habits—Like the Short-billed Marsh Wren, which it somewhat resembles in haunts and habits, Henslow's Sparrow is usually found in little scattered colonies. Wet, grassy meadows are its favorite haunts, as well as drier waste fields grown up to weeds and high grasses. So local are its preferences, however, that each colony keeps within certain bounds, although there may be large areas adjacent that to all appearances are just as suitable. These retreats Henslow's Sparrow shares with such other species as the Grasshopper and Savannah sparrows, the Meadowlark, and the Bobolink. The excellent studies made by Mr. Harlow, Dr. Dickey, and Dr. Sutton of the breeding habits of this elusive sparrow leave little to be desired. The last-named observer states (1928) that when the species was first noted at Hartstown "on May 11 the full population seemed to be on hand. The male birds were singing all over the field, in the subdued, mellow light of evening. Quaintly unmusical and abbreviated was the performance. They were extremely tame and often allowed us to approach within ten feet, as they crouched mouselike in the clusters of mustard flowers. Then after summoning sufficient courage they stood erect with tail down, threw back their heads, and with their large, pale-colored bills wide open, gave forth the slight syllables 'Chislick,' as though they were producing fine music.

"When they were closely approached, they seemed nervous, but instead of jerking their tails, or elevating the crest-feathers, as so many species do in expressing excitement, they lowered their heads, leaned toward the ground, and *jerked all*

[1]The writer is still unable to find grounds for the recognition of two races of this species. (Compare *Wilson Bulletin*, 1926, 38:217.)

[2]L. E. Hicks, *Ohio State University Studies*, 1935, 40:177.

over, a movement seemingly governed by the action of the knees and tarsi. They acted as though they wished to forsake their perches, but could not determine whether to drop to the grass, or to fly away. In this respect they were noticeably different from the Grasshopper Sparrows, which always flew away whenever they were even remotely approached. Often the Henslow's Sparrows, upon being too closely pressed, would drop twelve or eighteen inches to the ground, without spreading their wings to break the fall, and scuttle away through the grass.

"The flight of the two species under consideration is quite dissimilar. That of the Henslow's Sparrow is much more erratic and undulating, and the tail and rump twist or twirl in a very peculiar and characteristic way, just a second or two after the bird has flushed or left its perch. This twisting motion seems to be accompanied by a temporary change in the beat of the wings, and gives the impression that the propellent power ceases for an instant, while the bird rearranges its body. The reddish brown color of the tail and back is a good field-mark as the bird flies away, and of course the large bill, the greenish cast of the neck, and the ludicrously short tail are all noticeable. The Grasshopper Sparrow always seems very dusty in comparison.

"The alarm note of the two species, while admittedly similar, is stronger in the case of the Grasshopper Sparrow, and sometimes two-syllabled; the call-note of Henslow's Sparrow is weak, and at a distance scarcely to be heard at all."

Dr. Sutton intimates that "Mr. P. L. Jouy's description of a rather elaborate song attributed to this species" may possibly have pertained to the Grasshopper Sparrow instead. He continues:

"Although the Henslow's Sparrows sang intermittently all day, their particular song-periods occurred just at sunrise, and in the evening. There was something delightfully picturesque about the birds, when just after sundown they mounted the mustard stalks, and outlined against the golden flowers, gave forth their queer, monotonous notes."

The nest and eggs of this sparrow are justly considered something of a prize. Those found in 1913 by Mr. Harlow and Dr. Dickey in Huntingdon County were discovered only after a systematic search over the nesting area had resulted in flushing the parent birds. Sets of four and five eggs were taken respectively on May 24 and June 4, and on the latter date a nest with very young birds was also found. Dr. Sutton located a nest at Hartstown on June 1, 1922, after watching a pair of birds for more than two hours, and found that it contained newly hatched young. "The parents in approaching the nest sneaked through the grass for several yards. The nest was built under a clump of grass, and the entrance between the blades of grass was so small that even from directly above the nest it was almost impossible to see it. The young were fed small grasshoppers and other insects." My own experience with the species has been similar. On May 22, 1934, our party from the Carnegie Museum located a colony of a half-dozen pairs in an unmown field near Pymatuning Lake, directly south of Linesville. Dragging the field with a rope resulted in flushing two females from their nests; in each nest was a set of five eggs, partially incubated. The nests were loosely constructed of coarse, dry grasses, lined with finer stalks; they were well concealed in the thick grass, and one was partially domed over. The eggs, which we collected, are pale greenish white, sparsely and rather finely spotted with rufous brown; in the more heavily marked of the two sets, the spots are clustered more thickly about the larger end. The eggs measure about .75 by .57 inches.

Passerherbulus henslowi henslowi Dickey, *Oölogist*, 1913, 30:299 ([Charter Oak], Huntingdon Co., nesting)—Harlow, *Auk*, 1918, 35:138 ([Charter Oak], Huntingdon Co., breeding)—Burleigh, *Wilson Bull.*, 1924, 36:72 ("State College, Centre Co." [Charter Oak, Huntingdon Co.], migration); 1931, 43:48 (near Charter Oak, Huntingdon Co., breeding).

Nemospiza henslowii susurrans Sutton, *Ann. Carnegie Mus.*, 1928, 18:179 (near Hartstown, Crawford Co., habits; nesting).

Passerherbulus henslowi susurrans Christy, *Cardinal*, 1932, 3:95 (Geneva, Crawford Co., May; habits).

NELSON'S SPARROW

AMMOSPIZA CAUDACUTA NELSONI (Allen)

Description—A bird the size of the Savannah Sparrow; tail feathers pointed. Upperparts dull olive brown, with some white markings; crown dark-colored, a little paler in the middle, forming a strong contrast with the *rich buff of the sides of the head and of the throat and breast;* a large dark (grayish) area below and behind the eyes; rest of underparts white, with some darker streaks on the sides; under tail coverts buffy. In *fall plumage* the colors are blended and less heavily contrasted than in the spring dress, but at any season the color pattern is unmistakable; the impression of the buffy color is distinct as the bird flushes.

Range—This sparrow breeds mainly in western Canada, but during migration it reaches the Atlantic coast, where it also winters (in the southern states). While its route must thus lie directly across western Pennsylvania, the species is scarcely known there except in the Erie region, where it is a transient, rare in the spring but common in the fall. It has not yet been detected in the Pymatuning region, and the only locality record outside Erie County is one supplied by R. B. Simpson for Warren.

Migration—Mr. Simpson's record pertains to a bird taken on May 27, 1904. In the spring of 1900, on Presque Isle, I saw and collected but one specimen—on May 24. Mr. Simpson reports a single bird at this locality on May 12, 1932. These dates indicate that the species is one of the later migrants in the spring. In the fall of 1900, it was not positively identified at Presque Isle until September 13, and no individuals were seen after October 6. Oddly enough, this bird does not appear on the lists of the local observers at Erie.

Habits—First detected at Erie in September, 1893, by S. E. Bacon, Nelson's Sparrow proved to be a rather common transient on Presque Isle in the fall of 1900. In reporting my investigations there, I wrote (1904): "Although found about nearly all of the ponds, Niagara and Big Ponds were its favorite resorts. The birds were wont to frequent the thin growth of rushes along the water's edge, where they would run and skulk and hide with the greatest dexterity, flushing only when closely pressed, and soon dropping down again, sometimes flying back to the growth of weeds and bushes adjoining. In such cases they were usually easily secured by noting where they alighted and 'squeaking' them up into sight."

Ammodramus nelsoni Todd, *Ann. Carnegie Mus.*, 1904, 2:572 (Erie and Presque Isle, Erie Co., transient).

"Nelson Sparrow" Simpson, *Oölogist*, 1911, 28:97 (Warren, Warren Co., May).

EASTERN VESPER SPARROW (Plate 21)

POOECETES GRAMINEUS GRAMINEUS (Gmelin)

Description—A streaked sparrow, about the size of the Song Sparrow. Upperparts sandy brown with dusky streaks; ear coverts more or less brownish by comparison; wings showing two inconspicuous paler bars; *tail* dusky, but *the outer feathers largely white*, very noticeable in flight; underparts dull white, the breast and sides with dusky-brown streaks, which are scarce or absent on the throat. In the fall the upperparts and underparts are more or less washed with brownish buff.

Range—The Vesper Sparrow ranges across the continent from coast to coast, as far north as southern Canada in summer and to the Gulf coast and Mexico in winter. Two of the three recognized races are western. The eastern race is a common summer resident throughout western Pennsylvania wherever suitable conditions exist, regardless of elevation. Its numbers, like those of other open-country birds, must have increased greatly since early times.

Migration—This sparrow is one of the earlier arrivals and usually reaches the Ohio Valley before the end of March. In a backward season it may be delayed until April; on the other hand, it may appear as early as March 20—a date supplied by B. H. Christy for Sewickley in 1921. A. D. Kirk gives February 26 (1938) as an exceptionally early date for its appearance at his banding-station in Wilkinsburg. In southern Somerset County the species has been noted by A. B. Miller as early as March 16 (1921), but farther north in the mountains its arrival is definitely later, and the average date at Renovo is April 6 (Pierce). R. B. Simpson does not look for it at Warren before April; and it becomes common everywhere long before the end of that month. Migrants often move in loose, straggling flocks. The departure of this hardy species in the fall is always delayed until late October, and a few laggards often remain into the following month. Some late records at this season are: Beaver, November 4, 1890 (Todd); Sewickley, November 11, 1928 (Christy); Pittsburgh, November 21, 1912 (Burleigh); Wilkinsburg, November 14, 1892 (Atkinson); State College, November 17, 1914 (Burleigh); Renovo, November 17, 1911 (Pierce). There is no suggestion that this sparrow winters in our region.

Habits—John Burroughs draws a charming pen picture of this bird, which he introduces as the "field sparrow"—a name not to be confused with the Field Sparrow (*Spizella pusilla*) discussed in this work. He writes: "Have you heard the song of the field sparrow? If you have lived in a pastoral country, with broad upland pastures, you could hardly have missed him. Wilson, I believe, calls him the grass finch, and was evidently unacquainted with his powers of song. The two white lateral quills of his tail, and his habit of running and skulking a few yards in advance of you as you walk through the fields, are sufficient to identify him. Not in meadows or orchards, but in high, breezy pasture-grounds, will you look for him. His song is most noticeable after sundown, when other birds are silent, for which reason he has been aptly called the vesper sparrow. The farmer following his team from the field at dusk catches his sweetest strain. His song is not so brisk and varied as is that of the song sparrow, being softer and wilder, sweeter and more plaintive. Add the best parts of the lay of the latter to the sweet vibrating chant of the wood sparrow [*Spizella pusilla*], and you have the evening hymn of the vesper-bird—the poet of the plain, unadorned pastures. Go to those broad, smooth, up-lying fields, where the cattle and sheep are grazing, and sit down on one of the warm, clean stones, and listen to this song. On every side, near and remote, from out the short grass which the herds are cropping, the strain rises. Two or three long, silver notes of rest and peace, ending in some subdued trills or quavers, constitute each separate song. Often you will catch only one or two of the bars, the breeze having blown the minor part away. Such unambitious, unconscious melody! It is one of the most characteristic sounds in Nature. The grass, the stones, the stubble, the furrow, the quiet herds, and the warm twilight among the hills, are all subtly expressed in this song."[1]

The Vesper Sparrow also sings in the morning hours and more or less throughout the day, sometimes from the ground, but oftener from a fence post or other elevation. It is fond of working along the dirt roads; and when it rises at the approach of a passer-by, it will fly ahead of him as if reluctant to retire into the adjoining fields. The month of May finds nesting in progress. In fact, full sets of eggs have actually been found in Allegheny County as early as April 27 (Atkinson) and in Centre County on April 30 (Burleigh), but the first or second week in May is the usual time. The nest is loosely constructed of dry grasses and weed stalks and is lined with finer bits of the same material and frequently with horsehair; it is placed in an open field, often without much regard for concealment from above, and is sunk so that its brim is flush with the level of the ground. Many nests, built early in May in stubble fields, are destroyed in the spring plowing, and second nests are often disturbed in the same fields by subsequent cultivation of the land. D. A. Atkinson states that he once found a vesper sparrow's nest two feet from the ground in the shelter of a bunch of weeds that had grown up through a brush pile.

Two broods are usually reared in a season. The second set of eggs is laid late in June or early in July, and delayed nestings have been noted even as late as August 11 (Atkinson). Four or five eggs are usual; occasionally only three are laid, and very rarely six. The ground-color ranges from pale grayish or greenish to buffy white, and the markings, even of eggs in the same set, vary considerably. Some eggs are more or less uniformly clouded with a vinaceous-rufous shade, in the manner of those of the Savannah Sparrow; others show fine rufous or brown flecks and perhaps some blotches on the larger end; and others again have well-defined spots and scrawls, which suggest the

[1] *Wake-Robin*, 1913 edition, p. 17.

eggs of certain of the Icteridae—the Orchard Oriole, for example. The size and density of the markings vary greatly. The eggs, averaging .83 by .61 inches, are a little larger than those of the Song Sparrow.

Pocœcetes gramineus TOWNSEND, *Proc. Acad. Nat. Sci. Philadelphia*, 1883, 62 (Latrobe, Westmoreland Co., breeding) —TEULON, *Jour. Boston Zoöl. Soc.*, 1883, 2:8 (Bradford, McKean Co., May)—COPE, *Cassinia*, 1902, 5:16 (Germania, Potter Co., June)—TODD, *Ann. Carnegie Mus.*, 1904, 2:571 (Erie, Erie Co., nesting)—TODD, in Bausman, *Hist. Beaver Co., Pa.*, 1904, 2:1200 (Beaver Co., summer)—KEIM, *Cassinia*, 1905, 8:39 (Port Allegany, McKean Co., summer).

Poocœtes gramineus JACOBS, *Summer Birds Greene Co., Pa.*, 1893, 10 (Greene Co., nesting)—DWIGHT, *Auk*, 1892, 9:137 (Cresson, Cambria Co., June)—TODD, *Auk*, 1893, 10:40 (Two Lick, Indiana Co., June), 44 (Coalport, Clearfield Co., June)—BAILY, *Auk*, 1896, 13:294 (Williamsville, Elk Co., nesting).

"Vesper Sparrow" STONE, *Cassinia*, 1906, 9:44 (McConnellsburg, Fulton Co., June)—PITCAIRN, *Bird-Lore*, 1907, 9:155 (Riverview Park, Allegheny Co., breeding)—PITCAIRN, *Auk*, 1908, 25:476 (Leetsdale, Allegheny Co., June)—COOKE, *Bird-Lore*, 1911, 13:86 (Beaver, Beaver Co., and Renovo, Clinton Co., migration)—HARLOW, *Oölogist*, 1912, 29:279 (State College, Centre Co., nesting)—MCCONNELL, *Oölogist*, 1918, 35:150 ("Christy Park," Allegheny Co., breeding)—MCCLELLAND, *Am. Mid. Nat.*, 1922, 8:37 (Washington, Washington Co., summer)—STREET, *Cassinia*, 1924, 1923, 24:15 (Greencastle to Ft. Loudon, Franklin Co., June)—SUTTON, *Bird-Lore*, 1924, 26:190 (Turtle Creek and Aspinwall, Allegheny Co., spring)—CHRISTY, *Cardinal*, v. 1, no. 4, p. 10 (Big Traverse Valley, Beaver Co., June)—EASTWOOD, *Bird-Lore*, 1926, 28:207 (Pittsburgh region, Allegheny Co., March), 343 (Dixmont and vicinity, Allegheny Co., July, *fide* Auerswald), 402 (Clinton and vicinity, Allegheny Co., October); 1927, 29:196 (Pittsburgh region, Allegheny Co., March), 197 (Springs, Somerset Co., March, *fide* Miller)—BOULTON, *Bird-Lore*, 1928, 30:13 (Powers Run, Allegheny Co., October, *fide* Auerswald)—MCCLINTOCK, *Cardinal*, 1933, 3:128 (Ligonier, Westmoreland Co., summer).

Pocœcetes gramineus gramineus HARLOW, *Auk*, 1912, 29:474 (southern Centre Co., nesting)—CHRISTY, *Cardinal*, 1923, v. 1, no. 1, [p. 9] (Sewickley, Allegheny Co., breeding)—BURLEIGH, *Wilson Bull.*, 1923, 35:93 (Allegheny Co., summer); 1924, 36:72; and 1931, 43:47 (State College, Centre Co., migration, nesting)—CHRISTY and SUTTON, *Cardinal*, 1928, 2:72 (near Cook Forest, Clarion Co., nesting)—SUTTON, *Ann. Carnegie Mus.*, 1928, 18:176 (Crawford Co. localities, summer).

EASTERN LARK SPARROW

CHONDESTES GRAMMACUS GRAMMACUS (Say)

Description—A rather large sparrow; head broadly streaked, and tail extensively white at the tip. Upperparts grayish brown, with dusky streaks; wings dusky, with a white spot and paler edgings; *two broad chestnut stripes* (blackish in front), separated by a paler stripe, *on the crown;* another pale stripe over the eye, and a large *chestnut spot on the ear coverts;* a white spot below the eye; a black stripe on either side of the throat, and a small black spot in the middle of the breast; underparts otherwise dull white; tail dusky black, the feathers with white tips, largest on the outermost pair.

Range—The typical or eastern race of the Lark Sparrow is properly a bird of the Mississippi Valley and ranges as far north as Manitoba. It favors the prairie region of that section and seems to be gradually extending its range eastward as the forest gives way to open country. Already, according to L. E. Hicks, it has been found summering in many counties in Ohio, as far east and north as Ashtabula, which adjoins Erie and Crawford counties in Pennsylvania. He writes: "This species was first reported in Ohio by Dr. Wheaton in 1861, and is generally believed to have greatly increased in numbers during the last fifty years, though it has been found repeatedly to establish itself in new territory and then disappear after a few years. Very local everywhere and variable from year to year."[1] In the course of its eastward expansion, the Lark Sparrow has reached western Pennsylvania, where it may become semiregular as a summer resident. The records listed below outline its known range in the southwestern part of the state, from the Ohio Valley southward. The outlying records from Bedford and Huntingdon counties are most interesting, as they indicate that the species has actually crossed the Allegheny divide and is trying to establish itself in the Atlantic drainage.

Migration—There is little information concerning the arrival and departure of this species. One bird noted at the head of Pymatuning Lake, near Linesville, on May 2, 1937 (Irons); one seen near Sewickley on May 4, 1919 (Christy); and another

[1]*Ohio State University Studies*, 1935, 40:178.

seen near Waynesburg on April 30, 1936 (Dickey), may have recently arrived in those localities.

Habits—The following account has been extracted from the notes of S. S. Dickey: "The Lark Sparrow is among the rarest members of the extensive sparrow clan breeding in the uplands of Greene County. It is a shapely sparrow with grayish-brown streaks and a notably long tail. It is somewhat larger than the Grasshopper, Song, and Vesper sparrows. It arrives from the South late in April and remains until September. Hillside pastures and extensive cattle and sheep ranges are its favorite resorts. Here the male displays himself with marked activity. Perched in a tree in plain sight, he pours forth a potent song, which to my mind is not unlike that of the Indigo Bunting, although it is longer and decidedly more vigorous. The songster repeats his strain in spells or periods and languishes at times into an almost inaudible refrain, only to strike up once more in full voice. The female generally remains concealed among the herbage of the fields, at least until after her eggs are hatched and the fledglings are able to fly. A singing male as a rule is careful to keep away from the female and to avoid betraying the location of the nest. I have heard of one set of eggs that was collected near the village of Jefferson some years ago, but most of my experience with this bird has been in Monongalia County, West Virginia."

My personal experience with the Lark Sparrow is limited to a single occasion. On May 11, 1902, I positively identified a pair by the roadside at a point now known as "Barclay's Crossing," some four miles below Beaver, and I watched the female collecting nest material. Returning the next day, I searched the vicinity thoroughly and finally located and secured the male in a plowed field on the hillside near by. His song, which I heard a few times, reminded me of the Vesper Sparrow's. D. A. Atkinson never saw the bird himself, but reports a nest (presumably of this species) that was found by W. H. Ross near Bridgeville, Allegheny County, on June 3, 1897. Dr. Atkinson writes: "This nest was built three feet from the ground in a berry bush; it looked somewhat like a song sparrow's nest. The eggs were fresh, and their color and markings were characteristic of the eggs of the Lark Sparrow." A set of five eggs in the collection of J. W. Jacobs was found under similar circumstances: the parent bird was not seen. There is little chance for error in the identifications, however, since the eggs of this species are unmistakable and not easily confused with those of any other Pennsylvania bird. They are white, rather sparsely and irregularly spotted and scrawled with purplish black and with paler shell-markings. Thus they resemble those of the Baltimore Oriole, but they are of course smaller and more rounded ovate. They measure .78 by .60 inches.

Chondestes grammacus Jacobs, *Summer Birds Greene Co., Pa.*, 1893, 10 (Greene Co., nesting)—Stone, *Birds E. Pa. and N. J.*, 1894, 115 ("Fayette" [Bedford] Co., June, *fide* Rhoads)—Rhoads, *Auk*, 1899, 16:312 (between Bedford Springs and Hyndman, Bedford Co., June, and "Leetsdale" [Fair Oaks], Allegheny Co., May)—Todd, *Ann. Carnegie Mus.*, 1902, 1:504 ("Oakwood Station," Beaver Co., May)—Todd, in Bausman, *Hist. Beaver Co., Pa.*, 1904, 2:1200 (Beaver Co., summer)—Pitcairn, *Auk*, 1908, 25:476; 1910, 27:211 (Leetsdale, Allegheny Co., June and August).

Chondestes grammacus grammacus Harlow, *Auk*, 1918, 35:138 (Allegheny, Allegheny Co., May)—Christy, *Cardinal*, 1923, v. 1, no. 1, [p. 9] (Sewickley, Allegheny Co., May)—Wood, *Auk*, 1932, 49:98 (8 miles south of State College, Centre Co. [in Huntingdon Co.], nesting, *fide* Wiley)—(?)West, *Redstart*, 1936, 4:5 ([Linesville], Crawford Co., October)—Brooks, *Cardinal*, 1938, 4:181 (range; w. Pa. records, etc.).

BACHMAN'S SPARROW

AIMOPHILA AESTIVALIS BACHMANI (Audubon)

Description—A plainly colored, medium-sized sparrow, with strongly rounded tail. Upperparts showing rufous, grayish, and (on the middle of the back) dusky streaks, the rufous color predominating on the crown and nape; sides of head buffy gray, with a rufous stripe behind the eye; wings and tail dusky, with slight paler edgings, the secondaries and coverts more rufescent; underparts soiled whitish, with a buffy shade on the throat, breast, and sides; feet pale.

Range—Bachman's Sparrow is essentially a southern species, common in suitable localities in the South Atlantic and Gulf states. According to W. W. Cooke (1914), it is "an example of a bird that is apparently extending its range. Within recent years it has become common locally in southern Virginia, and has increased around Washington, D. C., until it is now known in four localities. It has invaded Ohio, even to the northern part of the state, and also western Pennsylvania." The bird's present status in Ohio has been outlined by L. E. Hicks: "As the first Ohio records for this species were in 1897, 1900, and 1901, it seems reasonably certain that this species has invaded the state from the south and southwest during the last half-century. It now occurs in numbers locally in 32 counties of southern and eastern Ohio."[1] I added the species to the Pennsylvania list in the spring of 1910, when I secured an adult male about a mile north of the town of Beaver. A nest (with one egg), supposed to belong to this species but never fully identified, had been taken near Waynesburg, however, on May 16, 1909, by J. B. Carter. Later research by S. S. Dickey has revealed that Bachman's Sparrow is a regular, although not common, summer resident in various other parts of Greene County. B. H. Christy has traced it to Allegheny and southern Beaver counties; and on July 6, 1937, about two miles east of Washington, G. M. Sutton observed a brood of young with their parents. The local range of this bird in our region will probably be found to approximate the ranges of such species as the Mockingbird and the Carolina Chickadee.

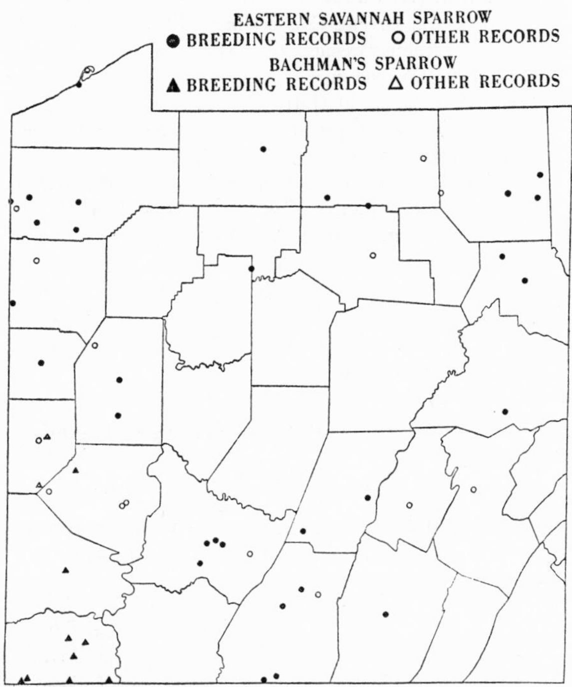

LOCAL RANGES OF THE SAVANNAH SPARROW AND OF BACHMAN'S SPARROW

Migration—In 1922, Dr. Dickey noted two singing males on April 15, about four miles south of Waynesburg. These were probably recent arrivals—as may also have been the bird that I secured near Beaver on April 29, 1910. No fall records are available.

Habits—My first encounter with this interesting little sparrow was in the spring of 1903 in western Florida, where I found it in the open pine woods and heard it sing. Imagine my surprise seven years later on hearing and recognizing this same song in Beaver County! The bird was soon located on the edge of a wooded ravine and was secured for identification; it was an adult male with enlarged gonads. Since that time, I have seen no other birds of this species, but Dr. Dickey has sent me a full account of his observations in Greene County, the greater part of which is here reproduced:

"Bachman's Sparrow is a drab-colored, inconspicuous, and rather retiring member of its tribe. Were it not for its exquisite song, it might readily be overlooked altogether or confused with some of the other sparrows. In southwestern Pennsylvania it is partial to open, scattered groves of white, red, and black oaks and to waste fields grown up to poverty grass (*Danthonia spicata*), intermixed with briers, saplings, small shrubs, and herbage. In such places the penetrating notes of the males may be heard from mid-April until sometime in August. The song is markedly different from that of any other indigenous sparrow; it may be transliterated *thee-ee-ee-ee-lut-lut-lut-lut.* It carries well and may be heard half a mile away.

"My first experience with this sparrow was in the summer of 1913, when with two companions I was engaged in trying to locate some old Indian trails across Greene County. On July 29, southwest of Kirby, an unfamiliar bird song attracted my attention. It came from an open grove of old

[1]*Ohio State University Studies,* 1935, 40:178.

white oaks, where the ground was covered with poverty grass. After some maneuvering, I contrived to spot the singer, which was perched on a dead branch, and to identify it satisfactorily as a Bachman's sparrow. During the next two days our journey took us across hills and valleys to the general vicinity of Brock and Rosedale, and two more males were encountered—one in a waste field, grown over with poverty grass, briers, and saplings, on the north side of the valley of Dunkard Creek; the other in a rolling pasture about four miles west of the Monongahela River and only half a mile from the West Virginia border.

"Some four years before this, Mr. J. B. Carter had stumbled across a strange nest in a hillside field adjoining an oak copse, close to Waynesburg. It had somewhat the appearance of a nest of the Grasshopper Sparrow, and it was tucked in a tussock of dead grass near a thicket. It held but one egg, which was pure glossy white in color and measured .74 by .53 inches. The discovery of this nest gave me some pause. It was apparently deserted, and it seemed not to belong to any species with which I was then familiar. Subsequent disclosures, however, pointed to its having been a nest of a Bachman's sparrow. This is the first actual record of the breeding of this species within our borders.

"On May 10, 1916, while traversing a grove of white oaks (used as a picnic resort) just north of Waynesburg, I saw a small brown bird fly from the ground into a tree and heard it burst into a song that at once disclosed its identity as a Bachman's sparrow. Soon its mate joined it, and the pair dallied about the grassy plots and then went into a near-by pasture dotted with hawthorn shrubbery. Returning to the spot two days later, I found the female gathering material for her nest, the location of which was thus betrayed. It was found in a clump of dry poverty grass in a wide aisle of the grove. On May 20 I returned again and collected the nest, which contained a set of five fresh eggs. The nest was a dome-shaped affair with a foundation of dry grass stems and blades. It was rather loosely arched over and was lined with finer grasses and horsehair. The eggs were white, with a faint bluish cast, and were slightly glossy in texture. The parent birds divided their time between the oak trees and the ground, feeding in both; they repeatedly perched in plain sight and manifested little fear.

"Later experience with this sparrow has confirmed my opinion that it prefers sterile fields and open oak groves. It thus occupies an ecological niche that, generally speaking, is otherwise unattractive to bird life. Since 1922, however, although I have often been afield, I have failed to meet with the species. Either it has dwindled in numbers, or I have completely overlooked it."

Peucæa æstivalis bachmani Cooke, *Bird-Lore*, 1914, 16:176 (Beaver, Beaver Co., April)—Dickey, *Oölogist*, 1914, 31:42 (Waynesburg, Greene Co., nesting)—Dickey, *Auk*, 1917, 34:212 (southern Greene Co., nesting)—Carter, *Oölogist*, 1917, 34:92 (Waynesburg, Greene Co., nesting)—Christy, *Cardinal*, 1929, 2:130 (Little Sewickley Creek, Allegheny Co., June)—Brooks, *Wilson Bull.*, 1938, 50:86 (range; w. Pa. records, etc.).

"Bachman Sparrow" Dickey, *Oölogist*, 1914, 31:8 (Greene Co., summer)—Christy, *Cardinal*, 1924, v. 1, no. 4, p. 11 ("Patton's Point," Beaver Co., May).

SLATE-COLORED JUNCO

JUNCO HYEMALIS HYEMALIS (Linnaeus)

Description—A bird the size of the Song Sparrow; general coloration slate gray and white; bill light-colored. *Adult: slaty gray*, the *underparts* (except the sides and flanks) *white from the breast down*, and the *outer tail feathers conspicuously white. Females* are duller, and in the fall the dark areas of both sexes are more or less washed with brown. *Young in juvenal plumage:* upperparts showing dusky streaks on a brown ground; underparts dull whitish, the throat and breast showing heavy dusky streaks; outer tail feathers white, as in the adult; bill pale.

Range—*Junco* is a genus peculiar to North America, where it is represented in the West by a number of species and races of comparatively restricted range, and in the East by a single species of wide range. *Junco hyemalis* occurs in summer throughout the Hudsonian, Canadian, and upper Transition life zones from Newfoundland and Labrador northwestward to Alaska, and southward in the

Appalachian highlands to North Carolina and Tennessee, where it appears as a slightly differentiated subspecies. Its breeding range in New England and in New York has been worked out with some precision by E. H. Forbush and by E. H. Eaton, and its range in western Pennsylvania has now likewise been determined. Audubon must have seen this species on his several trips across the Allegheny Mountains, but there is no record of it in his writings. Indeed, for a long time its breeding in this region was inferred rather than established. Then came J. A. Teulon's and B. H. Warren's records for McKean County; H. K. Jamison's and Jonathan Dwight's for Cresson, Cambria County; and those of others, as cited below. During the years from 1892 to 1899, when I was actively engaged in field work in western Pennsylvania, I paid especial attention to the Junco. Because it is common and easy to observe and identify, its local breeding range as shown on the accompanying map is doubtless fairly correct.

As now determined, this range is continuous across the entire plateau region, from the New York boundary southward in the mountains to Maryland and West Virginia. Its western edge crosses the Allegheny River near Tionesta at an elevation of about 1,100 feet; continues south to Clarion at the same altitude; and then swings off to the southeast through southern Jefferson County and eastern Indiana County to Laurel Hill, which it follows to the Maryland border. A narrow tongue also extends northward across the high country adjoining Chestnut Ridge in Fayette County, but not beyond. The eastern limit of the range follows in general the Allegheny divide but in places continues across the crest and down the eastern flank of the mountains to as low as 1,000 feet. Early in July, 1895, I encountered the Junco in considerable numbers in the hemlock growth at the western base of Blue Knob, in the northwestern corner of Bedford County. A single bird seen (but not secured) at Entriken, Huntingdon County, on June 3, 1898, by Thaddeus Surber was probably a stray. Other than these reports, there are no summer records for this species anywhere in the ridge and valley section; and if it ever occurred in summer in the Seven Mountains region of Huntingdon and Centre counties, it assuredly would not have been overlooked by the several observers who have worked there.

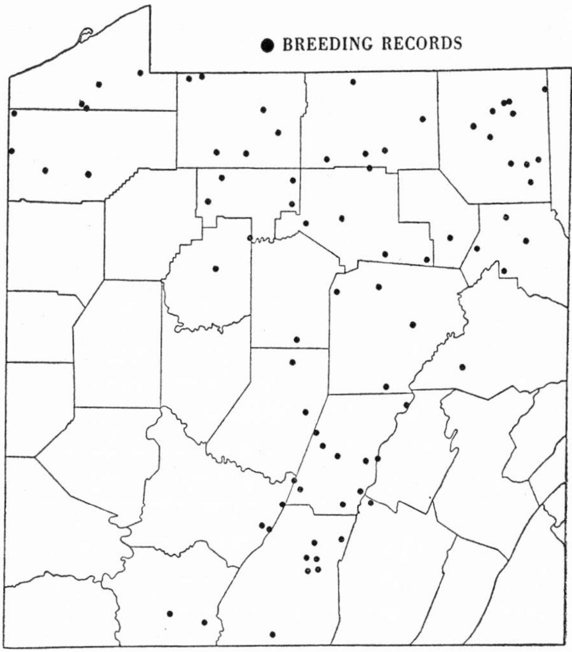

SUMMER RANGE OF THE SLATE-COLORED JUNCO

The status of the Junco in the Erie-Crawford district calls for special remark. While the species is a common winter resident and abundant migrant there, just as it is farther south (in the Ohio Valley), there is a strip of country, embracing the divide between the Lake Erie drainage, on the one hand, and the headwaters of French Creek and the Shenango River, on the other, where it is locally distributed in summer also. This extension of its recognized breeding range continues into Ashtabula County, Ohio (Hicks), and evidently coincides with the former distribution of the white pine, now virtually extirpated in that area. Under primitive conditions, the Junco was doubtless much more generally distributed there, but its present breeding stations are isolated.

Within its regular breeding area, the Junco is resident as a species, although migration may be noted in the spring and fall. Outside this area it is merely a winter resident, common and well known, as attested by the frequency with which it appears in the "Christmas Census" lists.

Migration—In the Ohio Valley, the Junco is more numerous in October and April, when transients are passing through, than at other times. I look for it at Beaver during the first week in October, and have never observed it there before September 26 (1891). September 11 (1913) is an exceptionally early date of arrival at Pittsburgh, and September 19 (1914), reported by T. D. Burleigh, is an early one at State College. The first comers are usually few and scattered, but by October 20 the birds have reached their maximum numbers. November finds the Junco population stabilized for the winter. The winter-resident birds loiter into April before moving north, and their place is then taken by birds from farther south; thus juncos may commonly be found until the latter part of that month. Stragglers have remained at Beaver as late as May 10 (1890), although by that time nesting is already under way in Crawford County.

Habits—Wintertime finds the Junco one of our commonest and most conspicuous small birds, swarming about brushy hedges, waste fields, the edges of woodland, and other places where weed seeds are plentiful. Under stress of weather, the birds may come to orchards or to the neighborhood of houses, where they often become very tame and will enter stables and dooryards to pick up seeds and crumbs, or will roost in holes in haystacks. Juncos travel in loose, straggling flocks, often in company with kindred spirits, such as tree sparrows or even chickadees; but they are always ready to strike out for themselves, and then they soon leave their companions behind. They fly in a peculiar, jerky manner, flashing the white on their tails and uttering a rapidly reiterated chirp that is characteristic. They have also an odd clicking note, and in the spring still another, which is rapidly repeated and may be transliterated by the syllable *tew*. The regular song of the Junco, which may be heard on its breeding grounds and sometimes also in its winter quarters, just before the species leaves for the North, is a trill almost exactly like that of the Chipping Sparrow. Besides this, I have heard at times a song of a different character, somewhat on the order of that of the American Goldfinch—a mellow, rambling ditty without any special form or pattern, but very pleasing when heard in chorus.

In summer the Junco seems rather more subdued than it is in winter, although this impression may be the result of finding it at the former season in isolated pairs instead of in restless, roving flocks. The male sings his simple little song (sometimes with variations) from the top of a tree or stub while the female is building the nest and incubating the eggs. Not only in the depths of the forest itself, but also along its outskirts, in second-growth woodland and thickets, and in underbrush, may the Junco be found. It shows a preference for conifers but in their absence seems well satisfied with deciduous growth. The nest is built on the ground, sometimes in an open spot, but oftener in the shelter of an overhanging bank. Warren (1890) says that in McKean County he has found nests "often within a few yards of each other, in the sides of the banks" along the railroad, and other observers have also noted the species' preference for this type of situation. Of eleven nests with eggs, collected at Kane by A. K. Pierce and now in the Carnegie Museum, no less than nine were in the roots of upturned stumps of fallen trees. At Warren, R. B. Simpson has even found nests in crevices in large tree trunks overhanging streams.

Wherever placed, the nest is a fairly compact, well-built, and deeply cupped structure. A rather large amount of green moss is usually included in its composition. Otherwise it is built of dry weed stalks, rootlets, grasses, and perhaps some fine dead twigs; the lining is of finer material of the same sort, supplemented by cow hair, horsehair, and similar substances. A typical nest measures about five inches in diameter by five in depth, and has a cavity two and one-fourth inches wide and two inches deep. Four or five eggs are usual; three are occasional; and sets of six are rare. The ground-color is generally a pale greenish white, but the markings vary considerably in density and character. A frequent pattern is a vinaceous-rufous spotting, which is wreathed around, or confluent at, the larger end. Other eggs are blotched irregularly with a paler, brownish shade, and still others are very lightly spotted. Average measurements are .76 by .58 inches. Almost certainly two or more broods are raised in a season; for full sets of eggs have been taken at Kane from early May until late July, and young in the streaked plumage are on the wing from June to August inclusive.

"Snow Bird" WILSON, *Am. Orn.*, 1811, 3:21 (near Somerset, Somerset Co., February); Ord ed., 1828, v. 1, Intro., p. cv (Pittsburgh, Allegheny Co.)—WICKHAM, *Oölogist*, 1888, 5:92 (Beaver, Beaver Co., winter).

Junco hiemalis TOWNSEND, *Proc. Acad. Nat. Sci. Philadelphia*, 1883, 63 (Latrobe, Westmoreland Co., winter).

Junco hyemalis TEULON, *Jour. Boston Zoöl. Soc.*, 1883, 2:8 (Bradford, McKean Co., resident; nesting)—VAN FLEET, *Ornithologist and Oölogist*, 1884, 9:108 (DuBois, Clearfield Co.)—TODD, *Oölogist*, 1888, 5:125 (Beaver, Beaver Co., winter; habits)—JAMISON, *Ornithologist and Oölogist*, 1888, 13:134 (Cresson, Cambria Co., June)—WARREN, *Birds Pa.*, 1888, 242 (Crawford and McKean Co., breeding, *fide* Sennett); ed. 2, 1890, 240 (Kane and vicinity, McKean Co., nesting)—WARREN, *Forest and Stream*, 1891, 37:83 (Kane, McKean Co., summer)—DWIGHT, *Auk*, 1892, 9:137 (Cresson, Cambria Co., June)—TODD, *Auk*, 1893, 10:43, 44 (Coalport, Clearfield Co., June)—HOMER, *Ornithologist and Oölogist*, 1893, 18:61 (Elmer, Potter Co., June)—BAILY, *Auk*, 1896, 13:294 (Williamsville, Elk Co., nesting)—RHOADS, *Auk*, 1899, 16:312 (Laurel Hill, near Laughlintown, Westmoreland Co.; Cresson and Summit, Cambria Co.; Round Island, Clinton Co., breeding)—COPE, *Cassinia*, 1902, 5:16 (Kettle Creek Valley, Oleona to New Bergen, and Germania, Potter Co., June)—TODD, *Ann. Carnegie Mus.*, 1904, 2:574 (Erie and Presque Isle, Erie Co., winter)—TODD, in Bausman, *Hist. Beaver Co., Pa.*, 1904, 2:1200 (Beaver Co., winter)—KEIM, *Cassinia*, 1905, 8:39 (Port Allegany, McKean Co., nesting).

"Black Snow Bird" JACOBS, *Hoosier Nat.*, 1887, 2:78 (Waynesburg, Greene Co., winter).

Junco hyemalis hyemalis RIDGWAY, *Bull. U. S. Nat. Mus.* no. 50, part 1, 1901, 279 (mountains of Pa., breeding)—HARLOW, *Auk*, 1912, 29:478 (southern Centre Co., spring); 1918, 35:139 (Cameron, Elk, Forest, Clinton, Blair, Warren, and Fayette Co., breeding)—STONE, *Cassinia*, 1915, 18:58 (State College, Centre Co., migration, *fide* Mason); 1919, 22:34 (Altoona, Blair Co., winter, *fide* McGraw)—DWIGHT, *Bull. Am. Mus. Nat. Hist.*, 1918, 38:286 (Gallitzin and Cresson, Cambria Co.; [near] Altoona, Blair Co.; and McKean Co., breeding)—CHRISTY, *Cardinal*, 1923, v. 1, no. 1, [p. 10] (Sewickley, Allegheny Co., winter)—STONE, *Cassinia*, 1923, 24:31; etc. (Greencastle, Franklin Co., winter, *fide* Ziegler)—BURLEIGH, *Wilson Bull.*, 1923, 35:94 (Allegheny Co., winter resident); 1924, 36:129 (State College, Centre Co., winter)—CHRISTY and SUTTON, *Cardinal*, 1928, 2:72, 75 (Cook Forest, Clarion Co., nesting; winter)—SUTTON, *Ann. Carnegie Mus.*, 1928, 18:185 (Crawford Co. localities, transient and winter resident; Linesville and Meadville, Crawford Co., breeding)—EASTWOOD, *Wilson Bull.*, 1929, 41:102 (Harmarville, Allegheny Co., May; plumage)—BURLEIGH, *Cardinal*, 1932, 3:83 (Summit, Fayette Co., nesting)—HICKS, *Auk*, 1933, 50:449 (Pymatuning region, Crawford Co., nesting).

"Junco" SIMPSON, *Oölogist*, 1907, 24:182; etc. (Warren, Warren Co., nesting, etc.)—MILLER, *Bird-Lore*, 1908, 10:32; etc. (Springs, Somerset Co., December)—PITCAIRN, *Bird-Lore*, 1908, 10:32 (West View, Allegheny Co., December)—SIMPSON, *Oölogist*, 1912, 29:330 (head of Tionesta Creek, Warren Co., nesting)—WARFIELD, *Bird-Lore*, 1919, 21:37; etc. (Chambersburg, Franklin Co., December)—MCCONNELL, *Bird-Lore*, 1920, 22:31; etc. (Emsworth, Allegheny Co., December)—SAVAGE, *Bird-Lore*, 1920, 22:31 (Crafton, Allegheny Co., December)—STAHL, *et al.*, *Bird-Lore*, 1921, 23:18 (Forest Hills to Deer Creek, Allegheny Co., December)—NICHOLSON, *Bird-Lore*, 1921, 23:18 (Grove City, Mercer Co., December)—MCCLELLAND, *Am. Mid. Nat.*, 1922, 8:35 (Washington, Washington Co., winter)—SUTTON, *Bird-Lore*, 1923, 25:132, 194; 1924, 26:122 (Pittsburgh region, Allegheny Co., winter)—CHRISTY and HEGNER, *Bird-Lore*, 1924, 26:30 (Raccoon Creek Valley, Beaver Co., December)—ALSOP, *Bird-Lore*, 1925, 27:41; etc. (Ridgway, Elk Co., December)—EASTWOOD, *Bird-Lore*, 1926, 28:58 (Hartstown, Crawford Co., November; Thompsonville to Finleyville, Washington Co., November), 136 ("Slack Hollow," Pittsburgh, Allegheny Co., January, *fide* Grimm; Raccoon Creek, Beaver Co., *fide* Todd; Thompsonville, Washington Co., *fide* Blair).

"Slate-colored Junco" COOKE, *Bird-Lore*, 1914, 16:438 (Beaver, Beaver Co., migration)—MCGRAW, *et al.*, *Bird-Lore*, 1919, 21:37; etc. (Altoona, Blair Co., December)—SUTTON, *Bird-Lore*, 1924, 26:266 (Warren, Warren Co., nesting, *fide* Simpson and Granquist; "Ligonier, Westmoreland Co." [summit of Laurel Hill, west of Johnstown, Cambria Co.], nesting, *fide* Jennings), 337 (Wattsburg, Erie Co., nesting, *fide* Allen)—EASTWOOD, *Bird-Lore*, 1926, 28:343 (Cooksburg, Forest Co., nesting, *fide* Elliott)—MATUSZAK, *Bird-Lore*, 1926, 28:29 (Hyde Park, Westmoreland Co., December)—ELLAIR, *et al.*, *Bird-Lore*, 1927, 29:29 (Thompsonville and vicinity, Washington Co., December)—BERKHEIMER, *Bird-Lore*, 1933, 35:27; etc. (Osterburg, Bedford Co., December)—ELLIOTT, *Cardinal*, 1934, 3:170 (Raccoon Creek, Beaver Co., December)—COPE and HAWKINS, *Forest Leaves*, 1934, 24:26 (E. Tionesta Forest Reserve, Warren and McKean Co., summer).

EASTERN TREE SPARROW (Plate 22)

SPIZELLA ARBOREA ARBOREA (Wilson)

Description—Larger than the Chipping Sparrow. *Cap and a stripe behind the eye, rufous;* sides of head deep gray; back showing dusky and brown streaks; tail dusky; wings dusky brown, with white bars and edgings; underparts grayish white, unstreaked, but with a *small dark spot in the middle of the breast;* bill dark above, pale beneath. In fresh fall plumage the upperparts and underparts are more or less washed with buff.

Range—The eastern race of the Tree Sparrow

breeds in the Hudsonian Life Zone and winters mainly in the northern United States and the adjoining provinces of Canada. It is thus a very common and generally distributed winter resident throughout western Pennsylvania.

Migration—In the fall this species is a late migrant and does not ordinarily reach our region until the end of October or early in November. Earliest fall dates for certain localities are: Erie, October 26, 1889 (Sennett); Meadville, October 31, 1913 (First); Beaver, October 30, 1909 (Todd); Sewickley, October 30, 1921 (Christy); State College, October 28, 1915 (Burleigh). From Renovo, the earliest record (supported by a specimen) is that of October 16, 1906 (Pierce). Any occurrences earlier than this could scarcely be more than accidental. By the end of November the species has attained its normal winter numbers; and no noticeable increase takes place until March, when migrants from the South begin to appear. The movement continues into April. "Last-seen" dates are: Pittsburgh, April 15, 1912 (Burleigh); Wilkinsburg, April 21, 1899 (Atkinson); Springs, Somerset County, April 16, 1927 (Miller); Claysville, Washington County, April 17, 1927 (Sutton); Sewickley, April 16, 1928 (Christy); Warren, April 20, 1904 (Simpson); Beaver, April 23, 1909 (Todd); Waynesburg, April 19, 1892 (Jacobs); Hartstown, April 29, 1922 (Sutton); Erie, April 18, 1900 (Todd); State College, April 20, 1919 (Burleigh). It is exceptional, however, to note the Tree Sparrow after the middle of April, since the majority of birds pass through earlier in the season.

Habits—The Tree Sparrow is the winter representative of the Chipping Sparrow, which it somewhat resembles but from which it may easily be distinguished by its larger size and brighter coloration and by the small dark spot in the center of the breast. Arriving from the North in the fall, it settles in waste fields grown over with weeds and bushes and providing seeds in abundance. Always it appears in loose, straggling flocks, which sometimes number scores or even hundreds and which often include juncos and other species. A given flock may stay in one favorite spot throughout the winter, if the food supply is adequate. The quantity of weed seeds consumed by one of these flocks in the course of a season is enormous. A feeding flock usually scatters out more or less, so that only a few birds are in sight at any one time; the rest remain hidden in the thick covert. While thus engaged, they carry on among themselves an animated twittering, which sounds like the simultaneous squeaking of many pairs of scissors. At the approach of an intruder, the birds suddenly cease their chatter, leave the shelter of the weeds and bushes, and fly in alarm to the nearest trees—whence the name "Tree Sparrow."

With the approach of spring, the birds grow restless and tend to wander about. Perhaps they move on northward, and migrants from farther south take their place. This is the time when the males begin to sing, and they continue to do so until their departure. It is somewhat surprising to learn that this unassuming little bird is a vocalist of no mean ability. It has an exquisite song, not loud, but sweet and warbler-like, which it reserves for mild days in March and April, just before leaving for its summer home. Several males singing at the same time produce a concert effect well worth hearing.

Spizella monticola Townsend, *Proc. Acad. Nat. Sci. Philadelphia*, 1883, 63 (Latrobe, Westmoreland Co., winter)—Todd, *Ann. Carnegie Mus.*, 1904, 2:573 (Erie and Presque Isle, Erie Co., winter)—Todd, in Bausman, *Hist. Beaver Co., Pa.*, 1904, 2:1200 (Beaver Co., winter).

"Tree Sparrow" Miller, *Bird-Lore*, 1908, 10:32; etc. (Springs, Somerset Co., December)—Pitcairn, *Bird-Lore*, 1908, 10:32 (West View, Allegheny Co., December)—Gerberding, *Bird-Lore*, 1912, 14:29 (Greenville, Mercer Co., December)—Simpson, *Oölogist*, 1913, 30:50 (Warren, Warren Co., March)—Christy and Hegner, *Bird-Lore*, 1924, 26:30; etc. (Raccoon Creek Valley, Beaver Co., December)—McConnell, *Oölogist*, 1918, 35:151 ("Christy Park," Allegheny Co., winter)—McGraw, *et al.*, *Bird-Lore*, 1919, 21:37; etc. (Altoona, Blair Co., December)—Warfield, *Bird-Lore*, 1919, 21:37; etc. (Chambersburg, Franklin Co., December)—Savage, *Bird-Lore*, 1920, 22:31 (Crafton, Allegheny Co., December)—McConnell, *Bird-Lore*, 1920, 22:31; etc. (Emsworth, Allegheny Co., December)—Nicholson, *Bird-Lore*, 1921, 23:18 (Grove City, Mercer Co., December)—McClelland, *Am. Mid. Nat.*, 1922, 8:35 (Washington, Washington Co., winter)—Jones, *et al.*, *Bird-Lore*, 1923, 25:25 (Deer Creek, Allegheny Co., December)—Alsop, *Bird-Lore*, 1925, 27:41; etc. (Ridgway, Elk Co., December)—Matuszak, *Bird-Lore*, 1926, 28:29 (Hyde Park, Westmoreland Co., December)—Portman, *et al.*, *Bird-Lore*, 1926, 28:31 (Thompsonville and vicinity, Washington Co., December)—Eastwood, *Bird-Lore*, 1926, 28:58 (Ribold, Butler Co., December; etc.); 1927, 29:197 (Springs, Somerset Co., April, *fide* Miller)—Christy and Sutton, *Cardinal*, 1928, 2:75 (Cook Forest, Clarion Co., winter)—Chaney, *Bird-Lore*, 1932, 34:47 (Uniontown and vicinity, Fayette Co., December)—Berkheimer, *Bird-Lore*, 1933, 35:27; etc. (near Osterburg, Bedford Co., De-

cember)—ELLIOTT, *Cardinal*, 1934, 3:170 (Raccoon Creek, Beaver Co., December).
Spizella monticola monticola STONE, *Cassinia*, 1919, 22:34 (Altoona, Blair Co., winter, *fide* McGraw)—CHRISTY, *Cardinal*, 1923, v. 1, no. 1, [p. 10] (Sewickley, Allegheny Co., winter)—BURLEIGH, *Wilson Bull.*, 1923, 35:94 (Allegheny Co., winter); 1924, 36:129 (State College, Centre Co., winter)—[Editor], *Cassinia*, 1926, 25:31 (Greencastle, Franklin Co., winter, *fide* Ziegler).
Spizella arborea arborea SUTTON, *Ann. Carnegie Mus.*, 1928, 18:183 (Meadville and Pymatuning Swamp, Crawford Co., transient and winter resident).

EASTERN CHIPPING SPARROW (Plate 22)

SPIZELLA PASSERINA PASSERINA (Bechstein)

Description—A small sparrow, with a rather long and slightly forked tail. *Adult in spring: crown chestnut, blackish in front* and bounded by a grayish-white stripe over the eye; a narrow dusky stripe through the eye; back sandy brown, with dusky streaks; wings dusky brown, with lighter-colored edgings; tail plain dusky brown; *underparts plain grayish white; bill black.* In *fall plumage* the upperparts are more or less washed with rufous buff, and the chestnut crown is duller and shows dusky streaks; the bill is paler. In *juvenal plumage the underparts* also show *heavy dusky streaks.*

Range—Resident races of this species are known from Mexico and Central America. The two northern races are migratory and together occupy the whole width of the continent; they range northward in summer through the Canadian Life Zone and southward in winter to the Gulf coast and Mexico. The eastern race is an abundant summer resident throughout western Pennsylvania and is especially numerous in cultivated districts. There is one winter record of a single bird observed by W. G. Pitcairn at West View, Allegheny County, on December 21, 1907.

Migration—The Chipping Sparrow begins its northward movement in March and as a rule reaches the Ohio Valley during the last week in that month or, if weather conditions permit, a little earlier (Beaver, March 19, 1891; Sewickley, March 19, 1889). In backward seasons, such as have prevailed in recent years, its appearance may be delayed until the first week in April, but seldom later. In the Erie-Crawford district, however, the average date of its arrival is later by several days, and in the highlands there is a definite retardation of its northward progress, which is indicated in a series of arrival records made by A. K. Pierce at Renovo. All these records are for April (except one for March 30, 1905), and the arrival has been noted even as late as April 23. R. B. Simpson's earliest date for Warren is April 12 (1895). At Springs, Somerset County, in the mountains of our southern border, the species arrives between March 24 and April 9, the average date being April 2 (Miller). At State College the earliest date is April 1 (1916—Burleigh).

In the fall this sparrow lingers until the last of October or the early part of November. Some late dates at this season are: Beaver, November 3, several years (Todd); Pittsburgh, October 30, 1913 (Burleigh); Erie, October 27, 1888 (Sennett); State College, November 4, 1916 (Burleigh); Renovo, October 28, 1901 and 1910 (Pierce).

Habits—No other native bird—not even the Robin or the House Wren—is so thoroughly at home about human habitations as the little Chipping Sparrow. It comes familiarly into the dooryard in search of crumbs of food, and it builds its nest in the vines and bushes about the house. The domestic cat is undoubtedly its worst enemy; otherwise its confidence is rarely betrayed. A few pairs, it is true, still cling to their original haunts in the forest (I have found them in June in the scattered pine growth on the Allegheny divide in Centre County), but the vast majority settle in orchards and cultivated grounds, where they do good service in consuming injurious insects, particularly caterpillars, weevils, grasshoppers, and leaf beetles. During the month of June, when the young are being reared, fully 93 per cent of the food consists of insects.[1] In the fall months, the percentage of weed seed consumed rises to a high figure. Thus this diminutive sparrow is economically one of the most useful birds.

The arrival of the species in the spring is announced by the male with his simple, unassuming song—a single trilled note. There is a surprising amount of individual variation in this song, par-

[1] S. D. JUDD, U. S. Department of Agriculture, Biological Survey, *Bulletin*, no. 15, 1901, p. 78.

ticularly in speed of delivery; the pitch also varies. The bird usually sings from a low perch in a tree, but occasionally from the ground. Two or three weeks—sometimes more—elapse between the time of arrival and the beginning of nesting. D. A. Atkinson reports finding a full set of eggs on April 22 (1896), but in a normal season, laying takes place during the first half of May. Two broods are usually reared, and the eggs for the second are laid sometime in July. The nest is built at no great height in an orchard or shade tree, or often in a vine or low bush. In Centre County, according to T. D. Burleigh, the red cedar is a favorite nesting site, and presumably this tree is also chosen in other counties where it is common. Ground nests are unusual, but they have been reported by several different observers; I have noted two, one of which was in my dooryard. Wherever situated, the nest is a well-built structure, more or less rough and irregular outside, but firmly and neatly cupped. A typical nest is composed of dry grasses and weed stalks and is lined with fine rootlets and horsehair. It holds together well enough to outlast the season for which it was intended, but it is often so insecurely fixed that it may be dislodged by a wind storm. I have never found more than four eggs in a nest, and often there are only three. The eggs are distinctive in color and markings and are thus easy to distinguish from those of any other native sparrow. They are pale bluish green, with some black or reddish-brown spots disposed thickly about the larger end and irregularly over the rest of the surface; in different sets the markings vary greatly in density. The average size is .72 by .51 inches.

Young in spotted plumage follow the parents for a time, insistently clamoring for attention. A brood raised on my premises in 1925 included one almost pure albino, which was conspicuous among its fellows. Before it disappeared, I saw it daily for over a week. In September and October, after the young have molted into the first winter plumage, the birds forsake the vicinity of houses for weed-grown fields, bushy thickets, and the edges of woods, where they travel about in straggling companies, often with associates of similar habits. They leave for the South just about the time that the Tree Sparrow comes down from the North to occupy their late haunts.

Spizella socialis Teulon, *Jour. Boston Zoöl. Soc.*, 1883, 2:9 (Bradford, McKean Co., breeding)—Jamison, *Ornithologist and Oölogist*, 1888, 13:134; and Dwight, *Auk*, 1892, 9:137 (Cresson, Cambria Co., June)—Todd, *Auk*, 1893, 10:40 (Two Lick, Indiana Co., June), 44 (Coalport, Clearfield Co., June)—Jacobs, *Summer Birds Greene Co., Pa.*, 1893, 10 (Greene Co., nesting)—Baily, *Auk*, 1896, 13:294 (Williamsville, Elk Co., nesting)—Cope, *Cassinia*, 1902, 5:10, 16 (Galeton and Germania, Potter Co., and Tamarack Swamp, Clinton Co., June)—Todd, *Ann. Carnegie Mus.*, 1904, 2:573 (Erie, Erie Co., summer)—Todd, in Bausman, *Hist. Beaver Co., Pa.*, 1904, 2:1200 (Beaver Co., summer)—Keim, *Cassinia*, 1905, 8:39 (Port Allegany, McKean Co., summer)—Forrest, *Oölogist*, 1911, 28:115 (Washington, Washington Co., breeding).

Spizella domestica Townsend, *Proc. Acad. Nat. Sci. Philadelphia*, 1883, 63 (Latrobe, Westmoreland Co., nesting).

"Chipping Sparrow" Jacobs, *Nat. Companion*, 1886, 2:59 (Waynesburg, Greene Co., November)—Stone, *Cassinia*, 1906, 9:44 (McConnellsburg, Fulton Co., June)—Pitcairn, *Bird-Lore*, 1907, 9:155 (Riverview Park, Allegheny Co., nesting); 1908, 10:32 (West View, Allegheny Co., December)—Dickey, *Oölogist*, 1911, 28:107 (Waynesburg, Greene Co., nesting)—Burleigh, *Oölogist*, 1911, 28:156 (Harmarville, Allegheny Co., nesting)—McConnell, *Oölogist*, 1918, 35:151 (McKeesport, Allegheny Co.)—Blair, *In the Open*, June, 1920, 10:22 ([Plains Church], Butler Co., June)—McClelland, *Am. Mid. Nat.*, 1922, 8:36 (Washington, Washington Co., summer)—Street, *Cassinia*, 1923, 24:15 (Greencastle to Ft. Loudon, and Jordan's Knob, Franklin Co., June)—Miller, *Oölogist*, 1923, 40:152 (Charter Oak, Huntingdon Co., nesting)—Sutton, *Bird-Lore*, 1924, 26:190 (Pittsburgh, Allegheny Co., April)—Christy, *Cardinal*, 1924, v. 1, no. 4, p. 10 (Big Traverse Valley, Beaver Co., June)—Lehman, *Bird-Lore*, 1925, 27:245 ([Chambersburg, Franklin Co.], habits)—Eastwood, *Bird-Lore*, 1925, 27:337 (Bradford Woods, Allegheny Co., August, *fide* Frederick), 406 (Dixmont, Allegheny Co., September, *fide* Reiter); 1926, 28:207 (Pittsburgh region, Allegheny Co., March), 273 (Rector, Westmoreland Co., May, *fide* Knauz), 402 (Aspinwall, Allegheny Co., September, *fide* Auerswald); 1927, 29:56 (Logan's Ferry, Allegheny Co., October), 197 (Springs, Somerset Co., March, *fide* Miller)—Boulton, *Bird-Lore*, 1928, 30:13 (Little Pucketa Creek [New Kensington], Westmoreland Co., October, *fide* Manley and Taylor), 196 (Beaver, Beaver Co., April, *fide* Todd)—Thompson, *Bird-Lore*, 1933, 35:320 (Erie, Erie Co., nesting).

Spizella passerina passerina Harlow, *Auk*, 1912, 29:474 (southern Centre Co., nesting)—Christy, *Cardinal*, 1923, v. 1, no. 1, [p. 10] (Sewickley, Allegheny Co., breeding)—Burleigh, *Wilson Bull.*, 1923, 35:94 (Allegheny Co., nesting); 1924, 36:72; 1931, 43:48 (State College, Centre Co., migration, nesting)—Christy and Sutton, *Cardinal*, 1928, 2:72 (Cook Forest, Clarion Co., summer)—Sutton, *Ann. Carnegie Mus.*, 1928, 18:183 (Crawford Co. localities, summer; nesting)—Burleigh, *Cardinal*, 1932, 3:83 ([Summit], Fayette Co., summer).

EASTERN FIELD SPARROW (Plate 22)

SPIZELLA PUSILLA PUSILLA (Wilson)

Description—A small sparrow, in size and proportions similar to the Chipping Sparrow. *Adult:* crown rufescent brown; eye-region grayish, but ear coverts brownish; back showing rufescent-brown and dusky streaks; tail dusky, with narrow edgings and gray upper coverts; wings dull brown, with two whitish or buffy bars; underparts dull grayish, the breast and sides with a buffy wash; *bill pale reddish brown. Young in juvenal plumage:* similar in general to the adult, but *breast and sides* showing *conspicuous dusky streaks.*

Range—This species (including the western race, *arenacea*) is confined to the region east of the Rocky Mountains. Like the Chipping Sparrow, it is migratory, but it does not range nearly so far north as that species, and it enters the Canadian Fauna only to a limited extent. It winters mainly in the southern states and occasionally farther north. It is a common and generally distributed summer resident in western Pennsylvania.

Migration—The Field Sparrow comes a little earlier in the spring than the Chipping Sparrow. It reaches the Ohio Valley, according to my observations at Beaver, between March 12 (1890) and 30 (1917), but not until April does it become really common. At Springs, in southern Somerset County, it has been noted as early as March 6 (1921), but the average date is March 29 (Miller). Allegheny County arrival records coincide in general with mine from Beaver County, but those from farther north are later by a few days. The available dates from Renovo, ranging from March 17 to April 16 (Pierce), also correspond. At State College the species arrives about April 3, while March 26 (1917) is the earliest recorded date.

In the fall the Field Sparrow remains until late in October or early in November, and leaves at just about the same time as the Chipping Sparrow. Late dates of record are: Erie, October 26, 1900 (Todd); Warren, November 1, 1903 (Simpson); Beaver, November 4, 1890 (Todd); Renovo, November 2, 1911 (Pierce); McConnellsburg, November 29, 1924—one bird seen with a flock of tree sparrows (Sutton). This last may have been a wintering individual.

Habits[1]—The Field Sparrow is one of the smaller summer-resident sparrows in western Pennsylvania and one of the more abundant. From every pasture, from every briery waste, from meadow, and from hilltop, rises its springtime chant. Indeed, it is fairly to be supposed that the number of field sparrows resident in the region is greater today than ever before. It is a bird of the open, particularly of waste places. Our region was originally forested and not well suited to the bird's needs; in the early days of settlement, cultivation of the newly cleared land was so intense that conditions were not greatly improved; but, with the decline of agriculture, which began fifty or seventy-five years ago, Nature reclaimed the fields, caused brambles, haws, huckleberries, and many another wild growth to spring up, and at length brought about conditions that suit the Field Sparrow perfectly. Its usual associates are the Vesper Sparrow, the Towhee, and the Meadowlark; to the north, the Savannah Sparrow; and in the southwestern counties, Bachman's Sparrow.

About one-third of the food of the species, according to the United States Biological Survey, consists of insects. Vegetable matter, largely weed seeds, comprises the remainder.

The Chipping and Field sparrows have several important characters in common. They are equal in size, or nearly so, and alike in proportions. Both birds are brown above, ashy white and immaculate below, and chestnut-capped. But the side of the Chipping Sparrow's head is clearly and emphatically striped, with a line of black through the eye and a line of white above; and the bill is black. The Field Sparrow lacks pronounced facial markings, and its bill is flesh-colored. These differences are so obvious that it is impossible to mistake one bird for the other.

The songs of the two species are not unlike; both consist essentially of the rapid repetition of a single note—a trill, if that term may be extended to include a simple reiteration. The Chipping Sparrow's song, however, is rather thin in quality and mechanical and monotonous in execution; while that of the Field Sparrow is, to human ears, rich and sweet and delightfully varied. Ordinarily it

[1]Account contributed by Bayard H. Christy.

begins with three or four slow repetitions of a single note, and then, sometimes without change of pitch, sometimes on a lower, but oftener on a higher key, it is accelerated to a rapid trill. There may even be a second change of key within the course of a single song. It is by such small features of variation that the songs of particular birds may be distinguished.

April is the month of sparrows, as May is the month of warblers. By the first of April the Junco and the Tree Sparrow, still on their winter feeding grounds, have begun to sing; on fine mornings the transient Fox Sparrow may be heard rehearsing faintly its rare strains; the Vesper and Field sparrows have appeared and in ever increasing numbers are swelling the volume of bird music. Presently the Chipping Sparrow will be trilling in the dooryards, and the Grasshopper and Savannah sparrows, in the fields. In the wet meadows of the northwestern counties, the humblest of all, Henslow's Sparrow, will be repeating his ridiculous lay. As the month advances, the handsome White-throated and White-crowned sparrows will be loitering in the thickets and tuning their sweet pipes, and at last the gay-colored, voluble Indigo Bunting will be repeating endlessly from the margin of every wood his sprightly though shallow song. But as April passes and May progresses, the northern sparrows will have gone, and the songs of those remaining will have become merely orchestration for the melodies of greater musicians—thrushes, grosbeaks, orioles, and many others.

Birds' nests are often masterpieces, and the nest of the Field Sparrow is certainly one. It is a deep and lovely cup of dry grasses, all rough and casual-looking without, all symmetry and delicate artistry within. It is commonly placed a few inches above the ground between supporting stalks of bramble or weed. The eggs are normally four in number; sets of five are rare. They are usually pale greenish white in ground-color, but the markings vary greatly in shade, density, and character. In the more usual type they take the form of reddish-brown spots clustered around the larger end, but in some sets they resemble pale, longitudinal splashes. The average egg is .70 by .52 inches.

In the following excellent summary of the status of the species in Allegheny County, D. A. Atkinson says that the Field Sparrow is "an abundant summer resident, found in all the fields, meadows, and thickets, as well as along the roadsides and the borders of woods. It arrives here about the middle of March but does not become common until after April 1. It starts nesting in May and rears two broods in a season. Fresh eggs have been taken as early as May 3 and as late as August 9, but the latter date is exceptional, even for the second set. The nest is built in a thicket or in the bushes along a road or pasture. The height from the ground varies from two inches to five or six feet, but the nest is usually placed in a bush or weed-bunch at an elevation of ten or fifteen inches. The Cowbird persecutes this species probably more than any other, and one or two eggs of the parasite, together with those of the rightful owner, are frequently found in a field sparrow's nest. During September and October, the field sparrows gather into small flocks; after the middle of October they gradually become scarcer, and toward the first week of November they finally disappear."

The nest, although ordinarily elevated, sometimes rests on the ground. Of the nests of the Song Sparrow and the Towhee, it has been remarked that the nest for the first brood is sunk in the ground (perhaps for purposes of heat conservation), while later ones are in elevated positions. I cannot say whether or not this generalization is applicable to the nests of the Field Sparrow.

Spizella agrestis Townsend, *Proc. Acad. Nat. Sci. Philadelphia*, 1883, 63 (Latrobe, Westmoreland Co., summer).

Spizella pusilla Teulon, *Jour. Boston Zoöl. Soc.*, 1883, 2:9 (Bradford, McKean Co.)—Jamison, *Ornithologist and Oölogist*, 1888, 13:134; and Dwight, *Auk*, 1892, 9:137 (Cresson, Cambria Co., June)—Todd, *Auk*, 1893, 10:40 (Two Lick, Indiana Co., June)—Jacobs, *Summer Birds Greene Co., Pa.*, 1893, 10 (Greene Co., nesting)—Baily, *Auk*, 1896, 13:294 (Williamsville, Elk Co., nesting)—Jacobs, *Gleanings from Nature*, 1898, 1:27 (Greene Co., nesting)—Cope, *Cassinia*, 1902, 5:16 (Clinton and Potter Co., June)—Todd, *Ann. Carnegie Mus.*, 1904, 2:574 (Erie, Erie Co., summer)—Todd, in Bausman, *Hist. Beaver Co., Pa.*, 1904, 2:1200 (Beaver Co., summer)—Keim, *Cassinia*, 1905, 8:39 (Port Allegany, McKean Co., summer).

"Field Sparrow" Stone, *Cassinia*, 1906, 9:44 (McConnellsburg, Fulton Co., June)—Pitcairn, *Bird-Lore*, 1907, 9:155 (Riverview Park, Allegheny Co., nesting)—Burleigh, *Oölogist*, 1911, 28:156 (Harmarville, Allegheny Co., nesting)—McConnell, *Oölogist*, 1918, 35:151 (McKeesport, Allegheny Co.)—Miller (R. F.), *Oölogist*, 1919, 36:156 (Charter Oak, Huntingdon Co., nesting)—Scoville, *Cassinia*, 1920, 23:15, 19 ([Charter Oak, Huntingdon Co.], nesting, etc.)—Blair, *In the Open*, June, 1920, 10:22 ([Plains Church], Butler Co., nesting)—Miller (M. H.), *In the Open*, June, 1920, 10:24

(Thornhill, Allegheny Co., nesting)—McClelland, *Am. Mid. Nat.*, 1922, 8:36 (Washington, Washington Co., summer)—Street, *Cassinia*, 1923, 24:15 (Greencastle to Ft. Loudon, Jordan's Knob and Horse Valley, Franklin Co., June)—Sutton, *Bird-Lore*, 1924, 26:190 (Pittsburgh, Allegheny Co., April)—Christy, *Cardinal*, 1924, v. 1, no. 4, p. 10 (Big Traverse Valley, Beaver Co., June)—Eastwood, *Bird-Lore*, 1925, 27:337 (Bradford Woods, Allegheny Co., August, *fide* Frederick), 406 (Dixmont, Allegheny Co., September, *fide* Reiter); 1926, 28:207 (Pittsburgh region, Allegheny Co., March), 402 (Aspinwall, Allegheny Co., September, *fide* Auerswald); 1927, 29:56 (Pittsburgh region, Allegheny Co., October), 197 (Pittsburgh region, Allegheny Co., March; Springs, Somerset Co., March, *fide* Miller)—Boulton, *Bird-Lore*, 1928, 30:13 (Sewickley, Allegheny Co., October, *fide* Christy).

Spizella pusilla pusilla Harlow, *Auk*, 1912, 29:474 (southern Centre Co., nesting)—Christy, *Cardinal*, 1923, v. 1, no. 1, [p. 10] (Sewickley, Allegheny Co., breeding)—Burleigh, *Wilson Bull.*, 1923, 35:94 (Allegheny Co., nesting); 1924, 36:72; and 1931, 43:48 (State College, Centre Co., migration; nesting)—Christy and Sutton, *Cardinal*, 1928, 2:72 (Cook Forest, Clarion Co., summer)—Sutton, *Ann. Carnegie Mus.*, 1928, 18:184 (Meadville and Pymatuning region, Crawford Co., summer)—Burleigh, *Cardinal*, 1932, 3:83 ([Summit], Fayette Co., nesting).

"Eastern Field Sparrow" Wood, *Oölogist*, 1932, 49:103 (State College, Centre Co., song).

WHITE-CROWNED SPARROW (Plate 22)

ZONOTRICHIA LEUCOPHRYS LEUCOPHRYS (Forster)

Description—A fairly large sparrow, with plain underparts and white wing-bars. *Adult: crown white in the middle, black on the sides;* a white stripe running from above the eye to the nape, and below this a black stripe; upperparts dull grayish, the back streaked with chestnut brown, the rump washed with brown, and unstreaked; wings grayish to brownish, with two white bars; tail plain dark brown; underparts white, shaded with gray on the breast and sides; flanks and under tail coverts shaded with buff; *bill reddish brown. Young in the fall:* similar to the adult, but the upperparts browner, and the black-and-white head pattern absent; crown rich brown, paler in the middle, and bounded below on either side by a pale superciliary stripe; ear coverts pale brown. This species may readily be distinguished from the White-throated Sparrow by its differently colored bill and by the *lack of a sharply defined white area on the throat.*

Range—The White-crowned Sparrow ranges in summer across the continent in the Hudsonian Life Zone from Labrador to Alaska, and farther south in the mountains of the West. It winters from the southern part of the Mississippi Valley to Mexico, and casually in the Ohio and Potomac valleys. In western Pennsylvania it occurs as a transient visitant, fairly common in the spring and more irregular in the fall. It has been observed in various parts of our region, in the highlands as well as in the low country, but is not nearly so well known as the White-throated Sparrow.

Migration—The White-crowned Sparrow is regularly a later migrant than the White-throated; arriving ten days or two weeks behind the latter, it is common when the White-throated is represented by only a few laggards. There are several authentic April records for the White-crowned species: Meadville, April 23, 1908 (Kirkpatrick); Renovo, April 22, 1903 (Pierce); Buckhorn, Cambria County, April 26, 1918 (McGraw); Endeavor, Forest County, April 29, 1923 (Dickey); Greenville, April 29, 1929 (Seiple). Under the impression that some of the published references are probably in error, I have eliminated all but those cited below. May 7 is the average date of arrival at Beaver, as shown by my records for fourteen years, which range from May 2 (1926) to 11 (1908). At Springs, Somerset County, the average arrival date is May 8 (Miller). Other observers, however, report somewhat earlier dates. In general, this sparrow should appear sometime during the first or second week in May and remain until about May 20 or 25, when it leaves with most of the transient warblers. D. A. Atkinson reports a belated migrant at Wilkinsburg on June 5, 1898.

The fall migration is more extended. The earliest migrants appear in September: Erie, September 19, 1900 (Todd); Hartstown, September 24, 1925 (Sutton); State College, September 28, 1916 (Burleigh); Renovo, September 23, 1915 (Pierce). The species is not ordinarily common (if at all) until the first week of October, and the great host of migrants passes through during that month. Some late dates at this season are: Meadville, October 25, 1908 (Kirkpatrick); Renovo, October 18, 1914

(Pierce); State College, October 28, 1916 (Burleigh); Wilkinsburg, October 30, 1891 (Atkinson); Indiana, October 30, 1933 (Smyth).

Habits—The White-crown is the aristocrat of the sparrow tribe. No shrinking, shy recluse is he, keeping under cover in the heavy grass or dense thicket, as do so many of his relatives. A wandering adventurer, he comes boldly into the open and makes his presence known. Distinguished in appearance by his striped headdress and white crown-spot, which is occasionally fluffed up in display, he flaunts himself for a few days in late spring and is gone again. Alone or in small groups, he haunts bushes and shrubbery along fences, at the edge of the forest, and even in orchards and gardens. Once from my dooryard in Beaver I watched a white-crown hopping over the lawn and feeding on dandelion seed. The males sing intermittently—sometimes antiphonally, sometimes in pleasing chorus. The song is not loud but is exquisitely sweet and plaintive—a haunting bit of melody, bringing to mind the bird's summer home in the Canadian wilderness. Usually it consists of five syllables, which I would transliterate *hee-zur-se-se-see*. The White-crowns seldom associate with other species, but troop by themselves, even in the fall. Finding a flock at the same spot in several successive Octobers suggested that the same birds were returning each year. In other instances, their return has actually been proved by banding.

Zonotrichia leucophrys TOWNSEND, *Proc. Acad. Nat. Sci. Philadelphia*, 1883, 63 (Latrobe, Westmoreland Co.)—TEULON, *Jour. Boston Zoöl. Soc.*, 1883, 2:8 (Bradford, McKean Co., May)—RHOADS, *Abstr. Proc. Delaware Valley Orn. Club*, 1900, 3:8 ([Round Island], Clinton Co., October)—TODD, *Ann. Carnegie Mus.*, 1904, 2:572 (Presque Isle, Erie Co., transient)—TODD, in Bausman, *Hist. Beaver Co., Pa.*, 1904, 2:1200 (Beaver Co., transient)—SUTTON, *Ann. Carnegie Mus.*, 1928, 18:182 (Crawford Co. localities, transient).

"White-crowned Sparrow" ENTY, *Ornithologist and Oölogist*, 1885, 10:79 (Templeton, Armstrong Co., May)—COOKE, *Bird-Lore*, 1912, 14:98 (Beaver, Beaver Co., and Renovo, Clinton Co., migration)—HARLOW, *Cassinia*, 1912, 15:20 (Center Furnace Swamp, Centre Co., spring)—MCCLELLAND, *Am. Mid. Nat.*, 1922, 8:37 (Washington, Washington Co., transient)—EASTWOOD, *Bird-Lore*, 1925, 27:262 (Raccoon Creek, Beaver Co., May, *fide* Jones)—BOULTON, *Bird-Lore*, 1928, 30:271 ([?]Frick Park, Pittsburgh, Allegheny Co., *fide* Knauz), 401 (Millvale, Allegheny Co., October, *fide* Auerswald).

Zonotrichia leucophrys leucophrys CHRISTY, *Cardinal*, 1923, v. 1, no. 1, [p. 9] (Sewickley, Allegheny Co., transient)—STONE, *Cassinia*, 1923, 24:47 (Greencastle, Franklin Co., May, *fide* Ziegler)—BURLEIGH, *Wilson Bull.*, 1923, 35:93 (Allegheny Co., spring transient); 1924, 36:128 (State College, Centre Co., migration).

WHITE-THROATED SPARROW (Plate 22)

ZONOTRICHIA ALBICOLLIS (Gmelin)

Description—A fairly large sparrow, about the size of the White-crowned. *Adult:* upperparts streaked with rich brown and black; wings and tail dull brown, the former with narrow white bars and edgings; *crown* showing two black stripes on either side, reaching the nape, and separated by a narrow *grayish-white stripe;* a broad *superciliary stripe*, white behind the eye and *yellow in front;* below this a black stripe; sides of the head dull gray, continuous with the gray on the sides of the neck and on the breast; *throat abruptly white*, forming a strong contrast; rest of underparts dull whitish; bill dark. *Young birds in the fall* resemble the adults, but the black markings on the head are replaced by brown, and the light ones by gray or buff; the yellow spot before the eye is duller or absent; and the breast is sometimes indistinctly streaked.

Range—The White-throated Sparrow is more southern, generally speaking, than the White-crowned, since by far the larger part of the individuals composing the species breed in the Canadian Fauna. It is also more decidedly eastern and does not range west of the Rocky Mountains. It winters abundantly in the southern states and less commonly farther north. There are several winter records among the published references cited below; most of them are from Allegheny County, although A. B. Miller writes that one bird remained at his feeding-station at Springs, Somerset County, throughout the winter of 1915–16. This is certainly an unusual record for that altitude. The breeding of the species in our area is not nearly so well established as its wintering. Common though the bird is in summer in the highlands of western Massachusetts and in the Adirondack and Catskill Mountains of New York, it is rare and local at that season across the border in northeastern Pennsylvania. In the highlands of the western part of the state, I have searched in vain for the White-throated Sparrow in summer, although the Junco—a frequent associate in the north country—is common there. Van Fleet, however, includes this sparrow provisionally in his manuscript list of the summer birds of DuBois, remarking that it is casual and "may breed occasionally." R. B. Simpson has no summer records from Warren County, but L. E. Hicks noted two birds early in July, 1931, at Heart's Content. He also saw the species in Pymatuning Swamp on June 14, 1932, and on the same date, in the Ohio portion of the swamp, found a nest containing three small young. Again, he noted one bird in extreme northwestern Crawford County on July 16, 1929. F. B. Chapman (1937) states that on May 17, 1937, in the Pymatuning sanctuary, he saw a female white-throat carrying nesting material. These various records strongly suggest that under more primitive conditions this sparrow may have had a rather extensive breeding range in western Pennsylvania, although it was probably never so common as are the Junco and others. Our region is evidently close to its southern breeding limit. Its status here is mainly that of a regular and abundant transient.

Migration—White-throated sparrows recorded in March by various observers were possibly wintering individuals; for the first migrants rarely appear until sometime in April. My arrival records for Beaver range from April 10 (1891) to 30 (1905), and the average date is April 22. The spring dates for Allegheny County and the surrounding region in general are about the same, although in the more northern counties the vernal movement tends to be later by a few days. The A. K. Pierce arrival records for Renovo cover twenty-six years and also yield April 22 as the average date, and April 13 (1918) as the earliest. About a week after its arrival the species is common, and some birds linger until the second week in May or even later. In the spring of 1900, this sparrow was first observed at Presque Isle on April 18, reached its maximum numbers on May 2, and was last seen on May 10. In 1911 and 1924, I noted it at Beaver as late as May 19; and in 1922, G. M. Sutton observed it at Hartstown until May 18 and found one loiterer (or possibly a breeding bird) as late as May 29.

The autumnal movement begins in September and continues for about a month; stragglers often remain into November. In the fall of 1900, the White-throat was present on Presque Isle from September 15 to October 29. It arrives at Beaver between September 17 and 25 (the average date being September 22) and departs between October 18 and 29. There is one record for November 7 (1926). B. H. Christy has also noted it as late as November 7 at Sewickley. Extreme dates for the neighborhood of Pittsburgh reported by T. D. Burleigh are September 11 (1913) and November 16 (1912); these are certainly exceptional. The same observer recorded it at State College in 1914 from September 19 to November 19. The Pierce records for Renovo range from September 10 (1903) to November 3 (1906) and yield September 19 as the average arrival date. Most of the white-throats, however, pass through our region in October. Although the species is common throughout the fall season, there is usually a day or two (about October 10) when it is even more abundant than usual; at these times of excessive movement, the birds swarm everywhere—in the thickets, in the woods, in orchards, and in the shrubbery along the roads.

Habits—A charming pen picture of the White-throated Sparrow is quoted from E. H. Forbush: "It is April. At last winter has gone, after many days of snow and others of northerly and easterly gales, and the sun rises on a perfect day. The morning opens with a chorus of Robin song, mingled a little later with the trill of the Chipping Sparrow, the jingle of the Song Sparrow, the clanging of Grackles and the love notes of Flickers. Soft southeasterly breezes stir last year's leaves; flies and gnats buzz about in the sunlight; a few great bees are mumbling about in the green grass on the lawn, and frogs are croaking hoarsely at the head of the pond, as if uneasily bestirring themselves and trying their voices after the long winter sleep. Among the brush heaps, bushes, briers and sprouts of second growth clearings, along bush-bordered roads and in the edges of the pine woods where patches of snow still lie in shady places, the White-

throated Sparrows range, rustling the dead leaves on the ground as they scratch with both feet. They are on their leisurely way from the sunny south to northern New England and Canada.

"They prefer to stay on or near the ground, and although they alight in trees they seldom perch very high. When danger threatens they are likely to fly to some thicket or heap of brush for safety. In the spring migration they seem to prefer low thickets in moist places, but in their summer home they may be found almost anywhere in bushy pastures, thickets and woods, and in fall migration numbers visit weedy gardens and cornfields."[1]

The White-throat has an exquisite song, heard during the northward migration. Morning and evening are the hours when it is most frequently delivered, but the birds occasionally sing at intervals during the night. The song begins on a single fairly high note; jumps at once to another much higher, which is repeated several times; and trails off in a quavering tremolo, sweet and plaintive. I have heard the bird sing in the fall at odd times, although its usual note at that season is a rather metallic, squeaky chirp.

Zonotrichia albicollis TOWNSEND, *Proc. Acad. Nat. Sci. Philadelphia*, 1883, 63 (Latrobe, Westmoreland Co.)—TEULON, *Jour. Boston Zoöl. Soc.*, 1883, 2:8 (Bradford, McKean Co.)—TODD, *Ann. Carnegie Mus.*, 1904, 2:573 (Presque Isle, Erie Co., transient)—TODD, in Bausman, *Hist. Beaver Co., Pa.*, 1904, 2:1200 (Beaver Co., transient)—PITCAIRN, *Oölogist*, 1907, 24:41 (Riverview Park, Allegheny Co., migration)—STONE, *Cassinia*, 1919, 22:34; and 1920, 23:35 (Altoona, Blair Co., May, *fide* McGraw)—CHRISTY, *Cardinal*, 1923, v. 1, no. 1, [p. 10] (Sewickley, Allegheny Co., transient)—BURLEIGH, *Wilson Bull.*, 1923, 35:93 (Allegheny Co., transient; rare in winter); 1924, 36:128 (State College, Centre Co., migration)—[Editor], *Cassinia*, 1926, 25:32 (Greencastle, Franklin Co., spring, *fide* Ziegler)—SUTTON, *Ann. Carnegie Mus.*, 1928, 18:182 (Meadville and Pymatuning Swamp, Crawford Co., transient).

"White-throated Sparrow" COOKE, *Bird-Lore*, 1912, 14:101 (Beaver, Beaver Co., and Renovo, Clinton Co., migration)—HARLOW, *Cassinia*, 1912, 15:20 (Center Furnace Swamp, Centre Co., spring)—MILLER, *Bird-Lore*, 1916, 18:28 (Springs, Somerset Co., December)—MCCONNELL, *Oölogist*, 1918, 35:150 ("Christy Park," Allegheny Co., transient)—WARFIELD, *Bird-Lore*, 1919, 21:37 (Chambersburg, Franklin Co., December)—MCCLELLAND, *Am. Mid. Nat.*, 1922, 8:37 (Washington, Washington Co., transient)—SUTTON, *Bird-Lore*, 1924, 26:55 (Harmarville, Allegheny Co., November), 190 (Wildwood, Allegheny Co., April, *fide* Tracht)—EASTWOOD, *Bird-Lore*, 1925, 27:262 (Pittsburgh region, Allegheny Co., April), 406 (Dixmont, Allegheny Co., *fide* Reiter); 1926, 28:274 (Pittsburgh region, Allegheny Co., spring); 1927, 29:56 (Pittsburgh, Allegheny Co., October; Logan's Ferry, Allegheny Co., October; Thompsonville, Washington Co., November, *fide* Ellair), 273 (Springs, Somerset Co., April, *fide* Miller)—BOULTON, *Bird-Lore*, 1928, 30:14 (Guys Run, Allegheny Co., November, *fide* Reiter, *et al.*), 401 (Millvale, Allegheny Co., October, *fide* Auerswald)—CHAPMAN, *Cardinal*, 1937, 4:108 (Pymatuning Lake, Crawford Co., May; nesting?).

[1] *Birds of Massachusetts*, 1929, 3:74.

EASTERN FOX SPARROW (Plate 22)

PASSERELLA ILIACA ILIACA (Merrem)

Description—A large sparrow, with bright rufous tail and heavily spotted breast and sides. General color above, rich brown, in a streaked pattern; crown duller; *wings and tail bright rufous;* sides of head (below and behind the eye), rufous chestnut; underparts white, the *breast and sides of the neck showing rufous-chestnut spots*, more or less fused; flanks and sides showing browner spots and streaks; bill dark above, paler below.

Range—The eastern race of the Fox Sparrow breeds in the Hudsonian and Canadian life zones from Newfoundland to northwestern Alaska. West of the continental divide, the species splits up into a number of races, which in the United States are of alticoline distribution. The eastern race does not range southward in summer along the Appalachian highlands as do many Canadian Zone species; indeed, it is not known to breed south of the St. Lawrence River and Gulf. On the other hand, small numbers pass the winter as far north as New England, although as a rule the species retires to the southern states at that season. In western Pennsylvania it is an irregularly common transient and a rare winter resident.

Migration—This hardy sparrow is one of the earlier spring migrants. Usually it appears in March, before all the snow is gone, and terminates its stay before the end of April; most of the birds pass through rather hurriedly during the first two weeks of the latter month. Some early spring records are: Springs, Somerset County, February 24, 1922 (Miller); Frick Park, Pittsburgh,

February 29, 1936 (Malley); State College, March 1, 1919 (Burleigh); Shermansville, Crawford County, March 8, 1925 (Bergstrom); Hollidaysburg, March 8, 1921 (Berg); Lakemont, Blair County, March 10, 1918 (McGraw); Schenley Park, Pittsburgh, March 11, 1921 (Sutton); Sewickley, March 13, 1898 (Christy); Renovo, March 16, 1899 (Pierce); Warren, March 18, 1893 (Simpson). On days of great movement the species may be very numerous indeed; large flights were observed at Hillside, Westmoreland County, on March 18, 1922 (Boulton), and at Warren on April 17, 1932 (Simpson). Seldom does this sparrow linger into May, but a few late dates appear in the records of A. K. Pierce for Renovo: May 5, 1903; May 7, 1911; May 8, 1916; May 10, 1906; May 16, 1908.

October is the month of the Fox Sparrow's return and the time of its greatest abundance. It was once taken at Carnegie, Allegheny County, as early as September 28 (1896—Atkinson). I noted it at Presque Isle on October 5 in 1900, and at Beaver on October 3 in 1908, but usually it does not arrive until the second week of that month or even later. Mild weather in November tends to prolong its stay, as suggested by the following records: Sewickley, November 6, 1901, and November 18, 1903 (Christy); Washington, November 11, 1888 (Nease); Presque Isle, November 12, 1903 (Simpson); Pittsburgh, November 16, 1912, and November 23, 1913 (Burleigh); State College, November 23, 1915 (Burleigh); Renovo, November 14, 1896 (Pierce); near Lambertsville, Somerset County, November 17, 1935 (Mostoller). Some of these later dates suggest wintering, although the only certain winter record is one reported from McKeesport on December 26, 1915 (McConnell).

Habits—The Fox Sparrow and the Hermit Thrush have several points in common: they look somewhat alike; they migrate at the same time; and both are shy and retiring. The Sparrow, however, is a bird of the thicket and underbrush rather than of the deep forest; it is fond of briery areas on the outskirts of woods, and of dense willow and weedy growths along streams. The latter habitat is strikingly reminiscent of its usual haunts in the north country. Actually the bird is a sort of sublimated Song Sparrow; it is often found associated with that species and with the Towhee, the Junco, and the Tree Sparrow—birds of kindred tastes. Compared with these, the Fox Sparrow, according to G. M. Sutton, "gives one the idea of a more robust, more dignified bird. The head, for instance, is not lowered so often as is that of the Song Sparrow, nor is the tail twitched so nervously. At a short distance the eye seems a little larger than that of the latter species. The reddish tail is of course at once apparent when the bird takes flight, and it is never raised and lowered as it so often is with the Song Sparrow. The notes are also quite different, and the deeper 'chuck' note reminds one rather indistinctly of the Brown Thrasher's harsh call note, although in some respects it also suggests that of the Junco."

This sparrow spends much of its time on the ground, scratching about in the dry leaves, in the manner of the Towhee, and at times making a considerable disturbance. It is, according to E. H. Forbush, "one of the few of our sparrows that scratches with both feet at once. It leaps into the air, and while off the ground scratches or kicks quickly with both its powerful feet, making them fly as well as everything they touch, before it lands on them again. Thus it is able to excavate rapidly, throwing leaves and dirt sometimes a yard or more. If after it arrives, a snowstorm comes on, covering the ground with several inches of snow and cutting off most of the smaller birds from their chief source of food supply, this does not inconvenience the lusty Fox Sparrow. He excavates! Jumping and scratching he makes the snow fly, and soon is at the bottom of a hole and at his usual occupation of turning over the dead leaves and searching for seeds and insects. It is a pretty and stirring sight to see a flock of Fox Sparrows all at work in this manner, and throwing little jets of snow over the white carpet."[1]

Single birds are the rule in our region, and seldom are more than a few seen together. Occasionally in the spring, and rarely in the fall, some enterprising males break into song. In my opinion, no other sparrow quite equals this bird in musical ability, although it seems not to attain its full powers as a vocalist before reaching its summer home in the north country. There it is at its best as a musician of the wild, when its melody rings out full and clear from an evergreen thicket or a willow copse, within which the singer remains concealed. The song has all the sweetness of the

[1]*Birds of Massachusetts*, 1929, 3:105.

Song Sparrow's and is about as long, but it is much louder and carries for a greater distance. In the fall it is usually abbreviated and toned down.

Passerella iliaca TOWNSEND, *Proc. Acad. Nat. Sci. Philadelphia*, 1883, 63 (Latrobe, Westmoreland Co., fall)—TODD, *Ann. Carnegie Mus.*, 1904, 2:575 (Presque Isle, Erie Co., transient)—TODD, in Bausman, *Hist. Beaver Co., Pa.*, 1904, 2:1200 (Beaver Co., transient).

"Fox Sparrow" SIMPSON, *Oölogist*, 1910, 27:32; 1913, 30:50 (Warren, Warren Co., transient)—MCCONNELL, *Bird-Lore*, 1916, 18:27 (McKeesport, Allegheny Co., December)—MCCONNELL, *Oölogist*, 1918, 35:151 ("Christy Park," Allegheny Co., transient)—MCCLELLAND, *Am. Mid. Nat.*, 1922, 8:37 (Washington, Washington Co., transient)—SUTTON, *Bird-Lore*, 1923, 25:194; 1924, 26:56 (Pittsburgh region, Allegheny Co., migration), 190 (Pittsburgh, Allegheny Co., March, *fide* Norwind)—EASTWOOD, *Bird-Lore*, 1926, 28:207; 1927, 29:196, 197 (Pittsburgh region, Allegheny Co., March)—BOULTON, *Bird-Lore*, 1928, 30:13 (Cook Forest, Clarion Co., October), 14 (Guys Run, Allegheny Co., November, *fide* Reiter, *et al.*), 195 ("Slack Hollow," Allegheny Co., March, *fide* Grimm)—MALLEY and SHOEMAKER, *Redstart*, 1937, 4:70 (Pittsburgh, Allegheny Co., migration).

Passerella iliaca iliaca CHRISTY, *Cardinal*, 1923, v. 1, no. 1, [p. 10] (Sewickley, Allegheny Co., transient)—BURLEIGH, *Wilson Bull.*, 1923, 35:95 (Allegheny Co., transient); 1924, 36:129 (State College, Centre Co., migration)—SUTTON, *Ann. Carnegie Mus.*, 1928, 18:188 (Crawford Co. localities, transient).

LINCOLN'S SPARROW (Plate 22)

MELOSPIZA LINCOLNI LINCOLNI (Audubon)

Description—Similar to the Song Sparrow, but a little smaller; streaks on underparts much narrower; sides of head gray, with a greenish cast; and *breast crossed by a band of buff*, which forms a contrast with the white throat.

Range—This sparrow has a transcontinental range, within which geographic variation is slight as compared to the variation exhibited by the Song Sparrow. The bird summers in the Canadian Life Zone and winters in Mexico and the southern United States. It breeds at appropriate elevations in the mountains of the West, but does not range southward in the Appalachians, as do many other birds of this zone. Over the greater part of the eastern United States it is known only as a transient, but in recent years, several winter occurrences have been recorded in our region and also in eastern Pennsylvania. This erratic behavior on the part of the species was previously unsuspected, and it is certainly surprising and hard to explain. I completely overlooked this sparrow during the early years of my field activities in Beaver County, but later experience has convinced me that it is a regular, though not common, spring and fall transient there and can indeed be found at those seasons if search is made in the right place and at the right time. Records from other counties are remarkably few; notwithstanding their paucity, I believe that the species is far more numerous and more impartially distributed than has been supposed. Observers often seem to confuse it with the Song Sparrow, and identification in the field cannot be made in an offhand way.

Migration—The occurrence of Lincoln's Sparrow as early in the season as March 30 (1900), when D. A. Atkinson took a specimen (now in the Carnegie Museum) at Wilkinsburg, was a puzzle until certain winter records from eastern Pennsylvania were published.[1] I now believe that this individual must have been a winter resident. In partial confirmation, I have received from R. L. Keesler a record of a single Lincoln's sparrow that was seen with a small group of tree sparrows at Forestville, Butler County, and positively identified, on January 14, 1929. The regular spring migration does not begin here until May, when the warblers are passing through in large numbers. My earliest and latest dates at Beaver are respectively May 6 (1913) and 17 (1924). Miss Ruth Trimble saw one bird near Latrobe, Westmoreland County, on May 12, 1934. In the Pymatuning region of Crawford County, Lincoln's sparrows have been seen on May 15 and 24 (Sutton, and others), and they have been noted at Warren between May 11 and 16 (Granquist; Simpson). In the fall they pass through quickly and quietly, mainly during the first week in October (between September 30 and October 8, 1910, at Beaver). Exceptionally late dates are: Raccoon Creek, Beaver County, October 20 (1923—Boulton); and Sewickley Heights, Allegheny County, October 23 (1932—Christy and Hegner). On the other hand, the species has been observed at State College as early as September 21 (1930) by H. B. Curry.

[1] R. J. MIDDLETON, *Auk*, 1929, 46:392; E. S. WEYL, *Cassinia*, 1935, 29:53.

Habits—Jonathan Dwight[1] emphasizes shyness as the prevailing characteristic of this sparrow, and with this opinion I agree, insofar as spring transients are concerned. For in the spring, Lincoln's Sparrow ordinarily frequents bushy places and briery thickets, where it skulks about close to the ground, usually out of sight. On one occasion, however, I was surprised to encounter a single bird in an orchard, working through the terminal branches of the trees in true warbler-fashion. Shy and secretive though this bird is, the song of the male is distinctive and is an infallible clue to his presence, even when the singer himself is invisible. But he sings only spasmodically during his northward journey. The song is utterly unlike that of the Song Sparrow; in fact, in its hurried delivery it suggests the song of the Northern Water-Thrush or that of the House Wren, but in its length and fullness it emulates that of the American Goldfinch. Only a chirping note is heard in the fall, when, according to my experience, this sparrow is much easier to observe and study, because at that season it is less shy. Its favorite haunts are elderberry thickets intergrown with high weeds, where it often associates with song sparrows. Like the latter, it responds readily to "squeaking," and it will usually come into sight long enough to reveal its identity. Most of my fall records are from a restricted area near the town of Beaver.

"Lincoln Sparrow" SIMPSON, *Oölogist*, 1909, 26:152 (Warren, Warren Co., May)—WOOD, *Wilson Bull.*, 1932, 44:239 (State College, Centre Co., fall).

Melospiza lincolni lincolni SUTTON, *Ann. Carnegie Mus.*, 1928, 18:186 (Shermansville, Crawford Co., May; Crystal Lake, Crawford Co., May, *fide* Blair).

Melospiza lincolni CHRISTY, *Cardinal*, 1933, 3:149 (Sewickley Heights, Allegheny Co., October).

[1]In F. M. CHAPMAN, *Handbook of Birds of Eastern North America*, revised edition, 1932, p. 539.

SWAMP SPARROW (Plate 22)

MELOSPIZA GEORGIANA (Latham)

Description—A little smaller than the Song Sparrow; underparts without distinct spots or streaks. *Adult in spring: cap chestnut, blackish in front;* nape and sides of head grayish, with some darker mottling; back brown, with broad black streaks; wings and tail externally, rufous brown, the wing coverts spotted with black; *underparts dull white,* the breast washed with ashy gray and the flanks with brown. *Adult and young in fall:* similar to the spring adult, but crown deep brown, streaked with black and divided in the middle by a pale stripe. *Juvenal plumage:* black and brown streaks above; throat, breast, and sides showing dusky streaks on a whitish ground; wings and tail as in the adult.

Range—In summer this sparrow ranges northward to Newfoundland, James Bay, and northern Manitoba; southward to northern Nebraska in the interior and to New Jersey on the Atlantic coast; and somewhat farther south in the mountains. It winters mainly in the southern states and sporadically farther north. It has been noted by H. C. Kirkpatrick at Meadville in December, January, and March; and by G. M. Sutton at Hartstown in February. Its regular status in the Pymatuning area, however, is that of a common and characteristic summer resident. It is common also on Presque Isle and has been noted in virtually all the smaller swamps in the northwestern part of the state, north of the terminal moraine. So absolutely dependent is it upon a particular kind of habitat that in the Ohio and lower Allegheny valleys, where there are no suitable swamps, it is unknown as a summer resident and rare even as a migrant. D. A. Atkinson writes that "careful search of the small swamps at Claremont, Harmarville, and Pitcairn has failed to add this species to our list of summer birds." J. W. Jacobs has found it nesting in Greene County, however, although not recently. It occurs in the highlands also but is strictly local. Records have been received from widely separated points: Lake Seaton, Fayette County (Burleigh); the marshes near the head of Glade Run, Somerset County (Todd; Miller); DuBois (Van Fleet); Clarendon, Warren County (Simpson; Dickey); and Tamarack Swamp, Clinton County (Cope, 1902). The only June record from east of the Allegheny divide comes from Center Furnace Swamp in Centre County (Harlow, 1912). In Blair County, the species is a rare migrant (McGraw; Berg), as it doubtless is also in the other counties of the ridge and valley section.

Migration—In Crawford County, according to

G. M. Sutton (1928), the Swamp Sparrow "usually arrives in late March or early April: March 23, 1907, and April 7, 1914, Meadville (First); April 10, 1925, Conneaut Lake (Langdon); and becomes commoner by mid-April." In 1926 it was observed at Conneaut Lake on March 27, and in 1929, at Hartstown on April 6 (Seiple). On Presque Isle, however, it has not been noted before April 16 (1933 and 1934—Guynes). Earliest and average dates of arrival for State College are respectively April 8 (1919) and April 15 (Burleigh). The earliest date for Allegheny County (Frick Park, Pittsburgh) is April 7 (1937—Malley). In 1923, B. H. Christy saw this sparrow at Clinton Pond, in the same county, several times between April 23 and May 14, and in 1927 he noted it on May 15. I have recorded it at Beaver from April 28 (1911) to May 13 (1910). May dates naturally suggest breeding, but it is fairly certain that these particular ones pertained to late migrants. One bird was seen along Canoe Creek in Blair County as late as May 20 in 1917 (McGraw). In the fall, the main movement occurs from the middle of September until about October 10, while stragglers loiter into November. I have not seen the Swamp Sparrow at Beaver later than October 15 (1909), but it has been noted at Renovo on November 3 (1906—Pierce) and at State College as late as November 28 (1916—Burleigh).

Habits—The Swamp Sparrow is aptly named, although it is by no means the only sparrow that is partial to swampy ground. During the migration period, I have occasionally found it in habitat where it seemed out of place, as for instance in weedy, briery thickets in the uplands—far removed from its accustomed haunts—or in the willow brush along the Ohio River, or in open areas of marsh grass. On Presque Isle it haunts the thick bushes near the margins of the ponds, as well as the growths of flags and cattails in moist places, and there it keeps well hidden. At Pymatuning Swamp, where it is likewise common, it frequents the alders as well as the cattail areas, and often nests in weedy growths along the woodlands or about the small ponds. In western Pennsylvania, according to all observers, the alder growths nearly always harbor swamp sparrows. The bird delights to skulk and hide in the recesses of the heavier growth and will occasionally venture into sight in an exposed situation. Like its relative, the Song Sparrow, it feeds on or near the ground. Mr. Christy once watched swamp sparrows at Clinton Pond "beachcombing" at the water's edge. I have never heard the species sing during migration, but it is a persistent singer on its nesting grounds. Its song is a simple trill, like that of the Junco, with very little individual variation. Its ordinary call note is similar to that of the Song Sparrow, but is softer in tone and more metallic in timbre.

Dr. Sutton's interesting account (1928) of the nesting of this species at Pymatuning is here reproduced: "Nests just ready for eggs were found on May 3 and 4, 1922, characteristically situated between or on last year's cat-tail stalks. On May 11 two sets of four fresh eggs were found. From then on no less than sixty-six nests were located (including those found in 1923, 1924, and 1925) and enough data were gathered to make possible some definite statements concerning the nesting habits of the species.

"Nests were found to be, on the average, completed and ready for eggs by May 7. The eggs, laid daily, usually numbered four or five, but were sometimes three, and never, so far as we found, six. Nests were almost never placed on the ground, but were built between the cat-tail stalks, or upon the bent-down clumps of stalks and leaves, and were often completely hidden from above by the broad, dead leaf-blades. Entrances to the nests were almost always from the side and rarely from above. The material of the lining varied but little. It was always of fine grasses, and not varied with plant-fiber, roots, or hair, as might have been expected. The material forming the foundations of the nests was often coarse and bulky, and some of the structures were huge, sprawling affairs. Nests were often built directly above the water, where the depth varied from six to twenty-four inches, and were usually built about a foot or more above the surface. Nests with small young were found on June 1 and 3, 1922, and from June 4, 1923, onward.

"The eggs, which vary from pale apple-green to clear pale blue in color, were usually handsomely blotched with deep brown. Occasionally, however, the eggs much resembled those of the Song Sparrow, being evenly sprinkled with gray and dull brown spots, and lacking the blue ground-color which usually distinguishes the eggs of the present species. [Eggs of the Swamp Sparrow measure about .76 by .57 inches.]

"Female birds, which did not flush close at hand thus disclosing the location of their nests, slipped off at a distance of twenty feet or more and either skulked away like mice or fluttered off among the cat-tails. Nests were most often found in the open cat-tail stretches; but frequently they were built far back in the recesses of the wooded swamp in the little open spaces, where cat-tails and alders still maintained a foothold."

Melospiza palustris TOWNSEND, *Proc. Acad. Nat. Sci. Philadelphia*, 1883, 62 (Latrobe, Westmoreland Co.)—TEULON, *Jour. Boston Zoöl. Soc.*, 1883, 2:9 (Bradford, McKean Co.).

Melospiza georgiana JACOBS, *Summer Birds Greene Co., Pa.*, 1893, 11 (Greene Co., nesting)—RHOADS, *Auk*, 1899, 16:312 (Beaver, Beaver Co., May)—COPE, *Cassinia*, 1902, 5:17 (Tamarack Swamp, Clinton Co., June)—TODD, *Ann. Carnegie Mus.*, 1904, 2:574 (Presque Isle, Erie Co., summer)—TODD, in Bausman, *Hist. Beaver Co., Pa.*, 1904, 2:1200 (Beaver Co., transient)—HARLOW, *Auk*, 1912, 29:478 (Center Furnace Swamp, Centre Co.); 1918, 35:139 (Fayette Co., breeding)—CHRISTY, *Cardinal*, 1923, v. 1, no. 1, [p. 10] ([Flaugherty Run, west of] Sewickley, Allegheny Co., May)—BURLEIGH, *Wilson Bull.*, 1924, 36:129 (State College [Scotia, and Center Furnace], Centre Co. [and Charter Oak, Huntingdon Co.], migration)—CHRISTY, *Cardinal*, 1926, v. 1, no. 7, p. 25 (Clinton Pond, Allegheny Co., October)—SUTTON, *Ann. Carnegie Mus.*, 1928, 18:187 (Pymatuning Swamp, Crawford Co., summer; Meadville, occasional in winter, *fide* Kirkpatrick)—BURLEIGH, *Cardinal*, 1932, 3:83 (Lake Seaton, Fayette Co., August).

"Swamp Sparrow" HARLOW, *Oölogist*, 1912, 29:309 (Center Furnace Swamp, Centre Co., June)—CHRISTY, *Cardinal*, 1923, v. 1, no. 2, [p. 17] (Clinton Pond, Allegheny Co., spring)—EASTWOOD, *Bird-Lore*, 1925, 27:263 (Pittsburgh region, Allegheny Co., May); 1926, 28:274 (Sandy Lake, Mercer Co., May, *fide* Squier).

Additional breeding records: Tamarack Swamp, Erie Co.; Tamarack Swamp, Warren Co.; Cambridge Springs (2 miles east), Crawford Co. (Dickey)—Black Swamp and Gardner Swamp, Lawrence Co.; Canadohta Lake and Clear Lake, Crawford Co.; Benson Swamp, Warren Co. (Todd)—Half Moon Swamp (2–3 miles west) and Sandy Lake, Mercer Co.; Sugar Lake, Crawford Co.; Waterford and Edinboro, Erie Co. (Homer)—Forestville (2 miles northwest), Butler Co. (Keesler)—Sharon and vicinity, Mercer Co. (McQuiston)—Jamisonville (3 miles north), Butler Co., breeds regularly (Elliott).

EASTERN SONG SPARROW

MELOSPIZA MELODIA MELODIA (Wilson)

MISSISSIPPI SONG SPARROW (Plate 22)

MELOSPIZA MELODIA BEATA Bangs

Description—A medium-sized, brown-streaked sparrow, without white on the wings or tail. *Adult:* streaked above with two shades of brown on a grayish-brown background; wings and tail plain dull brown; a paler (grayish) stripe in the middle of the crown, and another over each eye; a dark (brownish) stripe behind the eye, and another below the ear coverts; a heavier dark stripe on either side of the throat, joining the dark stripes on the breast, sides, and flanks; underparts otherwise dull white. Sometimes the stripes on the breast tend to fuse into a spot in the middle. In *fall and winter*, all the colors are more blended, the brown prevailing. *Juvenal plumage:* similar to the adult plumage, but much browner, the color pattern merely indicated; underparts washed with buff.

The differences between the races *melodia* and *beata* are slight and are obvious only on comparison of good series of carefully selected specimens. They are not perceptible in life.

Range—*Melospiza melodia* is a North American species of wide range and great plasticity, especially in the West. It was long supposed that in the East there was but one race, but my researches and those of others show that the Song Sparrow of the Mississippi Valley (*beata*) is slightly but appreciably different from the race of the cis-Appalachian region (true *melodia*) and that of the Atlantic littoral (*atlantica*). The relationships of the two races in the mountains of Pennsylvania remain to be determined; presumably, however, *beata* occurs west of the Allegheny divide, while in the ridge and valley section the population may verge toward *melodia*.[1] (No attempt has been made to separate the two in the references cited below, or in the present text.)

Next to the Robin, the Song Sparrow is the

[1]According to ALEXANDER WETMORE, *Smithsonian Miscellaneous Collections*, 1936, v. 95, no. 17, p. 1, the name *beata* has been misapplied, and the race of the interior should be called *euphonia*.

commonest and most universally distributed bird in our region. It is an abundant summer resident everywhere, and although many individuals retire southward for the winter, a certain number remain. Even as far north as Erie a few birds winter every year, although at Warren the species is rare in the dead of winter. Toward the south the number of wintering birds increases, until in Greene County the Song Sparrow is fairly common. It reaches its maximum numbers in spring and fall, when the transients appear in force.

Migration—In late February and early March, the Song Sparrow population increases markedly with the coming of the early migrants. The movement lasts for two or three weeks, until the transients have all gone; the species then assumes its normal numbers for the summer. Again, in late September and through most of October, there is an observable increase as the transients move in the reverse direction. Just what determines the migration of this species is not yet known. Mrs. M. M. Nice has shown that some members of a given brood may leave in the fall, while others may remain. Transient birds may often be distinguished from resident birds by their cleaner, brighter plumage.

Habits—A bird of modest garb and rather retiring disposition, but friendly and sociable; a seed-eater by choice, but insectivorous in season; and an irrepressible songster—that is the Song Sparrow. Look for it, not in the deep woods, nor yet in the open fields that some of its tribe affect, but in underbrush, in briery thickets, in second-growth woods, in the high weeds and herbage along streams and wet areas, or even in gardens and about orchards. In the winter the birds favor dense thickets, brush heaps, and other sheltered situations. Often several song sparrows will congregate, and sometimes they will be found with other kinds, such as the Junco and the Tree Sparrow. Shocks of corn that have been left standing in the field sometimes serve as shelter, and the dry weeds all around supply an abundance of food. Although the birds feed mostly on or near the ground, they sing from higher and more exposed perches. The Song Sparrow is a cheerful optimist; and a mild, sunny day in winter is almost sure to invoke a song. Indeed, I have heard the species sing during every month in the year. Although the song attracts attention at any time, because of the liquid sweetness of its tone, it is more compelling in the early spring than at any other season. Never have I heard two individual songs exactly alike; yet in spite of this diversity, the songs are very similar in form and pattern and are not easily confused with those of any other species. Springtime in our region offers no greater musical treat than the medley of song-sparrow voices, vying with each other from adjoining territories.

Nesting begins fairly early, and three broods are usually raised. I have found highly incubated eggs in Beaver County as early as April 21, and other observers supply similar records. The first week in May, however, is a more usual time for fresh sets for the first brood, while those for the second are laid about the third week in June. There is considerable irregularity in the time of laying, and, according to T. D. Burleigh, fresh eggs have been found as late as August 6. He writes (1923): "As a general rule the first nests are found on the ground, while the later ones are almost invariably in bushes or small saplings, varying in height in proportion to the density of the foliage. It is probably just a coincidence, but the nest found August 6, 1915, was also higher from the ground than any I have ever found before or since, being twenty feet up in a red maple at the side of the road." I once found a nest some five feet from the ground in a natural cavity in an orchard tree—a peculiar situation. G. M. Sutton (1928) states that during 1922 he found twenty-six nests in the Pymatuning region: "While the majority of them were on the ground, some were built in the cat-tails; one was beautifully situated twenty inches from the ground in a clump of *Equisetum;* one was hidden in a low hemlock tree; and one was placed at least six feet up in a thick bush." The nests are built of dry leaves, weed stems, and grasses, and are lined with horsehair (if available) or other fine materials; when above the ground they are often quite bulky. Four or five eggs are laid; occasionally only three; and rarely six. The ground-color is usually pale green or greenish white, but the markings vary greatly in intensity. They are indeterminate small spots, or sometimes larger blotches, of dull reddish brown, evenly distributed over the surface but more or less confluent around the larger end of the egg. Average measurements are .76 by .60 inches. The young are usually out of the nest in about two weeks, but they follow their parents until after the postjuvenal molt.

Melospiza meloda TEULON, *Jour. Boston Zoöl. Soc.*, 1883, 2:9 (Bradford, McKean Co.).

Melospiza fasciata TOWNSEND, *Proc. Acad. Nat. Sci. Philadelphia*, 1883, 62 (Latrobe, Westmoreland Co., breeding)—JAMISON, *Ornithologist and Oölogist*, 1888, 13:134; and DWIGHT, *Auk*, 1892, 9:138 (Cresson, Cambria Co., June)—TODD, *Auk*, 1893, 10:40 (Two Lick, Indiana Co., June), 45 (Coalport, Clearfield Co., June)—JACOBS, *Summer Birds Greene Co., Pa.*, 1893, 11 (Greene Co., nesting)—BAILY, *Auk*, 1896, 13:294 (Williamsville, Elk Co., nesting).

"Song Sparrow" ENTY, *Ornithologist and Oölogist*, 1885, 10:78 (Templeton, Armstrong Co., March)—JACOBS, *Hoosier Nat.*, 1887, 2:78 (Waynesburg, Greene Co., resident; description nest and eggs)—WICKHAM, *Oölogist*, 1888, 5:92 (Beaver, Beaver Co., winter)—STONE, *Cassinia*, 1906, 9:44 (McConnellsburg, Fulton Co., June)—PITCAIRN, *Bird-Lore*, 1907, 9:155 (Riverview Park, Allegheny Co., nesting); 1908, 10:32 (West View, Allegheny Co., December)—MILLER (M. H.), *Bird-Lore*, 1908, 10:32; etc. (McKinley Park, Allegheny Co., December)—MILLER (A. B.), *Bird-Lore*, 1908, 10:32; etc. (Springs, Somerset Co., December)—SIMPSON, *Oölogist*, 1909, 26:170 (Warren, Warren Co., nesting)—HARLOW, *Cassinia*, 1912, 15:20, 22 (Center Furnace Swamp, Centre Co., nesting, etc.)—MILLER (M. H.), *In the Open*, April, 1920, 10:27 (Guyasuta, Allegheny Co., nesting)—CHRISTY and HEGNER, *Bird-Lore*, 1924, 26:30; etc. (Raccoon Creek Valley, Beaver Co., December)—MCCONNELL, *Oölogist*, 1918, 35:151 (McKeesport, Allegheny Co.)—MILLER, *Oölogist*, 1919, 36:157 (Pine Grove Mills, Centre Co., nesting)—MCGRAW, *et al.*, *Bird-Lore*, 1919, 21:37 (Altoona, Blair Co., December)—WARFIELD, *Bird-Lore*, 1919, 21:37; etc. (Chambersburg, Franklin Co., December)—SCOVILLE, *Atlantic Monthly*, 1920, 126:37 (Treaster Valley, Centre Co., March)—SAVAGE, *Bird-Lore*, 1920, 22:31 (Crafton, Allegheny Co., December)—MCCONNELL, *Bird-Lore*, 1920, 22:31; etc. (Emsworth, Allegheny Co., December)—BLAIR, *In the Open*, July, 1920, 10:22 (Plains Church, Butler Co., June)—STAHL, *et al.*, *Bird-Lore*, 1921, 23:18 (Forest Hills to Deer Creek, Allegheny Co., December)—NICHOLSON, *Bird-Lore*, 1921, 23:18 (Grove City, Mercer Co., December)—MCCLELLAND, *Am. Mid. Nat.*, 1922, 8:35 (Washington, Washington Co., resident)—BOULTON, *Oölogist*, 1922, 39:71 (near Beaver, Beaver Co., nesting)—HOFFMAN, *et al.*, *Bird-Lore*, 1923, 25:23 (Grove City, Mercer Co., December)—CHRISTY, *Cardinal*, 1923, v. 1, no. 2, [p. 17] (Clinton Pond, Allegheny Co., nesting)—STREET, *Cassinia*, 1923, 24:15 (Greencastle to Ft. Loudon, Franklin Co., June; Conococheague Creek, near Mercersburg, Franklin Co., nesting)—SUTTON, *Bird-Lore*, 1923, 25:194 (Duquesne, Allegheny Co., March, *fide* Galloway)—CHRISTY, *Cardinal*, 1924, v. 1, no. 4, p. 10 (Big Traverse Valley, Beaver Co., June)—ALSOP, *Bird-Lore*, 1925, 27:41 (Ridgway, Elk Co., December)—EASTWOOD, *Bird-Lore*, 1925, 27:337 (Bradford Woods, Allegheny Co., August, *fide* Frederick), 406 (Dixmont, Allegheny Co., September, *fide* Reiter); 1926, 28:273 (Millvale, Allegheny Co., nesting, *fide* Auerswald)—MATUSZAK, *Bird-Lore*, 1926, 28:29 (Hyde Park, Westmoreland Co., December)—PORTMAN, *et al.*, *Bird-Lore*, 1926, 28:31 (Thompsonville and vicinity, Washington Co., December)—BOULTON, *Bird-Lore*, 1928, 30:13 (Sewickley, Allegheny Co., October, *fide* Christy), 196 (Pittsburgh region, spring song, *fide* Jennings)—CHRISTY, *Cardinal*, 1931, 3:43, 46 (McDonald Reservoir, Washington Co., May)—MCCLINTOCK, *Cardinal*, 1933, 3:128 (Ligonier, Westmoreland Co., summer)—ELLIOTT, *Cardinal*, 1934, 3:170 (Raccoon Creek, Beaver Co., December).

Melospiza melodia COPE, *Cassinia*, 1902, 5:17 (Clinton and Potter Co., June).

Melospiza cinerea melodia TODD, *Ann. Carnegie Mus.*, 1904, 2:574 (Erie and Presque Isle, Erie Co., summer; occasional in winter)—TODD, in Bausman, *Hist. Beaver Co., Pa.*, 1904, 2:1200 (Beaver Co., resident)—KEIM, *Cassinia*, 1905, 8:39 (Port Allegany, McKean Co., summer).

Melospiza melodia melodia HARLOW, *Auk*, 1912, 29:474 (southern Centre Co., summer)—CHRISTY, *Cardinal*, 1923, v. 1, no. 1, [p. 10] (Sewickley, Allegheny Co., resident)—BURLEIGH, *Wilson Bull.*, 1923, 35:95 (Allegheny Co., resident; nesting); 1924, 36:72; 1931, 43:48 (State College, Centre Co., migration; nesting)—CHRISTY and SUTTON, *Cardinal*, 1928, 2:72 (Cook Forest, Clarion Co., summer)—SUTTON, *Ann. Carnegie Mus.*, 1928, 18:185 (Meadville and Pymatuning Swamp, Crawford Co., resident; nesting)—BURLEIGH, *Cardinal*, 1932, 3:83 (near Uniontown, Fayette Co., summer).

LAPLAND LONGSPUR

CALCARIUS LAPPONICUS LAPPONICUS (Linnaeus)

Description—A large, long-winged sparrow, resembling the Snow Bunting in size and proportions. *Spring plumage* (March): upperparts variegated with black, brown, and sandy buff, the *back of the neck chestnut;* a conspicuous buffy stripe over the eye; a blackish patch on the sides of the head joining a *veiled black area on the throat and breast;* rest of underparts soiled white; outer tail feathers partly buffy white. (Later in the season, the crown, the sides of the head, the throat, and the breast, become wholly black.) *Fall plumage* (October): similar to the spring plumage, but the chestnut collar and the black throat and breast scarcely evident; underparts strongly tinged with buff; brown prevailing above.

Range—The Lapland Longspur, like the Snow Bunting, breeds in the Arctic Life Zone of both Eurasia and North America and in the winter migrates southward, more or less irregularly, to the middle states. Warren gained the impression that it was fairly common and regular in the region of Lake Erie, but he was far from right, although the species is perhaps likelier to be encountered there than elsewhere in our region. Even at Warren, R. B. Simpson has seen it on only a few occasions, and always in the company of horned larks. D. A. Atkinson supplies a few records from Allegheny County, but no observers have seen it there in recent years. It should be looked for as a possible component of flocks of horned larks and snow buntings.

Migration—Sennett took specimens of this species at Erie on October 3, 1889, and also on March 25, 1875; these two dates are respectively the earliest for the fall and the latest for the spring. One bird was seen at State College on March 22, 1917 (Burleigh). The species is a winter wanderer, irregular and erratic in its movements, so that dates of occurrence for any given place are not necessarily significant.

Habits—The Lapland Longspur is a frequent associate of the Snow Bunting, and the call notes and general habits of the two birds are similar. S. E. Bacon remarked that the Longspur was much wilder and more difficult to procure than the other. Dr. Atkinson supplies the following note: "Mr. John Watson took this bird on two occasions: first, on January 14, 1892, when he shot a male from a flock of about twenty birds on the bank of the Allegheny River near Aspinwall; and again, on January 27, 1896, when he discovered a flock of fifty or more eating weed seeds in a field along the Ohio River at Sewickley. On both dates the ground was covered with snow and the weather was quite severe. I have myself encountered this species only once—during a severe cold snap from January 13 to 16 in 1896 —when a flock of about twenty birds had a rendezvous on a farm near Wilkinsburg. They spent much of their time in the shelter of the corn shocks and fed upon the weed seeds in the surrounding fields. I secured a pair on the first day."

Calcarius lapponicus WARREN, *Birds Pa.*, ed. 2, 1890, 232 (Erie, Erie Co., winter)—WARREN, *Forest and Stream*, 1890 34:64 (Erie, Erie Co., October, *fide* Sennett)—TODD, *Ann. Carnegie Mus.*, 1904, 2:570 (Erie, Erie Co., transient).

"Lapland Longspur" SIMPSON, *Oölogist*, 1912, 29:370 (Warren, Warren Co., February)—UPSON, *et al.*, *Bird-Lore*, 1935, 37: 47 (Presque Isle, Erie Co., December).

Calcarius lapponicus lapponicus BURLEIGH, *Wilson Bull.*, 1924, 36:128 (State College, Centre Co., March).

EASTERN SNOW BUNTING

PLECTROPHENAX NIVALIS NIVALIS (Linnaeus)

Description—One of the larger sparrows, with *white prevailing*. Upperparts buffy brown, with darker streaks; *wings and tail* black, with *large white areas;* underparts white, the breast and sides washed with light brown; sides of head white, with a brownish spot on the ear coverts; bill light-colored; feet dark.

Range—This is strictly an arctic and circumpolar species, which ranges in winter to the Temperate Zone. Its southward dispersion depends largely on the season, and a severe winter with much snow tends to carry it farther south than usual. It seems to be commoner and more regular along the shores of Lake Erie than elsewhere in our region, but even there the mild winters of recent years have made it less numerous than formerly. In the Pymatuning region of Crawford County it is more or less irregular, while in the Ohio Valley it appears only during spells of intensely cold weather, when, however, it may be locally abundant. In the mountain section it is rare, but it has been observed at Renovo in January, 1914, by A. K. Pierce; at State College by R. C. Harlow and T. D. Burleigh; and at Springs, Somerset County, by A. B. Miller.

Migration—In my 1904 report, I wrote of the Snow Bunting: "For a species of such cold weather proclivities, the date of its arrival [at Erie] in 1900—October 17—seems remarkably early, yet by October 22 it was already recorded as common. That this is not exceptional, however, is shown by Mr. Bacon's record of the same date in 1892, and of October 21 in 1901, as the time of the first fall appearance of the species in those years, while Dr. Warren says that in 1889 one was shot as early as October 12." On November 3, 1934, W. E. Dilley saw "thousands" of "snowflakes" at the open, or eastern, end of Presque Isle. At

Greenville, in Mercer County, the species was once seen as early as October 23 (1925—Seiple). On November 2, 1919, I was surprised to find a single stray bird feeding along the roadside near Beaver. Other than this record, there are no early dates reported from the Ohio Valley and southward; the species appears there as a rule only in the dead of winter. It is seldom common after February but usually does not finally disappear until sometime in March, and it has been observed as late as April 9 (1928) at Shermansville, Crawford County, by C. A. Bergstrom.

Habits—On Presque Isle, where the "snowflakes" sometimes appear in seasons other than winter, "they throng the outside beach in flocks

of from a few birds up to a hundred or more, while stray individuals are occasionally found along the shore of the bay. Sometimes they are found associated with Prairie Horned Larks, but as a rule they keep separate. They usually keep close to the edge of the water, and although not especially shy, are very restless and erratic in their movements, flying in a jerky, hesitating fashion, as if about to alight every instant" (Todd, 1904). Winter's coming may indeed force them to retire southward for a time, but it cannot chill their spirits nor quiet their twittering chatter. A bitterly cold day in midwinter, with an icy blast sweeping down from the north and the snow swirling in blinding clouds and piling in great drifts, finds the "snowflakes" in their wonted element. They seem to revel in the fury of the storm. Quieter days may discover them spread out over the stubble fields, where weed seeds are abundant. They are more restless than the horned larks, with which they often associate, and flocks are continually flying up, only to swing around and settle again, perhaps in the same place. Wherever the snow is partly melted they rather favor the bare spots. I once saw a flock that must have numbered several thousand birds; usually, however, snow buntings travel in flocks of smaller size. Mr. Burleigh once saw a flock of about fifty birds alight in the upper branches of a large tree, but this occurrence was unusual.

E. W. Arthur's interesting account (1926) of a flock that he saw in February near Slippery Rock, Butler County, may fittingly close the account of this species in particular, and of the *Birds of Western Pennsylvania* in general:

"None of the rest of us had ever before seen any of these little visitors from the far north. They were black-striped over a white body, with reddish brown on head and breast. From time to time, about to alight, the whole flock banked up against the wind and then the white patches under their wings flickered among the real snowflakes that were drifting about in the air, and we caught the quaint imagery of the name.

"Even while we watched, there came others from across the road to join the throng. Now the flock would alight for a few seconds. Then, with a succession of little voices, an odd sound that resembled somewhat a faint or far away whinny, they would rise as one mass and wheel and turn in marvellous fashion. For much of the time the whole battalion would fairly roll over the surface of the ground in swift progress. Specifically, that means that the vanguard of those in the air would suddenly drop to the earth; those behind them would fly beyond them and alight, and so on through the whole flock until those who had alighted first found themselves in the rear rank, whereupon they would rise and repeat the performance. It was surprising how rapidly the whole flock in this manner would pass across the ten-acre field. One of our party ran back perhaps a thousand feet through the snow, which on that windswept field was not so deep as elsewhere, up over the rolling ground in an effort to drive the flock toward us. Three times they massed to fly by him, and three times his shouts and frantic capers turned the trick. Finally the entire flock came winging back almost over our heads.

"We watched them for ten minutes or more, and all the while from the lower ground out of sight to the west of the road, up into our range of vision came others by fives and tens and fifties, almost as though rising out of the earth itself, until the whole great flock in motion, from the road back five hundred feet to the tree-covered hill beyond, aggregated certainly not less than a thousand birds. My companions were sure fifteen hundred was nearer the correct figure.

"I never saw such a multitude. They kept ever in motion except for such brief intervals as some were on the ground in the rolling maneuver described above. Now and then these comprised several hundred birds, and ever and anon as they rose came the low, musical whinnying chorus of voices, itself a distinctive feature of the exhibition. It was with mingled emotions of regret and large satisfaction—incidentally with chilled hands and feet—that we left the flock to battle with the squalls and ourselves took up again our journey."

Plectrophanes nivalis Gibson, *Ornithologist and Oölogist*, 1883, 8:94 (Renovo, Clinton Co., October)—Townsend, *Proc. Acad. Nat. Sci. Philadelphia*, 1883, 62 (Latrobe, Westmoreland Co., winter).

Plectrophenax nivalis Warren, *Birds Pa.*, ed. 2, 1890, 232 (Erie and vicinity, Erie Co., winter, *fide* Sennett)—Warren, *Forest and Stream*, 1890, 34:64 (Erie, Erie Co., winter; October, *fide* Russell).

Passerina nivalis Todd, *Ann. Carnegie Mus.*, 1904, 2:570 (Erie and Presque Isle, Erie Co., winter)—Todd, in Bausman, *Hist. Beaver Co., Pa.*, 1904, 2:1200 (Beaver Co., winter).

"Snowflake" Simpson, *Oölogist*, 1910, 27:100; and 1912, 29:370 (Warren, Warren Co., winter)—Arthur, *Cardinal*, 1926, v. 1, no. 8, p. 9 (Slippery Rock, Butler Co., winter; habits; Beaver, Beaver Co., February, *fide* Todd; Quaker Valley, Allegheny Co., *fide* Miller).

"Snow Bunting" [Editor], *Oölogist*, 1924, 41:37 (Port Allegany, McKean Co., February, *fide* Abbott)—Boulton, *Bird-Lore*, 1928, 30:127 (Sandy Lake, Mercer Co., February, *fide* Homer, *et al.*)—Upson, *et al.*, *Bird-Lore*, 1935, 37:47 (Presque Isle, Erie Co., December).

Plectrophenax nivalis nivalis Christy, *Cardinal*, 1923, v. 1, no. 1, [p. 9] (Sewickley, Allegheny Co., February)—Burleigh, *Wilson Bull.*, 1923, 35:93 ([Mt. Oliver], Allegheny Co., December); 1924, 36:128 (State College, Centre Co., winter)—Sutton, *Ann. Carnegie Mus.*, 1928, 18:175 (Crawford Co. localities, winter; records and references)—Bergstrom, *Cardinal*, 1930, 2:186 (Shermansville and Conneaut Lake, Crawford Co., winter).

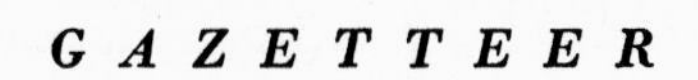

GAZETTEER

GAZETTEER

In this work, which is primarily concerned with local distribution of birds, geographical precision is of paramount importance. Not all the published articles on western Pennsylvania birds are beyond criticism in this respect, and some are quite unusable. Records giving only the county, such as many of those in Warren's 1890 *Report*, are of little value. The use of locality names that cannot be found on accessible maps is almost as deplorable as the complete omission of localities. Efforts to check these dubious and missing locality names have entailed much correspondence, some personal interviews, the study of original records when these were available, and examination of various maps. The results of these investigations are discussed in the Bibliography, and appear (generally enclosed in brackets) in the lists of references under the several species.

In order to identify all the places mentioned in the text of this work, an alphabetical list has been compiled. Annotations appear where necessary; and in some instances the names of the observers follow in italics, in parentheses. With the few exceptions of localities that are too close together to be indicated (designated by an asterisk), all the places listed in the Gazetteer may be found on the folding map at the back of the book. Strictly local names, that is, those that do not appear on the topographic sheets of the United States Geological Survey or on the official map of the City of Pittsburgh, are enclosed in quotation marks. Place names that have been changed are listed under both the old and the new names and are cross-referenced. Fixing the position of certain abandoned railroad stops and other remote localities has involved considerable research. Only a very few names, however, have defied final location. The list includes the names of all mountains, hills, gaps, valleys, streams, islands, lakes, ponds, bays, swamps, cities, towns, villages, crossings, mills, parks, forests, and other areas (excluding counties and townships), referred to in the text. Absolute uniformity and consistency have not been attained, but the orthography adopted is in general that found on the United States topographic maps, or, in the case of Pittsburgh, on the available city maps. Wherever possible, the use of the possessive form of names of localities or streams has been avoided.

Adams, Butler County, a stop on the Harmony Electric Line (now abandoned), one-half mile north of Mars.

Adamsville, Crawford County. (*Sutton; Seiple*)

Alan Seeger Forest, Huntingdon County, a fine stand (30 acres) of virgin timber along Detweiler Run, about three miles north of Greenwood Furnace. (*Sutton*)

Albion, Erie County.

Aliquippa, Beaver County.

Allegheny (City), now Pittsburgh (North Side), Allegheny County.

Allegheny Mountain (or Mountains), the culminating ridge of the Appalachian Chain in western Pennsylvania, forming the watershed or divide between the drainage systems of the Ohio River, on the one hand, and of the Juniata and the Potomac rivers, on the other. Entering Somerset County with a general northeastward trend, which increases in Centre and Clinton counties, the ridge rises to 2,000 or 2,500 feet or even more, the general elevation decreasing from south to north. Its eastern face, which is comparatively steep, is often called the Allegheny Front, or Escarpment, while the ridge itself is referred to as the Allegheny Divide, or Crest. (The original spelling, "Alleghany," is used on the map.)

Allegheny River, one of the two main affluents and constituents of the Ohio River, draining a large area in the northern and western counties of Pennsylvania. It rises in the highlands of Potter County, takes a northward bend into New York state, re-enters Pennsylvania in Warren County, and thence follows an irregular southward course to its junction with the Monongahela River at Pittsburgh. It has carved out a deep valley, and its course is crooked.

Allegrippus, Blair County, a former flag stop on the main line of the Pennsylvania Railroad, about two miles due east of the Gallitzin tunnel. (*Todd*)

Althom (formerly Thompson), Warren County.

Altoona, Blair County, a city in the valley at the base of the Allegheny Front; a "railroad town." Lake Altoona, the third and lowest reservoir of the city's water-supply system, is situated two and one-half miles due west of the southern extremity of the city, along the railroad. (*McGraw*)

Ambridge, Beaver County.

Amity, Washington County.

Anderson Creek, Clearfield County, the present name of a locality visited by the author in June, 1899, en route from Clearfield to Winterburn.

"Ant Hills," Blair County, one-half mile north of Hollidaysburg. (*McGraw*)

Arden, Washington County, on Chartiers Creek.

Ardenheim, Huntingdon County.

Aspinwall, Allegheny County.

Atlantic, Crawford County. (*Sutton*)

Avalon, Allegheny County.

Avella, Washington County.

Baden, Beaver County.

Bailey Run, Cameron County, a small stream in Grove Township, about seven miles from Sinnemahoning, emptying into Sinnemahoning Creek.

Bakerstown, Allegheny County. (Numerous specimens collected by R. L. Fricke were taken three miles southeast of the town.)

Bald Eagle Creek, Centre County, a stream draining the valley between Bald Eagle Mountain and the main Allegheny range.

Bald Eagle Mountain, a ridge running parallel to the main Allegheny Mountain, from Tyrone, Blair County, to Lock Haven, Clinton County. It rises to 1,500–1,800 feet.

Bald Knob, an elevation on the edge of the Seven Mountains region of Centre County, about one and one-half miles southeast of Boalsburg. It rises to 2,300 feet.

"Barclay's Crossing" (formerly "Oakwood Station"), Beaver County, the local name for a railroad crossing two miles above Industry.

Barmore Lake, Mercer County, a shallow body of water a few acres in extent, on a golf course about one mile southwest of Grove City.

Barmore Run, Mercer County, the outlet of Barmore Lake, emptying into Wolf Creek.

Barree, Huntingdon County.

Bavington, Washington County.

Bear Lake, a small lake in the northwestern part of Warren County, about one mile east of the village of the same name. It was once fringed all around by trees and shrubbery, but the original conditions have been greatly modified. See W. R. Van Dersal, *Proceedings Pennsylvania Academy of Science*, 1936, 10:142. (*Todd*, 1898, 1934)

Bear Meadows, a peat bog about one square mile in extent, situated in a depression in the Seven Mountains region of southern Centre County, at an altitude of about 1,800 feet. In the middle is an open area, overgrown with sedges and other semiaquatic plants; this area was originally surrounded by a high forest of white pine, hemlock, black spruce, balsam fir, and certain deciduous trees, with dense rhododendron thickets below. The whole association was decidedly boreal in character and was unique in the region. When visited by the author in June, 1895, the place had been laid waste by the lumbermen and was nothing but a tangled mass of debris. For a description of this spot in its pristine condition, see W. A. Buckhout, *Forest Leaves*, January, 1889, p. 5; and *Garden and Forest*, 5:314.

Beatty, Westmoreland County, a former station on the main line of the Pennsylvania Railroad, southwest of Latrobe.

Beaver, Beaver County, the home of the author and the center of his local ornithological activities since 1886. Brighton, Borough, Industry, and Potter townships have been the chief field of his labors.

"Beaver Dams," the name applied to the cove at the head of Canoe Creek in eastern Blair County. It is a wild, uninhabited region. (*McGraw*)

Beaver River (formerly the Big Beaver), formed by the junction of the Mahoning and Shenango rivers below New Castle. It flows southward through Lawrence and Beaver counties to join the Ohio River opposite Monaca.

Bedford, Bedford County.

Bedford Springs, Bedford County.

Beech Creek, a stream draining the northern part of Centre County and the adjoining parts of Clinton County, after having cut its way across the Allegheny divide.

Beech Creek Mountain, the name given in this book to an outlying spur of the Alleghenies that runs through parts of Centre and Clinton counties, between the West Branch of the Susquehanna River and Beech Creek. Its crest is at an elevation of 2,000 feet or more.

Bellefonte, Centre County.

Belleville, Mifflin County. (*Todd*)

Bellevue, Allegheny County.

Bellowsville, Beaver County, a village of a few houses on the south bank of the Ohio River opposite Vanport.

Belsano, Cambria County.

"Bemis Dam," Crawford County, on French Creek, three miles north of Meadville.

Ben Avon, Allegheny County.

Benjamin Run, a small stream flowing down the south slope of Beech Creek Mountain, about three and one-half miles due west of Glen Union, Clinton County.

Benson Swamp, a wooded swamp beginning about three miles east of Columbus, Warren County, and extending eastward for another three miles on either side of the Erie Railroad. One of the few places in the state where the balsam fir grows. For a full description, see W. R. Van Dersal, *Proceedings Pennsylvania Academy of Science*, 1936, 10:142. (*Todd*, 1934)

Berlin, Somerset County.

Betula, McKean County.

Big Beaver, the old name for the Beaver River, used to distinguish it from the Little Beaver.

Big Bend of the Shenango River, Mercer County.

Big Cove Tannery, Fulton County. (*Phelps; Stone*)

Big Knob (1,300 feet), the highest elevation in Beaver County, four miles east by north of Rochester.

Big Pond,* one of the ponds on Presque Isle, Erie County.

Big Sewickley Creek,* a stream emptying into the Ohio River at Fair Oaks and forming the boundary between Allegheny and Beaver counties over much of its course.

Big Spring, Somerset County, a pool about 50 feet across, just north of Glade Mountain in Elklick Township, at an altitude of 2,600 feet. It is fed by underground springs. (*Todd*)

Big Traverse Creek, a tributary of Raccoon Creek in southern Beaver County. (Sometimes written "Travis.") (*Christy*)

Black Log Mountain, a ridge extending from Juniata County through eastern Huntingdon County to northern Fulton County, where it joins a similar and nearly parallel ridge, Shade Mountain. Black Log Valley lies between these two ridges.

Black Swamp, Lawrence County, an alder swamp about three miles east of Volant, close to the Mercer County line. (*Todd*)

"Blackburn," the local name for a place a little over two miles northeast of Glen Osborne, Allegheny County.

Blacklick Creek, a stream rising in Cambria County and flowing westward through southern Indiana County. It joins the Conemaugh River below Blairsville.

Blairsville, Indiana County.

Blairsville Intersection (now Torrance), Westmoreland County.

Blooming Valley, Crawford County.

Blue Jay Creek, Forest County, a tributary of Tionesta Creek, in Howe Township. (*Simpson*)

Blue Knob (2,366 feet), a village in Blair County.

Blue Knob (3,136 feet), the highest of a group of irregular round-topped mountain masses in northwestern Bedford County and southwestern Blair County. They are separated from each other, and from the main Allegheny divide, by narrow valleys.

Blue Mountain, a ridge in Mifflin County, lying between Black Log Mountain and the Juniata River and parallel with both. (Its southern tip reaches Huntingdon County.) At one point it rises to 2,000 feet.

Boalsburg, Centre County.

Boggsville, Armstrong County.

Bolivar, Westmoreland County.

Boston, Allegheny County.

"Bowman's Station" (now Mance), Somerset County.

Boydstown, Butler County, at the lower end of Oneida Lake.

Brackenridge, Allegheny County.

Braddock, Allegheny County.

Braddock Reservoir,* northeast of Braddock, Allegheny County.

Bradford, McKean County. (*Teulon*)

Bradford Woods, Allegheny County.

Braeburn, Westmoreland County.

Brentwood, Allegheny County.

Bridgeville, Allegheny County.

Brilliant, Allegheny County.

Brinkerton, Westmoreland County.

Broad Mountain, northern Huntingdon County, between Standing Stone Creek and its eastern branch. It reaches a height of 2,300 feet.

Broad Top Mountain, in Fulton, Bedford, and Huntingdon counties, well described by its name. Its area (roughly stated) is about 60 square miles, and its general elevation is 2,000 feet. It is a plateau drained by several streams leading off in different directions.

Brock, Greene County.

Brookline, a section of Pittsburgh, Allegheny County, occupying part of the "South Hills" district.

Brookville, Jefferson County.

Brown Station (now Brown's Crossing), on the electric line one mile southwest of Thompsonville, Washington County.

Brown's Crossing, *see* Brown Station.

Buchanan, Crawford County, a railroad junction point some two miles south of Meadville.

"Buchanan's Ravine,"* a wooded ravine in the French Creek Valley, east of Buchanan, Crawford County.

Buckhorn (2,368 feet), a point on the crest of the Alleghenies between Cambria and Blair counties, northwest of Altoona. (*McGraw*)

Buckstown, Somerset County. One of the last remaining tracts of virgin timber in this county was located south of this place. (*Todd; Mostoller*)

Buffalo Creek, a stream draining parts of Armstrong and Butler counties and emptying into the Allegheny River at Freeport. The name, Buffalo Creek region, as used in this book, refers to that part of the creek valley and its adjacent uplands lying between Boggsville and the mouth of Little Buffalo Creek, near Monroe. This region has been a favorite field for the author since 1889.

Buffalo Run, Centre County.

Burns Run, a small stream heading on Beech Creek Mountain and emptying into the West Branch of the Susquehanna River just above Keating, Clinton County. It was explored by the author in June, 1894.

Burnt Cabins, Fulton County.

"Bushy Run Battlefield," Westmoreland County, about two miles northeast of Jeannette.

Butcher Run, Butler County, a stream emptying into Connoquenessing Creek just below Butler.

Butler, Butler County. (*Roth*)

Butler Knob (2,360 feet), on Jacks Mountain, five miles west of Shirleysburg, Huntingdon County.

Callery, Butler County. (*Todd*)

Calvin, Huntingdon County. (*Todd*)

Cambridge Springs, Crawford County. (*Dickey*)

Canadohta Lake (formerly Oil Creek Lake), Crawford County, one mile long and one-third mile wide. It was at one time surrounded by low, swampy woodland; but use of the lake as a summer resort has greatly changed conditions. (*Todd*)

Canoe Creek, Blair County, a stream emptying into the Frankstown Branch of the Juniata River at Canoe Creek village. (*McGraw*)

Canoe Creek, a stream draining parts of northern Indiana County and southern Jefferson County.

Canonsburg, Washington County.

"Canonsburg Waterworks,"* three miles east of Canonsburg, Washington County.

Carlton, Mercer County.

Carnegie (formerly Mansfield), Allegheny County.

Carter Camp, the post-office name for New Bergen, Potter County.

Casselman, Somerset County.

Casselman River, a stream draining a large area in Somerset County and joining the Youghiogheny River at Confluence. It is a shallow, swift stream, flowing in a valley with steep slopes on either side.

Cassville, Huntingdon County.

Castle Shannon, Allegheny County.

Cataract, Clearfield County.

Center Furnace, Centre County, a point less than a mile northeast of State College.

Center Furnace Swamp,* a marshy area near Center Furnace, Centre County. (*Harlow, et al.*)

Centerville, Crawford County.

Centerville, Somerset County.

Chalk Hill, Fayette County, on the National Pike three miles east of Summit. (*Burleigh*)

"Chambers Dam," four and one-half miles due south of Washington, Washington County.

Chambersburg, Franklin County.

Charlesville, Bedford County (placed too far west on map).

Charlesville Cove (or Friends Cove), Bedford County, the entire valley drained by Cove Creek.

Charter Oak, northern Huntingdon County. (*Harlow; Burleigh; Miller*)

Chartiers Creek, a stream draining an area in northern Washington County and southwestern Allegheny County. It enters the Ohio River at McKees Rocks.

Cherry Island, Pymatuning Swamp, less than a mile southeast of Hartstown, Crawford County. (*Sutton*)

Cherry Run, a small tributary of Oil Creek, which it enters from the northeast at Rouseville, Venango County.

Cherry Run Reservoir, Indiana County. (*Smyth*)

Cherry Spring, Potter County. The railroad station is three miles south of the village. (*Todd*)

Cherryhill, Erie County.

Chestnut Ridge, a low ridge (1,600 feet) in western Bedford County. (Not to be confused with the ridge of the same name farther west.) (*Preble*)

Chestnut Ridge, the westernmost ridge of the Appalachian chain in Pennsylvania, extending across Fayette and Westmoreland counties into Indiana County. (See page 4)

"Christy Park," an outlying section of McKeesport, Allegheny County, along the Youghiogheny River two miles above its mouth.

Claremont, Allegheny County.

Clarendon, Warren County.

Clarington, Forest County.

Clarion, Clarion County, on the Clarion River.

Clarion Junction, Clarion County. (*Todd*)

Clarion River, a stream draining a large area in Elk, Forest, and Clarion counties. It enters the Allegheny River below Foxburg.

Clarksboro (formerly Clarksville), Mercer County.

Claysville, Washington County.

Clear Lake (formerly Mill Pond), Crawford County, an artificial lake occupying a depression north of Spartansburg. Its shores are boggy, with a fringe of alders farther back. (*Todd*)

Clearfield, Clearfield County.

Clearville, Bedford County. (*Phelps*)

Clermont, McKean County. (*Todd*)

Clifton, Allegheny County, a way station on the Pennsylvania Railroad, between Dixmont and Emsworth.

Climax, Armstrong County. (The railroad station is in Clarion County.) (*Todd*)

Clinton, Allegheny County.

Clinton Pond,* a small body of water along the highway one-half mile northeast of Clinton, Allegheny County.

Coalport, Clearfield County. The observations of the author in 1892 were made about two miles east of the town and thence southward to a tract of original forest along the Pennsylvania and Northwestern Railroad.

Cobham, Warren County.

Cochranton, Crawford County.

Colfax, Huntingdon County. (*Todd*)

College Hill, Beaver County.

Columbus, Warren County.

Conemaugh, Cambria County, near Johnstown.

Conemaugh Furnace, Westmoreland County, at the lower end of the Conemaugh River gap through Laurel Hill. (*Todd*)

Conemaugh River, a stream rising on the western slope of the Allegheny divide in Cambria County and flowing west, over a very irregular and crooked course, to the Allegheny River. Below its junction with Loyalhanna Creek, it is called the Kiskiminetas River. The main line of the Pennsylvania Railroad follows its course where it has cut deep gaps through Laurel Hill and Chestnut Ridge.

Conewango Creek, an affluent of the Allegheny River, which it enters at Warren, Warren County, from the north.

Confluence, Somerset County, at the junction of Laurel Hill Creek, the Casselman River, and the Youghiogheny River.

Conneaut Creek, a stream draining an area in western Crawford and Erie counties. It turns to the west in the latter county and empties into Lake Erie at Conneaut, Ohio. The West Branch of this creek is divided into three branches.

Conneaut Lake, Crawford County, at the lower or southern end of the lake of the same name.

Conneaut Lake, Crawford County, the largest natural lake in the state. It is now so completely a summer resort that its ecological importance is greatly lessened. There remain some small marshy areas on its western and southern shores. See G. M. Sutton, *Annals Carnegie Museum*, 1928, 18:36.

Conneaut Marsh (or Swamp), Crawford County, an extensive marsh reaching from the lower end of Conneaut Lake to French Creek. It is wooded in part and open in part, but not easy to explore.

Conneaut Outlet, Crawford County, a stream flowing through Conneaut Marsh. See G. M. Sutton, *Annals Carnegie Museum*, 1928, 18:37. It must here be noted that because of unwarranted editorial changes in the text of Dr. Sutton's article, Conneaut Outlet is often called "the outlet of Conneaut Lake."

Conneauttee Lake (now Edinboro Lake), southern Erie County. It is about one mile long by one-half mile wide, with marshy ground at its upper or northern end. (*Homer; Roth*)

Conneautville, Crawford County.

Connoquenessing Creek, a stream draining most of southern Butler County and emptying into the Beaver River at Rock Point, Lawrence County.

Conococheague Creek, a stream draining the western part of Franklin County and flowing southward into the Potomac River.

Conrad, Potter County (railroad name, Hull). (*Sutton*)

Conway, Beaver County.

Cook Forest, a tract comprising 7,219 acres, situated where Clarion, Forest, and Jefferson counties meet, north of the Clarion River. It is now a state park, and it contains one of the few stands of virgin white pine and hemlock left in the state, as well as much hardwood and second-growth timber. For a full description of this tract, see B. H. Christy, *Cardinal*, 1928, 2:49–51.

Cooks Run, western Clinton County, a stream emptying into the West Branch of the Susquehanna River at the village of Cooks Run.

Cooksburg, Forest County, at the lower end of Cook Forest.

Cooperstown, Venango County.

Coraopolis, Allegheny County.

"Coraopolis Heights,"* Allegheny County, on the hilltop overlooking Coraopolis.

Corydon, Warren County.

Coudersport, Potter County. (*Todd*)

Cove Creek, Bedford County, a stream rising in Martin Hill southwest of Rainsburg. It drains "Charlesville Cove" (Friends Cove) and flows northward into the Raystown Branch of the Juniata River.

Cove Gap, the post-office name for Foltz, Franklin County.

Cove Mountain, a ridge entering the state from the south between Fulton and Franklin counties, but soon merging with Tuscarora Mountain.

Cowan Gap, Tuscarora Mountain, on the line between Fulton and Franklin counties close to the northern border of the former.

Crafton, Allegheny County.

Cranberry Swamp, Warren County, along Tionesta Creek between Clarendon and Tiona. It is a wooded swamp that has been cut over and spoiled. (*Todd*)

Cresson (or "Cresson Springs"), Cambria County, on the crest of the Alleghenies. (*Dwight; Jamison; Todd; Dickey*)

Crooked Creek, a stream draining the upper or eastern arm of Pymatuning Swamp and flowing southward into the Shenango River.

Cross Fork, Potter County. (*Todd; Cope*)

Cross Fork Junction, Potter County, on the Buffalo and Susquehanna Railroad. (*Todd*)

"Crouse's Run,"* at Wildwood, Allegheny County.

Croyland, Elk County. (*Todd*)

Crumb, Somerset County. (*Preble*)

Crystal Lake, Pymatuning Swamp, east of Hartstown, Crawford County. (Formerly called Mud Lake, *fide* Sutton, and so named on the map.)

Crystal Point,* Erie County, the site of the Perry Monument, at the western entrance to Misery Bay, Presque Isle.

Cussewago Creek (and Valley), Crawford County, a stream entering French Creek opposite Meadville.

Custards, Crawford County.

"Dan Hollow,"* Benzinger Township, Elk County, about two miles southeast of Glenhazel.

Darlington, Westmoreland County.

Davis Island, a small island in the Ohio River, due west of Bellevue, Allegheny County.

Dee, Armstrong County.

Deer Creek,* Allegheny County, a stream entering the Allegheny River from the north at Harmarville. The term Deer Creek region, as used in this book, refers to the lower valley of the stream, within about three miles of its mouth.

"Dell Delight," a park just west of Hollidaysburg, Blair County.

Denny, Allegheny County.

"Denny Pond,"* a small pond in the flat land along the Allegheny River, near Denny, Allegheny County.

Detweiler Run, a small stream in extreme northeastern Huntingdon County, draining into Standing Stone Creek. (*Todd*)

Diamond Valley, West Township, Huntingdon County, east of Tussey Mountain.

Dixmont, Allegheny County, at the mouth of Toms Run.

"Doan's Pond," a small pond near the highway about one and one-half miles west and a little south of Guys Mill, Crawford County.

Dollar Lake, Pymatuning Swamp, a small circular body of water east of Hartstown, Crawford County, close to the state highway.

Donaldson, Warren County.

Donegal, Westmoreland County.

Donohoe, Westmoreland County, a station on the main line of the Pennsylvania Railroad.

Dorseyville, Allegheny County.

Douthett, Allegheny County, a stop on the Harmony Electric Line (now abandoned).

Drake's Mill, Crawford County.

Dravosburg, Allegheny County.

Driftwood, Cameron County. (*Todd*)

Drury Run, Clinton County, a stream rising in Tamarack Swamp and flowing into the West Branch of the Susquehanna River just above Renovo. (*Todd*)

DuBois, Clearfield County. (*Van Fleet*)

Duncansville, Blair County.

Dunkard, Greene County.

Dunkard Creek, a stream draining the southern part of Greene County.

Dunlo, Cambria County. (*Todd*)

Duquesne, Allegheny County.

Dutch Run, Indiana and Cambria counties, an affluent of Blacklick Creek (north branch). (*Todd*)

Eagle Rock, Venango County.

East Altoona, Blair County.

East Brook, Lawrence County.

East Freedom, Blair County.

East Hickory Creek, Warren County.

East Pittsburgh, Allegheny County.

East Springfield, Erie County.

East Tionesta Forest Reserve, a tract comprising 3,836 acres of virgin forest in Warren and McKean counties. The tract belongs to the federal government and has been set aside as a natural laboratory for scientific and educational research. See A. F. Hough, *Ecology*, January, 1936, v. 17, no. 1, p. 9–28; and articles by several authors in *Forest Leaves*, April, July, October, 1934, v. 24, nos. 2, 3, 4, p. 19–27.

East Titusville (or Fieldmore Springs), Crawford County.

Ebensburg, Cambria County. (*Todd*)

Economy, Beaver County.

Edgebrook,* a section of Pittsburgh, Allegheny County, one and one-eighth miles due south of McKinley Park.

Edgecliff, Westmoreland County.

Edgewood, Allegheny County.

Edgeworth, Allegheny County.

Edinboro, Erie County.

Edinboro Lake, *see* Conneauttee Lake.

Ekastown, Butler County.

Elderton, Armstrong County.

Ellis Island,* Pymatuning Swamp, Crawford County, close to Cherry Island, southeast of Hartstown.

Ellisburg, Potter County.

Elmer, Potter County. (*Homer*)

Elulalia, the post-office name for Sheffield Junction, Forest County.

Emmaville, Fulton County. (*Phelps*)

Emporium, Cameron County.

Emsworth, Allegheny County.

Endeavor, Forest County. (*Dickey*)

Entriken, Huntingdon County. (*Surber*)

Erie, Erie County.

Erie Bay (or Presque Isle Bay), an arm of Lake Erie.

Espyville, Crawford County, one mile west of Espyville railroad station.

Euclid, Butler County.

Everett, Bedford County.

Everson, Fayette County.

Evitts Mountain, an elevation entering Bedford County from the south and continuing into Blair County under another name.

Fair Oaks, Allegheny County, a former station and post office (now abandoned) near the mouth of Big Sewickley Creek.

Fannettsburg, Franklin County.

Fenelton, Butler County.

Fieldmore Springs, *see* East Titusville.

Fillmore, Centre County.

Finleyville, Washington County.

First Mountain, southern Centre County, one of the Seven Mountains.

Firstfork, Cameron County.

Fish Creek, a stream draining an area in southwestern Greene County.

Flaugherty Run,* in Moon Township, Allegheny County, a stream entering the Ohio River from the west at Shousetown (now Glenwillard).

Flowing Spring, Blair County. (*Todd*)

Foltz, Franklin County (Cove Gap post office).

Fool Creek, a tributary of Tionesta Creek, in southern Cherry Grove Township, Warren County.

Forbes Forest, Westmoreland County, a state forest on the summit and west slope of Laurel Hill, south of Laughlintown.

Forest Hills, Allegheny County, east of Edgewood and Swissvale.

Forestville, Butler County.

Fort Loudon, Franklin County.

Four-mile Run, Brighton Township, Beaver County, a stream emptying into the Ohio River from the north at Merrill.

Foxburg, Clarion County. (*Harlow*)

Frankfort Springs, southern Beaver County. (*Christy*)

Franklin, Venango County.

Frankstown Branch of the Juniata River. It drains the larger part of Blair County, whence it flows through Huntingdon County to meet the Raystown Branch below Huntingdon.

Freeport, Armstrong County, at the mouth of Buffalo Creek. (*Todd*)

French Creek, a stream draining southern Erie County and central Crawford County. It enters the Allegheny River at Franklin, Venango County.

Frick Park, on the eastern edge of the city limits of Pittsburgh, Allegheny County.

Friends Cove, *see* Charlesville Cove.

"Fruits Mill," Mercer County.

Furnace Run, eastern Westmoreland County, a tributary of Loyalhanna Creek.

Gaibleton, Indiana County. (*Trimble*)

Galbraith Gap (or Reitz Gap), one mile east of Bald Knob, southern Centre County.

Galeton, Potter County. (*Cope*)

Gallitzin, Cambria County.

Gardner Swamp, a cattail swamp a few acres in extent, with an area of open water in the middle, lying about four miles southeast of the center of New Castle, Lawrence County.

Garland, Warren County.

Garrison, Greene County.

Gastown, Armstrong County. (*Todd*)

Gayly, Allegheny County.

Geneva, Crawford County.

Georgetown, Beaver County.

Germania, Potter County.

Glade Mountain, a spur of Negro Mountain in western Elklick Township, Somerset County, rising to an altitude of 3,040 feet.

Glade Run, Somerset County, a stream flowing along the southern base of Glade Mountain and through an extensive open marsh called Glade Run Marsh, or simply the Glades.

Glade Run, Warren County, a small stream entering the Allegheny River from the north, just above Warren.

Glen Osborne (or Osborne), Allegheny County.

Glen Union, Clinton County.

Glenfield, Allegheny County.

Glenhazel, Elk County.

Glenn Island,* Pymatuning Swamp, Crawford County, a small island just west of the "spillway" south of Linesville.

Glenshaw, Allegheny County.

Glenwillard (formerly Shousetown), Allegheny County.

Gold, Potter County. (*Todd*)

Gordon Lake, a small lake about two miles southwest of Bedford Springs, Bedford County.

Grant (formerly Grantonia), Elk County.

Grant Run,* near Grant, Elk County.

Grantonia (now Grant), Elk County.

Great Trough Creek, an affluent of the Raystown Branch of the Juniata River, in southwestern Huntingdon County.

Green Garden, Beaver County.

Greencastle, Franklin County.

Greendale, Valley Township, Armstrong County.

Greensburg, Westmoreland County.

Greensburg Reservoir, on the hilltop two and one-half miles southeast of Greensburg, Westmoreland County.

Greenville, Mercer County. (*Seiple*)

Greenwood Furnace, Huntingdon County. (*Todd*)

Grove City, Mercer County.

Grove Run, Clinton County, a small stream entering the West Branch of the Susquehanna River from the northwest, in West Keating Township.

Grunder Run, Warren County, a stream entering the Allegheny River from the south four miles due west of the mouth of Conewango Creek.

Guyasuta, Allegheny County, between Sharpsburg and Aspinwall.

Guyasuta Run,* a stream entering the Allegheny River at Guyasuta, Allegheny County.

Guys Mill, Crawford County.

Guys Run,* a small stream flowing into Deer Creek just before the latter joins the Allegheny River at Harmarville, Allegheny County.

Hackney, Washington County.

Haffey, the post-office name for Milltown, Allegheny County.

Half Moon Swamp, Fairview Township, Mercer County.

Hallton, Elk County.

Hares Valley, Cass Township, Huntingdon County, a former post office on the present site of Cornelius Chapel, two and one-half miles north of Saltillo. In a larger sense the name applies to the entire valley section. (*Phelps*)

Harlansburg, Lawrence County. (*Todd*)

Harmarville, Allegheny County. (*Burleigh, et al.*)

Harmonsburg, Crawford County.

Harmony, Butler County.

Harrisville, Butler County. (*Todd; Keesler*)

"Harry's Valley," Huntingdon County, a name used by R. F. Miller instead of the more usual name of "Stone Valley." Strictly speaking, however, the two are not identical.

Harshaville, Beaver County.

Hart's Run,* a small stream in southern Hampton Township, Allegheny County, tributary to Pine Creek.

Hartstown, Crawford County. (*Todd; Sutton; et al.*)

Hasson Gap,* Tussey Mountain, Centre County, one mile southeast of Shingletown.

Hazelhurst, McKean County. (*Todd*)

Heart's Content, Warren County, the site of a tract of 121 acres of virgin forest. See H. J. Lutz, *Ecology*, 1930, 11:1–29; and H. F. Morey, *Ecology*, 1936, 17:43–55.

Hemlock Island, Pymatuning Swamp. Now nearly all covered by the waters of the new lake. (*Hicks*)

"Hemlock Point," Pymatuning Swamp, Crawford County, three and one-half miles due west of Linesville.

Hero, Greene County.

Hickory, Washington County.

"Hickory Bottom Swamp,"* northwest of Lakemont, Blair County.

Hickory Creek (Middle Branch), a stream rising near Heart's Content, Warren County, and flowing southwestward to join the Allegheny River. (Middle Hickory Creek on map.)

Hidden Lake, *see* Lower Lake.

Highland Park, within the city limits of Pittsburgh, Allegheny County, opposite Aspinwall. It contains three reservoirs, where waterfowl sometimes alight.

"Highouse's Eddy,"* on the Allegheny River, Warren County, near Warren.

Hillside, Westmoreland County.

Hiram, Fulton County.

"Hoag's Ravine," one and one-half miles south of Meadville, Crawford County, on the west side of French Creek.

Holbrook, Greene County.

Hollidaysburg, Blair County. (*Berg*)

Homer City, Indiana County.

Homer Gap Run, a stream rising on the east flank of the Allegheny divide, north of Altoona, Blair County. It flows into the Little Juniata River at the lower (north) end of the city of Juniata.

Homestead, Allegheny County.

Homestead Park,* Allegheny County.

Homewood Junction, the railroad name for Racine, Beaver County.

Hookstown, Beaver County.

Hoover's Run, Wayne Township, Greene County, an affluent of Dunkard Creek.

Hooversville, Somerset County. (*Preble*)

Hopewell, Bedford County.

Horse Valley, a cove in Franklin County, northeast of Jordan's Knob.

"Horseshoe Curve,"* on the Pennsylvania Railroad, at Kittanning Point, Blair County.

Houston, Washington County.

Howard, Centre County. (*Todd*)

Howard Hill* (2,258 feet), an elevation in McKean County, upon which the town of Mount Jewett stands.

Howards, Cameron County.

Hull, the railroad name for Conrad, Potter County.

Huntingdon, Huntingdon County.

Huntley, Cameron County.

Hustontown, Fulton County. (*Todd*)

Hyde Park, Westmoreland County.

Hydetown, Crawford County.

Hyndman, Bedford County. (*Surber*)

Hyner, Clinton County.

Idaho, Armstrong County. (*Todd*)

Idlewild, a picnic resort at the eastern end of the gap of Loyalhanna Creek through Chestnut Ridge, Westmoreland County. (*Preble*)

"Immel Reservoir," on the western flank of Laurel Hill, about one and one-half miles east of Lycippus, Westmoreland County.

Indian Creek, Fayette County.

Indiana, Indiana County.

Industry, Beaver County.

Ingram, Allegheny County.

Iron Bridge, Armstrong County.

Irwin, Westmoreland County.

Jacks Mountain, a ridge extending from Huntingdon County into Mifflin County, with a gap between Mapleton and Mount Union through which the Juniata River flows.

Jacks Run,* Versailles Township, Allegheny County, east of McKeesport. ("Jacks Run," in G. M. Sutton, *Annals Carnegie Museum*, 1928, 18:153, 220, should read "Jackson Run.")

Jackson Run, Conewango Township, Warren County, a stream flowing into Conewango Creek about two miles above the mouth of the latter.

Jackson Run, east of Hartstown, Crawford County. Erroneously called "Jacks Run" by G. M. Sutton, *Annals Carnegie Museum*, 1928, 18:153, 220.

Jacobs Creek, Westmoreland County. (*Medsger*)

Jamestown, Mercer County.

Jamisonville, Butler County. H. H. Elliott's observations were made about one mile south of this point.

Jeannette, Westmoreland County.

Jefferson, Greene County.

Jenner Crossroads, Somerset County, one mile southeast of Jennerstown, on the Lincoln Highway.

Jennerstown, Somerset County. ("Jennertown" on the map.)

Johnsburg, Somerset County.

Johnsonburg, Elk County.

Johnstown, Cambria County. Johnstown Airport* is one and one-half miles west of the town. (*Canan; Mostoller*)

Jordan's Knob (1,800 feet), an elevation at the head of Horse Valley, western Franklin County.

"Jumbo Woods,"* an area of high forest in northwestern Beaver Township, Crawford County, one and one-half miles southeast of Wing.

Jumonville, Fayette County, on the western flank of Chestnut Ridge. (*Preble*)

"Junction Hill" (1,423 feet), on the west side of French Creek, two miles south of Meadville, Crawford County.

Juniata, the lower (northern) section of Altoona, Blair County.

Juniata Crossing, eastern Bedford County, where the Lincoln Highway crosses the Raystown Branch of the Juniata River.

Juniata River, the principal western affluent of the Susquehanna River, draining the larger part of the ridge and valley section. Below Huntingdon it divides into the Frankstown Branch and the Raystown Branch.

Kane, McKean County. (*Pierce; Todd*)

Karthaus, Clearfield County.

Katrine Swamp, or Katrine Pond Swamp, a wooded swamp in southern McKean County. When visited by the author in June, 1895, it had already been lumbered over, and only a suggestion of its original avifauna remained.

Keating, Clinton County. (*Todd*)

Keating Summit, Potter County.

Kennard, Mercer County.

"Kennedy's Riffles," on French Creek, one-half mile north of Buchanan, Crawford County.

Kettle Creek, a stream draining southeastern Potter and western Clinton counties. It enters the West Branch of the Susquehanna River near Westport.

Keystone (formerly Keystone Junction), Somerset County, a point on the Baltimore & Ohio Railroad where the road passes through a gorge in the Allegheny Mountains. (*Preble*)

"Kidds Mill," on the Shenango River about two miles south of Shenango, Mercer County.

Kimberlen Run (Kimberly Run on some maps), about one mile south of Somerset, Somerset County. (*Preble*)

Kingston, Westmoreland County, at the western end of the gap in Chestnut Ridge through which Loyalhanna Creek flows. (*Todd*)

Kinzua, Warren County.

Kirby, Greene County.

Kittanning, Armstrong County.

Kittanning Point, Blair County, the site of the "Horseshoe Curve" on the Pennsylvania Railroad.

Kladder, Blair County.

Klink Run, a stream flowing into Pymatuning Swamp from the west a little over one mile north of Hartstown, Crawford County.

Knobsville, Fulton County. (*Todd*)

Knoxville, Allegheny County.

Lake Altoona, *see* Altoona.

Lake Le Bœuf, Erie County, near Waterford, 1,166 feet above tide. The lake is of irregular outline and about one-half mile in greatest diameter. It drains into French Creek through Le Bœuf Creek.

Lake Pleasant, Erie County, about one-half mile long. It lies in open country at an elevation of 1,301 feet. (*Sennett; Todd*)

Lake Seaton, Fayette County, a shallow artificial lake about four miles east of Summit, at an elevation of 1,900 feet. (*Burleigh*)

Lakemont, Blair County, the site of a small artificial lake formed by damming a small stream. (*McGraw*)

Lakeville, Crawford County, on Canadohta or Oil Creek Lake.

Lambertsville, Somerset County.

Latrobe, Westmoreland County. (*Townsend*)

Laughlintown, Westmoreland County, at the western base of Laurel Hill. (*Rhoads*)

Laurel Gap, on the Allegheny crest three miles due east of Lilly, Cambria County.

Laurel Hill, a well-marked ridge parallel with the main Allegheny crest and about 20–25 miles west thereof. It enters the state from the south in Fayette County and continues (interrupted by the gaps of the Youghiogheny and Conemaugh rivers) to western Cambria County, where its identity is lost in the general level. It rises to 2,800 feet in many places, and at one point to 3,000 feet.

Laurel Hill Creek, a stream draining southwestern Somerset County and flowing into the Casselman River at Confluence.

Laurel Run, a small stream in extreme northern Huntingdon County, emptying into Standing Stone Creek.

Lawrenceville, a section of Pittsburgh, Allegheny County, adjacent to the Allegheny River.

Leasuresville, Butler County. The name as used in this book refers to a point one mile southeast of the village, in Armstrong County, from which the Buffalo Creek region was worked. (*Todd*)

Le Bœuf Creek, *see* Lake Le Bœuf.

Leckrone, Fayette County.

Leech's Corners, Mercer County.

Leetsdale, Allegheny County. Records attributed to this locality by S. N. Rhoads were actually made along Big Sewickley Creek, above Fair Oaks, by William Seager.

Legionville, Beaver County, a way station on the Pennsylvania Railroad.

Lemont, Centre County.

Licking Creek, a stream draining the greater part of Fulton County (from Sideling Hill to Cove Mountain) and flowing southward into the Potomac River.

Ligonier, Westmoreland County.

Ligonier Valley, the name applied to the region between Chestnut Ridge and Laurel Hill, in Westmoreland and Fayette counties.

Lilly, Cambria County.

Linesville, Crawford County, just north of Pymatuning Lake.

Little Beaver Creek, a stream rising in Lawrence County and flowing across northwestern Beaver County into Ohio. It re-enters Pennsylvania just before emptying into the Ohio River below Smiths Ferry.

Little Beaver Run, an affluent of Moshannon Creek, in southern Decatur and eastern Woodward townships, Clearfield County.

Little Cove,* a valley between Tuscarora Mountain and Cove Mountain in southwestern Franklin County. It is closed at the northern end and is drained by Little Cove Creek.

Little Deer Creek,* an eastern branch of Deer Creek, draining the eastern part of West Deer and Indiana townships, Allegheny County.

Little Kettle Creek, a stream joining Kettle Creek from the north at Oleona, Potter County.

Little Pucketa Creek, a stream draining parts of Upper Burrell and Lower Burrell townships, Westmoreland County. It flows into Pucketa Creek just above the mouth of the latter below New Kensington.

Little Sewickley Creek,* a stream emptying into the Ohio at Shields, Allegheny County, after following an irregular course across Sewickley Heights Township.

Little Traverse Creek (or Run), an affluent of Raccoon Creek, entering the latter from the northwest just below "Patton's Point," southern Beaver County.

Lloydville, Cambria County (2,184 feet), on the Allegheny crest. (*Surber*)

Lock Mountain, a ridge in Blair County east of the Frankstown Branch of the Juniata River. It attains a height of over 2,200 feet at its southern end, near Martinsburg.

Locust Grove, Fulton County. (*Phelps*)

Logan's Ferry, Allegheny County.

Long Hollow, Mifflin County, a valley drained by a stream entering the Juniata River from the north at Mount Union, Huntingdon County.

Long Run,* in Versailles Township, Allegheny County, a stream entering the Youghiogheny River one-third mile below "Christy Park."

Loop Run (or Loup Run), a small tributary of Tipton Run, Blair County, flowing down the eastern face of the Allegheny Front.

Loretto, Cambria County.

Lower Lake (or Hidden Lake), Pymatuning Swamp, southeast of Hartstown, Crawford County.

Lowrie Run,* a stream entering the Ohio River from the north at Emsworth station, Allegheny County.

Loyalhanna Creek, a fairly large creek that drains the Ligonier Valley in Westmoreland County, cuts through Chestnut Ridge in a deep gap, and joins the Kiskiminetas River at Saltsburg, Indiana County.

Lycippus, Westmoreland County.

McAlevy's Fort, Huntingdon County. (*Todd*)

McBride Gap, a gap in Nittany Mountain, three and one-half miles northeast of Lemont, Centre County.

McClure, Fayette County.

McConnell's Mills, Lawrence County.

McConnellsburg, Fulton County.

McConnellstown, Huntingdon County.

McDonald Reservoir, Washington County, one and one-half miles southwest of the Allegheny County line and the same distance east of Bavington.

"McGinnis Run," a tributary of Furnace Run, about one mile south of Laughlintown, Westmoreland County.

McKean, Erie County.

McKee Gap, Blair County. (*Todd*)

McKees Rocks, Allegheny County.

McKeesport, Allegheny County.

McKinley Park (South Side), Pittsburgh, Allegheny County.

McVeytown, Mifflin County. (*Todd*)

Madison, Westmoreland County.

Mahoningtown, Lawrence County. ("Mahonington" on the map.)

Mammoth Reservoir, one-half mile north of Mammoth, Westmoreland County.

Mance (formerly "Bowman's Station"), Somerset County.

Mann's Choice, Bedford County.

Mansfield (Mansfield Valley post office), now Carnegie, Allegheny County.

Mapleton, Huntingdon County. (*Todd*)

Mapletown, Greene County.

Marklesburg, Huntingdon County.

Martin Hill, an irregular ridge connecting Evitts Mountain with Tussey Mountain in southern Bedford County. It attains a height of 2,700 feet.

Martinsburg, Blair County. (*Todd*)

Masseyburg, Huntingdon County.

Mattawana, Mifflin County.

Mayport (formerly Maysville—New Mayville post office), Clarion County. (*Todd*)

Maysville, *see* Mayport.

Mead Island, in the Allegheny River opposite Starbrick, Warren County.

Meadville, Crawford County. (*Kirkpatrick*)

Meadville Junction, Crawford County, on the Bessemer & Lake Erie Railroad.

Mercer, Mercer County.

Mercer Junction, Mercer County, on the Bessemer & Lake Erie Railroad (northeast of Mercer).

Mercersburg, Franklin County.

Merrill, Beaver County, a former station on the Pennsylvania Railroad opposite the mouth of Raccoon Creek.

Metal, Franklin County.

Metcalf, Westmoreland County.

Meyersdale, Somerset County. (*Preble*)

Middle Hickory Creek, *see* Hickory Creek.

Miles Grove (now North Girard), Erie County.

Milesburg, Centre County.

Mill Creek, Huntingdon County.

Mill Pond, *see* Clear Lake.

Mill Run, a stream rising in a tamarack bog southeast of Meadville and entering French Creek at that town.

Millers (Station), Crawford County, on the Erie Railroad.

Millport, Potter County.

Milltown, Allegheny County (Haffey post office).

Millvale, Allegheny County.

Monaca, Beaver County. As used in this book, the name refers to the south bank of the Ohio River, below the town.

Monongahela River, one of the two main affluents of the Ohio River. It rises in West Virginia and flows northward to join the Allegheny River at Pittsburgh. Its tributaries drain a large area in the southern part of western Pennsylvania.

Monroe, Butler County, a way station on the Butler Branch of the Pennsylvania Railroad, near Buffalo Creek.

Monroe Furnace (abandoned), northern Huntingdon County, on the southeastern flank of Tussey Mountain.

"Montgomery Mill," on Wolf Creek about four miles north of Grove City, Mercer County.

Moon Run, Allegheny County.

Mooresville,* northern Huntingdon County (exact position unknown).

Morganza, Washington County. (*Van Ostrand*)

Mosgrove, Armstrong County.

Moshannon, Centre County. (*Surber*)

Mount Chestnut, Butler County.

Mount Jewett, McKean County.

Mount Oliver, Allegheny County.

Mount Pleasant, Westmoreland County. (*Preble*)

Mount Union, Huntingdon County. (*Todd*)

Mud Lake, *see* Crystal Lake.

Muddy Creek, Butler County, an affluent of Slippery Rock Creek, entering that stream from the east.

Murdocksville, Washington County.

Musser Gap, southern Centre County, in the southeastern part of Ferguson Township.

Natrona, Allegheny County.

Needmore, Fulton County.

Negro Mountain, an outlying spur of the main Allegheny range in southern Somerset County, where the mountain widens out to occupy a considerable area. It attains an altitude of 3,220 feet at the head of Glade Run; but north of the gorge of the Casselman River, its general elevation decreases, and its identity is lost in the general level.

Neville Island, nearly five miles long, in the Ohio River between Coraopolis and Bellevue, Allegheny County.

New Alexandria, Westmoreland County.

New Bergen, Potter County (Carter Camp post office).

New Bethlehem, Clarion County.

New Castle, Lawrence County. (*Raney*)

New Florence, Westmoreland County.

New Galilee, Beaver County. An open cattail swamp, a few acres in extent, lies to the west of this town, along the Pennsylvania Railroad. (*Todd*)

New Hamburg, Mercer County. (*Homer*)

New Kensington, Westmoreland County.

New Lexington, Somerset County. Warren's Somerset County records attributed to H. D. Moore presumably came from this place.

New Mayville, *see* Mayport.

New Paris, Bedford County, at the western base of Chestnut Ridge. (*Preble*)

Newburg, Huntingdon County (Trough Creek post office).

Newfield Junction, Potter County.

Newmansville, Clarion County.

Newton Hamilton, Mifflin County. (*Phelps*)

Niagara Pond,* near the eastern end of Presque Isle, Erie County.

Nineveh (now Seward), Westmoreland County. (*Todd*)

Nittany Mountain, Centre County, a broad-topped ridge (1,800 feet) running northeast from Lemont.

Nittany Valley, Centre County, northwest of Nittany Mountain.

Noblestown,* Allegheny County.

North Bend, Clinton County.

North East, Erie County.

North Girard (formerly Miles Grove), Erie County.

North Park, in Pine and McCandless townships, Allegheny County.

North Springfield, Erie County.

Norwich, McKean County.

Oak Hall, Centre County.

Oakdale, Allegheny County.

Oakland, a section of Pittsburgh, Allegheny County.

Oakmont, Allegheny County.

"Oakwood Station," *see* Barclay's Crossing.

Ohio River, formed by the junction of the Allegheny and Monongahela rivers at Pittsburgh. Its general course is at first northwesterly, but after receiving the waters of the Beaver River it turns to the southwest, and leaves the state a little below the village of Smiths Ferry, Beaver County.

Ohiopyle, Fayette County. (*Preble; Todd*)

Oil City, Venango County.

Oil Creek, a stream entering the Allegheny River from the north at Oil City, Venango County.

Oil Creek Lake, *see* Canadohta Lake.

Oleona, Potter County. (*Cope*)

"Olympia Park,"* McKeesport, Allegheny County.

"Oneida Lake," an artificial lake on Connoquenessing Creek near Boydstown, Butler County.

Orbisonia, Huntingdon County.

Osborne, *see* Glen Osborne.

Oscar, Armstrong County.

Osceola Mills, Clearfield County.

Osgood, Mercer County.

Osterburg, Bedford County.

Ott Run, Warren County, a stream entering the Allegheny River from the south a short distance above Warren.

"Packsaddle," the gorge of the Conemaugh River through Chestnut Ridge, east of Torrance, Westmoreland County.

Parrish, Forest County. (*Todd*)

"Patton's Point," the name applied to the hilltop and lower ground enclosed in a loop of Raccoon Creek opposite the mouths of Big and Little Traverse creeks, southern Beaver County. (*Christy*)

Pearl, Venango County.

Pennsylvania Furnace, Huntingdon County.

Peru Mills, Juniata County.

Philipsburg, Centre County.

Pine Bank, Greene County.

Pine Barrens, the name applied to an area in Centre County, south of Scotia.

Pine Creek,* a stream draining the central part of the north side of Allegheny County. It enters the Allegheny River below Sharpsburg.

Pine Creek (with two main branches), a stream draining an area in eastern Armstrong County and entering the Allegheny River at Mosgrove.

Pine Creek, a stream draining a part of eastern Potter County toward the east. It flows into Tioga County.

Pine Flats, Indiana County. (*Todd*)

Pine Glen, Centre County. (*Surber*)

"Pine Grove," a ravine, formerly with bottomland-hardwood forest and dense hemlock growth, about two miles northeast of Industry, Beaver County. (*Todd*)

Pine Grove Mills, Centre County.

Pine Swamp, Mercer County, two miles west of Harrisville.

Pine Valley, Warren County.

Pitcairn, Allegheny County.

Pittsburgh, Allegheny County.

Plains Church, Butler County, a station on the Harmony Electric Line (now abandoned).

Plumer, Venango County.

Polk, Venango County.

Port Allegany, McKean County. (*Todd; Keim; Scherer*)

Port Matilda, Centre County. (*Todd*)

Portage, Cambria County. (*Todd*)

Portersville, Butler County.

Potter's Mills, Centre County.

Powers Run,* a small stream entering the Allegheny River from the west opposite Verona, Allegheny County.

Presque Isle, the peninsula jutting into Lake Erie near the city of Erie, enclosing Presque Isle, or Erie, Bay. For a full account of its physical features and bird life, see Todd, *Annals Carnegie Museum*, 1904, 2:481–596.

Presque Isle Bay, *see* Erie Bay.

Prospect, Butler County.

Pulaski, Lawrence County.

Punxsutawney, Jefferson County. (*Todd*)

Purchase Line, Indiana County.

Putneyville, Armstrong County.

Pymatuning Lake, Crawford County, an artificial lake extending from Linesville to Jamestown.

Pymatuning Swamp, Crawford County, once comprising some 10,400 acres and running over the Pennsylvania boundary into Ohio. It was a wooded bog of the sphagnum-tamarack type, but it has now been cleared for the greater part and converted into a shallow lake. Only at the upper end, near Hartstown, do original conditions still obtain. For a full description of this region and its bird life, see G. M. Sutton, *Annals Carnegie Museum*, 1928, 18:19–239.

Quaker Valley, Allegheny County, a former station on the Pennsylvania Railroad between Sewickley and Edgeworth.

Queen, Bedford County.

Raccoon Creek, a stream rising in northern Washington County and flowing thence northward through Beaver County to join the Ohio River opposite Merrill. Bird records by the author were all made on the lower course of the stream; those by B. H. Christy were made farther up, from "Patton's Point" southward into Washington County.

Racine, Beaver County (railroad name, Homewood Junction). (*Hunter*)

Rainsburg, Bedford County. (*Phelps*)

Randolph Run, a small stream joining Crooked Creek from the east about one and one-half miles south of Hartstown, Crawford County.

Rasselas, Elk County.

Rathbun, Elk County.

Raymilton, Venango County.

Raystown Branch of the Juniata River. It rises in Bedford County and flows thence northward through Huntingdon County to join the Frankstown Branch below Huntingdon. Its course is meandering, with wide loops and oxbows.

Rector, Westmoreland County.

Red Mill, Centre County.

"Red Mill Pond," Centre County, just west of the village of Red Mill.

Redbank, Clarion County. (*Todd*)

Redbank Creek, a stream entering the Allegheny River from the east at Redbank. It forms the boundary between Clarion and Armstrong counties.

Reed's Furnace, Mercer County.

Reitz Gap, *see* Galbraith Gap.

Renovo, Clinton County. (*Pierce*)

Reynoldsville, Jefferson County.

Ribold, Butler County.

Richmond, Indiana County (Rochester Mills post office).

Richmond Furnace, Franklin County.

Riddlesburg, Bedford County. (*Surber*)

Ridgway, Elk County. (*Todd; Alsop*)

"Riley's Ford,"* Allegheny County (location unknown).

Riverview Park, Pittsburgh (North Side), Allegheny County.

Rochester, Beaver County.

Rochester Mills, the post-office name for Richmond, Indiana County.

Rock Point, a picnic resort (now abandoned) at the mouth of Connoquenessing Creek, Lawrence County.

Rockwood, Somerset County. (*Preble*)

Rocky Ridge, a short, irregularly shaped ridge in southern Huntingdon County, east of Broad Top Mountain.

Rogersville, Greene County.

"Rolling Rock," a country-club estate situated about one mile west and a little north of Laughlintown, Westmoreland County, and facing on Loyalhanna Creek.

Rosebud, Clearfield County.

Rosedale, Greene County.

Ross Mountain Park, northeastern Westmoreland County, at the western base of Laurel Hill near West Fairfield.

Roulette, Potter County.

Round Island, Clinton County. (*Rhoads; Todd*)

Round Mountain (2,000 feet), a knob north of Newburg, Huntingdon County.

"Round Top" (1,500 feet), a hill about two miles northwest of Meadville, Crawford County.

Rouseville, Venango County.

Rowan, Butler County, a stop on the Harmony Electric Line (now abandoned).

Rowena, Somerset County.

Rural Ridge, on Little Deer Creek, Allegheny County, three miles north of the Allegheny River. Erroneously called "Rural Bridge" by R. L. Fricke, in the *Cardinal*, 1927, 2:16.

Russell, Warren County.

Ryot (formerly Six Roads), Bedford County.

"Saint Clair Dam," about two miles west and a little north of the center of Johnstown, Cambria County.

Saint Marys, Elk County. (*Sutton*)

Salisbury, Somerset County.

Saltillo, Huntingdon County.

Saltsburg, Indiana County.

Sandy Creek, Allegheny County.

Sandy Lake, Mercer County, one mile long by one-half mile wide. It is bordered by alders, with some cattails along its northern margin. See G. M. Sutton, *Annals Carnegie Museum*, 1928, 18:38. (*Homer*)

Sandy Ridge, Centre County. (*Todd*)

"Sang Hollow," a former stop on the Pennsylvania Railroad, three miles or more northwest of Johnstown, in the gorge through Laurel Hill, Cambria County.

Sarversville, Butler County.

Savage Mountain, southeastern Somerset County, a high ridge roughly parallel with the main Allegheny range to the west. It is divided by a small stream into two ridges: Big Savage Mountain, and Little Savage Mountain.

Sawmill Run, a stream entering the Ohio River from the south less than one mile below the "Point," Pittsburgh, Allegheny County.

"Schaeffer's Pond," Pymatuning Swamp, a small pond on the north side of the highway, above Dollar Lake, Crawford County.

Schellsburg, Bedford County.

Schenley Park, a large park in the Oakland district of Pittsburgh, Allegheny County.

Scotch Hill, Clarion County.

Scotia, Centre County.

Scottdale, Westmoreland County. (*Medsger*)

Scrub Ridge, central Fulton County, about ten miles long and attaining an elevation of 1,900 feet.

Second Mountain,* Centre County (exact position unknown).

Seven-mile Run, a stream flowing southward past Williamsville, Elk County.

Seven Mountains, the name applied to the irregular aggregation of mountain ridges on the border between Centre and Huntingdon counties.

Seward (formerly Nineveh), Westmoreland County.

Sewickley, Allegheny County. (*Christy, et al.*)

Sewickley Heights,* a township of Allegheny County. The name, as generally used, applies to the hilltop section northeast of the town of Sewickley.

Shade Gap, Huntingdon County. (*Phelps*)

Shade Mountain, an elevation extending from northern Fulton County through Huntingdon County and thence into Juniata County, parallel with Black Log Mountain, with which it is connected at its southern extremity.

Shade Valley, Huntingdon County, east of Shade Mountain. It is drained by Shade Creek.

Shadyside, a section of Pittsburgh (East End), Allegheny County; with a station of the same name on the Pennsylvania Railroad.

Shanksville, Somerset County.

Sharon, Mercer County. (*McQuiston*)

Sharpsburg, Allegheny County.

Shaver Creek, a stream rising in the Seven Mountains region of Huntingdon County. It follows a general southwestern course to join the Frankstown Branch of the Juniata River.

Shawmut, Elk County.

"Shaw's Landing" (or Shaws), on French Creek, Crawford County.

Sheakleyville, Mercer County.

Sheffield, Warren County.

Sheffield Junction, Forest County (Elulalia post office).

Shenango, Mercer County.

Shenango River, an affluent of the Beaver River. It rises in Pymatuning Swamp and follows a devious but general southward course through Mercer and Lawrence counties to join the Mahoning River; the combined streams form the Beaver.

Sheriff, Forest County.

Sheriff Run, Upper and Lower, two small streams rising in southern Warren County and flowing south to join Tionesta Creek at Sheriff, Forest County.

Shermansville, Crawford County.

Shields, Allegheny County.

"Shiery's Hill,"* said to be "about two miles northwest of Ligonier," Westmoreland County (*fide* Christy).

Shingletown, Centre County.

"Shingletown Gap,"* Centre County, a local name for Hasson Gap, Tussey Mountain.

Shintown, Clinton County.

Shirleysburg, Huntingdon County.

Shousetown (now Glenwillard), Allegheny County.

Sideling Hill, a ridge extending (with several gaps and interruptions) from the Juniata River southward through Huntingdon and Fulton counties into Maryland. Its general elevation increases from north to south, rising to 2,310 feet at one point.

Sigel, Jefferson County.

Singers Gap, in Jacks Mountain, five miles south of the Juniata River, Huntingdon County.

Sinnemahoning Creek, a stream entering the West Branch of the Susquehanna River at Keating, Clinton County. It drains nearly all of Cameron County, as well as parts of Potter and Elk counties. (Misspelled "Sinnemaghoning" on the map.)

Six-mile Island,* Allegheny River, one-half mile long, between Aspinwall and Highland Park, Allegheny County.

Six Roads (now Ryot), Bedford County.

Sizerville, Cameron County.

"Slack Hollow," the valley and ravine of a small stream flowing into Sawmill Run from the west, about three miles south of metropolitan Pittsburgh, Allegheny County.

Slate Lick, Armstrong County.

Slippery Rock, Butler County.

Slippery Rock Creek, a stream draining parts of Mercer, Butler, and Lawrence counties and joining Connoquenessing Creek a few miles above the mouth of the latter.

"Smith Hill" (1,798 feet), an elevation about four and one-half miles northwest of Youngsville, Warren County.

Smith Run, a small stream flowing along the western base of Sideling Hill. It joins the Juniata River above Mapleton, Huntingdon County.

Smiths Ferry, Beaver County.

Snowshoe, Centre County.

Somerfield, Somerset County.

Somerset, Somerset County. (*Preble*)

South Bethlehem, Armstrong County.

South Bradford, McKean County.

"South Hills,"* the name applied to that part of Pittsburgh, Allegheny County, on the hilltops beyond the Monongahela River.

South Park, in Bethel and Snowden townships, Allegheny County.

South Side Cemetery, Pittsburgh, Allegheny County.

Spartansburg, Crawford County, south of Clear Lake.

Spraggs, Greene County.

Spring Creek, a stream rising near State College, Centre County, and flowing northeastward to join Bald Eagle Creek.

Spring Creek, in eastern Forest County and western Elk County. It flows into the Clarion River at Hallton.

Spring Lake, Crawford County, a small lake about two miles southeast of the center of Meadville.

Springdale, Allegheny County.

Springfield, Erie County.

Springs (formerly Tub), Somerset County. (*Miller*)

Springville, Bedford County, on the present site of St. Marks Church, Colerain Township.

Spruce Creek, Huntingdon County, at the mouth of the stream by the same name.

Squaw Run,* a small stream entering the Allegheny River from the north just east of Claremont, Allegheny County.

Squirrel Hill, a section of Pittsburgh, Allegheny County, east of Schenley Park.

Standing Stone Creek, a stream in eastern Huntingdon County, rising in the Seven Mountains and entering the Juniata River (Frankstown Branch) below Huntingdon.

Standing Stone Mountain, eastern Huntingdon County, an elevation bounding the valley of Standing Stone Creek on the east.

Starbrick, Warren County.

State College, Centre County. (*Harlow; Burleigh; Buckhout; Musgrave; Todd; et al.*) Numerous records attributed to this place really came from the mountains to the southward.

"State College Nature Study Camp," northern Huntingdon County, just north of the Alan Seeger Forest.

Sterling Run, Cameron County.

Stewart's Corners (or Stewartville), Crawford County, about two miles east of Espyville railroad station.

Stewartville, *see* Stewart's Corners.

"Stone Valley," the name loosely applied by R. C. Harlow and others to the entire region south of the Seven Mountains in northern Huntingdon County. It does not appear on any published map of this region.

Stoneboro, Mercer County, south of Sandy Lake.

Stony Point, Crawford County.

Stoops Ferry, Allegheny County.

"Stout's Island,"* in the West Branch of the Susquehanna River at Renovo, Clinton County. (*Pierce*)

Stoyestown, Somerset County.

Straight Creek, a stream in northeastern Elk County, flowing into the Clarion River.

Sugar Lake, Crawford County, one-half mile long and a little less in width. (*Homer*)

Sugar Run, a small stream rising on the Allegheny crest east of Gallitzin, Cambria County, and flowing eastward into the valley near Altoona, Blair County. The Pennsylvania Railroad follows its gorge for a distance.

Sugar Valley, on the east side of the Juniata River opposite Newton Hamilton, Mifflin County.

Sugarloaf Mountain (2,700 feet), an elevation on the west slope of Laurel Hill in Fayette County, southeast of Ohiopyle. (*Preble; Todd*)

Sulphur Spring, on the edge of Tamarack Swamp, about one and one-half miles northwest of Pine Valley, Warren County. Sulphur Spring Lake, an oval pool one hundred yards long, adjoins on the west. Relicts of a boreal character persist here. See W. R. Van Dersal, *Proceedings Pennsylvania Academy of Science*, 1936, 10:138–140.

Summit, Cambria County. (*Rhoads*)

Summit, Fayette County, on the crest of Chestnut Ridge.

Susquehanna River (West Branch), the shallow river that drains a large part of the Allegheny Plateau; its course passes through Clearfield and Clinton counties in a gorge with steep sides and a comparatively narrow valley.

Swarts, Greene County.

Swede Hill, Westmoreland County.

Sweden Valley, Potter County. (*Todd*)

Swissvale, Allegheny County.

Tamarack Swamp, Clinton County, at the head of Drury Run, a wooded bog of the sphagnum-tamarack type, with an outer fringe of spruce and balsam fir, and this surrounded in its turn by hemlock. Several visits (the first in 1894) were paid to this interesting locality by the author, and it has also been visited by F. R. Cope, Jr. See *Cassinia*, 1902, 5:8–21.

"Tamarack Swamp," Crawford County, southeast of Meadville, at the head of Mill Run.

Tamarack Swamp, Erie County, about two and one-half miles northwest of Lake Le Bœuf. (*Homer; Dickey*)

Tamarack Swamp, Warren County, two miles west of Bear Lake. It has been cut over and reduced to an alder thicket. See W. R. Van Dersal, *Proceedings Pennsylvania Academy of Science*, 1936, 10:141.

Tambine, Elk County.

Tarentum, Allegheny County.

Tatman Run, a stream cutting a gap through Terrace Mountain and entering the Raystown Branch of the Juniata River opposite Entriken, Huntingdon County.

Templeton, Armstrong County. (*Enty*)

Ten-mile Creek, the stream on which Waynesburg is situated. It drains a large part of Greene County.

Terrace Mountain, Huntingdon County, an elevation closing in the valley of the Raystown Branch of the Juniata River on the east. It joins Sideling Hill at its northern end. It does not rise much above 1,600 feet.

Thompson (now Althom), Warren County.

"Thompson's Spring,"* one mile northeast of State College (*i.e.*, near Center Furnace), Centre County.

Thompsonville, Washington County.

Thoms Run, a stream draining the Cook Forest area in northeastern Clarion County and flowing into the Clarion River at Cooksburg.

Thornburg, Allegheny County.

Thornhill, Allegheny County.

Tidioute, Warren County. (*Homer*)

Tiona, Warren County. (*Todd*)

Tionesta, Forest County. (*Homer*)

Tionesta Creek, a stream draining most of southeastern Warren County and also Forest County. It enters the Allegheny River at Tionesta in the latter county. The "head of Tionesta Creek" refers to a point near what is now called Heart's Content.

Tipton, Blair County.

"Tipton Dam," three miles northwest of Tipton, Blair County, on Tipton Run.

Titusville, Crawford County.

Toms Run, a stream entering the Ohio River from the north just below Dixmont, Allegheny County.

Torpedo, Warren County.

Torrance (formerly Blairsville Intersection), Westmoreland County.

Town Hill, western Fulton County, a ridge connecting two other ridges diagonally, forming coves on either side. It reaches an elevation of 1,900 feet or more.

Trafford (or Trafford City), Westmoreland County.

Transfer, Mercer County.

Trauger, Westmoreland County.

Treaster Valley, about three miles long, immediately southeast of First Mountain, southern Centre County.

Trough Creek, the post-office name for Newburg, Huntingdon County.

Trough Creek Valley, Huntingdon County, an extensive area between Terrace Mountain on the west and Sideling Hill on the east.

Trout Run, Portage Township, Cambria County, a stream rising on the Allegheny divide and flowing northwestward to empty into the Conemaugh River at Portage.

Tub (now Springs), Somerset County.

Tubmill Reservoir, Ross Mountain Park, northeastern Westmoreland County.

Turnerville, Crawford County.

Turtle Creek, Allegheny County.

Tuscarora Mountain, an elevation forming the western boundary of Franklin County.

Tussey Mountain, a well-defined ridge entering Bedford County from the south and continuing (with certain interruptions by sundry streams) to southern Centre County, where it merges with the Seven Mountains. For considerable stretches it maintains an elevation of 2,000 feet.

Tussey Mountain Barrens, an area in southern Huntingdon County, covered by a growth of pitch pine and dense underbrush. The soil is sandy and stony, and the drainage is underground.

"Tussey Valley,"* Centre County (location unknown).

Tusseyville, Centre County.

Two Lick, Indiana County. (*Todd*)

Two Lick Creek, a stream draining part of central and eastern Indiana County.

Two-mile Run, a small stream northwest of Beaver, Beaver County, entering the Ohio River at Vanport. A favorite collecting ground of the author.

Tyler, Clearfield County.

Tyrone, Blair County.

Union City, Erie County.

Uniontown, Fayette County.

United, Westmoreland County.

Upper Talleycavey, Allegheny County.

Utica, Venango County.

Vail, Blair County. (*Todd*)

Valencia, Butler County.

Vanderbilt, Fayette County.

Van Horne Run (or Creek), a stream in Vernon Township, Crawford County, flowing southeast to join French Creek one mile or more below Meadville.

Vanport, Beaver County.

Verona, Allegheny County.

Versailles,* Allegheny County.

Volant, Lawrence County. (*Todd*)

"Von Hofen Spring,"* three and one-half miles northeast of Leetsdale, Allegheny County.

Waddle, Centre County.

"Waggoner's Hollow," a ravine three miles due northeast of Shields, Allegheny County.

"Waldameer Park," an amusement resort on the mainland at the head of Erie Bay, Erie County.

Wall Rose, Beaver County.

Walnut Creek, Erie County, a stream entering Lake Erie in a deep ravine five miles west of the head of Erie Bay.

Wampum, Lawrence County.

Warren, Warren County. (*Simpson*)

Warriorsmark, Huntingdon County.

Washington, Washington County. (*Nease, Montgomery, Forrest, McClelland*)

Waterford, Erie County, north of Lake Le Bœuf.

"Watson Run," a small stream flowing into Buffalo Creek from the north, one-half mile below the Butler-Armstrong county line. Its lower course is through a ravine heavily wooded with hemlock. (*Todd*)

Wattsburg, Erie County.

Waynesburg, Greene County. (*Jacobs; Dickey*)

Weedville, Elk County. (*Todd*)

Wells Tannery, Fulton County. (*Todd*)

Wendel, Westmoreland County.

Wesley, Venango County.

West Branch Conneaut Creek, Erie County, formed by the union of three branches in Crawford County, flowing north.

West Branch Susquehanna River, *see* Susquehanna River.

West Dublin, Fulton County, one-half mile west of Hiram.

West Elizabeth, Allegheny County.

West Finley, Washington County.

West View, Allegheny County.

Westford, Crawford County.

Westport, Clinton County.

Wexford, Allegheny County.

Whaley Island, Pymatuning Lake, southwest of Linesville, Crawford County.

Wharton Furnace, Fayette County, on the east slope of Chestnut Ridge.

Wheeling Creek, a stream forming part of the boundary between Washington and Greene counties. Its course is westward to the Ohio River in West Virginia.

Whips Cove, southwestern Fulton County, between Town Hill and Sideling Hill.

"Wightman Pond," a small pond on the west side of French Creek, one-half mile southwest of "Shaw's Landing," Crawford County.

Wilbur Mine, Somerset County.

Wilcox, Elk County.

Wildboy Run, a stream entering Sinnemahoning Creek from the north at Conrad, Potter County.

Wildcat Run, a small stream entering Tionesta Creek (West Branch) six miles east of a point one mile south of Althom (formerly Thompson), Warren County.

Wildwood, Hampton Township, Allegheny County.

Wilkinsburg, Allegheny County.

Williamsville, on the boundary line between McKean and Elk counties, where Seven-mile Run crosses. (*Baily*)

Willow Run, a stream in Juniata County draining the lower (northeastern) end of Shade Valley.

Wills Mountain, an elevation entering Bedford County from Maryland and terminating at the Juniata River (Raystown Branch) west of Bedford. At a few points it reaches an elevation of 2,600 feet.

Wilmerding, Allegheny County.

"Wilson's Grove,"* on the edge of Washington, Washington County.

Wing, Crawford County.

Winterburn, Clearfield County.

Wolf Creek, a stream draining southeastern Mercer County and emptying into Slippery Rock Creek in Butler County.

Wolfsburg, Bedford County.

Woodcock, Crawford County.

Woodcock Creek, a stream entering French Creek from the east about four miles north of Meadville, Crawford County.

Woodland, Clearfield County. (*Todd*)

Woodlawn, Beaver County.

Wopsononock Mountain (2,540 feet), a summit on the Allegheny divide northwest of Altoona, Blair County. (*Dwight*)

Yellow Bass Pond,* on Presque Isle, Erie County.

Yellow Creek, a stream entering Two Lick Creek from the east after cutting through Chestnut Ridge in Indiana County.

Youghiogheny River, a large affluent of the Monongahela River, which it joins at McKeesport, Allegheny County.

Young Womans Creek, a stream rising in southern Potter County and flowing southward through Clinton County to empty into the West Branch of the Susquehanna River at North Bend.

Youngstown, Westmoreland County.

Youngsville, Warren County.

BIBLIOGRAPHY

BIBLIOGRAPHY

THE FOLLOWING list of titles comprises all those thus far found that deal with the birds of western Pennsylvania as such, except articles in sportsmen's journals. The latter are listed only when they are of sufficient interest and authority to warrant mention. The object has been to include only articles and publications containing original contributions; those that merely cite, or quote from, earlier sources have been excluded. Authors' names are arranged alphabetically; the titles of their papers are in chronological sequence. These titles have been transcribed literally; required additions and emendations are in brackets; and titles have been supplied where necessary. All names of periodicals have been given in full without abbreviations. All but two titles have been personally verified. Annotations have been reduced to a minimum and allude mainly to errors, omissions of localities, and questionable identifications. Many of the titles deal only incidentally with the birds of this region. Less than 18 per cent of the entries were published before 1901.

"Christmas Census" reports are here listed under the name of the editor who compiled them; in the references they are attributed to the observers themselves.

"A. A. A."

Snowy Owl. *Forest and Stream*, February 3, 1887, 28:24. At North East, Erie County.

ABBOTT, GERALD A.

A Snipe Episode. *Oölogist*, April, 1924, 41:49. At Port Allegany, McKean County.

Introducing Pennsylvania. *Oölogist*, May, 1924, 41:59–60. Incidental references to birds.

ALLEN, JOEL A.

The Bæolophus bicolor-atricristatus Group. *Bulletin American Museum of Natural History*, June, 1907, 23:467–481. Lists specimens of *Baeolophus bicolor* from a few localities in western Pennsylvania (p. 478).

ANONYMOUS

Pigeons by the Million. The Great Nesting Grounds in Pennsylvania. *Cassinia*, 1913, 16:21–25. Editor's footnote: "This article, offered for reprinting by Dr. Louis B. Bishop, appeared in the Sunday issue of the New York Times, May 9, 1886, and is valuable as a contemporary account of a species virtually extinct. Although some of the statements are rendered dubious by a context of astonishing theories, there is a residue, sufficiently reliable to warrant a reprint almost in full." Describes the nesting colony in the Spring Creek region of Forest and Warren counties. Comments by the editor are interspersed.

Official Canadian Record of Bird-Banding Returns. *Canadian Field-Naturalist*, April, 1928, 42:107–110; September, 1928, 42:151–161. Two Black Duck recoveries from near Erie.

ARTHUR, EDMUND W.

[Holboell's Grebe in Mercer County]. *Cardinal*, January, 1926, v. 1, no. 7, p. 25.

Snowflakes. *Cardinal*, July, 1926, v. 1, no. 8, p. 9–10. Near Slippery Rock, Butler County.

[Turkey Vulture Nesting in Mercer County]. *Cardinal*, July, 1927, 2:43–44.

After a Week End at Presque Isle. *Cardinal*, July, 1928, 2:97–98.

An Episode with Golden-wings [Golden-winged Warbler]. *Cardinal*, January, 1932, 3:55–56.

Courtship Dance of the Pileated Woodpecker. *Cardinal*, January, 1934, 3:173. As observed in Mercer County.

The Country Rambler. Pittsburgh, 1934. 271 p., 1 pl. Review: *Cardinal*, 1934, 3:203.

A Mockingbird in Bellevue. *Cardinal*, July, 1934, 3:198–199. In Allegheny County.

Mockingbird in Bellevue. *Cardinal*, January, 1935, 4:16. Article unsigned.

An Egret in May. *Cardinal*, July, 1936, 4:95. At Linesville, Crawford County.

AUDUBON, JOHN JAMES

Ornithological Biography. Vol. 1. Edinburgh, 1831. xxiv, 512 p. *Tetrao umbellus* (p. 218) and *Troglodytes ludovicianus* (p. 401) from the vicinity of Pittsburgh.

Ornithological Biography. Vol. 2. Edinburgh, 1834. xxxi, 588 p. Incidental western Pennsylvania records for *Muscicapa canadensis* (p. 18), *Icteria viridis* (p. 223), and *Corvus americanus* (p. 322).

Ornithological Biography. Vol. 3. Edinburgh, 1835. xvi, 638 p. *Fuligula marila* from Pittsburgh (p. 225).

Ornithological Biography. Vol. 4. Edinburgh, 1838. xxvii, 618 p. *Strix otus* nesting near the Juniata River (perhaps east of our limits?) (p. 573).

BACON, SAMUEL E.

[Great Northern Shrike and Robin at Erie]. *Oölogist*, April, 1888, 5:60. Article initialed.

[Notes from Erie]. *Oölogist*, July, 1889, 6:134.

[Note on the Nesting of the Virginia Rail at Erie]. *Ornithologist and Oölogist*, July, 1891, 16:108.

Old Squaw (Clangula hiemalis). *Ornithologist and Oölogist*, March, 1892, 17:45. Abundance on Lake Erie and destruction by fishermen's nets.

BAILY, WILLIAM L.

Summer Birds of Northern Elk County, Pa. *Auk*, October, 1896, 13:289–297. An annotated list of 69 species observed from June 18 to July 2, 1894, with a full description of the region and a discussion of its faunal character. Carefully prepared and entirely reliable.

BAIRD, DONALD M.

A Grasshopper Sparrow's Nest. *Cardinal*, January, 1936, 4:73. In Sewickley Township, Allegheny County.

BAKER, WILLIAM C.

Some Sight Records from Ohio. *Wilson Bulletin*, March, 1933, 45:35–36. Carolina Chickadee in Beaver County.

[Barnes, R. Magoon, editor]

[Note on Richard C. Harlow's Collection of Birds' Eggs]. *Oölogist*, August, 1918, 35:119.

Red-tail Hawk Eggs. *Oölogist*, January, 1919, 36:16. Describes two sets from Waynesburg.

A Carefully Prepared Scientific Collection of Birds' Eggs of Unique Historical Importance. *Oölogist*, December, 1923, 40:191–200, 5 figs. A historical account of the collection of J. W. Jacobs, with figures of sets of Red-tailed Hawk and Ruby-throated Hummingbird from Greene County.

[The Goshawk and Snow Bunting at Port Allegany]. *Oölogist*, March, 1924, 41:[37]. Reported by G. A. Abbott.

Golden Eagle. *Oölogist*, May, 1931, 48:70. Quotes a newspaper account of the killing of one of these birds near Washington.

True Newspaper Ornithology. *Oölogist*, November, 1937, 54:139. Great Blue Heron entangled in power line in Greene County.

Barrows, Walter B.

The English Sparrow in North America. U. S. Department of Agriculture, Division of Economic Ornithology and Mammalogy, *Bulletin*, no. 1, 1889. 405 p., 1 map. Incidental western Pennsylvania references to certain native birds (p. 89, 90, 279).

The Food of Crows. U. S. Department of Agriculture, *Annual Report. Report of the Ornithologist and Mammalogist for 1888*, 1889, p. 498–535. Crow record from East Brook, Lawrence County (p. 518).

Barrows, Walter B., and E. A. Schwarz

The Common Crow of the United States. U. S. Department of Agriculture, Division of Ornithology and Mammalogy, *Bulletin*, no. 6, 1895. 98 p., 1 pl. Western Pennsylvania locality records (p. 39, 96).

Beal, Foster E. L.

The Food of Cuckoos. U. S. Department of Agriculture, Biological Survey, *Bulletin*, no. 9, 1898, p. 7–14. Incidental reference to a yellow-billed cuckoo from western Pennsylvania (p. 14).

Bent, Arthur C.

Life Histories of North American Shore Birds. Order Limicolæ (Part 1). U. S. National Museum, *Bulletin*, no. 142, 1927. ix, 420 p., 55 pls. Many of the local migration dates cited in this volume are taken from previous papers by W. W. Cooke and others. New data, however, appear under the following species: *Rubicola minor*, *Capella gallinago delicata*, *Pisobia bairdi*, *Pisobia minutilla*, *Ereunetes pusillus*, and *Totanus flavipes*.

——(Part 2). *Ibid.*, no. 146, 1929. ix, 412 p., 66 pls. Western Pennsylvania records cited in this volume are all from published sources, except one for the Spotted Sandpiper. The Renovo record for the Hudsonian Curlew (p. 123) is an error.

Life Histories of North American Gallinaceous Birds. Orders Galliformes and Columbiformes. U. S. National Museum, *Bulletin*, no. 162, 1932. xi, 490 p., 93 pls. In the account of the Passenger Pigeon, contributed by Charles W. Townsend, migration dates from three localities in western Pennsylvania are given (p. 401).

Life Histories of North American Woodpeckers. Order Piciformes. U. S. National Museum, *Bulletin*, no. 174, 1939. viii, 334 p., 39 pls. In the account of the Northern Pileated Woodpecker (p. 171–189), contributed by B. H. Christy, is a reference (p. 179) to a nest found in Fulton County (near Fort Loudon).

Bergner, Harold J.

A Field Trip in the Pymatuning Area. *Redstart*, April, 1938, 5:44–46. A nominal list of 63 species observed April 9–10, 1938, with brief notes on a few.

Bergstrom, C. Albert

[Northern Shrike in Crawford County]. *Cardinal*, July, 1928, 2:107.

[American Pipit in Crawford County]. *Cardinal*, July, 1928, 2:107.

Notes from Pymatuning. *Cardinal*, January, 1930, 2:186. Nine species briefly mentioned.

Blair, Helen M.

Demmler House Outing [at Plains Church, Butler County]. *In the Open*, July, 1920, 10:22. Notes on a few species observed by the Audubon Society, June 19, 1920.

Audubon Outings. *Bulletin Audubon Society of Western Pennsylvania*, April, 1923, 1:41–43.

Boggs, Ira B.

A Field Trip in Northwestern Pennsylvania. *Redstart*, September, 1936, 3:92. Brief record of species noted on Presque Isle and at Pymatuning Lake, June 1–4, 1936.

Notes on Two Visits to Pymatuning Lake and Vicinity. *Redstart*, October, 1937, 5:1–3. Rambling notes on the birds observed by a group on two visits (September 4–5; October 10–11, 1937) to Pymatuning Lake and Erie (Soldiers' Home grounds and Presque Isle). The finding of 3 species of rail in one small area at the former place receives notice at some length, while other and important-if-true occurrences are dismissed with casual mention. The author enumerates 15 species of shore birds observed at Erie, including several that others familiar with the locality consider rare, and one (the Buff-breasted Sandpiper) that is certainly erroneously listed (*fide* R. T. Peterson, in a letter).

Gadwall Nesting at Pymatuning. *Cardinal*, January, 1939, 5:19. A footnote by the editor calls attention to the fact that this case of "nesting" is not the first for the region, as supposed by the author.

Boulton, W. Rudyerd

My Bluebirds. *Bird-Lore*, April, 1916, 18:123–125. Observations on nesting at Beaver in the spring of 1915.

[Note on Screech Owl and Flicker at Beaver]. *Bird-Lore*, February, 1918, 20:67, 1 fig.

Camp in a Coal Mine. *Oölogist*, May, 1922, 39:70–73. With a nominal list of 97 species observed May 12–13, 1921, on the south bank of the Ohio River opposite Beaver, and thence to Raccoon Creek and return.

The Relations of Birds and Man. *Cardinal*, January, 1926, v. 1, no. 7, p. 1–6. Contains several incidental references to the birds of western Pennsylvania.

The Season: Pittsburgh Region. *Bird-Lore*, February, 1928, 30:13–14; April, 1928, 30:127–128; June, 1928, 30:195–196; August, 1928, 30:270–271; October, 1928, 30:336–337; December, 1928, 30:400–401.

[Pileated Woodpecker Nesting in Mercer County]. *Cardinal*, July, 1928, 2:105.

[Further Notes on the Upland Plover in Westmoreland County]. *Cardinal*, July, 1930, 2:233.

Brooks, Earle A.

Notes from West Virginia. *Auk*, April, 1908, 25:235–238. Contains a note on the breeding of *Otocoris alpestris praticola* in Schenley Park, Pittsburgh—as previously recorded by other observers.

Brooks, Margaret, editor

Bird-Lore's Thirty-ninth Christmas Bird Census. *Bird-Lore*, February, 1939 (supplement), 41:1–56. Lists from Osterburg, Bedford County (D. and R. Berkheimer); Deer Creek, Allegheny County (W. H. Seybolt, *et al.*); Linesville, Crawford County (F. A. Hegner); scattered localities, Allegheny and Washington counties (A. Hardie, *et al.*); and Springs, Somerset County (A. B. Miller).

Bird-Lore's Fortieth Christmas Bird Census. *Bird-Lore*, February, 1940 (supplement), 42:66–136. Lists from (Osterburg), Bedford County (D. and R. Berkheimer); Deer

Creek, Allegheny County (H. B. Stere, *et al.*); Pittsburgh and vicinity, Allegheny County (C. and D. Auerswald, *et al.*); and Warren, Warren County (H. E. Johnson).

BROOKS, MAURICE
The Erie Meeting. *Redstart*, April, 1936, 3:49–50. Lists 28 species observed at Erie, March 14–15, 1936.

Bachman's Sparrow in the North-Central Portion of Its Range. *Wilson Bulletin*, June, 1938, 50:86–109, figs. 17–19. Some of the data are quoted from the manuscript of the present work.

The Eastern Lark Sparrow in the Upper Ohio Valley. *Cardinal*, July, 1938, 4:181–200, 1 pl., 1 map. Western Pennsylvania records are listed (the exact localities are not accurately given in all cases).

BRUMBAUGH, C. LEON
July Horizons (Wilkinsburg, Allegheny County, Pa.). *Wilson Bulletin*, September, 1905, 12:100. A nominal list of 53 species, including such improbabilities as the Black-throated Blue Warbler and Pigeon Hawk.

BURLEIGH, THOMAS D.
Yellow Warbler. *Oölogist*, December, 1910, 27:147. A two-storied nest at Harmarville, Allegheny County.

Nesting Birds of Harmarville, Pa. *Oölogist*, September, 1911, 28:155–156. Author's name inadvertently omitted.

Late Nesting of the Towhee. *Oölogist*, October, 1911, 28:168. Near Uniontown, Fayette County.

Late Nesting of the Cedar Waxwing. *Oölogist*, October, 1911, 28:168. Near Uniontown, Fayette County.

Some Unusual Nesting Sites. *Oölogist*, November, 1911, 28:180.

The Cardinal at Harmarville, Pa. *Oölogist*, July, 1912, 29: 316–317.

The Scarlet Tanager. *Oölogist*, October, 1912, 29:363.

Field Notes. *Oölogist*, December, 1912, 29:395.

Unusual Nesting Sites. *Oölogist*, March, 1913, 30:55. Although not so stated in the text, all these observations were made in Allegheny County. The "Purple" Grackle is of course the Bronzed Grackle.

Bird Life on the National Pike. *Oölogist*, October, 1913, 30:253–255. Observations made in Fayette County, where the pike crosses Chestnut Ridge.

A July Tramp in Allegheny Co., Pa. *Oölogist*, October, 1913, 30:258, 263. With list of 48 species observed.

Unusual Wintering of the Catbird at Pittsburgh, Pa. *Oölogist*, November, 1913, 30:279.

Unusual Winter Birds [in Allegheny County]. *Oölogist*, November, 1913, 30:281. Winter records for several summer residents.

Birds Seen on a Day's Tramp in Allegheny Co., Pa., May 2, 1914. *Oölogist*, October, 1914, 31:190–191. 66 species. "Yellow Palm" Warbler should read "Palm" Warbler.

Birds Seen on a Day's Tramp in Allegheny County, Pa. *Oölogist*, January, 1915, 32:20. Reprint from 1914, 31: 190–191.

A Tame Chickadee. *Oölogist*, July, 1915, 32:119.

A White Robin at State College, Pa. *Oölogist*, July, 1915, 32:119.

Breeding of the Pied-billed Grebe (*Podilymbus podiceps*) near State College, Center Co., Pa. *Auk*, April, 1918, 35: 218–219.

Notes on the Bird Life of Allegheny County, Pennsylvania. *Wilson Bulletin*, June, 1923, 35:79–99; September, 1923, 35:138–147. Lists 146 native species, with full annotations on migration, nesting dates, etc., based solely on the observations of the author between 1910 and 1917, mainly in the several parks of Pittsburgh proper; in the region of Squaw Run, Harmarville; and in the valley of Deer Creek. A carefully prepared list, showing only a few discrepancies from the author's field notebook. *Dendroica palmarum hypochrysea* (p. 140) is misidentified; it should be *D. p. palmarum.*

Migration Notes from State College, Center County, Pennsylvania. *Wilson Bulletin*, June, 1924, 36:68–77; September, 1924, 36:128–132. A résumé of the author's observations from the fall of 1914 through the spring of 1919. The species are classified according to seasonal status. There are 22 residents, 74 summer residents, 79 migrants (including winter residents), and 4 stragglers (one of these, however, is from an extralimital locality). The date "April 18, 1919," for the Broad-winged Hawk refers to a locality in Luzerne County. Through a printer's error, the dates for the Purple Grackle are misplaced and appear at the bottom of p. 71.

Further Notes on the Birds of Allegheny County, Pennsylvania. *Cardinal*, January, 1929, 2:117–120. Supplement to the author's list in the *Wilson Bulletin*, 1923; 28 species.

Personal Experiences with the Northern Pileated Woodpecker, *Phlœotomus pileatus abieticola. Oölogists' Record*, March, 1929, 9:22–24.

[Supplementary] Notes on the Breeding Birds of State College, Center Co., Pennsylvania. *Wilson Bulletin*, March, 1931, 43:37–54.

Notes on the Breeding Birds of Fayette County, Pennsylvania. *Cardinal*, July, 1932, 3:73–83. List of 82 species observed on Chestnut Ridge between Uniontown and Summit, and at Chalk Hill and Lake Seaton, Fayette County, in the summers from 1909 to 1926 (with many gaps). Wherever possible in the present work, exact localities have been added (from Mr. Burleigh's manuscript notes) under the head of the several species involved.

Concerning Wintering Robins. *Cardinal*, July, 1934, 3:199–200.

BURNS, FRANK L.
The American Crow. *Wilson Ornithological Chapter Agassiz Association Bulletin*, no. 5, March, 1895. 41 p. A few incidental western Pennsylvania references (p. 12, 15, 33).

A Monograph of the Flicker. *Wilson Bulletin*, no. 31, April, 1900. 83 p. Nesting and migration data from Waynesburg, by J. W. Jacobs.

[A Monograph of the] Broad-winged Hawk (Buteo platypterus). *Wilson Bulletin*, December, 1911, 23:145–320. Contains a few records from western Pennsylvania.

BUTLER, ARTHUR G.
Foreign Finches in Captivity. London, 1894. viii, 332 p., 60 pls. Contains an extract from a letter of W. J. Holland concerning the Cardinal Grosbeak in "southwestern Pennsylvania" (p. 86).

"C. S. L."
[Baltimore Oriole Nests]. *Oölogist*, April, 1888, 5:60. At Warriorsmark, Huntingdon County.

CARTER, JAMES B.
Just Notes. *Oölogist*, December, 1914, 31:231. Bewick's Wren, Robin, Red-winged Blackbird, and Louisiana Water-Thrush in Greene County.

My First Set of Maryland Yellow-throat. *Oölogist*, June, 1915, 32:102. Presumably refers to Greene County.

Nesting of the Bachman's Sparrow in Southwestern Pennsylvania. *Oölogist*, May, 1917, 34:92–93. Cf. S. S. Dickey, *Auk*, 1917, 34:212.

CHAPMAN, FLOYD B.
The Pymatuning Excursion. *Cardinal*, January, 1937, 4:108.

CHAPMAN, FRANK M.
A Preliminary Study of the Grackles of the Subgenus Quiscalus. *Bulletin American Museum of Natural History*, February, 1892, 4:1–20. Contains several references to Erie specimens in the Sennett Collection.

A Study of the Genus Sturnella. *Bulletin American Museum of Natural History*, December, 1900, 13:297–320. Mentions specimens of *S. magna* from Erie (p. 316).

The Warblers of North America. New York, March, 1907. ix, 306 p., 24 pls. The migration tables are taken from W. W. Cooke's articles in *Bird-Lore*, 1903–6. Nesting dates for several species in Greene County were contributed by J. W. Jacobs.

[CHAPMAN, FRANK M., editor]

The Eighth Christmas Bird Census. *Bird-Lore*, January, 1908, 10:22–39. List from Springs, Somerset County (A. B. Miller).

The Ninth Christmas Bird Census. *Bird-Lore*, February, 1909, 11:15–36. List from McKinley Park, Pittsburgh (M. H. Miller).

Bird-Lore's Tenth Christmas Census. *Bird-Lore*, February, 1910, 12:19–36. List from Springs, Somerset County (A. B. Miller).

Bird-Lore's Eleventh [Christmas] Bird Census. *Bird-Lore*, February, 1911, 13:18–44. Two short lists from Pittsburgh (Naomi Wright and M. H. Miller).

Bird-Lore's Twelfth Christmas Bird Census. *Bird-Lore*, February, 1912, 14:18–44. List from Greenville, Mercer County (R. H. Gerberding).

Bird-Lore's Thirteenth [Christmas] Bird Census. *Bird-Lore*, February, 1913, 15:20–45. Lists from Aspinwall and Pittsburgh, Allegheny County; and Springs, Somerset County (T. D. Burleigh, A. W. Honywill, and A. B. Miller, respectively).

CHATHAM, JOHN H.

The Bald Eagle on the Susquehanna River. Being a Brief Life History of the Bird of Freedom in Pennsylvania. With an Introduction (p. 3–8) by Henry W. Shoemaker. Altoona, Pa., 1919. 15 p. This brochure is a curious mixture of fact and fancy. It contains a few references to localities in western Pennsylvania.

CHRISTY, BAYARD H.

A List of Birds of Sewickley, Pennsylvania. *Cardinal*, January, 1923, v. 1, no. 1, [p. 1–15]. Lists 161 native species, 1 of which (the King Rail) is included by mistake. The paper is a résumé of the author's notes covering thirty-odd years. His observations do not apply solely to the Sewickley region proper, but were made as far away in some cases (he is careful to explain) as Clinton Pond (southwest of the Ohio River), the upper reaches of Raccoon Creek in Beaver County, and the Beaver River in the same county. A number of unrecorded species that should occur in the region are included in brackets.

Crossbill Visitors. *Bulletin Audubon Society of Western Pennsylvania*, April, 1923, 1:10–12, 1 pl.

Notes [on Local Birds]. *Cardinal*, July, 1923, v. 1, no. 2, [p. 8–10]. Canvas-back, Bald Eagle, Long-eared Owl (nesting), and Crossbills. Article unsigned.

Spring Migration at Clinton Pond. *Cardinal*, July, 1923, v. 1, no. 2, [p. 11–18], maps. List of 39 species observed during the spring of 1923.

Passenger Pigeon Reminiscences. *Cardinal*, January, 1924, v. 1, no. 3, p. 7–11. By three of the older residents of Sewickley. Article unsigned.

Bewick's Wren in Allegheny County. *Cardinal*, January, 1924, v. 1, no. 3, p. 12–15.

Notes [on Local Birds]. *Cardinal*, January, 1924, v. 1, no. 3, p. 18–19. Article unsigned.

Revision of the Cardinal's Bird List. *Cardinal*, January, 1924, v. 1, no. 3, p. 20. Adds 11 native species to the original list and cancels 1. Most of these records had been published before. Article unsigned.

Warblers of the Big Travis. *Cardinal*, July, 1924, v. 1, no. 4, p. 8–14. Big Traverse Creek, one of the affluents of Raccoon Creek, in southern Beaver County. Includes an informal list of all the birds observed, and a census of the warblers.

Audubon in Pittsburgh. *Cardinal*, July, 1924, v. 1, no. 4, p. 16–20, 1 pl. With several quotations from his works. Article unsigned.

Notes [on Local Birds]. *Cardinal*, July, 1924, v. 1, no. 4, p. 21–24. Nesting of the Woodcock, Great Horned Owl, etc. Article unsigned.

Lambdin's Museum. *Cardinal*, January, 1925, v. 1, no. 5, p. 15–17. Further information on the white crows mentioned by Audubon. Article unsigned.

Notes [on Local Birds]. *Cardinal*, January, 1925, v. 1, no. 5, p. 19–21. Least Bittern, Little Blue Heron, Belted Kingfisher (in December), Purple Martin. Article unsigned.

Revision of the Cardinal's Bird List. *Cardinal*, January, 1925, v. 1, no. 5, p. 24. Adds 11 species, but nearly all actually from outlying localities. Some of these records had been published before. Article unsigned.

[Notes from Clinton Pond]. *Cardinal*, July, 1925, v. 1, no. 6, p. 21.

[Brewster's Warbler in Southern Beaver County]. *Cardinal*, July, 1925, v. 1, no. 6, p. 23.

[Notes from Clinton Pond]. *Cardinal*, January, 1926, v. 1, no. 7, p. 25.

Revision of the Cardinal's Bird List. *Cardinal*, January, 1926, v. 1, no. 7, p. 28. Five species added.

[Notes from Clinton Pond]. *Cardinal*, July, 1926, v. 1, no. 8, p. 15.

[The Yellow-bellied Flycatcher near Sewickley]. *Cardinal*, July, 1926, v. 1, no. 8, p. 17–18.

[Prairie Horned Lark Nesting near Clinton Pond]. *Cardinal*, July, 1926, v. 1, no. 8, p. 18. Article unsigned.

[Robins in Winter]. *Cardinal*, July, 1926, v. 1, no. 8, p. 20. Article unsigned.

[A February Trip to Cook Forest]. *Cardinal*, July, 1926, v. 1, no. 8, p. 21. Article unsigned.

[Ring-billed Gull near Dixmont]. *Cardinal*, January, 1927, 2:11.

[Canada Geese at Clinton Pond]. *Cardinal*, January, 1927, 2:11. Article unsigned.

[A Nest of the Ruffed Grouse]. *Cardinal*, January, 1927, 2:13. In the Little Sewickley Valley, Allegheny County (Christy, MS.). Article unsigned.

[Local Range of the Turkey Vulture]. *Cardinal*, January, 1927, 2:13. Article unsigned.

[Unusual Winter Visitors]. *Cardinal*, January, 1927, 2:16–18. Rough-legged Hawk, Goshawk, and Snowy Owl. Article unsigned.

[A Redstart in November]. *Cardinal*, January, 1927, 2:18. Article unsigned.

[Snowy Owl in Allegheny County]. *Cardinal*, July, 1927, 2:41. Article unsigned.

[Common Tern Nesting on Presque Isle]. *Cardinal*, July, 1927, 2:42. *Fide* J. E. Perry. Article unsigned.

[Blue Goose on Presque Isle]. *Cardinal*, July, 1927, 2:42–43. *Fide* J. E. Perry. Article unsigned.

[Persistence of the Crow]. *Cardinal*, July, 1927, 2:44–45. Article initialed.

A Page from Jack Miner and a Footnote. *Cardinal*, July, 1927, 2:46–48. Discusses the changes in the bird life observed in Allegheny County, and especially the diminution in numbers of many breeding species.

[Notes from Clinton Pond]. *Cardinal*, July, 1928, 2:104.

[Nighthawk Migration]. *Cardinal*, July, 1928, 2:105–106.

[Cedar Waxwings Feeding on Ants]. *Cardinal*, July, 1928, 2:106.

[Mockingbird Nesting in Washington County]. *Cardinal*, July, 1928, 2:107. Article unsigned.

[Notes on the Green Heron]. *Cardinal*, January, 1929, 2:129.

[Wintering Mourning Doves]. *Cardinal*, 1929, 2:129.

[Red-bellied Woodpecker at Sewickley]. *Cardinal*, January, 1929, 2:130. Article unsigned.

[Bachman's Sparrow near Sewickley]. *Cardinal*, January, 1929, 2:130.

[Palm Warbler near Frankfort Springs]. *Cardinal*, January, 1929, 2:131.

A Vulture Nest. *Cardinal*, January, 1930, 2:192–193, 1 fig. Near Frankfort Springs, Beaver County.

[Mourning Dove Nesting in September]. *Cardinal*, January, 1930, 2:201.

[Goshawk near Sewickley]. *Cardinal*, January, 1930, 2:201.

[Singing of a Young Robin]. *Cardinal*, January, 1930, 2:202.

A Bobolink Nest. *Cardinal*, July, 1930, 2:218–219. In Sewickley Township, Allegheny County.

A Legislative Mistake. *Cardinal*, July, 1930, 2:226–232. A strong indictment of the act placing a bounty on the Goshawk.

[White-eyed Vireo in Southern Beaver County]. *Cardinal*, July, 1930, 2:234.

[Unusual Nesting Site of the House Wren]. *Cardinal*, July, 1930, 2:234.

Woodcocks in a Dry Season. *Cardinal*, January, 1931, 3: 13–14.

Goshawk, *Astur atricapillus* [at Sewickley Heights, Allegheny County]. *Cardinal*, January, 1931, 3:15.

Sanderling (*Crocethia alba*) and Black Tern (*Chlidonias nigra surinamensis*) [at Dixmont, Allegheny County]. *Cardinal*, January, 1931, 3:16–17.

A Passenger-Pigeon Item. *Cardinal*, January, 1931, 3:19. Quotation from a letter written in 1857 relating to a flight of pigeons at Pittsburgh. Article unsigned.

A Cliff-Swallow Colony. *Cardinal*, January, 1931, 3:20–21, 1 fig. Near Harmony, Butler County.

Water-Birds at McDonald Reservoir. *Cardinal*, July, 1931, 3:43.

Nesting of Red-bellied Woodpecker in Beaver County. *Cardinal*, July, 1931, 3:44–45. At "Patton's Point," upper Raccoon Creek Valley.

Bird and Aeroplane. *Cardinal*, July, 1931, 3:45–46. Prairie Horned Lark at the Butler airport.

The Short-billed Marsh Wren at McDonald Reservoir. *Cardinal*, July, 1931, 3:46.

Barn Owl, *Aluco pratincola* (Bonaparte), in Allegheny County. *Cardinal*, January, 1932, 3:68–69.

The Summer Range of the Savannah Sparrow, *Passerculus sandwichensis savanna* (Wilson). *Cardinal*, January, 1932, 3:70–71.

Swans at Presque Isle. *Cardinal*, July, 1932, 3:85–91, 1 pl.

Barn Owl, *Tyto pratincola* (Bonaparte). *Cardinal*, July, 1932, 3:93.

[Further Note concerning the Prairie Horned Lark]. *Cardinal*, July, 1932, 3:93–94.

Henslow's Sparrow, *Passerherbulus henslowi susurrans* Brewster, in Conneaut Marsh. *Cardinal*, July, 1932, 3:95.

Ruddy Turnstone in Crawford County. *Cardinal*, July, 1933, 3:147–148.

The Hummingbird's Nest Material. *Cardinal*, July, 1933, 3:148.

Lincoln's Sparrow on Sewickley Heights. *Cardinal*, July, 1933, 3:149.

The American Egret in Summer. *Cardinal*, January, 1934, 3:164–169, map. With a summary of the western Pennsylvania records to date.

Shore-birds at Erie. *Cardinal*, January, 1934, 3:172–173. Seen September 4, 1933. No new records are involved.

Wintering Robins. *Cardinal*, 1934, 3:173–175. Speculates on their origin, suggesting that they may come from the North.

Connecticut Warbler in Beaver County. *Cardinal*, January, 1934, 3:176. On the Beaver County side of Big Sewickley Creek, May 28, 1933.

City Sparrow Hawks. *Cardinal*, January, 1935, 4:10–12, 2 figs.

Kingbird Migration. *Cardinal*, January, 1935, 4:18–19. At Hartstown, Crawford County.

A Raven's Nest. *Cardinal*, July, 1935, 4:43–47, 1 fig. Near Mill Creek, Huntingdon County.

Woodpeckers' Winter Quarters. *Cardinal*, July, 1936, 4:97.

Cliff Swallow Colony in Butler County. *Cardinal*, July, 1936, 4:97. Cf. *Cardinal*, 1931, 3:20.

Winter-killing of Carolina Wren, Bachman's Sparrow, and Mockingbird. *Cardinal*, July, 1936, 4:97–98.

Early Appearance of Pine Siskin. *Cardinal*, July, 1936, 4:98.

The Robin's Nesting Habits. *Cardinal*, January, 1937, 4:121. Article initialed.

Chimney Swifts at Sunrise. *Cardinal*, January, 1938, 4:166.

Autumn Robins. *Cardinal*, January, 1938, 4:176–177.

Great White Heron at Pymatuning. *Cardinal*, July, 1938, 4:202–203.

Bob-White Survival. *Cardinal*, January, 1939, 5:19–20. A review of P. L. Errington and F. N. Hamerstrom's paper, with incidental notes on predator "control" in Allegheny County. Article initialed.

Orchard Oriole at Pymatuning. *Cardinal*, January, 1939, 5:21.

Mourning Doves in Winter. *Cardinal*, July, 1939, 5:45. Near Murdocksville, Washington County.

Robin Migration. *Cardinal*, July, 1939, 5:45–46. In Allegheny County.

Nesting of Rough-winged Swallow. *Cardinal*, July, 1939, 5:46. At Sewickley.

Red-throated Loon in Allegheny County. *Cardinal*, January, 1940, 5:68. At Noblestown. Includes also a note on the occurrence of the Common Loon at Versailles.

Horned Grebe at Pymatuning. *Cardinal*, January, 1940, 5:68.

[Christy, Bayard H., editor]

[Whistling Swan Records]. *Cardinal*, July, 1926, v. 1, no. 8, p. 15.

[Nesting of the Broad-winged Hawk]. *Cardinal*, July, 1926, v. 1, no. 8, p. 15–16.

[Bald Eagle on Presque Isle]. *Cardinal*, July, 1926, v. 1, no. 8, p. 16.

[Barn Owl Nesting at Blairsville]. *Cardinal*, July, 1926, v. 1, no. 8, p. 17, 1 pl.

[Mockingbird Nesting in Washington County]. *Cardinal*, July, 1926, v. 1, no. 8, p. 19.

[Making a Bird Census in February]. *Cardinal*, July, 1926, v. 1, no. 8, p. 20–21.

An English Sparrow Foster Parent. *Cardinal*, January, 1930, 2:191–192. English Sparrow feeding the young of a Red-eyed Vireo—in Schenley Park, Pittsburgh.

[Pileated Woodpecker on Laurel Hill]. *Cardinal*, July, 1930, 2:233. *Fide* O. C. Reiter.

[Western Pennsylvania Notes]. *Cardinal*, July, 1933, 3:150. Notes on 14 species, contributed by members of the Audubon Society.

Geese and Swans at Erie. *Cardinal*, January, 1935, 4:17–18. Quotes from letter of J. E. Perry.

Marbled Godwit at Erie. *Cardinal*, January, 1935, 4:18. *Fide* J. E. Perry.

[Note on the Migrant Shrike]. *Cardinal*, January, 1940, 5:66, footnote. Allegheny County records are specified. The nest found by D. A. Atkinson in "northern Allegheny County" actually came from Sewickley.

CHRISTY, BAYARD H., and RUDYERD BOULTON
Upland Plover in Westmoreland County. *Cardinal*, January, 1929, 2:122–128, 1 fig.

CHRISTY, BAYARD H., and GEORGE M. SUTTON
Bob-white in Pennsylvania. *Cardinal*, January, 1926, v. 1, no. 7, p. 7–19. An account of the introduction of birds from other parts of the country to replace the original stock. A valuable historical record, carefully compiled.

The Summer Birds of Cook Forest. *Cardinal*, January, 1928, 2:68–75. List of 88 species observed at intervals from May to July during several seasons, with a supplemental (nominal) list of winter visitors.

The Turkey in Pennsylvania. *Cardinal*, January, 1929, 2: 109–116, 1 pl.

CLARK, HUBERT L.
The Pterylography of certain American Goatsuckers and Owls. *Proceedings U. S. National Museum*, for 1894, May, 1895, 17:551–572. Records a specimen of ***Megascops asio*** from Pittsburgh (p. 565).

CLARKE, WILLIAM S., JR.
Notes from State College, Pa. *Bird-Lore*, December, 1930, 32:422–423. Evening Grosbeak; Downy and Hairy woodpeckers.

[COGGINS, HERBERT L., secretary]
[Bird Life of Warren]. *Cassinia*, 1908, 11:81–82. From letters of R. B. Simpson.

CONOVER, HENRY B.
A New Race of Ruffed Grouse from Vancouver Island. *Condor*, July, 1935, 37:204–206. Lists specimens of ***Bonasa umbellus umbellus*** from western Pennsylvania.

CONKLIN, W. GARD.
The Pymatuning State Game Refuge and Museum. *Bulletin Pennsylvania Game Commission*, no. 19, October, 1938. 40 p., map, and numerous figures. A popular account of the history and development of the Pymatuning Game Refuge, with a nominal list of the birds (*ex* Sutton, 1928) and other references to the bird life of the area. A revised and enlarged edition appeared in June, 1939.

COOKE, WELLS W.
The Migration of Warblers. First Paper. *Bird-Lore*, December, 1903, 5:188–193, 1 pl. American Redstart at Beaver and Renovo (p. 189).

——Second Paper. *Ibid.*, February, 1904, 6:21–24, 2 pls. Hooded Warbler and Yellow-breasted Chat in western Pennsylvania.

——Third Paper. *Ibid.*, April, 1904, 6:57–60, 2 pls. Black-throated Green, Wilson's, and Canada warblers in western Pennsylvania.

——Fourth Paper. *Ibid.*, June, 1904, 6:91–92, 2 pls. Beaver and Waynesburg records for the Blue-winged and Golden-winged warblers.

——Sixth Paper. *Ibid.*, October, 1904, 6:162–163, 1 pl. Bay-breasted and Chestnut-sided warblers in western Pennsylvania.

——Seventh Paper. *Ibid.*, December, 1904, 6:199–200, 2 pls. Western Pennsylvania records for the Magnolia Warbler.

——Eighth Paper. *Ibid.*, February, 1905, 7:32–35, 1 pl. Western Pennsylvania dates for the Yellow Warbler.

——Ninth Paper. *Ibid.*, April, 1905, 7:135–136, 1 pl. Western Pennsylvania dates for the Kentucky Warbler.

——Tenth Paper. *Ibid.*, June, 1905, 7:169–170, 1 pl. Western Pennsylvania dates for the Mourning Warbler.

——Eleventh Paper. *Ibid.*, August, 1905, 7:203–206, 1 pl. Western Pennsylvania dates for the Black and White and Black-poll warblers.

——Twelfth Paper. *Ibid.*, October, 1905, 7:237–239, 1 pl. Local records for the Nashville and Tennessee warblers.

——Thirteenth Paper. *Ibid.*, December, 1905, 7:275–278, 2 pls. Local records for the Cape May and Palm warblers, and the Maryland Yellow-throat.

——Fourteenth Paper. *Ibid.*, February, 1906, 8:26–27, 1 pl. Worm-eating Warbler at Beaver.

——Fifteenth Paper. *Ibid.*, April, 1906, 8:61–62, 1 pl. Local records for the Myrtle Warbler.

——Sixteenth Paper. *Ibid.*, June, 1906, 8:100–102, 1 pl. Local records for the Oven-bird, Northern Water-Thrush, and Louisiana Water-Thrush.

——Eighteenth Paper. *Ibid.*, October, 1906, 8:168–169, 1 pl. Local records for the Parula Warbler. The date "April 24, 1899," does not apply to Beaver, but to the Buffalo Creek region of Butler County.

——Nineteenth Paper. *Ibid.*, December, 1906, 8:203–204, 1 pl. Local records for the Black-throated Blue and Cerulean warblers. The record for the latter at Beaver on September 14, 1889, is probably an error—see p. 520 of the present work.

Distribution and Migration of North American Warblers. U. S. Department Agriculture, Biological Survey, *Bulletin*, no. 18, 1904. 142 p. Includes western Pennsylvania migration records for various species (contributed by A. K. Pierce, Renovo; J. W. Jacobs, Waynesburg; and W. E. C. Todd and H. H. Wickham, Beaver).

Distribution and Migration of North American Ducks, Geese, and Swans. U. S. Department of Agriculture, Biological Survey, *Bulletin*, no. 26, 1906. 90 p. Contains western Pennsylvania records for sundry species.

The Migration of Thrushes. First Paper. *Bird-Lore*, February, 1907, 9:32–34, 1 pl. Dates for the Wood Thrush at Beaver.

——Second Paper. *Ibid.*, April, 1907, 9:76–78, 1 pl. Local records for the Robin.

——Third Paper. *Ibid.*, June, 1907, 9:121–125, 1 pl. Local records for the Gray-cheeked, Olive-backed, and Hermit thrushes. One record is an error—see p. 449 of the present work.

The Migration of Flycatchers. Fourth Paper. *Bird-Lore*, June, 1908, 10:114–117, 1 pl. Local records for the Green-crested (Acadian), Alder, and Least flycatchers. "Waynesboro" (p. 115), should read "Waynesburg."

——Fifth Paper. *Ibid.*, August, 1908, 10:116–170, 1 pl. Local records for the Kingbird and Wood Pewee.

——Sixth Paper. *Ibid.*, September, 1908, 10:210–212, 1 pl. Local records for the Phoebe.

——Eighth Paper. *Ibid.*, February, 1909, 11:12–14, 1 pl. Local records for the Crested Flycatcher.

The Migration of Vireos. First Paper. *Bird-Lore*, April, 1909, 11:78–79, 1 pl. Local records for the Philadelphia, Warbling, and Red-eyed vireos.

——Third Paper. *Ibid.*, August, 1909, 11:165–168, 1 pl. Local records for the Yellow-throated and Blue-headed vireos. The Beaver records for the former species, however, are almost certainly errors—see p. 476 of the present work.

The Migration of North American Sparrows. Fifth Paper. *Bird-Lore*, July, 1910, 12:139–141, 1 pl. Fall migration dates for the Pine Siskin at Renovo.

——Ninth Paper. *Ibid.*, April, 1911, 13:83–88. Vesper Sparrow at Renovo and Beaver.

——Eleventh Paper. *Ibid.*, August, 1911, 13:198–201. Indigo Bunting at Beaver and Renovo.

——Fifteenth Paper. *Ibid.*, April, 1912, 14:98–105, 1 pl. Local records for the White-crowned and White-throated sparrows.

——Sixteenth Paper. *Ibid.*, June, 1912, 14:158–161, 1 pl. Local records for the Rose-breasted Grosbeak.

——Eighteenth Paper. *Ibid.*, October, 1912, 14:287–290. Towhee at Beaver and Renovo.

——Twenty-sixth Paper. *Ibid.*, February, 1914, 16:19–23, 1 pl. Redpoll records in this paper are second-hand.

Purple Finch dates are from Renovo and Beaver. "September 10, 1890," should read "September 10, 1910."

——Twenty-eighth Paper. *Ibid.*, June, 1914, 16:176–178, 1 pl. Bachman's Sparrow at Beaver.

——Thirty-first Paper. *Ibid.*, December, 1914, 16:438–442. Junco at Beaver.

Distribution and Migration of North American Shorebirds. U. S. Department of Agriculture, Biological Survey, *Bulletin*, no. 35, 1910. 100 p., 4 pls. Some western Pennsylvania migration dates for certain species. The Solitary Sandpiper record for Beaver, November 28, 1901 (p. 60), is an error of transcription on the part of the author; it properly refers to the Woodcock. The Spotted Sandpiper record for Beaver, April 2, 1888 (p. 69), is also an error; it should read April 4.

Distribution and Migration of North American Herons and their Allies. U. S. Department of Agriculture, Biological Survey, *Bulletin*, no. 45, 1913. 70 p., 21 maps. Contains a few western Pennsylvania migration records for certain species. "Waynesboro" (in table on p. 57) should read "Waynesburg."

Distribution and Migration of North American Rails and their Allies. U. S. Department of Agriculture, Biological Survey, *Bulletin*, no. 128, September, 1914. 50 p. Western Pennsylvania records and dates for several species.

The Migration of North American Kinglets. *Bird-Lore*, April, 1915, 17:118–125, 1 pl. Dates for Beaver and Renovo (the latter incorrect—see p. 462 of the present work).

The Migration of North American Birds. *Bird-Lore*, June, 1915, 17:199–203, 1 pl. Blue-gray Gnatcatcher at Waynesburg and Beaver.

Distribution and Migration of North American Gulls and their Allies. U. S. Department of Agriculture, Biological Survey, *Bulletin*, no. 292, October, 1915. 70 p., 31 figs. Western Pennsylvania records for several species.

The Migration of North American Birds [Nuthatches]. *Bird-Lore*, December, 1915, 17:443–445. Red-breasted Nuthatch at Beaver.

Coon, W. Edwin

A Note on the Barred Owl. *Bird-Lore*, October, 1917, 19: 266–267. Its food habits, as shown by an examination of pellets found near Conneautville, Crawford County.

Fours—Right! *Bird-Lore*, October, 1923, 25:317–318. Refers to a brood of killdeer in western Crawford County.

Cope, Francis R., Jr.

Observations on the Summer Birds of Parts of Clinton and Potter Counties, Pa. *Cassinia*, 1902, 5:8–21. A list of 76 species observed June 21–28, 1900, at Tamarack Swamp, Clinton County, and thence north along the Kettle Creek Valley in Potter County. The paper is written from the faunal standpoint, and the changes in the bird life due to deforestation are fully discussed.

Cope, Theodora M., and Arthur S. Hawkins

A Preliminary Survey of the Flora and Fauna of the East Tionesta Virgin Forest, Pennsylvania. *Forest Leaves*, April–July–October, 1934, p. 23–27. A nominal list of 66 species observed June 14–July 15, and July 29–August 10.

Crawford, Stanton C.

Crepuscular Life Viewed from a City Lot. *Proceedings Pennsylvania Academy of Science*, 1934, 8:96–99. Observations at Edgewood, Allegheny County.

Curry, Haskell B.

Louisiana Heron in Centre County, Pennsylvania. *Auk*, October, 1933, 50:428–429.

Cushman, L. B.

Was this Bird Fighting Vermin? *Wilson Bulletin*, March, 1916, 28:39–40. Comment on the action of an Indigo Bunting at North East, Erie County.

Deane, Ruthven

Unusual Abundance of the Snowy Owl (*Nyctea nyctea*). *Auk*, July, 1906, 23:283–298. Record from Erie (p. 292).

Extracts from the Field Notes of George B. Sennett. *Auk*, October, 1923, 40:626–633. Numerous records from Erie and vicinity made in 1874–76.

Debes, V. A.

Winter Robins IV. *Bird-Lore*, April, 1912, 14:111. Flocks seen at several (unspecified) localities in Allegheny and Washington counties. Also records the Prairie Horned Lark.

Dickey, Samuel S.

Strange Nesting Sites. *Oölogist*, December, 1909, 26:224. The Sparrow Hawk and Cardinal in Greene County.

Unusual. *Oölogist*, December, 1909, 26:224. The Mourning Dove nesting near Waynesburg.

Prairie Horned Lark. *Oölogist*, April, 1910, 27:48–49. With list of nests found in Greene County, 1907–9.

Hairy Woodpecker. *Oölogist*, April, 1911, 28:74–75. Nesting data for Greene County.

Chipping Sparrow Nesting Upon the Ground in Green[e] County, Pa. *Oölogist*, June, 1911, 28:107.

The Great Horned Owl. *Oölogist*, February, 1912, 29:219–222.

The Bewick's Wren. *Oölogist*, June, 1912, 29:299–301.

The Cerulean Warbler Nesting in Greene County, Pennsylvania. *Oölogist*, June, 1912, 29:302.

The Kentucky Warbler. *Oölogist*, June, 1912, 29:302–303.

The Red-shouldered Hawk, a Summer Resident in Greene County, Pa. *Oölogist*, February, 1913, 30:23.

Nesting of the Prairie Horned Lark in Southern Pennsylvania. *Oölogist*, March, 1913, 30:48.

Nesting of the Whip Poor Will. *Oölogist*, May, 1913, 30: 74–75.

Nesting of the American Sparrow Hawk. *Oölogist*, May, 1913, 30:75–76.

Nesting of the Bewick's Wren. *Oölogist*, July, 1913, 30:119–120.

The Louisiana Water Thrush. *Oölogist*, August, 1913, 30:135.

The Red-Bellied Woodpecker. *Oölogist*, September, 1913, 30:146, 148.

Nesting of the Grasshopper Sparrow. *Oölogist*, September, 1913, 30:148.

Tufted Titmouse. *Oölogist*, September, 1913, 30:149.

The Northern Pileated Woodpecker. *Oölogist*, November, 1913, 30:280. Nesting in northern Huntingdon County.

The Henslow's Sparrow a Summer Resident in Central Pennsylvania. *Oölogist*, December, 1913, 30:299–300. Nesting in northern Huntingdon County, May, 1913—the first record for western Pennsylvania.

Bachman's Sparrow, a Summer Resident in Southern Pennsylvania. *Oölogist*, January, 1914, 31:8–10. In southwestern Greene County.

Some Experiences with the Red-tailed Hawk. *Oölogist*, February, 1914, 31:28–29.

Possible Nesting of Bachman's Sparrow (Peu[c]aea aestivalis bachmani.) in Southern [Southwestern] Pennsylvania. *Oölogist*, March, 1914, 31:42.

A Great Tree Climber. *Oölogist*, April, 1914, 31:63–64. Climbing to a nest of the Red-tailed Hawk.

The Pileated Woodpecker in Southwestern Pennsylvania. *Oölogist*, April, 1914, 31:65.

Nesting of the White-breasted Nuthatch in Central Pennsylvania. *Oölogist*, April, 1914, 31:66–67.

The Worm-Eating Warbler. *Oölogist*, June, 1914, 31:96–98.

The Golden-winged Warbler. *Oölogist*, June, 1914, 31:99–100.

An Unmarked Set of Kentucky Warbler's Eggs. *Oölogist*, June, 1914, 31:118–119.

Rough Winged and Bank Swallows. *Oölogist*, August, 1914, 31:154–155. Questions the breeding of the Bank Swallow in Greene County.

Sets of Five Eggs from the Yellow Breasted Chat. *Oölogist*, August, 1914, 31:156–157.

The Carolina Wren. *Oölogist*, August, 1914, 31:158–160.

Some Central Pennsylvania Birds. *Oölogist*, September, 1914, 31:168–171. The locality is not precisely stated, but was near Charter Oak, Huntingdon County.

The Killdeer. *Oölogist*, October, 1914, 31:184, 186.

Early June Birds of Cresson, Cambria County, Pa. *Oölogist*, November, 1914, 31:206–207.

The Value of Hawks and Owls. *Oölogist*, February, 1915, 32:21–22. Based mainly on data from western Pennsylvania.

The Great Horned Owl. *Oölogist*, March, 1915, 32:49.

Rare Birds near Waynesburg, Pa. *Auk*, April, 1915, 32:236. Yellow-crowned Night Heron, Bald Eagle, and Florida Gallinule.

The Blue-Gray Gnatcatcher. *Oölogist*, April, 1915, 32:67–71, 2 figs.

The Northern Raven. *Oölogist*, July, 1915, 32:106–107.

The Resident Chickadee of Southwestern Pennsylvania. *Auk*, October, 1915, 32:498–499. *Penthestes carolinensis*, not *P. atricapillus* as formerly supposed.

The Northern Pileated Woodpecker. *Oölogist*, April, 1916, 33:64–70, 7 figs.

First Recorded Nesting of Bachman's Sparrow in Pennsylvania. *Auk*, April, 1917, 34:212. In Greene County, May, 1916.

Collecting Whippoorwill's Eggs. *Oölogist*, July, 1918, 35:105–106.

[Note on Migration of Red-tailed Hawk]. *Oölogist*, October, 1918, 35:140.

Sandpipers. *Oölogist*, January, 1919, 36:6–8.

Unusual Nesting Site of the Rough-winged Swallow. *Oölogist*, January, 1919, 36:18.

A Mountain Home of the Parula Warbler. *Oölogist*, February, 1919, 36:33. The locality referred to is Spruce Creek, Huntingdon County (Dickey, MS.).

In the Haunts of the Duck Hawk. *Oölogist*, March, 1919, 36:43–44. The locality is unspecified, but is Spruce Creek, Huntingdon County (Dickey, MS.).

Days with the Ruby-throated Hummer. *Oölogist*, March, 1919, 36:48–49.

Early Nesting of Some Common Birds. *Oölogist*, April, 1919, 36:67.

An English Sparrow Makes Its Home in the Nest of a Hawk. *Oölogist*, June, 1919, 36:101.

Days with the Cerulean Warbler. *Oölogist*, August, 1920, 37:88–91, 2 figs. With a full description of the nests and eggs found in Greene County.

The Great Horned Owl. *Bulletin Audubon Society of Western Pennsylvania*, April, 1923, 1:21–25, 3 figs.

Getting Friendly with the Woodcock. *Nature Magazine*, September, 1926, p. 176, 1 fig. Juniata River—exact locality unspecified.

The Worm-eating Warbler. *Cardinal*, July, 1934, 3:179–184, 1 pl. With data on 24 nests—mostly in Greene and Huntingdon counties.

The White-eyed Vireo in Greene County, Pennsylvania. *Cardinal*, January, 1938, 4:158–163, 1 pl.

DONALDSON, JOHN J.

Egret (Casmerodius egretta) at Greenville, Mercer Co., Pa. *Auk*, October, 1926, 43:537.

[DWIGHT, JONATHAN, JR., recording secretary]

[Abstract Proceedings] Linnæan Society of New York. *Auk*, April, 1889, 6:196–204. Records of 4 species from Erie (p. 198).

Abstract [No. 2] Proceedings Linnæan Society of New York, for the Year Ending March 7, 1890. 10 p. Note on the King Eider at Erie (p. 10).

Abstract [No. 3] Proceedings Linnæan Society of New York, for the Year Ending March 6, 1891. 11 p. Advance notice of Mr. Dwight's paper in the *Auk*, 1892, 9:129–141, with a few species mentioned.

DWIGHT, JONATHAN, JR.

The Horned Larks of North America. *Auk*, April, 1890, 7:138–158. Erie records (p. 142, 145).

Summer Birds of the Crest of the Pennsylvania Alleghanies. *Auk*, April, 1892, 9:129–141. List of 81 species observed in the vicinity of Altoona, Blair County, and Cresson, Cambria County, June 18–25, 1890; and at North Mountain, etc., in 1891. The first paper dealing faunistically with the birds of the mountains of western Pennsylvania.

The Geographical Distribution of Color and of other Variable Characters in the Genus Junco: a New Aspect of Specific and Subspecific Values. *Bulletin American Museum of Natural History*, June, 1918, 38:269–309, pls. 11–13, 5 maps. Lists Pennsylvania specimens examined (p. 286).

EASTWOOD, SIDNEY K.

Blue-gray Gnatcatcher Nesting in Western Pennsylvania. *Bird-Lore*, August, 1925, 27:254. Near Murdocksville, Washington County.

The Season: Pittsburgh Region. *Bird-Lore*, August, 1925, 27:261–263. Questionable records are those of the Olive-backed and Gray-cheeked thrushes, April 17; White-crowned Sparrow, April 19; and Connecticut Warbler, April 26. All these dates are much too early for the species named.

——*Ibid.*, October, 1925, 27:337–338.

——*Ibid.*, December, 1925, 27:406–407. The arrival dates for several warblers reported by W. C. Grimm are much too late to be correct.

——*Ibid.*, February, 1926, 28:58–59.

——*Ibid.*, April, 1926, 28:136–137. A supposed winter record for the Brown Thrasher is questionable. The alleged locality, "Patterson, Mercer County," must be an error.

——*Ibid.*, June, 1926, 28:207–208.

——*Ibid.*, August, 1926, 28:272–274. Several doubtful records occur in this paper—those for the Blue-winged and Connecticut warblers, White-winged Scoter, Greater Scaup, etc. Twenty-seven species are listed from Forbes Forest, near Rector, Westmoreland County, on the authority of Marie Knauz.

——*Ibid.*, October, 1926, 28:342–343.

——*Ibid.*, December, 1926, 28:402–403. Kingbird, Pine Siskin, Yellow Palm Warbler(!) and Yellow-breasted Chat, observed as late as October 10(!).

——*Ibid.*, February, 1927, 29:55–56.

——*Ibid.*, April, 1927, 29:126–127.

——*Ibid.*, June, 1927, 29:196–197.

——*Ibid.*, August, 1927, 29:196–197.

——*Ibid.*, August, 1927, 29:272–273.

Cuckoo Acrobatics. *Bird-Lore*, April, 1926, 28:130.

A Freak Junco. *Wilson Bulletin*, June, 1929, 41:102.

The Northern Pileated Woodpecker in Westmoreland County, Pennsylvania. *Wilson Bulletin*, March, 1930, 42:54.

Notes on the Feeding of the Least Bittern. *Wilson Bulletin*, March, 1932, 44:42. At Boydstown, Butler County.

American Egret in Butler County, Pennsylvania. *Wilson Bulletin*, December, 1932, 44:240. At Boydstown, Butler County.

EIFRIG, C. W. GUSTAVE

Remarkable Flight of Gulls at Cumberland, Md. *Auk*, January, 1902, 19:75. Herring and Bonaparte's gulls from Confluence, Somerset County, April.

Birds of Allegany and Garrett Counties, Western Maryland. *Auk*, April, 1904, 21:234–250. A few incidental records from Somerset County, Pa.

ELLIOT, DANIEL G.
North American Shore Birds. London, 1895. 268 p., 74 pls. The Marbled Godwit is said to breed "as far east as Western Pennsylvania, as I am informed by Mr. George B. Sennett" (p. 105).

ELLIOTT, GEORGE P.
Dove vs. Robin. *Young Oölogist,* December, 1884, 1:113. At Mercer.

White-rumped Shrike (*Lanius ludovicianus excubitorides*). *Ornithologist and Oölogist,* January, 1886, 11:15. Nesting at Mercer in May, 1885.

Red-tailed Hawk (*Buteo borealis*). *Ornithologist and Oölogist,* March, 1886, 11:34–35. A general account, with some local observations made at Mercer.

ELLIOTT, HOWARD H.
[The Myrtle Warbler in Winter]. *Cardinal,* January, 1930, 2:202. In Allegheny County.

The Intelligence of a Robin. *Cardinal,* July, 1933, 3:130–131, 1 pl. (With afterword by B. H. Christy.) At Wilkinsburg.

American Pipit in Crawford County. *Cardinal,* July, 1933, 3:149.

Winter Birds on Raccoon Creek. *Cardinal,* 1934, 3:169–171. (With editorial note by B. H. Christy.) A summary of the records made by the author and other observers on the "Christmas Bird Census" trips during seven years, from Monaca to a point below the mouth of Raccoon Creek, Beaver County. In the present work, references have been cited from this account instead of from the original lists appearing in *Bird-Lore.*

Saw-whet Owl in Butler County.—*Cardinal,* January, 1935, 4:18.

Western Meadowlark in Crawford County. *Cardinal,* January, 1936, 4:72.

Pipit in Butler County. *Cardinal,* January, 1940, 5:71–72.

ELLIOTT, W. C.
A History of Reynoldsville and Vicinity. Reynoldsville, Pa., 1894. 58 p. Contains a nominal list (English names only) of 97 species of birds (p. 14). Ornithologically of no value or importance.

ENTY, GEORGE
Notes from Templeton, Pennsylvania. *Ornithologist and Oölogist,* May, 1885, 10:78–79. Dates of spring arrival for certain species in 1881 and 1882. The White-eyed Vireo record is certainly questionable, while the "Broad-winged" Hawk was probably actually the Red-shouldered.

[EVANS, WILLIAM B., secretary]
Abstract of the Proceedings of the Delaware Valley Ornithological Club for 1905. *Cassinia,* 1906, 9:69–76. Note by J. A. G. Rehn on the occurrence of the Wild Turkey in Diamond Valley, Huntingdon County (p. 74).

FAXON, WALTER
Brewster's Warbler. *Memoirs Museum Comparative Zoölogy,* January, 1911, 40:57–78, 1 pl. A specimen of *Helminthophila chrysoptera* from Beaver is discussed and figured.

FISCHER, MORITZ
A Vanished Race. *Bird-Lore,* April, 1913, 15:77–84. Refers (p. 84) to the nesting of the Wild Pigeon near Sheffield, Warren County, in 1878 (authority not cited).

FISHER, ALBERT K.
The Hawks and Owls of the United States in Their Relation to Agriculture. U. S. Department of Agriculture, Division of Ornithology and Mammalogy, *Bulletin,* no. 3, 1893. 210 p., 25 pls. Contains a note on the food of an *Accipiter cooperi* taken at Beaver (contributed by W. E. C. Todd) (p. 38).

FOERSTER, NORMAN O.
The Seasons and the Birds. *Amateur Naturalist* (Binghamton, N. Y.), March, 1904, 1:26–30. Refers to western Pennsylvania (Allegheny County?).

Bird-Song Studies. *Amateur Naturalist,* September, 1904, 1:82–86. Refers to western Pennsylvania (Allegheny County?).

FORBUSH, EDWARD H.
Birds of Massachusetts and Other New England States. Vol. 2. Boston, 1927. 461 p., pls. 34–62. Contains a reference to the Bald Eagle in Blair County, *fide* McGraw (p. 156).

FORREST, EARLE R.
Least Bitterns Observed in Pennsylvania. *Oölogist,* April, 1900, 17:58–59. In July at Hackney, Washington County.

"Some Twice Occupied Nests." *Oölogist,* September, 1901, 18:136–137. Observations in Washington County.

Photographing Some Difficult Nests. *Oölogist,* October, 1910, 27:114–116. Chimney Swift and American Crow in Washington County.

Black Birds. *Oölogist,* November, 1910, 27:134. Species not stated. Locality, Washington.

A List of the Birds on a City Lot. *Oölogist,* July, 1911, 28: 114–116. Within the city limits of Washington, 1901–3; 27 species. The Brown Creeper is erroneously stated to breed.

FRENCH, JOHN C.
The Passenger Pigeon in Pennsylvania. Its Remarkable History, Habits and Extinction, with Interesting Side Lights on the Folk and Forest Lore of the Alleghanian Region of the Old Keystone State. Altoona, Pa., 1919. 257 p. Reviews: *Auk,* 1919, 36:605–606; *Cardinal,* 1926, v. 1, no. 8, p. 24. As a scientific work, this publication has no standing. It is a loose compilation, without plan or system, of information about pigeons in general and the Passenger Pigeon in particular, not only in Pennsylvania but also in other parts of the country. Wilson and Audubon are quoted at some length, but on the same basis as are later newspaper accounts and reports from pigeon hunters. Much extraneous matter is included in the general hodgepodge. Many of the statements are fanciful and misleading. The most trustworthy observations would seem to be those of the author himself, in recounting his experiences in Potter County. "The book serves one good end: it identifies in time and place a large number of Pigeon nestings in Pennsylvania" (Christy). Some of the data here presented seemed of sufficient value to be utilized in the preparation of the account of this species in the present work (p. 266–272).

FRICKE, REINHOLD L.
[Broad-winged Hawk Nesting at Rural Bridge, Allegheny County]. *Cardinal,* January, 1927, 2:16. The locality should read "Rural Ridge."

[Short-billed Marsh Wren in Westmoreland County]. *Cardinal,* January, 1929, 2:131.

[King Rail in Westmoreland County]. *Cardinal,* January, 1930, 2:201.

Unusual Observations for Western Pennsylvania. *Auk,* October, 1930, 47:572–573. Short-billed Marsh Wren nesting at Pymatuning Swamp; Dowitcher taken at the same place; Little Blue Heron in Westmoreland County.

Water-fowl in Pymatuning Swamp. *Cardinal,* July, 1931, 3:42.

[Sora Nesting in Pymatuning Swamp—a Photograph]. *Cardinal,* January, 1934, 3: opposite p. 154.

Snowy Egrets at Pymatuning Lake, Pennsylvania. *Wilson Bulletin,* December, 1937, 49:302. Specimens collected.

Lawrence's Warbler in Crawford County. *Cardinal,* July, 1939, 5:46–47. Collected near Linesville.

The Common Black Duck. *Carnegie Magazine,* September, 1939, 13:116–118, 1 fig. Based mainly on observations made at Pymatuning Lake.

FRIEDMANN, HERBERT
Further Additions to the List of Birds Victimized by the Cowbird. *Wilson Bulletin,* March, 1934, 46:25–36; June,

1934, 46:104–114. Refers to a set of eggs of the White-breasted Nuthatch from State College that included an egg of the Cowbird (p. 31).

GIBSON, CHARLES D.
Snow Buntings and Pileated Woodpeckers. *Ornithologist and Oölogist*, December, 1883, 8:94. Near Renovo, Clinton County.

[GILL, THEODORE N.(?), editor]
Wild Turkeys Abundant. *Osprey*, September–October, 1900, 5:14. Recorded from "Bowman's Station" (now Mance), Somerset County.

GRAHAM, EDWARD H.
Purple Martins at Ambridge. *Cardinal*, July, 1924, v. 1, no. 4, p. 4–7, 1 fig.

GRIMM, WILLIAM C.
The Sapsucker and Hornbeam. *Bird-Lore*, October, 1925, 27:329–330.

GRISCOM, LUDLOW
A Monographic Study of the Red Crossbill. *Proceedings Boston Society of Natural History*, January, 1937, 41:77–210. Several western Pennsylvania records.

HARLOW, RICHARD C.
The Little Blue Heron in New Jersey. *Auk*, April, 1909, 26:189–190. Said also to be occasional in "the Alleghanies" of Pennsylvania.

A Redpoll Invasion. *Bird-Lore*, June, 1909, 11:121–122. A well-written account of the Redpoll as observed at State College in the winter of 1908–9.

Wilson's Snipe wintering in Pennsylvania. *Auk*, July, 1909, 26:305. At State College in January.

The Lesser Yellow-legs in Center County, Pennsylvania. *Auk*, July, 1909, 26:305. The dates cited (April 1 and 20) are certainly remarkably early for this species. Could they have referred to the Greater Yellow-legs?

Breeding of the Raven in Pennsylvania. *Cassinia*, 1911, 14:11–18. (See also p. 50–51). A résumé of Pennsylvania breeding records, and an account of the nesting of this species in southern Centre County. "Renovo" (p. 12, line 8) should read "Warren."

Breeding of the Raven in Pennsylvania. *Auk*, April, 1911, 28:266. An abstract of the author's article in *Cassinia* of even date.

The Orange-crowned Warbler in Pennsylvania. *Auk*, April, 1911, 28:268. The date does not agree with that cited in *Cassinia*, 1911, 14:51, nor with the author's manuscript notes, where it is given as May 8, 1909.

The Black-bellied Plover in Center County, Pa. *Auk*, October, 1911, 28:484.

The Bewick's Wren in Center Co., Pa. *Auk*, October, 1911, 28:489.

Late Nesting of the Cedar Waxwing and Indigo Bird. *Oölogist*, October, 1911, 28:167. At State College (Harlow, MS.).

The Center Furnace Swamp. *Cassinia*, 1912, 15:19–23. An informal account of the birds of a five-acre swamp at Center Furnace, Centre County.

Nesting of the Savannah Sparrow in Center County, Pa. *Oölogist*, May, 1912, 29:279.

Nesting of the Virginia and Sora Rails in Pennsylvania. *Oölogist*, July, 1912, 29:308–309. Another version, with a few changes and additions, of the author's article in *Cassinia*, 1912, 15:19–23.

Pennsylvania and New Jersey Nesting Dates for 1912. *Oölogist*, October, 1912, 29:354. Localities are omitted, but some of the records seem (from the author's manuscript notes) to have been made in western Pennsylvania —Warren and State College.

The Breeding Birds of Southern Center County, Pennsylvania. *Auk*, October, 1912, 29:465–478. An annotated list of 88 breeding species, with a hypothetical list of 19 more. The region covered has State College as the center, but extends southward to include the Seven Mountains and northern Huntingdon (consistently misspelled "Hundington") County. The observations cover about four years (1908–12). Nesting dates are given for many species, and exact localities for some of the rarer ones.

Nesting Dates for Pennsylvania and New Jersey. *Oölogist*, April, 1914, 31:71–73. The omission of localities seriously detracts from the value of the list.

Nesting of the Northern Pileated Woodpecker. *Oölogist*, May, 1914, 31:82–85.

Elevated Nests of the Towhee. *Oölogist*, May, 1914, 31:86.

Nesting of the Black and White Warbler. *Oölogist*, June, 1914, 31:95. In "Stone Valley" (near Charter Oak), Huntingdon County.

Nesting of the Worm-eating Warbler in Hundington [Huntingdon] County, Pa. *Oölogist*, June, 1914, 31:98–99. Near Charter Oak.

A Broad Wing's Nest. *Oölogist*, February, 1915, 32:29–31. Near Pine Grove Mills, Huntingdon County (Harlow, MS.).

May Day with the Sparrow Hawks. *Oölogist*, April, 1917, 34:62–64.

Early Nesting of the Solitary Vireo in Pennsylvania. *Oölogist*, September, 1917, 34:165. Near Charter Oak, Huntingdon County (Harlow, MS.).

Notes on the Breeding Birds of Pennsylvania and New Jersey. *Auk*, January, 1918, 35:18–29; April, 1918, 35: 136–147. This article, prepared at the special request of the then editor of the *Auk*, Witmer Stone, is an attempt to summarize the results of the author's field work in Pennsylvania and New Jersey from 1904 to 1917. "Under each species are given the number of nests examined; the average number of eggs in a complete set, as well as the extremes, in order to show the range of variation; and the average and extreme dates for complete sets. Additional information is given under certain species and in the case of rare species full data are given for each nest found." From the standpoint of the present reviewer and from that of the student of local geographic distribution, however, the article is disappointing. It is not too much to say that it should never have been published in its present form, as it is bound to give trouble to future workers in this field, just as Warren's *Report* of 1890 has done—and for precisely the same reason: too many loose statements. Where exact data are given for nests found, this criticism of course does not apply; but there are far too many attempts to outline distribution on the basis of county records alone—which in a state such as Pennsylvania are virtually valueless for this purpose. Had the author been content to confine himself to the use of his own records and to avoid generalizing, the result would have been less lamentable; but unfortunately he frequently includes the observations of others (published and otherwise), without any indication that they are not his own. Thus, all his references to Fayette County are based on hearsay reports from T. D. Burleigh. By checking the author's statements against his earlier papers and against a brief résumé of his field notes courteously placed at my disposal, it has been possible, in the present work, to supply fuller data for some of the species involved, as duly noted in the references thereunder. Many records, however, still remain obscure, and there are numerous discrepancies. In view of Mr. Harlow's wide experience and wonderful opportunities, it is unfortunate that so many of his records have been found unsatisfactory and unusable in the preparation of this book. Misspellings of proper names have been corrected in the references.

The Breeding Habits of the Northern Raven in Pennsylvania. *Auk*, July, 1922, 39:399–410. An authoritative paper, which has been freely used in preparing the account of the species in the present work (p. 382–386).

Hartung, Dorothy
Black-throated Green Warbler at McConnell's Mills. *Cardinal*, July, 1934, 3:200.

Hayes, Samuel P.
Speed of Flying Hummingbird. *Auk*, January, 1929, 46:116. Near Erie.

Hazzard, Thomas L.
Bird Caught by a Spider—Albino English Sparrow. *Ornithologist and Oölogist*, February, 1884, 9:23. From "Allegheny" (now Pittsburgh, North Side).

Heard, John J.
Swans in Westmoreland County. *Cardinal*, January, 1935, 4:17. At Tubmill Reservoir, Ross Mountain Park.

Hegner, Frank A.
[Sora at Edgeworth]. *Cardinal*, January, 1926, v. 1, no. 7, p. 25.

Nesting of the Prairie Horned Lark, *Otocoris alpestris praticola* Henshaw, in Allegheny County. *Cardinal*, July, 1932, 3:93 (pl., p. 84).

Red Crossbill, *Loxia curvirostra pusilla* Gloger, in Allegheny County. *Cardinal*, July, 1932, 3:95.

Turkey Vulture's Re-Use of Nesting Site. *Cardinal*, January, 1934, 3:172, 1 fig. Near Frankfort Springs, Beaver County.

Barn Owl in Sewickley. *Cardinal*, January, 1934, 3:172.

Hegner, Frank A., and Bayard H. Christy
The Veery in the North Park. *Cardinal*, January, 1931, 3:22. "Deer" Creek should read "Pine" Creek.

Henrici, Max
[Upland Plover in Butler County]. *Cardinal*, January, 1926, v. 1, no. 7, p. 25.

Herrick, Francis H.
An Eagle Observatory. *Auk*, January, 1924, 41:89–105, pls. 10–12. Incidental reference (p. 92) to a nest of the Bald Eagle at North Springfield, Erie County (erroneously stated to be in Ohio).

Nests and Nesting Habits of the American Eagle. *Auk*, April, 1924, 41:213–231, pls. 13–15. Refers in part to nests found in Erie County. North Springfield is in this county (not in Ohio).

The American Eagle. A Study in Natural and Civil History. New York, 1934. xx, 267 p., 94 pls. and figs. Reviews: *Auk*, 1935, 52:206; *Cardinal*, 1935, 4:20–21. A summary of the author's extensive field observations of this species, some of which were made in Erie County.

Hicks, Lawrence E.
Some Breeding Records for Ohio. *Auk*, October, 1933, 50:448–449. Includes also some breeding records for the Slate-colored Junco from the Pymatuning region of Pennsylvania.

The Breeding Birds of Ashtabula County, Ohio. *Wilson Bulletin*, December, 1933, 45:168–195. Contains incidental Pennsylvania breeding records.

Avocet taken in Ohio. *Auk*, October, 1937, 54:538. One observed also at Erie.

Hitchcock, Henrietta
Foster Parents. *Bird-Lore*, April, 1930, 32:134–135. A pair of Robins adopt a young bird.

[Holland, William J., editor]
[Breeding of the Prairie Horned Lark in Schenley Park, Pittsburgh]. *Annals Carnegie Museum*, March, 1901, 1:3.

[The White Pelican in Western Pennsylvania]. *Annals Carnegie Museum*, March, 1901, 1:3. On Conneaut Lake, Crawford County.

Holt, Ernest G.
[Effects of a Hailstorm on Bird Life]. *Cardinal*, July, 1925, v. 1, no. 6, p. 24.

Turkey Vulture Nesting in Beaver County, Pennsylvania. *Auk*, October, 1926, 43:542.

Unusual Nest-Sites of Chimney Swift and Robin. *Bird-Lore*, June, 1927, 29:183–184. At Cooksburg, Forest County.

Yellow-headed Blackbird in Pennsylvania. *Auk*, July, 1929, 46:390. Questioning—on purely negative evidence—the sight record published in the *Auk*, 1929, 46:119.

Homer, Fred L.
The Purple Grackle and the Robin Laying in the Same Nest. *Ornithologist and Oölogist*, June, 1889, 14:88. At New Hamburg, Mercer County.

[Capture of Bewick's Wren at New Hamburg]. *Ornithologist and Oölogist*, March, 1891, 16:46. A Carolina Wren, misidentified. Cf. *Auk*, 1894, 11:330.

Among the Birds of Northern Pennsylvania. *Ornithologist and Oölogist*, April, 1893, 18:60–61. June notes on a few species at Elmer, Potter County.

The Carolina Wren in Winter in Mercer County, Pennsylvania. *Auk*, October, 1894, 11:330–331.

Young Nighthawks. *Bulletin Audubon Society of Western Pennsylvania*, April, 1923, 1:36–37.

Some Common Birds and Wild Flowers. Pittsburgh, 1923. 32 p. Privately printed. Brief popular accounts of 25 species of birds.

Horton, William C.
An Attempt to Establish a Purple Martin Colony. *Bird-Lore*, September, 1907, 9:204. With eggs taken at Waynesburg.

[Howell, Arthur H., secretary]
Abstract [No. 4] Proceedings Linnæan Society of New York, for the Year Ending March 2, 1892. 8 p. Contains a reference to certain observations made by S. E. Bacon at Erie (read by G. B. Sennett).

Huidekoper, Edgar
Breeding of Wilson Snipe. *Forest and Stream*, November, 1877, 9:326. The first Pennsylvania record. At Conneaut Marsh, near Geneva, Crawford County, *fide* H. C. Kirkpatrick, MS.

"J. N. C."
A Wild Pigeon Fake. *Forest and Stream*, November, 1907, 69:811. Once abundant in the woods of Chestnut Ridge, Fayette County, in the fall.

Jackson, R. M. S.
The Mountain. Philadelphia, 1860, xii, 632 p. Contains a list of 150 species (p. 317–360), alleged to represent the avifauna of the region about Cresson, Cambria County. I mention this list only to discredit it. Many impossibilities are included solely on the ground of their general ranges as given by Thomas Nuttall and John Cassin, who, in addition, are freely quoted. The list has been entirely disregarded in compiling the present work.

Jackson, Thomas H.
The Mourning Warbler in Warren Co., Pa. *Cassinia*, 1909, 12:9–13, 1 pl. Describes a successful search for its nest, with R. B. Simpson.

Young Goshawk. *Oölogist*, March, 1911, 28:47, 1 pl.

Jacobs, J. Warren
The Red-tailed Hawk. (Buteo borealis). *Naturalists' Companion*, August, 1886, 2:4–5. Nest and eggs found near Waynesburg, April, 1886.

Blue Gray Gnatcatcher. *Hoosier Naturalist*, October, 1886, 2:30–31. Nesting at Waynesburg.

Birds of Green[e] County, Pennsylvania. *Naturalists' Companion*, November, 1886, 2:58; December, 1886—January, 1887, 2:81–82 (not completed). A list of 28 species, briefly annotated. "*Dendrœca pennsylvanica*" erroneously listed as a summer resident.

[Nesting of the Bluebird]. *Naturalists' Companion*, November, 1886, 2:59. One pair laid five sets of eggs in succession.

Whippoor-will. (*Caprimulgus Vociferus.*). *Curiosity World* (Lake Village, N. H.), January, 1887, v. 1, no. 5, [p. 2]. A brief account of its nesting habits, etc., at Waynesburg.

Our Winter Birds. *Hoosier Naturalist*, January, 1887, 2:78. With notes on the nesting of certain species resident at Waynesburg.

The American Woodcock. *Oölogist*, March–May, 1887, 4:74. Nesting at Waynesburg (erroneously called "Waynesboro").

The Red-tailed Hawk. *West American Scientist*, September, 1887, 3:184–185. Nesting near Waynesburg, April, 1887.

Acadian Flycatcher. *Oölogist*, January, 1888, 5:13. Fourteen sets from Waynesburg, May–July, 1887.

The White-breasted Nuthatch. *Bay State Oölogist*, January, 1888, 1:3–4. Nesting at Waynesburg.

Tufted Titmouse. *Bay State Oölogist*, February, 1888, 1:15. An egg of the Cowbird found with the set.

Carolina Wren. *Hawkeye Ornithologist and Oölogist*, March, 1888, 1:37. Nesting at Waynesburg.

The Pileated Woodpecker. *Bay State Oölogist*, April, 1888, 1:31. Nesting near Waynesburg.

Migration Reports . . . Waynesburg, Pa. *Hawkeye Ornithologist and Oölogist*, May, 1888, 1:75. Arrival of 15 species, February–March, 1888.

The Blue-Gray Gnatcatcher. *Bay State Oölogist*, June, 1888, 1:46–47. Nesting at Waynesburg, May, 1887.

Nesting of the White-breasted Nuthatch. *Hawkeye Ornithologist and Oölogist*, October, 1888, 1:120–121. Records for 6 sets of eggs taken near Waynesburg.

Nesting of the Maryland Yellow-throat in Southwestern Pennsylvania. *Hawkeye Ornithologist and Oölogist*, March, 1889, 2:27–28.

Nesting of the Kentucky Warbler in Southwestern Pennsylvania. *Hawkeye Ornithologist and Oölogist*, April, 1889, 2:38–41.

Nesting of the Tufted Tit. *Oölogist*, April, 1889, 6:72–73.

Nesting of the Ruby-throated Hummingbird. *Ornithologists' and Oölogists' Semi-Annual*, July, 1889, v. 1, no. 2, p. 34–36.

Great Horned Owl. *Oölogist*, July, 1890, 7:144–145.

The Kentucky Warbler *The Taxidermist* (Akron, Ohio), March, 1892, 1:108–109. Description of nest and eggs as observed in Greene County.

Some Trips for Hawk's Eggs. *Oölogist*, November, 1892, 9:247–249. In Greene County (not Franklin).

Summer Birds of Greene County, Pennsylvania. Waynesburg, Pa., August, 1893. 15 p. Review: *Auk*, 1893, 10:353. A carefully prepared list of 90 species, summarizing the author's observations on their nesting. *Quiscalus quiscula* and *Q. q. aeneus* are both included. *Parus atricapillus* of this author is now known to be *P. carolinensis.*

Eggs of Native Pennsylvania Birds. Waynesburg, Pa., December, 1895. 10 p., 3 pls. Reviews: *Osprey*, 1898, 3:62; *Wilson Ornithological Chapter Agassiz Association Bulletin*, no. 7, 1896, p. 10. A list of the collection of eggs exhibited by the author at the Chicago World's Fair in 1893; with dates, but unfortunately without localities. The greater part of the collection must have been made by the author in Greene County, but a number of sets came from outside the state. Faunistically, the paper is unusable.

Ruby-throated Humming-bird Breeding in the Same Location for Ten Consecutive Years. *Wilson Ornithological Chapter Agassiz Association Bulletin*, no. 16, September, 1897, p. 62.

Nest of Mourning Dove, *Zenaidura macroura*, Containing Three Eggs. *Wilson Ornithological Chapter Agassiz Association Bulletin*, no. 17, November, 1897, p. 71.

Oölogical Abnormalities. *Gleanings from Nature*, no. 1, January, 1898. 36 p., 4 pls. Contains a number of records of sets taken by the author in Greene County.

Nesting of the Black-and-white Warbler. *Osprey*, January, 1899, 3:71–72.

The Story of a Martin Colony. *Gleanings*, no. 2, January, 1903, 24 p., 3 pls. Reviews: *Auk*, 1903, 20:226; *Wilson Bulletin*, 1903, 10:39; *Bird-Lore*, 1903, 5:31. A full account of the author's celebrated colony at Waynesburg from 1896 to 1902. An instructive and valuable study.

The Yellow-throated Vireo. *Wilson Bulletin*, March, 1903, 10:17–20.

Purple Martin Notes from Waynesburg, Pa. *Bulletin Michigan Ornithological Club*, December, 1903, 4:87–88. Describes the mortality among young and old martins due to unseasonable weather conditions.

The Haunts of the Golden-winged Warbler (*Helminthophila chrysoptera*). *Gleanings*, no. 3, March, 1904, 30 p., 7 pls. Reviews: *Auk*, 1904, 21:339; *Wilson Bulletin*, 1904, 11:62; *Bird-Lore*, 1904, 6:206. "The most complete biography of the Golden-winged Warbler extant" (Chapman).

Unique Martin Boxes. *Bird-Lore*, January, 1905, 7:20. In southern Greene County.

Nesting of the Grasshopper Sparrow in Southwestern Pennsylvania. *Wilson Bulletin*, March, 1905, 12:18–20.

Unusual Red-tailed Hawk Eggs. *Oölogist*, April, 1910, 27:50–51.

Bringing Back the Purple Martins. *Nature and Culture*, February, 1911, 2:18–29, 9 figs.

Where are the Bluebirds? *Bird-Lore*, June, 1912, 14:163.

Mocking-birds in Pennsylvania. *In the Open*, August, 1914, 4:41–42. Nesting near Waynesburg in 1913.

Unusual Sets of Red-tailed Hawk Eggs. *Oölogist*, March, 1918, 35:45–46.

Two Species of Birds Use One Nest. Other "Emergency Cases" or Double Sets. *Oölogist*, March, 1920, 37:36. The Bluebird and Carolina Chickadee use one nest; near Waynesburg.

On the Occurrence of the Snowy Owl in Southwestern Pennsylvania. *Oölogist*, August, 1922, 39:123–124.

Cowbird (*Molothrus ater ater*) Lays Eggs Direct from Oviduct into the Nest of Its Victim. *Oölogists' Record*, March, 1923, 3:19–21. (With letter of transmission, p. 18.)

The Purple Martin. *Bulletin Audubon Society of Western Pennsylvania*, April, 1923, 1:34–35.

The Other Egg in the Nest. *Oölogist*, May, 1924, 41:52–54. With a list of species parasitized by the Cowbird.

Celebrating My Fiftieth Year as an Oölogist. *Oölogist*, March, 1932, 49:30–33. Nesting of the Great Horned Owl.

Forty Years Ago—and More. *Oölogist*, October, 1932, 49:110–111. Nesting of the Red-tailed Hawk.

Forty Years Ago—and More. Paper No. 3. *Oölogist*, January, 1933, 50:2–6. Author's reminiscences of the Pileated Woodpecker in Greene County.

Most Southern Pennsylvania Breeding Record of the Bobolink. *Auk*, January, 1933, 50:119. Near Springs, Somerset County.

Observations on Some Oölogical Abnormalities. *Oölogist*, December, 1933, 50:154–156.

A Surprised Cardinal. *Oölogist*, February, 1934, 51:19–20. Yellow-billed Cuckoo laying in a Cardinal's nest.

Mocking Birds in Pennsylvania. *Oölogist*, December, 1934, 51:149.

Nesting of the Mockingbird in Southwestern Pa. *Oölogist*, December, 1934, 51:147–149.

An Ill Wind That Blew Some Good, and Incidentally Landed Some Nice Sets of Sharp-shinned Hawk's Eggs Into Our Cabinets. *Oölogist*, May, 1936, 53:55–57.

Forty Years Ago. *Oölogist*, July, 1937, 54:81–84. Reminiscences of the author's oölogical career.

Forty Years Ago—and More. *Oölogist*, November, 1937, 54:134–139.

On the Reasoning Instinct of the Tufted Titmouse (Baeolophus Bicolor). *Oölogist*, January, 1938, 55:6–7.

JACOBS, MARION KENT

Pet Birds. *Oölogist*, January, 1931, 48:7. Crow at Waynesburg.

JACOBS, WILLIAM F.
My First Offense. *Oölogist*, April, 1922, 39:64–66. Sparrow Hawk nesting in a building at Waynesburg.

JAMES, EDWIN
Account of an Expedition from Pittsburgh to the Rocky Mountains, Performed in the Years 1819 and '20 . . . under the Command of Major Stephen H. Long. Vol. 1. Philadelphia, 1823. 503 p. "At evening we heard the cry of the whip-poor-will [*Caprimulgus vociferus*]; and among other birds saw the pelicanus carbo, several turkey vultures, and the tell tale sandpiper" (p. 4). These were noted while the expedition was descending the Ohio River, probably not far from Beaver, on May 5, 1919.

JAMISON, HARRY K.
A Collecting Trip to Cresson Springs, Penn. *Ornithologist and Oölogist*, September, 1888, 13:133–134. A list of 22 species observed on June 27, 1888.

JENNINGS, OTTO E.
Bird Notes from Presque Isle. *Cardinal*, January, 1930, 2:181–185, map. With especial reference to the establishment of the Common Tern colony, etc.

Peregrinating Presque Isle. *Carnegie Magazine*, November, 1930, 4:171–175. Incidental references to birds.

Some Interrelations of Plants and Birds on Presque Isle, Pennsylvania. *Proceedings Pennsylvania Academy of Science*, 1933, 7:192–195.

JOHN, THOMAS
Nesting of the Mockingbird in Washington County, Pennsylvania. *Redstart*, September, 1936, 3:91. The date "April 6" is a typographical error; it should read "July 6."

JONES, JESSE L.
[King Rail at Sandy Lake, Mercer County]. *Cardinal*, July, 1925, v. 1, no. 6, p. 20.

JONES, LYNDS
Record of the Work of the Wilson Chapter for 1893 and 1894, on the Mniotiltidæ. *Wilson Ornithological Chapter [Agassiz Association] Bulletin*, no. 4, January, 1895. 20 p. Contains a few records from Greene County (Waynesburg) contributed by J. W. Jacobs.

JORDAN, A. H. B.
[Note on Ruby-throated Hummingbird at Johnsonburg]. *Ornithologist and Oölogist*, July, 1893, 18:105.

JUDD, SYLVESTER D.
The Grouse and Wild Turkeys of the United States, and Their Economic Value. U. S. Department of Agriculture, Biological Survey, *Bulletin*, no. 24, 1905. 55 p., 2 pls. Refers to a nest of the Wild Turkey found in Somerset County by E. A. Preble (p. 49).

KEESLER, R. L.
Birds. *Oölogist*, December, 1921, 38:170–171. Nesting of the Bluebird at Harrisville, Butler County, and occurrence of the Redpoll in winter. The Bachman Warbler record is of course an error.

KEIM, THOMAS D.
Summer Birds of Port Alleghany [Allegany], McKean County, Pennsylvania. *Cassinia*, 1905, 8:36–41. A list of 68 species noted by H. W. Fowler and the author from July 30 to August 6.

KEMERY, V. MAX
A Nighthawk's Unusual Home Ties. *Bird-Lore*, August, 1925, 27:251–252. Nesting on a railroad track at Johnstown (presumably), Cambria County.

KIBBEE, A. E.
A Young Naturalist. *Nidiologist*, April, 1894, 1:124. Loon captured at Warren by R. B. Simpson.

KIRKPATRICK, HARRY C.
Cardinal Grosbeaks in Winter. *Forest and Stream*, January, 1884, 21:474. At Meadville, December 25, 1883.

A December Robin's Nest. *Forest and Stream*, December 19, 1889, 33:422. At Meadville, December 9, 1889.

Absence of the Bluebird at Meadville, Pa. *Auk*, July, 1895, 12:309–310.

KIRTLAND, JARED P.
Report on the Zoology of Ohio. *Second Annual Report Geological Survey of the State of Ohio* (Columbus), 1838, p. 157–200. *Cathartes aura* nesting along Little Beaver Creek, Beaver County (p. 177). *Psittacus carolinensis* recorded from the mouth of the Big Beaver, "on perhaps doubtful authority" (p. 179).

KOCH, FRED O.
Nesting of Wilson's Thrush in Pennsylvania. *Ornithologist and Oölogist*, May, 1890, 15:74–75. At Lloydville, Cambria County.

KRIEBLE, C. GORDON
The Great White Heron in Pennsylvania. *Cardinal*, January, 1939, 5:15. Note on the occurrence of this species on Pymatuning Lake in October; identity established by a motion picture.

LEETE, R. M. [Miss]
Tufted Titmouse [at North East, Erie County]. *Wilson Bulletin*, March, 1909, 21:48.

LEHMAN, EDWARD S.
In Defense of the House Wren. *Bird-Lore*, August, 1925, 27:245. The locality is Chambersburg.

LINCOLN, FREDERICK C.
Returns from Banded Birds, 1920 to 1923. U. S. Department of Agriculture, *Department Bulletin*, no. 1268, October, 1924. 56 p., 4 pls. Loon banded at "Altoona," i. e., Lakemont, Blair County.

The Migration of Young North American Herring Gulls. *Auk*, January, 1928, 45:49–59, 3 figs. Banded birds returned from Presque Isle, Erie County, and Holbrook, Greene County.

LITTLE, ROBERT
Coot, *Fulica americana* [at Clinton, Allegheny County]. *Cardinal*, January, 1931, 3:16.

Great Horned Owl, *Bubo virginianus* [Molesting Poultry]. *Cardinal*, January, 1931, 3:17–18.

[LIVINGSTON, PHILIP ATLEE, editor]
Report on Spring Migration [etc.] for the Years 1927–28. *Cassinia*, December, 1929, 27:21–37. A few records from western Pennsylvania.

LUTTRINGER, LEO A., JR.
The Whistling Swan. *Oölogist*, April, 1928, 45:42. One taken alive at Sheffield, Warren County.

Controlling the Goshawk. *Cardinal*, July, 1930, 2:220–226, 1 map.

[Short-eared Owl in Butler County]. *Cardinal*, July, 1930, 2:233.

American Egrets in Pennsylvania. *Oölogist*, September, 1930, 47:116. Reported from "as far north as Potter County."

Rough-legged Hawk in Western Pennsylvania. *Cardinal*, July, 1931, 3:42.

Pennsylvania Bird-Life. *Bulletin Pennsylvania Game Commission*, no. 17, August, 1938. 64 p., 1 pl. Contains a list of Pennsylvania birds with indications of their local ranges.

MCATEE, W. L.
Food Habits of the Grosbeaks. U. S. Department of Agriculture, Biological Survey, *Bulletin*, no. 32, 1908. 92 p., 4 pls. Abundance of the Rose-breasted Grosbeak in western Pennsylvania (p. 34).

M'CLELLAND, DR. and MRS. W. C.
Notes on Birds of the Vicinity of Washington, Pennsylvania. *American Midland Naturalist*, January, 1922, 8:35–38. An informal list of birds observed between 1911 and 1921, with a running commentary; spring arrival dates for some species.

MCCLINTOCK, NORMAN
A Successful Failure. *Bird-Lore*, October, 1909, 11:198–204. A study of the House Wren at Pittsburgh.

The Gray-cheeked Thrush. *Cardinal*, January, 1926, v. 1, no. 7, p. 20–22. As observed in migration in Pittsburgh.

Ligonier Bird Notes. *Cardinal*, July, 1933, 3:125–129. Random notes on several species.

McCONNELL, THOMAS L.

The Diary of a New Purple Martin Colony for the Season of 1913. *Bird-Lore*, April, 1914, 16:116–117. At McKeesport, Allegheny County.

Chickadee Notes from McKeesport, Pennsylvania. *Oölogist*, February, 1915, 32:35.

Bird Brevities. *Oölogist*, June, 1916, 33:114.

Crow Roost near Boston, Pennsylvania. *Auk*, October, 1917, 34:478.

High Mortality among the Purple Martins in Western Pennsylvania during April, 1917. *Bird-Lore*, April, 1918, 20:130–131.

Some Common Land Birds Found in the Immediate Vicinity of McKeesport, Penn. *Oölogist*, November, 1918, 35:150–152. 86 species. Citations in the present work are from this list rather than from the "Christmas Bird Census" reports by the same observer.

The Bird-House for Purple Martins. *Bird-Lore*, April, 1921, 23:75–77. Colonies in McKeesport, Allegheny County.

McCONNELL, THOMAS L., and L. F. SAVAGE

Prothonotary Warbler at Erie, Pa. *Bird-Lore*, August, 1919, 21:242.

McCRACKEN, JOHN C.

Another Tame Grouse. *Bird-Lore*, April, 1930, 32:127.

McDOWELL, R. W.

The History of a Martin-House. *Bird-Lore*, June, 1917, 19:146–148, 1 fig. At Uniontown, Fayette County.

McGAVERN, C. S.

A Spring Adventure. *Bird-Lore*, April, 1926, 28:130–132. With a "Partridge" at Erie.

MACGOWAN, JANET

Birds about the House. *Transactions Warren Academy of Sciences*, for 1915–16, 1918, 3:12–17. Notes on several species common at Warren.

McGREW, ALBERT D.

Accipiter Velox. *Oölogist*, April, 1916, 33:72.

Observations on a Family of Winter Wrens. *Oölogist*, December, 1918, 35:162–164. Near Endeavor, Forest County.

McINTOSH, FRANKLIN G.

Robin and Snake. *Bird-Lore*, June, 1922, 24:152. At Franklin, Venango County.

McKNIGHT, WILLIAM J.

[*History of*] *Jefferson County Pennsylvania*. Vol. 1. Chicago, 1917. xxvi, 516 p. Pages 139–142 are devoted to a desultory account of the birds; of no scientific value. Some interesting personal reminiscences of the nesting of the Passenger Pigeon are included, however.

MALLEY, PHILIP P.

Herring Gulls on the Monongahela River During Flood. *Wilson Bulletin*, December, 1936, 48:310.

The Orange-crowned Warbler at Pittsburgh, Pennsylvania. *Wilson Bulletin*, December, 1936, 48:311.

Some Peculiar Experiences among Birds. *Oölogist*, April, 1938, 55:43–44. Observations made at Frick Park, Pittsburgh.

MALLEY, PHILIP P., and C. B. SHOEMAKER

A Comparison of Migration Dates, 1937. *Redstart*, August, 1937, 4:69–70. Notes on 32 species, with arrival dates as observed at Frick Park, Pittsburgh, etc.

MANLEY, C. H.

American Egret (*Casmerodius albus egretta*) [at Iron Bridge, Armstrong (!) County]. *Cardinal*, January, 1931, 3:15.

Red-shouldered Hawk (*Buteo lineatus*) [at Harmarville]. *Cardinal*, January, 1931, 3:15–16.

Robins and Sparrows, Co-tenants. *Cardinal*, January, 1934, 3:175–176.

Whistling Swans on Migration. *Cardinal*, July, 1938, 4:203. At Braeburn, Westmoreland County.

MERCUR, MARGARET SPEER

Cardinal Pathology. *Cardinal*, January, 1937, 4:122–123.

MERRIAM, C. HART

Preliminary Report of the Committee on Bird Migration. *Auk*, January, 1885, 2:53–65. Records for the Purple Martin (p. 58) and Baltimore Oriole (p. 60) at New Lexington, Somerset County, *fide* H. D. Moore.

MEYER, WILLIAM H.

Analysis of Barn Owl pellets in Pennsylvania. *Auk*, April, 1939, 56:187. Near State College.

MILLER, ANSEL B.

The Song Period of the Brown Thrasher. *Bird-Lore*, October, 1913, 15:311. At Springs, Somerset County.

Robin Nesting on Ground. *Bird-Lore*, August, 1918, 20:302.

Towhee Nesting in Bushes. *Bird-Lore*, December, 1925, 27:400.

A Gutter Nest [of a Robin]. *Bird-Lore*, June, 1930, 32:202.

Cuckoos and Caterpillars. *Bird-Lore*, October, 1934, 36:301, 1 fig.

MILLER, MILO H.

Bittern Caught in City. *In the Open*, November, 1912, 3:67. Knoxville, Allegheny County, September.

McKinley Park, a Sylvan Retreat for Birds and Bird-Lovers. *In the Open*, December, 1912, 3:40–41, 3 figs. With an informal list of birds found in the park at various seasons.

Bird Notes from Pymatuning. *In the Open*, August, 1913, 4:33–36.

The Screech Owl. *In the Open*, February, 1915, 5:48–49. In McKinley Park, Pittsburgh; with a general account from other sources.

Rose-breasted Grosbeak. *In the Open*, July, 1915, 5:23. McKinley Park, Pittsburgh.

House Wren. *In the Open*, August, 1915, 5:45–46. Nesting in McKinley Park, Pittsburgh.

Song Sparrow or Silver Tongue. *In the Open*, April, 1920, 10:27–28. Nesting in "Guyasuta Hollow," Allegheny County.

American or Red Crossbill at Pittsburgh. *Bird-Lore*, April, 1920, 22:97. At Brentwood, Allegheny County. Article reprinted in *In the Open*, June, 1920, 10:22–23.

The Bobolink and Cowbird. *In the Open*, June, 1920, 10:23.

The Thornhill Visit. *In the Open*, June, 1920, 10:23–24. With notes on a few of the species observed (Thornhill, Allegheny County).

MILLER, RICHARD F.

Early Nesting of the Northern Pileated Woodpecker in Pennsylvania. *Auk*, October, 1918, 35:479–480.

Pennsylvania and New Jersey Nesting Data for 1918. *Oölogist*, September, 1919, 36:155–157. Numerous records from Centre and Huntingdon counties.

Large Sets of Birds' Eggs. *Oölogist*, February, 1922, 39:27–28. Set of the White-breasted Nuthatch from State College.

Unusual Nesting Site of the Chipping Sparrow. *Oölogist*, September, 1923, 40:152. A nest found in an old woodpecker-hole at Charter Oak, Huntingdon County.

Nesting of the White-breasted Nuthatch in Center County, Pa. *Oölogist*, October, 1928, 45:134–138.

MITCHELL, HAROLD D.

Northern Phalarope at Pymatuning. *Cardinal*, January, 1940, 5:70–71.

MORISON, FRED T.

The Prize Crow Essay. *Bird-Lore*, February, 1902, 4:31–32. Based on data secured "in northwestern Pennsylvania, but a short distance from Lake Chautauqua, N. Y."

MUNSON, S. A.
Golden Eagles. *Ornithologist and Oölogist*, February, 1882, 6:94. One captured at Millers Station, Crawford County. Recorded also by G. B. Sennett, *Bulletin Nuttall Ornithological Club*, 1882, 7:58.

NELLIS, PETER
A Robin Feud. *Bird-Lore*, April, 1933, 35:97–98. Two females at the same nest; Schenley Park, Pittsburgh.

NETTING, M. GRAHAM, and WILLIAM R. VAN DERSAL
The Future of the Ecology of Pymatuning Swamp. *Cardinal*, January, 1934, 3:151–163, 2 maps. A suggestive paper of interest to the ornithologist, although birds are treated only incidentally. A full bibliography is attached.

NEWTON, F. N.
The Passenger Pigeon's Nesting. *Forest and Stream*, June, 1910, 74:934. At Coudersport, Potter County.

[NICHOLS, JOHN T., for editor]
Bird-Lore's Nineteenth Christmas Census. *Bird-Lore*, February, 1919, 21:25–49. Lists from Altoona (H. A. McGraw, *et al.*), Chambersburg (Benjamin and Robert Warfield), and McKeesport (T. L. McConnell and L. F. Savage).

Bird-Lore's Twentieth Christmas Census. *Bird-Lore*, February, 1920, 22:14–45. Lists from Altoona (H. A. McGraw and H. P. Hays); Chambersburg (B. and R. Warfield); Sewickley (B. H. Christy and F. A. Hegner); Springs, Somerset County (A. B. Miller); "Crafton," i. e., Moon Run, Thornburg, etc. (L. F. Savage); and Emsworth, Allegheny County (T. L. McConnell).

Bird-Lore's Twenty-first Christmas Census. *Bird-Lore*, February, 1921, 23:3–31. Lists from "Forest Hills to Deer Creek," Allegheny County (R. H. Stahl, *et al.*); Grove City, Mercer County (Nevin Nicholson); and Emsworth, Allegheny County (T. L. McConnell, *et al.*).

Bird-Lore's Twenty-second Christmas Census. *Bird-Lore*, February, 1922, 24:9–41. Lists from Emsworth, Allegheny County (T. L. McConnell, *et al.*); Clinton Pond to Sewickley (B. H. Christy and F. A. Hegner); and Springs, Somerset County (A. B. Miller).

Bird-Lore's Twenty-third Christmas Census. *Bird-Lore*, February, 1923, 25:8–45. Lists from Chambersburg (B. and R. Warfield); Grove City, Mercer County (John Hoffman, *et al.*); McKeesport (L. F. Savage); Monaca to Raccoon Creek, Beaver County (G. M. Sutton, *et al.*); Deer Creek region, Allegheny County (J. L. Jones, *et al.*); Sewickley (B. H. Christy and F. A. Hegner); and Springs, Somerset County (A. B. Miller).

Bird-Lore's Twenty-fourth Christmas Census. *Bird-Lore*, February, 1924, 26:14–52. Lists from McKeesport (L. F. Savage); "Pittsburgh," i. e., Deer Creek region, Allegheny County (H. H. Elliott, *et al.*); "Sewickley," i. e., upper Raccoon Creek Valley, etc., in Beaver County (B. H. Christy and F. A. Hegner); and Springs, Somerset County (A. B. Miller). The Broad-winged Hawk and Pigeon Hawk records in these lists are certainly questionable.

Bird-Lore's Twenty-fifth Christmas Census. *Bird-Lore*, February, 1925, 27:23–60. Lists from "Pittsburgh," i. e., Deer Creek region, Allegheny County (P. F. Squier and H. H. Elliott); Monaca to Raccoon Creek, Beaver County (J. L. Jones and O. C. Reiter); Ridgway, Elk County (Elizabeth B. Alsop); and "Sewickley," i. e., upper Raccoon Creek Valley, Beaver County, to Clinton Pond, Allegheny County (B. H. Christy and F. A. Hegner).

Bird-Lore's Twenty-sixth Christmas Census. *Bird-Lore*, February, 1926, 28:15–53. Lists from Hyde Park, Westmoreland County (R. and M. P. Matuszak); McKeesport (L. F. Savage, *et al.*); Deer Creek region, Allegheny County (J. L. Jones, *et al.*); "Pittsburgh," i. e., Monaca to Raccoon Creek, Beaver County (P. F. Squier, *et al.*); same locality (W. E. C. Todd, *et al.*); and Thompsonville, etc., Washington County (Agnes C. Portman, *et al.*).

Bird-Lore's Twenty-seventh Christmas Census. *Bird-Lore*, February, 1927, 29:12–52. Lists from Deer Creek region, Allegheny County (C. H. Manley, *et al.*); McKeesport (L. F. Savage, *et al.*); Monaca to Raccoon Creek to Industry, Beaver County (O. C. Reiter and P. F. Squier); Ridgway, Elk County (Elizabeth B. Alsop); Sewickley (B. H. Christy and F. A. Hegner); and Thompsonville, etc., Washington County (F. Ellair, *et al.*).

Bird-Lore's Twenty-eighth Christmas Census. *Bird-Lore*, February, 1928, 30:25–69. Lists from Deer Creek region, Allegheny County (C. Wells, *et al.*); Hyde Park, Westmoreland County (R. Matuszak); McKeesport (L. F. Savage, *et al.*); Monaca to Raccoon Creek, Beaver County (P. F. Squier); and "Sewickley," i. e., upper Raccoon Creek Valley, Beaver County (B. H. Christy and F. A. Hegner).

Bird-Lore's Twenty-ninth Christmas Census. *Bird-Lore*, February, 1929, 31:21–66. Lists from McKeesport (L. F. Savage, *et al.*); "Pittsburgh," i. e., Deer Creek region, Allegheny County (H. H. Elliott and P. F. Squier); and "Sewickley," i. e., upper Raccoon Creek Valley (Frankfort Springs, Beaver County) to Clinton, Allegheny County (B. H. Christy and F. A. Hegner).

Bird-Lore's Thirtieth Christmas Census. *Bird-Lore*, February, 1930, 32:19–66. Lists from Deer Creek region, Allegheny County (C. S. Taylor and C. H. Manley); McKeesport (L. F. Savage, *et al.*); and "Sewickley," i. e., upper Raccoon Creek Valley, Beaver County (B. H. Christy and F. A. Hegner).

Bird-Lore's Thirty-first Christmas Census. *Bird-Lore*, February, 1931, 33:25–78. Lists from Deer Creek region, Allegheny County (W. H. Seybolt, *et al.*); "Ohio River, near Pittsburgh," i. e., Monaca to Raccoon Creek, Beaver County (H. H. Elliott and P. F. Squier); Sewickley (B. H. Christy and F. A. Hegner); and South Side, Pittsburgh (Helen Blair and Agnes C. Portman).

Bird-Lore's Thirty-second Christmas Census. *Bird-Lore*, February, 1932, 34:24–80. Lists from Aliquippa (to Raccoon Creek), Beaver County (L. J. Reed); Erie (Presque Isle, etc.) (J. Savage); McKeesport (L. F. Savage, *et al.*); Pittsburgh (near Allegheny County airport) (P. P. Malley); "Sewickley," i. e., upper Raccoon Creek Valley, Beaver County (B. H. Christy and F. A. Hegner); Springs, Somerset County (A. B. Miller); and Uniontown, etc., Fayette County (W. M. Chaney). The Erie list is of particular interest and value.

Bird-Lore's Thirty-third Christmas Census. *Bird-Lore*, February, 1933, 35:13–58. Lists from Osterburg, Bedford County (D. Berkheimer); Presque Isle, Erie (E. Upson, *et al.*); and "Sewickley," i. e., Big Traverse Creek Valley, Beaver County (B. H. Christy and F. A. Hegner).

Bird-Lore's Thirty-fourth Christmas Census. *Bird-Lore*, February, 1934, 36:17–66. Lists from Erie (C. M. Beal and R. T. Peterson); Osterburg, Bedford County (D. Berkheimer); "Sewickley," i. e., Big Traverse Creek, southern Beaver County (B. H. Christy and F. A. Hegner); and Springs, Somerset County (A. B. Miller). The Erie list is unusually large and includes the Little Gull, a European species.

NICHOLSON, NEVIN G.
Cormorant in Western Pennsylvania. *Bird-Lore*, April, 1918, 20:180. Double-crested Cormorant seen at Barmore Lake, near Grove City, Mercer County. Records also a Barrow's Golden-eye—possible but not probable.

NORRIS, J. PARKER
A Series of Eggs of the Red-tailed Hawk. *Ornithologist and Oölogist*, May, 1886, 11:67–69. Sets from Washington, Pa.

NUSS, GHALE M.
Brown Thrasher in Southwestern Pennsylvania. *Oölogist*, November, 1910, 27:129. Locality not given.

Oberholser, Harry C.
A Revision of the Wrens of the Genus Thryomanes Sclater. *Proceedings U. S. National Museum*, November, 1898, 21:421–450. Records breeding specimens of *Thryomanes bewickii bewickii* (in the Biological Survey Collection, collected by W. H. Phelps) from four localities in Bedford and Fulton counties.
A Review of the Larks of the Genus Otocoris. *Proceedings U. S. National Museum*, June, 1902, 24:801–884, 4 maps. Lists specimens of *Otocoris alpestris praticola* from two points in western Pennsylvania (p. 828).
A Revision of the forms of the Hairy Woodpecker (Dryobates villosus [Linnaeus]). *Proceedings U. S. National Museum*, June, 1911, 40:595–621. Lists specimens from a number of localities in western Pennsylvania.
A Revision of the Subspecies of the Green Heron (Butorides virescens [Linnaeus]). *Proceedings U. S. National Museum*, August, 1912, 42:529–577. Specimens from McKee Gap, Blair County, and Erie (p. 538).
A Revision of the Forms of the Great Blue Heron (Ardea herodias Linnaeus). *Proceedings U. S. National Museum*, December, 1912, 43:531–559. Records a specimen from Conneauttee Lake, Erie County (p. 538).
A Monograph of the Genus Chordeiles Swainson, Type of a New Family of Goatsuckers. U. S. National Museum, *Bulletin*, no. 86, April, 1914. vii, 123 p., 6 maps. Records a specimen of *Chordeiles virginianus virginianus* from Erie (Sennett Collection).
Critical Notes on the Eastern Subspecies of *Sitta carolinensis* Latham. *Auk*, April, 1917, 34:181–187. Records specimens from a few localities in western Pennsylvania.
The Migration of North American Birds. Second Series. I. Five Swallows. *Bird-Lore*, December, 1917, 19:320–330, 1 pl. Migration dates from western Pennsylvania localities for 3 species.
——II. The Scarlet and Louisiana Tanagers. *Ibid.*, February, 1918, 20:16–19, 1 pl. Scarlet Tanager migration dates from Beaver and Renovo.
——III. The Summer and Hepatic Tanagers, Martins, and Barn Swallows. *Ibid.*, April, 1918, 20:145–152. Barn Swallow migration dates from Renovo.
——V. The Shrikes. *Ibid.*, August, 1918, 20:286–290, 1 pl. Migration dates for the Northern Shrike at Erie (*ex* Todd, 1904—error in part) and Renovo.
——XIII. European Starling and the Bobolink. *Ibid.*, August, 1920, 22:213–217, 1 pl. Bobolink migration dates from Beaver.
——XIV. Cowbirds. *Ibid.*, December, 1920, 22:343–345. Cowbird migration dates from Beaver and Renovo.
——XV. Yellow-headed Blackbird and Meadowlarks. *Ibid.*, April, 1921, 23:78–82, 1 pl. Cites two local published records for the former species, and Beaver and Renovo migration dates for the latter.
——XVI. Purple Grackle. *Ibid.*, August, 1921, 23:192–193. Migration dates from Beaver and Renovo.
——XVII. Rusty Blackbird and Brewer Blackbird. *Ibid.*, November, 1921, 23:295–299. Migration dates for the Rusty Blackbird at Pittsburgh and Renovo.
——XVIII. Red-winged Blackbirds. *Ibid.*, April, 1922, 24:85–88, 1 pl. Red-winged Blackbird migration dates from Renovo and Beaver.
——XX. Baltimore Oriole. *Ibid.*, December, 1922, 24:339–341, 1 pl. Migration dates from Renovo and Beaver.
——XXI. Orchard Oriole. *Ibid.*, April, 1923, 25:119–120, 1 pl. Spring migration dates from Beaver.
——XXIV. Ruby-throated, Black-chinned, and Calliope Hummingbirds. *Ibid.*, April, 1924, 26:108–111, 1 pl. Ruby-throated Hummingbird migration dates from Renovo.
——XXIX. The Swifts. *Ibid.*, February, 1926, 28:9–13. Chimney Swift migration dates from Renovo and Beaver.
——XXX. Chuck-will's-widow and Whip-poor-will. *Ibid.*, April, 1926, 28:117–120, 1 pl. Whip-poor-will migration dates from Renovo and Beaver.
——XXXI. The Nighthawks. *Ibid.*, August, 1926, 28:255–261, 1 pl. Nighthawk migration dates from Beaver and Renovo. The date "April 27, 1911," for the former locality is an error.
——XXXIII. The Flickers. *Ibid.*, April, 1927, 29:110–112, 1 pl. Northern Flicker migration dates from Renovo.
——XXXV. Red-headed and Lewis's Woodpeckers. *Ibid.*, December, 1927, 29:411–413. Red-headed Woodpecker migration dates from Beaver.
——XXXVII. Yellow-bellied and Red-breasted Sapsuckers. *Ibid.*, August, 1928, 30:253–257. The Beaver records for the Yellow-bellied Sapsucker cited in this article almost certainly actually pertain to the Red-bellied Woodpecker. They were supplied by H. H. Wickham.
——XLVI. Yellow-billed, Mangrove, and Black-billed Cuckoos. *Ibid.*, August, 1931, 33:249–254, 1 pl. Migration dates from Beaver and Renovo.
The Geographic Races of Cyanocitta cristata. *Auk*, January, 1921, 38:83–89. Records specimens of *Cyanocitta cristata bromia* from Redbank, Clarion County, and Leasuresville, Butler County (in the Biological Survey Collection).
A Revision of the North American House Wrens. *Ohio Journal of Science*, March, 1934, 34:86–96. The House Wren from west of the mountains is described as new, under the name *baldwini*. Western Pennsylvania specimens are listed under both races.
Description of a New Chickadee from the Eastern United States. *Proceedings Biological Society of Washington*, December 28, 1937, 50:219–220. The range of the new race (*practicus*) is given as including "southwestern Pennsylvania."
The Great White Heron in Pennsylvania. *Cardinal*, January, 1939, 5:15–16. Critical remarks on the specimen in the Pymatuning Museum, and on the two known occurrences.

Oldys, Henry
Individual Variety of Bird Songs. *Cassinia*, 1915, 18:24–29. Refers to songs of Meadowlark heard near Washington (p. 28).

Oliver, D. Leet
The Philadelphia Vireo in Western Pennsylvania. *Auk*, April, 1902, 19:206. At Shields and Pittsburgh, Allegheny County; and near Industry, Beaver County, *fide* Todd.

O'Neil, Edward, II.
[Migrant Shrike near Sewickley in March]. *Cardinal*, July, 1930, 2:234.
[Two Local Records for the] Short-eared Owl, *Asio flammeus*. *Cardinal*, January, 1931, 3:18. Beaver and Allegheny counties.

Oudette, Burt L.
American Brant on Pymatuning Lake. *Cardinal*, July, 1936, 4:96.
White Pelican at Pymatuning. *Cardinal*, January, 1937, 4:121.
Blue Goose at Pymatuning. *Cardinal*, January, 1937, 4:121.
Bald Eagle at Pymatuning. *Cardinal*, July, 1938, 4:203. Nesting in 1937 and 1938.
Migration at Pymatuning. *Cardinal*, July, 1939, 5:47–48. Spring records for waterfowl.
Blue Goose and Snow Goose at Pymatuning. *Cardinal*, January, 1940, 5:68.

Palmer, William
Our Small Eastern Shrikes. *Auk*, July, 1898, 15:244–258. Ascribes the Migrant Shrike to the western tier of counties in Pennsylvania (p. 249).
Ecology of the Maryland Yellow-throat, and Its Relatives. *Auk*, July, 1900, 17:216–242. Critical remarks on western Pennsylvania specimens (p. 234).

PARKER, C. W.
The Martin in Allegheny County. *Cardinal*, July, 1924, v. 1, no. 4, p. 1–4.

PERRY, J. ELMER
Whistling Swans at Erie. *Cardinal*, January, 1932, 3:68.
Marbled Godwit at Erie. *Cardinal*, July, 1935, 4:49. (With editorial comment by B. H. Christy.) The same occurrence that was reported in the *Cardinal*, 1935, 4:18.
Bird Notes from Erie. *Cardinal*, January, 1938, 4:177. *Larus hyperboreus*, *Cryptoglaux acadica*, and other interesting species.

PETERSON, ROGER T.
Snowy Egret and Bald Eagle at Pymatuning. *Cardinal*, January, 1938, 4:175–176.

PETTINGILL, OLIN SEWALL, JR.
The American Woodcock *Philohela minor* (Gmelin). *Memoirs Boston Society of Natural History*, April, 1936, 9:169–391, pls. 12–21. Western Pennsylvania records (p. 225–226).

PIERCE, H. B.
The Pigeon and the Muzzle-loader. *In the Open*, March, 1920, 10:28–30. Recollections of a flight in the fall of 1874, ten miles west of Pittsburgh.

PITCAIRN, WILLIAM G.
[Bird life in Riverview Park, Allegheny]. *Oölogist*, March, 1907, 24:41. With mention of a few common species.
A Report on the Nesting Birds in the Vicinity of Riverview Park, Allegheny, Pa., for 1906. *Bird-Lore*, July, 1907, 9:155.
Lark Sparrow (*Chondestes grammacus*) in Southwestern Pennsylvania. *Auk*, October, 1908, 25:476. At Leetsdale, Allegheny County, in June.
[Note on Nesting of American Robin and Brown Thrasher]. *Oölogist*, March, 1910, 27:23. At Rowan, Butler County, and Allegheny (now North Side, Pittsburgh), as shown in the original data for the specimens.
Further Notes on the Lark Sparrow in Southwestern Pennsylvania. *Auk*, April, 1910, 27:211. At Leetsdale, Allegheny County, in August.
Wilson's Thrush (*Hylocichla fuscescens*) a common Breeder Near Allegheny, Pennsylvania. *Auk*, April, 1910, 27:213. According to the author's original records, this species was actually found breeding no nearer "Allegheny" than Rowan, Butler County.

[POTTER, JULIAN K., secretary]
Abstract of the Proceedings of the Delaware Valley Ornithological Club, 1920. *Cassinia*, 1923, 24:50–54. Loon captured at Greencastle, Franklin County, by G. F. Ziegler, Jr. (p. 54).
Report on Spring Migration for the Years 1922–24. *Cassinia*, February, 1926, 25:21–52. Records of a few species from Greencastle, Franklin County, contributed by G. F. Ziegler, Jr.
Abstract of the Proceeding[s] of the Delaware Valley Ornithological Club, 1924. *Cassinia*, February, 1926, 25:62–66. Nesting of the Duck Hawk at Tyrone, Blair County (p. 63).

PUTNAM, XENO W.
A Pennsylvania Relic Ground. *Forest and Stream*, September 22, 1906, 67:450. The Wild Pigeon roost in Pymatuning Swamp is described.

RANEY, EDWARD C.
Robin and Mourning Dove use the same nest. *Auk*, July, 1939, 56:337–338. At New Castle.

REITER, OSCAR C.
Eggs of the Whip-poor-will. *Cardinal*, July, 1931, 3:43–44, 1 pl. Near "Patton's Point," southern Beaver County.

RHOADS, SAMUEL N.
Notes on Some of the Rarer Birds of Western Pennsylvania. *Auk*, October, 1899, 16:308–313. This article is a potpourri of ornithological records from various sources, first-hand and otherwise, with virtually nothing to tie them together. It bears the marks of hasty and careless composition and is disfigured by typographical and other errors; and its scientific value is open to criticism. The article is based in part upon the author's own field work in western Pennsylvania (mainly in Beaver, Westmoreland, and Cambria counties in 1898; and at Round Island, Clinton County, in 1896), and in part upon the word-of-mouth statements of certain local observers. In some instances there are discrepancies between the author's published records and the records in his notebooks (which it has been my privilege to examine). For the purposes of the present work, every effort has been made to check and correct all the records in this article, as noted under the head of the several species involved; but many cannot now be verified. It may here be noted that the specimen of Connecticut Warbler said to have been taken at "Leetsdale" (i.e., Fair Oaks), Allegheny County, on May 24, 1898, has been proved to be a Mourning Warbler instead. The Allegheny County record for the Green-winged Teal is also an error.

RIDGWAY, ROBERT
The Birds of North and Middle America. Part I. U. S. National Museum, *Bulletin*, no. 50, October, 1901. xxxiii, 715 p., 20 pls. A few western Pennsylvania records for certain Fringillidae.
——Part II. *Ibid.*, October, 1902. xx, 834 p., 22 pls. Critical remarks on western Pennsylvania specimens of the Black-throated Blue Warbler (p. 542, 545–546).
——Part III. *Ibid.*, December, 1904. xx, 801 p., 19 pls. A few incidental western Pennsylvania references.
——Part VI. *Ibid.*, April, 1914. xx, 882 p., 36 pls. Western Pennsylvania records for *Phloeotomus pileatus abieticola* (p. 156, 160) and *Dryobates villosus villosus* (p. 202).

RIVES, WILLIAM C.
The Summer Birds of the West Virginia Spruce Belt. *Auk*, April, 1898, 15:131–137. Incidental reference to the summering of the Lesser Scaup Duck in western Pennsylvania, *fide* Todd (p. 134).

[ROGERS, CHARLES H., for editor]
Bird-Lore's Fourteenth Christmas Census. *Bird-Lore*, February, 1914, 16:26–50. Lists from McKeesport (T. L. McConnell); Pittsburgh (A. W. Honywill) to Harmarville (T. D. Burleigh and H. K. Anderson); and Springs, Somerset County (A. B. Miller).
Bird-Lore's Fifteenth Christmas Census. *Bird-Lore*, February, 1915, 17:22–48. Lists from McKeesport (Charles Lindberg and T. L. McConnell); Pittsburgh to Harmarville (T. D. Burleigh); Sewickley (B. H. Christy and F. A. Hegner); and Springs, Somerset County (A. B. Miller).
Bird-Lore's Sixteenth Christmas Census. *Bird-Lore*, February, 1916, 18:18–42. Lists from Beaver (W. R. Boulton); McKeesport (T. L. McConnell); Pittsburgh to Harmarville (T. D. Burleigh and A. D. McGrew); Sewickley (H. C. Morrison, *et al.*); and Springs, Somerset County (A. B. Miller).
Bird-Lore's Seventeenth Christmas Census. *Bird-Lore*, February, 1917, 19:11–39. Lists from McKeesport (T. L. McConnell and L. F. Savage); Pittsburgh (T. D. Burleigh and A. D. McGrew); and Springs, Somerset County (A. B. Miller).
Bird-Lore's Eighteenth Christmas Census. *Bird-Lore*, February, 1918, 20:25–50. Lists from Beaver (W. R. Boulton); McKeesport (L. F. Savage and T. L. McConnell); and Springs, Somerset County (A. B. Miller).

ROGERS, CHARLES H.
A Coöperative Study of Bird Migration. *Bird-Lore*, June, 1914, 16:180–185; August, 1914, 16:270–274. Migration dates for several common species from Pittsburgh, contributed by T. D. Burleigh.

ROTH, PAUL W.
A Set of [Great Horned] Owl's Eggs. *Thielensian* (Thiel

College, Greenville, Pa.), January, 1896, 13:70–71. Locality not specified.

Rutledge, Archibald
Nonpareil (Passerina ciris) in Pennsylvania. *Auk*, October, 1921, 38:606–607. Seen near Mercersburg, Franklin County, May 16, 1921.

Sage, John H.
Albino [Robin]. *Ornithologist and Oölogist*, July, 1881, 6:38. At Sewickley, Allegheny County. Quoted from newspaper account.

[Sage, John H., secretary]
Seventh Congress of the American Ornithologists' Union. *Auk*, January, 1890, 7:66–71. Note on an abnormal specimen of the Carolina (Sora) Rail from Erie (p. 71).

[Sansom, James B., editor]
Mamma Woodcock on the Job. *In the Open*, May–June, 1914, 4:46, fig. Nest found at Oakmont, Allegheny County.

Schacklett, Turner W.
Spring Activities. *Bird-Lore*, June, 1924, 26:177–178. House Wren nesting at Erie.

Scherer, Lloyd E.
Passenger Pigeons in Northwestern Pennsylvania. *Cardinal*, July, 1939, 5:25–42. Account drawn from diary and records of J. B. Oviatt; applies to McKean and Potter counties.

Schlag, Carl W.
Hummingbirds and Their Nests. *Cardinal*, January, 1930, 2:195–200, 1 pl. (With afterword by B. H. Christy.) A careful and thoroughly scientific study of this species near Glenshaw, Allegheny County.

Hummingbirds in Time of Drought. *Cardinal*, January, 1931, 3:10–12. Additional interesting observations, supplementing a previous article.

The Struggle for Existence. *Cardinal*, July, 1931, 3:34–35. Tufted Titmouse nesting in a bird box.

Hummingbird Habits. *Cardinal*, January, 1935, 4:13–16.

Hummingbird Notes—*Cardinal*, January, 1939, 5:17–18. Suggests that polygamy may obtain in this species.

More Hummingbird Notes. *Cardinal*, January, 1940, 5:57–65.

Scoville, Samuel, Jr.
The Pileated Woodpecker. *Cassinia*, 1920, 23:14–22, 1 pl. An entertaining account of the author's experiences in search of the nest of this species in northern Huntingdon County (Charter Oak), in company with R. C. Harlow. Other species noted are referred to more or less at length.

The Raven's Nest. *Atlantic Monthly*, July, 1920, 126:32–37. (Reprinted in *Everyday Adventures*, 1920, Atlantic Monthly Press.) An interesting account of a successful quest for the nest of this bird, in company with R. C. Harlow ("the Collector"). The region covered was the Seven Mountains in Centre County.

Runaway Days. New York, 1927. 254 p. Review: *Auk*, 1927, 44:455. A series of delightfully written sketches, among which are accounts of trips to the mountains of Huntingdon County in search of the Raven and Pileated Woodpecker (p. 189, 225).

Scroggs, G. A.
Early Birds. *Forest and Stream*, March 31, 1892, 38:296. First arrivals at Beaver—a few common species.

Seiple, Stanley J.
American Egret at Conneaut Lake, Pennsylvania. *Auk*, January, 1929, 46:104.

[Snowy Owl in Greenville]. *Cardinal*, January, 1929, 2:130.

Egret in Crawford County, Pa. *Auk*, January, 1930, 47:74.

White Herons near Hartstown, Crawford Co., Pa. *Auk*, January, 1931, 48:113. With a list of other water birds noted late in August. "Semipalmated Sandpiper" should read "Semipalmated Plover."

Semple, John B.
Nest Material of the Baltimore Oriole, *Icterus galbula* (Linnæus). *Cardinal*, January, 1932, 3:69–70.

Sennett, George B.
An Unusual Flight of Whistling Swans in Northwestern Pennsylvania. *Bulletin Nuttall Ornithological Club*, April, 1880, 5:125–126.

Capture of the Golden Eagle in Crawford County, Pennsylvania. *Bulletin Nuttall Ornithological Club*, January, 1882, 7:58. At Millers Station, December 10, 1881. Cf. S. A. Munson, *Ornithologist and Oölogist*, 1882, 6:94.

Troglodytes aëdon, House Wren, Breeding in a Sand Bank. *Auk*, January, 1889, 6:76. At Erie, in an old kingfisher-hole.

The King Eider (*Somateria spectabilis*) at Erie, Pennsylvania. *Auk*, January, 1890, 7:88–89.

Sharples, Robert P.
The Mourning Warbler. *Oölogist*, August, 1908, 25:121. Two nests found in Warren County.

On the Nesting of the Broad-winged Hawk (Buteo platypterus) and Goshawk (Astur atricapillus) in Pennsylvania. *Cassinia*, 1910, 13:25–28, 2 pls. Quotations from letters of R. B. Simpson on the nesting of the Goshawk in Warren County.

Shontz, Russell M.
Winter Robins at Sharon, Pa. *Bird-Lore*, June, 1933, 35:155.

[Shryock, William A., secretary]
Abstract Proceedings Delaware Valley Ornithological Club, no. 2, 1898, 42 p. A Raven taken in Clearfield County, *fide* W. G. Smith (p. 2). Seven species listed from Rasselas, Elk County, by W. L. Baily. Cf. *Auk*, 1896, 13:289.

Abstract Proceedings Delaware Valley Ornithological Club, no. 3, 1900. 28 p. "The Birds of [Round Island,] Clinton County," with mention of two species, by S. N. Rhoads (p. 8). A nest of the "Long-billed Water Thrush" from Somerset County is described by Stewardson Brown (p. 13). Old-squaw ducks and other birds noted at Waynesburg by J. W. Jacobs (p. 14).

Simpson, Ralph B.
[Winter Records of the Belted Kingfisher and Killdeer at Warren]. *Ornithologist and Oölogist*, April, 1890, 15:63.

[Notes from Warren, 1891]. *Ornithologist and Oölogist*, July, 1891, 16:111.

Fox vs. Crows. *Oölogist*, August, 1894, 11:256.

The Magnolia Warbler. *Nidiologist*, August, 1895, 2:164. With a list of other warblers nesting at Warren.

An Albino Crow. *Nidiologist*, October, 1895, 3:19.

From Warren Co., Penn. *Oölogist*, September, 1906, 23: 135–136. A brief informal list of breeding species.

[Notes from Warren]. *Oölogist*, June, 1907, 24:86–87. On the appearance of the Pine Grosbeak, Crossbill (both species), etc., during the winter of 1906–7.

A Decoration Day Trip. *Oölogist*, September, 1907, 24: 133–134.

A Morning's Egg Hunt. *Oölogist*, November, 1907, 24: 182–183. Notes on the nesting of the Magnolia Warbler, Olive-sided Flycatcher, etc. Author's name inadvertently omitted.

Three Freaks. *Oölogist*, November, 1908, 25:171. Albinistic Meadowlark.

[Letter on the Birds of Warren]. *Oölogist*, February, 1909, 26:25–26. Notes on the American Goshawk, Mourning Warbler, Olive-sided Flycatcher, etc.

American Goshawk Nesting in Pennsylvania. *Oölogist*, June, 1909, 26:85–87. The first circumstantial account of the nesting of this hawk within our limits.

More About the Pennsylvania Goshawks. *Oölogist*, August, 1909, 26:119–120.

Occurrence of Lincoln's Sparrow. *Oölogist*, September, 1909, 26:152.

From Erie, Pennsylvania. *Oölogist*, September, 1909, 26:153. Observations made July 4–6, 1909.

The Blackburnian Warbler. *Oölogist*, October, 1909, 26: 163–164. Notes on its appearance, habits, and nesting.

Pennsylvania. Nesting Dates for 1909. *Oölogist*, October, 1909, 26:169–170. Data on 28 species.

The Olive-sided Fly-Catcher in Pennsylvania. *Oölogist*, November, 1909, 26:193–195. A full account of its nesting in Warren County.

Fall Notes from Warren, Pa. *Oölogist*, March, 1910, 27:32.

The Cormorant in Western Pennsylvania. *Oölogist*, March, 1910, 27:34. At Warren, May 1, 1903.

Turkey Vulture in Pennsylvania. *Oölogist*, March, 1910, 27:35. One taken alive in Warren County in July.

The Black-throated Blue Warbler. *Oölogist*, May, 1910, 27:64–65. Habits and nesting in Warren County.

Winter Wren Nesting [in Warren County]. *Oölogist*, August, 1910, 27:98.

Spring and Winter Birds. *Oölogist*, August, 1910, 27:100.

The Northern Pileated Woodpecker. *Oölogist*, December, 1910, 27:147–149. Habits and nesting in Warren County.

Some Rare Waterfowl. *Oölogist*, February, 1911, 28:33.

An April Blow on Lake Erie. *Oölogist*, February, 1911, 28:38–39.

A Flight of Swans. *Oölogist*, February, 1911, 28:39–40.

A Flight of Loons. *Oölogist*, February, 1911, 28:41–42.

A Costly Holb[o]ells [Grebe]. *Oölogist*, February, 1911, 28:42–43.

A Flight of Buffleheads. *Oölogist*, February, 1911, 28:44.

Goshawk, Nesting Again. *Oölogist*, March, 1911, 28:47.

A Barred Owl's Breakfast. *Oölogist*, March, 1911, 28:52.

An Adult Pigeon Hawk. *Oölogist*, March, 1911, 28:52.

The Sharp-shinned Hawk. *Oölogist*, March, 1911, 28:54–56.

Nesting of the Pileated Woodpecker. *Oölogist*, April, 1911, 28:72.

Occurrence of Black Terns. *Oölogist*, April, 1911, 28:76.

Nelson's Sparrow and Dunlin [at Warren]. *Oölogist*, June 1911, 28:97.

Evening Grosbeaks [at Warren]. *Oölogist*, June, 1911, 28:102. A flock seen during February and March, 1911.

Two September Days [at Presque Isle]. *Oölogist*, September, 1911, 28:142–144.

Among the Rocks. *Oölogist*, October, 1911, 28:161–162.

Pileated Woodpecker. *Oölogist*, October, 1911, 28:165.

Chat and Golden Wing[ed Warbler]. *Oölogist*, October, 1911, 28:165–166.

A Young Acadian [Owl]. *Oölogist*, December, 1911, 28:184.

After Birds and Eggs. *Oölogist*, December, 1911, 28:201–202.

Piping Plover in Pennsylvania. *Oölogist*, January, 1912, 29:212–213. Nesting on Presque Isle.

A Friday's Hunt. *Oölogist*, March, 1912, 29:246–247. On Presque Isle, May 17–20, 1905.

Some Ducks and a Hawk. *Oölogist*, March, 1912, 29:247–249. American Rough-legged Hawk, American Merganser, etc., at Warren.

A Day on the Peninsula. *Oölogist*, March, 1912, 29:249–250. Birds observed on Presque Isle in early June.

Hunting Warblers Nests. *Oölogist*, May, 1912, 29:276–277.

On the Tionesta. *Oölogist*, August, 1912, 29:328–330. Informal account of the bird life at the head of Tionesta Creek, Warren County.

[Note on the Breeding of the Quail near Warren]. *Oölogist*, August, 1912, 29:335.

Some Erie, Pa., Notes. *Oölogist*, September, 1912, 29:350.

Winter Notes. *Oölogist*, November, 1912, 29:370.

The Pine Siskin. *Oölogist*, November, 1912, 29:372–373. An interesting account of its nesting in the spring of 1912.

Robin vs. Snake. *Oölogist*, December, 1912, 29:402.

Some Raptore Notes. *Oölogist*, February, 1913, 30:32.

Along the High Water. *Oölogist*, March, 1913, 30:50–51.

Large Set of [Black-billed] Cuckoo [Eggs]. *Oölogist*, March, 1913, 30:53.

After Ducks and Shore Birds. *Oölogist*, September, 1913, 30:149–150. An October hunt on Presque Isle.

Broad-winged Hawk. *Oölogist*, February, 1914, 31:27.

Cliff Swallow and Sparrow. *Oölogist*, February, 1914, 31:40. English sparrows appropriating the nests of cliff swallows.

A Flight of Pine Grosbeaks. *Oölogist*, March, 1914, 31:53–54. During the winter of 1906–7.

Cardinal at Warren, Pa. *Oölogist*, May, 1914, 31:80.

A Day of Records. *Oölogist*, May, 1914, 31:91–92.

The Warblers of Warren Co., Penna. *Oölogist*, June, 1914, 31:119–122. A list of 30 species, of which 16 are known to breed.

The Winter Wren. *Oölogist*, October, 1914, 31:186, 188.

A Great Flight of Grebes. *Oölogist*, December, 1914, 31: 210, 212.

The Solitary Vireo. *Oölogist*, December, 1914, 31:229–230.

The Barred Owl. *Oölogist*, January, 1915, 32:9–10, 1 fig.

The Great Horned Owl. *Oölogist*, January, 1915, 32:10–12, 1 fig.

Goshawk Notes. *Oölogist*, February, 1915, 32:29.

Fur and Feathers. *Oölogist*, February, 1920, 37:24–26.

The Maryland Yellow Throat. *Oölogist*, April, 1920, 37: 43–45.

Nesting of the Goshawk. *Oölogist*, August, 1920, 37:91–93.

Sharp-shins and Pileateds. *Oölogist*, November, 1920, 37:134.

Two May Days. *Oölogist*, December, 1920, 37:142–143. On the nesting of the Magnolia, Blackburnian, Black-throated Blue, and Black-throated Green warblers; Brown Creeper; and others.

Birds Freezing. *Oölogist*, October, 1921, 38:135. Cardinal and Bob-white.

The Brown Creeper. *Oölogist*, November, 1921, 38:153–154. Nesting in Warren County.

Hunting Hawks' Nests. *Oölogist*, March, 1922, 39:33, 36. Half-tone illustrations for this article appear on p. 19, 21, 26, and 30 of the February number.

Unexpected Takes. *Oölogist*, April, 1922, 39:54–56. Chiefly about mammals, but with notes on the Acadian Owl and Duck Hawk.

Some Blackburnian [Warbler] Nests. *Oölogist*, July, 1922, 39:86–87.

SKAGGS, MERIT B.

White Herons in Ohio. *Wilson Bulletin*, March, 1937, 49:47. The observations here recorded were actually made on the Pennsylvania side of Pymatuning Lake, near Linesville.

Gull Records for Lake Erie. *Wilson Bulletin*, December, 1937, 49:294. Great Black-backed Gull and Common Redpoll at Presque Isle, February, 1937.

Red-throated Loon and Herring Gull in Western Pennsylvania. *Wilson Bulletin*, September, 1938, 50:202.

STONE, WITMER

Work of the Delaware Valley Ornithological Club During 1890. *Auk*, April, 1891, 8:244–245. Records a specimen of *Corvus corax "sinuatus"* from "Delaware" [Fulton] County. Compare the author's *Birds E. Pa. and N. J.*, 1894, p. 103.

The Birds of Eastern Pennsylvania and New Jersey. Prepared under the direction of the Delaware Valley Ornithological Club. Philadelphia, 1894. vii, 185 p., 1 pl., 2 maps. A few incidental original references to western Pennsylvania birds (p. 91, 96, 103, 113, 115).

Breeding of Sitta canadensis in Pennsylvania. *Auk*, July, 1897, 14:324. The species noted at Round Island, Clinton County, May 26–June 1, 1896, by S. N. Rhoads.

Report on the Spring Migration of 1904. *Cassinia*, 1905, 8:46–61. Note on the Mourning and Hooded warblers in Blair County in June (p. 59).

June Birds of Fulton County, Pa. *Cassinia*, 1906, 9:40–44. Account of a trip taken by W. L. Baily and W. E. Hughes from Mercersburg across the mountains to McConnellsburg and Big Cove Tannery in June, 1905. Includes a discussion of forest and faunal conditions; random notes on some of the more interesting birds; and a nominal list of 72 species.

Report on the Spring Migration of 1905. *Cassinia*, 1906, 9:52–67. Contains a list of known occurrences of Bewick's Wren in western Pennsylvania, contributed by W. E. C. Todd (p. 65–66). Specimens taken before 1898 are in the Biological Survey Collection.

Report on the Spring Migration of 1914. *Cassinia*, 1915, 18:38–61. Includes records by C. R. Mason for several species at State College.

Report on the Spring Migration of 1918. *Cassinia*, 1919, 22:22–37. Contains records by H. A. McGraw for several species at Altoona.

Report of the Spring Migration of 1919. *Cassinia*, 1920, 23:23–39. Contains records by H. A. McGraw of a number of species at Altoona.

Report on the Spring Migration—1920. *Cassinia*, 1923, 24:20–34. Contains a few migration dates from Greencastle, Franklin County, contributed by G. F. Ziegler, Jr.

Report on the Spring Migration—1921. *Cassinia*, 1923, 24:35–49. Contains a few migration dates from Greencastle, Franklin County, contributed by G. F. Ziegler, Jr.

[STREET, J. FLETCHER, secretary]

Abstract of the Proceedings of the Delaware Valley Ornithological Club, 1910. *Cassinia*, 1911, 14:49–53. Note on the occurrence of the Snow Bunting at Orbisonia, Huntingdon County; on the nesting of the Raven near State College; and on the capture of the Orange-crowned Warbler at the latter locality (p. 50–51). Note on the Sora and Virginia Rail breeding at "State College," i.e., Center Furnace (p. 53).

Abstract of the Proceedings of the D. V. O. C., 1912. *Cassinia*, 1912, 16:56–59. Note on "Birds and Chestnut Blight," with reference to species observed in Huntingdon County, by L. S. Pearson (p. 59).

STREET, J. FLETCHER

Summer Birds of Adams and Franklin Counties, Pennsylvania. *Cassinia*, 1923, 24:8–19. List of 81 species, observed by W. L. Baily, S. N. Rhoads, Witmer Stone, and J. F. Street during an automobile trip, June 16–19, 1920, from Greencastle through Mercersburg to Foltz (Cove Gap post office), Ft. Loudon, and Metal—localities in Franklin County on the eastern flank of Tuscarora Mountain—and across Jordan's Knob to Horse Valley. A notable record is that of a pair of blue grosbeaks. The record of the Fish Crow is scarcely acceptable.

SURFACE, HARVEY A.

Annual Report of the Division of Zoology. *Ninth Annual Report Pennsylvania Department of Agriculture [for] 1903*, 1904, p. 159–191. Reference to a few unusual birds observed at State College—*Cathartes aura, Loxia curvirostra minor*, etc. (p. 178–179). Compare *Wilson Bulletin*, 1905, 12:28.

Report of the Ornithologist. *Ibid.*, p. 227–232. *Loxia curvirostra minor* and *Cardinalis cardinalis* at State College (p. 232).

Report of the Ornithologist. *Tenth Annual Report Pennsylvania Department of Agriculture [for] 1904*, 1905, p. 418–424. A wild pigeon, taken in 1902 in McKean County, exhibited (p. 422).

Report of the Ornithologist. *Nineteenth Annual Report Pennsylvania Department of Agriculture [for] 1913*, 1914, p. 358–366. Reprint of a newspaper article (p. 359) from Indiana County with regard to the Robin being forced to winter in the North because of persecution in the South by gunners(!).

SUTTON, GEORGE M.

A Trip to Waynesburg, Pa. *Oölogist*, January, 1915, 32:14, 16, 18. Notes on the collections of birds' eggs of S. S. Dickey, J. B. Carter, and J. W. Jacobs, and on the nest tree of a pileated woodpecker.

Field Identification of Our Winter Birds. *Bulletin Audubon Society of Western Pennsylvania*, April, 1923, 1:4–9.

The Starling in Southwestern Pennsylvania. *Bulletin Audubon Society of Western Pennsylvania*, April, 1923, 1:38–40, 1 pl.

The Season: Pittsburgh Region. *Bird-Lore*, April, 1923, 25: 132. The first of a series of interesting sketches of the seasonal bird life of this area, compiled from the author's notes and those supplied by other local observers. An unusual influx of boreal birds is here recorded. The flock of cowbirds mentioned was seen at Squaw Run, while the crossbills were observed by B. H. Christy at Frankfort Springs, Beaver County (not Sewickley).

——*Ibid.*, June, 1923, 25:193–195. Includes also some records from Huntingdon County, made by the author; and others from as far north as Mercer County, made by the Messrs. Homer.

——*Ibid.*, August, 1923, 25:260. Includes also some notes from Pymatuning Swamp and other outlying localities.

——*Ibid.*, February, 1924, 26:55–56. Includes notes from several outlying localities. "Greensburg," Mercer County, should read "Greenville."

——*Ibid.*, April, 1924, 26:122–123. Unusual number of summer residents wintering.

——*Ibid.*, June, 1924, 26:189–190.

——*Ibid.*, August, 1924, 26:266–267. The records cover a wide area in western Pennsylvania.

——*Ibid.*, October, 1924, 26:336–337.

——*Ibid.*, December, 1924, 26:418–419. Notes from Erie, Greenville, Gordon Lake (Bedford County), Bethany (W. Va.), etc.

Notes on the Nesting of the Wilson's Snipe in Crawford County, Pennsylvania. *Wilson Bulletin*, December, 1923, 35:191–202, 3 figs. One of the best accounts of the nesting habits of this species, but not the first record for this region. Compare Huidekoper, *Forest and Stream*, November, 1877, 9:326.

The Ruffed Grouse Situation in Pennsylvania. *Cardinal*, January, 1925, v. 1, no. 5, p. 17–19.

The Ruffed Grouse Situation in Pennsylvania. *Wild Life Magazine* (Greenville, Pa.), January–February, 1925, v. 3, no. _, p. _.

A Natural Zoological Garden in Western Pennsylvania: Pymatuning Swamp. *Wild Life Magazine*, April, 1925, v. _, no. _, p. 4–5. "A popular account of the more interesting features of the Swamp."

Swimming and Diving Activity of the Spotted Sandpiper (Actitis macularia). *Auk*, October, 1925, 42:580–581. Refers in part to observations made at Chambersburg.

The American Egret (Casmerodius egretta) in Eastern and Central Pennsylvania. *Auk*, October, 1925, 42:583. The only record given from western Pennsylvania is one from Mount Union, Huntingdon County.

Strange Nesting-site of the Chimney Swift (Chætura pelagica). *Auk*, October, 1925, 42:586. In Potter County.

Notes on the Nesting of the Goshawk in Potter County, Pennsylvania. *Wilson Bulletin*, December, 1925, 37: 193–199, 1 pl., 1 fig.

Long-eared Owl capturing Ruffed Grouse. *Auk*, April, 1926, 43:236. In Cameron County.

A Loon Strangled by Its Fish Food. *Wilson Bulletin*, March, 1927, 39:39, 1 fig. At Presque Isle.

The Invasion of Goshawks and Snowy Owls during the Winter of 1926–1927. *Cardinal*, July, 1927, 2:35–41, 2 maps. With a record of food habits.

[Turkey Vulture Nesting in Crawford County]. *Cardinal*, July, 1927, 2:44.

Flocking, Mating, and Nest-building Habits of the Prairie Horned Lark. *Wilson Bulletin*, September, 1927, 39: 132–141, 1 pl., 4 figs. Observations made mainly in Allegheny, Beaver, and Crawford counties.

Madeira Petrel (Oceanodroma castro) in Pennsylvania. *Auk*, October, 1927, 44:556–557. At Chambersburg.

Goshawk Nesting in Clarion County, Pennsylvania. *Auk*, October, 1927, 44:563.

The Birds of Pymatuning Swamp and Conneaut Lake, Crawford County, Pennsylvania. *Annals Carnegie Museum*, March, 1928, 18:19–239, pls. 2–10. Reviews: *Auk*, 1928, 45:397, 398; *Wilson Bulletin*, 1928, 40:120; *Cardinal*, 1928, 2:100–103. This is the most notable local list that has thus far appeared from western Pennsylvania. It is based in the main on the author's own field work in this region from 1922 to 1927, with the inclusion of data contributed by other observers. The area treated covers not only Pymatuning Swamp, but also Conneaut Lake and Marsh, and the adjacent region as far east as Meadville. Sandy Lake, Mercer County, is referred to parenthetically. Ecological conditions are fully discussed, and seasonal lists and a bibliography are included. There are 244 native species listed, with full annotations under each; nesting and migration are given special attention. The nesting habits of certain lesser-known species are described in considerable detail, and some of these accounts are the first for western Pennsylvania. While there are a few minor errors, the article as a whole is carefully prepared, readable and interesting, and extremely valuable as a record of the conditions originally prevailing in a section that has since undergone a tremendous transformation. The list has been freely used in the preparation of the present work and is cited throughout as "Sutton, 1928."

Abundance of the Golden Eagle in Pennsylvania in 1927–1928. *Auk*, July, 1928, 45:375. Potter's Mills is in Centre County (not Huntingdon). The exact locality is doubtful.

Notes on the Flight of the Chimney Swift. *Cardinal*, July, 1928, 2:85–92. Based on observations made in part in western Pennsylvania.

[A Snowy Owl Invasion]. *Cardinal*, July, 1928, 2:104. One Washington County record. Article unsigned.

An Introduction to the Birds of Pennsylvania. Harrisburg, Pa., 1928. ix, 169 p., 1 pl., numerous figs. Review: *Auk*, 1929, 46:133.

Extension of the Breeding Range of the Turkey Vulture in Pennsylvania. *Auk*, October, 1928, 45:501–503.

Yellow-headed Blackbird in Pennsylvania. *Auk*, January, 1929, 46:119.

Bird Notes from Pymatuning Swamp. *Cardinal*, January, 1929, 2:121. Notes on 9 species.

[A Golden Eagle Capture]. *Cardinal*, January, 1929, 2:129.

[Saw-whet Owl Incident]. *Cardinal*, January, 1929, 2:129.

[Northern Shrike in Jefferson County]. *Cardinal*, January, 1929, 2:130.

Photographing Wild Turkey Nests in Pennsylvania. *Auk*, July, 1929, 46:326–328, pl. 18.

The Nesting Wrens of Brooke County, West Virginia. *Wilson Bulletin*, March, 1930, 42:10–17, 3 figs. With incidental references to observations in western Pennsylvania.

Notes on the Northern Pileated Woodpecker in Pennsylvania. *Cardinal*, July, 1930, 2:207–217, 1 pl., 1 map. An exhaustive account of its local range, present status, etc.

The Status of the Goshawk in Pennsylvania. *Wilson Bulletin*, June, 1931, 43:108–113, 2 maps. The invasions of 1926–27 and 1927–28 are described.

"T. L. A."

"Siamese" Robins' Nests. *Young Oölogist*, December, 1884, 1:119. At Meadville.

Teulon, James A. (Wrongly spelled "Tuelon")

A List of Birds Observed near Bradford, Penn. *Quarterly Journal Boston Zoölogical Society*, October, 1882, 1:47–52; January, 1883, 2:8–11. Review: *Bulletin Nuttall Ornithological Club*, 1883, 8:171. The earliest annotated list of western Pennsylvania birds, and valuable despite Elliott Coues's derogation in his review. 77 species.

Thomas, William S.

Trails and Tramps in Alaska and Newfoundland. New York, 1913. xv, 330 p. Illustrated. The title of this book is misleading, since four of the eight chapters actually relate to Allegheny County, Pennsylvania. This fact is not stated in the text. The last two chapters are mainly concerned with birds, and the observations, according to T. D. Burleigh, were made in the Deer Creek region. The illustration on p. 296, purporting to show the nest and eggs of the Blue-winged Warbler, actually portrays those of the Golden-winged.

[Habits of the American Bittern]. *In the Open*, June, 1920, 10:23. At Mud Lake, near Hartstown, Crawford County.

The Deer Creek Hike [of the Audubon Society]. *In the Open*, June, 1920, 10:24–25. With an informal list of birds seen in the lower Deer Creek Valley, Allegheny County (date not given). Article unsigned.

Thompson, Alice [Mrs.]

Notes from Erie. *Bird-Lore*, December, 1933, 35:320. The "Snowy Egret" here mentioned was an American Egret.

Thompson, W. W.

The Passenger Pigeon. Coudersport, Pa., [1921]. 17 p. Published by the Potter County *Journal*. Unscientific, but interesting.

Todd, W. E. Clyde

Beaver County, Pa., Notes. *Oölogist*, June–September, 1887, 4:89. All common species. The author's initial effort.

Black Snowbird. *Oölogist*, August–September, 1888, 5:125–126. Winter habits at Beaver.

Breeding of Dendroica maculosa in Western Pennsylvania. *Auk*, January, 1891, 8:116. In the Buffalo Creek region of Butler County.

Breeding of Totanus solitarius and Otocoris alpestris praticola in Western Pennsylvania. *Auk*, April, 1891, 8:236. In Beaver and Butler counties, respectively.

Nesting of the Cerulean Warbler (*Dendroica cœrulea*) in Beaver County, Pennsylvania. *Auk*, April, 1891, 8:238–239. One of the earliest accounts of the nesting of this species.

Notes on the Occurrence of Uncommon Species at Beaver, Pa. *Auk*, 1891, 8:240. *Clangula hyemalis*, *Phalaropus lobatus*, *Tringa bairdii*, and *Geothlypis philadelphia*.

Nesting of Wilson's Thrush in Western Pennsylvania. *Ornithologist and Oölogist*, April, 1891, 16:50–51. In the Buffalo Creek region of Butler and Armstrong counties.

Further Note on Otocoris alpestris praticola. *Auk*, October, 1891, 8:395. Observed near Beaver in June.

Notes on the Mniotiltidæ of Western Pennsylvania. *Auk*,

October, 1891, 8:397–399. A discussion of the status of 20 species of this group in Beaver County and in the Buffalo Creek region of Butler and Armstrong counties.

The Ruddy Duck. *Ornithologist and Oölogist*, April, 1892, 17:61–62. As observed during migration at Beaver.

Nesting of the Blue-gray Gnatcatcher. *Ornithologist and Oölogist*, May, 1892, 17:73–74. In Beaver County. Quoted in greater part on p. 458 of the present work.

Summer Birds of Indiana and Clearfield Counties, Pennsylvania. *Auk*, January, 1893, 10:35–46. (Correction, p. 305.) Lists 65 species from Indiana County and 55 from Clearfield County, with brief annotations. From a faunal standpoint, this article supplements and extends Jonathan Dwight's article of the preceding year.

The Occurrence in Summer of Certain Warblers at Beaver, Pennsylvania. *Auk*, April, 1893, 10:209. *Helminthophila pinus, Geothlypis formosa*, and *Sylvania mitrata*.

The Olive-Sided Flycatcher (*Nuttallornis borealis* (Swainson)) in Warren Co., Pennsylvania. *Annals Carnegie Museum*, March, 1901, 1:4. Two pairs located in June, 1900.

The Lark Sparrow (*Chondestes grammacus* (Say)) in Beaver County, Pennsylvania. *Annals Carnegie Museum*, September, 1902, 1:504. A pair found building near "Oakwood Station" (now "Barclay's Crossing"), Beaver County.

The Birds of Erie and Presque Isle, Erie County, Pennsylvania. *Annals Carnegie Museum*, August, 1904, 2:481–596, 3 pls., 1 map. Reviews: *Auk*, 1904, 21:505; *Bird-Lore*, 1904, 6:169; *Wilson Bulletin*, 1904, 11:95. Based mainly on the observations and collections made by W. W. Worthington and the author during the spring and fall of 1900, supplemented by data contributed by S. E. Bacon and by information gleaned from all other available sources, including the collection of G. B. Sennett. Included are a list of 237 species, fully annotated; an introduction treating of the physical features, etc., of the locality; and a brief bibliography. This article has been freely used in preparing the present work, but a few of the species are now relegated to the doubtful list. Other doubtful records are noted in the text and references.

The Mammal and Bird Fauna of Beaver County, Pennsylvania. In Bausman (J. H.), *History of Beaver County, Pennsylvania*. Appendix No. III. New York, November, 1904, p. 1198–1202. A list of 178 species, with a mere indication of seasonal status and abundance, and a short introduction.

The Life Zones of Western Pennsylvania. *Cardinal*, January, 1924, v. 1, no. 3, p. 1–6. With an introduction of a general nature and lists of the local species characterizing the several zones. From the list of Canadian Life Zone species, a few names were inadvertently omitted—cf. p. 11 of the present work.

Two Rare Warblers at Beaver. *Cardinal*, January, 1925, v. 1, no. 5, p. 20. Connecticut and Orange-crowned Warblers.

The Bird Collection of the Carnegie Museum. *Cardinal* July, 1925, v. 1, no. 6, p. 15–18.

[Saw-whet Owl in Pittsburgh]. *Cardinal*, July, 1927, 2:44.

Chickadees of Western Pennsylvania. *Cardinal*, July, 1936, 4:90–95. This article is extracted from the present work (with omission of the published references).

The Redhead and Ring-necked Duck Breeding at Pymatuning Lake, Pennsylvania. *Auk*, October, 1936, 53:440.

Critical Remarks on the Long-billed Marsh Wren. *Proceedings Biological Society of Washington*, February 23, 1937, 50:23.

Two New Races of North American Birds. *Auk*, January, 1938, 55:116–118. With incidental references to specimens of *Penthestes atricapillus atricapillus* and *Ammospiza caudacuta nelsoni* from western Pennsylvania.

Type locality of the American Robin. *Auk*, April, 1939, 56:190–191. Breeding robins from western Pennsylvania are intermediates between *migratorius* and *achrusterus*, but nearer the latter.

TODD, W. E. CLYDE, and GEORGE M. SUTTON

Taxonomic Remarks on the Carolina Chickadee, *Penthestes carolinensis*. *Proceedings Biological Society of Washington*, July, 1936, 49:69–70. Refers to specimens from western Pennsylvania.

TOWNSEND, CHARLES H.

Note on the Long-tailed Duck. *Bulletin Nuttall Ornithological Club*, October, 1882, 7:251. At Latrobe, Westmoreland County, February, 1881.

Notes on the Birds of Westmoreland County, Penna. *Proceedings Academy of Natural Sciences of Philadelphia*, April, 1883, p. 59–68. Review: *Auk*, 1884, 1:184. List of 136 species, briefly annotated; the seasonal occurrence is sometimes left open to conjecture. The area covered is from Latrobe to Chestnut Ridge.

Old Times with the Birds: Autobiographical. *Condor*, September, 1927, 29:224–232. Early experiences with the Wild Pigeon in Westmoreland County.

TRIMBLE, RUTH

Some Recent Developments in the Pymatuning Region, Western Pennsylvania. *Cardinal*, January, 1937, 4:102–108.

Moving Day for the Birds. *Carnegie Magazine*, September, 1939, 13:106–109. Contains references to various birds observed at Erie, Pymatuning Lake, and elsewhere in western Pennsylvania.

TROTTER, SPENCER

The Red-headed Woodpecker as a Pennsylvania and New Jersey Bird. *Cassinia*, 1904, 7:6–10. Note on its occurrence at State College, *fide* H. A. Surface (p. 9).

VAN FLEET, WALTER

Notes from DuBois, Pa., July 24, 1884. *Ornithologist and Oölogist*, September, 1884, 9:108. Random notes on the summer birds. Article initialed.

VAN OSTRAND, H. T.

Poke Berry Coloring. *Osprey*, November, 1896, 1:38. Observations at Morganza, Washington County, on staining of the viscera of birds that eat pokeberries.

[VOGT, WILLIAM, editor]

Bird-Lore's Thirty-fifth Christmas Census. *Bird-Lore*, February, 1935, 37:31–85. Lists from Osterburg, Bedford County (J. and D. Berkheimer); Erie (Presque Isle and Erie Bay) (E. Upson, *et al.*); "Sewickley," i.e., Big Traverse Creek, southern Beaver County (B. H. Christy and F. A. Hegner); and Springs, Somerset County (A. B. Miller).

Bird-Lore's Thirty-sixth Christmas Bird Census. *Bird-Lore*, February, 1936, 38:41–85. Lists from Osterburg, Bedford County (D. and R. Berkheimer); Erie (Presque Isle and Erie Bay) (Gertrude Reilly, *et al.*); and Springs, Somerset County (A. B. Miller).

Bird-Lore's Thirty-seventh Christmas Census. *Bird-Lore*, February, 1937, 39:28–72. Lists from Osterburg, Bedford County (D. and R. Berkheimer); Deer Creek region, Allegheny County (V. Bennett, *et al.*); "Sewickley," i.e., Pymatuning Lake, Crawford County (!) (B. H. Christy, *et al.*); and Springs, Somerset County (A. B. Miller).

Bird-Lore's Thirty-eighth Christmas Census. *Bird-Lore*, February, 1938, 40:22–71. Lists from Osterburg, Bedford County (D. and R. Berkheimer); Deer Creek region, Allegheny County (F. S. Bennett, *et al.*); Linesville (M. B. Skaggs, *et al.*); Springs, Somerset County (A. B. Miller); and several separate localities in Allegheny County (C. and D. Auerswald, *et al.*).

WALLACE, EGBERT, JR.

A Progressive Baby Wren. *Bird-Lore*, October, 1933, 35:268. At McKean, Erie County.

WARREN, BENJAMIN HARRY

Report on the Birds of Pennsylvania. Harrisburg, Pa., 1888. xii, 260 p., 50 pls. Review: *Auk*, 1889, 6:170. The Appendix (p. 229–249) contains a number of references to the birds of the Erie region, inserted on the authority of G. B. Sennett. The main text of the *Report* refers almost entirely to the avifauna of the southeastern part of Pennsylvania, to which the author's field work had been confined.

Report on the Birds of Pennsylvania. Edition 2. Harrisburg, 1890. xiv, 434 p., 100 pls. Review: *Auk*, 1891, 8:101. "The primary purpose of the Report is not to lay before the scientific public the outcome of the author's investigations, though a great deal of important original matter is actually given; its object is simply to instruct the people of Pennsylvania in regard to the birds of their State, and especially to give the farmers all available information as to the bearing upon their own interests of the food habits of the various species" (*Auk*, p. 102). From this standpoint, the book was an undoubted success and did a great deal of good (especially in correcting the popular misconception as to the birds of prey); and it was in great demand. As a scientific publication, however, it is woefully lacking—even judged by the standards of fifty years ago—and not to be compared with other state lists of the time. It was hastily and carelessly prepared ("compiled" would be a better word), without any critical analysis of the data on which it was based, or any apparent conception of the significance of the records. Indeed, the author casually cites record after record for various rare species without giving the slightest indication that he was aware of their unusual character. He seems to have accepted virtually everything that he received from his correspondents, without any attempt whatever to separate the chaff from the wheat; for this reason, he repeatedly falls into error. Seldom does he include enough data for rare species to enable an independent judgment, and there is evidence that he sometimes confused the records for different species. In the interim between the first and second editions of his report, Warren himself visited the western part of the state (his earlier field work had been confined to the southeastern part). Scattered through the pages of the book are many references to his observations in the western counties. Unfortunately, however, he failed to realize the importance of citing exact localities and dates, and as a rule he gives only the county. From the standpoint of the present work, such records have little value. Still more unfortunately, all his original notebooks, lists, etc., were destroyed in the Capitol fire at Harrisburg in 1897, so that it is now impossible to check or amplify these dubious and imperfect records. In the present work, an effort has been made to evaluate all these records, insofar as the evidence permits in each case. Many are quite unacceptable.

Notes on Pennsylvania Birds. *Forest and Stream*, February 13, 1890, 34:64. *Plectrophenax nivalis* and *Calcarius lapponicus* at Erie.

Evening Grosbeak in Pennsylvania. *Forest and Stream*, March 6, 1890, 34:123. One shot at Warren, January 22.

Pennsylvania Notes. *Forest and Stream*, August 20, 1891, 37:83. List of 16 species found breeding or summering at Kane, McKean County—including the Passenger Pigeon and several "northern" kinds. The "Large-billed" Water Thrush should read "Northern" Water Thrush. Article signed "W."

Pennsylvania Bird Notes. *Forest and Stream*, September 24, 1891, 37:182–183. Records the summering of the Tree Swallow at Renovo (probably an error) and the capture of the Raven in Centre County. Article signed "W."

Enemies of Poultry. *Bulletin Pennsylvania State Department of Agriculture*, no. 17, 1897. xxiii, 749 p. This book, written in newspaper style, is padded far in excess of actual requirements; its publication was the occasion for a political scandal that completely discredited its author. Most of the subject matter is adapted from his 1890 *Report*, but the book includes some new data on the Raven and some of the birds of prey, involving records for western Pennsylvania.

Evening Grosbeaks in Pennsylvania. *Auk*, July, 1914, 31: 400. Bedford County, February, 1914.

WARRICK, W. T.

Oölogical Notes for June. *Oölogist* (S. L. Willard, publisher), June, 1878, 4:27. Four sets (25 eggs) taken from a single pair of Flickers in one season. Robins (erroneously) supposed to be young were found building nests.

Chewink, Cowbird, and Wood Thrush [at Washington]. *Ornithologist and Oölogist*, February, 1883, 8:15. Author's name misprinted "Warwick."

Late Nesting [of the Mourning Dove at Washington]. *Ornithologist and Oölogist*, February, 1883, 8:15. Author's name misprinted "Warwick."

Owls and Horned Grebe. *Ornithologist and Oölogist*, April, 1883, 8:31–32. Notes from Washington.

Cardinal Grosbeak. *Ornithologist and Oölogist*, June, 1883, 8:46.

White Herons. *Ornithologist and Oölogist*, October, 1883, 8:80.

WEST, RUSSELL

The A. O. U. Field Trip to the Pymatuning Region. *Redstart*, October, 1936, 4:4–5. With a partial list of the species observed.

WETMORE, ALEXANDER

Observations on the Birds of West Virginia. *Proceedings U. S. National Museum*, August 24, 1937, 84:401–441. Refers specimens from "Johnstown," Pennsylvania, to *togata* (p. 407). As revealed by the records, however, there is no assurance that the specimens in question (in the collection of the U. S. National Museum) actually came from that place.

WHITE, I. C.

The Geology of Huntingdon County. *Second Geological Survey of Pennsylvania*, (Report of Progress T.³), Harrisburg, 1885. xv, 471 p. Mention of the Wild Turkey in the Tussey Mountain Barrens (p. 281).

WICKHAM, HURLBURT H.

Black-Capped Chickadee. *Oölogist*, October–December, 1887, 4:102. Nesting at Beaver, April, 1887.

Notes on Birds of Beaver, Pa. *Oölogist*, June, 1888, 5:92. List of birds noted during the winter of 1887–88—all common species. The "Yellow-bellied" Woodpecker should read "Red-bellied" Woodpecker.

WIED, MAXIMILIAN, PRINZ ZU

Reise in das Innere Nord-America in den Jahren 1832 bis 1834. Vol. 1. Coblenz, 1839. xvi, 653 p. Four species of woodpeckers (*Picus villosus*, *P. pubescens*, *P. varius*, and *P. pileatus*), the "Fasan" (elsewhere called *Tetrao umbellus*), *Columba migratoria*, and the "Blue-bird" were noted near Ebensburg late in September or early in October, 1832 (p. 131–132). Several of these names are omitted in the English translation by H. Evans Lloyd, 1843.

Verzeichniss der Vögel, welche auf eine Reise in Nord-America beobachtet wurden. *Journal für Ornithologie*, 1858, 6:1–29, 97–124, 177–205, 257–284, 337–354, 417–445; 1859, 7:81–96, 161–180, 241–260. *Astur fuscus* from Ebensburg, Cambria County (p. 15), *Bubo asio* (p. 25), *Sialia wilsoni* (p. 121), *Pipilo erythrophthalmus* (p. 267), *Picus pileatus* (p. 352), and *Picus villosus* (p. 254) from the "Alleghany-Gebirge" (exact locality not specified). *Pelecanus fuscus* supposedly from Economy, Beaver County—possible but highly improbable.

WILSON, ALEXANDER

American Ornithology. Vol. 3. Philadelphia, 1811. 120 p., pls. 19–27. Contains western Pennsylvania records for *Alauda magna* and the "Snow-bird" (*Junco*) (p. 20–21); and for the Carolina Wren (p. 83).

American Ornithology. Vol. 4. Philadelphia, 1811. 100 p., pls. 28–36. *Strix nyctea* at Pittsburgh (p. 53).

WILSON, ALEXANDER (George Ord, editor)
American Ornithology. Vol. 1. New York and Philadelphia, 1828. cxix, 231 p. On pages cv and cvii of the introduction are incidental references to the Snow-bird and Redbird, included in Wilson's letters to Alexander Lawson, and referring to Pittsburgh and the Ohio River, respectively.

WOOD, HAROLD B.
Observations at a Barn Swallow's Nest. *Wilson Bulletin*, June, 1937, 49:96–100. At Cherry Spring, Potter County.

WOOD, MERRILL
Eastern Lark Sparrow Breeding in Central Pennsylvania. *Auk*, January, 1932, 49:98. In Huntingdon County, about 8 miles south of State College. The record was authenticated by a photograph, which has been examined.

Night Singing. *Oölogist*, September, 1932, 49:103. Field and Grasshopper sparrows.

An Abundance of Color. *Oölogist*, September, 1932, 49:106. Seventeen species (mostly warblers) seen "on the trickling filter bed of the sewage plant" at State College.

New Birds for State College, Pennsylvania. *Wilson Bulletin*, December, 1932, 44:238–239. Some of these records (i.e., Fish Crow, Boat-tailed Grackle) are obviously errors. Nearly all are sight records and should be received with caution.

A Partial Albino Red-tailed Hawk. *Wilson Bulletin*, June, 1933, 45:79. From Bradford, McKean County.

WOODWARD, ARTHUR J.
European Widgeon at Erie. *Cardinal*, July, 1933, 3:147.

WRIGHT, ALBERT HAZEN
Some Early Records of the Passenger Pigeon. *Auk*, October, 1910, 27:428–442. Cites Thomas Ashe's reference (1808) for Pennsylvania (Erie?) (p. 437).

Early Records of the Wild Turkey. II. *Auk*, October, 1914, 31:463–473. Quotes Christian Schultz's observations (1810) on this species, made on the Allegheny River (p. 470).

Early Records of the Wild Turkey. III. *Auk*, January, 1915, 32:61–81. Quotes a few records from various sources pertaining to western Pennsylvania (p. 73–74).

WRIGHT, JOHN E.
Three Broods of Cardinals. *Cardinal*, July, 1935, 4:49.

ZIEGLER, G. FRED, JR.
Notes on a Purple Martin Colony. *Auk*, July, 1923, 40:431–436. At Greencastle, Franklin County.

INDEX OF BIRD NAMES

INDEX OF BIRD NAMES

COLOR PLATES

PLATE 1

→

COMMON MALLARD

(page 77)

Female

Male

COMMON BLACK DUCK

(page 80)

George Miksch Sutton

George Miksch Sutton

PLATE 2

→

SHOVELLER
(page 92)

Female

Male

BLUE-WINGED TEAL
(page 90)

Male

Female

George Miksch Sutton

George Miksch Sutton

PLATE 3

→

BALDPATE
(page 86)

Male **Female**

REDHEAD
(page 96)

Male **Female**

George Miksch Sutton

George Miksch Sutton

PLATE 4

→

RING-NECKED DUCK

(page 98)

Male

Female

LESSER SCAUP DUCK

(page 102)

Female

Male

George Miksch Sutton

George Miksch Sutton

PLATE 5

→

OLD-SQUAW

(page 108)

Male

Female

BUFFLE-HEAD

(page 107)

Female

Male

George Miksch Sutton

George Miksch Sutton

PLATE 6

→

SHARP-SHINNED HAWK

(page 134)

Immature

Adult Female

Adult Male

COOPER'S HAWK

(page 137)

Adult

Immature

George Miksch Sutton

George Miksch Sutton

PLATE 7

→

NORTHERN RED-SHOULDERED HAWK

(page 142)

Adult

Immature

EASTERN RED-TAILED HAWK

(page 139)

Adult

Immature

George Miksch Sutton

PLATE 8

→

MARSH HAWK

(page 155)

Male

Female

BROAD-WINGED HAWK

(page 146)

Immature

Adult

George Miksch Sutton

PLATE 9

→

SEMIPALMATED SANDPIPER
(page 237)

LEAST SANDPIPER
(page 232)

SPOTTED SANDPIPER
(page 219)

Summer

Winter

GREATER YELLOW-LEGS
(page 225)

LESSER YELLOW-LEGS
(page 227)

PECTORAL SANDPIPER
(page 229)

EASTERN SOLITARY SANDPIPER
(page 221)

PLATE 10

→

RING-BILLED GULL
(page 249)

Immature

Adult

BONAPARTE'S GULL
(page 251)

Adult

Immature

George Miksch Sutton

George Miksch Sutton

PLATE 11

→

COMMON TERN
(page 254)

Immature **Adult**

BLACK TERN
(page 258)

Immature **Adults**

George Miksch Sutton

George Miksch Sutton

PLATE 12

→

LONG-EARED OWL (page 292)	BARN OWL (page 278)
SHORT-EARED OWL (page 294)	NORTHERN BARRED OWL (page 290)

George Miksch Sutton

George Miksch Sutton

George Miksch Sutton

George Miksch Sutton

PLATE 13

→

RED-BELLIED WOODPECKER (page 325)	YELLOW-BELLIED SAPSUCKER (page 331)
Male	Immature Male
EASTERN HAIRY WOODPECKER (page 334)	**NORTHERN DOWNY WOODPECKER** (page 337)
Male	Female Male
BLACK-BILLED CUCKOO (page 275)	**YELLOW-BILLED CUCKOO** (page 273)

George Miksch Sutton
George Miksch Sutton
George Miksch Sutton
George Miksch Sutton
George Miksch Sutton
George Miksch Sutton

PLATE 14

→

NORTHERN CRESTED FLYCATCHER (page 342)	EASTERN PHOEBE (page 344)	EASTERN WOOD PEWEE (page 354)
OLIVE-SIDED FLYCATCHER (page 356)	LEAST FLYCATCHER (page 352)	EASTERN KINGBIRD (page 339)
YELLOW-BELLIED FLYCATCHER (page 346)	ACADIAN FLYCATCHER (page 348)	ALDER FLYCATCHER (page 350)

George Miksch Sutton
George Miksch Sutton
George Miksch Sutton
George Miksch Sutton

PLATE 15

→

BANK SWALLOW (page 367)	NORTHERN CLIFF SWALLOW (page 373)	ROUGH-WINGED SWALLOW (page 369)
CAROLINA CHICKADEE (page 395)	BLACK-CAPPED CHICKADEE (page 392)	RED-BREASTED NUTHATCH (page 402)
CAROLINA WREN (page 420)	BEWICK'S WREN (page 417)	EASTERN WINTER WREN (page 414)

George Miksch Sutton
George Miksch Sutton
George Miksch Sutton
George Miksch Sutton
George Miksch Sutton
George Miksch Sutton

PLATE 16

→

EASTERN RUBY-CROWNED KINGLET (page 462)	EASTERN GOLDEN-CROWNED KINGLET (page 460)	BLUE-GRAY GNATCATCHER (page 457)
Female Male	Male	Male Female
VEERY (page 450)	EASTERN BLUEBIRD (page 453) Adult Juvenal	WOOD THRUSH (page 440)
GRAY-CHEEKED THRUSH (page 448)	EASTERN HERMIT THRUSH (page 443)	OLIVE-BACKED THRUSH (page 446)

PLATE 17

→

RED-EYED VIREO (page 480)	PHILADELPHIA VIREO (page 482)	YELLOW-THROATED VIREO (page 475)
EASTERN WARBLING VIREO (page 483)	BLUE-HEADED VIREO (page 477)	AMERICAN PIPIT (page 464)
MIGRANT SHRIKE (page 471)	NORTHERN SHRIKE (page 470) Adult Immature	CEDAR WAXWING (page 467)

George Miksch Sutton

PLATE 18

→

TENNESSEE WARBLER (page 498) Immature Adult	**NASHVILLE WARBLER** (page 500) Adult Immature	**ORANGE-CROWNED WARBLER** (page 499) Adult Immature
MAGNOLIA WARBLER (page 507) Adult Male Immature Male	**CAPE MAY WARBLER** (page 510) Adult Male Immature Male Immature Female	**NORTHERN PARULA WARBLER** (page 502) Adult Male Immature
BLACK-THROATED BLUE WARBLER (page 512) Male Female	**MYRTLE WARBLER** (page 515) Immature Male Adult Male	**CERULEAN WARBLER** (page 519) Male Female

George Miksch Sutton
George Miksch Sutton
George Miksch Sutton
George Miksch Sutton
George Miksch Sutton
George Miksch Sutton
George Miksch Sutton

PLATE 19

→

CHESTNUT-SIDED WARBLER (page 525)	BLACK-THROATED GREEN WARBLER (page 516)	WESTERN PALM WARBLER (page 533)
Adult Male Immature Male Immature Female	Adult Male Adult Female Immature Female Immature Male	Adult Immature
BAY-BREASTED WARBLER (page 527)	**BLACK-POLL WARBLER (page 528)**	**NORTHERN PINE WARBLER (page 530)**
Adult Female Immature Adult Male	Adult Male Adult Female Immature	Female Male
BLACKBURNIAN WARBLER (page 522)	**NORTHERN WATER-THRUSH (page 537)**	**LOUISIANA WATER-THRUSH (page 541)**
Adult Male Adult Female Immature Male Immature Female		

George Miksch Sutton
George Miksch Sutton
George Miksch Sutton
George Miksch Sutton

PLATE 20 →

WILSON'S WARBLER (page 560) Adult Male Adult Female Immature	**HOODED WARBLER** (page 557) Female Male	**CANADA WARBLER** (page 561) Male Female
MARYLAND YELLOW-THROAT (page 551) Adult Male Immature Male Adult Female Immature Female	**AMERICAN REDSTART** (page 564) Immature Male Adult Male Adult Female	**KENTUCKY WARBLER** (page 545)
OVEN-BIRD (page 534)	**MOURNING WARBLER** (page 548) Male Female	**CONNECTICUT WARBLER** (page 547) Adult Male Immature

George Miksch Sutton
George Miksch Sutton
George Miksch Sutton
George Miksch Sutton
George Miksch Sutton

PLATE 21

→

EASTERN GOLDFINCH (page 617) Adult Male in Winter Adult Male in Summer	NORTHERN PINE SISKIN (page 614)	EASTERN SAVANNAH SPARROW (page 627)
EASTERN GRASSHOPPER SPARROW (page 629)	HENSLOW'S SPARROW (page 631)	EASTERN VESPER SPARROW (page 633)
RUSTY BLACKBIRD (page 582) Adult Male Immature	PURPLE GRACKLE (page 584)	BRONZED GRACKLE (page 585)

George Miksch Sutton
George Miksch Sutton
George Miksch Sutton
George Miksch Sutton
George Miksch Sutton
George Miksch Sutton
George Miksch Sutton
George Miksch Sutton
George Miksch Sutton

PLATE 22

→

EASTERN TREE SPARROW (page 641)	**WHITE-CROWNED SPARROW** (page 647) Adult Immature	**WHITE-THROATED SPARROW** (page 648)
EASTERN FIELD SPARROW (page 645)	**EASTERN CHIPPING SPARROW** (page 643) Adult Juvenal	**MISSISSIPPI SONG SPARROW** (page 655)
SWAMP SPARROW (page 653)	**LINCOLN'S SPARROW** (page 652)	**EASTERN FOX SPARROW** (page 650)

George Miksch Sutton
George Miksch Sutton
George Miksch Sutton

PLATE 23

→

FLIGHT PATTERNS OF EASTERN HAWKS

BROAD-WINGED or MOUSE HAWKS

ROUGH-LEGGED HAWK

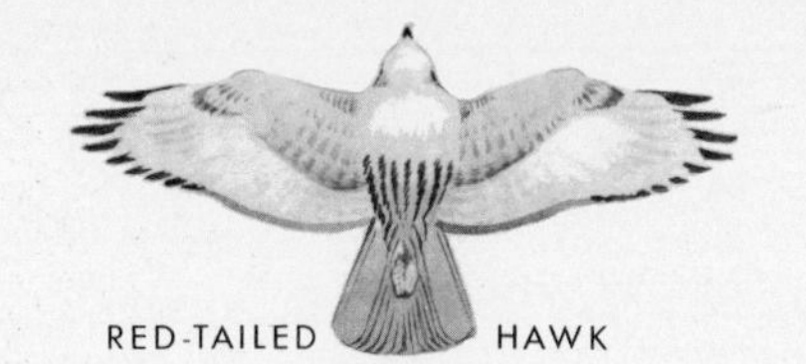

RED-TAILED HAWK

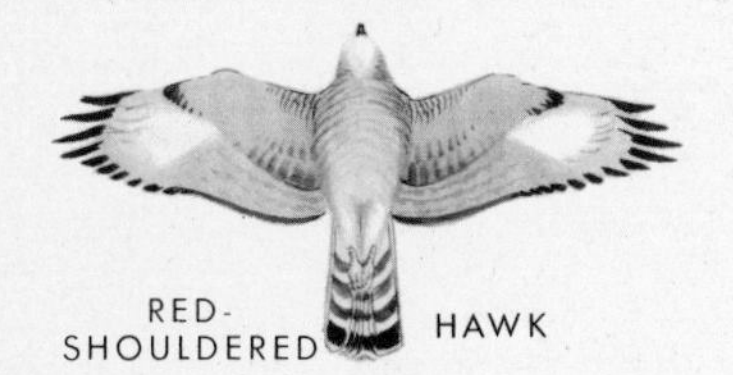

RED-SHOULDERED HAWK

BROAD-WINGED HAWK

POINTED-WINGED FALCONS

DUCK HAWK

PIGEON HAWK

SPARROW HAWK

MARSH HAWK

SHORT-WINGED or BIRD HAWKS

GOSHAWK

COOPER'S HAWK

SHARP-SHINNED HAWK

SMALL-HEADED or CARRION BIRDS

TURKEY VULTURE

BLACK VULTURE

WHITE-HEADED or WATER-FREQUENTING BIRDS

BALD EAGLE ADULT

BALD EAGLE IMMATURE

OSPREY

R.T. PETERSON

Courtesy of National Association of Audubon Societies

TOPOGRAPHIC MAP